Chemistry ^6e

The Molecular Nature of Matter and Change

Silberberg
University of Cincinnati

Volume 1
Chem 1040

Mc Graw Hill **Learning Solutions**

Boston   Burr Ridge, IL   Dubuque, IA   New York   San Francisco   St. Louis
Bangkok   Bogotá   Caracas   Lisbon   London   Madrid
Mexico City   Milan   New Delhi   Seoul   Singapore   Sydney   Taipei   Toronto

Chemistry: The Molecular Nature of Matter and Change, Sixth Edition
Volume 1
Chem 1040
University of Cincinnati

1 2 3 4 5 6 7 8 9 0 BOM BOM 14 13 12

ISBN-13: 978-0-07-769841-6
ISBN-10: 0-07-769841-X
Part of
ISBN-13: 978-0-07-769842-3
ISBN-10: 0-07-769842-8

Learning Solutions Consultant: Bradley Ritter
Production Editor: Mark Bodensteiner
Printer/Binder: BookMasters, Inc.
Cover Images © 2012 JupiterImages Corporation

To Ruth and Daniel, with all my love,
and
In Memory of my Mother,
Gert Mazur,
Whose unfailing belief in me, I have finally come to realize,
has been a driving force in my life.

BRIEF CONTENTS

DETAILED CONTENTS

CHAPTER 3 • Stoichiometry of Formulas and Equations 82

CHAPTER 4 • Three Major Classes of Chemical Reactions 134

CHAPTER 5 • Gases and the Kinetic-Molecular Theory 180

CHAPTER 6 • Thermochemistry: Energy Flow and Chemical Change 228

CHAPTER 7 • Quantum Theory and Atomic Structure 260

CHAPTER 8 • Electron Configuration and Chemical Periodicity 294

CHAPTER 9 • Models of Chemical Bonding 328

CHAPTER 10 • The Shapes of Molecules 362

CHAPTER 24 • Nuclear Reactions and Their Applications 976

Martin S. Silberberg received a B.S. in Chemistry from the City University of New York and a Ph.D. in Chemistry from the University of Oklahoma. He then accepted a position as research associate in analytical biochemistry at the Albert Einstein College of Medicine in New York City, where he developed methods to study neurotransmitter metabolism in Parkinson's disease and other neurological disorders. Following six years as research associate, Dr. Silberberg joined the faculty of Bard College at Simon's Rock, a liberal arts college known for its excellence in teaching small classes of highly motivated students. As head of the Natural Sciences Major and Director of Premedical Studies, he taught courses in general chemistry, organic chemistry, biochemistry, and liberal-arts chemistry. The small class size and close student contact afforded him insights into how students learn chemistry, where they have difficulties, and what strategies can help them succeed. Dr. Silberberg decided to apply these insights in a broader context and established a textbook writing, editing, and consulting company. Before writing his own texts, he worked as a consulting and development editor on chemistry, biochemistry, and physics texts for several major college publishers. He resides with his wife Ruth and son in the Pioneer Valley near Amherst, Massachusetts, where he enjoys the rich cultural and academic life of the area and relaxes by cooking and singing.

Preface

At the core of natural science, chemistry is so crucial to an understanding of medicine, molecular biology, genetics, pharmacology, ecology, atmospheric science, engineering, nuclear studies, materials science, and many other fields that it has become a central requirement for an increasing number of academic majors. Furthermore, chemical principles are at the core of many key societal issues, including climate change, energy options, materials recycling, diet and nutrition, and medicine and disease. Clearly, the study of chemistry plays an essential role in our world.

WHAT SETS THIS BOOK APART

For five editions, *Chemistry: The Molecular Nature of Matter and Change* has been recognized for setting the standard among general chemistry textbooks. This sixth edition maintains that unparalleled reputation by keeping pace with the evolution of student learning. The text still contains the most accurate macroscopic-to-molecular illustrations, consistent step-by-step worked problems, and an extensive collection of end-of-chapter problems, with a wide range of difficulties and applications targeting student interests in engineering, medicine, materials, and environmental studies. Changes throughout the text have made it more succinct, the artwork more teachable and modern, and the design more open and inviting. And, while the content has certainly been updated to reflect chemistry's growing impact in the world, the mechanisms of the text—the teaching approaches that are so admired and emulated—have remained the same. Three hallmarks make this text a market leader.

Visualizing Chemical Models— Macroscopic to Molecular

Chemistry deals with observable changes caused by unobservable atomic-scale events, requiring an understanding of a size gap of mind-boggling proportions. One of the text's goals coincides with that of so many instructors: to help the student visualize chemical events on the molecular scale. Thus, concepts are explained first at the macroscopic level and then from a molecular point of view, with the text's groundbreaking illustrations always placed next to the discussion to bring the point home for today's visually oriented students.

Thinking Logically to Solve Problems

The problem-solving approach, based on the four-step method widely accepted by experts in chemical education, is introduced in Chapter 1 and employed *consistently* throughout the text. It encourages students to *plan* a logical approach to a problem, and only then proceed to *solve* it. Each sample problem includes a *check,* which fosters the habit of "taking a breath" to assess the reasonableness and magnitude of the answer. Finally, for *practice* and reinforcement, each sample problem is followed immediately by a similar follow-up problem, for which an abbreviated solution, not merely a numerical answer, is given at the end of the chapter. In this edition, solving problems and visualizing models have been married through an increasing number of molecular-scene problems in both worked examples and homework sets.

Applying Ideas to the Real World

An understanding of modern chemistry influences attitudes about climate change and health care, while also explaining the spring in a running shoe and the display of a laptop screen. Today's students may enter one of the emerging chemistry-related hybrid fields—biomaterials science or planetary geochemistry, for example—and their text should point out the relevance of chemical concepts to such career directions. The *Chemical Connections* and *Tools of the Laboratory* boxed essays (which now include problems to reinforce learning), the fewer but more pedagogic margin notes, and the many applications woven into the chapter content are up-to-date, student-friendly features that complement the text content.

REFINING THE STANDARD: AN EVOLVING LEARNING SYSTEM

Just as the field of chemistry is addressing major changes in the world, the student learning experience is changing as well—different math and reading preparation, less time for traditional studying, electronic media as part of daily lectures and homework, new challenges and options in career choices, and so on. To address these dynamic times, a modern general chemistry text supported by a suite of robust electronic tools for professor and student must continue to evolve, as this text has through all previous editions. From first to second edition, a major emphasis was placed on creating more molecular art to help students visualize chemistry at that level. The third edition incorporated many revised sample problems and a plethora of new end-of-chapter problems. The fourth edition gave birth to molecular-scene sample problems to help students understand concepts through simple molecular depictions. Molecular scenes became so popular that the fifth edition tripled the number of sample problems and doubled the number of end-of-chapter problems using them. During these revisions, major content improvements took place in limiting-reactant stoichiometry, green chemistry, biomolecular structure, kinetics and equilibrium, entropy and free energy, and nuclear chemistry, among many other areas.

With each edition, students and instructors alike have been involved in refining the text. Especially in preparation for the sixth edition, the author, together with key members of the editorial, sales, and marketing teams, consulted extensively with student and faculty users. From chapter reviews, focus groups, symposia, class tests, and one-on-one interviews with instructors, we were gratified to learn that everyone loved the pioneering, and still the most accurate, molecular art; the stepwise problem-solving approach, time-honored and consistent with decades of education research; the abundant mix of qualitative, basic quantitative, and applied end-of-chapter problems; and the thorough, student-friendly coverage of mainstream topics.

Based on this feedback, our revision for this edition focuses on "refining the standard" set earlier: distilling the writing to be concise and direct, opening up the overall appearance of pages, and improving illustrations by shortening legends and adding explanations into the art. We are delighted to introduce the sixth edition of *Chemistry: The Molecular Nature of Matter and Change,* which moves further toward perfecting content and approach in these ways:

Chapter openings, simplified. A familiar application and photo engage the student, followed by a bulleted list of main topics covered in the chapter.

Writing style and content presentation. Every line of every discussion has been revised to optimize clarity, readability, and a more direct presentation of ideas. The use of additional subheads, numbered (and titled) paragraphs, and bulleted (and titled) lists has eliminated long unbroken paragraphs. Main ideas are delineated and highlighted, making for more efficient study and lectures. As a result, the text is over 70 pages shorter, yet no key topics have been removed.

Problem-solving format. The much admired and duplicated four-part (plan, solution, check, practice) *Sample Problems* are displayed cleanly. Both data-based and molecular-scene problems occur throughout, and, to deepen understanding, most *Follow-Up Problems* have worked-out solutions at the back of each chapter, with a road map when appropriate, effectively doubling the number of worked problems. This edition has 15 more sample problems—many in the earlier chapters, where students need the most practice and confidence.

Art and figure legends. The innovative art that raised the bar in chemistry textbooks is still present, with many figures made more realistic and modern. Moreover, figure legends have been greatly shortened and their explanations added to neighboring text and the figures themselves for greater comprehension and less redundancy.

Page design and layout. A more open look invites the reader with cleaner margins and more white space, yet with the same attention to keeping text, figures, and tables near each other for easier viewing and studying.

Incorporating relevance. Applications make chemistry meaningful, so many exciting ideas from the margin notes and galleries of the fifth edition have been incorporated directly into the text, where they are more likely to be read. The boxed essays—*Chemical Connections* and *Tools of the Laboratory*—are more concise and are now accompanied by several homework problems to make them more useful for student and teacher.

Section Summaries. This universally approved feature is even easier to use in its new bulleted format.

Chapter review. Our unique *Chapter Review Guide* aids study by presenting concepts to understand and skills to master, key terms, key equations, and the multistep *Brief Solutions to Follow-Up Problems* (rather than simple numerical answers).

End-of-chapter problem sets. With an enhanced design to improve readability and traditional and molecular-scene problems updated and revised, these problem sets, more extensive than in most other texts, provide students and teachers with abundant choices in a wide range of difficulty and set in real-life scenarios.

Content Changes to Individual Chapters

- Chapter 2 presents a new figure and table on molecular modeling.
- Discussion of empirical formulas has been moved from Chapter 2 to Chapter 3 so it appears just before molecular formulas.
- Within Chapter 3, some sample problems have been segmented and seven new sample problems introduced to better focus problem-solving on distinct concepts.
- Chapter 3 contains more extensive use of stoichiometry reaction tables in limiting-reactant problems.
- Chapter 4 presents a new molecular-scene sample problem on depicting an ionic compound in aqueous solution.
- Chapter 5 includes a new subsection on how gas laws apply to breathing.
- Chapter 5 also contains new short discussions on the relevance of gas density.
- Also in Chapter 5, coverage of reaction stoichiometry has been more logically grouped with other rearrangements of the ideal gas law.
- Chapter 5 contains new illustrations of diffusion and origin of pressure.
- In Chapter 5, *Chemical Connections to Atmospheric Science* uses the gas laws to explain why the troposphere has a uniform composition.
- Chapter 7 includes a new sample problem on using the Rydberg equation.
- Chapter 8 contains a new subsection covering electron configuration, chemical reactivity, and redox behavior.

- In Chapter 9, *Tools of the Laboratory: Infrared Spectroscopy* contains a new discussion of carbon dioxide in global warming.
- Chapter 11 includes a new discussion of limitations to *d*-orbital hybridization.
- Chapter 12 presents new short discussions of everyday applications of surface tension, capillarity, and viscosity.
- Chapter 13 presents everyday applications of freezing point depression and osmotic pressure.
- The fifth edition's *Interchapter* has been deleted, but key figures have been placed in relevant locations within other chapters.
- Chapter 14 provides a thorough, focused survey of main-group descriptive chemistry.
- Chapter 15 contains new art for the molecular biology of protein synthesis and DNA replication.
- Chapter 16 incorporates two of the fifth edition's boxed features—on measuring reaction rates and on enzymes—into the chapter text.
- Chapter 17 makes consistent use of benchmarks for determining when an assumption is valid.
- Chapter 17 incorporates the fifth edition's boxed feature on ammonia production into the chapter text.
- Chapter 19 incorporates the fifth edition's boxed feature on cave formation into the chapter text.

Flexibility in Topic and Chapter Presentation

Chemistry: The Molecular Nature of Matter and Change has been revised to keep the mainstream topic sequence working optimally for teacher and student. But every course is unique, so flexibility has been built in: many section and subsection breaks allow topics to be rearranged with minimal loss of continuity. For example, redox balancing can be covered in Chapter 4, in Chapter 21, or, as done in the text, in both Chapter 4 (oxidation-number method) *and* Chapter 21 (half-reaction method, in preparation for electrochemistry). Likewise, several chapters can be taught in different orders. For instance, gases (Chapter 5) can be covered in sequence to explore the mathematical modeling of physical behavior or, with no loss of continuity, just before liquids and solids (Chapter 12) to show the effects of intermolecular forces on the three states of matter. In fact, feedback has indicated that many instructors move chapters, sections, and topics around, for example, covering descriptive chemistry (Chapter 14) and organic chemistry (Chapter 15) in

the more traditional placement at the end of the course. Because the topic sequence is so flexible, any instructor can feel comfortable making such changes to suit his or her course.

KEEPING PACE WITH THE EVOLUTION OF STUDENT LEARNING

Many of us don't have the same cell phones, computers, or cars that we did just a few years ago—because technology is improving. In much the same way, the Silberberg Learning System has also been improving. The fifth edition of this text was accompanied by an online homework program called ARIS. Through careful observation of students and collaboration with instructors, the online homework tool has evolved into an online learning and engagement tool: **Connect:™ Chemistry.** The goal of Connect: Chemistry is to usher in a new era of meaningful online learning that balances the conceptual and quantitative aspect of this most vital discipline.

With this sixth edition, McGraw-Hill is offering students and instructors a greatly enhanced digital homework experience through Connect: Chemistry. Each problem formerly in the ARIS system has been carefully converted into the new program. Within Connect: Chemistry, each problem retains Silberberg's problem-solving methodology and is enhanced with specific hints, as well as feedback for common incorrect answers—all authored and accuracy-checked by teams of dedicated chemistry professors with many years of classroom experience. Several rounds of editorial revising and more expert checking, in addition to numerous instructor and student tests of all problems, ensure the accuracy and pedagogic soundness of all content.

In addition to the specific hints and feedback, many problems offer students the opportunity to engage in chemical drawing that can be assessed directly within their homework. To provide this important pedagogic experience, Connect: Chemistry has partnered with CambridgeSoft's® ChemDraw, widely considered the "gold standard" of scientific drawing programs and *the* cornerstone application for drawing and annotating molecules, reactions, and pathways. This collaboration of Connect: Chemistry and ChemDraw features an easy-to-use, intuitive, and comprehensive course management and homework system with professional-grade drawing capabilities.

THE SILBERBERG LEARNING SYSTEM

Many pedagogic tools are woven throughout the chapters to guide students on their learning journey.

Chapter Openers

Each chapter introduces a familiar application and photo relating to the main topic of the chapter, followed by a bulleted list of main topics. The chapter outline shows the sequence of topics and subtopics. At the top of the opposite page, *Concepts and Skills to Review* lists key material from earlier chapters that students should understand before starting to read the current one.

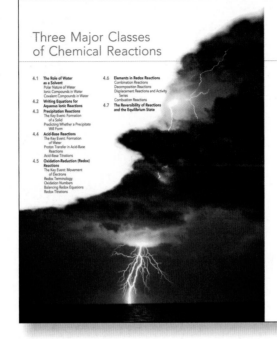

Problem Solving

A worked-out *Sample Problem* appears whenever an important new concept or skill is introduced. The problem-solving step helps students think through chemistry problems logically and systematically. The universally accepted four-step approach of plan, solve, check, and practice is used consistently for every sample problem in the text. The steps are:

- **Plan** analyzes the problem so that students can use what is known to find what is unknown. This step develops the habit of thinking through the solution before performing calculations. Most quantitative problems are accompanied in the margin by a *Road Map*, a block diagram that is specific to the problem and leads students visually through the planned steps.
- **Solution** presents the calculation steps *in the same order* as they appear in the plan and in the road map.
- **Check** fosters the habit of going over one's work with a rough calculation to make sure the answer is both chemically and mathematically reasonable—a great way to avoid careless errors. In many cases, this step is followed by a *Comment* that identifies an additional insight, alternative approach, or common mistake to avoid.
- **Follow-Up Problem** presents a similar problem to provide immediate practice, with an abbreviated multistep solution appearing at the end of the chapter. Where appropriate in the first several chapters, students are asked to draw their own road map to solve the follow-up problem.

Sample Problem 3.13 **Balancing an Equation from a Molecular Scene**

Problem The following molecular scenes depict an important reaction in nitrogen chemistry (nitrogen is blue; oxygen is red):

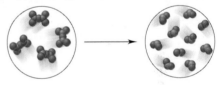

Write a balanced equation for this reaction.

Plan To write a balanced equation, we first have to determine the formulas of the molecules and obtain coefficients by counting the number of each molecule. Then, we arrange this information in the correct equation format, using the smallest whole-number coefficients and including states of matter.

Solution The reactant circle shows only one type of molecule. It has two N and five O atoms, so the formula is N_2O_5; there are four of these molecules. The product circle shows two different molecules, one with one N and two O atoms, and the other with two O atoms; there are eight NO_2 and two O_2. Thus, we have:

$$4N_2O_5 \longrightarrow 8NO_2 + 2O_2$$

Writing the balanced equation with the smallest whole-number coefficients and all substances as gases:

$$2N_2O_5(g) \longrightarrow 4NO_2(g) + O_2(g)$$

Check Reactant (4 N, 10 O) $\longrightarrow$ products (4 N, 8 + 2 = 10 O)

Follow-Up Problem 3.13 Write a balanced equation for the important atmospheric reaction depicted below (carbon is black; oxygen is red):

Three-Level Illustrations

As the art that set the standard for chemistry textbooks, these illustrations connect the macroscopic and molecular levels of reality with the symbolic level in the form of a chemical equation.

Figure 5.12 Collecting a water-insoluble gaseous product and determining its pressure.

Annotated Figures

Modern, explanatory figures describe chemical processes through instructional labeling and realistic, three-dimensional art.

Optimized Presentation

Text paragraphs have been made more concise, with presentation of content optimized through the use of subheads, numbered paragraphs, and lists. Main ideas are delineated, resulting in a more student-friendly study format.

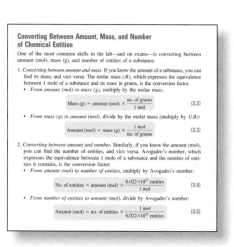

Applications

Chemical Connections essays show the interdisciplinary nature of chemistry by applying chemical principles directly to related scientific fields, including physiology, geology, biochemistry, engineering, and environmental science. *Tools of the Laboratory* essays describe the key instruments and techniques that chemists use in modern practice to obtain the data that underlie their theories. Both essay features now include several problems to enhance learning and relevance.

Section Summaries

Concise, bulleted summary lists conclude each section, restating the major ideas just covered.

Chapter Review Guide

A rich catalog of study aids ends each chapter to help students review its content.

- **Learning Objectives,** with section and/or sample problem numbers, focus on key concepts and skills.
- **Key Terms** are boldfaced and defined within the chapter and listed here by section (with page numbers), as well as being defined again in the *Glossary*.
- **Key Equations and Relationships** are screened and numbered within the chapter and listed here with page numbers.
- **Brief Solutions to Follow-Up Problems** double the number of worked problems by providing multistep calculations at the ends of the chapters, rather than just a numerical answer at the back of the book. Road maps are supplied for those follow-up problems that ask students to prepare one in planning their solution.

End-of-Chapter Problems

An exceptionally large number of qualitative, quantitative, and molecular-scene homework problems end each chapter. Three types of problems are keyed by chapter section, with comprehensive problems following:

- **Concept Review Questions** test students' qualitative understanding of key ideas.
- **Skill-Building Exercises** are grouped in pairs that cover a similar idea, with one of each pair answered in the back of the book. These exercises begin with simple questions and increase in difficulty, gradually eliminating students' need for multistep directions.
- **Problems in Context** apply the skills learned in the skill-building exercises to interesting scenarios, including examples from industry, medicine, and the environment.
- **Comprehensive Problems,** most based on realistic applications, are more challenging and rely on concepts and skills from any section of the current chapter or from previous chapters.

LEARNING SYSTEM RESOURCES FOR INSTRUCTORS

www.mcgrawhillconnect.com/chemistry

McGraw-Hill Connect is a web-based, interactive assignment and assessment platform that incorporates cognitive science principles to customize the learning process. The chemical drawing tool found within Connect: Chemistry is CambridgeSoft's ChemDraw, which is widely considered the "gold standard" of scientific drawing programs and the cornerstone application for drawing and annotating molecules, reactions, and pathways. This combination of Connect and ChemDraw is an easy-to-use, intuitive, and comprehensive course management and homework system with professional-grade drawing capabilities.

End-of-chapter problems from this textbook are available in Connect: Chemistry for instructors to build assignments that are automatically graded and tracked through reports that export easily to Excel. Instructors can edit existing problems and write entirely new problems; track individual student performance—by problem, assignment, concept, or in relation to the class overall—with automatic grading; provide instant feedback to students; and store detailed grade reports securely online. Grade reports can be easily integrated with learning management systems such as WebCT and Blackboard. Single sign-on integration is available with the Blackboard course management system. Within Connect, instructors can also create and share materials with colleagues. Ask your McGraw-Hill representative for more information, and then check it out at www.mcgrawhillconnect.com/chemistry.

Blackboard Course Management Integration with McGraw-Hill Content

Do More

McGraw-Hill Higher Education and Blackboard, the Web-based course-management system, have teamed up to allow students and faculty to easily use online materials and activities to complement face-to-face teaching. Blackboard features exciting social learning and teaching tools that foster more logical, visually impactful, and active learning opportunities for students. This partnership transforms closed-door classrooms into communities where students remain connected to their educational experience 24 hours a day.

This partnership allows instructors and students access to McGraw-Hill's Connect™ and Create™ from within Blackboard—with a single sign-on.

Instructors also get deep integration of McGraw-Hill content and content engines into Blackboard. Whether choosing a book for your course or building Connect™ assignments, all the tools you need are right where you want them—inside Blackboard.

Gradebooks are now seamless. When a student completes an integrated Connect™ assignment, the grade for that assignment is automatically (and instantly) fed to the Blackboard grade center.

McGraw-Hill and Blackboard now offer easy access to industry-leading technology and content, whether your campus hosts it, or we do. Be sure to ask your local McGraw-Hill representative for details.

Presentation Center   Accessed from your textbook's Connect website, Presentation Center is an online digital library containing McGraw-Hill owned photos, artwork, animations, and other types of media that can be used to create customized lectures, visually enhanced tests and quizzes, compelling course websites, or attractive printed support materials for classroom purposes. The visual resources in this collection include the following:

- **Art** Full-color digital files of all illustrations in the book can be readily incorporated into lecture presentations, exams, or custom-made classroom materials. In addition, all files have been inserted into PowerPoint slides for ease of lecture preparation.
- **Photos** The photo collection contains digital files of photographs from the text, which can be reproduced for multiple classroom uses.
- **Tables** Every table that appears in the text has been saved in electronic form for use in classroom presentations and/or classroom materials.

- **Animations** Numerous full-color animations illustrating important processes are also provided. Harness the visual impact of concepts in motion by importing these files into classroom presentations or online course materials.

PowerPoint materials can also be accessed through your textbook's Connect website:

- **PowerPoint Lecture Outlines** Ready-made presentations that combine art and lecture notes are provided for each chapter of the text.
- **PowerPoint Slides** For instructors who prefer to create their lectures from scratch, all illustrations, photos, sample problems, and tables have been inserted into blank PowerPoint slides, arranged by chapter.

The Presentation Center library includes thousands of assets from many McGraw-Hill titles. This ever-growing resource gives instructors the power to utilize assets specific to an adopted textbook as well as content from all other books in the library. Accessed through the instructor side of your textbook's Connect website, Presentation Center's dynamic search engine allows you to explore by discipline, course, textbook chapter, asset type, or keyword. Simply browse, select, and download the files you need to build engaging course materials. To access Connect, request registration information from your McGraw-Hill sales representative.

Tegrity campus

Digital Lecture Capture: Tegrity McGraw-Hill *Tegrity Campus* records and distributes your lecture with just a click of a button. Students can view anytime/anywhere via computer, iPod, or mobile device. *Tegrity* indexes as it records your slideshow presentations and anything shown on your computer, so students can use keywords to find exactly what they want to study.

Computerized Test Bank Prepared by Walter Orchard, Professor Emeritus of Tacoma Community College, over 2300 test questions to accompany *Chemistry: The Molecular Nature of Matter and Change* are available utilizing Brownstone's Diploma testing software. *Diploma's* software allows you to quickly create a customized test using McGraw-Hill's supplied questions or by authoring your own. *Diploma* allows you to create your tests without an Internet connection—just download the software and question files directly to your computer.

Instructor's Solutions Manual This supplement, prepared by Patricia Amateis of Virginia Tech, contains complete, worked-out solutions for *all* the end-of-chapter problems in the text. It can be found within the Instructors Resources, on the Connect: Chemistry site.

Content Delivery Flexibility *Chemistry: The Molecular Nature of Matter and Change,* by Martin Silberberg, is available in other formats in addition to the traditional textbook, giving instructors and students more choices for the format of their chemistry text.

create

- **Customizable Textbooks: Create** McGraw-Hill Create™ is a new, self-service website that allows you to create custom course materials—print or eBook—by drawing on McGraw-Hill's comprehensive, cross-disciplinary content. Add your own content quickly and easily. Tap into other rights-secured third-party sources as well. Then, arrange the content in a way that makes the most sense for your course. Even personalize your book with your course name and information. Choose the best format for your course: color print, black-and-white print, or ebook (which is viewable on an iPad). And when you are finished customizing, you will receive a free PDF review copy in just minutes. Visit McGraw-Hill Create at www.mcgrawhillcreate.com today and begin building your perfect book.
- **ConnectPlus eBook** McGraw-Hill's ConnectPlus eBook takes digital texts beyond a simple PDF. With the same content as the printed book, but optimized for the screen, the ConnectPlus eBook has embedded media, including animations and videos, which bring concepts to life and provide "just in time" learning for students. Additionally, fully integrated homework problems allow students to interact with the problems to determine if they're gaining mastery of the content, and the problems can also be assigned by the instructor.

Cooperative Chemistry Laboratory Manual Prepared by Melanie Cooper of Clemson University, this innovative manual features open-ended problems designed to simulate experience in a research lab. Working in groups, students investigate one problem over a period of several weeks, so they might complete three or four projects during the semester, rather than one preprogrammed experiment per class. The emphasis is on experimental design, analytic problem solving, and communication.

LEARNING SYSTEM RESOURCES FOR STUDENTS

Student Study Guide   This valuable study guide, prepared by Libby Bent Weberg, is designed to help you recognize your learning style; understand how to read, classify, and create a plan for solving a problem; and practice your problem-solving skills. For each section of each chapter, the guide provides study objectives and a summary of the corresponding text. Following the summary are sample problems with detailed solutions. Each chapter has true-false questions and a self-test, with all answers provided at the end of the chapter.

Student Solutions Manual   This supplement, prepared by Patricia Amateis of Virginia Tech, contains detailed solutions and explanations for all problems in the main text that have colored numbers.

Connect: Chemistry   With Connect: Chemistry, you can practice solving assigned homework problems using the Silberberg problem-solving methodology applied in the textbook. Algorithmic problems serve up multiple versions of similar problems for mastery of content, with hints and feedback for common incorrect answers to help you stay on track. Where appropriate, you engage in accurate, professional-grade chemical drawing through the use of CambridgeSoft's ChemDraw tool, which is implemented directly into homework problems. Check it out at www.mcgraw-hillconnect.com/chemistry.

LearnSmart™

LearnSmart™   This adaptive diagnostic learning system, powered by Connect: Chemistry and based on artificial intelligence, constantly assesses your knowledge of the course material. As you work within the system, LearnSmart develops a personal learning path adapted to what you have actively learned and retained. This innovative study tool also has features to allow your instructor to see exactly what you have accomplished, with a built-in assessment tool for graded assignments. You can access LearnSmart for general chemistry by going to www.mcgraw-hillconnect.com/chemistry.

Animations for MP3/iPod   A number of animations are available for download to your MP3/iPod through the textbook's Connect website.

Acknowledgments

The sixth edition and its associated learning system are the culmination of numerous chapter reviews, insightful suggestions, brainstorming sessions, focus groups, interviews, and class tests. Each person involved played an important part in the revision of the text and its ancillaries.

I feel very fortunate to have a relationship with my publisher based on mutual respect, shared goals, and warm friendship. Heading the McGraw-Hill Higher Education team with their advice and support were Publisher Ryan Blankenship and Executive Editor Jeff Huettman, Developmental Editor Donna Nemmers, Director of Digital Content David Spurgeon, Digital Project Manager Daryl Bruflodt, Project Manager Peggy Selle, Designer David Hash, and Marketing Manager Tami Hodge.

Patricia Amateis, Virginia Tech, helped revise several chapters and prepared Appendix E as well as the Instructor's and Student Solutions Manuals. Krishnan Rajeshwar, University of Texas–Arlington, updated the discussion of the future of energy use.

I am very grateful to the Board of Advisors, who helped me make this text the optimum teaching tool: Debra Feakes, Texas State University–San Marcos, Derek Gragson, California Polytechnic State University–San Luis Obispo, and James Reeves, University of North Carolina–Wilmington. Also, my deepest gratitude extends to the following individuals, who attended focus groups or symposia, provided content reviews, and class-tested materials in preparation for the Sixth Edition and its associated learning system:

Patricia Amateis, *Virginia Tech*
Margaret Asirvatham, *University of Colorado—Boulder*
Yiyan Bai, *Houston Community College–Central*
Laurance Beauvais, *San Diego State University*
Thomas Bertolini, *University of Southern California*
Fereshteh Billiot, *Texas A&M University–Corpus Christi*
Deborah Booth, *University of Southern Mississippi*
Simon Bott, *University of Houston*
Stacey Lowery Bretz, *Miami University of Ohio*
Karen Brewer, *Virginia Tech*
Les Butler, *Louisiana State University*
Bindu Chakravarty, *Houston Community College–Northeast Campus*
Chris Cheatum, *University of Iowa*
Liwei Chen, *Ohio University*
Tom Clausen, *University of Alaska–Fairbanks*
Erin Dahlke, *Loras College*
Michelle Driessen, *University of Minnesota*
Jack Duff, *Southern Polytechnic State University*
Bill Durham, *University of Arkansas*
Emmanuel Ewane, *Houston Community College–Northwest*
Deborah Exton, *University of Oregon*
Paul Fazen, *Villanova University*
David Frank, *California State University–Fresno*
John Gelder, *Oklahoma State University*
Greg Gellene, *Texas Tech University*
Dimitri Giarikos, *Nova Southeastern University*

Michael Greenlief, *University of Missouri–Columbia*
Todor Gounev, *University of Missouri–Kansas City*
John Hagen, *California Polytechnic State University–San Luis Obispo*
Michael Hailu, *Columbus State Community College*
John Halpin, *New York University*
Narayan Hosmane, *Northern Illinois University*
Larry Houk, *University of Memphis*
Eihab Jaber, *Worcester State University*
Heiko Jacobsen, *Tulane University*
Richard Jarman, *College of DuPage*
Steve Keller, *University of Missouri*
San Kim, *Northern Virginia Community College*
Chuck Kirkpatrick, *St. Louis University*
Marina Koether, *Kennesaw State University*
Patric Kolniak, *Louisiana State University*
Pamela Kraemer, *Northern Virginia Community College*
Jothi Kumar, *North Carolina A&T State University*
Dorothy B. Kurland, *Emeritus, West Virginia Institute of Technology*
Anna Larsen, *Ithaca College*
Allison Long, *Georgia Southern University*
Jeanette Madea, *Broward Community College*
Diana Malone, *Clarke University*
Lisa McGaw, *University of Central Oklahoma*
Thomas McGrath, *Baylor University*
Danny McGuire, *Cameron University*
Bill McLaughlin, *Montana State University*
Lauren McMills, *Ohio University*
Joyce Miller, *San Jacinto College–South*

Kristine Miller, *Anne Arundel Community College*
Jeremy Mitchell-Koch, *Emporia State University*
Debbie Mohler, *James Madison University*
Kereen Monteyne, *University of Northern Kentucky*
Mahesh Narayan, *University of Texas–El Paso*
Jessica Orvis, *Georgia Southern University*
Jason Overby, *College of Charleston*
Richard Paselk, *Humboldt State University*
Louis Pignolet, *Emeritus, University of Minnesota*
John Pollard, *The University of Arizona*
Bernard Powell, *University of Texas–San Antonio*
William Quintana, *New Mexico State University*
Edward Quitevis, *Texas Tech University*
Jeff Rack, *Ohio University*
Lisa Reece, *Ozarks Technical Community College*
Michelle Richards-Babb, *West Virginia University*
Dawn Rickey, *Colorado State University*
Thomas Ridgway, *University of Cincinnati*
Steven Rowley, *Middlesex County College*
Raymond Sadeghi, *University of Texas–San Antonio*
Issa Salame, *The City College of New York*
Jim Satterlee, *Washington State University*
Colleen Scott, *Southern Illinois University–Carbondale*
Thomas Selegue, *Pima Community College*
Steve Shore, *Oklahoma City Community College*
Michael Sommer, *University of Wyoming*
Jie Song, *University of Michigan–Flint*

David Speckhard, *Loras College*
Rick Spinney, *Ohio State University*
Emelyn S. Q. Tan, *National University of Singapore*
Kimberly Trick, *University of Dayton*

Cyriacus Uzomba, *Austin Community College*
Debbie Warnaar, *James Madison University*
Lyle Wescott, *University of Mississippi*
Wayne Wesolowski, *The University of Arizona*

Daniel Williams, *Kennesaw State University*
Stephanie Wunder, *Temple University*
Timothy Zauche, *University of Wisconsin–Platteville*
Lin Zhu, *IUPUI*

Connect: Chemistry has been greatly enhanced by the efforts of Kereen Monteyne, University of Northern Kentucky; MaryKay Orgill, University of Nevada–Las Vegas; and Yasmin Patell, Kansas State University; who did a masterful job of authoring hints and feedback to augment all of the system's homework problems. The following individuals helped write and review learning goal–oriented content for **LearnSmart for General Chemistry:** Margaret Asirvatham, University of Colorado–Boulder; William Burns, Arkansas State University; Cabot-Ann Christofferson, South Dakota School of Mines; Christina Johnson, University of California–San Diego; Adam I. Keller, Columbus State Community College; Willem R. Leenstra, University of Vermont; Margaret Ruth Leslie, Kent State University; Benjamin R. Martin, Texas State University–San Marcos; Kathy Thrush Shaginaw, Particular Solutions, Inc.; and Erin Whitteck.

Several expert freelancers contributed as well. As always, Jane Hoover did an excellent copyediting of the textbook, and Francine Banwarth and Rose Kramer followed with meticulous proofreading. John Murdzek and LaurelTech exercised careful skill in accuracy-checking content within Connect: Chemistry.

Over the years and editions, I've always had the great benefit of the expertise of my "in-home" team. This time around, my son, Daniel, offered his keen artist's eye to the figures revised, the photos selected, and the cover devised. And my wife, Ruth, made this text come to fruition—literally. She worked closely with the McGraw-Hill production team and provided indispensable, detailed input to the compositor, copy editor, and proof readers. And, of course, they both kept the author going with their love and support.

Keys to the Study of Chemistry

Concepts and skills to review before you study this chapter

- exponential (scientific) notation (Appendix A)

Maybe you're taking this course because chemistry is fundamental to understanding other natural sciences. Maybe it's required for your medical or engineering major. Or maybe you just want to learn more about the impact of chemistry on society or even on a personal, everyday level. For example, did you have cereal, fruit, and coffee for breakfast today? In chemical terms, you enjoyed nutrient-enriched, spoilage-retarded carbohydrate flakes mixed in a white emulsion of fats, proteins, and monosaccharides, with a piece of fertilizer-grown, pesticide-treated fruit, and a cup of hot aqueous extract of stimulating alkaloid. Earlier, you may have been awakened by the sound created as molecules aligned in the liquid-crystal display of your clock and electrons flowed to create a noise. You might have thrown off a thermal insulator of manufactured polymer and jumped in the shower to emulsify fatty substances on your skin and hair with purified water and formulated detergents. Perhaps you next adorned yourself in an array of pleasant-smelling pigmented gels, dyed polymeric fibers, synthetic footwear, and metal-alloy jewelry. After breakfast, you probably abraded your teeth with a colloidal dispersion of artificially flavored, dental-hardening agents, grabbed your laptop (an electronic device containing ultrathin, microetched semiconductor layers powered by a series of voltaic cells), collected some books (processed cellulose and plastic, electronically printed with light- and oxygen-resistant inks), hopped in your hydrocarbon-fueled, metal-vinyl-ceramic vehicle, electrically ignited a synchronized series of controlled gaseous explosions, and took off for class!

But the true impact of chemistry extends much farther than the commercial products of daily life. The truth is the most profound biological and environmental questions ultimately have chemical answers: How does an organism reproduce, grow, and age? What are the underlying explanations for health and disease? How can we sustain a planetary ecosystem in which plant, animal, and human populations thrive? Is there life on other worlds?

So, no matter what your reason for studying chemistry, you're going to learn some amazing ideas. And, this course comes with a bonus for developing two mental skills. The first, common to all science courses, is the ability to solve problems systematically. The second is specific to chemistry, for as you comprehend its ideas, you begin to view a hidden reality, one filled with incredibly minute particles moving at fantastic speeds, colliding billions of times a second, and interacting in ways that allow your brain to translate fluxes of electric charge into thoughts and that determine how all the matter inside and outside of you behaves. This chapter holds the keys to unlock and enter this new world.

IN THIS CHAPTER . . . We discuss some central ideas about matter and energy, the process of science, units of measurement, and how scientists handle data.
- We begin with fundamental concepts about matter and energy and their changes.
- A brief discussion of chemistry's origins, including some major missteps, leads to an overview of how scientists build models to study nature.
- We consider systematic chemical problem solving, including unit conversion and modern unit systems for mass, length, volume, density, and temperature.
- We see that data collection always includes some uncertainty and examine the distinction between accuracy and precision.

1.1 • SOME FUNDAMENTAL DEFINITIONS

A good place to begin our exploration of chemistry is to define it and a few central concepts. **Chemistry** is *the study of matter and its properties, the changes that matter undergoes, and the energy associated with those changes.*

The Properties of Matter

Matter is the "stuff" of the universe: air, glass, planets, students—*anything that has mass and volume.* (In Section 1.5, we discuss the meanings of mass and volume in terms of how they are measured.) Chemists want to know the **composition** of matter, *the types and amounts of simpler substances that make it up.* A *substance* is a type of matter that has a defined, fixed composition.

We learn about matter by observing its **properties,** *the characteristics that give each substance its unique identity.* To identify a person, we might observe height, weight, hair and eye color, fingerprints, and, now, even DNA pattern, until we arrive at a unique identification. To identify a substance, we observe two types of properties, physical and chemical, which are closely related to two types of change that matter undergoes:

- **Physical properties** are characteristics a substance shows *by itself, without changing into or interacting with another substance.* These properties include melting point, electrical conductivity, and density. A **physical change** occurs when a substance *alters its physical properties, **not** its composition.* For example, when ice melts, several physical properties change, such as hardness, density, and ability to flow. But the composition of the sample does *not* change: it is still water. The photograph in Figure 1.1A shows what this change looks like in everyday life. The "blow-up" circles depict a magnified view of the particles making up the sample. In the icicle, the particles lie in a repeating pattern, whereas they are jumbled in the droplet, but *the particles are the same* in both forms of water.

  Physical change (same substance before and after):

  Water (solid form) $\longrightarrow$ water (liquid form)

- **Chemical properties** are characteristics a substance shows *as it changes into or interacts with another substance (or substances).* Chemical properties include flammability, corrosiveness, and reactivity with acids. A **chemical change,** also called a **chemical reaction,** occurs when *a substance (or substances) is converted into a different substance (or substances).* Figure 1.1B shows the chemical change (reaction) that occurs when you pass an electric current through water: the water decomposes

Solid water

Liquid water

Hydrogen gas

Oxygen gas

A Physical change:
*Solid form of water becomes liquid form. Particles before and after remain the same, which means composition did **not** change.*

B Chemical change:
*Electric current decomposes water into different substances (hydrogen and oxygen). Particles before and after are different, which means composition **did** change.*

Figure 1.1 The distinction between physical and chemical change.

(breaks down) into two other substances, hydrogen and oxygen, that bubble into the tubes. The composition *has* changed: the final sample is no longer water.

Chemical change (different substances before and after):

$$\text{Water} \xrightarrow{\text{electric current}} \text{hydrogen} + \text{oxygen}$$

Let's work through a sample problem that uses atomic-scale scenes to distinguish between physical and chemical change.

Sample Problem 1.1 | **Visualizing Change on the Atomic Scale**

Problem The scenes below represent an atomic-scale view of a sample of matter, A, undergoing two different changes, left to B and right to C:

Decide whether each depiction shows a physical or a chemical change.

Plan Given depictions of the changes, we have to determine whether each represents a physical or a chemical change. The number and colors of the little spheres that make up each particle tell its "composition." Samples with particles of the *same* composition but in a different arrangement depict a *physical* change, whereas samples with particles of a *different* composition depict a *chemical* change.

Solution In A, each particle consists of one blue and two red spheres. The particles in A change into two types in B, one made of red and blue spheres and the other made of two red spheres; therefore, they have undergone a chemical change to form different particles. The particles in C are the same as those in A, but they are closer together and arranged differently; therefore, they have undergone a physical change.

Follow-Up Problem 1.1 Is the following change chemical or physical? (Compare your answer with the one in Brief Solutions to Follow-Up Problems at the end of the chapter.)

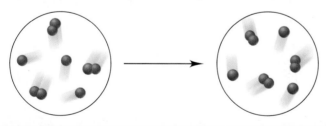

Like water, hydrogen, oxygen, or any other real substance, copper is also identified by *its own set* of physical and chemical properties (Table 1.1 on the next page).

The States of Matter

Matter occurs commonly in *three physical forms* called **states:** solid, liquid, and gas. We'll define the states and see how temperature can change them.

Defining the States On the macroscopic scale, each state of matter is defined by the way the sample fills a container (Figure 1.2, next page, *flasks at top*):

- A **solid** has a fixed shape that does not conform to the container shape. Solids are *not* defined by rigidity or hardness: solid iron is rigid and hard, but solid lead is flexible, and solid wax is soft.

Table 1.1 Some Characteristic Properties of Copper

Physical Properties	Chemical Properties
Easily shaped into sheets (malleable) and wires (ductile)	Slowly forms a blue-green carbonate in moist air
Can be melted and mixed with zinc to form brass	Reacts with nitric or sulfuric acid
Density = 8.95 g/cm³ Melting point = 1083°C Boiling point = 2570°C	Slowly forms deep-blue solution in aqueous ammonia

- A **liquid** has a varying shape that conforms to the container shape, but only to the extent of the liquid's volume; that is, a liquid has *an upper surface.*
- A **gas** also has a varying shape that conforms to the container shape, but it fills the entire container and, thus, does *not* have a surface.

On the atomic scale, each state is defined by the relative positions of its particles (Figure 1.2, *circles at bottom*):

- In a *solid,* the particles lie next to each other in a regular, three-dimensional *array.*
- In a *liquid,* the particles also lie close together but move randomly around each other.
- In a *gas,* the particles have large distances between them and move randomly throughout the container.

Figure 1.2 The physical states of matter.

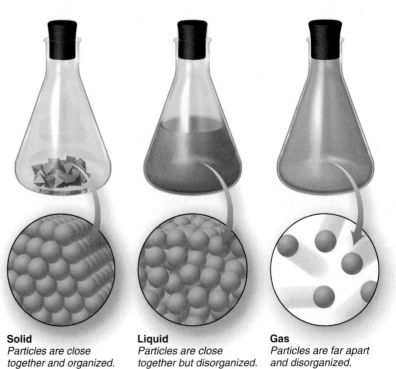

Solid
Particles are close together and organized.

Liquid
Particles are close together but disorganized.

Gas
Particles are far apart and disorganized.

Temperature and Changes of State Depending on the temperature and pressure of the surroundings, many substances can exist in each of the three physical states and undergo changes in state as well. For example, as the temperature increases, solid water melts to liquid water, which boils to gaseous water (also called *water vapor*). Similarly, as the temperature drops, water vapor condenses to liquid water, and with further cooling, the liquid freezes to ice. In a steel plant, solid iron melts to liquid (molten) iron and then cools to the solid again. And, far beyond the confines of a laboratory or steel plant, lakes of molten sulfur lie on Jupiter's moon Io (*see photo*), which is capped by poles of frozen hydrogen sulfide, a gas on Earth.

The main point is that *a physical change caused by heating can generally be reversed by cooling*. This is *not* generally true for a chemical change. For example, heating iron in moist air causes a chemical reaction that yields the brown, crumbly substance known as rust. Cooling does not reverse this change; rather, another chemical change (or series of them) is required.

The following sample problem provides practice in distinguishing some familiar examples of physical and chemical change.

What common substances occur in unusual states on other worlds?

Sample Problem 1.2 Distinguishing Between Physical and Chemical Change

Problem Decide whether each of the following processes is primarily a physical or a chemical change, and explain briefly:
(a) Frost forms as the temperature drops on a humid winter night.
(b) A cornstalk grows from a seed that is watered and fertilized.
(c) A match ignites to form ash and a mixture of gases.
(d) Perspiration evaporates when you relax after jogging.
(e) A silver fork tarnishes slowly in air.

Plan The basic question we ask to decide whether a change is chemical or physical is, "Does the substance change composition or just change form?"

Solution **(a)** Frost forming is a physical change: the drop in temperature changes water vapor (gaseous water) in humid air to ice crystals (solid water).
(b) A seed growing involves chemical change: the seed uses water, substances from air, fertilizer, and soil, and energy from sunlight to make complex changes in composition.
(c) The match burning is a chemical change: the combustible substances in the match head are converted into other substances.
(d) Perspiration evaporating is a physical change: the water in sweat changes its form, from liquid to gas, but not its composition.
(e) Tarnishing is a chemical change: silver changes to silver sulfide by reacting with sulfur-containing substances in the air.

Follow-Up Problem 1.2 Decide whether each of the following processes is primarily a physical or a chemical change, and explain briefly (see Brief Solutions at the end of the chapter):
(a) Purple iodine vapor appears when solid iodine is warmed.
(b) Gasoline fumes are ignited by a spark in an automobile engine's cylinder.
(c) A scab forms over an open cut.

The Central Theme in Chemistry

Understanding the properties of a substance and the changes it undergoes leads to the central theme in chemistry: *macroscopic-scale* properties and behavior, those we can see, are the results of *atomic-scale* properties and behavior that we cannot see. The distinction between chemical and physical change is defined by composition, which we study macroscopically. But composition ultimately depends on the makeup of substances at the atomic scale. Similarly, macroscopic properties of substances in any of the three states arise from atomic-scale behavior of their particles. Picturing

Methane and oxygen form carbon dioxide and water in the flame of a lab burner. (Carbon is black, oxygen red, and hydrogen blue.)

a chemical event on the molecular scale, even one as common as the flame of a laboratory burner (*see margin*), helps clarify what is taking place. What is happening when water boils or copper melts? What events occur in the invisible world of minute particles that cause a seed to grow, a neon light to glow, or a nail to rust? Throughout the text, we return to this central idea:

> We study **observable** changes in matter to understand their **unobservable** causes.

The Importance of Energy in the Study of Matter

Physical and chemical changes are accompanied by energy changes. **Energy** is often defined as *the ability to do work.* Essentially, all work involves moving something. Work is done when your arm lifts a book, when a car's engine moves the wheels, or when a falling rock moves the ground as it lands. The object doing the work (arm, engine, rock) transfers some of the energy it possesses to the object on which the work is done (book, wheels, ground).

The total energy an object possesses is the sum of its potential energy and its kinetic energy.

- **Potential energy** is *the energy due to the **position** of the object relative to other objects.*
- **Kinetic energy** is *the energy due to the **motion** of the object.*

Let's examine four systems that illustrate the relationship between these two forms of energy: a weight raised above the ground, two balls attached by a spring, two electrically charged particles, and a fuel and its waste products. Two concepts central to all these cases are

1. *When energy is converted from one form to the other, it is conserved, not destroyed.*
2. *Situations of lower energy are more stable, and therefore favored, over situations of higher energy (less stable).*

The four cases are

- *A weight raised above the ground* (Figure 1.3A). The energy you exert to lift a weight against gravity, increases the weight's potential energy (energy due to its position). When you drop the weight, that additional potential energy is converted to kinetic energy (energy due to motion). The situation with the weight elevated and higher in potential energy is *less stable,* so the weight will fall when released to result in a situation that is lower in potential energy and *more stable.*
- *Two balls attached by a spring* (Figure 1.3B). When you pull the balls apart, the energy you exert to stretch the relaxed spring increases the system's potential energy. This change in potential energy is converted to kinetic energy when you release the balls. The system of balls and spring is less stable (has more potential energy) when the spring is stretched than when it is relaxed.
- *Two electrically charged particles* (Figure 1.3C). Due to interactions known as *electrostatic forces, opposite charges attract each other, and like charges repel each other.* When energy is exerted to move a positive particle away from a negative one, the potential energy of the system increases, and that increase is converted to kinetic energy when the particles are pulled together by the electrostatic attraction. Similarly, when energy is used to move two positive (or two negative) particles together, their potential energy increases and changes to kinetic energy when they are pushed apart by the electrostatic repulsion. Charged particles move naturally to a more stable situation (lower energy).
- *A fuel and its waste products* (Figure 1.3D). Matter is composed of positively and negatively charged particles. *The chemical potential energy of a substance results from the relative positions of and the attractions and repulsions among its particles.*

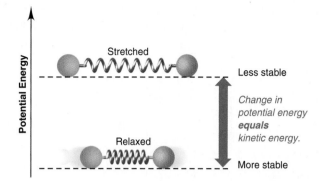

A **A gravitational system.** *Potential energy is gained when a weight is lifted. It is converted to kinetic energy as the weight falls.*

B **A system of two balls attached by a spring.** *Potential energy is gained when the spring is stretched. It is converted to the kinetic energy of the moving balls as the spring relaxes.*

C **A system of oppositely charged particles.** *Potential energy is gained when the charges are separated. It is converted to kinetic energy as the attraction pulls the charges together.*

D **A system of fuel and exhaust.** *A fuel is higher in chemical potential energy than the exhaust. As the fuel burns, some of its potential energy is converted to the kinetic energy of the moving car.*

Some substances are higher in potential energy than others. For example, gasoline and oxygen have more chemical potential energy than the exhaust gases they form. This difference is converted into kinetic energy, which moves the car, heats the interior, makes the lights shine, and so on. Similarly, the difference in potential energy between the food and air we take in and the wastes we excrete enables us to move, grow, keep warm, study chemistry, and so on.

Figure 1.3 Potential energy is converted to kinetic energy. The dashed horizontal lines indicate the potential energy of each system before and after the change.

◼ Summary of Section 1.1

- Chemists study the composition and properties of matter and how they change.
- Each substance has a unique set of *physical* properties (attributes of the substance itself) and *chemical* properties (attributes of the substance as it interacts with or changes to other substances). Changes in matter can be *physical* (different form of the same substance) or *chemical* (different substance).
- Matter exists in three physical states—solid, liquid, and gas. The behavior of each state is due to the arrangement of the particles.
- A physical change caused by heating may be reversed by cooling. But a chemical change caused by heating can be reversed only by other chemical changes.
- Macroscopic changes result from submicroscopic changes.
- Changes in matter are accompanied by changes in energy.
- An object's potential energy is due to its position; an object's kinetic energy is due to its motion. Energy used to lift a weight, stretch a spring, or separate opposite charges increases the system's potential energy, which is converted to kinetic energy as the system returns to its original condition. Energy changes form but is conserved.
- Chemical potential energy arises from the positions and interactions of a substance's particles. When a higher energy (less stable) substance is converted into a more stable (lower energy) substance, some potential energy is converted into kinetic energy.

Figure 1.4 Alchemical apparatus.

1.2 • CHEMICAL ARTS AND THE ORIGINS OF MODERN CHEMISTRY

This brief overview of early breakthroughs, and a few false directions, describes how the modern science of chemistry arose and progressed.

Prechemical Traditions

Chemistry had its origin in a prescientific past that incorporated three overlapping traditions—alchemy, medicine, and technology:

1. *The alchemical tradition. Alchemy* was an occult study of nature that began in the 1st century AD and dominated thinking for over 1500 years. Originally influenced by the Greek idea that matter strives for "perfection," alchemists later became obsessed with converting "baser" metals, such as lead, into "purer" ones, such as gold. The alchemists' names for substances and their belief that matter could be altered magically were very difficult to correct over the centuries. Their legacy to chemistry was in technical methods. They invented distillation, percolation, and extraction and devised apparatus still used routinely today (Figure 1.4). But perhaps even more important was that alchemists encouraged observation and experimentation, which replaced the Greek approach of explaining nature solely through reason.

2. *The medical tradition.* Alchemists also influenced medical practice in medieval Europe. And ever since the 13th century, distillates and extracts of roots, herbs, and other plant matter have been used as sources of medicines. The alchemist and physician Paracelsus (1493–1541) considered the body to be a chemical system and illness an imbalance that could be restored by treatment with drugs. Although many early prescriptions were useless, later ones had increasing success. Thus began the alliance between medicine and chemistry that thrives today.

3. *The technological tradition.* For thousands of years, pottery making, dyeing, and especially metallurgy contributed greatly to people's experience with materials. During the Middle Ages and the Renaissance, books were published that described how to purify, assay, and coin silver and gold, how to use balances, furnaces, and crucibles, and how to make glass and gunpowder. Some introduced quantitative measurement, which was lacking in alchemical writings. Many creations from those times are still marveled at throughout the world. Nevertheless, the skilled artisans showed little interest in *why* a substance changes or *how to predict* its behavior.

The Phlogiston Fiasco and the Impact of Lavoisier

Chemical investigation in the modern sense—inquiry into the causes of changes in matter—began in the late 17th century. At that time, most scientists explained **combustion,** the process of burning, with the *phlogiston theory*. It proposed that combustible materials contain *phlogiston,* an undetectable substance released when the material burns. Highly combustible materials like charcoal were thought to contain a lot of phlogiston, and slightly combustible materials like metals only a little.

But inconsistencies continuously arose.

Phlogiston critics: Why is air needed for combustion, and why does charcoal stop burning in a closed vessel?
Phlogiston supporters: Air "attracts" phlogiston out of the charcoal, and burning stops when the air in the vessel is "saturated" with phlogiston.

Critics also noted that when a metal burns, it forms its *calx,* which weighs more than the metal, leading them to ask,

Critics: How can the *loss* of phlogiston cause a *gain* in mass?
Supporters: Phlogiston has negative mass.

As ridiculous as these responses seem now, it's important to remember that, even today, scientists may dismiss conflicting evidence rather than abandon an accepted idea.

The conflict over phlogiston was resolved when the young French chemist Antoine Lavoisier (1743–1794) performed several experiments:

1. Heating mercury calx decomposed it into two products—mercury and a gas—whose *total mass equaled the starting mass of the calx.*
2. Heating mercury with the gas reformed the calx, yielded mercury and, again, *the total mass remained constant.*
3. Heating mercury in a measured volume of air yielded mercury calx and left four-fifths of the air remaining.
4. A burning candle placed in the remaining air was extinguished.

Lavoisier named the gas *oxygen* and gave metal calxes the name *metal oxides.* His explanation of his results made the phlogiston theory irrelevant:

- Oxygen, a normal component of air, combines with a substance when it burns.
- In a closed container, a combustible substance stops burning when it has combined with all the available oxygen.
- A metal calx (metal oxide) weighs more than the metal because its mass includes the mass of the oxygen.

This new theory triumphed because it relied on *quantitative, reproducible measurements,* not on strange properties of undetectable substances. Because this approach is at the heart of science, many propose that the *science* of chemistry began with Lavoisier.

◼ Summary of Section 1.2

- Alchemy, medicine, and technology placed little emphasis on objective experimentation, focusing instead on mystical explanations or practical experience, but these traditions contributed some apparatus and methods that are still important today.
- Lavoisier overthrew the phlogiston theory by showing quantitatively that oxygen, a component of air, is required for combustion and combines with a burning substance.

1.3 • THE SCIENTIFIC APPROACH: DEVELOPING A MODEL

Unlike our prehistoric ancestors, who survived through *trial and error*—gradually learning which types of stone were hard enough to shape others, which plants were edible and which poisonous—we employ the *quantitative theories* of chemistry to understand materials, make better use of them, and create new ones: specialized drugs, advanced composites, synthetic polymers, and countless others (Figure 1.5).

Figure 1.5 Modern materials in a variety of applications. **A,** High-tension polymers in synthetic hip joints. **B,** Specialized polymers in clothing and sports gear. **C,** Liquid crystals and semiconductors in electronic devices. **D,** Medicinal agents in pills.

Figure 1.6 The scientific approach to understanding nature. Hypotheses and models are mental pictures that are revised to match observations and experimental results, *not* the other way around.

To understand nature, scientists use an approach called the **scientific method.** It is not a stepwise checklist, but rather a process involving creative propositions and tests aimed at objective, verifiable discoveries. There is no single procedure, and luck often plays a key role in discovery. In general terms, the scientific approach includes the following parts (Figure 1.6):

- **Observations.** These are the facts our ideas must explain. The most useful observations are quantitative because they can be analyzed to reveal trends. Pieces of quantitative information are **data.** When the same observation is made by many investigators in many situations with no clear exceptions, it is summarized, often in mathematical terms, as a **natural law.** The observation that mass remains constant during chemical change—made by Lavoisier and numerous experimenters since—is known as the law of mass conservation (Chapter 2).
- **Hypothesis.** Whether derived from observation or from a "spark of intuition," a hypothesis is a proposal made to explain an observation. A sound hypothesis need not be correct, but it must be *testable by experiment.* Indeed, a hypothesis is often the reason for performing an experiment: if the results do not support it, the hypothesis must be revised or discarded. Hypotheses can be altered, but experimental results cannot.
- **Experiment.** A set of procedural steps that tests a hypothesis, an experiment often leads to a revised hypothesis and new experiments to test it. An experiment typically contains at least two **variables,** quantities that can have more than one value. A well-designed experiment is **controlled** in that it measures the effect of one variable on another while keeping all other variables constant. Experimental results must be *reproducible* by others. Both skill and creativity play a part in experimental design.
- **Model.** Formulating conceptual models, or **theories,** based on *experiments* that test *hypotheses* about *observations* distinguishes scientific thinking from speculation. As hypotheses are revised according to experimental results, a model emerges to explain how the phenomenon occurs. A model is a *simplified,* not an exact, representation of some aspect of nature that we use to *predict* related phenomena. Ongoing experimentation refines the model to account for new facts.

Lavoisier's overthrow of the phlogiston theory demonstrates the scientific method of thinking. *Observations* of burning and smelting led to the *hypothesis* that combustion involved the loss of phlogiston. *Experiments* showing that air is required for burning and that a metal gains mass during combustion led Lavoisier to propose a new *hypothesis,* which he tested repeatedly with quantitative *experiments.* Accumulating evidence supported his developing *model (theory)* that combustion involves combination with a component of air (oxygen). Innumerable *predictions* based on this theory have supported its validity, and Lavoisier himself extended the theory to account for animal respiration and metabolism.

■ Summary of Section 1.3

- The scientific method is a process designed to explain and predict phenomena.
- Observations lead to hypotheses about how or why a phenomenon occurs. When repeated with no exceptions, observations may be expressed as a natural law.
- Hypotheses are tested by controlled experiments and revised when necessary.
- If reproducible data support a hypothesis, a model (theory) can be developed to explain the observed phenomenon. A good model predicts related phenomena but must be refined whenever conflicting data appear.

1.4 • CHEMICAL PROBLEM SOLVING

In many ways, learning chemistry is learning how to solve chemistry problems, not only those in exams or homework, but the more complex ones in life and society. The sample problems in this book are designed to strengthen your skills for solving problems. In this section, we describe the problem-solving approach. Most problems include calculations, so let's first discuss how to handle measured quantities.

Units and Conversion Factors in Calculations

All measured quantities consist of a number *and* a unit: a person's height is "5 feet, 10 inches," not "5, 10." Ratios of quantities have ratios of units, such as miles/hour. (We discuss some important units in Section 1.5.) To minimize errors, make it a habit to *include units in all calculations.*

The arithmetic operations used with quantities are the same as those used with pure numbers; that is, units can be multiplied, divided, and canceled:

- A carpet measuring 3 feet by 4 feet (ft) has an area of

$$\text{Area} = 3 \text{ ft} \times 4 \text{ ft} = (3 \times 4)(\text{ft} \times \text{ft}) = 12 \text{ ft}^2$$

- A car traveling 350 miles (mi) in 7 hours (h) has a speed of

$$\text{Speed} = \frac{350 \text{ mi}}{7 \text{ h}} = \frac{50 \text{ mi}}{1 \text{ h}} \text{ (often written 50 mi·h}^{-1}\text{)}$$

- In 3 hours, the car travels a distance of

$$\text{Distance} = 3 \text{ h} \times \frac{50 \text{ mi}}{1 \text{ h}} = 150 \text{ mi}$$

Constructing a Conversion Factor **Conversion factors** are *ratios used to express a quantity in different units.* Suppose we want to know the distance of that 150-mile car trip in feet. To convert miles to feet, we use *equivalent quantities,*

$$1 \text{ mi} = 5280 \text{ ft}$$

from which we can construct two conversion factors. Dividing both sides by 5280 ft gives one conversion factor (shown in blue):

$$\frac{1 \text{ mi}}{5280 \text{ ft}} = \frac{5280 \text{ ft}}{5280 \text{ ft}} = 1$$

And, dividing both sides by 1 mi gives the other conversion factor (the inverse):

$$\frac{1 \text{ mi}}{1 \text{ mi}} = \frac{5280 \text{ ft}}{1 \text{ mi}} = 1$$

Since the numerator and denominator of a conversion factor are equal, multiplying a quantity by a conversion factor is the same as multiplying by 1. Thus, *even though the number and unit change, the size of the quantity remains the same.*

To convert the distance from miles to feet, we choose the conversion factor with miles in the denominator, because it cancels miles and gives the answer in feet:

$$\text{Distance (ft)} = 150 \text{ mi} \times \frac{5280 \text{ ft}}{1 \text{ mi}} = 792,000 \text{ ft}$$

$$\text{mi} \quad \Rightarrow \quad \text{ft}$$

Choosing the Correct Conversion Factor It is easier to convert if you first decide whether the answer expressed in the new units should have a larger or smaller number. In the previous case, we know that a foot is *smaller* than a mile, so the distance in feet should have a *larger* number (792,000) than the distance in miles (150). The conversion factor has the larger number (5280) in the numerator, so it gave a larger number in the answer.

Most importantly, the *conversion factor you choose must cancel all units except those you want in the answer.* Therefore, set the unit you are converting *from* (beginning unit) in the *opposite position in the conversion factor* (numerator or denominator) so that it cancels and you are left with the unit you are converting *to* (final unit):

$$\text{beginning unit} \times \frac{\text{final unit}}{\text{beginning unit}} = \text{final unit} \qquad \text{as in} \qquad \text{mi} \times \frac{\text{ft}}{\text{mi}} = \text{ft}$$

Or, in cases that involve units raised to a power:

$$(\text{beginning unit} \times \text{beginning unit}) \times \frac{\text{final unit}^2}{\text{beginning unit}^2} = \text{final unit}^2$$

$$\text{as in} \qquad (\text{ft} \times \text{ft}) \times \frac{\text{mi}^2}{\text{ft}^2} = \text{mi}^2$$

Or, in cases that involve a ratio of units:

$$\frac{\text{beginning unit}}{\text{final unit}_1} \times \frac{\text{final unit}_2}{\text{beginning unit}} = \frac{\text{final unit}_2}{\text{final unit}_1} \qquad \text{as in} \qquad \frac{\text{mi}}{\text{h}} \times \frac{\text{ft}}{\text{mi}} = \frac{\text{ft}}{\text{h}}$$

Converting Between Unit Systems We use the same procedure to convert between systems of units, for example, between the English (or American) unit system and the International System (a revised metric system; Section 1.5). Suppose we know that the height of Angel Falls in Venezuela (the world's highest) is 3212 ft, and we find its height in miles as

$$\text{Height (mi)} = 3212 \text{ ft} \times \frac{1 \text{ mi}}{5280 \text{ ft}} = 0.6083 \text{ mi}$$
$$\text{ft} \qquad \Rightarrow \qquad \text{mi}$$

Now, we want its height in kilometers (km). The equivalent quantities are

$$1.609 \text{ km} = 1 \text{ mi}$$

Because we are converting *from* miles *to* kilometers, we use the conversion factor with miles in the denominator in order to cancel miles:

$$\text{Height (km)} = 0.6083 \text{ mi} \times \frac{1.609 \text{ km}}{1 \text{ mi}} = 0.9788 \text{ km}$$
$$\text{mi} \qquad \Rightarrow \qquad \text{km}$$

Notice that kilometers are *smaller* than miles, so this conversion factor gave us an answer with a *larger* number (0.9788 is larger than 0.6083).

If we want the height of Angel Falls in meters (m), we use the equivalent quantities 1 km = 1000 m to construct the conversion factor:

$$\text{Height (m)} = 0.9788 \text{ km} \times \frac{1000 \text{ m}}{1 \text{ km}} = 978.8 \text{ m}$$
$$\text{km} \qquad \Rightarrow \qquad \text{m}$$

In longer calculations, we often string together several conversion steps:

$$\text{Height (m)} = 3212 \text{ ft} \times \frac{1 \text{ mi}}{5280 \text{ ft}} \times \frac{1.609 \text{ km}}{1 \text{ mi}} \times \frac{1000 \text{ m}}{1 \text{ km}} = 978.8 \text{ m}$$
$$\text{ft} \qquad \Rightarrow \quad \text{mi} \quad \Rightarrow \quad \text{km} \quad \Rightarrow \qquad \text{m}$$

The use of conversion factors in calculations is also referred to as the factor-label method or **dimensional analysis** (because units represent physical dimensions). We use this approach throughout the text.

A Systematic Approach to Solving Chemistry Problems

The approach used in this book to solve problems emphasizes reasoning, not memorizing, and is based on a simple idea: plan how to solve the problem *before* you try to solve it, then check your answer, and practice with a similar follow-up problem. In general, the sample problems consist of several parts:

1. **Problem.** This part states all the information you need to solve the problem, usually framed in some interesting context.

2. **Plan.** This part helps you *think* about the solution *before* juggling numbers and pressing calculator buttons. There is often more than one way to solve a problem, and the given plan is one possibility. The plan will
   - Clarify the known and unknown: what information do you have, and what are you trying to find?
   - Suggest the steps from known to unknown: what ideas, conversions, or equations are needed?
   - Present a road map (especially in early chapters), a flow diagram of the plan. The road map has a box for each intermediate result and an arrow showing the step (conversion factor or operation) used to get to the next box.

3. **Solution.** This part shows the calculation steps in the same order as in the plan (and the road map).

4. **Check.** This part helps you check that your final answer makes sense: Are the units correct? Did the change occur in the expected direction? Is it reasonable chemically? To avoid a large math error, we also often do a rough calculation and see if we get an answer "in the same ballpark" as the actual result. Here's a typical "ballpark" calculation from everyday life. You are at a music store and buy three CDs at $14.97 each. With a 5% sales tax, the bill comes to $47.16. In your mind, you know that $14.97 is about $15, and 3 times $15 is $45; with the sales tax, the cost should be a bit more. So, your quick mental calculation *is* in the same ballpark as the actual cost.

5. **Comment.** This part appears occasionally to provide an application, an alternative approach, a common mistake to avoid, or an overview.

6. **Follow-Up Problem.** This part presents a similar problem that requires you to apply concepts and/or methods used in solving the sample problem.

Of course, you can't learn to solve chemistry problems, any more than you can learn to swim, by reading about it, so here are a few suggestions:

- Follow along in the sample problem with pencil, paper, and calculator.
- Try the follow-up problem as soon as you finish the sample problem. A feature called Brief Solutions to Follow-Up Problems appears at the end of each chapter, allowing you to compare your solution steps and answer.
- Read the sample problem and text again if you have trouble.
- Try the practice quizzes in the Online Learning Center at www.mhhe.com/silberberg. For each chapter, two interactive quizzes provide conceptual and problem-solving practice and offer feedback for review.
- The end-of-chapter problems review and extend the concepts and skills in the chapter, so work as many as you can. (Answers are given in the back of the book for problems with a colored number.)

Let's apply this systematic approach in a unit-conversion problem.

Sample Problem 1.3 Converting Units of Length

Problem To wire your stereo equipment, you need 325 centimeters (cm) of speaker wire that sells for $0.15/ft. How much does the wire cost?

Plan We know the length of wire in centimeters (325 cm) and the price in dollars per foot ($0.15/ft). We can find the unknown cost of the wire by converting the length from centimeters to inches (in) and from inches to feet. The price gives us the equivalent quantities (1 ft = $0.15) to convert feet of wire to cost in dollars. The road map starts with the known and moves through the calculation steps to the unknown.

Solution Converting the known length from centimeters to inches: The equivalent quantities alongside the road map arrow are needed to construct the conversion factor. We choose 1 in/2.54 cm, rather than the inverse, because it gives an answer in inches:

$$\text{Length (in)} = \text{length (cm)} \times \text{conversion factor} = 325 \ \text{cm} \times \frac{1 \ \text{in}}{2.54 \ \text{cm}} = 128 \ \text{in}$$

Converting the length from inches to feet:

$$\text{Length (ft)} = \text{length (in)} \times \text{conversion factor} = 128 \ \text{in} \times \frac{1 \ \text{ft}}{12 \ \text{in}} = 10.7 \ \text{ft}$$

Converting the length in feet to cost in dollars:

$$\text{Cost (\$)} = \text{length (ft)} \times \text{conversion factor} = 10.7 \ \text{ft} \times \frac{\$0.15}{1 \ \text{ft}} = \boxed{\$1.60}$$

Check The units are correct for each step. The conversion factors make sense in terms of the relative unit sizes: the number of inches is *smaller* than the number of centimeters (an inch is *larger* than a centimeter), and the number of feet is *smaller* than the number of inches. The total cost seems reasonable: a little more than 10 ft of wire at $0.15/ft should cost a little more than $1.50.

Comment 1. We could also have strung the three steps together:

$$\text{Cost (\$)} = 325 \ \text{cm} \times \frac{1 \ \text{in}}{2.54 \ \text{cm}} \times \frac{1 \ \text{ft}}{12 \ \text{in}} \times \frac{\$0.15}{1 \ \text{ft}} = \boxed{\$1.60}$$

2. There are usually alternative sequences in unit-conversion problems. Here, for example, we would get the same answer if we first converted the cost of wire from $/ft to $/cm and kept the wire length in cm. Try it yourself.

Follow-Up Problem 1.3 A furniture factory needs 31.5 ft² of fabric to upholster one chair. Its Dutch supplier sends the fabric in bolts of exactly 200 m². How many chairs can be upholstered with 3 bolts of fabric (1 m = 3.281 ft)? Draw a road map to show how you plan the solution. (See Brief Solutions.)

Road Map

Length (cm) of wire

↓ 2.54 cm = 1 in

Length (in) of wire

↓ 12 in = 1 ft

Length (ft) of wire

↓ 1 ft = $0.15

Cost ($) of wire

■ Summary of Section 1.4

- A measured quantity consists of a number and a unit.
- A conversion factor is a ratio of equivalent quantities (and, thus, equal to 1) that is used to express a quantity in different units.
- The problem-solving approach used in this book has four parts: (1) plan the steps to the solution, which often includes a flow diagram (road map) of the steps, (2) perform the calculations according to the plan, (3) check to see if the answer makes sense, and (4) practice with a similar problem and compare your solution with the one at the end of the chapter.

1.5 • MEASUREMENT IN SCIENTIFIC STUDY

Measurement has a rich history characterized by the search for *exact, invariable standards*. Measuring for purposes of trade, building, and surveying began thousands of years ago, but for most of that time, it was based on standards that could vary: a yard was the distance from the king's nose to the tip of his outstretched arm, and an acre was the area tilled in one day by a man with a pair of oxen. Our current system of measurement began in 1790 in France, when a committee, of which Lavoisier was a member, developed the *metric system.* Then, in 1960, another committee in France revised the metric system and established the universally accepted **SI units** (from the French **S**ystème **I**nternational d'Unités).

General Features of SI Units

The SI system is based on seven **fundamental units,** or **base units,** each identified with a physical quantity (Table 1.2). All other units are **derived units,** combinations of the seven base units. For example, the derived unit for speed, meters per second (m/s), is the base unit for length (m) divided by the base unit for time (s). (Derived units that are a ratio of base units can be used as conversion factors.) For quantities much smaller or larger than the base unit, we use decimal prefixes and exponential (scientific) notation (Table 1.3). (If you need a review of exponential notation, see Appendix A.) Because the prefixes are based on powers of 10, SI units are easier to use in calculations than English units.

Some Important SI Units in Chemistry

Here, we discuss units for length, volume, mass, density, temperature, and time; other units are presented in later chapters. Table 1.4 (*on the next page*) shows some SI quantities for length, volume, and mass, along with their English-system equivalents.

Table 1.2 SI Base Units

Physical Quantity (Dimension)	Unit Name	Unit Abbreviation
Mass	kilogram	kg
Length	meter	m
Time	second	s
Temperature	kelvin	K
Electric current	ampere	A
Amount of substance	mole	mol
Luminous intensity	candela	cd

Table 1.3 Common Decimal Prefixes Used with SI Units

Prefix*	Prefix Symbol	Word	Conventional Notation	Exponential Notation
tera	T	trillion	1,000,000,000,000	1×10^{12}
giga	G	billion	1,000,000,000	1×10^{9}
mega	M	million	1,000,000	1×10^{6}
kilo	k	thousand	1,000	1×10^{3}
hecto	h	hundred	100	1×10^{2}
deka	da	ten	10	1×10^{1}
—	—	one	1	1×10^{0}
deci	d	tenth	0.1	1×10^{-1}
centi	c	hundredth	0.01	1×10^{-2}
milli	m	thousandth	0.001	1×10^{-3}
micro	μ	millionth	0.000001	1×10^{-6}
nano	n	billionth	0.000000001	1×10^{-9}
pico	p	trillionth	0.000000000001	1×10^{-12}
femto	f	quadrillionth	0.000000000000001	1×10^{-15}

*The prefixes most frequently used by chemists appear in bold type.

Table 1.4 Common SI-English Equivalent Quantities

Quantity	SI	SI Equivalents	English Equivalents	English to SI Equivalent
Length	1 kilometer (km)	1000 (10^3) meters	0.6214 mile (mi)	1 mile = 1.609 km
	1 meter (m)	100 (10^2) centimeters	1.094 yards (yd)	1 yard = 0.9144 m
		1000 millimeters (mm)	39.37 inches (in)	1 foot (ft) = 0.3048 m
	1 centimeter (cm)	0.10 (10^{-2}) meter	0.3937 inch	1 inch = 2.54 cm (exactly)
Volume	1 cubic meter (m^3)	1,000,000 (10^6) cubic centimeters	35.31 cubic feet (ft^3)	1 cubic foot = 0.02832 m^3
	1 cubic decimeter (dm^3)	1000 cubic centimeters	0.2642 gallon (gal)	1 gallon = 3.785 dm^3
			1.057 quarts (qt)	1 quart = 0.9464 dm^3
				1 quart = 946.4 cm^3
	1 cubic centimeter (cm^3)	0.001 dm^3	0.03381 fluid ounce	1 fluid ounce = 29.57 cm^3
Mass	1 kilogram (kg)	1000 grams	2.205 pounds (lb)	1 pound = 0.4536 kg

Length The SI base unit of length is the **meter (m).** In the metric system, it was originally defined as 1/10,000,000 of the distance from the equator to the North Pole, and later as the distance between two fine lines engraved on a corrosion-resistant metal bar. More recently, the first exact, unchanging standard was adopted: 1,650,763.73 wavelengths of orange-red light from electrically excited krypton atoms. The current standard is exact and invariant: 1 meter is the distance light travels in a vacuum in 1/299,792,458 of a second.

A meter is a little longer than a yard (1 m = 1.094 yd); a centimeter (10^{-2} m) is about two-fifths of an inch (1 cm = 0.3937 in; 1 in = 2.54 cm). Biological cells are often measured in micrometers (1 μm = 10^{-6} m). On the atomic scale, nanometers (10^{-9} m) and picometers (10^{-12} m) are used. Many proteins have diameters of about 2 nm; atomic diameters are about 200 pm (0.2 nm). An older unit still in use is the angstrom (1 Å = 10^{-10} m = 0.1 nm = 100 pm).

Volume Any sample of matter has a certain **volume (V),** the amount of space it occupies. The SI unit of volume is the **cubic meter (m^3).** In chemistry, we often use non-SI units, the **liter (L)** and the **milliliter (mL)** (note the uppercase L). Physicians and other medical practitioners measure body fluids in cubic decimeters (dm^3), which are equivalent to liters:

$$1\,L = 1\,dm^3 = 10^{-3}\,m^3$$

And 1 mL, or $\frac{1}{1000}$ of a liter, is equivalent to 1 cubic centimeter (cm^3):

$$1\,mL = 1\,cm^3 = 10^{-3}\,dm^3 = 10^{-3}\,L = 10^{-6}\,m^3$$

A liter is slightly larger than a quart (qt) (1 L = 1.057 qt; 1 qt = 946.4 mL); 1 fluid ounce ($\frac{1}{32}$ of a quart) equals 29.57 mL (29.57 cm^3).

Figure 1.7 is a life-size depiction of the two 1000-fold decreases in volume from 1 dm^3 to 1 cm^3 and then to 1 mm^3. The edge of a 1-m^3 cube would be about 2.5 times the width of this text opened flat.

Figure 1.8A shows some laboratory glassware for working with volumes. Erlenmeyer flasks and beakers are used to contain liquids. Graduated cylinders, pipets, and burets are used to measure and transfer them. Volumetric flasks and pipets have a fixed volume indicated by a mark on the neck. Solutions are prepared quantitatively in volumetric flasks, and specific amounts are put into cylinders, pipets, or burets to transfer to beakers or flasks for further steps. In Figure 1.8B, an automatic pipet transfers liquid accurately *and* quickly.

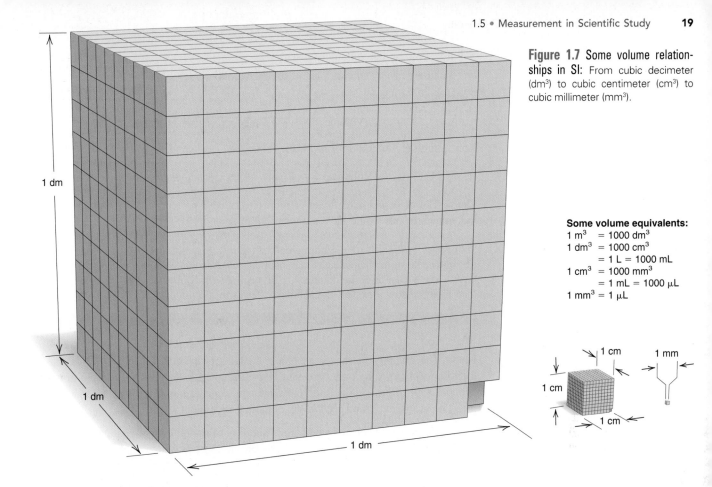

Figure 1.7 Some volume relationships in SI: From cubic decimeter (dm³) to cubic centimeter (cm³) to cubic millimeter (mm³).

Some volume equivalents:
1 m³ = 1000 dm³
1 dm³ = 1000 cm³
       = 1 L = 1000 mL
1 cm³ = 1000 mm³
       = 1 mL = 1000 µL
1 mm³ = 1 µL

A

B

Figure 1.8 Common laboratory volumetric glassware. **A,** From left to right are two graduated cylinders, a pipet being emptied into a beaker, a buret delivering liquid to an Erlenmeyer flask, and two volumetric flasks. **Inset,** In contact with the glass neck of the flask, the liquid forms a concave meniscus (curved surface). **B,** An automatic pipet delivers a given volume of liquid to each test tube.

Road Map

Sample Problem 1.4   **Converting Units of Volume**

Problem The volume of an irregularly shaped solid can be determined from the volume of water it displaces. A graduated cylinder contains 19.9 mL of water. When a small piece of galena, an ore of lead, is added, it sinks and the volume increases to 24.5 mL. What is the volume of the piece of galena in cm³ and in L?

Plan We have to find the volume of the galena from the change in volume of the cylinder contents. The volume of galena in mL is the difference before (19.9 mL) and after (24.5 mL) adding it. Since mL and cm³ represent identical volumes, the volume in mL equals the volume in cm³. We then use equivalent quantities (1 mL = 10^{-3} L) to convert mL to L. The road map shows these steps.

Solution Finding the volume of galena:

$$\text{Volume (mL)} = \text{volume after} - \text{volume before} = 24.5 \text{ mL} - 19.9 \text{ mL} = 4.6 \text{ mL}$$

Converting the volume from mL to cm^3:

$$\text{Volume (cm}^3\text{)} = 4.6 \text{ mL} \times \frac{1 \text{ cm}^3}{1 \text{ mL}} = \boxed{4.6 \text{ cm}^3}$$

Converting the volume from mL to L:

$$\text{Volume (L)} = 4.6 \text{ mL} \times \frac{10^{-3} \text{ L}}{1 \text{ mL}} = \boxed{4.6 \times 10^{-3} \text{ L}}$$

Check The units and magnitudes of the answers seem correct, and it makes sense that the volume in mL would have a number 1000 times larger than the same volume in L.

Follow-Up Problem 1.4 Within a cell, proteins are synthesized on particles called ribosomes. Assuming ribosomes are spherical, what is the volume (in dm^3 and μL) of a ribosome whose average diameter is 21.4 nm (V of a sphere $= \frac{4}{3}\pi r^3$)? Draw a road map to show how you plan the solution. (See Brief Solutions.)

Mass The quantity of matter an object contains is its **mass.** The SI unit of mass is the **kilogram (kg),** the only base unit whose standard is an object—a platinum-iridium cylinder kept in France—and the only one whose name has a prefix.*

The terms *mass* and *weight* have distinct meanings:

- *Mass is constant* because an object's quantity of matter cannot change.
- *Weight* is *variable* because it depends on the local gravitational field acting on the object.

Because the strength of the gravitational field varies with altitude, you (and other objects) weigh slightly less on a high mountain than at sea level.

Does this mean that a sample weighed on laboratory balances in Miami (sea level) and in Denver (about 1.7 km above sea level) give different results? No, because these balances measure mass, not weight. (We actually "mass" an object when we weigh it on a balance, but we don't use that term.) Mechanical balances compare the object's mass with masses built into the balance, so the local gravitational field pulls on them equally. Electronic (analytical) balances generate an electric field that counteracts the local field, and the current needed to restore the pan to zero is converted to the equivalent mass and displayed.

Road Map

Length (km) of fiber

$\downarrow$ 1 km = 10^3 m

Length (m) of fiber

$\downarrow$ 1 m = 1.19×10^{-3} lb

Mass (lb) of fiber

$\downarrow$ 6 fibers = 1 cable

Mass (lb) of cable

$\downarrow$ 2.205 lb = 1 kg

Mass (kg) of cable

Sample Problem 1.5 Converting Units of Mass

Problem Many international computer communications are carried by optical fibers in cables laid along the ocean floor. If one strand of optical fiber weighs 1.19×10^{-3} lb/m, what is the mass (in kg) of a cable made of six strands of optical fiber, each long enough to link New York and Paris (8.84×10^3 km)?

Plan We have to find the mass of cable (in kg) from the given mass/length of fiber (1.19×10^{-3} lb/m), number of fibers/cable (6), and length of cable (8.84×10^3 km). Let's first find the mass of one fiber and then the mass of cable. As shown in the road map, we convert the length of one fiber from km to m and then find its mass (in lb) by converting m to lb. Then we multiply the fiber mass by 6 to get the cable mass, and finally convert lb to kg.

Solution Converting the fiber length from km to m:

$$\text{Length (m) of fiber} = 8.84 \times 10^3 \text{ km} \times \frac{10^3 \text{ m}}{1 \text{ km}} = 8.84 \times 10^6 \text{ m}$$

---

*The names of the other base units are used as the root words, but for units of mass we attach prefixes to the word "gram," as in "microgram" and "kilogram"; thus, we say "milligram", never "microkilogram."

Converting the length of one fiber to mass (lb):

$$\text{Mass (lb) of fiber} = 8.84 \times 10^6 \; \text{m} \times \frac{1.19 \times 10^{-3} \; \text{lb}}{1 \; \text{m}} = 1.05 \times 10^4 \; \text{lb}$$

Finding the mass of the cable (lb):

$$\text{Mass (lb) of cable} = \frac{1.05 \times 10^4 \; \text{lb}}{1 \; \text{fiber}} \times \frac{6 \; \text{fibers}}{1 \; \text{cable}} = 6.30 \times 10^4 \; \text{lb/cable}$$

Converting the mass of cable from lb to kg:

$$\text{Mass (kg) of cable} = \frac{6.30 \times 10^4 \; \text{lb}}{1 \; \text{cable}} \times \frac{1 \; \text{kg}}{2.205 \; \text{lb}} = \boxed{2.86 \times 10^4 \; \text{kg/cable}}$$

Check The units are correct. Let's think through the relative sizes of the answers to see if they make sense: The number of m should be 10^3 larger than the number of km. If 1 m of fiber weighs about 10^{-3} lb, about 10^7 m should weigh about 10^4 lb. The cable mass should be six times as much, or about 6×10^4 lb. Since 1 lb is about $\frac{1}{2}$ kg, the number of kg should be about half the number of lb.

Follow-Up Problem 1.5 An intravenous nutrient solution is delivered to a hospital patient at a rate of 1.5 drops per second. If a drop of solution weighs 65 mg on average, how many kilograms are delivered in 8.0 h? Draw a road map to show how you plan the solution. (See Brief Solutions.)

Figure 1.9 shows the ranges of some common lengths, volumes, and masses.

Figure 1.9 Some interesting quantities of length (**A**), volume (**B**), and mass (**C**). The vertical scales are exponential.

Table 1.5 Densities of Some Common Substances*		
Substance	**Physical State**	**Density (g/cm³)**
Hydrogen	gas	0.0000899
Oxygen	gas	0.00133
Grain alcohol	liquid	0.789
Water	liquid	0.998
Table salt	solid	2.16
Aluminum	solid	2.70
Lead	solid	11.3
Gold	solid	19.3

*At room temperature (20°C) and normal atmospheric pressure (1 atm).

Density The **density** (d) of an object is its mass divided by its volume:

$$\text{Density} = \frac{\text{mass}}{\text{volume}} \tag{1.1}$$

We isolate each of these variables by treating density as a conversion factor:

$$\text{Mass} = \text{volume} \times \text{density} = \text{volume} \times \frac{\text{mass}}{\text{volume}}$$

or,

$$\text{Volume} = \text{mass} \times \frac{1}{\text{density}} = \text{mass} \times \frac{\text{volume}}{\text{mass}}$$

Because volume can change with temperature, so can density. But, at a given temperature and pressure, the *density of a substance is a characteristic physical property and, thus, has a specific value.*

The SI unit of density is kilograms per cubic meter (kg/m³), but in chemistry, density has units of g/L (g/dm³) or g/mL (g/cm³) (Table 1.5). The densities of gases are much lower than the densities of liquids or solids (see Figure 1.2).

Sample Problem 1.6   **Calculating Density from Mass and Volume**

Problem Lithium, a soft, gray solid with the lowest density of any metal, is a key component of advanced batteries, such as the one in your laptop. A slab of lithium weighs 1.49×10^3 mg and has sides that are 20.9 mm by 11.1 mm by 11.9 mm. Find the density of lithium in g/cm³.

Plan To find the density in g/cm³, we need the mass of lithium in g and the volume in cm³. The mass is 1.49×10^3 mg, so we convert mg to g. We convert the lengths of the three sides from mm to cm, and then multiply them to find the volume in cm³. Dividing the mass by the volume gives the density (see the road map).

Solution Converting the mass from mg to g:

$$\text{Mass (g) of lithium} = 1.49 \times 10^3 \, \text{mg} \left(\frac{10^{-3} \, \text{g}}{1 \, \text{mg}} \right) = 1.49 \, \text{g}$$

Converting side lengths from mm to cm:

$$\text{Length (cm) of one side} = 20.9 \, \text{mm} \times \frac{1 \, \text{cm}}{10 \, \text{mm}} = 2.09 \, \text{cm}$$

Similarly, the other side lengths are 1.11 cm and 1.19 cm.
Multiplying the sides to get the volume:

$$\text{Volume (cm}^3) = 2.09 \, \text{cm} \times 1.11 \, \text{cm} \times 1.19 \, \text{cm} = 2.76 \, \text{cm}^3$$

Calculating the density:

$$\text{Density of lithium} = \frac{\text{mass}}{\text{volume}} = \frac{1.49 \, \text{g}}{2.76 \, \text{cm}^3} = \boxed{0.540 \, \text{g/cm}^3}$$

Check Since 1 cm = 10 mm, the number of cm in each length should be $\frac{1}{10}$ the number of mm. The units for density are correct, and the size of the answer (~0.5 g/cm³) seems correct since the number of g (1.49) is about half the number of cm³ (2.76). Also, the problem states that lithium has a very low density, so this answer makes sense.

Road Map

Follow-Up Problem 1.6 The piece of galena in Sample Problem 1.4 has a volume of 4.6 cm³. If the density of galena is 7.5 g/cm³, what is the mass (in kg) of that piece of galena? Draw a road map to show how you plan the solution. (See Brief Solutions.)

Temperature There is a noteworthy distinction between temperature and heat:

- **Temperature (T)** is *a measure* of how hot or cold one object is relative to another.
- **Heat** is *the energy* that flows from the object with the higher temperature to the object with the lower temperature. When you hold an ice cube, it feels like the "cold" flows into your hand, but actually, heat flows from your hand to the ice.

In the laboratory, we measure temperature with a **thermometer,** a narrow tube containing a fluid that expands when heated. When the thermometer is immersed in a substance hotter than itself, heat flows from the substance through the glass into the fluid, which expands and rises in the thermometer tube. If a substance is colder than the thermometer, heat flows to the substance from the fluid, which contracts and falls within the tube.

We'll consider three temperature scales: the Celsius (°C, formerly called centigrade), the Kelvin (K), and the Fahrenheit (°F) scales. The SI base unit of temperature is the **kelvin (K,** with no degree sign, °). Figure 1.10 shows some interesting temperatures in the Kelvin scale, which is preferred in scientific work (although the Celsius scale is still used frequently). In the United States, the Fahrenheit scale is used for weather reporting, body temperature, and so forth.

The three scales differ in the size of the unit and/or the temperature of the zero point. Figure 1.11 shows the freezing and boiling points of water in the three scales. The **Celsius scale** sets water's freezing point at 0°C and its boiling point (at normal atmospheric pressure) at 100°C. The **Kelvin (absolute) scale** uses the *same size degree* as the Celsius scale—$\frac{1}{100}$ of the difference between the freezing and boiling points of water—but it has a *different zero point;* that is, 0 K, or *absolute zero,* equals −273.15°C. Thus, in the Kelvin scale, *all temperatures are positive;* for example, water freezes at +273.15 K (0°C) and boils at +373.15 K (100°C).

10^4 K —

6×10³: Surface of the Sun (interior ≈ 10^7 K)

3683: Highest melting point of a metallic element (tungsten)

1337: Melting point of gold

10^3 K —

600: Melting point of lead

373: Boiling point of H_2O
370: Day on Moon
273: Melting point of H_2O

140: Jupiter cloud top

10^2 K —
120: Night on Moon
90: Boiling point of oxygen

NEON

27: Boiling point of neon

10^1 K —

0 K — Absolute zero (lowest attained temperature ≈ 10^{-9} K)

Figure 1.10 Some interesting temperatures.

Celsius, °C   Kelvin, K   Fahrenheit, °F

Boiling point of water — 100°C   373.15 K   212°F

100 Celsius degrees   100 kelvins   180 Fahrenheit degrees

Freezing point of water — 0°C   273.15 K   32°F

0°C   273 K   32°F

−5°C   268 K   23°F

Figure 1.11 Freezing and boiling points of water in the Celsius, Kelvin (absolute), and Fahrenheit scales. At the bottom of the figure, a portion of each of the three thermometer scales is expanded to show the sizes of the units.

Table 1.6 The Three Temperature Scales

Scale	Unit	Size of Degree (Relative to K)	Freezing Point of H_2O	Boiling Point of H_2O	T at Absolute Zero	Conversion
Kelvin (absolute)	kelvin (K)	—	273.15 K	373.15 K	0 K	to °C (Equation 1.2)
Celsius	Celsius degree (°C)	1	0°C	100°C	−273.15°C	to K (Equation 1.3) to °F (Equation 1.4)
Fahrenheit	Fahrenheit degree (°F)	$\frac{5}{9}$	32°F	212°F	−459.67°F	to °C (Equation 1.5)

We convert between the Celsius and Kelvin scales by remembering the different zero points: 0°C = 273.15 K, so

$$T \text{ (in K)} = T \text{ (in °C)} + 273.15 \tag{1.2}$$

And, therefore,

$$T \text{ (in °C)} = T \text{ (in K)} - 273.15 \tag{1.3}$$

The Fahrenheit scale differs from the other scales in its zero point *and* in the size of its degree. Water freezes at 32°F and boils at 212°F. Therefore, 180 Fahrenheit degrees (212°F − 32°F) represents the same temperature change as 100 Celsius degrees (or 100 kelvins). Because 100 Celsius degrees equal 180 Fahrenheit degrees,

$$1 \text{ Celsius degree} = \tfrac{180}{100} \text{ Fahrenheit degrees} = \tfrac{9}{5} \text{ Fahrenheit degrees}$$

To convert a temperature from °C to °F, first change the degree size and then adjust the zero point:

$$T \text{ (in °F)} = \tfrac{9}{5}T \text{ (in °C)} + 32 \tag{1.4}$$

To convert a temperature from °F to °C, do the two steps in the opposite order: adjust the zero point and then change the degree size. In other words, solve Equation 1.4 for T (in °C):

$$T \text{ (in °C)} = [T \text{ (in °F)} - 32]\tfrac{5}{9} \tag{1.5}$$

Table 1.6 compares the three temperature scales.

Sample Problem 1.7 Converting Units of Temperature

Problem A child has a body temperature of 38.7°C, and normal body temperature is 98.6°F. Does the child have a fever? What is the child's temperature in kelvins?

Plan To see if the child has a fever, we convert from °C to °F (Equation 1.4) and compare it with 98.6°F. Then, to convert the child's temperature in °C to K, we use Equation 1.2.

Solution Converting the temperature from °C to °F:

$$T \text{ (in °F)} = \tfrac{9}{5}T \text{ (in °C)} + 32 = \tfrac{9}{5}(38.7°C) + 32 = 101.7°F; \quad \boxed{\text{yes, the child has a fever.}}$$

Converting the temperature from °C to K:

$$T \text{ (in K)} = T \text{ (in °C)} + 273.15 = 38.7°C + 273.15 = \boxed{311.8 \text{ K}}$$

Check From everyday experience, you know that 101.7°F is a reasonable temperature for someone with a fever. In the second step, we can check for a large error as follows: 38.7°C is almost 40°C, and 40 + 273 = 313, which is close to our answer.

Follow-Up Problem 1.7 Mercury melts at 234 K, lower than any other pure metal. What is its melting point in °C and °F?

Time The SI base unit of time is the **second (s),** which is now based on an atomic standard. The best pendulum clock is accurate to within 3 seconds per year, and the best quartz clock is 1000 times more accurate. The most recent version of the atomic clock is over 6000 times more accurate than that—within 1 second in 20 million years! Rather than the oscillations of a pendulum, the atomic clock measures the oscillations of microwave radiation absorbed by gaseous cesium atoms cooled to around 10^{-6} K: 1 second is defined as 9,192,631,770 of these oscillations. Chemists now use lasers to measure the speed of extremely fast reactions that occur in a few picoseconds $(10^{-12}$ s) or femtoseconds $(10^{-15}$ s).

Extensive and Intensive Properties Some variables are *dependent* on the amount of substance present; these are called **extensive properties.** On the other hand, **intensive properties** are *independent* of the amount of substance. Mass and volume, for example, are extensive properties, but density is an intensive property. Thus, a gallon of water has four times the mass of a quart of water, but it also has four times the volume, so the density, the *ratio* of mass to volume, is the same for both samples.

Another important example concerns heat, an extensive property, and temperature, an intensive property: a vat of boiling water has more heat, that is, more energy, than a cup of boiling water, but both samples have the same temperature.

▌Summary of Section 1.5

- The SI unit system consists of seven base units and numerous derived units.
- Exponential notation and prefixes based on powers of 10 are used to express very small and very large numbers.
- The SI base unit of length is the meter (m); on the atomic scale, the nanometer (nm) and picometer (pm) are used commonly.
- Volume (*V*) units are derived from length units, and the most important volume units are the cubic meter (m³) and the liter (L).
- The *mass* of an object—the quantity of matter in it—is constant. The SI unit of mass is the kilogram (kg). The *weight* of an object varies with the gravitational field.
- Density (*d*) is a characteristic physical property of a substance and is the ratio of its mass to its volume.
- Temperature (*T*) is a measure of the relative hotness of an object. Heat is energy that flows from an object at higher *T* to one at lower *T*.
- Temperature scales differ in the size of the degree unit and/or the zero point. For scientific uses, temperature is measured in kelvins (K) or degrees Celsius (°C).
- Extensive properties, such as mass, volume, and energy, depend on the amount of a substance. Intensive properties, such as density and temperature, do not.

1.6 • UNCERTAINTY IN MEASUREMENT: SIGNIFICANT FIGURES

All measuring devices—balances, pipets, thermometers, and so forth—are made to limited specifications, and we use our imperfect senses and skills to read them. Therefore, we can *never* measure a quantity exactly; put another way, every measurement includes some **uncertainty.** The device we choose depends on how much uncertainty is acceptable. When you buy potatoes, a supermarket scale that measures in 0.1-kg increments is acceptable; it tells you that the mass is, for example, 2.0 ± 0.1 kg. The "± 0.1 kg" term expresses the uncertainty: the potatoes weigh between 1.9 and 2.1 kg. Needing more certainty than that to weigh a substance, a chemist uses a balance that measures in 0.001-kg increments and finds the substance weighs 2.036 ± 0.001 kg, that is, between 2.035 and 2.037 kg. The greater number of digits in this measurement means we know the mass of the substance with *more certainty* than we know the mass of potatoes.

We *always estimate the rightmost digit* of a measurement. The uncertainty can be expressed with the ± sign, but generally we drop the sign and *assume an uncertainty of one unit in the rightmost digit.* The digits we record, both the certain and the uncertain ones, are called **significant figures.** There are four significant figures in 2.036 kg

Figure 1.12 The number of significant figures in a measurement. The thermometer on the left is graduated in increments of 0.1°C; the one on the right is graduated in increments of 1°C.

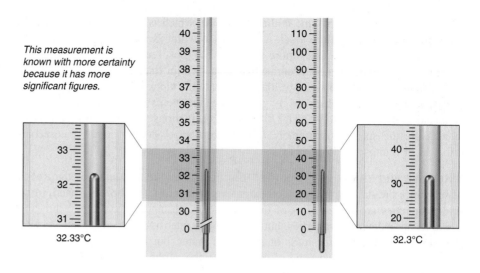

This measurement is known with more certainty because it has more significant figures.

32.33°C

32.3°C

and two in 2.0 kg. *The greater the number of significant figures, the greater is the certainty of a measurement.* Figure 1.12 shows this point for two thermometers.

Determining Which Digits Are Significant

When you take a measurement or use one in a calculation, you must know the number of digits that are significant: *all digits are significant, except zeros used only to position the decimal point.* The following procedure applies this point:

1. Make sure the measurement has a decimal point.
2. Start at the left, and move right until you reach the first nonzero digit.
3. Count that digit and every digit to its right as significant.

A complication can arise when zeros end a number:

- If there *is* a decimal point and the zeros lie either after or before it, they *are* significant: 1.1300 g has five significant figures and 6500. has four.
- If there is *no* decimal point, we assume that the zeros are *not* significant, unless exponential notation clarifies the quantity: 5300 L is *assumed* to have two significant figures, but 5.300×10^3 L has four, 5.30×10^3 L has three, and 5.3×10^3 L has two.
- A terminal decimal point indicates that zeros are significant: 500 mL has one significant figure, but 500. mL has three (as do 5.00×10^2 mL and 0.500 L).

Sample Problem 1.8 Determining the Number of Significant Figures

Problem For each of the following quantities, underline the zeros that are significant figures (sf) and determine the total number of significant figures. For (d) to (f), express each quantity in exponential notation first.
(a) 0.0030 L   **(b)** 0.1044 g   **(c)** 53,069 mL
(d) 0.00004715 m   **(e)** 57,600. s   **(f)** 0.0000007160 cm³

Plan We determine the number of significant figures by counting digits, as just presented, paying particular attention to the position of zeros in relation to the decimal point, and underline the zeros that are significant.

Solution **(a)** 0.0030 L has 2 sf
(b) 0.1044 g has 4 sf
(c) 53,069 mL has 5 sf
(d) 0.00004715 m, or 4.715×10^{-5} m, has 4 sf
(e) 57,600. s, or 5.7600×10^4 s, has 5 sf
(f) 0.0000007160 cm³, or 7.160×10^{-7} cm³, has 4 sf

Check Be sure that every zero counted as significant comes after nonzero digit(s) in the number.

Follow-Up Problem 1.8 For each of the following quantities, underline the zeros that are significant figures and determine the total number of significant figures (sf). For (d) to (f), express each quantity in exponential notation first.
(**a**) 31.070 mg   (**b**) 0.06060 g   (**c**) 850.°C
(**d**) 200.0 mL   (**e**) 0.0000039 m   (**f**) 0.000401 L

Significant Figures: Calculations and Rounding Off

Measuring several quantities typically results in data with differing numbers of significant figures. In a calculation, we keep track of the number in each quantity so that we don't have more significant figures (more certainty) in the answer than in the data. If we do have too many significant figures, we must **round off** the answer.

The general rule for rounding is that *the least certain measurement sets the limit on certainty for the entire calculation and determines the number of significant figures in the final answer.* Suppose you want to find the density of a new ceramic. You measure the mass of a piece of it on a precise laboratory balance and obtain 3.8056 g; you measure the volume as 2.5 mL by displacement of water in a graduated cylinder. The mass has five significant figures, but the volume has only two. Should you report the density as 3.8056 g/2.5 mL = 1.5222 g/mL or as 1.5 g/mL? The answer with five significant figures implies more certainty than the answer with two. But you didn't measure the volume to five significant figures, so you can't possibly know the density with that much certainty. Therefore, you report 1.5 g/mL, the answer with two significant figures.

Rules for Arithmetic Operations The two rules in arithmetic calculations are

1. *For multiplication and division.* The answer contains the same number of significant figures as there are in the measurement with the *fewest significant figures*. Suppose you want to find the volume of a sheet of a new graphite composite. The length (9.2 cm) and width (6.8 cm) are obtained with a ruler, and the thickness (0.3744 cm) with a set of calipers. The calculation is

$$\text{Volume (cm}^3) = 9.2 \text{ cm} \times 6.8 \text{ cm} \times 0.3744 \text{ cm} = 23.4225 \text{ cm}^3 = 23 \text{ cm}^3$$

Even though your calculator may show 23.4225 cm^3, you report 23 cm^3, the answer with two significant figures, the same as in the measurements with the lower number of significant figures. After all, if the length and width have two significant figures, you can't possibly know the volume with more certainty.

2. *For addition and subtraction.* The answer has the same number of decimal places as there are in the measurement with the *fewest decimal places*. Suppose you want the total volume after adding water to a protein solution: you have 83.5 mL of solution in a graduated cylinder and add 23.28 mL of water from a buret. The calculation is shown in the margin. Here the calculator shows 106.78 mL, but you report the volume as 106.8 mL, because the measurement with fewer decimal places (83.5 mL) has one decimal place (*see margin*).

$$
\begin{array}{r}
83.5 \text{ mL} \\
+\ 23.28 \text{ mL} \\
\hline
106.78 \text{ mL}
\end{array}
$$
Answer: Volume = 106.8 mL

Rules for Rounding Off You usually need to round off the final answer to the proper number of significant figures or decimal places. Notice that in calculating the volume of the graphite composite above, we removed the extra digits, but in calculating the total volume of the protein solution, we removed the extra digit and increased the last digit by one. The general rule for rounding is that *the least certain measurement sets the limit on the certainty of the final answer.* Here are detailed rules for rounding off:

1. If the digit removed is *more than 5*, the preceding number increases by 1: 5.379 rounds to 5.38 if you need three significant figures and to 5.4 if you need two.
2. If the digit removed is *less than 5*, the preceding number remains the same: 0.2413 rounds to 0.241 if you need three significant figures and to 0.24 if you need two.
3. If the digit removed *is 5*, the preceding number increases by 1 if it is odd and remains the same if it is even: 17.75 rounds to 17.8, but 17.65 rounds to 17.6. If the 5 is followed only by zeros, rule 3 is followed; if the 5 is followed by nonzeros, rule 1 is followed: 17.6500 rounds to 17.6, but 17.6513 rounds to 17.7.

Figure 1.13 Significant figures and measuring devices. The mass measurement (6.8605 g) has more significant figures than the volume measurement (68.2 mL).

4. *Always carry one or two additional significant figures through a multistep calculation and round off the final answer **only**.* Don't be concerned if you string together a calculation to check a sample or follow-up problem and find that your answer differs in the last decimal place from the one in the book. To show you the correct number of significant figures in text calculations, *we round off intermediate steps,* and that process may sometimes change the last digit.

Note that, unless you set a limit on your calculator, it gives answers with too many figures and you must round the displayed result.

Significant Figures in the Lab The measuring device you choose determines the number of significant figures you can obtain. Suppose an experiment requires a solution made by dissolving a solid in a liquid. You weigh the solid on an analytical balance and obtain a mass with five significant figures. It would make sense to measure the liquid with a buret or a pipet, which measures volumes to more significant figures than a graduated cylinder. If you do choose the cylinder, you would have to round off more digits, and some certainty in the mass value would be wasted (Figure 1.13). With experience, you'll choose a measuring device based on the number of significant figures you need in the final answer.

Exact Numbers **Exact numbers** have no uncertainty associated with them. Some are part of a unit conversion: by definition, there are exactly 60 minutes in 1 hour, 1000 micrograms in 1 milligram, and 2.54 centimeters in 1 inch. Other exact numbers result from actually counting items: there are exactly 3 coins in my hand, 26 letters in the English alphabet, and so forth. Therefore, unlike a measured quantity, *exact numbers do not limit the number of significant figures in a calculation.*

Sample Problem 1.9   **Significant Figures and Rounding**

Problem Perform the following calculations and round the answers to the correct number of significant figures:

(a) $\dfrac{16.3521 \text{ cm}^2 - 1.448 \text{ cm}^2}{7.085 \text{ cm}}$

(b) $\dfrac{(4.80 \times 10^4 \text{ mg})\left(\dfrac{1 \text{ g}}{1000 \text{ mg}}\right)}{11.55 \text{ cm}^3}$

Plan We use the rules just presented in the text: **(a)** We subtract before we divide. **(b)** We note that the unit conversion involves an exact number.

Solution (a) $\dfrac{16.3521 \text{ cm}^2 - 1.448 \text{ cm}^2}{7.085 \text{ cm}} = \dfrac{14.904 \text{ cm}^2}{7.085 \text{ cm}} = \boxed{2.104 \text{ cm}}$

(b) $\dfrac{(4.80 \times 10^4 \text{ mg})\left(\dfrac{1 \text{ g}}{1000 \text{ mg}}\right)}{11.55 \text{ cm}^3} = \dfrac{48.0 \text{ g}}{11.55 \text{ cm}^3} = \boxed{4.16 \text{ g/cm}^3}$

Check Note that in (a) we lose a decimal place in the numerator, and in (b) we retain 3 sf in the answer because there are 3 sf in 4.80. Rounding to the nearest whole number is always a good way to check: **(a)** $(16 - 1)/7 \approx 2$; **(b)** $(5 \times 10^4/1 \times 10^3)/12 \approx 4$.

Follow-Up Problem 1.9 Perform the following calculation and round the answer to the correct number of significant figures: $\dfrac{25.65 \text{ mL} + 37.4 \text{ mL}}{73.55 \text{ s}\left(\dfrac{1 \text{ min}}{60 \text{ s}}\right)}$

Precision, Accuracy, and Instrument Calibration

We may use the words "precision" and "accuracy" interchangeably in everyday speech, but for scientific measurements they have distinct meanings. **Precision,** or *reproducibility,* refers to how close the measurements in a series are to each other,

Figure 1.14 Precision and accuracy in a laboratory calibration.

and **accuracy** refers to how close each measurement is to the actual value. These terms are related to two widespread types of error:

1. **Systematic error** produces values that are *either* all higher or all lower than the actual value. This type of error is part of the experimental system, often caused by a faulty device or by a consistent mistake in taking a reading.
2. **Random error,** in the absence of systematic error, produces values that are higher *and* lower than the actual value. Random error *always* occurs, but its size depends on the measurer's skill and the instrument's precision.

Precise measurements have low random error, that is, small deviations from the average. *Accurate measurements have low systematic error and, generally, low random error.* In some cases, when many measurements have a high random error, the *average* may still be accurate.

Suppose each of four students measures 25.0 mL of water in a preweighed graduated cylinder and then weighs the water *plus* cylinder on a balance. If the density of water is 1.00 g/mL at the temperature of the experiment, the *actual* mass of 25.0 mL of water is 25.0 g. Each student performs the operation four times, subtracts the mass of the empty cylinder, and obtains one of four graphs (Figure 1.14). In graphs A and B, random error is small; that is, precision is high (the weighings are reproducible). In A, however, the accuracy is high as well (all the values are close to 25.0 g), whereas in B the accuracy is low (there is a systematic error). In graphs C and D, random error is large; that is, precision is low. Note, however, that in D there is also a systematic error (all the values are high), whereas in C the average of the values is close to the actual value.

Systematic error can be taken into account through **calibration,** comparing the measuring device with a known standard. The systematic error in graph B, for example, might be caused by a poorly manufactured cylinder that reads "25.0" when it actually contains about 27 mL. If that cylinder had been calibrated, the student could have adjusted all volumes measured with it. The students also should calibrate the balance with standardized masses.

▌ Summary of Section 1.6

- The final digit of a measurement is always estimated. Thus, all measurements have some uncertainty, which is expressed by the number of significant figures.
- The certainty of a calculated result depends on the certainty of the data, so the answer has as many significant figures as in the least certain measurement.
- Excess digits are rounded off in the final answer with a set of rules.
- The choice of laboratory device depends on the certainty needed.
- Exact numbers have as many significant figures as the calculation requires.
- Precision refers to how close values are to each other, and accuracy refers to how close values are to the actual value.
- Systematic errors give values that are either all higher or all lower than the actual value. Random errors give some values that are higher and some that are lower than the actual value.
- Precise measurements have low random error; accurate measurements have low systematic error and low random error.
- A systematic error is often caused by faulty equipment and can be compensated for by calibration.

CHAPTER REVIEW GUIDE

Learning Objectives   Relevant section (§) and/or sample problem (SP) numbers appear in parentheses.

Understand These Concepts

1. The distinction between physical and chemical properties and changes (§1.1; SPs 1.1, 1.2)
2. The defining features of the states of matter (§1.1)
3. The nature of potential and kinetic energy and their interconversion (§1.1)
4. The process of approaching a phenomenon scientifically and the distinctions between observation, hypothesis, experiment, and model (§1.3)
5. The common units of length, volume, mass, and temperature and their numerical prefixes (§1.5)
6. The distinctions between mass and weight, heat and temperature, and intensive and extensive properties (§1.5)

7. The meaning of uncertainty in measurements and the use of significant figures and rounding (§1.6)
8. The distinctions between accuracy and precision and between systematic and random error (§1.6)

Master These Skills

1. Using conversion factors in calculations and a systematic approach of plan, solution, check, and follow-up for solving problems (§1.4; SPs 1.3–1.5)
2. Finding density from mass and volume (SP 1.6)
3. Converting among the Kelvin, Celsius, and Fahrenheit scales (SP 1.7)
4. Determining the number of significant figures (SP 1.8) and rounding to the correct number of digits (SP 1.9)

Key Terms   Page numbers appear in parentheses.

Section 1.1
chemistry (4)
matter (4)
composition (4)
property (4)
physical property (4)
physical change (4)
chemical property (4)
chemical change (chemical reaction) (4)
state of matter (5)
solid (5)
liquid (6)
gas (6)
energy (8)
potential energy (8)
kinetic energy (8)

Section 1.2
combustion (10)

Section 1.3
scientific method (12)
observation (12)
data (12)
natural law (12)
hypothesis (12)
experiment (12)
variable (12)
controlled experiment (12)
model (theory) (12)

Section 1.4
conversion factor (13)
dimensional analysis (15)

Section 1.5
SI unit (17)
base (fundamental) unit (17)
derived unit (17)
meter (m) (18)
volume (V) (18)
cubic meter (m³) (18)
liter (L) (18)
milliliter (mL) (18)
mass (20)
kilogram (kg) (20)
weight (20)
density (d) (22)
temperature (T) (23)
heat (23)
thermometer (23)
kelvin (K) (23)

Celsius scale (23)
Kelvin (absolute) scale (23)
second (s) (25)
extensive property (25)
intensive property (25)

Section 1.6
uncertainty (25)
significant figures (25)
round off (27)
exact number (28)
precision (28)
accuracy (29)
systematic error (29)
random error (29)
calibration (29)

Key Equations and Relationships   Page numbers appear in parentheses.

1.1 Calculating density from mass and volume (22):

$$\text{Density} = \frac{\text{mass}}{\text{volume}}$$

1.2 Converting temperature from °C to K (24):

$$T \text{ (in K)} = T \text{ (in °C)} + 273.15$$

1.3 Converting temperature from K to °C (24):

$$T \text{ (in °C)} = T \text{ (in K)} - 273.15$$

1.4 Converting temperature from °C to °F (24):

$$T \text{ (in °F)} = \tfrac{9}{5}T \text{ (in °C)} + 32$$

1.5 Converting temperature from °F to °C (24):

$$T \text{ (in °C)} = [T \text{ (in °F)} - 32]\tfrac{5}{9}$$

Brief Solutions to Follow-Up Problems

1.1 Chemical. The red-and-blue and separate red particles on the left become paired red and separate blue particles on the right.

1.2 (a) Physical. Solid iodine changes to gaseous iodine.
(b) Chemical. Gasoline burns in air to form different substances.
(c) Chemical. In contact with air, substances in torn skin and blood react to form different substances.

1.3 No. of chairs

$$= 3 \text{ bolts} \times \frac{200 \text{ m}^2}{1 \text{ bolt}} \times \frac{(3.281)^2 \text{ ft}^2}{1 \text{ m}^2} \times \frac{1 \text{ chair}}{31.5 \text{ ft}^2}$$

$$= 205 \text{ chairs}$$

See Road Map 1.3.

Road Map 1.3

Fabric (bolts)
↓ 200 m² = 1 bolt
Fabric (m²)
↓ (3.281)² ft² = 1 m²
Fabric (ft²)
↓ 1 chair = 31.5 ft²
No. of chairs

Road Map 1.4

Diameter (dm)
↓ diameter = 2r
r (dm)
↓ $V = \frac{4}{3}\pi r^3$
V (dm³)
↓ 1 dm³ = 1 L
  1 L = 10⁶ μL
V (μL)

Road Map 1.5

Time (hr)
↓ 1 hr = 60 min
Time (min)
↓ 1 min = 60 s
Time (s)
↓ 1 s = 1.5 drops
No. of drops
↓ 1 drop = 65 mg
Mass (mg) of solution
↓ 10³ mg = 1 g
Mass (g) of solution
↓ 10³ g = 1 kg
Mass (kg) of solution

Road Map 1.6

V (cm³)
↓ multiply by density
Mass (g)
↓ 10³ g = 1 kg
Mass (kg)

1.4 Radius of ribosome (dm) $= \dfrac{21.4 \text{ nm}}{2} \times \dfrac{1 \text{ dm}}{10^8 \text{ nm}}$

$= 1.07 \times 10^{-7}$ dm

Volume of ribosome (dm³) $= \frac{4}{3}\pi r^3 = \frac{4}{3}(3.14)(1.07 \times 10^{-7} \text{ dm})^3$

$= 5.13 \times 10^{-21}$ dm³

Volume of ribosome (μL) $= (5.13 \times 10^{-21} \text{ dm}^3)\left(\dfrac{1 \text{ L}}{1 \text{ dm}^3}\right)\left(\dfrac{10 \text{ μL}}{1 \text{ L}}\right)$

$= 5.13 \times 10^{-15}$ μL

See Road Map 1.4.

1.5 Mass (kg) of solution

$= 8.0 \text{ h} \times \dfrac{60 \text{ min}}{1 \text{ h}} \times \dfrac{60 \text{ s}}{1 \text{ min}} \times \dfrac{1.5 \text{ drops}}{1 \text{ s}}$

$\times \dfrac{65 \text{ mg}}{1 \text{ drop}} \times \dfrac{1 \text{ g}}{10^3 \text{ mg}} \times \dfrac{1 \text{ kg}}{10^3 \text{ g}}$

$= 2.8$ kg

See Road Map 1.5.

1.6 Mass (kg) of sample $= 4.6 \text{ cm}^3 \times \dfrac{7.5 \text{ g}}{1 \text{ cm}^3} \times \dfrac{1 \text{ kg}}{10^3 \text{ g}}$

$= 0.034$ kg

See Road Map 1.6.

1.7 T (in °C) = 234 K − 273.15 = −39°C
T (in °F) = $\frac{9}{5}$(−39°C) + 32 = −38°F
Answer contains two significant figures (see Section 1.6).

1.8 (a) 31.0̲7̲0 mg, 5 sf   (b) 0.060̲6̲0 g, 4 sf
(c) 850̲.°C, 3 sf   (d) 2.0̲0̲0̲×10² mL, 4 sf
(e) 3.9×10⁻⁶ m, 2 sf   (f) 4.0̲1×10⁻⁴ L, 3 sf

1.9 $\dfrac{25.65 \text{ mL} + 37.4 \text{ mL}}{73.55 \text{ s}\left(\dfrac{1 \text{ min}}{60 \text{ s}}\right)} = 51.4$ mL/min

PROBLEMS

Problems with **colored** numbers are answered in Appendix E and worked in detail in the Student Solutions Manual. Problem sections match those in the text and provide the numbers of relevant sample problems. Most offer Concept Review Questions, Skill-Building Exercises (grouped in pairs covering the same concept), and Problems in Context. The Comprehensive Problems are based on material from any section.

Some Fundamental Definitions
(Sample Problems 1.1 and 1.2)

Concept Review Question

1.1 Scenes A–D represent atomic-scale views of different samples of substances:

(a) Under one set of conditions, the substances in A and B mix, and the result is depicted in C. Does this represent a chemical or a physical change?
(b) Under a second set of conditions, the same substances mix, and the result is depicted in D. Does this represent a chemical or a physical change?
(c) Under a third set of conditions, the sample depicted in C changes to that in D. Does this represent a chemical or a physical change?
(d) After the change in part (c) has occurred, does the sample have different chemical properties? Physical properties?

A   B   C   D

Skill-Building Exercises (grouped in similar pairs)

1.2 Describe solids, liquids, and gases in terms of how they fill a container. Use your descriptions to identify the physical state (at room temperature) of the following: (a) helium in a toy balloon; (b) mercury in a thermometer; (c) soup in a bowl.

1.3 Use your descriptions from Problem 1.2 to identify the physical state (at room temperature) of the following: (a) the air in your room; (b) tablets in a bottle of vitamins; (c) sugar in a packet.

1.4 Define *physical property* and *chemical property*. Identify each type of property in the following statements:
(a) Yellow-green chlorine gas attacks silvery sodium metal to form white crystals of sodium chloride (table salt).
(b) A magnet separates a mixture of black iron shavings and white sand.

1.5 Define *physical change* and *chemical change*. State which type of change occurs in each of the following statements:
(a) Passing an electric current through molten magnesium chloride yields molten magnesium and gaseous chlorine.
(b) The iron in discarded automobiles slowly forms reddish brown, crumbly rust.

1.6 Which of the following is a chemical change? Explain your reasoning: (a) boiling canned soup; (b) toasting a slice of bread; (c) chopping a log; (d) burning a log.

1.7 Which of the following changes can be reversed by changing the temperature: (a) dew condensing on a leaf; (b) an egg turning hard when it is boiled; (c) ice cream melting; (d) a spoonful of batter cooking on a hot griddle?

1.8 For each pair, which has higher potential energy?
(a) The fuel in your car or the gaseous products in its exhaust
(b) Wood in a fire or the ashes after the wood burns

1.9 For each pair, which has higher kinetic energy?
(a) A sled resting at the top of a hill or a sled sliding down the hill
(b) Water above a dam or water falling over the dam

Chemical Arts and the Origins of Modern Chemistry

Concept Review Questions

1.10 The alchemical, medical, and technological traditions were precursors to chemistry. State a contribution that each made to the development of the science of chemistry.

1.11 How did the phlogiston theory explain combustion?

1.12 One important observation that supporters of the phlogiston theory had trouble explaining was that the calx of a metal weighs more than the metal itself. Why was that observation important? How did the phlogistonists respond?

1.13 Lavoisier developed a new theory of combustion that overturned the phlogiston theory. What measurements were central to his theory, and what key discovery did he make?

The Scientific Approach: Developing a Model

Concept Review Questions

1.14 How are the key elements of scientific thinking used in the following scenario? While making toast, you notice it fails to pop out of the toaster. Thinking the spring mechanism is stuck, you notice that the bread is unchanged. Assuming you forgot to plug in the toaster, you check and find it is plugged in. When you take the toaster into the dining room and plug it into a different outlet, you find the toaster works. Returning to the kitchen, you turn on the switch for the overhead light and nothing happens.

1.15 Why is a quantitative observation more useful than a non-quantitative one? Which of the following is (are) quantitative? (a) The Sun rises in the east. (b) A person weighs one-sixth as much on the Moon as on Earth. (c) Ice floats on water. (d) A hand pump cannot draw water from a well more than 34 ft deep.

1.16 Describe the essential features of a well-designed experiment.

1.17 Describe the essential features of a scientific model.

Chemical Problem Solving
(Sample Problem 1.3)

Concept Review Question

1.18 When you convert feet to inches, how do you decide which part of the conversion factor should be in the numerator and which in the denominator?

Skill-Building Exercises (grouped in similar pairs)

1.19 Write the conversion factor(s) for
(a) in^2 to m^2 (b) km^2 to cm^2
(c) mi/h to m/s (d) lb/ft^3 to g/cm^3

1.20 Write the conversion factor(s) for
(a) cm/min to in/s (b) m^3 to in^3
(c) m/s^2 to km/h^2 (d) gal/h to L/min

Measurement in Scientific Study
(Sample Problems 1.4 to 1.7)

Concept Review Questions

1.21 Describe the difference between intensive and extensive properties. Which of the following properties are intensive: (a) mass; (b) density; (c) volume; (d) melting point?

1.22 Explain the difference between mass and weight. Why is your weight on the Moon one-sixth that on Earth?

1.23 For each of the following cases, state whether the density of the object increases, decreases, or remains the same:
(a) A sample of chlorine gas is compressed.
(b) A lead weight is carried up a high mountain.
(c) A sample of water is frozen.
(d) An iron bar is cooled.
(e) A diamond is submerged in water.

1.24 Explain the difference between heat and temperature. Does 1 L of water at 65°F have more, less, or the same quantity of energy as 1 L of water at 65°C?

1.25 A one-step conversion is sufficient to convert a temperature in the Celsius scale to the Kelvin scale, but not to the Fahrenheit scale. Explain.

Skill-Building Exercises (grouped in similar pairs)

1.26 The average radius of a molecule of lysozyme, an enzyme in tears, is 1430 pm. What is its radius in nanometers (nm)?

1.27 The radius of a barium atom is 2.22×10^{-10} m. What is its radius in angstroms (Å)?

1.28 What is the length in inches (in) of a 100.-m soccer field?

1.29 The center on your basketball team is 6 ft 10 in tall. How tall is the player in millimeters (mm)?

1.30 A small hole in the wing of a space shuttle requires a 20.7-cm^2 patch. (a) What is the patch's area in square kilometers (km^2)? (b) If the patching material costs NASA \$3.25/in^2, what is the cost of the patch?

1.31 The area of a telescope lens is 7903 mm². (a) What is the area in square feet (ft²)? (b) If it takes a technician 45 s to polish 135 mm², how long does it take her to polish the entire lens?

1.32 Express your body weight in kilograms (kg).

1.33 There are 2.60×10^{15} short tons of oxygen in the atmosphere (1 short ton = 2000 lb). How many metric tons of oxygen are present (1 metric ton = 1000 kg)?

1.34 The average density of Earth is 5.52 g/cm³. What is its density in (a) kg/m³; (b) lb/ft³?

1.35 The speed of light in a vacuum is 2.998×10^8 m/s. What is its speed in (a) km/h; (b) mi/min?

1.36 The volume of a certain bacterial cell is 2.56 μm³. (a) What is its volume in cubic millimeters (mm³)? (b) What is the volume of 10^5 cells in liters (L)?

1.37 (a) How many cubic meters of milk are in 1 qt (946.4 mL)? (b) How many liters of milk are in 835 gal (1 gal = 4 qt)?

1.38 An empty vial weighs 55.32 g. (a) If the vial weighs 185.56 g when filled with liquid mercury (d = 13.53 g/cm³), what is its volume? (b) How much would the vial weigh if it were filled with water (d = 0.997 g/cm³ at 25°C)?

1.39 An empty Erlenmeyer flask weighs 241.3 g. When filled with water (d = 1.00 g/cm³), the flask and its contents weigh 489.1 g. (a) What is the flask's volume? (b) How much does the flask weigh when filled with chloroform (d = 1.48 g/cm³)?

1.40 A small cube of aluminum measures 15.6 mm on a side and weighs 10.25 g. What is the density of aluminum in g/cm³?

1.41 A steel ball-bearing with a circumference of 32.5 mm weighs 4.20 g. What is the density of the steel in g/cm³ (V of a sphere = $\frac{4}{3}\pi r^3$; circumference of a circle = $2\pi r$)?

1.42 Perform the following conversions:
(a) 68°F (a pleasant spring day) to °C and K
(b) −164°C (the boiling point of methane, the main component of natural gas) to K and °F
(c) 0 K (absolute zero, theoretically the coldest possible temperature) to °C and °F

1.43 Perform the following conversions:
(a) 106°F (the body temperature of many birds) to K and °C
(b) 3410°C (the melting point of tungsten, the highest for any metallic element) to K and °F
(c) 6.1×10^3 K (the surface temperature of the Sun) to °F and °C

Problems in Context

1.44 A 25.0-g sample of each of three unknown metals is added to 25.0 mL of water in graduated cylinders A, B, and C, and the final volumes are depicted in the circles below. Given their densities, identify the metal in each cylinder: zinc (7.14 g/mL), iron (7.87 g/mL), or nickel (8.91 g/mL).

A   B   C

1.45 The distance between two adjacent peaks on a wave is called the *wavelength*.

(a) The wavelength of a beam of ultraviolet light is 247 nanometers (nm). What is its wavelength in meters?
(b) The wavelength of a beam of red light is 6760 pm. What is its wavelength in angstroms (Å)?

1.46 Each of the beakers depicted below contains two liquids that do not dissolve in each other. Three of the liquids are designated A, B, and C, and water is designated W.

(a) Which of the liquids is (are) more dense than water and which less dense?
(b) If the densities of W, C, and A are 1.0 g/mL, 0.88 g/mL, and 1.4 g/mL, respectively, which of the following densities is possible for liquid B: 0.79 g/mL, 0.86 g/mL, 0.94 g/mL, or 1.2 g/mL?

1.47 A cylindrical tube 9.5 cm high and 0.85 cm in diameter is used to collect blood samples. How many cubic decimeters (dm³) of blood can it hold (V of a cylinder = $\pi r^2 h$)?

1.48 Copper can be drawn into thin wires. How many meters of 34-gauge wire (diameter = 6.304×10^{-3} in) can be produced from the copper in 5.01 lb of covellite, an ore of copper that is 66% copper by mass? (*Hint:* Treat the wire as a cylinder: V of cylinder = $\pi r^2 h$; d of copper = 8.95 g/cm³.)

Uncertainty in Measurement: Significant Figures
(Sample Problems 1.8 and 1.9)

Concept Review Questions

1.49 What is an exact number? How are exact numbers treated differently from other numbers in a calculation?

1.50 Which procedure(s) decrease(s) the random error of a measurement: (1) taking the average of more measurements; (2) calibrating the instrument; (3) taking fewer measurements? Explain.

1.51 A newspaper reported that the attendance at Slippery Rock's home football game was 16,532. (a) How many significant figures does this number contain? (b) Was the actual number of people counted? (c) After Slippery Rock's next home game, the newspaper reported an attendance of 15,000. If you assume that this number contains two significant figures, how many people could actually have been at the game?

Skill-Building Exercises (grouped in similar pairs)

1.52 Underline the significant zeros in the following numbers:
(a) 0.41   (b) 0.041   (c) 0.0410   (d) 4.0100×10^4

1.53 Underline the significant zeros in the following numbers:
(a) 5.08   (b) 508   (c) 5.080×10^3 (d) 0.05080

1.54 Round off each number to the indicated number of significant figures (sf): (a) 0.0003554 (to 2 sf); (b) 35.8348 (to 4 sf); (c) 22.4555 (to 3 sf).

1.55 Round off each number to the indicated number of significant figures (sf): (a) 231.554 (to 4 sf); (b) 0.00845 (to 2 sf); (c) 144,000 (to 2 sf).

1.56 Round off each number in the following calculation to one fewer significant figure, and find the answer:

$$\frac{19 \times 155 \times 8.3}{3.2 \times 2.9 \times 4.7}$$

1.57 Round off each number in the following calculation to one fewer significant figure, and find the answer:

$$\frac{10.8 \times 6.18 \times 2.381}{24.3 \times 1.8 \times 19.5}$$

1.58 Carry out the following calculations, making sure that your answer has the correct number of significant figures:

(a) $\dfrac{2.795 \text{ m} \times 3.10 \text{ m}}{6.48 \text{ m}}$

(b) $V = \frac{4}{3}\pi r^3$, where $r = 17.282$ mm

(c) 1.110 cm $+ 17.3$ cm $+ 108.2$ cm $+ 316$ cm

1.59 Carry out the following calculations, making sure that your answer has the correct number of significant figures:

(a) $\dfrac{2.420 \text{ g} + 15.6 \text{ g}}{4.8 \text{ g}}$
(b) $\dfrac{7.87 \text{ mL}}{16.1 \text{ mL} - 8.44 \text{ mL}}$

(c) $V = \pi r^2 h$, where $r = 6.23$ cm and $h = 4.630$ cm

1.60 Write the following numbers in scientific notation:
(a) 131,000.0 (b) 0.00047 (c) 210,006 (d) 2160.5

1.61 Write the following numbers in scientific notation:
(a) 282.0 (b) 0.0380 (c) 4270.8 (d) 58,200.9

1.62 Write the following numbers in standard notation. Use a terminal decimal point when needed:
(a) 5.55×10^3 (b) 1.0070×10^4 (c) 8.85×10^{-7} (d) 3.004×10^{-3}

1.63 Write the following numbers in standard notation. Use a terminal decimal point when needed:
(a) 6.500×10^3 (b) 3.46×10^{-5} (c) 7.5×10^2 (d) 1.8856×10^2

1.64 Convert the following into correct scientific notation:
(a) 802.5×10^2 (b) 1009.8×10^{-6} (c) 0.077×10^{-9}

1.65 Convert the following into correct scientific notation:
(a) 14.3×10^1 (b) 851×10^{-2} (c) 7500×10^{-3}

1.66 Carry out each calculation, paying special attention to significant figures, rounding, and units (J = joule, the SI unit of energy; mol = mole, the SI unit for amount of substance):

(a) $\dfrac{(6.626\times10^{-34} \text{ J·s})(2.9979\times10^8 \text{ m/s})}{489\times10^{-9} \text{ m}}$

(b) $\dfrac{(6.022\times10^{23} \text{ molecules/mol})(1.23\times10^2 \text{ g})}{46.07 \text{ g/mol}}$

(c) $(6.022\times10^{23} \text{ atoms/mol})(2.18\times10^{-18} \text{ J/atom})\left(\dfrac{1}{2^2} - \dfrac{1}{3^2}\right)$,

where the numbers 2 and 3 in the last term are exact

1.67 Carry out each calculation, paying special attention to significant figures, rounding, and units:

(a) $\dfrac{4.32\times10^7 \text{ g}}{\frac{4}{3}(3.1416)(1.95\times10^2 \text{ cm})^3}$ (The term $\frac{4}{3}$ is exact.)

(b) $\dfrac{(1.84\times10^2 \text{ g})(44.7 \text{ m/s})^2}{2}$ (The term 2 is exact.)

(c) $\dfrac{(1.07\times10^{-4} \text{ mol/L})^2(3.8\times10^{-3} \text{ mol/L})}{(8.35\times10^{-5} \text{ mol/L})(1.48\times10^{-2} \text{ mol/L})^3}$

1.68 Which statements include exact numbers?
(a) Angel Falls is 3212 ft high.

(b) There are 8 known planets in the Solar System.
(c) There are 453.59 g in 1 lb.
(d) There are 1000 mm in 1 m.

1.69 Which of the following include exact numbers?
(a) The speed of light in a vacuum is a physical constant; to six significant figures, it is 2.99792×10^8 m/s.
(b) The density of mercury at 25°C is 13.53 g/mL.
(c) There are 3600 s in 1 h.
(d) In 2003, the United States had 50 states.

Problems in Context

1.70 How long is the metal strip shown below? Be sure to answer with the correct number of significant figures.

1.71 These organic solvents are used to clean compact discs:

Solvent	Density (g/mL) at 20°C
Chloroform	1.492
Diethyl ether	0.714
Ethanol	0.789
Isopropanol	0.785
Toluene	0.867

(a) If a 15.00-mL sample of CD cleaner weighs 11.775 g at 20°C, which solvent does the sample most likely contain?
(b) The chemist analyzing the cleaner calibrates her equipment and finds that the pipet is accurate to ±0.02 mL, and the balance is accurate to ±0.003 g. Is this equipment precise enough to distinguish between ethanol and isopropanol?

1.72 A laboratory instructor gives a sample of amino-acid powder to each of four students, I, II, III, and IV, and they weigh the samples. The true value is 8.72 g. Their results for three trials are
I: 8.72 g, 8.74 g, 8.70 g II: 8.56 g, 8.77 g, 8.83 g
III: 8.50 g, 8.48 g, 8.51 g IV: 8.41 g, 8.72 g, 8.55 g
(a) Calculate the average mass from each set of data, and tell which set is the most accurate.
(b) Precision is a measure of the average of the deviations of each piece of data from the average value. Which set of data is the most precise? Is this set also the most accurate?
(c) Which set of data is both the most accurate and the most precise?
(d) Which set of data is both the least accurate and the least precise?

1.73 The following dartboards illustrate the types of errors often seen in measurements. The bull's-eye represents the actual value, and the darts represent the data.

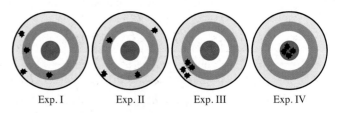

Exp. I   Exp. II   Exp. III   Exp. IV

(a) Which experiments yield the same average result?
(b) Which experiment(s) display(s) high precision?
(c) Which experiment(s) display(s) high accuracy?
(d) Which experiment(s) show(s) a systematic error?

Comprehensive Problems

1.74 Two blank potential energy diagrams appear below. Beneath each diagram are objects to place in the diagram. Draw the objects on the dashed lines to indicate higher or lower potential energy and label each case as more or less stable:

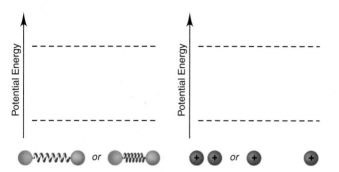

(a) Two balls attached to a relaxed *or* a compressed spring (b) Two positive charges near *or* apart from each other

1.75 The scenes below illustrate two different mixtures. When mixture A at 273 K is heated to 473 K, mixture B results.

A 273 K   **B** 473 K

(a) How many different chemical changes occur?
(b) How many different physical changes occur?

1.76 Bromine is used to prepare the pesticide methyl bromide and flame retardants for plastic electronic housings. It is recovered from seawater, underground brines, and the Dead Sea. The average concentrations of bromine in seawater ($d = 1.024$ g/mL) and the Dead Sea ($d = 1.22$ g/mL) are 0.065 g/L and 0.50 g/L, respectively. What is the mass ratio of bromine in the Dead Sea to that in seawater?

1.77 An Olympic-size pool is 50.0 m long and 25.0 m wide. (a) How many gallons of water ($d = 1.0$ g/mL) are needed to fill the pool to an average depth of 4.8 ft? (b) What is the mass (in kg) of water in the pool?

1.78 At room temperature (20°C) and pressure, the density of air is 1.189 g/L. An object will float in air if its density is less than that of air. In a buoyancy experiment with a new plastic, a chemist creates a rigid, thin-walled ball that weighs 0.12 g and has a volume of 560 cm^3.
(a) Will the ball float if it is evacuated?
(b) Will it float if filled with carbon dioxide ($d = 1.830$ g/L)?
(c) Will it float if filled with hydrogen ($d = 0.0899$ g/L)?
(d) Will it float if filled with oxygen ($d = 1.330$ g/L)?
(e) Will it float if filled with nitrogen ($d = 1.165$ g/L)?
(f) For any case in which the ball will float, how much weight must be added to make it sink?

1.79 Asbestos is a fibrous silicate mineral with remarkably high tensile strength. But it is no longer used because airborne asbestos particles can cause lung cancer. Grunerite, a type of asbestos, has a tensile strength of 3.5×10^2 kg/mm^2 (thus, a strand of grunerite with a 1-mm^2 cross-sectional area can hold up to 3.5×10^2 kg). The tensile strengths of aluminum and Steel No. 5137 are

2.5×10^4 lb/in^2 and 5.0×10^4 lb/in^2, respectively. Calculate the cross-sectional areas (in mm^2) of wires of aluminum and of Steel No. 5137 that have the same tensile strength as a fiber of grunerite with a cross-sectional area of 1.0 μm^2.

1.80 Earth's oceans have an average depth of 3800 m, a total surface area of 3.63×10^8 km^2, and an average concentration of dissolved gold of 5.8×10^{-9} g/L. (a) How many grams of gold are in the oceans? (b) How many cubic meters of gold are in the oceans? (c) Assuming the price of gold is $370.00/troy oz, what is the value of gold in the oceans (1 troy oz = 31.1 g; d of gold = 19.3 g/cm^3)?

1.81 Brass is an alloy of copper and zinc. Varying the mass percentages of the two metals produces brasses with different properties. A brass called *yellow zinc* has high ductility and strength and is 34%–37% zinc by mass. (a) Find the mass range (in g) of copper in 185 g of yellow zinc. (b) What is the mass range (in g) of zinc in a sample of yellow zinc that contains 46.5 g of copper?

1.82 Liquid nitrogen is obtained from liquefied air and is used industrially to prepare frozen foods. It boils at 77.36 K. (a) What is this temperature in °C? (b) What is this temperature in °F? (c) At the boiling point, the density of the liquid is 809 g/L and that of the gas is 4.566 g/L. How many liters of liquid nitrogen are produced when 895.0 L of nitrogen gas is liquefied at 77.36 K?

1.83 A jogger runs at an average speed of 5.9 mi/h. (a) How fast is she running in m/s? (b) How many kilometers does she run in 98 min? (c) If she starts a run at 11:15 am, what time is it after she covers 4.75×10^4 ft?

1.84 Scenes A and B depict changes in matter at the atomic scale:

A

B

(a) Which show(s) a physical change? (b) Which show(s) a chemical change? (c) Which result(s) in different physical properties? (d) Which result(s) in different chemical properties? (e) Which result(s) in a change in state?

1.85 If a temperature scale were based on the freezing point (5.5°C) and boiling point (80.1°C) of benzene and the temperature difference between these points was divided into 50 units (called °X), what would be the freezing and boiling points of water in °X? (See Figure 1.11, p. 23.)

1.86 Earth's surface area is 5.10×10^8 km^2; its crust has a mean thickness of 35 km and a mean density of 2.8 g/cm^3. The two most abundant elements in the crust are oxygen (4.55×10^5 g/t, where t stands for "metric ton"; 1 t = 1000 kg) and silicon (2.72×10^5 g/t), and the two rarest nonradioactive elements are ruthenium and rhodium, each with an abundance of 1×10^{-4} g/t. What is the total mass of each of these elements in Earth's crust?

The Components of Matter

Concepts and skills to review before you study this chapter

- physical and chemical change (Section 1.1)
- states of matter (Section 1.1)
- attraction and repulsion between charged particles (Section 1.1)

- meaning of a scientific model (Section 1.3)
- SI units and conversion factors (Section 1.5)
- significant figures in calculations (Section 1.6)

Look closely at almost any sample of matter—a rock, a piece of wood, a butterfly wing—and you'll see that it's made of smaller parts. With a microscope, you'll see still smaller parts. And, if you could zoom in a billion times closer, you'd find, on the atomic scale, the ultimate particles that make up all things.

Modern scientists are certainly not the first to wonder what things are made of. The philosophers of ancient Greece did too, and most believed that everything was made of one or, at most, a few elemental substances (elements), whose hotness, wetness, hardness, and other properties gave rise to the properties of everything else. Democritus (c. 460–370 BC), the father of atomism, took a different approach, and his reasoning went something like this: if you cut a piece of, say, aluminum foil smaller and smaller, you must eventually reach a particle of aluminum so small that it can no longer be cut. Therefore, matter is ultimately composed of indivisible particles with nothing but empty space between them. He called the particles *atoms* (Greek *atomos*, "uncuttable") and proclaimed: "According to convention, there is a sweet and a bitter, a hot and a cold, and . . . there is order. In truth, there are atoms and a void." But, Aristotle, one of the greatest and most influential philosophers of Western culture, said it was impossible for "nothing" to exist, and the concept of atoms was suppressed for 2000 years.

Finally, in the 17th century, the English scientist Robert Boyle argued that, by definition, an element is composed of "simple Bodies, not made of any other Bodies, of which all mixed Bodies are compounded, and into which they are ultimately resolved," a description remarkably close to our idea of an element, with atoms being the "simple Bodies." The next two centuries saw rapid progress in chemistry and the development of a "billiard-ball" image of the atom. Then, an early 20th-century burst of creativity led to our current model of an atom with a complex internal structure.

IN THIS CHAPTER . . . We examine the properties and composition of matter on the macroscopic and atomic scales.

- We relate the three types of matter—elements, compounds, and mixtures—to the chemical entities they consist of—atoms, ions, and molecules.
- We see how the defining properties of the types of matter relate to laws discovered in the 18th century concerning the masses of substances that react with each other.
- We examine the 19th-century atomic model proposed to explain these laws.
- We describe some 20th-century experiments that led to our current understanding of atomic structure and atomic mass.
- We focus on how the elements are organized in the periodic table and introduce the two major ways that elements combine.
- We derive names and formulas of compounds and calculate their masses.
- We examine the models chemists use to depict molecules.
- We classify mixtures and see how to separate them.
- We present a final overview of the components of matter.

2.1 • ELEMENTS, COMPOUNDS, AND MIXTURES: AN ATOMIC OVERVIEW

Matter can be classified into three types based on its composition—elements, compounds, and mixtures. Elements and compounds are the two kinds of substances: a **substance** is matter whose composition is fixed. Mixtures are not substances because they have a variable composition.

1. *Elements.* An **element** is the simplest type of matter with unique physical and chemical properties. *It consists of only one kind of atom* and, therefore, cannot be broken down into a simpler type of matter by any physical or chemical methods. Each element has a name, such as silicon, oxygen, or copper. A sample of silicon contains only silicon atoms. The *macroscopic* properties of a piece of silicon, such as color, density, and combustibility, are different from those of a piece of copper because the *submicroscopic* properties of silicon atoms are different from those of copper atoms; that is, *each element is unique because the properties of its atoms are unique.*

In nature, most elements exist as populations of atoms, either separated or in contact with each other, depending on the physical state. Figure 2.1A shows atoms of an element in its gaseous state. Several elements occur in molecular form: a **molecule** is an independent structure of two or more atoms bound together (Figure 2.1B). Oxygen, for example, occurs in air as *diatomic* (two-atom) molecules.

2. *Compounds.* A **compound** consists of *two or more different elements that are bonded chemically* (Figure 2.1C). That is, the elements in a compound are not just mixed together: their atoms have joined in a chemical reaction. Many compounds, such as ammonia, water, and carbon dioxide, consist of molecules. But many others, like sodium sulfate (which we'll discuss shortly) and silicon dioxide, do not. No matter what the compound, however, one defining feature is that *the elements are present in fixed parts by mass* (fixed mass ratio). This is so because *each unit of the compound consists of a fixed number of atoms of each element.* For example, consider a sample of ammonia. It is 14 parts nitrogen by mass and 3 parts hydrogen by mass *because* 1 nitrogen atom has 14 times the mass of 1 hydrogen atom, and each ammonia molecule consists of 1 nitrogen atom and 3 hydrogen atoms:

Ammonia gas is 14 parts N by mass and 3 parts H by mass.

1 N atom has 14 times the mass of 1 H atom.

Each ammonia molecule consists of 1 N atom and 3 H atoms.

Another defining feature of a compound is that *its properties are different from the properties of its component elements.* Table 2.1 shows a striking example: soft, silvery sodium metal and yellow-green, poisonous chlorine gas are very different from the compound they form—white, crystalline sodium chloride, common table salt!

Unlike an element, a compound *can* be broken down into simpler substances—its component elements. For example, an electric current breaks down molten sodium chloride into metallic sodium and chlorine gas. By definition, this breakdown is a *chemical change,* not a physical one.

Figure 2.1 Elements, compounds, and mixtures on the atomic scale. The samples depicted here are gases, but the three types of matter also occur as liquids and solids.

A Atoms of an element

B Molecules of an element

C Molecules of a compound

D Mixture of two elements and a compound

Table 2.1 Some Properties of Sodium, Chlorine, and Sodium Chloride

Property	Sodium	+	Chlorine	→	Sodium Chloride	
Melting point	97.8°C		−101°C		801°C	
Boiling point	881.4°C		−34°C		1413°C	
Color	Silvery		Yellow-green		Colorless (white)	
Density	0.97 g/cm³		0.0032 g/cm³		2.16 g/cm³	
Behavior in water	Reacts		Dissolves slightly		Dissolves freely	

3. *Mixtures.* A **mixture** consists of two or more substances (elements and/or compounds) that are physically intermingled. Because a mixture is *not* a substance, in contrast to a compound, *the components of a mixture **can** vary in their parts by mass.* A mixture of the compounds sodium chloride and water, for example, can have many different parts by mass of salt to water. On the atomic scale, a mixture consists of the individual units that make up its component elements and/or compounds (Figure 2.1D). It makes sense, then, that *a mixture retains many of the properties of its components.* Saltwater, for instance, is colorless like water and tastes salty like sodium chloride.

Unlike compounds, mixtures can be separated into their components by *physical changes;* chemical changes are not needed. For example, the water in saltwater can be boiled off, a physical process that leaves behind solid sodium chloride. The following sample problem will help differentiate these types of matter.

Sample Problem 2.1 | **Distinguishing Elements, Compounds, and Mixtures at the Atomic Scale**

Problem The scenes below represent atomic-scale views of three samples of matter:

Describe each sample as an element, compound, or mixture.

Plan We have to determine the type of matter by examining the component particles. If a sample contains only one type of particle, it is either an element or a compound; if it contains more than one type, it is a mixture. Particles of an element have only one kind of atom (one color), and particles of a compound have two or more kinds of atoms.

Solution (a) Mixture: there are three different types of particles. Two types contain only one kind of atom, either green or purple, so they are elements, and the third type contains two red atoms for every one yellow, so it is a compound.

(b) Element: the sample consists of only blue atoms.

(c) Compound: the sample consists of molecules that each have two black and six blue atoms.

Follow-Up Problem 2.1 Describe the following reaction in terms of elements, compounds, and mixtures. (See Brief Solutions at the end of the chapter.)

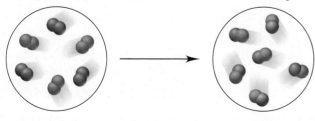

■ Summary of Section 2.1

- All matter exists as either elements, compounds, or mixtures.
- Elements and compounds are substances, types of matter with a fixed composition.
- An element consists of only one type of atom and occurs as collections of individual atoms or molecules.
- A compound contains two or more elements chemically combined and exhibits different properties from its component elements. The elements occur in fixed parts by mass because each unit of the compound has a fixed number of each type of atom. Only a chemical change can break down a compound into its elements.
- A mixture consists of two or more substances mixed together, not chemically combined. The components retain their individual properties, can be present in any proportion, and can be separated by physical changes.

2.2 • THE OBSERVATIONS THAT LED TO AN ATOMIC VIEW OF MATTER

Any model of the composition of matter had to explain the *law of mass conservation* and the *law of definite (or constant) composition.* As you'll see, an atomic theory developed by John Dalton in the early 19th century explained these mass laws and another now known as the *law of multiple proportions.*

Mass Conservation

The most fundamental chemical observation of the 18th century was the **law of mass conservation:** *the total mass of substances does not change during a chemical reaction.* The *number* of substances may change and, by definition, their properties must, but the *total amount* of matter remains constant. (Lavoisier had first stated this law on the basis of his combustion experiments.) Figure 2.2 illustrates mass conservation because the lead nitrate and sodium chromate solutions (*left*) have the same mass as the solid lead chromate in sodium nitrate solution (*right*) that forms when they react.

Even in a complex biochemical change, such as the metabolism of the sugar glucose, which involves many reactions, mass is conserved:

$$180 \text{ g glucose} + 192 \text{ g oxygen gas} \longrightarrow 264 \text{ g carbon dioxide} + 108 \text{ g water}$$
$$372 \text{ g material before} \longrightarrow 372 \text{ g material after}$$

Mass conservation means that, based on all chemical experience, *matter cannot be created or destroyed.*

To be precise about it, we now know, based on the work of Albert Einstein (1879–1955), that the mass before and after a reaction is not *exactly* the same. Some

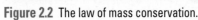

Figure 2.2 The law of mass conservation.

mass is converted to energy, or vice versa, but the difference is too small to measure, even with the best balance. For example, when 100 g of carbon burns, the carbon dioxide formed weighs 0.000000036 g (3.6×10^{-8} g) less than the carbon and oxygen that reacted. Because the energy changes of *chemical* reactions are so small, for all practical purposes, mass *is* conserved. Later in the text, you'll see that energy changes in *nuclear* reactions are so large that mass changes are easy to measure.

Definite Composition

The sodium chloride in your salt shaker is the same substance whether it comes from a salt mine, a salt flat, or any other source. This fact is expressed in the **law of definite (or constant) composition,** which states that *no matter what its source, a particular compound is composed of the same elements in the same parts (fractions) by mass.* The **fraction by mass (mass fraction)** is the part of the compound's mass that each element contributes. It is obtained by dividing the mass of each element by the mass of the compound. The **percent by mass (mass percent, mass %)** is the fraction by mass expressed as a percentage (multiplied by 100).

For an everyday example, consider a box that contains three types of marbles (*right*): yellow ones weigh 1.0 g each, purple 2.0 g each, and red 3.0 g each. Each type makes up a fraction of the total mass of marbles, 16.0 g. The *mass fraction* of yellow marbles is their number times their mass divided by the total mass: (3×1.0 g)/ 16.0 g = 0.19. The *mass percent* (parts per 100 parts) of yellow marbles is 0.19 × 100 = 19% by mass. The purple marbles have a mass fraction of 0.25 and are 25% by mass of the total, and the red marbles have a mass fraction of 0.56 and are 56% by mass.

Similarly, in a compound, each element has a *fixed* mass fraction (and mass percent). For example, calcium carbonate, the major compound in seashells, marble, and coral is composed of three elements—calcium, carbon, and oxygen. The following results are obtained from a mass analysis of 20.0 g of calcium carbonate:

Analysis by Mass (grams/20.0 g)	Mass Fraction (parts/1.00 part)	Percent by Mass (parts/100 parts)
8.0 g calcium	0.40 calcium	40% calcium
2.4 g carbon	0.12 carbon	12% carbon
9.6 g oxygen	0.48 oxygen	48% oxygen
20.0 g	1.00 part by mass	100% by mass

The mass of each element depends on the mass of the sample—that is, more than 20.0 g of compound would contain more than 8.0 g of calcium—but *the mass fraction is fixed no matter what the size of the sample.* The sum of the mass fractions (or mass percents) equals 1.00 part (or 100%) by mass. The law of definite composition tells us that pure samples of calcium carbonate, no matter where they come from, always contain 40% calcium, 12% carbon, and 48% oxygen by mass (Figure 2.3).

Because a given element always constitutes the same mass fraction of a given compound, we can use that mass fraction to find the actual mass of the element in any sample of the compound:

$$\text{Mass of element} = \text{mass of compound} \times \frac{\text{part by mass of element}}{\text{one part by mass of compound}}$$

Or, more simply, we can skip the need to find the mass fraction first and use the results of mass analysis directly:

$$\text{Mass of element in sample} = \text{mass of compound in sample} \times \frac{\text{mass of element in compound}}{\text{mass of compound}} \quad (2.1)$$

CALCIUM CARBONATE
40 mass % calcium
12 mass % carbon
48 mass % oxygen

Figure 2.3 The law of definite composition. Calcium carbonate occurs in many forms (such as marble, *top*, and coral, *bottom*), but the mass percents of its elements are always the same.

Sample Problem 2.2 — Calculating the Mass of an Element in a Compound

Problem Pitchblende is the most important compound of uranium. Mass analysis of an 84.2-g sample shows that it contains 71.4 g of uranium, with oxygen the only other element. How many grams of uranium are in 102 kg of pitchblende?

Plan We have to find the mass of uranium in a known mass (102 kg) of pitchblende, given the mass of uranium (71.4 g) in a different mass of pitchblende (84.2 g). The mass ratio of uranium to pitchblende is the same for any sample of pitchblende. Therefore, using Equation 2.1, we multiply the mass (in kg) of the pitchblende sample by the ratio of uranium to pitchblende from the mass analysis. This gives the mass (in kg) of uranium, and we convert kilograms to grams.

Solution Finding the mass (kg) of uranium in 102 kg of pitchblende:

$$\text{Mass (kg) of uranium} = \text{mass (kg) of pitchblende} \times \frac{\text{mass (kg) of uranium in pitchblende}}{\text{mass (kg) of pitchblende}}$$

$$= 102 \; \text{kg pitchblende} \times \frac{71.4 \; \text{kg uranium}}{84.2 \; \text{kg pitchblende}} = 86.5 \; \text{kg uranium}$$

Converting the mass of uranium from kg to g:

$$\text{Mass (g) of uranium} = 86.5 \; \text{kg uranium} \times \frac{1000 \; \text{g}}{1 \; \text{kg}} = \boxed{8.65 \times 10^4 \; \text{g uranium}}$$

Check The analysis showed that most of the mass of pitchblende is due to uranium, so the large mass of uranium makes sense. Rounding off to check the math gives:

$$\sim 100 \; \text{kg pitchblende} \times \frac{70}{85} = 82 \; \text{kg uranium}$$

Follow-Up Problem 2.2 How many metric tons (t) of oxygen are combined in a sample of pitchblende that contains 2.3 t of uranium? (*Hint:* Remember that oxygen is the only other element present.) See Brief Solutions.

Road Map

Mass (kg) of pitchblende

↓ multiply by mass ratio of uranium to pitchblende from analysis

Mass (kg) of uranium

↓ 1 kg = 1000 g

Mass (g) of uranium

Multiple Proportions

An observation that applies when two elements form more than one compound is now called the **law of multiple proportions:** *if elements A and B react to form two compounds, the different masses of B that combine with a fixed mass of A can be expressed as a ratio of small whole numbers.* Consider two compounds, let's call them I and II, that carbon and oxygen form. These compounds have very different properties: the density of carbon oxide I is 1.25 g/L, whereas that of II is 1.98 g/L; I is poisonous and flammable, but II is not. Mass analysis shows that

Carbon oxide I is 57.1 mass % oxygen and 42.9 mass % carbon
Carbon oxide II is 72.7 mass % oxygen and 27.3 mass % carbon

To see the phenomenon of multiple proportions, we use the mass percents of oxygen and of carbon to find their masses in a given mass, say 100 g, of each compound. Then we divide the mass of oxygen by the mass of carbon in each compound to obtain the mass of oxygen that combines with a fixed mass of carbon:

	Carbon Oxide I	Carbon Oxide II
g oxygen/100 g compound	57.1	72.7
g carbon/100 g compound	42.9	27.3
g oxygen/g carbon	$\dfrac{57.1}{42.9} = 1.33$	$\dfrac{72.7}{27.3} = 2.66$

If we then divide the grams of oxygen per gram of carbon in II by that in I, we obtain a ratio of small whole numbers:

$$\frac{2.66 \; \text{g oxygen/g carbon in II}}{1.33 \; \text{g oxygen/g carbon in I}} = \frac{2}{1}$$

The law of multiple proportions tells us that in two compounds of the same elements, the mass fraction of one element relative to the other element changes in *increments based on ratios of small whole numbers.* In this case, the ratio is 2/1—for a given mass of carbon, compound II contains *2 times* as much oxygen as I, not 1.583 times, 1.716 times, or any other intermediate amount. In the next section, we'll explain the mass laws on the atomic scale.

■ Summary of Section 2.2

- The law of mass conservation states that the total mass remains constant during a chemical reaction.
- The law of definite composition states that any sample of a given compound has the same elements present in the same parts by mass.
- The law of multiple proportions states that, in different compounds of the same elements, the masses of one element that combine with a fixed mass of the other can be expressed as a ratio of small whole numbers.

2.3 • DALTON'S ATOMIC THEORY

With 200 years of hindsight, it may be easy to see how the mass laws could be explained by an atomic model—matter existing in indestructible units, each with a particular mass—but it was a major breakthrough in 1808 when John Dalton (1766–1844) presented his atomic theory of matter in *A New System of Chemical Philosophy.*

Despite having no formal education, Dalton began teaching science at age 12 and then studied color blindness, a personal affliction still known as *daltonism.* At 21, he started recording daily weather data and continued this project for the rest of his life. His results on humidity and dew point led to a key discovery about gases (Section 5.4) and eventually to his atomic theory.

Postulates of the Atomic Theory

Dalton expressed his theory in a series of postulates. Like most great thinkers, he integrated the ideas of others into his own. As we go through the postulates, presented here in modern terms, let's see which were original and which came from others.

1. All matter consists of **atoms,** tiny indivisible particles of an element that cannot be created or destroyed. (This derives from the "eternal, indestructible atoms" proposed by Democritus more than 2000 years earlier and reflects mass conservation as stated by Lavoisier.)
2. Atoms of one element *cannot* be converted into atoms of another element. In chemical reactions, the atoms of the original substances recombine to form different substances. (This rejects the alchemical belief in the magical transmutation of elements.)
3. Atoms of an element are identical in mass and other properties and are different from atoms of any other element. (This contains Dalton's major new ideas: *unique mass and properties* for the atoms of a given element.)
4. Compounds result from the chemical combination of a specific ratio of atoms of different elements. (This follows directly from the law of definite composition.)

How the Theory Explains the Mass Laws

Let's see how Dalton's postulates explain the mass laws:

- *Mass conservation.* Atoms cannot be created or destroyed (postulate 1) or converted into other types of atoms (postulate 2). Therefore, a chemical reaction, in which atoms are combined differently, cannot possibly result in a mass change.
- *Definite composition.* A compound is a combination of a *specific* ratio of different atoms (postulate 4), each of which has a particular mass (postulate 3). Thus, each element in a compound constitutes a fixed fraction of the total mass.
- *Multiple proportions.* Atoms of an element have the same mass (postulate 3) and are indivisible (postulate 1). The masses of element B that combine with a fixed mass of element A give a small, whole-number ratio because different numbers of B atoms combine with each A atom in different compounds.

The *simplest* arrangement consistent with the mass data for carbon oxides I and II in our earlier example is that one atom of oxygen combines with one atom of carbon in compound I (carbon monoxide) and that two atoms of oxygen combine with one atom of carbon in compound II (carbon dioxide):

Carbon oxide I   Carbon oxide II
(carbon monoxide)   (carbon dioxide)

Let's work through a sample problem that reviews the mass laws.

Sample Problem 2.3 **Visualizing the Mass Laws**

Problem The scenes below represent an atomic-scale view of a chemical reaction:

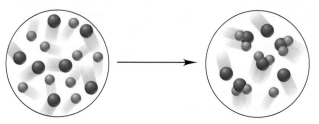

Which of the mass laws—mass conservation, definite composition, or multiple proportions—is (are) illustrated?

Plan From the depictions, we note the numbers, colors, and combinations of atoms (spheres) to see which mass laws pertain. If the numbers of each atom are the same before and after the reaction, the total mass did not change (mass conservation). If a compound forms that always has the same atom ratio, the elements are present in fixed parts by mass (definite composition). When the same elements form different compounds and the ratio of the atoms of one element that combine with one atom of the other element is a small whole number, the ratio of their masses is a small whole number as well (multiple proportions).

Solution There are seven purple and nine green atoms in each circle, so mass is conserved. The compound formed has one purple and two green atoms, so it has definite composition. Only one compound forms, so the law of multiple proportions does not pertain.

Follow-Up Problem 2.3 Which sample(s) best display(s) the fact that compounds of bromine (orange) and fluorine (yellow) exhibit the law of multiple proportions? Explain.

A   B   C

▌Summary of Section 2.3

- Dalton's atomic theory explained the mass laws by proposing that all matter consists of indivisible, unchangeable atoms of fixed, unique mass.
- Mass is conserved during a reaction because the atoms retain their identities but are combined differently.
- Each compound has a fixed mass fraction of each of its elements because it is composed of a fixed number of each type of atom.
- Different compounds of the same elements exhibit multiple proportions because they each consist of whole atoms.

2.4 • THE OBSERVATIONS THAT LED TO THE NUCLEAR ATOM MODEL

Dalton's model established that masses of reacting elements could be explained in terms of atoms but not why atoms bond as they do: why, for example, do two, and not three, hydrogen atoms bond with one oxygen atom in a water molecule?

Moreover, Dalton's "billiard ball" model of the atom did not predict the existence of subatomic charged particles, which were observed in later experiments that led to the discovery of *electrons* and the atomic *nucleus*. Let's examine some of these experiments and the more complex atomic model that emerged from them.

Discovery of the Electron and Its Properties

For many years, scientists had known that matter and electric charge were related. When amber is rubbed with fur, or glass with silk, positive and negative charges form—the same charges that make your hair crackle and cling to your comb on a dry day. They also knew that an electric current could decompose certain compounds into their elements. But they did not know what a current was made of.

Cathode Rays To discover the nature of an electric current, some investigators tried passing current through nearly evacuated glass tubes fitted with metal electrodes. When the electric power source was turned on, a "ray" could be seen striking the phosphor-coated end of the tube and emitting a glowing spot of light. The rays were called **cathode rays** because they originated at the negative electrode (cathode) and moved to the positive electrode (anode).

Figure 2.4 shows some properties of cathode rays based on these observations. The main conclusion was that *cathode rays consist of negatively charged particles found in all matter.* The rays appear when these particles collide with the few remaining gas molecules in the evacuated tube. Cathode ray particles were later named *electrons.* There are many familiar cases of the effects of charged particles colliding with gases or hitting a phosphor-coated screen:

- In a "neon" sign, electrons collide with the gas particles in the tube, causing them to give off light.
- The aurora borealis, or northern lights (*see photo*), occurs when Earth's magnetic field bends streams of charged particles coming from the Sun, which then collide with gas particles in the atmosphere to give off light.
- In older televisions and computer monitors, the cathode ray passes back and forth over the coated screen, creating a pattern that we see as a picture.

Why do the northern lights glow?

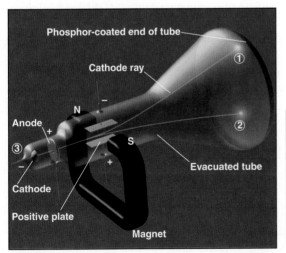

OBSERVATION	CONCLUSION
1. Ray bends in magnetic field.	Consists of charged particles
2. Ray bends toward positive plate in electric field.	Consists of negative particles
3. Ray is identical for any cathode.	Particles found in all matter

Figure 2.4 Observations that established the properties of cathode rays.

Mass and Charge of the Electron Two classic experiments and their conclusion revealed the mass and charge of the electron:

1. *Mass/charge ratio.* In 1897, the British physicist J. J. Thomson (1856–1940) measured the ratio of the mass of a cathode ray particle to its charge. By comparing this value with the mass/charge ratio for the lightest charged particle in solution, Thomson estimated that the cathode ray particle weighed less than $\frac{1}{1000}$ as much as hydrogen, the lightest atom! He was shocked because this implied that, contrary to Dalton's atomic theory, *atoms contain even smaller particles.* Fellow scientists reacted with disbelief to Thomson's conclusion, thinking he was joking.

2. *Charge.* In 1909, the American physicist Robert Millikan (1868–1953) measured the *charge* of the electron. He did so by observing the movement of oil droplets in an apparatus that contained electrically charged plates and an x-ray source (Figure 2.5). X-rays knocked electrons from gas molecules in the air within the apparatus, and the electrons stuck to an oil droplet falling through a hole in a positively charged plate. With the electric field off, Millikan measured the mass of the droplet from its rate of fall. Then, by adjusting the field's strength, he made the droplet hang suspended in the air and, thus, measured its total charge.

Figure 2.5 Millikan's oil-drop experiment for measuring an electron's charge. The total charge on an oil droplet is some whole-number multiple of the charge of the electron.

Fine mist of oil is sprayed into apparatus.

Oil droplets fall through hole in positively charged plate.

X-rays knock electrons from air molecules, and they stick to droplets.

Electrically charged plates influence droplet's motion.

Observer times droplet's motion and controls electric field.

X-ray source

After many tries, Millikan found that the total charge of the various droplets was always some *whole-number multiple of a minimum charge.* If different oil droplets picked up different numbers of electrons, he reasoned that this minimum charge must be the charge of the electron itself. Remarkably, the value that he calculated over a century ago was within 1% of the modern value of the electron's charge, -1.602×10^{-19} C (C stands for *coulomb,* the SI unit of charge).

3. *Conclusion: calculating the electron's mass.* The electron's mass/charge ratio from work by Thomson and others and the value for the electron's charge can be used to find the electron's mass, which is *extremely* small:

$$\text{Mass of electron} = \frac{\text{mass}}{\text{charge}} \times \text{charge} = \left(-5.686 \times 10^{-12} \frac{\text{kg}}{\text{C}}\right)(-1.602 \times 10^{-19} \text{ C})$$

$$= 9.109 \times 10^{-31} \text{ kg} = 9.109 \times 10^{-28} \text{ g}$$

Discovery of the Atomic Nucleus

The presence of electrons in all matter posed some major questions about the structure of atoms. Matter is electrically neutral, so atoms must be also. But if atoms contain negatively charged electrons, what positive charges balance them? And if an electron has such a tiny mass, what accounts for an atom's much larger mass? To address these issues, Thomson proposed his "plum-pudding" model—a spherical atom composed of diffuse, positively charged matter with electrons embedded like "raisins in a plum pudding."

In 1910, New Zealand–born physicist Ernest Rutherford (1871–1937) tested this model and obtained an unexpected result (Figure 2.6):

1. *Experimental design.* Figure 2.6B shows the experimental setup, in which tiny, dense, positively charged alpha (α) particles emitted from radium are aimed at gold foil. A circular, zinc-sulfide screen registers the deflection (scattering) of the α particles by emitting light flashes when the particles strike it.
2. *Expected results.* With Thomson's model in mind (Figure 2.6A), Rutherford expected only minor, if any, deflections of the α particles because they should act as bullets and go right through the gold atoms. After all, an electron would not deflect an α particle any more than a Ping-Pong ball would deflect a baseball.
3. *Actual results.* Initial results were consistent with this idea, but then the unexpected happened (Figure 2.6C). As Rutherford recalled: "I remember two or three days later Geiger [one of his coworkers] coming to me in great excitement and saying, 'We have been able to get some of the α particles coming backwards . . .' It was quite the most incredible event that has ever happened to me in my life. It was almost as incredible as if you fired a 15-inch shell at a piece of tissue paper and it came back and hit you." In fact, very few α particles were deflected at all, and only 1 in 20,000 was deflected by more than 90° ("coming backwards").
4. *Rutherford's conclusion.* Rutherford concluded that these few α particles were being repelled by something small, dense, and positive within the gold atoms. Calculations based on the mass, charge, and velocity of the α particles and the proportion of these large-angle deflections showed that
   • An atom is mostly space occupied by electrons.
   • In the center is a tiny region, which Rutherford called the **nucleus,** that contains all the positive charge and essentially all the mass of the atom.
   He proposed that positive particles lay within the nucleus and called them *protons.*

Rutherford's model explained the charged nature of matter, but it could not account for all the atom's mass. After more than 20 years, in 1932, James Chadwick discovered the *neutron,* an uncharged dense particle that also resides in the nucleus.

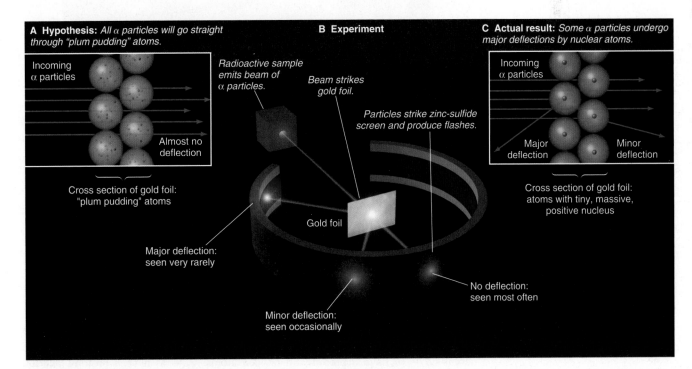

Figure 2.6 Rutherford's α-scattering experiment and discovery of the atomic nucleus.

▌Summary of Section 2.4

- Several major discoveries at the turn of the 20th century resolved questions about Dalton's model and led to our current model of atomic structure.
- Cathode rays were shown to consist of negative particles (electrons) that exist in all matter. J. J. Thomson measured their mass/charge ratio and concluded that they are much smaller and lighter than atoms.
- Robert Millikan determined the charge of the electron, which he combined with other data to calculate its mass.
- Ernest Rutherford proposed that atoms consist of a tiny, massive, positive nucleus surrounded by electrons.

● **The Tiny, Massive Nucleus** A few analogies can help you grasp the incredible properties of the atomic nucleus. A nucleus the size of the period at the end of a sentence would weigh about 100 tons, as much as 50 cars! An atom the size of the Houston Astrodome would have a nucleus the size of a green pea that would contain virtually all its mass. If the nucleus were the size depicted at the right in Figure 2.7 (about 1 cm across), the atom would be about 200 m across, or more than the length of two football fields!

2.5 • THE ATOMIC THEORY TODAY

Dalton's model of an indivisible particle has given way to our current model of an atom with an elaborate internal architecture of subatomic particles.

Structure of the Atom

An *atom* is an electrically neutral, spherical entity composed of a positively charged central nucleus surrounded by one or more negatively charged electrons (Figure 2.7). The electrons move rapidly within the available volume, held there by the attraction of the nucleus. An atom's diameter ($\sim 1 \times 10^{-10}$ m) is about 20,000 times the diameter of its nucleus ($\sim 5 \times 10^{-15}$ m). The nucleus contributes 99.97% of the atom's mass, occupies only about 1 quadrillionth of its volume, and is incredibly dense: about 10^{14} g/mL! ●

Figure 2.7 General features of the atom.

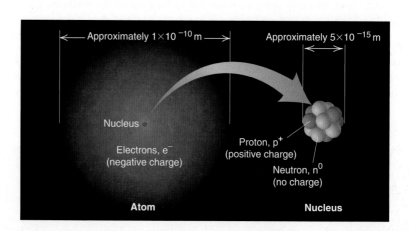

An *atomic nucleus consists of protons and neutrons* (the only exception is the simplest hydrogen nucleus, which is a single proton). The **proton (p⁺)** has a positive charge, and the **neutron (n⁰)** has no charge; thus, the positive charge of the nucleus results from its protons. The *magnitudes* of the charges possessed by a proton and by an **electron (e⁻)** are equal, but the *signs* of the charges are opposite. *An atom is neutral because the number of protons in the nucleus equals the number of electrons surrounding the nucleus.* Some properties of these three subatomic particles are listed in Table 2.2 on the next page.

Atomic Number, Mass Number, and Atomic Symbol

The **atomic number (Z)** of an element equals the number of protons in the nucleus of each of its atoms. *All atoms of an element have the same atomic number, and the atomic number of each element is different from that of any other element.* All carbon atoms ($Z = 6$) have 6 protons, all oxygen atoms ($Z = 8$) have 8 protons, and all

Table 2.2 Properties of the Three Key Subatomic Particles

Name (Symbol)	Charge		Mass		Location in Atom
	Relative	Absolute (C)*	Relative (amu)†	Absolute (g)	
Proton (p^+)	1+	$+1.60218\times10^{-19}$	1.00727	1.67262×10^{-24}	Nucleus
Neutron (n^0)	0	0	1.00866	1.67493×10^{-24}	Nucleus
Electron (e^-)	1-	-1.60218×10^{-19}	0.00054858	9.10939×10^{-28}	Outside nucleus

*The coulomb (C) is the SI unit of charge.
†The atomic mass unit (amu) equals 1.66054×10^{-24} g; discussed later in this section.

uranium atoms ($Z = 92$) have 92 protons. There are currently 117 known elements, of which 90 occur in nature and 27 have been synthesized by nuclear scientists.

The **mass number** (*A*) is the total number of protons and neutrons in the nucleus of an atom. Each proton and each neutron contributes one unit to the mass number. Thus, a carbon atom with 6 protons and 6 neutrons in its nucleus has a mass number of 12, and a uranium atom with 92 protons and 146 neutrons in its nucleus has a mass number of 238.

The **atomic symbol** (or *element symbol*) of an element is based on its English, Latin, or Greek name, such as C for carbon, S for sulfur, and Na for sodium (Latin *natrium*). Often written with the symbol are the atomic number (*Z*) as a left *sub*script and the mass number (*A*) as a left *super*script, so element X would be $^A_Z X$. Since the mass number is the sum of protons and neutrons, the number of neutrons (*N*) equals the mass number minus the atomic number:

$$\text{Number of neutrons} = \text{mass number} - \text{atomic number, or}\quad N = A - Z \quad \textbf{(2.2)}$$

Thus, a chlorine atom, symbolized $^{35}_{17}Cl$, has $A = 35$, $Z = 17$, and $N = 35 - 17 = 18$. Because each element has its own atomic number, we also know the atomic number given the symbol. For example, instead of writing $^{12}_6C$ for carbon with mass number 12, we can write ^{12}C (spoken "carbon twelve"), with $Z = 6$ understood. Another way to name this atom is carbon-12.

Isotopes

All atoms of an element have the same atomic number but not the same mass number. **Isotopes** of an element are atoms that have *different numbers of neutrons* and therefore different mass numbers. For example, all carbon atoms ($Z = 6$) have 6 protons and 6 electrons, but only 98.89% of naturally occurring carbon atoms have 6 neutrons ($A = 12$). A small percentage (1.11%) have 7 neutrons ($A = 13$), and even fewer (less than 0.01%) have 8 ($A = 14$). These are carbon's three naturally occurring isotopes—^{12}C, ^{13}C, and ^{14}C. *A natural sample of carbon has these three isotopes in these relative proportions.* Five other carbon isotopes—^9C, ^{10}C, ^{11}C, ^{15}C, and ^{16}C—have been created in the laboratory. Figure 2.8 depicts the atomic number, mass number, and symbol for four atoms, two of which are isotopes of the element uranium.

The chemical properties of an element are primarily determined by the number of electrons, so *all isotopes of an element have nearly identical chemical behavior,* even though they have different masses.

Figure 2.8 The $^A_Z X$ notations and spherical representations for four atoms. (The nuclei are not drawn to scale.)

Mass number ($p^+ + n^0$)   Atomic symbol
Atomic number (p^+)

$^6p^+$ $^6n^0$ $6e^-$ $^{12}_6C$
An atom of carbon-12

$8p^+$ $8n^0$ $8e^-$ $^{16}_8O$
An atom of oxygen-16

$92p^+$ $143n^0$ $92e^-$ $^{235}_{92}U$
An atom of uranium-235

$92p^+$ $146n^0$ $92e^-$ $^{238}_{92}U$
An atom of uranium-238

Sample Problem 2.4 | **Determining the Number of Subatomic Particles in the Isotopes of an Element**

Problem Silicon (Si) is a major component of semiconductor chips. It has three naturally occurring isotopes: ^{28}Si, ^{29}Si, and ^{30}Si. Determine the numbers of protons, neutrons, and electrons in each silicon isotope.

Plan The mass number (A; left superscript) of each of the three isotopes is given, which is the sum of protons and neutrons. From the elements list on the text's inside front cover, we find the atomic number (Z, number of protons), which equals the number of electrons. We obtain the number of neutrons by subtracting Z from A (Equation 2.2).

Solution From the elements list, the atomic number of silicon is 14. Therefore,

$$^{28}\text{Si has } 14\text{p}^+, 14\text{e}^-, \text{ and } 14\text{n}^0 (28 - 14)$$
$$^{29}\text{Si has } 14\text{p}^+, 14\text{e}^-, \text{ and } 15\text{n}^0 (29 - 14)$$
$$^{30}\text{Si has } 14\text{p}^+, 14\text{e}^-, \text{ and } 16\text{n}^0 (30 - 14)$$

Follow-Up Problem 2.4 How many protons, neutrons, and electrons are in **(a)** $^{11}_{5}\text{Q}$? **(b)** $^{41}_{20}\text{R}$? **(c)** $^{131}_{53}\text{X}$? What elements do Q, R, and X represent?

Atomic Masses of the Elements

The mass of an atom is measured *relative* to the mass of an atomic standard. The modern standard is the carbon-12 atom, whose mass is defined as *exactly* 12 atomic mass units. Thus, the **atomic mass unit (amu)** is $\frac{1}{12}$ the mass of a carbon-12 atom. Based on this standard, the ^1H atom has a mass of 1.008 amu; in other words, a ^{12}C atom has almost 12 times the mass of an ^1H atom. We will continue to use the term *atomic mass unit* in the text, although the name of the unit has been changed to the **dalton (Da)**; thus, one ^{12}C atom has a mass of 12 daltons (12 Da, or 12 amu). The atomic mass unit is a unit of relative mass, but it has an absolute mass of 1.66054×10^{-24} g.

The isotopic makeup of an element is determined by **mass spectrometry**, a method for measuring the relative masses and abundances of atomic-scale particles very precisely (which we discuss in the Tools of the Laboratory essay). For example, using a mass spectrometer, we measure the mass ratio of ^{28}Si to ^{12}C as

$$\frac{\text{Mass of }^{28}\text{Si atom}}{\text{Mass of }^{12}\text{C standard}} = 2.331411$$

From this mass ratio, we find the **isotopic mass** of the ^{28}Si atom, the relative mass of this silicon isotope:

$$\text{Isotopic mass of }^{28}\text{Si} = \text{measured mass ratio} \times \text{mass of }^{12}\text{C}$$
$$= 2.331411 \times 12 \text{ amu} = 27.97693 \text{ amu}$$

Along with the isotopic mass, the mass spectrometer gives the relative abundance as a percentage (or fraction) of each isotope in a sample of the element. For example, the relative abundance of ^{28}Si is 92.23% (or 0.9223).

From such data, we can obtain the **atomic mass** (also called *atomic weight*) of an element, the *average* of the masses of its naturally occurring isotopes weighted according to their abundances. Each naturally occurring isotope of an element contributes a certain portion to the atomic mass. For instance, multiplying the isotopic mass of ^{28}Si by its fractional abundance gives the portion of the atomic mass of Si contributed by ^{28}Si:

$$\text{Portion of Si atomic mass from }^{28}\text{Si} = 27.97693 \text{ amu} \times 0.9223 = 25.8031 \text{ amu}$$
$$\text{(retaining two additional significant figures)}$$

Similar calculations give the portions contributed by ^{29}Si (28.976495 amu $\times$ 0.0467 = 1.3532 amu) and by ^{30}Si (29.973770 amu $\times$ 0.0310 = 0.9292 amu). Adding the three portions together (rounding to two decimal places at the end) gives the atomic mass of silicon:

$$\text{Atomic mass of Si} = 25.8031 \text{ amu} + 1.3532 \text{ amu} + 0.9292 \text{ amu}$$
$$= 28.0855 \text{ amu} = 28.09 \text{ amu}$$

The atomic mass is an average value; thus, while no individual silicon atom has a mass of 28.09 amu, in the laboratory, we consider a sample of silicon to consist of atoms with this average mass.

Mass spectrometry is a powerful technique for measuring the mass and abundance of charged particles from their mass/charge ratio (m/e). When a high-energy electron collides with a particle, say, an atom of neon-20, one of the atom's electrons is knocked away and the resulting particle has one positive charge, Ne^+ (Figure B2.1). Thus, its m/e equals the mass divided by 1+.

Figure B2.2, part A, depicts the core of one type of mass spectrometer. The sample is introduced (and vaporized if liquid or solid), then bombarded by high-energy electrons to form positively charged particles, in this case, of the different neon isotopes. These are attracted toward a series of negatively charged plates with slits in them. Some particles pass through the slits into an evacuated tube exposed to a magnetic field. As the particles enter this region, their paths are bent, the lightest particles (lowest m/e) are deflected most and the heaviest particles (highest m/e) least. At the end of the magnetic region, the particles strike a detector, which records their relative positions and abundances (Figure B2.2, parts B and C).

Mass spectrometry is now employed to measure the mass of virtually any atom, molecule, or molecular fragment. The technique is being used to study catalyst surfaces, forensic materials, fuel mixtures, medicinal agents, and many other samples, especially proteins (Figure B2.2, part D); in fact, John B. Fenn and Koichi Tanaka shared part of the 2002 Nobel Prize in chemistry for developing methods to study proteins by mass spectrometry.

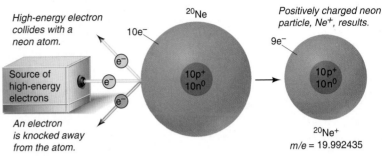

High-energy electron collides with a neon atom.

Source of high-energy electrons

An electron is knocked away from the atom.

^{20}Ne

$10e^-$

$10p^+$
$10n^0$

Positively charged neon particle, Ne^+, results.

$9e^-$

$10p^+$
$10n^0$

$^{20}Ne^+$
$m/e = 19.992435$

Figure B2.1 Formation of a positively charged neon particle (Ne^+).

Problems

B2.1 Chlorine has two naturally occurring isotopes, ^{35}Cl (abundance 76%) and ^{37}Cl (abundance 24%), and it occurs as diatomic (two-atom) molecules. In a mass spectrum, peaks are seen for the molecule and for the separated atoms.
(a) How many peaks are in the mass spectrum?
(b) What is the m/e value of the heaviest particle and of the lightest particle?

B2.2 When a sample of pure carbon is analyzed by mass spectrometry, peaks X, Y, and Z are obtained. Peak Y is taller than X and Z, and Z is taller than X. What is the m/e value of the isotope responsible for peak Z?

Sample enters chamber and is vaporized (if necessary).

Electron beam knocks electrons from atoms (see Figure B2.1).

Charged particle beam

Heater

Electron source

Electric field accelerates particles toward magnetic region.

Magnetic field separates particles by their mass/charge ratio.

Magnet

Detector

Lightest particles

$^{20}Ne^+$ $^{21}Ne^+$

$^{22}Ne^+$

Heaviest particles

A

Figure B2.2 The mass spectrometer and its data. **A,** Particles are separated by their m/e values. **B,** The relative abundances of three Ne isotopes. **C,** The percent abundance of each isotope. **D,** The mass spectrum of a protein molecule. Each peak represents a molecular fragment.

B

Abundance of Ne^+ particles

19 20 21 22
Mass/charge

$^{20}Ne^+$ (90.5%)

100
80
60
40
20

Percent abundance

$^{21}Ne^+$ (0.3%)

$^{22}Ne^+$ (9.2%)

20 21 22
Mass/charge

C

D

Sample Problem 2.5 Calculating the Atomic Mass of an Element

Problem Silver (Ag; $Z = 47$) has 46 known isotopes, but only two occur naturally, ^{107}Ag and ^{109}Ag. Given the following data, calculate the atomic mass of Ag:

Isotope	Mass (amu)	Abundance (%)
^{107}Ag	106.90509	51.84
^{109}Ag	108.90476	48.16

Road Map

Mass (g) of each isotope

↓ multiply by fractional abundance of each isotope

Portion of atomic mass from each isotope

↓ add isotopic portions

Atomic mass

Plan From the mass and abundance of the two Ag isotopes, we have to find the atomic mass of Ag (weighted average of the isotopic masses). We divide each percent abundance by 100 to get the fractional abundance and then multiply that by each isotopic mass to find the portion of the atomic mass contributed by each isotope. The sum of the isotopic portions is the atomic mass.

Solution Finding the fractional abundances:

Fractional abundance of ^{107}Ag = 51.84/100 = 0.5184; similarly, ^{109}Ag = 0.4816

Finding the portion of the atomic mass from each isotope:

Portion of atomic mass from ^{107}Ag = isotopic mass × fractional abundance
$$= 106.90509 \text{ amu} × 0.5184 = 55.42 \text{ amu}$$
Portion of atomic mass from ^{109}Ag = 108.90476 amu × 0.4816 = 52.45 amu

Finding the atomic mass of silver:

Atomic mass of Ag = 55.42 amu + 52.45 amu = $\boxed{107.87 \text{ amu}}$

Check The individual portions seem right: ~100 amu × 0.50 = 50 amu. The portions should be almost the same because the two isotopic abundances are almost the same. We rounded each portion to four significant figures because that is the number of significant figures in the abundance values. This is the correct atomic mass (to two decimal places); in the list of elements (inside front cover), it is rounded to 107.9 amu.

Follow-Up Problem 2.5 Boron (B; $Z = 5$) has two naturally occurring isotopes. Find the percent abundances of ^{10}B and ^{11}B given these data: atomic mass of B = 10.81 amu, isotopic mass of ^{10}B = 10.0129 amu, and isotopic mass of ^{11}B = 11.0093 amu. (*Hint:* The sum of the fractional abundances is 1. If x = abundance of ^{10}B, then $1 - x$ = abundance of ^{11}B.)

▌Summary of Section 2.5

- An atom has a central nucleus, which contains positively charged protons and uncharged neutrons and is surrounded by negatively charged electrons. An atom is neutral because the number of electrons equals the number of protons.
- An atom is represented by the notation $^A_Z X$, in which Z is the atomic number (number of protons), A the mass number (sum of protons and neutrons), and X the atomic symbol.
- An element occurs naturally as a mixture of isotopes, atoms with the same number of protons but different numbers of neutrons. Each isotope has a mass relative to the ^{12}C mass standard.
- The atomic mass of an element is the average of its isotopic masses weighted according to their natural abundances and is determined using modern instruments, especially the mass spectrometer.

2.6 • ELEMENTS: A FIRST LOOK AT THE PERIODIC TABLE

At the end of the 18th century, Lavoisier compiled a list of the 23 elements known at that time; by 1870, 65 were known; by 1925, 88; today, there are 117 and still counting! By the mid-19th century, enormous amounts of information concerning reactions, properties, and atomic masses of the elements had been accumulated. Several researchers noted recurring, or *periodic,* patterns of behavior and proposed schemes to organize the elements according to some fundamental property.

In 1871, the Russian chemist Dmitri Mendeleev (1836–1907) published the most successful of these organizing schemes as a table of the elements listed by increasing atomic mass and arranged so that elements with similar chemical properties fell in the same column. The modern **periodic table of the elements,** based on Mendeleev's version (but arranged by *atomic number,* not mass), is one of the great classifying schemes in science and an indispensable tool to chemists—and chemistry students.

Organization of the Periodic Table One common version of the modern periodic table appears in Figure 2.9 (and inside the front cover). It is formatted as follows:

1. Each element has a box that contains its atomic number, atomic symbol, and atomic mass. (A mass in parentheses is the mass number of the most stable isotope of that element.) The boxes lie, from left to right, in order of *increasing atomic number* (number of protons in the nucleus).
2. The boxes are arranged into a grid of **periods** (horizontal rows) and **groups** (vertical columns). Each period has a number from 1 to 7. Each group has a number from 1 to 8 *and* either the letter A or B. A newer system, with group numbers from 1 to 18 but no letters, appears in parentheses under the number-letter designations. (The text uses the number-letter system and shows the newer numbering system in parentheses.)
3. The eight A groups (two on the left and six on the right) contain the *main-group elements.* The ten B groups, located between Groups 2A(2) and 3A(13), contain the *transition elements.* Two horizontal series of *inner transition elements,* the lanthanides and the actinides, fit *between* the elements in Group 3B(3) and Group 4B(4) and are placed below the main body of the table.

Figure 2.9 The modern periodic table. As of mid-2010, elements 113–116 and 118 had not been named.

Classifying the Elements One of the clearest ways to classify the elements is as metals, nonmetals, and metalloids. The "staircase" line that runs from the top of Group 3A(13) to the bottom of Group 6A(16) is a dividing line:

- The **metals** (three shades of blue in Figure 2.9) lie in the large lower-left portion of the table. About three-quarters of the elements are metals, including many main-group elements and all the transition and inner transition elements. They are generally shiny solids at room temperature (mercury is the only liquid) that conduct heat and electricity well. They can be tooled into sheets (are malleable) and wires (are ductile).
- The **nonmetals** (yellow) lie in the small upper-right portion of the table. They are generally gases or dull, brittle solids at room temperature (bromine is the only liquid) and conduct heat and electricity poorly.
- The **metalloids** (green; also called **semimetals**), which lie along the staircase line, have properties between those of metals and nonmetals.

Figure 2.10 shows examples of these three classes of elements.

Figure 2.10 Some metals, metalloids, and nonmetals.

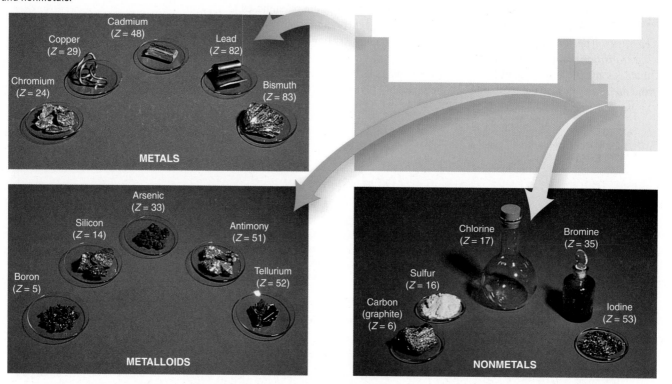

Two major points to keep in mind:

1. In general, elements in a group have **similar** chemical properties and elements in a period have **different** chemical properties.
2. Despite this classification of three types of elements, in reality, there is a gradation in properties from left to right and top to bottom.

It is important to learn some of the group (family) names. Group 1A(1), except for hydrogen, consists of the *alkali metals,* and Group 2A(2) consists of the *alkaline earth metals.* Both groups consist of highly reactive elements. The *halogens,* Group 7A(17), are highly reactive nonmetals, whereas the *noble gases,* Group 8A(18), are relatively unreactive nonmetals. Other main groups [3A(13) to 6A(16)] are often named for the first element in the group; for example, Group 6A(16) is the *oxygen family.*

Two of the major branches of chemistry have traditionally been defined by the elements that each studies. *Organic chemistry* studies the compounds of carbon, specifically those that contain hydrogen and often oxygen, nitrogen, and a few other elements. This branch is concerned with fuels, drugs, dyes, and the like. *Inorganic chemistry,* on the other hand, focuses on the compounds of all the other elements and is concerned with catalysts, electronic materials, metal alloys, mineral salts, and the like. With the explosive growth in biomedical and materials sciences, the line between these branches has all but disappeared.

▌Summary of Section 2.6

- In the periodic table, the elements are arranged by atomic number into horizontal periods and vertical groups.
- Nonmetals appear in the upper-right portion of the table, metalloids lie along a staircase line, and metals fill the rest of the table.
- Elements within a group have similar behavior, whereas elements within a period have dissimilar behavior.

2.7 • COMPOUNDS: INTRODUCTION TO BONDING

Only a few elements occur free in nature. The noble gases—helium (He), neon (Ne), argon (Ar), krypton (Kr), xenon (Xe), and radon (Rn)—occur in air as separate atoms. In addition to occurring in compounds, oxygen (O), nitrogen (N), and sulfur (S) occur in their most common elemental form as the molecules O_2, N_2, and S_8, and carbon (C) occurs in vast, nearly pure deposits of coal. And some metals—copper (Cu), silver (Ag), gold (Au), and platinum (Pt)—are also sometimes found uncombined. But, aside from these few exceptions, *the overwhelming majority of elements occur in compounds combined with other elements.*

Elements combine in two general ways and both involve *the electrons of the atoms of interacting elements:*

1. *Transferring electrons* from one element to another to form **ionic compounds**
2. *Sharing electrons* between atoms of different elements to form **covalent compounds**

These processes generate **chemical bonds,** the forces that hold the atoms together in a compound. This section introduces compound formation, which we'll discuss in much more detail in later chapters.

The Formation of Ionic Compounds

Ionic compounds are composed of **ions,** charged particles that form when an atom (or small group of atoms) gains or loses one or more electrons. The simplest type of ionic compound is a **binary ionic compound,** one composed of two elements. It typically forms *when a metal reacts with a nonmetal:*

- Each metal atom *loses* one or more electrons and becomes a **cation,** a positively charged ion.
- Each nonmetal atom *gains* one or more of the electrons lost by the metal atom and becomes an **anion,** a negatively charged ion.

In effect, the metal atoms *transfer electrons* to the nonmetal atoms. The resulting large numbers of cations and anions attract each other and form the ionic compound. A cation or anion derived from a single atom is called a **monatomic ion;** we'll discuss polyatomic ions, those derived from a small group of atoms, later.

The Case of Sodium Chloride *All binary ionic compounds are solid arrays of oppositely charged ions.* The formation of the binary ionic compound sodium chloride, common table salt, from its elements is depicted in Figure 2.11. In the electron transfer, a sodium atom *loses* one electron and forms a sodium cation, Na^+. (The charge on the ion is written as a *right superscript*.) A chlorine atom *gains* the electron and becomes a chloride anion, Cl^-. (The name change when the nonmetal atom becomes an anion is discussed in the next section.) The oppositely charged ions (Na^+ and Cl^-) attract each other, and the similarly charged ions (Na^+ and Na^+, or Cl^- and Cl^-) repel each other. The resulting solid aggregation is a regular array of alternating Na^+ and Cl^- ions that extends in all three dimensions. Even the tiniest visible grain of table salt contains an enormous number of sodium and chloride ions.

Coulomb's Law The strength of the ionic bonding depends to a great extent on the net strength of these attractions and repulsions and is described by *Coulomb's law,* which can be expressed as follows: *the energy of attraction (or repulsion) between two particles is directly proportional to the product of the charges and inversely proportional to the distance between them.*

$$\text{Energy} \propto \frac{\text{charge 1} \times \text{charge 2}}{\text{distance}}$$

In other words, as is summarized in Figure 2.12,

- Ions with higher charges attract (or repel) each other more strongly than ions with lower charges.
- Smaller ions attract (or repel) each other more strongly than larger ions, because their charges are closer together.

Predicting the Number of Electrons Lost or Gained *Ionic compounds are neutral* because they contain equal numbers of positive and negative *charges.* Thus, there are equal numbers of Na^+ and Cl^- ions in sodium chloride, because both ions are singly charged. But there are two Na^+ ions for each oxide ion, O^{2-}, in sodium oxide because two 1+ ions balance one 2− ion.

Can we predict the number of electrons a given atom will lose or gain when it forms an ion? For A-group elements, we usually find that metal atoms lose electrons and nonmetal atoms gain electrons to *form ions with the same number of electrons as in an atom of the nearest noble gas* [Group 8A(18)]. Noble gases have a stability that is related to their number (and arrangement) of electrons. Thus, a sodium atom ($11e^-$) can attain the stability of a neon atom ($10e^-$), the nearest noble gas, by

A The elements (lab view)

Chlorine gas

Sodium metal

B The elements (atomic view)

Chlorine atom (Cl)

$17p^+$
$18n^0$

Gains electron $17e^-$

Chloride ion (Cl^-)

$18e^-$

$17p^+$
$18n^0$

Cl^- Na^+

e^-

Sodium atom (Na)

$11p^+$
$12n^0$

$11e^-$

Loses electron

$11p^+$
$12n^0$

$10e^-$

Sodium ion (Na^+)

C Electron transfer

D The compound (atomic view): Na^+ and Cl^- in the crystal

E The compound (lab view): sodium chloride crystal

Figure 2.11 The formation of an ionic compound. A, The two elements as seen in the laboratory. **B,** The elements on the atomic scale. **C,** The electron transfer from Na atom to Cl atom to form Na^+ and Cl^- ions. **D,** Countless Na^+ and Cl^- ions attract each other and form a regular three-dimensional array. **E,** Crystalline NaCl occurs naturally as the mineral halite.

losing one electron. Similarly, a chlorine atom ($17e^-$) attains the stability of an argon atom ($18e^-$), its nearest noble gas, by gaining one electron. Thus, in general, when an element located near a noble gas forms a monatomic ion,

- *Metals lose electrons:* elements in Group 1A(1) lose one electron, elements in Group 2A(2) lose two, and aluminum in Group 3A(13) loses three.
- *Nonmetals gain electrons:* elements in Group 7A(17) gain one electron, oxygen and sulfur in Group 6A(16) gain two, and nitrogen in Group 5A(15) gains three.

In the periodic table in Figure 2.9, it looks like the elements in Group 7A(17) are "closer" to the noble gases than the elements in Group 1A(1). In truth, both groups are only one electron away from the number of electrons in the nearest noble gas. Figure 2.13 shows a periodic table of monatomic ions that is cut and rejoined as a cylinder. Note that fluorine (F; $Z = 9$) has one electron *fewer* than the noble gas neon (Ne; $Z = 10$) and sodium (Na; $Z = 11$) has one electron *more;* thus, they form the F^- and Na^+ ions. Similarly, oxygen (O; $Z = 8$) gains two electrons and magnesium (Mg; $Z = 12$) loses two to form the O^{2-} and Mg^{2+} ions and attain the same number of electrons as neon. In Figure 2.13, species in a row have the same number of electrons.

Figure 2.12 Factors that influence the strength of ionic bonding.

Figure 2.13 The relationship between ion formed and the nearest noble gas.

Sample Problem 2.6 | Predicting the Ion an Element Forms

Problem What monatomic ions do the following elements form?
(a) Iodine ($Z = 53$)   **(b)** Calcium ($Z = 20$)   **(c)** Aluminum ($Z = 13$)

Plan We use the given Z value to find the element in the periodic table and see where its group lies relative to the noble gases. Elements in Groups 1A, 2A, and 3A *lose* electrons to attain the same number as the nearest noble gas and become positive ions; those in Groups 5A, 6A, and 7A *gain* electrons and become negative ions.

Solution **(a)** I^- Iodine ($_{53}I$) is in Group 7A(17), the halogens. Like any member of this group, it gains 1 electron to attain the same number as the nearest Group 8A(18) member, in this case, $_{54}Xe$.
(b) Ca^{2+} Calcium ($_{20}Ca$) is in Group 2A(2), the alkaline earth metals. Like any Group 2A member, it loses 2 electrons to attain the same number as the nearest noble gas, $_{18}Ar$.
(c) Al^{3+} Aluminum ($_{13}Al$) is a metal in the boron family [Group 3A(13)] and thus loses 3 electrons to attain the same number as its nearest noble gas, $_{10}Ne$.

Follow-Up Problem 2.6 What monatomic ion does each of the following elements form: **(a)** $_{16}S$; **(b)** $_{37}Rb$; **(c)** $_{56}Ba$?

Atoms far apart: *No interactions.*

Atoms closer: *Attractions* (green arrows) *between nucleus of one atom and electron of the other increase. Repulsions between nuclei and between electrons are very weak.*

Optimum distance: *H_2 molecule forms because attractions* (green arrows) *balance repulsions* (red arrows).

Figure 2.14 Formation of a covalent bond between two H atoms.

The Formation of Covalent Compounds

Covalent compounds form when elements share electrons, which usually occurs between nonmetals. The simplest case of electron sharing occurs not in a compound but between two hydrogen atoms (H; $Z = 1$). Imagine two separated H atoms approaching each other (Figure 2.14). As they get closer, the nucleus of each atom attracts the electron of the other atom more and more strongly. As the separated atoms begin to interpenetrate each other, repulsions between the nuclei and between the electrons begin to increase. At some optimum distance between the nuclei, the two atoms form a **covalent bond,** a pair of electrons mutually attracted by the two nuclei. The result is a hydrogen molecule, in which each electron no longer "belongs" to a particular H atom: the two electrons are *shared* by the two nuclei. A sample of hydrogen gas consists of these diatomic molecules (H_2)—pairs of atoms that are chemically bound and behave as an independent unit—*not* separate H atoms. Figure 2.15 shows other nonmetals that exist as molecules at room temperature.

Figure 2.15 Elements that occur as molecules.

Atoms of different elements share electrons to form the molecules of a covalent compound. A sample of hydrogen fluoride, for example, consists of molecules in which one H atom forms a covalent bond with one F atom; water consists of molecules in which one O atom forms covalent bonds with two H atoms:

Hydrogen fluoride, HF   Water, H_2O

Distinguishing the Entities in Covalent and Ionic Substances There is a key distinction between the chemical entities in covalent substances and in ionic substances. *Most covalent substances consist of molecules.* A cup of water, for example, consists of individual water molecules lying near each other. In contrast, under ordinary conditions, *there are no molecules in an ionic compound.* A piece of sodium chloride, for example, is a continuous array in three dimensions of oppositely charged sodium and chloride ions, *not* a collection of individual sodium chloride "molecules."

Another key distinction between covalent and ionic substances concerns the nature of the particles attracting each other. Covalent bonding involves the mutual attraction between two (positively charged) nuclei and the two (negatively charged) electrons that reside between them. Ionic bonding involves the mutual attraction between positive and negative ions.

Polyatomic Ions: Covalent Bonds Within Ions Many ionic compounds contain **polyatomic ions,** which consist of two or more atoms bonded *covalently* and have a net positive or negative charge. For example, Figure 2.16 shows that a crystalline form of calcium carbonate (*left*) occurs on the atomic scale as an array of polyatomic carbonate anions and monatomic calcium cations (*center*). The carbonate ion (*right*) consists of a carbon atom covalently bonded to three oxygen atoms, and two additional electrons give the ion its 2− charge. In many reactions, the polyatomic ion stays together as a unit.

Figure 2.16 The carbonate ion in calcium carbonate.

Carbonate ion
CO_3^{2-}

▌ Summary of Section 2.7

- Although a few elements occur uncombined in nature, the great majority exist in compounds.
- Ionic compounds form when a metal *transfers* electrons to a nonmetal, and the resulting positive and negative ions attract each other to form a three-dimensional array. In many cases, metal atoms lose and nonmetal atoms gain enough electrons to attain the same number of electrons as in atoms of the nearest noble gas.
- Covalent compounds form when elements, usually nonmetals, *share* electrons. Each covalent bond is an electron pair mutually attracted by two atomic nuclei.
- Monatomic ions are derived from single atoms. Polyatomic ions consist of two or more covalently bonded atoms that have a net positive or negative charge due to a deficit or excess of electrons.

2.8 • FORMULAS, NAMES, AND MASSES OF COMPOUNDS

In a **chemical formula,** element symbols and, often, numerical subscripts show the type and number of each atom in the smallest unit of the substance. In this section, you'll learn how to write the names and formulas of ionic and simple covalent compounds, how to calculate the mass of a compound from its formula, and how to visualize molecules with three-dimensional models. To make learning the names and formula of compounds easier, we'll rely on various rules, so be prepared for a bit of memorization and a lot of practice.

Binary Ionic Compounds

Let's begin with two general rules:

- For *all* ionic compounds, *names and formulas give the positive ion (cation) first and the negative ion (anion) second.*
- For all *binary* ionic compounds, *the name of the cation is the name of the metal, and the name of the anion has the suffix -ide added to the root of the name of the nonmetal.*

For example, the anion formed from brom*ine* is named brom*ide* (brom+ide). Therefore, the compound formed from the metal calcium and the nonmetal bromine is named *calcium bromide.*

Table 2.3 Common Monatomic Ions*

Charge	Formula	Name
Cations		
1+	H⁺	hydrogen
	Li⁺	**lithium**
	Na⁺	**sodium**
	K⁺	**potassium**
	Cs⁺	cesium
	Ag⁺	**silver**
2+	**Mg²⁺**	**magnesium**
	Ca²⁺	**calcium**
	Sr²⁺	strontium
	Ba²⁺	**barium**
	Zn²⁺	**zinc**
	Cd²⁺	cadmium
3+	**Al³⁺**	**aluminum**
Anions		
1−	H⁻	hydride
	F⁻	**fluoride**
	Cl⁻	**chloride**
	Br⁻	**bromide**
	I⁻	**iodide**
2−	**O²⁻**	**oxide**
	S²⁻	**sulfide**
3−	**N³⁻**	nitride

*Listed by charge; those in **boldface** are most common.

In general, if the metal of a binary ionic compound is a main-group element (A groups) it usually forms a single type of ion; if it is a transition element (B groups), it often forms more than one. We discuss each case in turn.

Compounds of Elements That Form One Ion

The periodic table presents some key points about the formulas of main-group monatomic ions:

- Monatomic ions of main-group elements have the same ionic charge; the alkali metals—Li, Na, K, Rb, Cs, and Fr—form ions with a 1+ charge; the halogens—F, Cl, Br, and I—form ions with a 1− charge; and so forth.
- For cations, ion charge equals A-group number: Na is in Group 1A and forms Na^+, Ba is in Group 2A and forms Ba^{2+}. (Exceptions in Figure 2.17 are Sn^{2+} and Pb^{2+}.)
- For anions, ion charge equals A-group number minus 8; for example, S is in Group 6A $(6 - 8 = -2)$ and thus forms S^{2-}.

Try to memorize the A-group monatomic ions in Table 2.3 (all of these listed except Ag^+, Zn^{2+}, and Cd^{2+}) according to their positions in Figure 2.17. These ions have *the same number of electrons as an atom of the nearest noble gas.*

Because an ionic compound consists of an array of ions rather than separate molecules, its formula represents the **formula unit,** the *relative* numbers of cations and anions in the compound. The compound has zero net charge, so the positive charges of the cations balance the negative charges of the anions. For example, calcium bromide is composed of Ca^{2+} ions and Br^- ions, so two Br^- balance each Ca^{2+}. The formula is $CaBr_2$, not Ca_2Br. In this and all other formulas,

- The subscript refers to the element *preceding* it.
- The *subscript 1 is understood* from the presence of the element symbol alone (that is, we do not write Ca_1Br_2).
- The charge (without the sign) of one ion becomes the subscript of the other:

$$Ca^{2+} \times Br^{1-} \qquad \text{gives} \qquad Ca_1Br_2 \qquad \text{or} \qquad CaBr_2$$

- Reduce the subscripts to the smallest whole numbers that retain the ratio of ions. Thus, for example, for the Ca^{2+} and O^{2-} ions in calcium oxide, we get Ca_2O_2, which we reduce to the formula CaO.*

---

*Compounds of the mercury(I) ion, such as Hg_2Cl_2, and peroxides of the alkali metals, such as Na_2O_2, are the only two common exceptions to this step; in fact, reducing the subscripts for these compounds would give the incorrect formulas HgCl and NaO.

Figure 2.17 Some common monatomic ions of the elements. Most main-group elements form one monatomic ion. Most transition elements form two monatomic ions. (Hg_2^{2+} is a diatomic ion but is included for comparison with Hg^{2+}.)

The following two sample problems apply these rules. In Sample Problem 2.7, we name the compound from its elements, and in Sample Problem 2.8, we find the formula.

Sample Problem 2.7   Naming Binary Ionic Compounds

Problem Name the ionic compound formed from the following pairs of elements:
(a) Magnesium and nitrogen
(b) Iodine and cadmium
(c) Strontium and fluorine
(d) Sulfur and cesium

Plan The key to naming a binary ionic compound is to recognize which element is the metal and which is the nonmetal. When in doubt, check the periodic table. We place the cation name first, add the suffix *-ide* to the nonmetal root, and place the anion name last.

Solution (a) Magnes*ium* is the metal; *nitr-* is the nonmetal root: magnesium nitride
(b) Cadm*ium* is the metal; *iod-* is the nonmetal root: cadmium iodide
(c) Stront*ium* is the metal; *fluor-* is the nonmetal root: strontium fluoride (Note the spelling is flu*o*ride, not flo*u*ride.)
(d) Ces*ium* is the metal; *sulf-* is the nonmetal root: cesium sulfide

Follow-Up Problem 2.7 For the following ionic compounds, give the name and periodic table group number of each element present:
(a) Zinc oxide
(b) Silver bromide
(c) Lithium chloride
(d) Aluminum sulfide

Sample Problem 2.8   Determining Formulas of Binary Ionic Compounds

Problem Write formulas for the compounds named in Sample Problem 2.7.

Plan We write the formula by finding the smallest number of each ion that gives the neutral compound. These numbers appear as *right subscripts* to the element symbol.

Solution
(a) Mg^{2+} and N^{3-}; three Mg^{2+} ions (6+) balance two N^{3-} ions (6−): Mg_3N_2
(b) Cd^{2+} and I^-; one Cd^{2+} ion (2+) balances two I^- ions (2−): CdI_2
(c) Sr^{2+} and F^-; one Sr^{2+} ion (2+) balances two F^- ions (2−): SrF_2
(d) Cs^+ and S^{2-}; two Cs^+ ions (2+) balance one S^{2-} ion (2−): Cs_2S

Comment 1. The subscript 1 is understood and so not written; thus, in (b), we do *not* write Cd_1I_2.
2. Ion charges do *not* appear in the compound formula; thus, in (c), we do *not* write $Sr^{2+}F_2^-$.

Follow-Up Problem 2.8 Write the formulas of the compounds named in Follow-Up Problem 2.7.

Compounds with Metals That Form More Than One Ion As noted earlier, many metals, particularly the transition elements (B groups), can form more than one ion. Table 2.4 on the next page lists some examples; see Figure 2.17 for their placement in the periodic table. Names of compounds containing these elements include a *Roman numeral within parentheses* immediately after the metal ion's name to indicate its ionic charge. For example, iron can form Fe^{2+} and Fe^{3+} ions. The two compounds that iron forms with chlorine are $FeCl_2$, named iron(II) chloride (spoken "iron two chloride"), and $FeCl_3$, named iron(III) chloride.

Table 2.4 Some Metals That Form More Than One Monatomic Ion*

Element	Ion Formula	Systematic Name	Common (Trivial) Name
Chromium	Cr^{2+}	chromium(II)	chromous
	Cr^{3+}	**chromium(III)**	chromic
Cobalt	Co^{2+}	cobalt(II)	
	Co^{3+}	cobalt(III)	
Copper	**Cu^+**	**copper(I)**	cuprous
	Cu^{2+}	**copper(II)**	cupric
Iron	**Fe^{2+}**	**iron(II)**	ferrous
	Fe^{3+}	**iron(III)**	ferric
Lead	**Pb^{2+}**	**lead(II)**	
	Pb^{4+}	lead(IV)	
Mercury	Hg_2^{2+}	mercury(I)	mercurous
	Hg^{2+}	**mercury(II)**	mercuric
Tin	**Sn^{2+}**	**tin(II)**	stannous
	Sn^{4+}	tin(IV)	stannic

*Listed alphabetically by metal name; the ions in **boldface** are most common.

We are focusing here on systematic names, but some common (trivial) names are still used. In common names for certain metal ions, the Latin root of the metal is followed by either of two suffixes (see Table 2.4):

- The suffix *-ous* for the ion with the lower charge
- The suffix *-ic* for the ion with the higher charge

Thus, iron(II) chloride is also called ferr*ous* chloride and iron(III) chloride is ferr*ic* chloride. (Memory aid: there is an *o* in *-ous* and *lower,* and an *i* in *-ic* and *higher.*)

Table 2.5 Common Polyatomic Ions*

Formula	Name
Cations	
NH_4^+	**ammonium**
H_3O^+	**hydronium**
Anions	
CH_3COO^-	**acetate**
(or **$C_2H_3O_2^-$**)	
CN^-	cyanide
OH^-	**hydroxide**
ClO^-	hypochlorite
ClO_2^-	chlorite
ClO_3^-	**chlorate**
ClO_4^-	**perchlorate**
NO_2^-	nitrite
NO_3^-	**nitrate**
MnO_4^-	**permanganate**
CO_3^{2-}	**carbonate**
HCO_3^-	**hydrogen carbonate**
	(or **bicarbonate**)
CrO_4^{2-}	chromate
$Cr_2O_7^{2-}$	**dichromate**
O_2^{2-}	peroxide
PO_4^{3-}	**phosphate**
HPO_4^{2-}	hydrogen phosphate
$H_2PO_4^-$	dihydrogen
	phosphate
SO_3^{2-}	sulfite
SO_4^{2-}	**sulfate**
HSO_4^-	hydrogen sulfate
	(or **bisulfate**)

*Boldface ions are most common.

Sample Problem 2.9 Determining Names and Formulas of Ionic Compounds of Metals That Form More Than One Ion

Problem Give the systematic names for the formulas or the formulas for the names of the following compounds:
(a) Tin(II) fluoride   **(b)** CrI_3 **(c)** Ferric oxide   **(d)** CoS

Solution **(a)** Tin(II) ion is Sn^{2+}; fluoride is F^-. Two F^- ions balance one Sn^{2+} ion: tin(II) fluoride is SnF_2. (The common name is stannous fluoride.)
(b) The anion is I^-, iodide, and the formula shows three I^-. Therefore, the cation must be Cr^{3+}, chromium(III) ion: CrI_3 is chromium(III) iodide. (The common name is chromic iodide.)
(c) *Ferric* is the common name for iron(III) ion, Fe^{3+}; oxide ion is O^{2-}. To balance the charges, the formula is Fe_2O_3. [The systematic name is iron(III) oxide.]
(d) The anion is sulfide, S^{2-}, which requires that the cation be Co^{2+}. The name is cobalt(II) sulfide.

Follow-Up Problem 2.9 Give the systematic names for the formulas or the formulas for the names of the following compounds:
(a) Lead(IV) oxide   **(b)** Cu_2S **(c)** $FeBr_2$ **(d)** Mercuric chloride

Compounds That Contain Polyatomic Ions

Many ionic compounds contain polyatomic ions. Table 2.5 shows some common polyatomic ions. Remember that *the polyatomic ion stays together as a charged unit.* The formula for potassium nitrate is KNO_3: each K^+ balances one NO_3^-. The formula for sodium carbonate is Na_2CO_3: two Na^+ balance one CO_3^{2-}. *When two or more of the same polyatomic ion are present in the formula unit, that ion appears in parentheses with the subscript written outside.* For example, calcium nitrate contains one Ca^{2+} and two NO_3^- ions and has the formula $Ca(NO_3)_2$. Parentheses and a subscript are *only* used if *more than one* of a given polyatomic ion is present; thus, sodium nitrate is $NaNO_3$, *not* $Na(NO_3)$.

Families of Oxoanions As Table 2.5 shows, most polyatomic ions are **oxoanions** (or *oxyanions*), those in which an element, usually a nonmetal, is bonded to one or more oxygen atoms. There are several families of two or four oxoanions that differ only in the number of oxygen atoms. The following simple naming conventions are used with these ions.

With two oxoanions in the family:

- The ion with *more* O atoms takes the nonmetal root and the suffix *-ate.*
- The ion with *fewer* O atoms takes the nonmetal root and the suffix *-ite.*

For example, SO_4^{2-} is the sulf*ate* ion, and SO_3^{2-} is the sulf*ite* ion; similarly, NO_3^- is nitr*ate*, and NO_2^- is nitr*ite.*

With four oxoanions in the family (a halogen bonded to O) (Figure 2.18):

- The ion with *most* O atoms has the prefix *per-*, the nonmetal root, and the suffix *-ate.*
- The ion with *one fewer* O atom has just the root and the suffix *-ate.*
- The ion with *two fewer* O atoms has just the root and the suffix *-ite.*
- The ion with *least (three fewer)* O atoms has the prefix *hypo-*, the root, and the suffix *-ite.*

For example, for the four chlorine oxoanions,

ClO_4^- is *per*chlor*ate*, ClO_3^- is chlor*ate*, ClO_2^- is chlor*ite*, ClO^- is *hypo*chlor*ite*

	Prefix	Root	Suffix
No. of O atoms ↑	per	*root*	ate
		root	ate
		root	ite
	hypo	*root*	ite

Figure 2.18 Naming oxoanions. Prefixes and suffixes indicate the number of O atoms in the anion.

Hydrated Ionic Compounds Ionic compounds called **hydrates** have a specific number of water molecules in each formula unit, which is shown after a centered dot in the formula and noted in the name by a Greek numerical prefix before the word *hydrate.* Table 2.6 shows these prefixes. For example, Epsom salt has seven water molecules in each formula unit: the formula is $MgSO_4·7H_2O$, and the name is magnesium sulfate *hepta*hydrate. Similarly, the mineral gypsum has the formula $CaSO_4·2H_2O$ and the name calcium sulfate *di*hydrate. The water molecules, referred to as "waters of hydration," are part of the hydrate's structure. Heating can remove some or all of them, leading to a different substance. For example, when heated strongly, blue copper(II) sulfate pentahydrate ($CuSO_4·5H_2O$) is converted to white copper(II) sulfate ($CuSO_4$).

Table 2.6 Numerical Prefixes for Hydrates and Binary Covalent Compounds

Number	Prefix
1	mono-
2	di-
3	tri-
4	tetra-
5	penta-
6	hexa-
7	hepta-
8	octa-
9	nona-
10	deca-

Sample Problem 2.10 | **Determining Names and Formulas of Ionic Compounds Containing Polyatomic Ions**

Problem Give the systematic names for the formulas or the formulas for the names of the following compounds:
(a) $Fe(ClO_4)_2$ **(b)** Sodium sulfite   **(c)** $Ba(OH)_2·8H_2O$
Solution (a) ClO_4^- is perchlorate, which has a 1− charge, so the cation must be Fe^{2+}. The name is iron(II) perchlorate. (The common name is ferrous perchlorate.)
(b) Sodium is Na^+; sulfite is SO_3^{2-}, and two Na^+ ions balance one SO_3^{2-} ion. The formula is Na_2SO_3.
(c) Ba^{2+} is barium; OH^- is hydroxide. There are eight (*octa-*) water molecules in each formula unit. The name is barium hydroxide octahydrate.

Follow-Up Problem 2.10 Give the systematic names for the formulas or the formulas for the names of the following compounds:
(a) Cupric nitrate trihydrate   **(b)** Zinc hydroxide   **(c)** LiCN

Sample Problem 2.11 | **Recognizing Incorrect Names and Formulas of Ionic Compounds**

Problem Explain what is wrong with the name or formula at the end of each statement, and correct it:
(a) $Ba(C_2H_3O_2)_2$ is called barium diacetate.
(b) Sodium sulfide has the formula $(Na)_2SO_3$.
(c) Iron(II) sulfate has the formula $Fe_2(SO_4)_3$.
(d) Cesium carbonate has the formula $Cs_2(CO_3)$.

Solution **(a)** The charge of the Ba^{2+} ion *must* be balanced by *two* $C_2H_3O_2^-$ ions, so the prefix *di-* is unnecessary. For ionic compounds, we do not indicate the number of ions with numerical prefixes. The correct name is barium acetate.
(b) Two mistakes occur here. The sodium ion is monatomic, so it does *not* require parentheses. The sulfide ion is S^{2-}, *not* SO_3^{2-} (which is sulfite). The correct formula is Na_2S.
(c) The Roman numeral refers to the charge of the ion, *not* the number of ions in the formula. Fe^{2+} is the cation, so it requires one SO_4^{2-} to balance its charge. The correct formula is $FeSO_4$. [$Fe_2(SO_4)_3$ is the formula for iron(III) sulfate.]
(d) Parentheses are *not* required when only one polyatomic ion of a kind is present. The correct formula is Cs_2CO_3.

Follow-Up Problem 2.11 State why the formula or name at the end of each statement is incorrect, and correct it:
(a) Ammonium phosphate is $(NH_3)_4PO_4$.
(b) Aluminum hydroxide is $AlOH_3$.
(c) $Mg(HCO_3)_2$ is manganese(II) carbonate.
(d) $Cr(NO_3)_3$ is chromic(III) nitride.
(e) $Ca(NO_2)_2$ is cadmium nitrate.

Acid Names from Anion Names

Acids are an important group of hydrogen-containing compounds that have been used in chemical reactions since before alchemical times. In the laboratory, acids are typically used in water solution. When naming them and writing their formulas, we consider acids as anions that are connected to the number of hydrogen ions (H^+) needed for charge neutrality. The two common types of acids are binary acids and oxoacids:

1. *Binary acid* solutions form when certain gaseous compounds dissolve in water. For example, when gaseous hydrogen chloride (HCl) dissolves in water, it forms hydrochloric acid, that is,

    Prefix *hydro-* + nonmetal *root* + suffix *-ic* + separate word *acid*
    hydro   +   chlor   +   ic   +   acid

    or *hydrochloric acid*. This naming pattern holds for many compounds in which hydrogen combines with an anion that has an *-ide* suffix.

2. *Oxoacid* names are similar to those of the oxoanions, except for two suffix changes:
    • *-ate* in the anion becomes *-ic* in the acid
    • *-ite* in the anion becomes *-ous* in the acid
    The oxoanion prefixes *hypo-* and *per-* are retained. Thus,

    BrO_4^- is *per*brom*ate*, and $HBrO_4$ is *per*brom*ic* acid.
    IO_2^- is iod*ite*, and HIO_2 is iod*ous* acid.

Sample Problem 2.12 | **Determining Names and Formulas of Anions and Acids**

Problem Name each of the following anions and give the name and formula of the acid derived from it: **(a)** Br^- **(b)** IO_3^- **(c)** CN^- **(d)** SO_4^{2-} **(e)** NO_2^-.

Solution **(a)** The anion is bromide; the acid is hydrobromic acid, HBr.
(b) The anion is iodate; the acid is iodic acid, HIO_3.
(c) The anion is cyanide; the acid is hydrocyanic acid, HCN.
(d) The anion is sulfate; the acid is sulfuric acid, H_2SO_4. (In this case, the suffix is added to the element name *sulfur,* not to the root, *sulf-.*)
(e) The anion is nitrite; the acid is nitrous acid, HNO_2.

Comment We must add *two* H^+ ions to the sulfate ion to obtain sulfuric acid because SO_4^{2-} has a 2− charge.

Follow-Up Problem 2.12 Write the formula for the name or name for the formula of each acid: **(a)** chloric acid **(b)** HF **(c)** acetic acid **(d)** sulfurous acid **(e)** HBrO.

Binary Covalent Compounds

Binary covalent compounds are typically formed by the combination of two nonmetals. Some are so familiar that we use their common names, such as ammonia (NH_3), methane (CH_4), and water (H_2O), but most are named systematically:

- The element with the lower group number in the periodic table comes first in the name. The element with the higher group number comes second and is named with its root and the suffix *-ide*. For example, nitrogen [Group 5A(15)] and fluorine [Group 7A(17)] form a compound that has three fluorine atoms for every nitrogen atom. The name and formula are nitrogen trifluoride, NF_3 (*Exception:* When the compound contains oxygen and any of the halogens chlorine, bromine, or iodine, the halogen is named first.)
- If both elements are in the same group, the one with the higher period number is named first. Thus, the Group 6A(16) elements sulfur (Period 3) and oxygen (Period 2) form sulfur dioxide, SO_2.
- Covalent compounds use Greek numerical prefixes (see Table 2.6) to indicate the number of atoms of each element. The first element in the name has a prefix *only* when more than one atom of it is present; the second element *usually* has a prefix.

Sample Problem 2.13 | **Determining Names and Formulas of Binary Covalent Compounds**

Problem **(a)** What is the formula of carbon disulfide?
(b) What is the name of PCl_5?
(c) Give the name and formula of the compound whose molecules each consist of two N atoms and four O atoms.

Solution **(a)** The prefix *di-* means "two." The formula is CS_2.
(b) P is the symbol for phosphorus; there are five chlorine atoms, which is indicated by the prefix *penta-*. The name is phosphorus pentachloride.
(c) Nitrogen (N) comes first in the name (lower group number). The compound is dinitrogen tetraoxide, N_2O_4.

Follow-Up Problem 2.13 Give the name or formula for **(a)** SO_3; **(b)** SiO_2; **(c)** dinitrogen monoxide; **(d)** selenium hexafluoride.

Sample Problem 2.14 **Recognizing Incorrect Names and Formulas of Binary Covalent Compounds**

Problem Explain what is wrong with the name or formula at the end of each statement, and correct it: **(a)** SF_4 is monosulfur pentafluoride. **(b)** Dichlorine heptaoxide is Cl_2O_6. **(c)** N_2O_3 is dinitrotrioxide.

Solution **(a)** There are two mistakes. *Mono-* is not needed if there is only one atom of the first element, and the prefix for four is *tetra-,* not *penta-*. The correct name is sulfur tetrafluoride.
(b) The prefix *hepta-* indicates seven, not six. The correct formula is Cl_2O_7.
(c) The full name of the first element is needed, and a space separates the two element names. The correct name is dinitrogen trioxide.

Follow-Up Problem 2.14 Explain what is wrong with the name or formula at the end of each statement, and correct it: **(a)** S_2Cl_2 is disulfurous dichloride. **(b)** Nitrogen monoxide is N_2O. **(c)** $BrCl_3$ is trichlorine bromide.

The Simplest Organic Compounds: Straight-Chain Alkanes

Organic compounds typically have complex structures that consist of chains, branches, and/or rings of carbon atoms bonded to hydrogen atoms and, often, to atoms of oxygen, nitrogen, and a few other elements. At this point, we'll lay the groundwork for naming organic compounds by focusing on the simplest ones. Rules for naming more complex ones are detailed in Chapter 15.

Hydrocarbons, the simplest type of organic compound, contain *only* carbon and hydrogen. *Alkanes* are the simplest type of hydrocarbon; many function as important fuels, such as methane, propane, butane, and the mixture that makes up gasoline. The simplest alkanes to name are the *straight-chain alkanes* because the carbon chains have no branches. Alkanes are named with a *root,* based on the number of C atoms in the chain, followed by the suffix *-ane.* Table 2.7 gives the names, molecular formulas, and space-filling models (discussed shortly) of the first 10 straight-chain alkanes. Note that the roots of the four smallest ones are new, but those for the larger ones are the same as the Greek prefixes shown in Table 2.6.

Molecular Masses from Chemical Formulas

In Section 2.5, we calculated the atomic mass of an element. Using the periodic table and the formula of a compound, we calculate the **molecular mass** (also called *molecular weight*) of a formula unit of the compound as the sum of the atomic masses:

$$\text{Molecular mass} = \text{sum of atomic masses} \tag{2.3}$$

The molecular mass of a water molecule (using atomic masses to four significant figures from the periodic table) is

Molecular mass of H_2O = (2 × atomic mass of H) + (1 × atomic mass of O)
= (2 × 1.008 amu) + 16.00 amu = 18.02 amu

Ionic compounds don't consist of molecules, so the mass of a formula unit is termed the **formula mass** instead of *molecular mass.* To calculate the formula mass of a compound with a polyatomic ion, *the number of atoms of each element inside the parentheses is multiplied by the subscript outside the parentheses.* For barium nitrate, $Ba(NO_3)_2$,

Formula mass of $Ba(NO_3)_2$

= (1 × atomic mass of Ba) + (2 × atomic mass of N) + (6 × atomic mass of O)
= 137.3 amu + (2 × 14.01 amu) + (6 × 16.00 amu) = 261.3 amu

We can use atomic masses, not ionic masses, because electron loss equals electron gain, so electron mass is balanced. In the next two sample problems, the name or molecular depiction is used to find a compound's molecular or formula mass.

Table 2.7 **The First 10 Straight-Chain Alkanes**

Name (Formula)	Model
Methane (CH_4)	
Ethane (C_2H_6)	
Propane (C_3H_8)	
Butane (C_4H_{10})	
Pentane (C_5H_{12})	
Hexane (C_6H_{14})	
Heptane (C_7H_{16})	
Octane (C_8H_{18})	
Nonane (C_9H_{20})	
Decane ($C_{10}H_{22}$)	

Sample Problem 2.15 Calculating the Molecular Mass of a Compound

Problem Using the periodic table, calculate the molecular (or formula) mass of
(a) Tetraphosphorus trisulfide   **(b)** Ammonium nitrate

Plan We first write the formula, then multiply the number of atoms (or ions) of each element by its atomic mass (from the periodic table), and find the sum.

Solution **(a)** The formula is P_4S_3.

$$\text{Molecular mass} = (4 \times \text{atomic mass of P}) + (3 \times \text{atomic mass of S})$$
$$= (4 \times 30.97 \text{ amu}) + (3 \times 32.07 \text{ amu}) = \boxed{220.09 \text{ amu}}$$

(b) The formula is NH_4NO_3. We count the total number of N atoms even though they belong to different ions:

Formula mass

$$= (2 \times \text{atomic mass of N}) + (4 \times \text{atomic mass of H}) + (3 \times \text{atomic mass of O})$$
$$= (2 \times 14.01 \text{ amu}) + (4 \times 1.007 \text{ amu}) + (3 \times 16.00 \text{ amu}) = \boxed{80.05 \text{ amu}}$$

Check You can often find large errors by rounding atomic masses to the nearest 5 and adding: **(a)** $(4 \times 30) + (3 \times 30) = 210 \approx 220.09$. The sum has two decimal places because the atomic masses have two. **(b)** $(2 \times 15) + 4 + (3 \times 15) = 79 \approx 80.05$.

Follow-Up Problem 2.15 What is the molecular (or formula) mass of
(a) Hydrogen peroxide   **(b)** Cesium chloride
(c) Sulfuric acid   **(d)** Potassium sulfate?

Sample Problem 2.16 Using Molecular Depictions to Determine Formula, Name, and Mass

Problem Each scene represents a binary compound. Determine its formula, name, and molecular (or formula) mass.

(a)   **(b)**

● sodium
○ fluorine
● nitrogen

Plan Each of the compounds contains only two elements, so to find the formula, we find the simplest whole-number ratio of one atom to the other. From the formula, we determine the name and the molecular (or formula) mass.

Solution **(a)** There is one brown sphere (sodium) for each green sphere (fluorine), so the formula is NaF. A metal and nonmetal form an ionic compound, in which the metal is named first: sodium fluoride.

$$\text{Formula mass} = (1 \times \text{atomic mass of Na}) + (1 \times \text{atomic mass of F})$$
$$= 22.99 \text{ amu} + 19.00 \text{ amu} = \boxed{41.99 \text{ amu}}$$

(b) There are three green spheres (fluorine) for each blue sphere (nitrogen), so the formula is NF_3. Two nonmetals form a covalent compound. Nitrogen has a lower group number, so it is named first: nitrogen trifluoride.

$$\text{Molecular mass} = (1 \times \text{atomic mass of N}) + (3 \times \text{atomic mass of F})$$
$$= 14.01 \text{ amu} + (3 \times 19.00) = \boxed{71.01 \text{ amu}}$$

Check **(a)** For binary ionic compounds, we predict ionic charges from the periodic table (see Figure 2.13). Na forms a 1+ ion, and F forms a 1− ion, so the charges balance with one Na^+ per F^-. Also, ionic compounds are solids, consistent with the picture. **(b)** Covalent compounds often occur as individual molecules, as in the picture. Rounding in **(a)** gives $25 + 20 = 45$; in **(b)**, we get $15 + (3 \times 20) = 75$, so there are no large errors.

Follow-Up Problem 2.16 Each scene represents a binary compound. Determine its name, formula, and molecular (or formula) mass.

(a)   **(b)**

- sodium
- oxygen
- nitrogen

Representing Molecules with Formulas and Models

In order to represent objects too small to see, chemists employ a variety of formulas and models. Each conveys different information, as shown for water below:

- A **molecular formula** uses element symbols and, often, numerical subscripts to give the *actual* number of atoms of each element in a molecule of the compound. (Recall that, for ionic compounds, the *formula unit* gives the *relative* number of each type of ion.) The molecular formula of water is H_2O: there are two H atoms and one O atom in each molecule.

  H_2O

- A **structural formula** shows the relative placement and connections of atoms in the molecule. It uses symbols for the atoms *and* either a pair of dots *(electron-dot formula)* or a line *(bond-line formula)* to show the bonds between the atoms. In water, each H atom is bonded to the O atom, but not to the other H atom.

  H:O:H

  H–O–H

In models, colored balls represent atoms *(see margin)*.

- A *ball-and-stick model* shows atoms as balls and bonds as sticks, and the angles between the bonds are accurate. Note that water is a bent molecule (with a bond angle of 104.5°). This type of model doesn't show the bonded atoms overlapping (see Figure 2.14) or their relative sizes, so it exaggerates the distance between them.

- A *space-filling model* is an accurately scaled-up image of the molecule, so it shows the relative sizes of the atoms, the relative distances between the nuclei (centers of the spheres), and the angles between the bonds. However, bonds are not shown, and it can be difficult to see each atom in a complex molecule.

Every molecule is minute, but the range of molecular sizes, and thus molecular masses, is enormous. Table 2.8 shows some diatomic and small polyatomic molecules, and, at the other end of the size range two extremely large molecules, called *macromolecules,* deoxyribonucleic acid (DNA) and nylon.

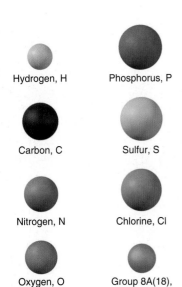

Hydrogen, H   Phosphorus, P

Carbon, C   Sulfur, S

Nitrogen, N   Chlorine, Cl

Oxygen, O   Group 8A(18), e.g., neon, Ne

Group 1A(1), e.g., lithium, Li

■ Summary of Section 2.8

- An ionic compound is named with cation first and anion second. For metals that can form more than one ion, the charge is shown with a Roman numeral.
- Oxoanions have suffixes, and sometimes prefixes, attached to the root of the element name to indicate the number of oxygen atoms.
- Names of hydrates have a numerical prefix indicating the number of associated water molecules.
- Acid names are based on anion names.
- For binary covalent compounds, the first word of the name is the element farther left or lower down in the periodic table, and prefixes show the numbers of each atom.
- The molecular (or formula) mass of a compound is the sum of the atomic masses.
- Chemical formulas give the number of atoms (molecular) or the arrangement of atoms (structural) of one unit of a compound.
- Molecular models convey information about bond angles (ball-and-stick) and relative atomic sizes and distances between atoms (space-filling).

Table 2.8 Representing Molecules

Name	Molecular Formula (Molecular Mass, in amu)	Bond-Line Formula	Ball-and-Stick Model	Space-Filling Model
Carbon monoxide	CO (28.01)			
Nitrogen dioxide	NO_2 (46.01)			
Butane	C_4H_{10} (58.12)			
Aspirin (acetylsalicylic acid)	$C_9H_8O_4$ (180.15)			

Deoxyribonucleic acid (DNA ~10,000,000 amu)

Nylon-66 (~15,000 amu)

2.9 • MIXTURES: CLASSIFICATION AND SEPARATION

In the natural world, *matter usually occurs as mixtures.* A sample of clean air, for example, consists of many elements and compounds physically mixed together, including O_2, N_2, CO_2, the noble gases [Group 8A(18)], and water vapor (H_2O). The oceans are complex mixtures of dissolved ions and covalent substances, including Na^+, Mg^{2+}, Cl^-, SO_4^{2-}, O_2, CO_2, and of course H_2O. Rocks and soils are mixtures of numerous compounds, including calcium carbonate ($CaCO_3$), silicon dioxide (SiO_2), aluminum oxide (Al_2O_3), and iron(III) oxide (Fe_2O_3). And living things contain thousands of substances—carbohydrates, lipids, proteins, nucleic acids, and many simpler ionic and covalent compounds.

There are two broad classes of mixtures:

- A **heterogeneous mixture** has one or more visible boundaries between the components. Thus, its composition is *not* uniform, but rather varies from one region to another. Many rocks are heterogeneous, having individual grains of different minerals. In some heterogeneous mixtures, such as milk and blood, the boundaries can be seen only with a microscope.
- A **homogeneous mixture** (or **solution**) has no visible boundaries because the components are individual atoms, ions, or molecules. Thus, its composition *is* uniform. A mixture of sugar dissolved in water is homogeneous, for example, because the sugar molecules and water molecules are uniformly intermingled on the molecular level. We have no way to tell visually whether a sample of matter is a substance (element or compound) or a homogeneous mixture.

Although we usually think of solutions as liquid, they can exist in all three physical states. For example, air is a gaseous solution of mostly oxygen and nitrogen molecules, and wax is a solid solution of several fatty substances. Solutions in water, called **aqueous solutions,** are especially important in the chemistry lab and comprise a major portion of the environment and of all organisms.

Recall that mixtures differ from compounds in three major ways:

1. The proportions of the components can vary.
2. The individual properties of the components are observable.
3. The components can be separated by physical means.

The difference between a mixture and a compound is well illustrated using iron and sulfur as components (Figure 2.19). Any proportion of iron metal filings and powdered sulfur forms a mixture. The components can be separated with a magnet because iron metal is magnetic. But if we heat the container strongly, the components form the compound iron(II) sulfide (FeS). The magnet can no longer remove the iron because it exists as Fe^{2+} ions chemically bound to S^{2-} ions.

Chemists have devised many procedures for separating a mixture into its components, and the Tools of the Laboratory essay describes some common ones.

An Overview of the Components of Matter

Understanding matter at the observable and atomic scales is the essence of chemistry. Figure 2.20 is a visual overview of many key terms and ideas in this chapter.

MIXTURE

S_8

Fe

A

COMPOUND

S^{2-}

Fe^{2+}

B

Figure 2.19 The distinction between mixtures and compounds. **A,** A *mixture* of iron and sulfur consists of the two elements. **B,** The *compound* iron(II) sulfide consists of an array of Fe^{2+} and S^{2-} ions.

▌ Summary of Section 2.9

- Heterogeneous mixtures have visible boundaries between the components.
- Homogeneous mixtures (solutions) have no visible boundaries because mixing occurs at the molecular level. They can occur in any physical state.
- Components of mixtures (unlike those of compounds) can have variable proportions, can be separated physically, and retain their properties.
- Separation methods are based on differences in physical properties and include filtration (particle size), crystallization (solubility), distillation (volatility), and chromatography (solubility).

Some of the most challenging laboratory procedures involve separating mixtures and purifying the components. All of the techniques described here depend on the *physical properties* of the substances in the mixture; no chemical changes occur.

Filtration is based on *differences in particle size* and is often used to separate a solid from a liquid, which flows through the tiny holes in filter paper as the solid is retained. In vacuum filtration, reduced pressure speeds the flow of the liquid through the filter. Filtration is used in the purification of tap water.

Crystallization is based on *differences in solubility.* The *solubility* of a substance is the amount that dissolves in a fixed volume of solvent at a given temperature. Since solubility often increases with temperature, the impure solid is dissolved in hot solvent and when the solution cools, the purified compound crystallizes. A key component of computer chips is purified by a type of crystallization.

Distillation separates components through *differences in volatility,* the tendency of a substance to become a gas. *Simple* distillation separates components with *large* differences in volatility, such as water from dissolved ionic compounds (Figure B2.3). As the mixture boils, the vapor is richer in the more volatile component, in this case, water, which is condensed and collected separately. *Fractional* distillation uses many vaporization-condensation steps to separate components with small volatility differences, such as those in petroleum (discussed in Chapter 13).

Chromatography is also based on *differences in solubility.* The mixture is dissolved in a gas or liquid, and the components are

Figure B2.4 Procedure for column chromatography.

Ink mixture is placed on stationary phase.

Solvent (mobile phase)

Fresh solvent flows through column.

Stationary phase packed in column

Components move at different rates.

Component most soluble in mobile phase (least soluble in stationary phase) moves fastest.

Collecting flasks

Later time

Components are collected separately.

separated as this solution, called the *mobile phase,* flows through a solid (or viscous liquid) called the *stationary phase.* A component with lower solubility in the stationary phase moves through it faster than a component with a higher solubility. Figure B2.4 depicts the separation of inks by *column chromatography.*

In a related technique called *gas-liquid chromatography (GLC),* the mobile phase is an inert gas, such as helium, that carries a gaseous mixture of components into a long tube packed with the stationary phase (Figure B2.5, part A). The components emerge separately and reach a detector. A chromatogram has numerous peaks, each representing the amount of a specific component (Figure B2.5, part B). *High-performance (high-pressure) liquid chromatography (HPLC)* is similar to GLC, but the mixture need not be vaporized, so more diverse mixtures can be separated.

Problem

B2.3 Name the technique(s) and briefly describe the procedure for separating each of the following mixtures into pure components: (a) table salt and pepper; (b) drinking water contaminated with soot; (c) crushed ice and crushed glass; (d) table sugar dissolved in ethanol; (e) two pigments (chlorophyll *a* and chlorophyll *b*) from spinach leaves.

Thermometer

Mixture is heated and volatile component vaporizes.

Vapors in contact with cool glass condense to form pure liquid distillate.

Water-cooled condenser

Distilling flask

Water out to sink

Water in

Distillate collected in separate flask.

Figure B2.3 Distillation.

He gas → He gas   **Time** ••• He gas → He gas

A *Gaseous mixture (blue and red) is carried into column with mobile phase.*

Component (blue) that is more soluble in stationary phase moves slower.

Solubility in stationary phase →

Detector response: 20, 18, 16, 14, 12, 10, 8, 6, 4, 2, 0

Time (minutes): 22 24 26 28 30 32 34 36

B

Figure B2.5 Principle of gas-liquid chromatography (GLC). The stationary phase is shown as a viscous liquid *(gray circles)* coating the solid beads *(yellow)* of an inert packing.

MATTER
- Anything with mass and volume
- Exists in three physical states: solid, liquid, gas

MIXTURES
- Two or more elements or compounds in variable proportions
- Components retain their properties

Heterogeneous Mixtures
- Visible parts
- Differing regional composition

Homogeneous Mixtures (Solutions)
- No visible parts
- Same composition throughout

PHYSICAL CHANGES

- Filtration
- Crystallization
- Distillation
- Chromatography

SUBSTANCES
- Fixed composition throughout

Elements
- Composed of one type of atom
- Classified as metal, nonmetal, or metalloid
- Simplest type of matter that retains characteristic properties
- May occur as individual atoms or diatomic or polyatomic molecules
- Atomic mass is average of isotopic masses weighted by abundance

Compounds
- Two or more elements combined in fixed parts by mass
- Properties differ from those of component elements
- Molecular mass is sum of atomic masses

CHEMICAL CHANGES

Atoms
- Protons (p^+) and neutrons (n^0) in tiny, massive, positive nucleus
- Atomic number (Z) = no. of p^+
- Mass number (A) = no. of p^+ + no. of n^0
- Electrons (e^-) occupy surrounding volume; no. of p^+ = no. of e^-

Ionic
- Ions arise through e^- transfer from metal to nonmetal
- Solids composed of array of mutually attracting cations and anions
- Formula unit represents the fixed cation/anion ratio

Covalent
- Often consist of separate molecules
- Atoms (usually nonmetals) bonded by e^- pair mutually attracted (shared) by both nuclei

Figure 2.20 The classification of matter from a chemical point of view.

CHAPTER REVIEW GUIDE

Understand These Concepts

1. The defining characteristics of the three types of matter—element, compound, and mixture—on the macroscopic and atomic levels (§2.1)
2. The significance of the three mass laws—mass conservation, definite composition, and multiple proportions (§2.2)
3. The postulates of Dalton's atomic theory and how it explains the mass laws (§2.3)
4. The major contribution of experiments by Thomson, Millikan, and Rutherford to our understanding of atomic structure (§2.4)
5. The structure of the atom, the main features of the subatomic particles, and the importance of isotopes (§2.5)
6. The format of the periodic table and general location and characteristics of metals, metalloids, and nonmetals (§2.6)
7. The essential features of ionic and covalent compounds and the distinction between them (§2.7)
8. The types of mixtures and their properties (§2.9)

Master These Skills

1. Distinguishing elements, compounds, and mixtures at the atomic scale (SP 2.1)
2. Using the mass ratio of element to compound to find the mass of an element in a compound (SP 2.2)
3. Visualizing the mass laws (SP 2.3)
4. Using atomic notation to express the subatomic makeup of an isotope (SP 2.4)
5. Calculating an atomic mass from isotopic composition (SP 2.5)
6. Predicting the monatomic ion formed from a main-group element (SP 2.6)
7. Naming and writing the formula of an ionic compound formed from the ions in Tables 2.3 to 2.5 (SPs 2.7–2.12, 2.16)
8. Naming and writing the formula of a binary covalent compound (SPs 2.13, 2.14, 2.16)
9. Calculating the molecular or formula mass of a compound (SP 2.15)

Key Terms Page numbers appear in parentheses.

Section 2.1
substance (38)
element (38)
molecule (38)
compound (38)
mixture (39)

Section 2.2
law of mass conservation (40)
law of definite (or constant) composition (41)
fraction by mass (mass fraction) (41)
percent by mass (mass percent, mass %) (41)
law of multiple proportions (42)

Section 2.3
atom (43)

Section 2.4
cathode ray (45)
nucleus (47)

Section 2.5
proton (p^+) (48)
neutron (n^0) (48)
electron (e^-) (48)
atomic number (Z) (48)
mass number (A) (49)
atomic symbol (49)
isotope (49)
atomic mass unit (amu) (50)
dalton (Da) (50)
mass spectrometry (50)
isotopic mass (50)
atomic mass (50)

Section 2.6
periodic table of the elements (53)

period (53)
group (53)
metal (54)
nonmetal (54)
metalloid (semimetal) (54)

Section 2.7
ionic compound (55)
covalent compound (55)
chemical bond (55)
ion (55)
binary ionic compound (55)
cation (55)
anion (55)
monatomic ion (55)
covalent bond (58)
polyatomic ion (59)

Section 2.8
chemical formula (59)
formula unit (60)

oxoanion (63)
hydrate (63)
binary covalent compound (65)
molecular mass (66)
formula mass (66)
molecular formula (68)
structural formula (68)

Section 2.9
heterogeneous mixture (70)
homogeneous mixture (solution) (70)
aqueous solution (70)
filtration (71)
crystallization (71)
distillation (71)
volatility (71)
chromatography (71)

Key Equations and Relationships Page numbers appear in parentheses.

2.1 Finding the mass of an element in a given mass of compound (41):

Mass of element in sample

$$= \text{mass of compound in sample} \times \frac{\text{mass of element}}{\text{mass of compound}}$$

2.2 Calculating the number of neutrons in an atom (49):

Number of neutrons = mass number − atomic number

or $N = A - Z$

2.3 Determining the molecular mass of a formula unit of a compound (66):

Molecular mass = sum of atomic masses

Brief Solutions to Follow-Up Problems

2.1 There are two types of particles reacting (left circle), one with two blue atoms and the other with two orange; the depiction shows a mixture of two elements. In the product (right circle), all the particles have one blue atom and one orange; this is a compound.

2.2 Mass (t) of pitchblende

$$= 2.3 \text{ t uranium} \times \frac{84.2 \text{ t pitchblende}}{71.4 \text{ t uranium}} = 2.7 \text{ t pitchblende}$$

Mass (t) of oxygen

$$= 2.7 \text{ t pitchblende} \times \frac{(84.2 - 71.4 \text{ t oxygen})}{84.2 \text{ t pitchblende}} = 0.41 \text{ t oxygen}$$

2.3 Sample B. Two bromine-fluorine compounds appear. In one, there are three fluorine atoms for each bromine; in the other, there is one fluorine for each bromine. Therefore, in the two compounds, the ratio of fluorines combining with one bromine is 3/1.

2.4 (a) $5p^+$, $6n^0$, $5e^-$; Q = B
(b) $20p^+$, $21n^0$, $20e^-$; R = Ca
(c) $53p^+$, $78n^0$, $53e^-$; X = I

2.5 $10.0129x + [11.0093(1 - x)] = 10.81$; $0.9964x = 0.1993$; $x = 0.2000$ and $1 - x = 0.8000$; % abundance of ^{10}B = 20.00%; % abundance of ^{11}B = 80.00%

2.6 (a) S^{2-}; (b) Rb^+; (c) Ba^{2+}

2.7 (a) Zinc [Group 2B(12)] and oxygen [Group 6A(16)]
(b) Silver [Group 1B(11)] and bromine [Group 7A(17)]
(c) Lithium [Group 1A(1)] and chlorine [Group 7A(17)]
(d) Aluminum [Group 3A(13)] and sulfur [Group 6A(16)]

2.8 (a) ZnO; (b) AgBr; (c) LiCl; (d) Al_2S_3

2.9 (a) PbO_2; (b) copper(I) sulfide (cuprous sulfide); (c) iron(II) bromide (ferrous bromide); (d) $HgCl_2$

2.10 (a) $Cu(NO_3)_2 \cdot 3H_2O$; (b) $Zn(OH)_2$; (c) lithium cyanide

2.11 (a) $(NH_4)_3PO_4$; ammonium is NH_4^+ and phosphate is PO_4^{3-}.
(b) $Al(OH)_3$; parentheses are needed around the polyatomic ion OH^-.
(c) Magnesium hydrogen carbonate; Mg^{2+} is magnesium and can have only a 2+ charge, so it does not need (II); HCO_3^- is hydrogen carbonate (or bicarbonate).
(d) Chromium(III) nitrate; the -*ic* ending is not used with Roman numerals; NO_3^- is nit*rate*.
(e) Calcium nitrite; Ca^{2+} is calcium and NO_2^- is nit*rite*.

2.12 (a) $HClO_3$; (b) hydrofluoric acid; (c) CH_3COOH (or $HC_2H_3O_2$); (d) H_2SO_3; (e) hypobromous acid

2.13 (a) Sulfur trioxide; (b) silicon dioxide; (c) N_2O; (d) SeF_6

2.14 (a) Disulfur dichloride; the -*ous* suffix is not used.
(b) NO; the name indicates one nitrogen.
(c) Bromine trichloride; Br is in a higher period in Group 7A(17), so it is named first.

2.15 (a) H_2O_2, 34.02 amu; (b) CsCl, 168.4 amu; (c) H_2SO_4, 98.09 amu; (d) K_2SO_4, 174.27 amu

2.16 (a) Na_2O. This is an ionic compound, so the name is sodium oxide.

Formula mass

$$= (2 \times \text{atomic mass of Na}) + (1 \times \text{atomic mass of O})$$
$$= (2 \times 22.99 \text{ amu}) + 16.00 \text{ amu} = 61.98 \text{ amu}$$

(b) NO_2. This is a covalent compound, and N has the lower group number, so the name is nitrogen dioxide.

Molecular mass

$$= (1 \times \text{atomic mass of N}) + (2 \times \text{atomic mass of O})$$
$$= 14.01 \text{ amu} + (2 \times 16.00 \text{ amu}) = 46.01 \text{ amu}$$

PROBLEMS

Problems with **colored** numbers are answered in Appendix E and worked in detail in the Student Solutions Manual. Problem sections match those in the text and provide the numbers of relevant sample problems. Most offer Concept Review Questions, Skill-Building Exercises (grouped in pairs covering the same concept), and Problems in Context. The Comprehensive Problems are based on material from any section or previous chapter.

Elements, Compounds, and Mixtures: An Atomic Overview

(Sample Problem 2.1)

Concept Review Questions

2.1 What is the key difference between an element and a compound?

2.2 List two differences between a compound and a mixture.

2.3 Which of the following are pure substances? Explain.
(a) Calcium chloride, used to melt ice on roads, consists of two elements, calcium and chlorine, in a fixed mass ratio.

(b) Sulfur consists of sulfur atoms combined into octatomic molecules.
(c) Baking powder, a leavening agent, contains 26% to 30% sodium hydrogen carbonate and 30% to 35% calcium dihydrogen phosphate by mass.
(d) Cytosine, a component of DNA, consists of H, C, N, and O atoms bonded in a specific arrangement.

2.4 Classify each substance in Problem 2.3 as an element, compound, or mixture, and explain your answers.

2.5 Explain the following statement: The smallest particles unique to an element may be atoms or molecules.

2.6 Explain the following statement: The smallest particles unique to a compound cannot be atoms.

2.7 Can the relative amounts of the components of a mixture vary? Can the relative amounts of the components of a compound vary? Explain.

Problems in Context

2.8 The tap water found in many areas of the United States leaves white deposits when it evaporates. Is this tap water a mixture or a compound? Explain.

2.9 Each scene below represents a mixture. Describe each one in terms of the number(s) of elements and/or compounds present.

(a)   (b)   (c)

2.10 Samples of illicit "street" drugs often contain an inactive component, such as ascorbic acid (vitamin C). After obtaining a sample of cocaine, government chemists calculate the mass of vitamin C per gram of drug sample, and use it to track the drug's distribution. For example, if different samples of cocaine obtained on the streets of New York, Los Angeles, and Paris all contain 0.6384 g of vitamin C per gram of sample, they very likely come from a common source. Do these street samples consist of a compound, element, or mixture? Explain.

The Observations That Led to an Atomic View of Matter

(Sample Problem 2.2)

Concept Review Questions

2.11 Why was it necessary for separation techniques and methods of chemical analysis to be developed before the laws of definite composition and multiple proportions could be formulated?

2.12 To which classes of matter—element, compound, and/or mixture—do the following apply: (a) law of mass conservation; (b) law of definite composition; (c) law of multiple proportions?

2.13 In our modern view of matter and energy, is the law of mass conservation still relevant to chemical reactions? Explain.

2.14 Identify the mass law that each of the following observations demonstrates, and explain your reasoning:
(a) A sample of potassium chloride from Chile contains the same percent by mass of potassium as one from Poland.
(b) A flashbulb contains magnesium and oxygen before use and magnesium oxide afterward, but its mass does not change.
(c) Arsenic and oxygen form one compound that is 65.2 mass % arsenic and another that is 75.8 mass % arsenic.

2.15 Which of the following scenes illustrate(s) the fact that compounds of chlorine (green) and oxygen (red) exhibit the law of multiple proportions? Name the compounds.

A   B   C

2.16 (a) Does the percent by mass of each element in a compound depend on the amount of compound? Explain.

(b) Does the mass of each element in a compound depend on the amount of compound? Explain.

2.17 Does the percent by mass of each element in a compound depend on the amount of that element used to make the compound? Explain.

Skill-Building Exercises (grouped in similar pairs)

2.18 State the mass law(s) demonstrated by the following experimental results, and explain your reasoning:

Experiment 1: A student heats 1.00 g of a blue compound and obtains 0.64 g of a white compound and 0.36 g of a colorless gas.

Experiment 2: A second student heats 3.25 g of the same blue compound and obtains 2.08 g of a white compound and 1.17 g of a colorless gas.

2.19 State the mass law(s) demonstrated by the following experimental results, and explain your reasoning:

Experiment 1: A student heats 1.27 g of copper and 3.50 g of iodine to produce 3.81 g of a white compound; 0.96 g of iodine remains.

Experiment 2: A second student heats 2.55 g of copper and 3.50 g of iodine to form 5.25 g of a white compound, and 0.80 g of copper remains.

2.20 Fluorite, a mineral of calcium, is a compound of the metal with fluorine. Analysis shows that a 2.76-g sample of fluorite contains 1.42 g of calcium. Calculate the (a) mass of fluorine in the sample; (b) mass fractions of calcium and fluorine in fluorite; (c) mass percents of calcium and fluorine in fluorite.

2.21 Galena, a mineral of lead, is a compound of the metal with sulfur. Analysis shows that a 2.34-g sample of galena contains 2.03 g of lead. Calculate the (a) mass of sulfur in the sample; (b) mass fractions of lead and sulfur in galena; (c) mass percents of lead and sulfur in galena.

2.22 Magnesium oxide (MgO) forms when the metal burns in air.
(a) If 1.25 g of MgO contains 0.754 g of Mg, what is the mass ratio of magnesium to oxide?
(b) How many grams of Mg are in 534 g of MgO?

2.23 Zinc sulfide (ZnS) occurs in the zinc blende crystal structure.
(a) If 2.54 g of ZnS contains 1.70 g of Zn, what is the mass ratio of zinc to sulfide?
(b) How many kilograms of Zn are in 3.82 kg of ZnS?

2.24 A compound of copper and sulfur contains 88.39 g of metal and 44.61 g of nonmetal. How many grams of copper are in 5264 kg of compound? How many grams of sulfur?

2.25 A compound of iodine and cesium contains 63.94 g of metal and 61.06 g of nonmetal. How many grams of cesium are in 38.77 g of compound? How many grams of iodine?

2.26 Show, with calculations, how the following data illustrate the law of multiple proportions:
Compound 1: 47.5 mass % sulfur and 52.5 mass % chlorine
Compound 2: 31.1 mass % sulfur and 68.9 mass % chlorine

2.27 Show, with calculations, how the following data illustrate the law of multiple proportions:
Compound 1: 77.6 mass % xenon and 22.4 mass % fluorine
Compound 2: 63.3 mass % xenon and 36.7 mass % fluorine

Problems in Context

2.28 Dolomite is a carbonate of magnesium and calcium. Analysis shows that 7.81 g of dolomite contains 1.70 g of Ca. Calculate the mass percent of Ca in dolomite. On the basis of the mass percent of Ca, and neglecting all other factors, which is the richer source of Ca, dolomite or fluorite (see Problem 2.20)?

2.29 The mass percent of sulfur in a sample of coal is a key factor in the environmental impact of the coal because the sulfur combines with oxygen when the coal is burned and the oxide can then be incorporated into acid rain. Which of the following coals would have the smallest environmental impact?

	Mass (g) of Sample	Mass (g) of Sulfur in Sample
Coal A	378	11.3
Coal B	495	19.0
Coal C	675	20.6

Dalton's Atomic Theory
(Sample Problem 2.3)

Concept Review Questions

2.30 Which of Dalton's postulates about atoms are inconsistent with later observations? Do these inconsistencies mean that Dalton was wrong? Is Dalton's model still useful? Explain.

2.31 Use Dalton's theory to explain why potassium nitrate from India or Italy has the same mass percents of K, N, and O.

The Observations That Led to the Nuclear Atom Model

Concept Review Questions

2.32 Thomson was able to determine the mass/charge ratio of the electron but not its mass. How did Millikan's experiment allow determination of the electron's mass?

2.33 The following charges on individual oil droplets were obtained during an experiment similar to Millikan's. Determine a charge for the electron (in C, coulombs), and explain your answer: -3.204×10^{-19} C; -4.806×10^{-19} C; -8.010×10^{-19} C; -1.442×10^{-18} C.

2.34 Describe Thomson's model of the atom. How might it account for the production of cathode rays?

2.35 When Rutherford's coworkers bombarded gold foil with α particles, they obtained results that overturned the existing (Thomson) model of the atom. Explain.

The Atomic Theory Today
(Sample Problems 2.4 and 2.5)

Concept Review Questions

2.36 Define *atomic number* and *mass number*. Which can vary without changing the identity of the element?

2.37 Choose the correct answer. The difference between the mass number of an isotope and its atomic number is (a) directly related to the identity of the element; (b) the number of electrons; (c) the number of neutrons; (d) the number of isotopes.

2.38 Even though several elements have only one naturally occurring isotope and all atomic nuclei have whole numbers of protons and neutrons, no atomic mass is a whole number. Use the data from Table 2.2 to explain this fact.

Skill-Building Exercises (grouped in similar pairs)

2.39 Argon has three naturally occurring isotopes, ^{36}Ar, ^{38}Ar, and ^{40}Ar. What is the mass number of each? How many protons, neutrons, and electrons are present in each?

2.40 Chlorine has two naturally occurring isotopes, ^{35}Cl and ^{37}Cl. What is the mass number of each isotope? How many protons, neutrons, and electrons are present in each?

2.41 Do both members of the following pairs have the same number of protons? Neutrons? Electrons?
(a) $^{16}_{8}$O and $^{17}_{8}$O   (b) $^{40}_{18}$Ar and $^{41}_{19}$K   (c) $^{60}_{27}$Co and $^{60}_{28}$Ni

Which pair(s) consist(s) of atoms with the same Z value? N value? A value?

2.42 Do both members of the following pairs have the same number of protons? Neutrons? Electrons?
(a) $^{3}_{1}$H and $^{3}_{2}$He   (b) $^{14}_{6}$C and $^{15}_{7}$N   (c) $^{19}_{9}$F and $^{18}_{9}$F

Which pair(s) consist(s) of atoms with the same Z value? N value? A value?

2.43 Write the $^{A}_{Z}$X notation for each atomic depiction:

(a)   (b)   (c)

2.44 Write the $^{A}_{Z}$X notation for each atomic depiction:

(a)   (b)   (c)

2.45 Draw atomic depictions similar to those in Problem 2.43 for (a) $^{48}_{22}$Ti; (b) $^{79}_{34}$Se; (c) $^{11}_{5}$B.

2.46 Draw atomic depictions similar to those in Problem 2.43 for (a) $^{207}_{82}$Pb; $^{9}_{4}$Be; $^{75}_{33}$As.

2.47 Gallium has two naturally occurring isotopes, ^{69}Ga (isotopic mass = 68.9256 amu, abundance = 60.11%) and ^{71}Ga (isotopic mass = 70.9247 amu, abundance = 39.89%). Calculate the atomic mass of gallium.

2.48 Magnesium has three naturally occurring isotopes, ^{24}Mg (isotopic mass = 23.9850 amu, abundance = 78.99%), ^{25}Mg (isotopic mass = 24.9858 amu, abundance = 10.00%), and ^{26}Mg (isotopic mass = 25.9826 amu, abundance = 11.01%). Calculate the atomic mass of magnesium.

2.49 Chlorine has two naturally occurring isotopes, ^{35}Cl (isotopic mass = 34.9689 amu) and ^{37}Cl (isotopic mass = 36.9659 amu). If chlorine has an atomic mass of 35.4527 amu, what is the percent abundance of each isotope?

2.50 Copper has two naturally occurring isotopes, ^{63}Cu (isotopic mass = 62.9296 amu) and ^{65}Cu (isotopic mass = 64.9278 amu). If copper has an atomic mass of 63.546 amu, what is the percent abundance of each isotope?

Elements: A First Look at the Periodic Table

Concept Review Questions

2.51 How can iodine ($Z = 53$) have a higher atomic number yet a lower atomic mass than tellurium ($Z = 52$)?

2.52 Correct each of the following statements:
(a) In the modern periodic table, the elements are arranged in order of increasing atomic mass.
(b) Elements in a period have similar chemical properties.
(c) Elements can be classified as either metalloids or nonmetals.

2.53 What class of elements lies along the "staircase" line in the periodic table? How do the properties of these elements compare with those of metals and nonmetals?

2.54 What are some characteristic properties of elements to the left of the elements along the "staircase"? To the right?

2.55 The elements in Groups 1A(1) and 7A(17) are all quite reactive. What is a major difference between them?

Skill-Building Exercises (grouped in similar pairs)

2.56 Give the name, atomic symbol, and group number of the element with each Z value, and classify it as a metal, metalloid, or nonmetal:
(a) $Z = 32$ (b) $Z = 15$ (c) $Z = 2$ (d) $Z = 3$ (e) $Z = 42$

2.57 Give the name, atomic symbol, and group number of the element with each Z value, and classify it as a metal, metalloid, or nonmetal:
(a) $Z = 33$ (b) $Z = 20$ (c) $Z = 35$ (d) $Z = 19$ (e) $Z = 13$

2.58 Fill in the blanks:
(a) The symbol and atomic number of the heaviest alkaline earth metal are _____ and _____.
(b) The symbol and atomic number of the lightest metalloid in Group 4A(14) are _____ and _____.
(c) Group 1B(11) consists of the *coinage metals*. The symbol and atomic mass of the coinage metal whose atoms have the fewest electrons are _____ and _____.
(d) The symbol and atomic mass of the halogen in Period 4 are _____ and _____.

2.59 Fill in the blanks:
(a) The symbol and atomic number of the heaviest nonradioactive noble gas are _____ and _____.
(b) The symbol and group number of the Period 5 transition element whose atoms have the fewest protons are _____ and _____.
(c) The elements in Group 6A(16) are sometimes called the *chalcogens*. The symbol and atomic number of the first metallic chalcogen are _____ and _____.
(d) The symbol and number of protons of the Period 4 alkali metal atom are _____ and _____.

Compounds: Introduction to Bonding
(Sample Problem 2.6)

Concept Review Questions

2.60 Describe the type and nature of the bonding that occurs between reactive metals and nonmetals.

2.61 Describe the type and nature of the bonding that often occurs between two nonmetals.

2.62 How can ionic compounds be neutral if they consist of positive and negative ions?

2.63 Given that the ions in LiF and in MgO are of similar size, which compound has stronger ionic bonding? Use Coulomb's law in your explanation.

2.64 Are molecules present in a sample of BaF_2? Explain.

2.65 Are ions present in a sample of P_4O_6? Explain.

2.66 The monatomic ions of Groups 1A(1) and 7A(17) are all singly charged. In what major way do they differ? Why?

2.67 Describe the formation of solid magnesium chloride ($MgCl_2$) from large numbers of magnesium and chlorine atoms.

2.68 Describe the formation of solid potassium sulfide (K_2S) from large numbers of potassium and sulfur atoms.

2.69 Does potassium nitrate (KNO_3) incorporate ionic bonding, covalent bonding, or both? Explain.

Skill-Building Exercises (grouped in similar pairs)

2.70 What monatomic ions do potassium ($Z = 19$) and iodine ($Z = 53$) form?

2.71 What monatomic ions do barium ($Z = 56$) and selenium ($Z = 34$) form?

2.72 For each ionic depiction, give the name of the parent atom, its mass number, and its group and period numbers:

(a)   (b)   (c)

2.73 For each ionic depiction, give the name of the parent atom, its mass number, and its group and period numbers:

(a)   (b)   (c)

2.74 An ionic compound forms when lithium ($Z = 3$) reacts with oxygen ($Z = 8$). If a sample of the compound contains 8.4×10^{21} lithium ions, how many oxide ions does it contain?

2.75 An ionic compound forms when calcium ($Z = 20$) reacts with iodine ($Z = 53$). If a sample of the compound contains 7.4×10^{21} calcium ions, how many iodide ions does it contain?

2.76 The radii of the sodium and potassium ions are 102 pm and 138 pm, respectively. Which compound has stronger ionic attractions, sodium chloride or potassium chloride?

2.77 The radii of the lithium and magnesium ions are 76 pm and 72 pm, respectively. Which compound has stronger ionic attractions, lithium oxide or magnesium oxide?

Formulas, Names, and Masses of Compounds
(Sample Problems 2.7 to 2.16)

Concept Review Questions

2.78 What information about the relative numbers of ions and the percent mass of elements is in the formula MgF_2?

2.79 How is a structural formula similar to a molecular formula? How is it different?

2.80 Consider a mixture of 10 billion O_2 molecules and 10 billion H_2 molecules. In what way is this mixture similar to a sample containing 10 billion hydrogen peroxide (H_2O_2) molecules? In what way is it different?

2.81 For what type(s) of compound do we use Roman numerals in the names?

2.82 For what type(s) of compound do we use Greek numerical prefixes in the names?

2.83 For what type of compound are we unable to write a molecular formula?

Skill-Building Exercises (grouped in similar pairs)

2.84 Give the name and formula of the compound formed from the following elements: (a) sodium and nitrogen; (b) oxygen and strontium; (c) aluminum and chlorine.

2.85 Give the name and formula of the compound formed from the following elements: (a) cesium and bromine; (b) sulfur and barium; (c) calcium and fluorine.

2.86 Give the name and formula of the compound formed from the following elements:
(a) $_{12}L$ and $_9M$ (b) $_{30}L$ and $_{16}M$ (c) $_{17}L$ and $_{38}M$

2.87 Give the name and formula of the compound formed from the following elements:
(a) $_{37}Q$ and $_{35}R$ (b) $_8Q$ and $_{13}R$ (c) $_{20}Q$ and $_{53}R$

2.88 Give the systematic names for the formulas or the formulas for the names: (a) tin(IV) chloride; (b) $FeBr_3$; (c) cuprous bromide; (d) Mn_2O_3.

2.89 Give the systematic names for the formulas or the formulas for the names: (a) Na_2HPO_4; (b) potassium carbonate dihydrate; (c) $NaNO_2$; (d) ammonium perchlorate.

2.90 Give the systematic names for the formulas or the formulas for the names: (a) CoO; (b) mercury(I) chloride; (c) $Pb(C_2H_3O_2)_2 \cdot 3H_2O$; (d) chromic oxide.

2.91 Give the systematic names for the formulas or the formulas for the names: (a) $Sn(SO_3)_2$; (b) potassium dichromate; (c) $FeCO_3$; (d) copper(II) nitrate.

2.92 Correct each of the following formulas:
(a) Barium oxide is BaO_2
(b) Iron(II) nitrate is $Fe(NO_3)_3$
(c) Magnesium sulfide is $MnSO_3$

2.93 Correct each of the following names:
(a) CuI is cobalt(II) iodide
(b) $Fe(HSO_4)_3$ is iron(II) sulfate
(c) $MgCr_2O_7$ is magnesium dichromium heptaoxide

2.94 Give the name and formula for the acid derived from each of the following anions:
(a) hydrogen sulfate   (b) IO_3^- (c) cyanide   (d) HS^-

2.95 Give the name and formula for the acid derived from each of the following anions:
(a) perchlorate   (b) NO_3^- (c) bromite   (d) F^-

2.96 Many chemical names are similar at first glance. Give the formulas of the species in each set:
(a) Ammonium ion and ammonia
(b) Magnesium sulfide, magnesium sulfite, and magnesium sulfate
(c) Hydrochloric acid, chloric acid, and chlorous acid
(d) Cuprous bromide and cupric bromide

2.97 Give the formulas of the compounds in each set:
(a) Lead(II) oxide and lead(IV) oxide
(b) Lithium nitride, lithium nitrite, and lithium nitrate
(c) Strontium hydride and strontium hydroxide
(d) Magnesium oxide and manganese(II) oxide

2.98 Give the name and formula of the compound whose molecules consist of two sulfur atoms and four fluorine atoms.

2.99 Give the name and formula of the compound whose molecules consist of two chlorine atoms and one oxygen atom.

2.100 Correct the name to match the formula of the following compounds: (a) calcium(II) dichloride, $CaCl_2$; (b) Copper(II) oxide, Cu_2O; (c) Stannous tetrafluoride, SnF_4; (d) Hydrogen chloride acid, HCl.

2.101 Correct the formula to match the name of the following compounds: (a) iron(III) oxide, Fe_3O_4; (b) chloric acid, HCl; (c) mercuric oxide, Hg_2O; (d) dichlorine heptaoxide, Cl_2O_6.

2.102 Give the number of atoms of the specified element in a formula unit of each of the following compounds, and calculate the molecular (formula) mass:
(a) Oxygen in aluminum sulfate, $Al_2(SO_4)_3$
(b) Hydrogen in ammonium hydrogen phosphate, $(NH_4)_2HPO_4$
(c) Oxygen in the mineral azurite, $Cu_3(OH)_2(CO_3)_2$

2.103 Give the number of atoms of the specified element in a formula unit of each of the following compounds, and calculate the molecular (formula) mass:
(a) Hydrogen in ammonium benzoate, $C_6H_5COONH_4$
(b) Nitrogen in hydrazinium sulfate, $N_2H_6SO_4$
(c) Oxygen in the mineral leadhillite, $Pb_4SO_4(CO_3)_2(OH)_2$

2.104 Write the formula of each compound, and determine its molecular (formula) mass: (a) ammonium sulfate; (b) sodium dihydrogen phosphate; (c) potassium bicarbonate.

2.105 Write the formula of each compound, and determine its molecular (formula) mass: (a) sodium dichromate; (b) ammonium perchlorate; (c) magnesium nitrite trihydrate.

2.106 Calculate the molecular (formula) mass of each compound: (a) dinitrogen pentaoxide; (b) lead(II) nitrate; (c) calcium peroxide.

2.107 Calculate the molecular (formula) mass of each compound: (a) iron(II) acetate tetrahydrate; (b) sulfur tetrachloride; (c) potassium permanganate.

2.108 Give the formula, name, and molecular mass of the following molecules:

(a)   (b)

2.109 Give the formula, name, and molecular mass of the following molecules:

(a)   (b)

Problems in Context

2.110 Before the use of systematic names, many compounds had common names. Give the systematic name for each of the following:
(a) Blue vitriol, $CuSO_4 \cdot 5H_2O$
(b) Slaked lime, $Ca(OH)_2$
(c) Oil of vitriol, H_2SO_4
(d) Washing soda, Na_2CO_3
(e) Muriatic acid, HCl
(f) Epsom salt, $MgSO_4 \cdot 7H_2O$
(g) Chalk, $CaCO_3$
(h) Dry ice, CO_2
(i) Baking soda, $NaHCO_3$
(j) Lye, $NaOH$

2.111 Each circle contains a representation of a binary compound. Determine its name, formula, and molecular (formula) mass.

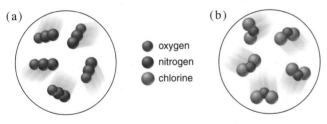

(a)   (b)

● oxygen
● nitrogen
● chlorine

Mixtures: Classification and Separation

Concept Review Questions

2.112 In what main way is separating the components of a mixture different from separating the components of a compound?

2.113 What is the difference between a homogeneous and a heterogeneous mixture?

2.114 Is a solution a homogeneous or a heterogeneous mixture? Give an example of an aqueous solution.

Skill-Building Exercises (grouped in similar pairs)

2.115 Classify each of the following as a compound, a homogeneous mixture, or a heterogeneous mixture: (a) distilled water; (b) gasoline; (c) beach sand; (d) wine; (e) air.

2.116 Classify each of the following as a compound, a homogeneous mixture, or a heterogeneous mixture: (a) orange juice; (b) vegetable soup; (c) cement; (d) calcium sulfate; (e) tea.

Problems in Context

2.117 Which separation method is operating in each of the following procedures?
(a) Pouring a mixture of cooked pasta and boiling water into a colander

(b) Removing colored impurities from raw sugar to make refined sugar

2.118 A quality-control laboratory analyzes a product mixture using gas-liquid chromatography. The separation of components is more than adequate, but the process takes too long. Suggest two ways, other than changing the stationary phase, to shorten the analysis time.

Comprehensive Problems

2.119 Helium is the lightest noble gas and the second most abundant element (after hydrogen) in the universe.
(a) The radius of a helium atom is 3.1×10^{-11} m; the radius of its nucleus is 2.5×10^{-15} m. What fraction of the spherical atomic volume is occupied by the nucleus (V of a sphere $= \frac{4}{3}\pi r^3$)?
(b) The mass of a helium-4 atom is 6.64648×10^{-24} g, and each of its two electrons has a mass of 9.10939×10^{-28} g. What fraction of this atom's mass is contributed by its nucleus?

2.120 From the following ions (with their radii in pm), choose the pair that forms the strongest ionic bond and the pair that forms the weakest:

Ion:	Mg^{2+}	K^+	Rb^+	Ba^{2+}	Cl^-	O^{2-}	I^-
Radius:	72	138	152	135	181	140	220

2.121 Give the molecular mass of each compound depicted below, and provide a correct name for any that are named incorrectly.

(a) boron fluoride   (b) monosulfur dichloride

(c) phosphorus trichloride   (d) dinitride pentaoxide

2.122 Polyatomic ions are named by patterns that apply to elements in a given group. Using the periodic table and Table 2.5, give the name of each of the following: (a) SeO_4^{2-}; (b) AsO_4^{3-}; (c) BrO_2^-; (d) $HSeO_4^-$; (e) TeO_3^{2-}.

2.123 Ammonium dihydrogen phosphate, formed from the reaction of phosphoric acid with ammonia, is used as a crop fertilizer as well as a component of some fire extinguishers. (a) What are the mass percentages of N and P in the compound? (b) How much ammonia is incorporated into 100. g of the compound?

2.124 Nitrogen forms more oxides than any other element. The percents by mass of N in three different nitrogen oxides are (I) 46.69%; (II) 36.85%; (III) 25.94%. For each compound, determine (a) the simplest whole-number ratio of N to O, and (b) the number of grams of oxygen per 1.00 g of nitrogen.

2.125 The number of atoms in 1 dm^3 of aluminum is nearly the same as the number of atoms in 1 dm^3 of lead, but the densities of these metals are very different (see Table 1.5). Explain.

2.126 You are working in the laboratory preparing sodium chloride. Consider the following results for three preparations of the compound:

Case 1: 39.34 g Na + 60.66 g Cl_2 $\longrightarrow$ 100.00 g NaCl
Case 2: 39.34 g Na + 70.00 g Cl_2 $\longrightarrow$
  100.00 g NaCl + 9.34 g Cl_2
Case 3: 50.00 g Na + 50.00 g Cl_2 $\longrightarrow$
  82.43 g NaCl + 17.57 g Na

Explain these results in terms of the laws of conservation of mass and definite composition.

2.127 Scenes A–I depict various types of matter on the atomic scale. Choose the correct scene(s) for each of the following:
(a) A mixture that fills its container
(b) A substance that cannot be broken down into simpler ones
(c) An element with a very high resistance to flow
(d) A homogeneous mixture
(e) An element that conforms to the walls of its container and displays an upper surface
(f) A gas consisting of diatomic particles
(g) A gas that can be broken down into simpler substances
(h) A substance with a 2/1 ratio of its component atoms
(i) Matter that can be separated into its component substances by physical means
(j) A heterogeneous mixture
(k) Matter that obeys the law of definite composition

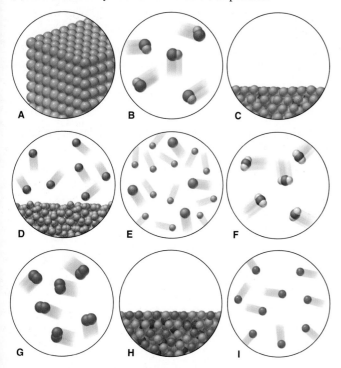

2.128 The seven most abundant ions in seawater make up more than 99% by mass of the dissolved compounds. Here are their abundances in units of mg ion/kg seawater: chloride 18,980; sodium 10,560; sulfate 2650; magnesium 1270; calcium 400; potassium 380; hydrogen carbonate 140.
(a) What is the mass % of each ion in seawater?
(b) What percent of the total mass of ions is sodium ion?
(c) How does the total mass % of alkaline earth metal ions compare with the total mass % of alkali metal ions?
(d) Which make up the larger mass fraction of dissolved components, anions or cations?

2.129 The scenes below represent a mixture of two monatomic gases undergoing a reaction when heated. Which mass law(s) is (are) illustrated by this change?

273 K ⟶ 450 K ⟶ 650 K

2.130 When barium (Ba) reacts with sulfur (S) to form barium sulfide (BaS), each Ba atom reacts with an S atom. If 2.50 cm³ of Ba reacts with 1.75 cm³ of S, are there enough Ba atoms to react with the S atoms (d of Ba = 3.51 g/cm³; d of S = 2.07 g/cm³)?

2.131 Succinic acid (*below*) is an important metabolite in biological energy production. Give the molecular formula, molecular mass, and the mass percent of each element in succinic acid.

2.132 Fluoride ion is poisonous in relatively low amounts: 0.2 g of F⁻ per 70 kg of body weight can cause death. Nevertheless, in order to prevent tooth decay, F⁻ ions are added to drinking water at a concentration of 1 mg of F⁻ ion per L of water. How many liters of fluoridated drinking water would a 70-kg person have to consume in one day to reach this toxic level? How many kilograms of sodium fluoride would be needed to treat a 8.50×10^7-gal reservoir?

2.133 Antimony has many uses, for example, in infrared devices and as part of an alloy in lead storage batteries. The element has two naturally occurring isotopes, one with mass 120.904 amu, the other with mass 122.904 amu. (a) Write the $_Z^A X$ notation for each isotope. (b) Use the atomic mass of antimony from the periodic table to calculate the natural abundance of each isotope.

2.134 Dinitrogen monoxide (N_2O; nitrous oxide) is a greenhouse gas that enters the atmosphere principally from natural fertilizer breakdown. Some studies have shown that the isotope ratios of ^{15}N to ^{14}N and of ^{18}O to ^{16}O in N_2O depend on the source, which can thus be determined by measuring the relative abundance of molecular masses in a sample of N_2O.
(a) What different molecular masses are possible for N_2O?
(b) The percent abundance of ^{14}N is 99.6%, and that of ^{16}O is 99.8%. Which molecular mass of N_2O is least common, and which is most common?

2.135 Use the box color(s) in the periodic table below to identify the element(s) described by each of the following:

(a) Four elements that are nonmetals
(b) Two elements that are metals
(c) Three elements that are gases at room temperature
(d) Three elements that are solid at room temperature
(e) One pair of elements likely to form a covalent compound
(f) Another pair of elements likely to form a covalent compound
(g) One pair of elements likely to form an ionic compound with formula MX
(h) Another pair of elements likely to form an ionic compound with formula MX
(i) Two elements likely to form an ionic compound with formula M_2X
(j) Two elements likely to form an ionic compound with formula MX_2

(k) An element that forms no compounds

(l) A pair of elements whose compounds exhibit the law of multiple proportions

2.136 The two isotopes of potassium with significant abundance in nature are ^{39}K (isotopic mass 38.9637 amu, 93.258%) and ^{41}K (isotopic mass 40.9618 amu, 6.730%). Fluorine has only one naturally occurring isotope, ^{19}F (isotopic mass 18.9984 amu). Calculate the formula mass of potassium fluoride.

2.137 Boron trifluoride is used as a catalyst in the synthesis of organic compounds. When this compound is analyzed by mass spectrometry (see Tools of the Laboratory, p. 51), several different 1+ ions form, including ions representing the whole molecule as well as molecular fragments formed by the loss of one, two, and three F atoms. Given that boron has two naturally occurring isotopes, ^{10}B and ^{11}B, and fluorine has one, ^{19}F, calculate the masses of all possible 1+ ions.

2.138 Nitrogen monoxide (NO) is a bioactive molecule in blood. Low NO concentrations cause respiratory distress and the formation of blood clots. Doctors prescribe nitroglycerin, $C_3H_5N_3O_9$, and isoamyl nitrate, $(CH_3)_2CHCH_2CH_2ONO_2$, to increase NO. If each compound releases one molecule of NO per atom of N it contains, calculate the mass percent of NO in each.

2.139 TNT (trinitrotoluene; *below*) is used as an explosive in construction. Calculate the mass of each element in 1.00 lb of TNT.

2.140 Nuclei differ in their stability, and some are so unstable that they undergo radioactive decay. The ratio of the number of neutrons to number of protons (*N/Z*) in a nucleus correlates with its stability. Calculate the *N/Z* ratio for (a) ^{144}Sm; (b) ^{56}Fe; (c) ^{20}Ne; (d) ^{107}Ag. (e) The radioactive isotope ^{238}U decays in a series of nuclear reactions that includes another uranium isotope,

^{234}U, and three lead isotopes, ^{214}Pb, ^{210}Pb, and ^{206}Pb. How many neutrons, protons, and electrons are in each of these five isotopes?

2.141 The anticancer drug Platinol (Cisplatin), $Pt(NH_3)_2Cl_2$, reacts with the cancer cell's DNA and interferes with its growth. (a) What is the mass % of platinum (Pt) in Platinol? (b) If Pt costs $32/g, how many grams of Platinol can be made for $1.00 million (assume that the cost of Pt determines the cost of the drug)?

2.142 In the periodic table below, give the name, symbol, atomic number, atomic mass, period number, and group number of (a) the *building-block elements (red)*, which occur in nearly every biological molecule, and (b) the *macronutrients (green)*, which are either essential ions in cell fluids or are part of many biomolecules.

2.143 The block diagram below classifies the components of matter on the macroscopic scale. Identify blocks (a)–(d).

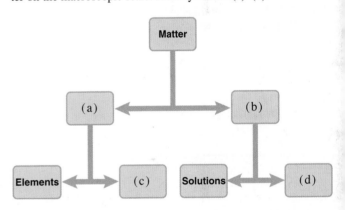

2.144 Which of the following steps in an overall process involve(s) a physical change and which involve(s) a chemical change?

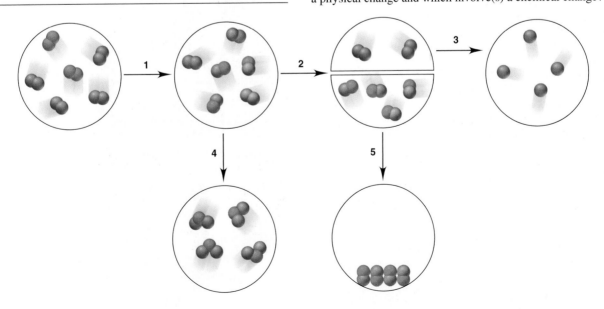

Stoichiometry of Formulas and Equations

Concepts and skills to review before you study this chapter

- atomic mass (Section 2.5)
- names and formulas of compounds (Section 2.8)
- molecular (or formula) mass (Section 2.8)
- molecular and structural formulas, and ball-and-stick and space-filling models (Section 2.8)

Chemistry is, above all, a practical science. Imagine that you're a biochemist who has extracted a substance with medicinal activity from a tropical plant: what is its formula, and what quantity of metabolic products will establish a safe dosage level? In 1785, the cardiac drug digitoxin was extracted from the foxglove (*photo*). (Since then, thousands of other biologically active compounds have been found in plants and many are used in modern medicines.) Or, suppose you're a chemical engineer studying rocket-fuel thrust: what amount of propulsive gases will a fuel produce? Perhaps you're on a team of environmental chemists examining coal samples: what quantity of air pollutants will a sample produce when burned? Or, maybe you're a polymer chemist preparing a plastic with unusual properties: how much of this new material will the polymerization reaction yield? You can answer countless questions like these with a knowledge of **stoichiometry** (pronounced "stoy-key-AHM-uh-tree"; from the Greek *stoicheion*, "element or part," and *metron*, "measure"), the study of the quantitative aspects of formulas and reactions.

IN THIS CHAPTER . . . We relate the mass of a substance to the number of chemical entities comprising it (atoms, ions, molecules, or formula units) and apply this relationship to formulas and equations.
- We discuss the *mole*, the chemist's unit for amount of a substance, and use it to convert between mass and number of entities.
- We also use it to derive a chemical formula from the results of mass analysis.
- We see whether two key types of formulas relate to molecular structures.
- We learn how to write chemical equations and how to balance them in terms of the amounts of substances reacting and produced.
- We calculate the amounts of reactants and products in a reaction and see why one of the reactants limits the amount of product that can form and, thus, the reaction yield.
- We discuss concentration and apply stoichiometry to reactions in solution.

3.1 • THE MOLE

In daily life, we often measure things by counting or by weighing: we weigh beans or rice, but we count eggs or pencils. And we use counting units (a dozen pencils) or mass units (a kilogram of beans) to express the amount. Similarly, daily life in the laboratory involves measuring substances. We want to know the numbers of chemical entities—atoms, ions, molecules, or formula units—that react with each other, but how can we possibly count or weigh such minute objects? As you'll see, chemists have devised a unit, called the *mole*, to *count chemical entities by weighing them.*

Defining the Mole

The **mole** (abbreviated **mol**) is the SI unit for *amount of substance.* It is defined as *the amount of a substance that contains the same number of entities as the number of atoms in 12 g of carbon-12.* This number, called **Avogadro's number** (in honor of the 19th-century Italian physicist Amedeo Avogadro), is enormous: ●

> One mole (1 mol) contains 6.022×10^{23} entities (to four significant figures) (3.1)

● **Imagine a Mole of . . .** A mole of any ordinary object is a staggering amount: a mole of periods (.) lined up side by side would equal the radius of our galaxy; a mole of marbles stacked tightly together would cover the United States 70 miles deep. However, atoms and molecules are not ordinary objects: you can swallow a mole of water molecules (about 18 mL) in one gulp!

A counting unit, like *dozen,* tells you the number of objects but not their mass; a mass unit, like *kilogram,* tells you the mass of the objects but not their number. The mole tells you both—the *number* of objects in a given *mass* of substance:

1 mol of carbon-12 contains 6.022×10^{23} carbon-12 atoms *and* has a mass of 12 g

What does it mean that the mole unit allows you to count entities by weighing the sample? Suppose you have a sample of carbon-12 and want to know the number of atoms present. You find that the sample weighs 6 g, so it is 0.5 mol of carbon-12 and contains 3.011×10^{23} atoms:

6 g of carbon-12 is 0.5 mol of carbon-12 and contains 3.011×10^{23} atoms

Knowing the amount (in moles), the mass (in grams), and the number of entities becomes very important when we mix different substances to run a reaction. The central relationship between masses on the atomic scale and on the macroscopic scale is the same for elements and compounds:

16
S
32.07

- *Elements.* The mass in *atomic mass units (amu)* of one atom of an element is the *same numerically* as the mass in *grams (g)* of 1 mole of atoms of the element. Recall from Chapter 2 that each atom of an element is considered to have the *atomic mass* given in the periodic table *(see margin).* Thus,

1 atom of S   has a mass of   32.07 amu   and   1 mol (6.022×10^{23} atoms) of S   has a mass of   32.07 g
1 atom of Fe   has a mass of   55.85 amu   and   1 mol (6.022×10^{23} atoms) of Fe   has a mass of   55.85 g

Note, also, that since atomic masses are relative, 1 Fe atom weighs 55.85/32.07 as much as 1 S atom, and 1 mol of Fe weighs 55.85/32.07 as much as 1 mol of S.

- *Compounds.* The mass in *atomic mass units (amu)* of one molecule (or formula unit) of a compound is the *same numerically* as the mass in *grams (g)* of 1 mole of the compound. Thus, for example,

1 molecule of H_2O has a mass of   18.02 amu   and   1 mol (6.022×10^{23} molecules) of H_2O has a mass of   18.02 g
1 formula unit of NaCl   has a mass of   58.44 amu   and   1 mol (6.022×10^{23} formula units) of NaCl   has a mass of   58.44 g

Here, too, because masses are relative, 1 H_2O molecule weighs 18.02/58.44 as much as 1 NaCl formula unit, and 1 mol of H_2O weighs 18.02/58.44 as much as 1 mol of NaCl.

The two key points to remember about the importance of the mole unit are

- The *mole* lets us relate the *number* of entities to the *mass* of a sample of those entities.
- The mole maintains the *same numerical relationship* between mass on the atomic scale (atomic mass units, amu) and mass on the macroscopic scale (grams, g).

In everyday terms, a grocer *does not* know there are 1 dozen eggs from their weight or that there is 1 kilogram of beans from their count, because eggs and beans do not have fixed masses. But, by weighing out 63.55 g (1 mol) of copper, a chemist *does* know that there are 6.022×10^{23} copper atoms, because all copper atoms have an atomic mass of 63.55 amu. Figure 3.1 shows 1 mole of some familiar elements and compounds.

Determining Molar Mass

The **molar mass** ($\mathcal{M}$) of a substance is the mass per mole of its entities (atoms, molecules, or formula units) and has units of grams per mole (g/mol). The periodic table is indispensable for calculating molar mass:

1. *Elements.* To find the molar mass, look up the atomic mass and note whether the element is monatomic or molecular.
- *Monatomic elements.* The molar mass is the periodic-table value in grams per mole.* For example, the molar mass of neon is 20.18 g/mol, and the molar mass of gold is 197.0 g/mol.

Figure 3.1 One mole (6.022×10^{23} entities) of some familiar substances. From left to right: 1 mol of copper (63.55 g), of liquid H_2O (18.02 g), of sodium chloride (table salt, 58.44 g), of sucrose (table sugar, 342.3 g), and of aluminum (26.98 g).

---

*The mass value in the periodic table has no units because it is a *relative* atomic mass, given by the atomic mass (in amu) divided by 1 amu ($\frac{1}{12}$ mass of one ^{12}C atom in amu):

$$\text{Relative atomic mass} = \frac{\text{atomic mass (amu)}}{\frac{1}{12} \text{ mass of } ^{12}C \text{ (amu)}}$$

Therefore, you use the same number for the atomic mass and for the molar mass.

- *Molecular elements.* You must know the formula to determine the molar mass (see Figure 2.15). For example, in air, oxygen exists most commonly as diatomic molecules, so the molar mass of O_2 is twice that of O:

$$\text{Molar mass } (\mathcal{M}) \text{ of } O_2 = 2 \times \mathcal{M} \text{ of } O = 2 \times 16.00 \text{ g/mol} = 32.00 \text{ g/mol}$$

The most common form of sulfur exists as octatomic molecules, S_8:

$$\mathcal{M} \text{ of } S_8 = 8 \times \mathcal{M} \text{ of } S = 8 \times 32.07 \text{ g/mol} = 256.6 \text{ g/mol}$$

2. *Compounds. The molar mass is the sum of the molar masses of the atoms in the formula.* Thus, from the formula of sulfur dioxide, SO_2, we know that 1 mol of SO_2 molecules contains 1 mol of S atoms and 2 mol of O atoms:

$$\mathcal{M} \text{ of } SO_2 = \mathcal{M} \text{ of } S + (2 \times \mathcal{M} \text{ of } O) = 32.07 \text{ g/mol} + (2 \times 16.00 \text{ g/mol}) = 64.07 \text{ g/mol}$$

Similarly, for ionic compounds, such as potassium sulfide (K_2S), we have

$$\mathcal{M} \text{ of } K_2S = (2 \times \mathcal{M} \text{ of } K) + \mathcal{M} \text{ of } S = (2 \times 39.10 \text{ g/mol}) + 32.07 \text{ g/mol} = 110.27 \text{ g/mol}$$

Thus, *subscripts in a formula refer to individual atoms (or ions) as well as to moles of atoms (or ions).* Table 3.1 summarizes these ideas for glucose, $C_6H_{12}O_6$ *(see margin),* the essential sugar in energy metabolism.

Glucose

Table 3.1 Information Contained in the Chemical Formula of Glucose, $C_6H_{12}O_6$ ($\mathcal{M}$ = 180.16 g/mol)

	Carbon (C)	Hydrogen (H)	Oxygen (O)
Atoms/molecule of compound	6 atoms	12 atoms	6 atoms
Moles of atoms/mole of compound	6 mol of atoms	12 mol of atoms	6 mol of atoms
Atoms/mole of compound	$6(6.022\times10^{23})$ atoms	$12(6.022\times10^{23})$ atoms	$6(6.022\times10^{23})$ atoms
Mass/molecule of compound	$6(12.01 \text{ amu}) = 72.06 \text{ amu}$	$12(1.008 \text{ amu}) = 12.10 \text{ amu}$	$6(16.00 \text{ amu}) = 96.00 \text{ amu}$
Mass/mole of compound	72.06 g	12.10 g	96.00 g

Converting Between Amount, Mass, and Number of Chemical Entities

One of the most common skills in the lab—and on exams—is converting between amount (mol), mass (g), and number of entities of a substance.

1. *Converting between amount and mass.* If you know the amount of a substance, you can find its mass, and vice versa. The molar mass ($\mathcal{M}$), which expresses the equivalence between 1 mole of a substance and its mass in grams, is the conversion factor.

- *From amount (mol) to mass (g),* multiply by the molar mass:

$$\text{Mass (g)} = \text{amount (mol)} \times \frac{\text{no. of grams}}{1 \text{ mol}} \qquad (3.2)$$

- *From mass (g) to amount (mol),* divide by the molar mass (multiply by $1/\mathcal{M}$):

$$\text{Amount (mol)} = \text{mass (g)} \times \frac{1 \text{ mol}}{\text{no. of grams}} \qquad (3.3)$$

2. *Converting between amount and number.* Similarly, if you know the amount (mol), you can find the number of entities, and vice versa. Avogadro's number, which expresses the equivalence between 1 mole of a substance and the number of entities it contains, is the conversion factor.

- *From amount (mol) to number of entities,* multiply by Avogadro's number:

$$\text{No. of entities} = \text{amount (mol)} \times \frac{6.022\times10^{23} \text{ entities}}{1 \text{ mol}} \qquad (3.4)$$

- *From number of entities to amount (mol),* divide by Avogadro's number:

$$\text{Amount (mol)} = \text{no. of entities} \times \frac{1 \text{ mol}}{6.022\times10^{23} \text{ entities}} \qquad (3.5)$$

Amount-Mass-Number Conversions Involving Elements We begin with amount-mass-number relationships of elements. As Figure 3.2 shows, *convert mass or number of entities to amount (mol) first.*

Figure 3.2 Mass-mole-number relationships for elements. To find the number of atoms (or molecules) in a given mass, or vice versa, convert to amount (mol) first. For molecular elements, Avogadro's number gives *molecules* per mole.

Let's work through a series of sample problems that show these conversions for both elements and compounds.

Sample Problem 3.1 | **Calculating the Mass of a Given Amount of an Element**

Problem Silver (Ag) is used in jewelry and tableware but no longer in U.S. coins. How many grams of Ag are in 0.0342 mol of Ag?

Plan We know the amount of Ag (0.0342 mol) and have to find the mass (g). To convert units of *moles* of Ag to *grams* of Ag, we multiply by the *molar mass* of Ag, which we find in the periodic table (see the road map).

Solution Converting from amount (mol) of Ag to mass (g):

$$\text{Mass (g) of Ag} = 0.0342 \text{ mol Ag} \times \frac{107.9 \text{ g Ag}}{1 \text{ mol Ag}} = \boxed{3.69 \text{ g Ag}}$$

Check We rounded the mass to three significant figures because the amount (mol) has three. The units are correct. About 0.03 mol × 100 g/mol gives 3 g; the small mass makes sense because 0.0342 is a small fraction of a mole.

Follow-Up Problem 3.1 Graphite is the crystalline form of carbon used in "lead" pencils. How many moles of carbon are in 315 mg of graphite? Include a road map that shows how you planned the solution. (See Brief Solutions at the end of the chapter for solutions to this and all other follow-up problems.)

Road Map

Sample Problem 3.2 | **Calculating the Number of Entities in a Given Amount of an Element**

Problem Gallium (Ga) is a key element in solar panels, calculators, and other light-sensitive electronic devices. How many Ga atoms are in 2.85×10^{-3} mol of gallium?

Plan We know the amount of gallium (2.85×10^{-3} mol) and need the number of Ga atoms. We multiply amount (mol) by Avogadro's number to find number of atoms (see the road map).

Solution Converting from amount (mol) of Ga to number of atoms:

$$\text{No. of Ga atoms} = 2.85 \times 10^{-3} \text{ mol Ga} \times \frac{6.022 \times 10^{23} \text{ Ga atoms}}{1 \text{ mol Ga}}$$

$$= \boxed{1.72 \times 10^{21} \text{ Ga atoms}}$$

Check The number of atoms has three significant figures because the number of moles does. When we round amount (mol) of Ga and Avogadro's number, we have $\sim(3 \times 10^{-3} \text{ mol})(6 \times 10^{23} \text{ atoms/mol}) = 18 \times 10^{20}$, or 1.8×10^{21} atoms, so our answer seems correct.

Follow-Up Problem 3.2 At rest, a person inhales 9.72×10^{21} nitrogen molecules in an average breath of air. How many moles of nitrogen atoms are inhaled? (*Hint:* In air, nitrogen occurs as a diatomic molecule.) Include a road map that shows how you planned the solution.

Road Map

Amount (mol) of Ga

multiply by
6.022×10^{23} atoms/mol

Number of Ga atoms

For the next problem, note that mass and number of entities relate directly to amount (mol), but *not* to each other. Therefore, *to convert between mass and number, first convert to amount.*

Sample Problem 3.3 | **Calculating the Number of Entities in a Given Mass of an Element**

Problem Iron (Fe) is the main component of steel and, thus, the most important metal in industrial society; it is also essential in the body. How many Fe atoms are in 95.8 g of Fe?

Plan We know the mass of Fe (95.8 g) and need the number of Fe atoms. We cannot convert directly from mass to number, so we first convert to amount (mol) by dividing mass of Fe by its molar mass. Then, we multiply amount (mol) by Avogadro's number to find number of atoms (see the road map).

Solution Converting from mass (g) of Fe to amount (mol):

$$\text{Moles of Fe} = 95.8 \text{ g Fe} \times \frac{1 \text{ mol Fe}}{55.85 \text{ g Fe}} = 1.72 \text{ mol Fe}$$

Converting from amount (mol) of Fe to number of Fe atoms:

$$\text{No. of Fe atoms} = 1.72 \text{ mol Fe} \times \frac{6.022 \times 10^{23} \text{ atoms Fe}}{1 \text{ mol Fe}}$$

$$= 10.4 \times 10^{23} \text{ atoms Fe}$$

$$= \boxed{1.04 \times 10^{24} \text{ atoms Fe}}$$

Check Rounding the mass and the molar mass of Fe, we have $\sim 100 \text{ g}/(\sim 60 \text{ g/mol}) = 1.7 \text{ mol}$. Therefore, the number of atoms should be a bit less than twice Avogadro's number: $<2(6 \times 10^{23}) = <1.2 \times 10^{24}$, so the answer seems correct.

Follow-Up Problem 3.3 Manganese (Mn) is a transition element essential for the growth of bones. What is the mass in grams of 3.22×10^{20} Mn atoms, the number found in 1 kg of bone? Include a road map that shows how you planned the solution.

Road Map

Mass (g) of Fe

divide by $\mathcal{M}$ of Fe

Amount (mol) of Fe

multiply by 6.022×10^{23} atoms/mol

Number of Fe atoms

Amount-Mass-Number Conversions Involving Compounds Only one new step is needed to solve amount-mass-number problems involving compounds: we need the chemical formula to find the molar mass and the amount of each element in the compound. The relationships are shown in Figure 3.3 on the next page, and Sample Problems 3.4 and 3.5 apply them to compounds with simple and more complicated formulas, respectively.

Figure 3.3 Amount-mass-number relationships for compounds. Use the chemical formula to find the amount (mol) of each element in a compound.

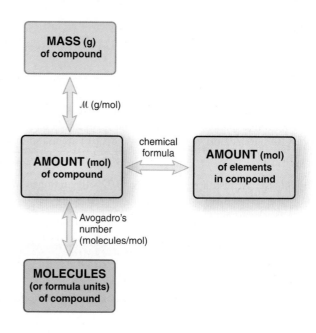

Road Map

Mass (g) of NO_2

divide by $\mathcal{M}$ (g/mol)

Amount (mol) of NO_2

multiply by Avogadro's number (molecules/mol)

Number of molecules of NO_2

Sample Problem 3.4 Calculating the Number of Chemical Entities in a Given Mass of a Compound I

Problem Nitrogen dioxide is a component of urban smog that forms from gases in car exhaust. How many molecules are in 8.92 g of nitrogen dioxide?

Plan We know the mass of compound (8.92 g) and need to find the number of molecules. As you just saw in Sample Problem 3.3, to convert mass to number of entities, we have to find the amount (mol). To do so, we divide the mass by the molar mass ($\mathcal{M}$), which we calculate from the molecular formula (see Sample Problem 2.15). Once we have the amount (mol), we multiply by Avogadro's number to find the number of molecules (see the road map).

Solution The formula is NO_2. Calculating the molar mass:

$$\mathcal{M} = (1 \times \mathcal{M} \text{ of N}) + (2 \times \mathcal{M} \text{ of O})$$
$$= 14.01 \text{ g/mol} + (2 \times 16.00 \text{ g/mol})$$
$$= 46.01 \text{ g/mol}$$

Converting from mass (g) of NO_2 to amount (mol):

$$\text{Amount (mol) of } NO_2 = 8.92 \text{ g } NO_2 \times \frac{1 \text{ mol } NO_2}{46.01 \text{ g } NO_2}$$
$$= 0.194 \text{ mol } NO_2$$

Converting from amount (mol) of NO_2 to number of molecules:

$$\text{No. of molecules} = 0.194 \text{ mol } NO_2 \times \frac{6.022 \times 10^{23} \text{ } NO_2 \text{ molecules}}{1 \text{ mol } NO_2}$$
$$= 1.17 \times 10^{23} \text{ } NO_2 \text{ molecules}$$

Check Rounding, we get $(\sim 0.2 \text{ mol})(6 \times 10^{23}) = 1.2 \times 10^{23}$, so the answer seems correct.

Follow-Up Problem 3.4 Fluoride ion is added to drinking water to prevent tooth decay. What is the mass (g) of sodium fluoride in a liter of water that contains 1.19×10^{19} formula units of the compound? Include a road map that shows how you planned the solution.

Sample Problem 3.5   Calculating the Number of Chemical Entities in a Given Mass of a Compound II

Problem Ammonium carbonate is a white solid that decomposes with warming. It has many uses, for example, as a component in baking powder, fire extinguishers, and smelling salts.
(a) How many formula units are in 41.6 g of ammonium carbonate?
(b) How many O atoms are in this sample?

Plan (a) We know the mass of compound (41.6 g) and need to find the number of formula units. As in Sample Problem 3.4, we find the amount (mol) and then multiply by Avogadro's number to find the number of formula units. [The road map shows the steps for part (a).] **(b)** To find the number of O atoms, we multiply the number of formula units by the number of O atoms in one formula unit.

Solution (a) The formula is $(NH_4)_2CO_3$ (see Table 2.5). Calculating the molar mass:

$$\mathscr{M} = (2 \times \mathscr{M} \text{ of N}) + (8 \times \mathscr{M} \text{ of H}) + (1 \times \mathscr{M} \text{ of C}) + (3 \times \mathscr{M} \text{ of O})$$
$$= (2 \times 14.01 \text{ g/mol N}) + (8 \times 1.008 \text{ g/mol H}) + 12.01 \text{ g/mol C}$$
$$+ (3 \times 16.00 \text{ g/mol O})$$
$$= 96.09 \text{ g/mol } (NH_4)_2CO_3$$

Converting from mass (g) to amount (mol):

$$\text{Amount (mol) of } (NH_4)_2CO_3 = 41.6 \text{ g } (NH_4)_2CO_3 \times \frac{1 \text{ mol } (NH_4)_2CO_3}{96.09 \text{ g } (NH_4)_2CO_3}$$
$$= 0.433 \text{ mol } (NH_4)_2CO_3$$

Converting from amount (mol) to formula units:

$$\text{Formula units of } (NH_4)_2CO_3 = 0.433 \text{ mol } (NH_4)_2CO_3$$
$$\times \frac{6.022 \times 10^{23} \text{ formula units } (NH_4)_2CO_3}{1 \text{ mol } (NH_4)_2CO_3}$$
$$= 2.61 \times 10^{23} \text{ formula units } (NH_4)_2CO_3$$

(b) Finding the number of O atoms:

$$\text{No. of O atoms} = 2.61 \times 10^{23} \text{ formula units } (NH_4)_2CO_3 \times \frac{3 \text{ O atoms}}{1 \text{ formula unit } (NH_4)_2CO_3}$$
$$= 7.83 \times 10^{23} \text{ O atoms}$$

Check In (a), the units are correct. Since the mass is less than half the molar mass ($\sim 42/96 < 0.5$), the number of formula units should be less than half Avogadro's number ($\sim 2.6 \times 10^{23}/6.0 \times 10^{23} < 0.5$).

Comment A *common mistake* is to forget the subscript 2 outside the parentheses in $(NH_4)_2CO_3$, which would give a much lower molar mass.

Road Map

Mass (g) of $(NH_4)_2CO_3$

↓ divide by $\mathscr{M}$ (g/mol)

Amount (mol) of $(NH_4)_2CO_3$

↓ multiply by 6.022×10^{23} formula units/mol

Number of formula units of $(NH_4)_2CO_3$

Follow-Up Problem 3.5 Tetraphosphorus decaoxide reacts with water to form phosphoric acid, a major industrial acid. In the laboratory, the oxide is a drying agent.
(a) What is the mass (g) of 4.65×10^{22} molecules of tetraphosphorus decaoxide?
(b) How many P atoms are present in this sample?

The Importance of Mass Percent

For many purposes, it is important to know how much of an element is present in a given amount of compound. A biochemist may want the ionic composition of a mineral nutrient; an atmospheric chemist may be studying the amount of carbon in a fuel; a materials scientist may want the metalloid composition of a semiconductor. In this section, we find the composition of a compound in terms of mass percent and use it to find the mass of each element in the compound.

Determining Mass Percent from a Chemical Formula Each element contributes a fraction of a compound's mass, and that fraction multiplied by 100 gives the element's mass percent. Finding the mass percent is similar on the molecular and molar scales:

- *For a molecule (or formula unit) of compound,* use the molecular (or formula) mass and chemical formula to find the mass percent of any element X in the compound:

$$\text{Mass \% of element X} = \frac{\text{atoms of X in formula} \times \text{atomic mass of X(amu)}}{\text{molecular (or formula) mass of compound (amu)}} \times 100$$

- *For a mole of compound,* use the molar mass and formula to find the mass percent of each element on a mole basis:

$$\text{Mass \% of element X} = \frac{\text{moles of X in formula} \times \text{molar mass of X (g/mol)}}{\text{mass (g) of 1 mol of compound}} \times 100 \quad \text{(3.6)}$$

As always, the individual mass percents add up to 100% (within rounding). In Sample Problem 3.6, we determine the mass percent of each element in a compound.

| Sample Problem 3.6 | Calculating the Mass Percent of Each Element in a Compound from the Formula |

Problem In mammals, lactose (milk sugar) is metabolized to glucose ($C_6H_{12}O_6$), the key nutrient for generating chemical potential energy. What is the mass percent of each element in glucose?

Plan We know the relative amounts (mol) of the elements from the formula (6 C, 12 H, 6 O), and we have to find the mass % of each element. We multiply the amount of each by its molar mass to find its mass. Dividing each mass by the mass of 1 mol of glucose gives the mass fraction of each element, and multiplying by 100 gives each mass %. The calculation steps for any element (X) are shown in the road map.

Solution Converting amount (mol) of C to mass (g):
We have 6 mol of C in 1 mol of glucose, so

$$\text{Mass (g) of C} = 6 \text{ mol C} \times \frac{12.01 \text{ g C}}{1 \text{ mol C}} = 72.06 \text{ g C}$$

Calculating the mass of 1 mol of glucose ($C_6H_{12}O_6$):

$$\mathcal{M} = (6 \times \mathcal{M} \text{ of C}) + (12 \times \mathcal{M} \text{ of H}) + (6 \times \mathcal{M} \text{ of O})$$
$$= (6 \times 12.01 \text{ g/mol C}) + (12 \times 1.008 \text{ g/mol H}) + (6 \times 16.00 \text{ g/mol O})$$
$$= 180.16 \text{ g/mol } C_6H_{12}O_6$$

Finding the mass fraction of C in glucose:

$$\text{Mass fraction of C} = \frac{\text{total mass of C}}{\text{mass of 1 mol glucose}} = \frac{72.06 \text{ g C}}{180.16 \text{ g glucose}} = 0.4000$$

Changing to mass %:

$$\text{Mass \% of C} = \text{mass fraction of C} \times 100 = 0.4000 \times 100$$
$$= 40.00 \text{ mass \% C}$$

Combining the steps for each of the other elements in glucose:

$$\text{Mass \% of H} = \frac{\text{mol H} \times \mathcal{M} \text{ of H}}{\text{mass of 1 mol glucose}} \times 100 = \frac{12 \text{ mol H} \times \dfrac{1.008 \text{ g H}}{1 \text{ mol H}}}{180.16 \text{ g glucose}} \times 100$$
$$= 6.714 \text{ mass \% H}$$

$$\text{Mass \% of O} = \frac{\text{mol O} \times \mathcal{M} \text{ of O}}{\text{mass of 1 mol glucose}} \times 100 = \frac{6 \text{ mol O} \times \dfrac{16.00 \text{ g O}}{1 \text{ mol O}}}{180.16 \text{ g glucose}} \times 100$$
$$= 53.29 \text{ mass \% O}$$

Road Map

| Amount (mol) of element X in 1 mol of glucose |

multiply by $\mathcal{M}$ (g/mol) of X

| Mass (g) of X in 1 mol of glucose |

divide by mass (g) of 1 mol of compound

| Mass fraction of X in glucose |

multiply by 100

| Mass % of X in glucose |

Check The answers make sense: even though there are equal numbers of moles of O and of C in the compound, the mass % of O is greater than the mass % of C because the molar mass of O is greater than the molar mass of C. The mass % of H is small because the molar mass of H is small. The sum of the mass percents is 100.00%.

Comment From here on, you should be able to determine the molar mass of a compound, so that calculation will no longer be shown.

Follow-Up Problem 3.6 Agronomists base the effectiveness of fertilizers on their nitrogen content. Ammonium nitrate is a common fertilizer. Calculate the mass percent of N in ammonium nitrate.

Determining the Mass of an Element from Its Mass Percent Sample Problem 3.6 shows that *an element always constitutes the same fraction of the mass of a given compound.* We obtained that fraction by dividing the total mass of element in a formula unit by the mass of one mole of the compound (see Equation 3.6). We can use that ratio directly to find the mass of element in any mass of a compound:

$$\text{Mass of element} = \text{mass of compound} \times \frac{\text{mass of element in 1 mol of compound}}{\text{mass of 1 mol of compound}} \quad \text{(3.7)}$$

For example, to find the mass of oxygen in 15.5 g of nitrogen dioxide, we have

$$\text{Mass (g) of O} = 15.5 \text{ g NO}_2 \times \frac{2 \text{ mol} \times \mathcal{M} \text{ of O (g/mol)}}{\text{mass (g) of 1 mol NO}_2}$$

$$= 15.5 \text{ g NO}_2 \times \frac{32.00 \text{ g O}}{46.01 \text{ g NO}_2} = 10.8 \text{ g O}$$

Sample Problem 3.7 | **Calculating the Mass of an Element in a Compound**

Problem Use the information in Sample Problem 3.6 to determine the mass (g) of carbon in 16.55 g of glucose.

Plan To find the mass of C in the sample of glucose, we multiply the mass of the sample by the mass of 6 mol of C divided by the mass of 1 mol of glucose.

Solution Finding the mass of C in a given mass of glucose:

$$\text{Mass (g) of C} = \text{mass (g) of glucose} \times \frac{6 \text{ mol C} \times \mathcal{M} \text{ of C (g/mol)}}{\text{mass (g) of 1 mol glucose}}$$

$$= 16.55 \text{ g glucose} \times \frac{72.06 \text{ g C}}{180.16 \text{ g glucose}} = \boxed{6.620 \text{ g C}}$$

Check Rounding shows that the answer is "in the right ballpark": 16 g times less than 0.5 parts by mass should be less than 8 g.

Follow-Up Problem 3.7 Use the information in Follow-Up Problem 3.6 to find the mass (g) of N in 35.8 kg of ammonium nitrate.

Summary of Section 3.1

- A mole of substance is the amount that contains Avogadro's number (6.022×10^{23}) of chemical entities (atoms, molecules, or formula units).
- The mass (in grams) of a mole of the entity has the same numerical value as the mass (in amu) of the individual entity. Thus, the mole allows us to count entities by weighing them.
- Using the molar mass ($\mathcal{M}$, g/mol) of an element (or compound) and Avogadro's number as conversion factors, we can convert among amount (mol), mass (g), and number of entities.
- The mass fraction of element X in a compound is used to find the mass of X in a given amount of the compound.

3.2 • DETERMINING THE FORMULA OF AN UNKNOWN COMPOUND

In Sample Problems 3.6 and 3.7, we used a compound's formula to find the mass percent (or mass fraction) of each element in it *and* the mass of each element in any size sample of it. In this section, we do the reverse: we use the masses of elements in a compound to find the formula. Then, we look briefly at the relationship between molecular formula and molecular structure.

Let's compare three common types of formula, using hydrogen peroxide as an example:

- The **empirical formula** is derived from mass analysis. It shows the *lowest* whole number of moles, and thus the *relative* number of atoms, of each element in the compound. For example, in hydrogen peroxide, there is 1 part by mass of hydrogen for every 16 parts by mass of oxygen. Because the atomic mass of hydrogen is 1.008 amu and that of oxygen is 16.00 amu, there is one H atom for every O atom. Thus, the empirical formula is HO.

Recall from Section 2.8, p. 59, that

- The **molecular formula** shows the *actual* number of atoms of each element in a molecule: the molecular formula is H_2O_2, twice the empirical formula.
- The **structural formula** shows the relative *placement and connections of atoms* in the molecule: the structural formula is $H-O-O-H$.

Let's see how to determine empirical and molecular formulas.

Empirical Formulas

A chemist studying an unknown compound goes through a three-step process to find the empirical formula:

1. Determine the mass (g) of each component element.
2. Convert each mass (g) to amount (mol), and write a preliminary formula.
3. Convert the amounts (mol) mathematically to whole-number (integer) subscripts. To accomplish this math conversion,
   - Divide each subscript by the smallest subscript, and
   - If necessary, multiply through by the *smallest integer* that turns all subscripts into integers.

Sample Problem 3.8 demonstrates these math steps.

Road Map

Amount (mol) of each element

↓ use nos. of moles as subscripts

Preliminary formula

↓ change to integer subscripts

Empirical formula

Sample Problem 3.8 | **Determining an Empirical Formula from Amounts of Elements**

Problem A sample of an unknown compound contains 0.21 mol of zinc, 0.14 mol of phosphorus, and 0.56 mol of oxygen. What is the empirical formula?

Plan We are given the amount (mol) of each element as fractions. We use these fractional amounts directly in a preliminary formula as subscripts of the element symbols. Then, we convert the fractions to whole numbers.

Solution Using the fractions to write a preliminary formula, with the symbols Zn for zinc, P for phosphorus, and O for oxygen:

$$Zn_{0.21}P_{0.14}O_{0.56}$$

Converting the fractions to whole numbers:
1. Divide each subscript by the smallest one, which in this case is 0.14:

$$Zn_{\frac{0.21}{0.14}}P_{\frac{0.14}{0.14}}O_{\frac{0.56}{0.14}} \longrightarrow Zn_{1.5}P_{1.0}O_{4.0}$$

2. Multiply through by the *smallest integer* that turns all subscripts into integers. We multiply by 2 to make 1.5 (the subscript for Zn) into an integer:

$$Zn_{(1.5\times2)}P_{(1.0\times2)}O_{(4.0\times2)} \longrightarrow Zn_{3.0}P_{2.0}O_{8.0}, \quad \text{or} \quad \boxed{Zn_3P_2O_8}$$

Check The integer subscripts must be the smallest integers with the same ratio as the original fractional numbers of moles: 3/2/8 is *the same ratio* as 0.21/0.14/0.56.

Comment A more conventional way to write this formula is $Zn_3(PO_4)_2$; this compound is zinc phosphate, formerly used widely as a dental cement.

Follow-Up Problem 3.8 A sample of a white solid contains 0.170 mol of boron and 0.255 mol of oxygen. What is the empirical formula?

Sample Problems 3.9–3.11 show how other types of compositional data are used to determine chemical formulas.

Sample Problem 3.9 | **Determining an Empirical Formula from Masses of Elements**

Problem Analysis of a sample of an ionic compound yields 2.82 g of Na, 4.35 g of Cl, and 7.83 g of O. What is the empirical formula and the name of the compound?

Plan This problem is similar to Sample Problem 3.8, except that we are given element *masses* that we must convert into integer subscripts. We first divide each mass by the element's molar mass to find amount (mol). Then we construct a preliminary formula and convert the amounts (mol) to integers.

Solution Finding amount (mol) of each element:

$$\text{Amount (mol) of Na} = 2.82 \text{ g Na} \times \frac{1 \text{ mol Na}}{22.99 \text{ g Na}} = 0.123 \text{ mol Na}$$

$$\text{Amount (mol) of Cl} = 4.35 \text{ g Cl} \times \frac{1 \text{ mol Cl}}{35.45 \text{ g Cl}} = 0.123 \text{ mol Cl}$$

$$\text{Amount (mol) of O} = 7.83 \text{ g O} \times \frac{1 \text{ mol O}}{16.00 \text{ g O}} = 0.489 \text{ mol O}$$

Constructing a preliminary formula: $Na_{0.123}Cl_{0.123}O_{0.489}$

Converting to integer subscripts (dividing all by the smallest subscript):

$$Na_{\frac{0.123}{0.123}}Cl_{\frac{0.123}{0.123}}O_{\frac{0.489}{0.123}} \longrightarrow Na_{1.00}Cl_{1.00}O_{3.98} \approx Na_1Cl_1O_4, \quad \text{or} \quad NaClO_4$$

The empirical formula is $\boxed{NaClO_4}$; the name is $\boxed{\text{sodium perchlorate.}}$

Check The numbers of moles seem correct because the masses of Na and Cl are slightly more than 0.1 of their molar masses. The mass of O is greatest and its molar mass is smallest, so it should have the greatest number of moles. The ratio of subscripts, 1/1/4, is the same as the ratio of moles, 0.123/0.123/0.489 (within rounding).

Follow-Up Problem 3.9 An unknown metal M reacts with sulfur to form a compound with the formula M_2S_3. If 3.12 g of M reacts with 2.88 g of S, what are the names of M and M_2S_3? [*Hint:* Determine the amount (mol) of S and use the formula to find the amount (mol) of M.]

Molecular Formulas

If we know the molar mass of a compound, we can use the empirical formula to obtain the molecular formula, which uses as subscripts the *actual* numbers of moles of each element in 1 mol of compound. For some compounds, such as water (H_2O), ammonia (NH_3), and methane (CH_4), the empirical and molecular formulas are identical, but for many others, the molecular formula is a *whole-number multiple* of the empirical formula. As you saw, hydrogen peroxide has the empirical formula HO. Dividing the molar mass of hydrogen peroxide (34.02 g/mol) by the empirical formula mass of HO (17.01 g/mol) gives the whole-number multiple:

$$\text{Whole-number multiple} = \frac{\text{molar mass (g/mol)}}{\text{empirical formula mass (g/mol)}} = \frac{34.02 \text{ g/mol}}{17.01 \text{ g/mol}} = 2.000 = 2$$

Multiplying the empirical formula subscripts by 2 gives the molecular formula:

$$H_{(1\times2)}O_{(1\times2)} \text{ gives } H_2O_2$$

Instead of giving compositional data as masses of each element, analytical laboratories provide mass percents. To find the molecular formula, we first determine the empirical formula and then the whole-number multiple:

1. Assume 100.0 g of compound to express each mass percent directly as mass (g).
2. Convert each mass (g) to amount (mol).
3. Derive the empirical formula.
4. Divide the compound's molar mass by the empirical formula mass to find the whole-number multiple.
5. Multiply each subscript in the empirical formula by the multiple.

Sample Problem 3.10 | Determining a Molecular Formula from Elemental Analysis and Molar Mass

Problem During excessive physical activity, lactic acid ($\mathcal{M}$ = 90.08 g/mol) forms in muscle tissue and is responsible for muscle soreness. Elemental analysis shows that this compound contains 40.0 mass % C, 6.71 mass % H, and 53.3 mass % O.
(a) Determine the empirical formula of lactic acid.
(b) Determine the molecular formula.

(a) Determining the empirical formula

Plan We know the mass % of each element and must convert each to an integer subscript. The mass of the sample of lactic acid is not given, but the mass percents are the same for any sample of it. Therefore, we assume there is 100.0 g of lactic acid and express each mass % as a number of grams. Then, we construct the empirical formula as in Sample Problem 3.9.

Solution Expressing mass % as mass (g) by assuming 100.0 g of lactic acid:

$$\text{Mass (g) of C} = \frac{40.0 \text{ parts C by mass}}{100 \text{ parts by mass}} \times 100.0 \text{ g} = 40.0 \text{ g C}$$

Similarly, we have 6.71 g of H and 53.3 g of O.

Converting from mass (g) of each element to amount (mol):

$$\text{Amount (mol) of C} = \text{mass of C} \times \frac{1}{\mathcal{M} \text{ of C}} = 40.0 \text{ g C} \times \frac{1 \text{ mol C}}{12.01 \text{ g C}} = 3.33 \text{ mol C}$$

Similarly, we have 6.66 mol of H and 3.33 mol of O.

Constructing the preliminary formula: $C_{3.33}H_{6.66}O_{3.33}$

Converting to integer subscripts:

$$C_{\frac{3.33}{3.33}}H_{\frac{6.66}{3.33}}O_{\frac{3.33}{3.33}} \longrightarrow C_{1.00}H_{2.00}O_{1.00} = C_1H_2O_1, \text{ the empirical formula is } \boxed{CH_2O}$$

Check The numbers of moles seem correct: the masses of C and O are each slightly more than 3 times their molar masses (e.g., for C, 40 g/(12 g/mol) > 3 mol), and the mass of H is over 6 times its molar mass of 1.

(b) Determining the molecular formula

Plan The molecular formula subscripts are whole-number multiples of the empirical formula subscripts. To find this multiple, we divide the given molar mass (90.08 g/mol) by the empirical formula mass, which we find from the sum of the elements' molar masses. Then we multiply each subscript in the empirical formula by the multiple.

Solution The empirical formula mass is 30.03 g/mol. Finding the whole-number multiple:

$$\text{Whole-number multiple} = \frac{\mathcal{M} \text{ of lactic acid}}{\mathcal{M} \text{ of empirical formula}} = \frac{90.08 \text{ g/mol}}{30.03 \text{ g/mol}} = 3.000 = 3$$

Determining the molecular formula:

$$C_{(1\times3)}H_{(2\times3)}O_{(1\times3)} = \boxed{C_3H_6O_3}$$

Check The calculated molecular formula has the same ratio of moles of elements (3/6/3) as the empirical formula (1/2/1) and corresponds to the given molar mass:

$\mathcal{M}$ of lactic acid $= (3 \times \mathcal{M} \text{ of } C) + (6 \times \mathcal{M} \text{ of } H) + (3 \times \mathcal{M} \text{ of } O)$

$\qquad\qquad = (3 \times 12.01 \text{ g/mol}) + (6 \times 1.008 \text{ g/mol}) + (3 \times 16.00 \text{ g/mol})$

$\qquad\qquad = 90.08 \text{ g/mol}$

Follow-Up Problem 3.10 One of the most widespread environmental carcinogens (cancer-causing agents) is benzo[*a*]pyrene ($\mathcal{M}$ = 252.30 g/mol). It is found in coal dust, cigarette smoke, and even charcoal-grilled meat. Analysis of this hydrocarbon shows 95.21 mass % C and 4.79 mass % H. What is the molecular formula of benzo[*a*]pyrene?

Combustion Analysis of Organic Compounds Still another type of compositional data is obtained through **combustion analysis,** used to measure the amounts of carbon and hydrogen in a combustible organic compound. The unknown compound is burned in an excess of pure O_2, and the H_2O and CO_2 that form are absorbed in separate containers (Figure 3.4). By weighing the absorbers before and after combustion, we find the masses of CO_2 and H_2O and use them to find the masses of C and H in the compound; from these results, we find the empirical formula. Many organic compounds also contain oxygen, nitrogen, or a halogen. As long as the third element doesn't interfere with the absorption of H_2O and CO_2, we calculate its mass by subtracting the masses of C and H from the original mass of the compound.

Figure 3.4 Combustion apparatus for determining formulas of organic compounds. A sample of an organic compound is burned in a stream of O_2. The resulting H_2O is absorbed by $Mg(ClO_4)_2$, and the CO_2 is absorbed by NaOH on asbestos.

Stream of O_2

Sample of compound containing C, H, and other elements

H_2O absorber

CO_2 absorber

Other substances not absorbed

Sample Problem 3.11 **Determining a Molecular Formula from Combustion Analysis**

Problem Vitamin C ($\mathcal{M}$ = 176.12 g/mol) is a compound of C, H, and O found in many natural sources, especially citrus fruits. When a 1.000-g sample of vitamin C is burned in a combustion apparatus, the following data are obtained:

$\qquad$ Mass of CO_2 absorber after combustion = 85.35 g
$\qquad$ Mass of CO_2 absorber before combustion = 83.85 g
$\qquad$ Mass of H_2O absorber after combustion = 37.96 g
$\qquad$ Mass of H_2O absorber before combustion = 37.55 g

What is the molecular formula of vitamin C?

Plan We find the masses of CO_2 and H_2O by subtracting the masses of the absorbers before and after the combustion. From the mass of CO_2, we use Equation 3.7 to find the mass of C. Similarly, we find the mass of H from the mass of H_2O. The mass of vitamin C (1.000 g) minus the sum of the masses of C and H gives the mass of O, the third element present. Then, we proceed as in Sample Problem 3.10: calculate amount (mol) of each element using its molar mass, construct the empirical formula, determine the whole-number multiple from the given molar mass, and construct the molecular formula.

Solution Finding the masses of combustion products:

$$\text{Mass (g) of CO}_2 = \text{mass of CO}_2 \text{ absorber after } - \text{ mass before}$$
$$= 85.35 \text{ g} - 83.85 \text{ g} = 1.50 \text{ g CO}_2$$
$$\text{Mass (g) of H}_2\text{O} = \text{mass of H}_2\text{O absorber after } - \text{ mass before}$$
$$= 37.96 \text{ g} - 37.55 \text{ g} = 0.41 \text{ g H}_2\text{O}$$

Calculating masses (g) of C and H using Equation 3.7:

$$\text{Mass of element} = \text{mass of compound} \times \frac{\text{mass of element in 1 mol of compound}}{\text{mass of 1 mol of compound}}$$

$$\text{Mass (g) of C} = \text{mass of CO}_2 \times \frac{1 \text{ mol C} \times \mathcal{M} \text{ of C}}{\text{mass of 1 mol CO}_2} = 1.50 \text{ g CO}_2 \times \frac{12.01 \text{ g C}}{44.01 \text{ g CO}_2}$$
$$= 0.409 \text{ g C}$$

$$\text{Mass (g) of H} = \text{mass of H}_2\text{O} \times \frac{2 \text{ mol H} \times \mathcal{M} \text{ of H}}{\text{mass of 1 mol H}_2\text{O}} = 0.41 \text{ g H}_2\text{O} \times \frac{2.016 \text{ g H}}{18.02 \text{ g H}_2\text{O}}$$
$$= 0.046 \text{ g H}$$

Calculating mass (g) of O:

$$\text{Mass (g) of O} = \text{mass of vitamin C sample} - (\text{mass of C} + \text{mass of H})$$
$$= 1.000 \text{ g} - (0.409 \text{ g} + 0.046 \text{ g}) = 0.545 \text{ g O}$$

Finding the amounts (mol) of elements: Dividing the mass (g) of each element by its molar mass gives 0.0341 mol of C, 0.046 mol of H, and 0.0341 mol of O.

Constructing the preliminary formula: $C_{0.0341}H_{0.046}O_{0.0341}$

Determining the empirical formula: Dividing through by the smallest subscript gives

$$C_{\frac{0.0341}{0.0341}} H_{\frac{0.046}{0.0341}} O_{\frac{0.0341}{0.0341}} = C_{1.00}H_{1.3}O_{1.00}$$

We find that 3 is the smallest integer that makes all subscripts into integers:

$$C_{(1.00\times3)}H_{(1.3\times3)}O_{(1.00\times3)} = C_{3.00}H_{3.9}O_{3.00} \approx C_3H_4O_3$$

Determining the molecular formula:

$$\text{Whole-number multiple} = \frac{\mathcal{M} \text{ of vitamin C}}{\mathcal{M} \text{ of empirical formula}} = \frac{176.12 \text{ g/mol}}{88.06 \text{ g/mol}} = 2.000 = 2$$
$$C_{(3\times2)}H_{(4\times2)}O_{(3\times2)} = \boxed{C_6H_8O_6}$$

Check The element masses seem correct: carbon makes up slightly more than 0.25 of the mass of CO_2 (12 g/44 g > 0.25), as do the masses in the problem (0.409 g/1.50 g > 0.25). Hydrogen makes up slightly more than 0.10 of the mass of H_2O (2 g/18 g > 0.10), as do the masses in the problem (0.046 g/0.41 g > 0.10). The molecular formula has the same ratio of subscripts (6/8/6) as the empirical formula (3/4/3) and the preliminary formula (0.0341/0.046/0.0341), and it gives the known molar mass:

$$(6 \times \mathcal{M} \text{ of C}) + (8 \times \mathcal{M} \text{ of H}) + (6 \times \mathcal{M} \text{ of O}) = \mathcal{M} \text{ of vitamin C}$$
$$(6 \times 12.01 \text{ g/mol}) + (8 \times 1.008 \text{ g/mol}) + (6 \times 16.00 \text{ g/mol}) = 176.12 \text{ g/mol}$$

Comment The subscript we calculated for H was 3.9, which we rounded to 4. But, if we had strung the calculation steps together, we would have obtained 4.0:

$$\text{Subscript of H} = 0.41 \text{ g H}_2\text{O} \times \frac{2.016 \text{ g H}}{18.02 \text{ g H}_2\text{O}} \times \frac{1 \text{ mol H}}{1.008 \text{ g H}} \times \frac{1}{0.0341 \text{ mol}} \times 3 = 4.0$$

Follow-Up Problem 3.11 A dry-cleaning solvent ($\mathcal{M} = 146.99$ g/mol) that contains C, H, and Cl is suspected to be a cancer-causing agent. When a 0.250-g sample was studied by combustion analysis, 0.451 g of CO_2 and 0.0617 g of H_2O formed. Find the molecular formula.

Chemical Formulas and Molecular Structures; Isomers

A formula represents a real, three-dimensional object. The structural formula makes this point, with its relative placement of atoms, but do empirical and molecular formulas contain structural information?

Table 3.2 Some Compounds with Empirical Formula CH₂O (Composition by Mass: 40.0% C, 6.71% H, 53.3% O)

Name	Molecular Formula	Whole-Number Multiple	$\mathcal{M}$ (g/mol)	Use or Function
Formaldehyde	CH_2O	1	30.03	Disinfectant; biological preservative
Acetic acid	$C_2H_4O_2$	2	60.05	Acetate polymers; vinegar (5% solution)
Lactic acid	$C_3H_6O_3$	3	90.08	Causes milk to sour; forms in muscles during exercise
Erythrose	$C_4H_8O_4$	4	120.10	Forms during sugar metabolism
Ribose	$C_5H_{10}O_5$	5	150.13	Component of many nucleic acids and vitamin B_2
Glucose	$C_6H_{12}O_6$	6	180.16	Major nutrient for energy in cells

CH_2O $C_2H_4O_2$ $C_3H_6O_3$ $C_4H_8O_4$ $C_5H_{10}O_5$ $C_6H_{12}O_6$

1. *Different compounds with the same empirical formula.* The empirical formula tells nothing about molecular structure because it is based solely on mass analysis. In fact, different compounds can have the *same* empirical formula. NO_2 and N_2O_4 are inorganic cases, and there are numerous organic ones. For example, many compounds have the empirical formula CH_2 (the general formula is C_nH_{2n}, with n an integer greater than or equal to 2), such as ethylene (C_2H_4) and propylene (C_3H_6), starting materials for two common plastics. Table 3.2 shows some biological compounds with the same empirical formula.

2. *Isomers: Different compounds with the same molecular formula.* A molecular formula also tells nothing about structure. Different compounds can have the *same* molecular formula because their atoms can bond in different arrangements to give more than one *structural formula.* **Isomers** are compounds with the same molecular formula, and thus molar mass, but different properties. *Constitutional,* or *structural, isomers,* occur when the atoms link together in different arrangements. Table 3.3 shows two pairs of examples. The left pair, butane and 2-methylpropane, share the molecular formula C_4H_{10}. One has a four-C chain and the other a one-C branch off a three-C chain. Both are small alkanes, so their properties are similar, but not identical. The two compounds with the molecular formula C_2H_6O have very different properties; indeed, they are different classes of organic compound—one is an alcohol and the other an ether.

Table 3.3 Two Pairs of Constitutional Isomers

Property	C_4H_{10}		C_2H_6O	
	Butane	**2-Methylpropane**	**Ethanol**	**Dimethyl Ether**
$\mathcal{M}$ (g/mol)	58.12	58.12	46.07	46.07
Boiling point	−0.5°C	−11.6°C	78.5°C	−25°C
Density (at 20°C)	0.579 g/mL (gas)	0.549 g/mL	0.789 g/mL (liquid)	0.00195 g/mL (gas)
Structural formula				
Space-filling model				

Figure 3.5 The antibiotic ampicillin.

As the number and kinds of atoms increase, the number of constitutional isomers—that is, the number of structural formulas that can be written for a given molecular formula—also increases: C_2H_6O has two structural formulas (Table 3.3), C_3H_8O has three, and $C_4H_{10}O$ seven. Imagine how many there are for $C_{16}H_{19}N_3O_4S$! Of all the possible isomers, only one is the antibiotic ampicillin (Figure 3.5). We'll discuss these and other types of isomerism fully later in the text.

■ Summary of Section 3.2

- From the masses of elements in a compound, their relative numbers of moles are found, which gives the empirical formula.
- If the molar mass of the compound is known, the molecular formula, the actual numbers of moles of each element, can also be determined.
- Combustion analysis provides data on the masses of C and H in an organic compound, which are used to obtain the formula.
- Atoms can bond in different arrangements (structural formulas). Two or more compounds with the same molecular formula are constitutional isomers.

3.3 • WRITING AND BALANCING CHEMICAL EQUATIONS

Thinking in terms of amounts, rather than masses, allows us to view reactions as large populations of interacting particles rather than as grams of material. For example, for the formation of HF from H_2 and F_2, if we weigh the substances, we find that

Macroscopic level (grams): 2.016 g of H_2 and 38.00 g of F_2 react to form 40.02 g of HF

This information tells us little except that mass is conserved. However, if we convert these masses (g) to amounts (mol), we find that

Macroscopic level (moles): 1 mol of H_2 and 1 mol of F_2 react to form 2 mol of HF

This information reveals that an enormous number of H_2 molecules react with just as many F_2 molecules to form twice as many HF molecules. Dividing by Avogadro's number shows the reaction between individual molecules:

Molecular level: 1 molecule of H_2 and 1 molecule of F_2 react to form 2 molecules of HF

Thus, *the macroscopic (molar) change corresponds to the submicroscopic (molecular) change* (Figure 3.6). This information forms the essence of a **chemical equation,** a statement that uses formulas to express the identities and quantities of substances in a chemical or physical change.

Figure 3.6 The formation of HF on the macroscopic and molecular levels.

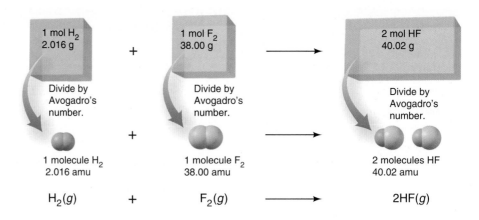

Steps for Balancing an Equation To present a chemical change quantitatively, the equation must be *balanced: the same number of each type of atom must appear on both sides.* As an example, here is a description of a chemical change that occurs in many fireworks and in a common lecture demonstration: a magnesium strip burns in oxygen gas to yield powdery magnesium oxide. (Light and heat are also produced, but we are concerned here only with substances.) Converting this description into a balanced equation involves the following steps:

1. *Translating the statement.* We first translate the chemical statement into a "skeleton" equation: the substances present *before* the change, called **reactants,** are placed to the left of a yield arrow, which points to the substances produced *during* the change, called **products:**

reactants   yield   product

___Mg + ___O$_2$ $\longrightarrow$ ___MgO

magnesium and oxygen   yield   magnesium oxide

At the beginning of the balancing process, we put a blank *in front of* each formula to remind us that we have to account for its atoms.

2. *Balancing the atoms.* By shifting our attention back and forth, we *match the numbers of each type of atom on the left and the right of the yield arrow.* In each blank, we place a **balancing (stoichiometric) coefficient,** a numerical multiplier of *all the atoms* in the formula that follows it. In general, balancing is easiest when we
   • Start with the most complex substance, the one with the largest number of different types of atoms.
   • End with the least complex substance, such as an element by itself.
   In this case, MgO is the most complex, so we place a coefficient 1 in that blank:

$$\text{___Mg + ___O}_2 \longrightarrow \underline{1}\,\text{MgO}$$

To balance the Mg in MgO, we place a 1 in front of Mg on the left:

$$\underline{1}\,\text{Mg + ___O}_2 \longrightarrow \underline{1}\,\text{MgO}$$

The O atom in MgO must be balanced by one O atom on the left. One-half an O$_2$ molecule provides one O atom:

$$\underline{1}\,\text{Mg} + \tfrac{1}{2}\,\text{O}_2 \longrightarrow \underline{1}\,\text{MgO}$$

In terms of numbers of each type of atom, the equation is balanced.

3. *Adjusting the coefficients.* There are several conventions about the final coefficients:
   • In most cases, *the smallest whole-number coefficients are preferred.* In this case, one-half of an O$_2$ molecule cannot exist, so we multiply the equation by 2:

$$2\text{Mg} + 1\text{O}_2 \longrightarrow 2\text{MgO}$$

   • We used the coefficient 1 to remind us to balance each substance. But, a coefficient of 1 is implied by the presence of the formula, so we don't write it:

$$2\text{Mg} + \text{O}_2 \longrightarrow 2\text{MgO}$$

(This convention is similar to not writing a subscript 1 in a formula.)

4. *Checking.* After balancing and adjusting the coefficients, always check that the equation is balanced:

$$\text{Reactants (2 Mg, 2 O)} \longrightarrow \text{products (2 Mg, 2 O)}$$

5. *Specifying the states of matter.* The final equation also indicates the physical state of each substance or whether it is dissolved in water. The abbreviations used for these states are shown in the margin. From the original statement, we know that a Mg "strip" is solid, O$_2$ is a gas, and "powdery" MgO is also solid. The balanced equation, therefore, is

$$2\text{Mg}(s) + \text{O}_2(g) \longrightarrow 2\text{MgO}(s)$$

g   for gas
l   for liquid
s   for solid
aq for aqueous solution

As you saw in Figure 3.6, *balancing coefficients refer to both individual chemical entities and moles of entities.* Thus,

2 atoms of Mg and 1 molecule of O_2 yield 2 formula units of MgO

2 moles of Mg and 1 mole of O_2 yield 2 moles of MgO

Figure 3.7 depicts this reaction on three levels:

- *Macroscopic level (photos),* as it appears in the laboratory
- *Molecular level (blow-up circles),* as chemists imagine it (with darker colored atoms representing the stoichiometry)
- *Symbolic level,* in the form of the balanced chemical equation

Keep in mind several key points about the balancing process:

- A coefficient operates on *all* the atoms in the formula that follows it:

  2MgO   *means* $2 \times (MgO)$,   or 2 Mg atoms + 2 O atoms

  $2Ca(NO_3)_2$ *means* $2 \times [Ca(NO_3)_2]$, or 2 Ca atoms + 4 N atoms + 12 O atoms

- Chemical formulas *cannot* be altered. In step 2 of the example, we *cannot* balance the O atoms by changing MgO to MgO_2 because MgO_2 is a different compound.
- Other reactants or products *cannot* be added. Thus, we *cannot* balance the O atoms by changing the reactant from O_2 molecules to O atoms or by adding an O atom to the products. The description of the reaction mentions oxygen gas, which consists of O_2 molecules, *not* separate O atoms.
- A balanced equation remains balanced if you multiply all the coefficients by the same number. For example,

$$4Mg(s) + 2O_2(g) \longrightarrow 4MgO(s)$$

is also balanced because the coefficients have just been multiplied by 2. However, *by convention,* we balance an equation with the *smallest* whole-number coefficients.

MACROSCOPIC VIEW

ATOMIC-SCALE VIEW

Mg   Mg

O_2

Mg^{2+}

O^{2-}

BALANCED EQUATION $2Mg(s)$ + $O_2(g)$ $2MgO(s)$

Figure 3.7 A three-level view of the reaction between magnesium and oxygen.

Sample Problem 3.12 Balancing Chemical Equations

Problem Within the cylinders of a car's engine, the hydrocarbon octane (C_8H_{18}), one of many components of gasoline, mixes with oxygen from the air and burns to form carbon dioxide and water vapor. Write a balanced equation for this reaction.

Solution 1. *Translate* the statement into a skeleton equation (with coefficient blanks). Octane and oxygen are reactants; "oxygen from the air" implies molecular oxygen, O_2. Carbon dioxide and water vapor are products:

$$\_C_8H_{18} + \_O_2 \longrightarrow \_CO_2 + \_H_2O$$

2. *Balance the atoms.* Start with the most complex substance, C_8H_{18}, and balance O_2 last:

$$\underline{1}\,C_8H_{18} + \_O_2 \longrightarrow \_CO_2 + \_H_2O$$

The C atoms in C_8H_{18} end up in CO_2. Each CO_2 contains one C atom, so 8 molecules of CO_2 are needed to balance the 8 C atoms in each C_8H_{18}:

$$\underline{1}\,C_8H_{18} + \_O_2 \longrightarrow \underline{8}\,CO_2 + \_H_2O$$

The H atoms in C_8H_{18} end up in H_2O. The 18 H atoms in C_8H_{18} require the coefficient 9 in front of H_2O:

$$\underline{1}\,C_8H_{18} + \_O_2 \longrightarrow \underline{8}\,CO_2 + \underline{9}\,H_2O$$

There are 25 atoms of O on the right (16 in $8CO_2$ plus 9 in $9H_2O$), so we place the coefficient $\frac{25}{2}$ in front of O_2:

$$\underline{1}\,C_8H_{18} + \tfrac{25}{2}\,O_2 \longrightarrow \underline{8}\,CO_2 + \underline{9}\,H_2O$$

3. *Adjust the coefficients.* Multiply through by 2 to obtain whole numbers:

$$2C_8H_{18} + 25O_2 \longrightarrow 16CO_2 + 18H_2O$$

4. *Check* that the equation is balanced:

$$\text{Reactants (16 C, 36 H, 50 O)} \longrightarrow \text{products (16 C, 36 H, 50 O)}$$

5. *Specify* states of matter. C_8H_{18} is liquid; O_2, CO_2, and H_2O vapor are gases:

$$2C_8H_{18}(l) + 25O_2(g) \longrightarrow 16CO_2(g) + 18H_2O(g)$$

Comment This is an example of a combustion reaction. *Any* compound containing C and H that burns in an excess of air produces CO_2 and H_2O.

Follow-Up Problem 3.12 Write a balanced equation for each of the following:
(a) A characteristic reaction of Group 1A(1) elements: chunks of sodium react violently with water to form hydrogen gas and sodium hydroxide solution.
(b) The destruction of marble statuary by acid rain: aqueous nitric acid reacts with calcium carbonate to form carbon dioxide, water, and aqueous calcium nitrate.
(c) Halogen compounds exchanging bonding partners: phosphorus trifluoride is prepared by the reaction of phosphorus trichloride and hydrogen fluoride; hydrogen chloride is the other product. The reaction involves gases only.
(d) Explosive decomposition of dynamite: liquid nitroglycerine ($C_3H_5N_3O_9$) explodes to produce a mixture of gases—carbon dioxide, water vapor, nitrogen, and oxygen.

Visualizing a Reaction with a Molecular Scene A great way to focus on the rearrangement of atoms from reactants to products is by visualizing an equation as a molecular scene. Here's a representation of the combustion of octane we just balanced:

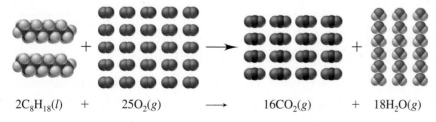

$$2C_8H_{18}(l) \quad + \quad 25O_2(g) \quad \longrightarrow \quad 16CO_2(g) \quad + \quad 18H_2O(g)$$

Now let's work through a sample problem to do the reverse—derive a balanced equation from a molecular scene.

Sample Problem 3.13 Balancing an Equation from a Molecular Scene

Problem The following molecular scenes depict an important reaction in nitrogen chemistry (nitrogen is blue; oxygen is red):

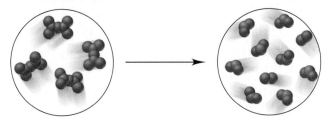

Write a balanced equation for this reaction.

Plan To write a balanced equation, we first have to determine the formulas of the molecules and obtain coefficients by counting the number of each molecule. Then, we arrange this information in the correct equation format, using the smallest whole-number coefficients and including states of matter.

Solution The reactant circle shows only one type of molecule. It has two N and five O atoms, so the formula is N_2O_5; there are four of these molecules. The product circle shows two different molecules, one with one N and two O atoms, and the other with two O atoms; there are eight NO_2 and two O_2. Thus, we have:

$$4N_2O_5 \longrightarrow 8NO_2 + 2O_2$$

Writing the balanced equation with the smallest whole-number coefficients and all substances as gases:

$$2N_2O_5(g) \longrightarrow 4NO_2(g) + O_2(g)$$

Check Reactant (4 N, 10 O) $\longrightarrow$ products (4 N, 8 + 2 = 10 O)

Follow-Up Problem 3.13 Write a balanced equation for the important atmospheric reaction depicted below (carbon is black; oxygen is red):

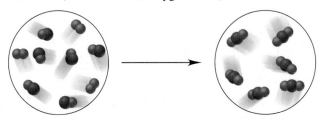

▌Summary of Section 3.3

- A chemical equation has reactant formulas on the left of a yield arrow and product formulas on the right.
- A balanced equation has the same number of each type of atom on both sides.
- Balancing coefficients are integer multipliers for *all* the atoms in a formula and apply to the individual entity or to moles of entities.

3.4 • CALCULATING QUANTITIES OF REACTANT AND PRODUCT

A balanced equation is essential for all calculations involving chemical change: *if you know the number of moles of one substance, the balanced equation tells you the number of moles of the others.*

Stoichiometrically Equivalent Molar Ratios from the Balanced Equation

In a balanced equation, *the amounts (mol) of substances are stoichiometrically equivalent to each other,* which means that a specific amount of one substance is formed from, produces, or reacts with a specific amount of the other. The quantitative relationships are expressed as *stoichiometrically equivalent molar ratios* that we use as conversion factors to calculate the amounts. For example, consider the equation for the combustion of propane, a hydrocarbon fuel used in cooking and water heating:

$$C_3H_8(g) + 5O_2(g) \longrightarrow 3CO_2(g) + 4H_2O(g)$$

If we view the reaction quantitatively in terms of C_3H_8, we see that

> 1 mol of C_3H_8 reacts with 5 mol of O_2
> 1 mol of C_3H_8 produces   3 mol of CO_2
> 1 mol of C_3H_8 produces   4 mol of H_2O

Therefore, in this reaction,

> 1 mol of C_3H_8 is stoichiometrically equivalent to 5 mol of O_2
> 1 mol of C_3H_8 is stoichiometrically equivalent to 3 mol of CO_2
> 1 mol of C_3H_8 is stoichiometrically equivalent to 4 mol of H_2O

We chose to look at C_3H_8, but any two of the substances are stoichiometrically equivalent to each other. Thus,

> 3 mol of CO_2 is stoichiometrically equivalent to 4 mol of H_2O
> 5 mol of O_2 is stoichiometrically equivalent to 3 mol of CO_2

and so on. A balanced equation contains a wealth of quantitative information relating individual chemical entities, amounts (mol) of substances, and masses of substances, and Table 3.4 presents the quantitative information contained in this equation.

   Here's a typical problem that shows how stoichiometric equivalence is used to create conversion factors: in the combustion of propane, how many moles of O_2 are consumed when 10.0 mol of H_2O are produced? To solve this problem, we have to find the molar ratio between O_2 and H_2O. From the balanced equation, we see that for every 5 mol of O_2 consumed, 4 mol of H_2O is formed:

> 5 mol of O_2 is stoichiometrically equivalent to 4 mol of H_2O

Table 3.4 Information Contained in a Balanced Equation

Viewed in Terms of	Reactants $C_3H_8(g)$ + $5O_2(g)$		$\longrightarrow$	Products $3CO_2(g)$ + $4H_2O(g)$	
Molecules	1 molecule C_3H_8	+ 5 molecules O_2	$\longrightarrow$	3 molecules CO_2	+ 4 molecules H_2O

Amount (mol)	1 mol C_3H_8	+ 5 mol O_2	$\longrightarrow$	3 mol CO_2	+ 4 mol H_2O
Mass (amu)	44.09 amu C_3H_8	+ 160.00 amu O_2	$\longrightarrow$	132.03 amu CO_2	+ 72.06 amu H_2O
Mass (g)	44.09 g C_3H_8	+ 160.00 g O_2	$\longrightarrow$	132.03 g CO_2	+ 72.06 g H_2O
Total mass (g)	204.09 g		$\longrightarrow$	204.09 g	

As with any equivalent quantities, we can construct two conversion factors, depending on the quantity we want to find:

$$\frac{5 \text{ mol } O_2}{4 \text{ mol } H_2O} \quad \text{or} \quad \frac{4 \text{ mol } H_2O}{5 \text{ mol } O_2}$$

Since we want to find amount (mol) of O_2 and we know amount (mol) of H_2O, we choose "5 mol O_2/4 mol H_2O" to cancel "mol H_2O":

$$\text{Amount (mol) of } O_2 \text{ consumed} = 10.0 \text{ mol } H_2O \times \frac{5 \text{ mol } O_2}{4 \text{ mol } H_2O} = 12.5 \text{ mol } O_2$$

$$\text{mol } H_2O \xrightarrow[\text{conversion factor}]{\text{molar ratio as}} \text{mol } O_2$$

*You **cannot** solve this type of problem without the balanced equation.* Here is an approach for solving *any* stoichiometry problem that involves a reaction:

1. Write the balanced equation.
2. When necessary, convert the known mass (or number of entities) of one substance to amount (mol) using its molar mass (or Avogadro's number).
3. Use the molar ratio to calculate the unknown amount (mol) of the other substance.
4. When necessary, convert the amount of that other substance to the desired mass (or number of entities) using its molar mass (or Avogadro's number).

Figure 3.8 summarizes the possible relationships among quantities of substances in a reaction, and Sample Problems 3.14–3.16 apply three of them in the first chemical step of converting copper ore to copper metal.

Figure 3.8 Summary of amount-mass-number relationships in a chemical equation. Start at any box (known) and move to any other (unknown) by using the conversion factor on the arrow. As always, convert to amount (mol) first.

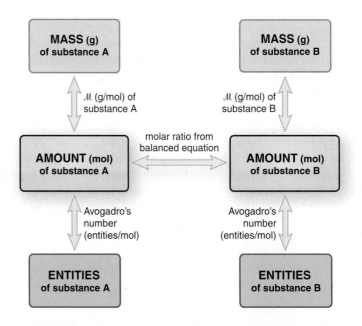

Sample Problem 3.14 Calculating Quantities of Reactants and Products: Amount (mol) to Amount (mol)

Problem In a lifetime, the average American uses 1750 lb (794 kg) of copper in coins, plumbing, and wiring. Copper is obtained from sulfide ores, such as chalcocite [copper(I) sulfide] by a multistep process. After grinding the ore, it is "roasted" (heated strongly with oxygen gas) to form powdered copper(I) oxide and gaseous sulfur dioxide. How many moles of oxygen are required to roast 10.0 mol of copper(I) sulfide?

Plan We *always* write the balanced equation first. The formulas of the reactants are Cu_2S and O_2, and the formulas of the products are Cu_2O and SO_2, so we have

$$2Cu_2S(s) + 3O_2(g) \longrightarrow 2Cu_2O(s) + 2SO_2(g)$$

We know the amount of Cu_2S (10.0 mol) and must find the amount (mol) of O_2 that is needed to roast it. The balanced equation shows that 3 mol of O_2 is needed for 2 mol of Cu_2S, so the conversion factor for finding amount (mol) of O_2 is "3 mol O_2/2 mol Cu_2S" (see the road map).

Solution Calculating the amount of O_2:

$$\text{Amount (mol) of } O_2 = 10.0 \text{ mol } Cu_2S \times \frac{3 \text{ mol } O_2}{2 \text{ mol } Cu_2S} = \boxed{15.0 \text{ mol } O_2}$$

Check The units are correct, and the answer is reasonable because this molar ratio of O_2 to Cu_2S (15/10) is identical to the ratio in the balanced equation (3/2).

Comment A *common mistake* is to invert the conversion factor; that calculation would be

$$\text{Amount (mol) of } O_2 = 10.0 \text{ mol } Cu_2S \times \frac{2 \text{ mol } Cu_2S}{3 \text{ mol } O_2} = \frac{6.67 \text{ mol}^2 \, Cu_2S}{1 \text{ mol } O_2}$$

The strange units should alert you that an error was made in setting up the conversion factor. Also note that this answer, 6.67, is *less* than 10.0, whereas the equation shows that there should be *more* moles of O_2 (3 mol) than moles of Cu_2S (2 mol). Be sure to think through the calculation when setting up the conversion factor and canceling units.

Follow-Up Problem 3.14 Thermite is a mixture of iron(III) oxide and aluminum powders that was once used to weld railroad tracks. It undergoes a spectacular reaction to yield solid aluminum oxide and molten iron. How many moles of iron(III) oxide are needed to form 3.60×10^3 mol of iron? Include a road map that shows how you planned the solution.

Road Map

> Amount (mol) of Cu_2S

↓ molar ratio

> Amount (mol) of O_2

Sample Problem 3.15   **Calculating Quantities of Reactants and Products: Amount (mol) to Mass (g)**

Problem During the roasting process, how many grams of sulfur dioxide form when 10.0 mol of copper(I) sulfide reacts?

Plan Referring to the balanced equation in Sample Problem 3.14, here we are given amount of reactant (10.0 mol of Cu_2S) and need the mass (g) of product (SO_2) that forms. We find the amount (mol) of SO_2 using the molar ratio (2 mol SO_2/2 mol Cu_2S) and then multiply by its molar mass (64.07 g/mol) to find mass (g) of SO_2 (see the road map).

Solution Combining the two conversion steps into one calculation, we have

$$\text{Mass (g) of } SO_2 = 10.0 \text{ mol } Cu_2S \times \frac{2 \text{ mol } SO_2}{2 \text{ mol } Cu_2S} \times \frac{64.07 \text{ g } SO_2}{1 \text{ mol } SO_2} = \boxed{641 \text{ g } SO_2}$$

Check The answer makes sense, since the molar ratio shows that 10.0 mol of SO_2 is formed and each mole weighs about 64 g. We rounded to three significant figures.

Follow-Up Problem 3.15 In the thermite reaction, what amount (mol) of iron forms when 1.85×10^{25} formula units of aluminum oxide reacts? Write a road map to show how to plan the solution.

Road Map

> Amount (mol) of Cu_2S

↓ molar ratio

> Amount (mol) of SO_2

↓ multiply by $\mathcal{M}$ (g/mol)

> Mass (g) of SO_2

Sample Problem 3.16   **Calculating Quantities of Reactants and Products: Mass to Mass**

Problem During the roasting of chalcocite, how many kilograms of oxygen are required to form 2.86 kg of copper(I) oxide?

Plan In this problem, we know the mass of the product, Cu_2O (2.86 kg), and we need the mass (kg) of O_2 that reacts to form it. Therefore, we must convert from mass of product to amount of product to amount of reactant to mass of reactant. We convert the mass of Cu_2O from kg to g and then to amount (mol). Then, we use the molar ratio (3 mol O_2/2 mol Cu_2O) to find the amount (mol) of O_2 required. Finally, we convert amount of O_2 to g and then kg (see the road map on the next page).

Road Map

Mass (kg) of Cu_2O

$\downarrow$ 1 kg = 10^3 g

Mass (g) of Cu_2O

$\downarrow$ divide by $\mathcal{M}$ (g/mol)

Amount (mol) of Cu_2O

$\downarrow$ molar ratio

Amount (mol) of O_2

$\downarrow$ multiply by $\mathcal{M}$ (g/mol)

Mass (g) of O_2

$\downarrow$ 10^3 g = 1 kg

Mass (kg) of O_2

Solution Converting from kilograms of Cu_2O to moles of Cu_2O: Combining the mass unit conversion with the mass-to-amount conversion gives

$$\text{Amount (mol) of } Cu_2O = 2.86 \text{ kg } Cu_2O \times \frac{10^3 \text{ g}}{1 \text{ kg}} \times \frac{1 \text{ mol } Cu_2O}{143.10 \text{ g } Cu_2O} = 20.0 \text{ mol } Cu_2O$$

Converting from moles of Cu_2O to moles of O_2:

$$\text{Amount (mol) of } O_2 = 20.0 \text{ mol } Cu_2O \times \frac{3 \text{ mol } O_2}{2 \text{ mol } Cu_2O} = 30.0 \text{ mol } O_2$$

Converting from moles of O_2 to kilograms of O_2: Combining the amount-to-mass conversion with the mass unit conversion gives

$$\text{Mass (kg) of } O_2 = 30.0 \text{ mol } O_2 \times \frac{32.00 \text{ g } O_2}{1 \text{ mol } O_2} \times \frac{1 \text{ kg}}{10^3 \text{ g}} = \boxed{0.960 \text{ kg } O_2}$$

Check The units are correct. Rounding to check the math, for example, in the final step, ~30 mol × 30 g/mol × 1 kg/10^3 g = 0.90 kg. The answer seems reasonable: even though the amount (mol) of O_2 is greater than the amount (mol) of Cu_2O, the mass of O_2 is less than the mass of Cu_2O because $\mathcal{M}$ of O_2 is less than $\mathcal{M}$ of Cu_2O.

Comment The three related sample problems (3.14–3.16) highlight the main point for solving stoichiometry problems: *convert the information given into amount (mol)*. Then, use the appropriate molar ratio and any other conversion factors to complete the solution.

Follow-Up Problem 3.16 During the thermite reaction, how many atoms of aluminum react for every 1.00 g of aluminum oxide that forms? Include a road map that shows how you planned the solution.

Reactions That Occur in a Sequence

In many situations, a product of one reaction becomes a reactant for the next in a sequence of reactions. For stoichiometric purposes, when the same (common) substance forms in one reaction and reacts in the next, we eliminate it in an **overall (net) equation**. The steps to writing the overall equation are

1. Write the sequence of balanced equations.
2. Adjust the equations arithmetically to cancel the common substance.
3. Add the adjusted equations together to obtain the overall balanced equation.

Sample Problem 3.17 shows the approach by continuing with the copper recovery process that started in Sample Problem 3.14.

Sample Problem 3.17 | **Writing an Overall Equation for a Reaction Sequence**

Problem Roasting is the first step in extracting copper from chalcocite. In the next step, copper(I) oxide reacts with powdered carbon to yield copper metal and carbon monoxide gas. Write a balanced overall equation for the two-step sequence.

Plan To obtain the overall equation, we write the individual equations in sequence, adjust coefficients to cancel the common substance (or substances), and add the equations together. In this case, only Cu_2O appears as a product in one equation and a reactant in the other, so it is the common substance.

Solution Writing the individual balanced equations:

$$2Cu_2S(s) + 3O_2(g) \longrightarrow 2Cu_2O(s) + 2SO_2(g) \text{ [equation 1; see Sample Problem 3.14]}$$
$$Cu_2O(s) + C(s) \longrightarrow 2Cu(s) + CO(g) \quad \text{[equation 2]}$$

Adjusting the coefficients: Since 2 mol of Cu_2O forms in equation 1 but 1 mol of Cu_2O reacts in equation 2, we double *all* the coefficients in equation 2 to use up the Cu_2O:

$$2Cu_2S(s) + 3O_2(g) \longrightarrow 2Cu_2O(s) + 2SO_2(g) \text{ [equation 1]}$$
$$2Cu_2O(s) + 2C(s) \longrightarrow 4Cu(s) + 2CO(g) \quad \text{[equation 2, doubled]}$$

Adding the two equations and canceling the common substance: We keep the reactants of both equations on the left and the products of both equations on the right:

$$2Cu_2S(s) + 3O_2(g) + \cancel{2Cu_2O(s)} + 2C(s) \longrightarrow \cancel{2Cu_2O(s)} + 2SO_2(g) + 4Cu(s) + 2CO(g)$$

or, $$2Cu_2S(s) + 3O_2(g) + 2C(s) \longrightarrow 2SO_2(g) + 4Cu(s) + 2CO(g)$$

Check Reactants (4 Cu, 2 S, 6 O, 2 C) $\longrightarrow$ products (4 Cu, 2 S, 6 O, 2 C)

Comment 1. Even though Cu_2O *does* participate in the chemical change, it is not involved in the reaction stoichiometry. An overall equation *may not* show which substances actually react; for example, C(s) and $Cu_2S(s)$ do not interact directly in this reaction sequence, even though both are shown as reactants.
2. The SO_2 formed in copper recovery contributes to acid rain, so chemists have devised microbial and electrochemical methods to extract metals without roasting sulfide ores. Such methods are examples of *green chemistry;* we'll discuss another on page 113.
3. These reactions were shown to explain how to obtain an overall equation. The actual extraction of copper is more complex, as you'll see in Chapter 22.

Follow-Up Problem 3.17 The SO_2 formed in copper recovery reacts in air with oxygen and forms sulfur trioxide. This gas, in turn, reacts with water to form a sulfuric acid solution that falls in rain. Write a balanced overall equation for this process.

Reaction Sequences in Organisms
Multistep reaction sequences called *metabolic pathways* occur throughout biological systems. (We discuss them again in Chapter 17.) For example, in most cells, the chemical energy in glucose is released through a sequence of about 30 individual reactions. The product of each reaction step is the reactant of the next, so that all the common substances cancel, and the overall equation is

$$C_6H_{12}O_6(aq) + 6O_2(g) \longrightarrow 6CO_2(g) + 6H_2O(l)$$

We eat food that contains glucose, inhale O_2, and excrete CO_2 and H_2O. In our cells, these reactants and products are many steps apart: O_2 never reacts *directly* with glucose, and CO_2 and H_2O are formed at various, often distant, steps along the sequence of reactions. Even so, the molar ratios in the overall equation are the same as if the glucose burned in a combustion chamber filled with O_2 and formed CO_2 and H_2O directly (Figure 3.9).

Figure 3.9 An overall equation equals the sum of the individual steps.

Reactions That Involve a Limiting Reactant
In problems up to now, the amount of *one* reactant was given, and we assumed there was enough of the other reactants to react with it completely. For example, suppose we want the amount (mol) of SO_2 that forms when 5.2 mol of Cu_2S reacts with O_2:

$$2Cu_2S(s) + 3O_2(g) \longrightarrow 2Cu_2O(s) + 2SO_2(g) \text{ [equation 1; see Sample Problem 3.14]}$$

We assume the 5.2 mol of Cu_2S reacts with as much O_2 as needed. Because all the Cu_2S reacts, its initial amount of 5.2 mol determines, or *limits*, the amount of SO_2 that can form, no matter how much more O_2 is present. In this situation, we call Cu_2S the **limiting reactant** (or *limiting reagent*).

Suppose, however, you know the amounts of both Cu_2S *and* O_2 and need to find out how much SO_2 forms. You first have to determine whether Cu_2S *or* O_2 is the limiting reactant—that is, which one is completely used up—because it limits how much SO_2 can form. The reactant that is *not* limiting is present *in excess*, which means the amount that doesn't react is left over. ● To determine which is the limiting reactant, we use the molar ratios in the balanced equation to perform a series of calculations to see *which reactant forms less product*.

Determining the Limiting Reactant
Let's clarify these ideas in a much more appetizing situation. Suppose you have a job making ice cream sundaes. Each sundae requires two scoops (12 oz) of ice cream, one cherry, and 50 mL of syrup:

$$2 \text{ scoops (12 oz)} + 1 \text{ cherry} + 50 \text{ mL syrup} \longrightarrow 1 \text{ sundae}$$

● **Limiting "Reactants" in Everyday Life**
Limiting-"reactant" situations arise in business all the time. A car assembly-plant manager must order more tires if there are 1500 car bodies and only 4000 tires, and a clothes manufacturer must cut more sleeves if there are 320 sleeves for 170 shirt bodies. You've probably faced such situations in daily life as well. A muffin recipe calls for 2 cups of flour and 1 cup of sugar, but you have 3 cups of flour and only $\frac{3}{4}$ cup of sugar. Clearly, the flour is in excess and the sugar limits the number of muffins you can make. Or, you're in charge of making cheeseburgers for a picnic, and you have 10 buns, 12 meat patties, and 15 slices of cheese. Here, the number of buns limits how many cheeseburgers you can make. Or, there are 26 students and only 23 microscopes in a cell biology lab. You'll find that limiting-"reactant" situations are almost limitless.

Figure 3.10 An ice cream sundae analogy for limiting reactants. **A,** The "reactants" form the "product" (sundae). **B,** Only two sundaes can be made before all the syrup is used up, so syrup is the limiting "reactant"; four scoops of ice cream and four cherries are "in excess."

A mob of 25 ravenous school kids enters, and each one wants a sundae with vanilla ice cream and chocolate syrup. You have 300 oz of vanilla ice cream (at 6 oz per scoop), 30 cherries, and 1 L of syrup: can you feed them all? A series of calculations based on the balanced equation shows the number of sundaes you can make from each ingredient:

$$\text{Ice cream: No. of sundaes} = 300 \text{ oz} \times \frac{1 \text{ scoop}}{6 \text{ oz}} \times \frac{1 \text{ sundae}}{2 \text{ scoops}} = 25 \text{ sundaes}$$

$$\text{Cherries: No. of sundaes} = 30 \text{ cherries} \times \frac{1 \text{ sundae}}{1 \text{ cherry}} = 30 \text{ sundaes}$$

$$\text{Syrup: No. of sundaes} = 1000 \text{ mL syrup} \times \frac{1 \text{ sundae}}{50 \text{ mL syrup}} = 20 \text{ sundaes}$$

Of the reactants (ice cream, cherry, syrup), the syrup forms the *least* product (sundaes), so it is the limiting "reactant." When all the syrup has been used up, some ice cream and cherries are "unreacted" so they are in excess:

300 oz (50 scoops) + 30 cherries + 1 L syrup $\longrightarrow$

20 sundaes + 60 oz (10 scoops) + 10 cherries

Figure 3.10 shows a similar example with different initial (starting) quantities.

Using Reaction Tables in Limiting-Reactant Problems A good way to keep track of the quantities in a limiting-reactant problem is with a *reaction table*. The balanced equation appears at the top for the column heads. The table shows the

- *Initial* quantities of reactants and products *before* the reaction
- *Change* in the quantities of reactants and products *during* the reaction
- *Final* quantities of reactants and products remaining *after* the reaction

For example, for the ice-cream sundae "reaction," the reaction table would be

Quantity	12 oz (2 scoops)	+ 1 cherry	+ 50 mL syrup	$\longrightarrow$ 1 sundae
Initial	300 oz (50 scoops)	30 cherries	1000 mL syrup	0 sundaes
Change	−240 oz (40 scoops)	−20 cherries	−1000 mL syrup	+20 sundaes
Final	60 oz (10 scoops)	10 cherries	0 mL syrup	20 sundaes

The body of the table shows the following important points:

- In the Initial line, "product" has not yet formed, so the entry is "0 sundaes."
- In the Change line, since the reactants (ice cream, cherries, syrup) are used during the reaction, their quantities decrease, so the changes in their quantities have a *negative* sign. At the same time, the quantity of product (sundaes) increases, so the change in its quantity has a *positive* sign.
- For the Final line, we *add* the Change and Initial lines. Notice that some reactants (ice cream and cherries) are in excess, while the limiting reactant (syrup) is used up.

Solving Limiting-Reactant Problems In limiting-reactant problems, *the quantities of two (or more) reactants are given, and we first determine which is limiting.* To do this, just as we did with the ice cream sundaes, we use the balanced equation to solve a series of calculations to see how much product forms from the given quantity of each reactant: the limiting reactant is the one that yields the *least* quantity of product.

The following problems examine these ideas from several aspects. In Sample Problem 3.18, we solve the problem by looking at a molecular scene; in Sample Problem 3.19, we start with the amounts (mol) of two reactants, and in Sample Problem 3.20, we start with masses of two reactants.

Sample Problem 3.18 **Using Molecular Depictions in a Limiting-Reactant Problem**

Problem Nuclear engineers use chlorine trifluoride to prepare uranium fuel for power plants. The compound is formed as a gas by the reaction of elemental chlorine and fluorine. The circle in the margin shows a representative portion of the reaction mixture before the reaction starts (chlorine is *green;* fluorine is *yellow*).
(a) Find the limiting reactant.
(b) Write a reaction table for the process.
(c) Draw a representative portion of the mixture after the reaction is complete. (*Hint:* The ClF_3 molecule has Cl bonded to three individual F atoms.)

Plan **(a)** We have to find the limiting reactant. The first step is to write the balanced equation, so we need the formulas and states of matter. From the name, chlorine trifluoride, we know the product consists of one Cl atom bonded to three F atoms, or ClF_3. Elemental chlorine and fluorine are the diatomic molecules Cl_2 and F_2, and all three substances are gases. To find the limiting reactant, we find the number of molecules of product that would form from the numbers of molecules of each reactant: whichever forms less product is the limiting reactant. **(b)** We use these numbers of molecules to write a reaction table. **(c)** We use the numbers in the Final line of the table to draw the scene.

Solution **(a)** The balanced equation is

$$Cl_2(g) + 3F_2(g) \longrightarrow 2ClF_3(g)$$

For Cl_2: Molecules of ClF_3 = 3 ~~molecules of Cl_2~~ × $\dfrac{\text{2 molecules of } ClF_3}{\text{1 ~~molecule of Cl_2~~}}$

$$= 6 \text{ molecules of } ClF_3$$

For F_2: Molecules of ClF_3 = 6 ~~molecules of F_2~~ × $\dfrac{\text{2 molecules of } ClF_3}{\text{3 ~~molecules of F_2~~}}$

$$= \tfrac{12}{3} \text{ molecules of } ClF_3 = 4 \text{ molecules of } ClF_3$$

Because it forms less product, F_2 is the limiting reactant.
(b) Since F_2 is the limiting reactant, all of it (6 molecules) is used in the "Change" line of the reaction table:

Molecules	$Cl_2(g)$	+	$3F_2(g)$	$\longrightarrow$	$2ClF_3(g)$
Initial	3		6		0
Change	−2		−6		+4
Final	1		0		4

(c) The representative portion of the final reaction mixture (*see margin*) includes 1 molecule of Cl_2 (the reactant in excess) and 4 molecules of product ClF_3.

Check The equation is balanced: reactants (2 Cl, 6 F) ⟶ products (2 Cl, 6 F). And, as shown in the circles, the numbers of each type of atom before and after the reaction are equal. Let's think through our choice of limiting reactant. From the equation, one Cl_2 needs three F_2 to form two ClF_3. Therefore, the three Cl_2 molecules in the circle depicting reactants need nine (3 × 3) F_2. But there are only six F_2, so there is not enough F_2 to react with the available Cl_2; or put the other way, there is too much Cl_2 to react with the available F_2. From either point of view, F_2 is the limiting reactant.

Follow-Up Problem 3.18 B_2 (B is *red*) reacts with AB as shown below:

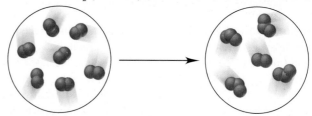

Write a balanced equation for the reaction, and determine the limiting reactant.

Sample Problem 3.19 **Calculating Quantities in a Limiting-Reactant Problem: Amount to Amount**

Problem In another preparation of ClF_3 (see Sample Problem 3.18), 0.750 mol of Cl_2 reacts with 3.00 mol of F_2. **(a)** Find the limiting reactant. **(b)** Write a reaction table.

Plan **(a)** We find the limiting reactant by calculating the amount (mol) of ClF_3 formed from the amount (mol) of each reactant: the reactant that forms fewer moles of ClF_3 is limiting. **(b)** We enter those values into the reaction table.

Solution **(a)** Determining the limiting reactant:
Finding amount (mol) of ClF_3 from amount (mol) of Cl_2:

$$\text{Amount (mol) of } ClF_3 = 0.750 \text{ mol } Cl_2 \times \frac{2 \text{ mol } ClF_3}{1 \text{ mol } Cl_2} = 1.50 \text{ mol } ClF_3$$

Finding amount (mol) of ClF_3 from amount (mol) of F_2:

$$\text{Amount (mol) of } ClF_3 = 3.00 \text{ mol } F_2 \times \frac{2 \text{ mol } ClF_3}{3 \text{ mol } F_2} = 2.00 \text{ mol } ClF_3$$

In this case, Cl_2 is limiting because it forms fewer moles of ClF_3.
(b) Writing the reaction table, with Cl_2 limiting:

Amount (mol)	$Cl_2(g)$ +	$3F_2(g)$ ⟶	$2ClF_3(g)$
Initial	0.750	3.00	0
Change	−0.750	−2.25	+1.50
Final	0	0.75	1.50

Check Let's check that Cl_2 is the limiting reactant by assuming, for the moment, that F_2 is limiting. If that were true, all 3.00 mol of F_2 would react to form 2.00 mol of ClF_3. However, based on the balanced equation, obtaining 2.00 mol of ClF_3 would require 1.00 mol of Cl_2, and only 0.750 mol of Cl_2 is present. Thus, Cl_2 must be the limiting reactant.

Comment A major point to note from Sample Problems 3.18 and 3.19 is that the relative quantities of reactants *do not* determine which is limiting, but rather the quantity of product formed, which is based on the *molar ratio in the balanced equation*. In both problems, there is more F_2 than Cl_2. However,
• Sample Problem 3.18 has an F_2/Cl_2 ratio of 6/3, or 2/1, which is less than the required molar ratio of 3/1, so F_2 is limiting and Cl_2 is in excess.
• Sample Problem 3.19 has an F_2/Cl_2 ratio of 3.00/0.750, which is greater than the required molar ratio of 3/1, so Cl_2 is limiting and F_2 is in excess.

Follow-Up Problem 3.19 For the reaction in Follow-Up Problem 3.18, how many moles of product form from 1.5 mol of each reactant?

Sample Problem 3.20   Calculating Quantities in a Limiting-Reactant Problem: Mass to Mass

Problem A fuel mixture used in the early days of rocketry consisted of two liquids, hydrazine (N_2H_4) and dinitrogen tetraoxide (N_2O_4), which ignite on contact to form nitrogen gas and water vapor.
(a) How many grams of nitrogen gas form when 1.00×10^2 g of N_2H_4 and 2.00×10^2 g of N_2O_4 are mixed?
(b) Write a reaction table for this process.

Plan The amounts of two reactants are given, which means this is a limiting-reactant problem. **(a)** To determine the mass of product formed, we must find the limiting reactant by calculating which of the given masses of reactant forms *less* nitrogen gas. As always, we first write the balanced equation. We convert the grams of each reactant to moles using its molar mass and then use the molar ratio from the balanced equation to find the number of moles of N_2 each reactant forms. Next, we convert the lower amount of N_2 to mass (see the road map). **(b)** We use the values based on the limiting reactant for the reaction table.

Road Map

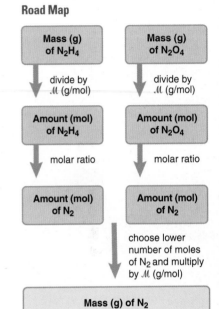

Solution **(a)** Writing the balanced equation:
$$2N_2H_4(l) + N_2O_4(l) \longrightarrow 3N_2(g) + 4H_2O(g)$$

Finding the amount (mol) of N_2 from the amount (mol) of each reactant

For N_2H_4: Amount (mol) of $N_2H_4 = 1.00 \times 10^2 \text{ g } N_2H_4 \times \dfrac{1 \text{ mol } N_2H_4}{32.05 \text{ g } N_2H_4} = 3.12 \text{ mol } N_2H_4$

Amount (mol) of $N_2 = 3.12 \text{ mol } N_2H_4 \times \dfrac{3 \text{ mol } N_2}{2 \text{ mol } N_2H_4} = 4.68 \text{ mol } N_2$

For N_2O_4: Amount (mol) of $N_2O_4 = 2.00 \times 10^2 \text{ g } N_2O_4 \times \dfrac{1 \text{ mol } N_2O_4}{92.02 \text{ g } N_2O_4} = 2.17 \text{ mol } N_2O_4$

Amount (mol) of $N_2 = 2.17 \text{ mol } N_2O_4 \times \dfrac{3 \text{ mol } N_2}{1 \text{ mol } N_2O_4} = 6.51 \text{ mol } N_2$

Thus, N_2H_4 is the limiting reactant because it yields less N_2.

Converting from amount (mol) of N_2 to mass (g):

$$\text{Mass (g) of } N_2 = 4.68 \text{ mol } N_2 \times \dfrac{28.02 \text{ g } N_2}{1 \text{ mol } N_2} = \boxed{131 \text{ g } N_2}$$

(b) With N_2H_4 as the limiting reactant, the reaction table is

Amount (mol)	$2N_2H_4(g)$ +	$N_2O_4(g)$ $\longrightarrow$	$3N_2(g)$ +	$4H_2O(g)$
Initial	3.12	2.17	0	0
Change	−3.12	−1.56	+4.68	+6.24
Final	0	0.61	4.68	6.24

Check The number of grams of N_2O_4 is more than that of N_2H_4, but there are fewer moles of N_2O_4 because its $\mathcal{M}$ is much higher. Rounding for N_2H_4: 100 g $N_2H_4 \times$ 1 mol/32 g ≈ 3 mol; ~3 mol × $\frac{3}{2}$ ≈ 4.5 mol N_2; ~4.5 mol × 30 g/mol ≈ 135 g N_2.

Comment 1. Recall this *common mistake* in solving limiting-reactant problems: The limiting reactant is not the *reactant* present in fewer moles (or grams). Rather, it is the reactant that forms fewer moles (or grams) of *product*.
2. An *alternative approach* to finding the limiting reactant compares "How much is needed?" with "How much is given?" That is, based on the balanced equation,
• Find the amount (mol) of each reactant needed to react with the other reactant.
• Compare that *needed* amount with the *given* amount in the problem statement. There will be *more* than enough of one reactant (excess) and *less* than enough of the other (limiting).
For example, the balanced equation for this problem shows that 2 mol of N_2H_4 reacts with 1 mol of N_2O_4. The amount (mol) of N_2O_4 needed to react with the given 3.12 mol of N_2H_4 is

$$\text{Amount (mol) of } N_2O_4 \text{ needed} = 3.12 \text{ mol } N_2H_4 \times \dfrac{1 \text{ mol } N_2O_4}{2 \text{ mol } N_2H_4} = 1.56 \text{ mol } N_2O_4$$

The amount of N_2H_4 needed to react with the given 2.17 mol of N_2O_4 is

$$\text{Amount (mol) of } N_2H_4 \text{ needed} = 2.17 \text{ mol } N_2O_4 \times \dfrac{2 \text{ mol } N_2H_4}{1 \text{ mol } N_2O_4} = 4.34 \text{ mol } N_2H_4$$

We are given 2.17 mol of N_2O_4, which is *more* than the 1.56 mol of N_2O_4 needed, and we are given 3.12 mol of N_2H_4, which is *less* than the 4.34 mol of N_2H_4 needed. Therefore, N_2H_4 is limiting, and N_2O_4 is in excess.

Follow-Up Problem 3.20 How many grams of solid aluminum sulfide can be prepared by the reaction of 10.0 g of aluminum and 15.0 g of sulfur? How many grams of the nonlimiting reactant are in excess?

Theoretical, Actual, and Percent Reaction Yields

Up until now, we've assumed that 100% of the limiting reactant becomes product, that ideal methods exist for isolating the product, and that we have perfect lab technique and collect all the product. In theory, this may happen, but in reality, it doesn't, and chemists recognize three types of reaction yield:

1. *Theoretical yield.* The amount of product calculated from the molar ratio in the balanced equation is the **theoretical yield.** But, there are several reasons why the theoretical yield is *never* obtained:
   - Reactant mixtures often proceed through **side reactions** that form different products (Figure 3.11). In the rocket fuel reaction in Sample Problem 3.20, for example, the reactants might form some NO in the following side reaction:
   $$N_2H_4(l) + 2N_2O_4(l) \longrightarrow 6NO(g) + 2H_2O(g)$$
   This reaction decreases the amounts of reactants available for N_2 production.
   - Even more important, many reactions seem to stop before they are complete, so some limiting reactant is unused. (We'll see why in Chapter 4.)
   - Physical losses occur in every step of a separation (see Tools of the Laboratory, Section 2.9): some solid clings to filter paper, some distillate evaporates, and so forth. With careful technique, you can minimize, but never eliminate, such losses.

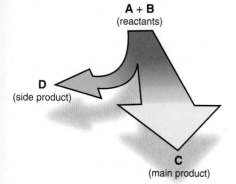

A + B
(reactants)

D
(side product)

C
(main product)

Figure 3.11 The effect of a side reaction on the yield of the main product.

2. *Actual yield.* Given these reasons for obtaining less than the theoretical yield, the amount of product actually obtained is the **actual yield.** Theoretical and actual yields are expressed in units of amount (moles) or mass (grams).

3. *Percent yield.* The **percent yield (% yield)** is the actual yield expressed as a percentage of the theoretical yield:

$$\% \text{ yield} = \frac{\text{actual yield}}{\text{theoretical yield}} \times 100 \qquad (3.8)$$

By definition, the actual yield is less than the theoretical yield, so the percent yield is *always* less than 100%.

Road Map

Mass (kg) of SiO_2

1. convert kg to g
2. divide by $\mathcal{M}$ (g/mol)

Amount (mol) of SiO_2

molar ratio

Amount (mol) of SiC

1. multiply by $\mathcal{M}$ (g/mol)
2. convert g to kg

Mass (kg) of SiC

Eq. 3.8

% Yield of SiC

Sample Problem 3.21   Calculating Percent Yield

Problem Silicon carbide (SiC) is an important ceramic material made by reacting sand (silicon dioxide, SiO_2) with powdered carbon at a high temperature. Carbon monoxide is also formed. When 100.0 kg of sand is processed, 51.4 kg of SiC is recovered. What is the percent yield of SiC from this process?

Plan We are given the actual yield of SiC (51.4 kg), so we need the theoretical yield to calculate the percent yield. After writing the balanced equation, we convert the given mass of SiO_2 (100.0 kg) to amount (mol). We use the molar ratio to find the amount of SiC formed and convert it to mass (kg) to obtain the theoretical yield. Then, we use Equation 3.8 to find the percent yield (see the road map).

Solution Writing the balanced equation:

$$SiO_2(s) + 3C(s) \longrightarrow SiC(s) + 2CO(g)$$

Converting from mass (kg) of SiO_2 to amount (mol):

$$\text{Amount (mol) of } SiO_2 = 100.0 \text{ kg } SiO_2 \times \frac{1000 \text{ g}}{1 \text{ kg}} \times \frac{1 \text{ mol } SiO_2}{60.09 \text{ g } SiO_2} = 1664 \text{ mol } SiO_2$$

Converting from amount (mol) of SiO_2 to amount (mol) of SiC:
The molar ratio is 1 mol SiC/1 mol SiO_2, so

$$\text{Amount (mol) of } SiO_2 = \text{moles of SiC} = 1664 \text{ mol SiC}$$

Converting from amount (mol) of SiC to mass (kg):

$$\text{Mass (kg) of SiC} = 1664 \; \cancel{\text{mol SiC}} \times \frac{40.10 \text{ g SiC}}{1 \; \cancel{\text{mol SiC}}} \times \frac{1 \text{ kg}}{1000 \text{ g}} = 66.73 \text{ kg SiC}$$

Calculating the percent yield:

$$\% \text{ yield of SiC} = \frac{\text{actual yield}}{\text{theoretical yield}} \times 100 = \frac{51.4 \; \cancel{\text{kg SiC}}}{66.73 \; \cancel{\text{kg SiC}}} \times 100 = \boxed{77.0\%}$$

Check Rounding shows that the mass of SiC seems correct: ~1500 mol × 40 g/mol × 1 kg/1000 g = 60 kg. The molar ratio of SiC/SiO_2 is 1/1, and M of SiC is about two-thirds $\left(\sim\frac{40}{60}\right)$ of M of SiO_2, so 100 kg of SiO_2 should form about 66 kg of SiC.

Follow-Up Problem 3.21 Marble (calcium carbonate) reacts with hydrochloric acid solution to form calcium chloride solution, water, and carbon dioxide. Find the percent yield of carbon dioxide if 3.65 g is collected when 10.0 g of marble reacts.

Yields in Multistep Syntheses In the multistep synthesis of a complex compound, the overall yield can be surprisingly low, even if the yield of each step is high. For example, suppose a six-step synthesis has a 90.0% yield for each step. To find the overall percent yield, *express the yield of each step as a decimal, multiply them together, and then convert back to percent.* The overall recovery is only slightly more than 50%:

Overall % yield = (0.900 × 0.900 × 0.900 × 0.900 × 0.900 × 0.900) × 100 = 53.1%

Such multistep sequences are common in laboratory syntheses of medicines, dyes, pesticides, and many other organic compounds. For example, the antidepressant Sertraline is prepared from a simple starting compound in six steps, with yields of 80%, 80%, 50%, 100%, 48%, and 30%, respectively, and an overall percent yield of only 4.6% (Figure 3.12). Because a typical synthesis begins with large amounts of inexpensive, simple reactants and ends with small amounts of expensive, complex products, the overall yield greatly influences the commercial potential of a product.

Atom Economy: A Green Chemistry Perspective on Yield In the relatively new field of **green chemistry**, academic, industrial, and government chemists develop methods that reduce or prevent the release of harmful substances into the environment and the wasting of energy resources.

One way that green chemists evaluate a synthetic route is to focus on its *atom economy*, the proportion of reactant atoms that end up in the desired product. The efficiency of a synthesis is quantified in terms of the *percent atom economy:*

$$\% \text{ atom economy} = \frac{\text{no. of moles} \times \text{molar mass of desired product}}{\text{sum of (no. of moles} \times \text{molar mass) for all products}} \times 100$$

Consider two synthetic routes—one starting with benzene (C_6H_6), the other with butane (C_4H_{10})—for the production of maleic anhydride ($C_4H_2O_3$), a key substance in the manufacture of polymers, dyes, medicines, pesticides, and other products:

Route 1. $2C_6H_6(l) + 9O_2(g) \longrightarrow \cdots \longrightarrow 2C_4H_2O_3(l) + 4H_2O(l) + 4CO_2(g)$

Route 2. $2C_4H_{10}(g) + 7O_2(g) \longrightarrow \cdots \longrightarrow 2C_4H_2O_3(l) + 8H_2O(l)$

Let's compare the efficiency of these routes in terms of percent atom economy:

Route 1.

$$\% \text{ atom economy} = \frac{2 \times M \text{ of } C_4H_2O_3}{(2 \times M \text{ of } C_4H_2O_3) + (4 \times M \text{ of } H_2O) + (4 \times M \text{ of } CO_2)} \times 100$$

$$= \frac{2 \times 98.06 \text{ g}}{(2 \times 98.06 \text{ g}) + (4 \times 18.02 \text{ g}) + (4 \times 44.01 \text{ g})} \times 100$$

$$= 44.15\%$$

Starting with 100 g of 1,2-dichlorobenzene,

↓80%
↓80%
↓50%
↓100%
↓48%
↓30%

Sertraline

the yield of Sertraline is only 4.6 g.

Figure 3.12 Low overall yield for a multistep biomedical synthesis.

Route 2.

$$\% \text{ atom economy} = \frac{2 \times M \text{ of } C_4H_2O_3}{(2 \times M \text{ of } C_4H_2O_3) + (8 \times M \text{ of } H_2O)} \times 100$$

$$= \frac{2 \times 98.06 \text{ g}}{(2 \times 98.06 \text{ g}) + (8 \times 18.02 \text{ g})} \times 100$$

$$= 57.63\%$$

From the perspective of atom economy, route 2 is preferable because a larger percentage of reactant atoms end up in the desired product. It is also a "greener" approach than route 1 because it avoids the use of the toxic reactant benzene and does not produce CO_2, a gas that contributes to global warming.

■ Summary of Section 3.4

- The substances in a balanced equation are related to each other by stoichiometrically equivalent molar ratios, which are used as conversion factors to find the amount (mol) of one substance given the amount of another.
- In limiting-reactant problems, the quantities of two (or more) reactants are given, and the limiting reactant is the one that forms the lower quantity of product. Reaction tables show the initial and final quantities of all reactants and products, as well as the changes in those quantities.
- In practice, side reactions, incomplete reactions, and physical losses result in an actual yield of product that is less than the theoretical yield (the quantity based on the molar ratio from the balanced equation), giving a percent yield less than 100%. In multistep reaction sequences, the overall yield is found by multiplying the yields for each step.
- Atom economy, or the proportion of reactant atoms found in the product, is one criterion for choosing a "greener" reaction process.

3.5 • FUNDAMENTALS OF SOLUTION STOICHIOMETRY

In popular media, you may see a chemist in a lab coat, surrounded by glassware, mixing colored solutions that froth and give off billowing fumes. Most reactions in solution are not this dramatic, and good technique requires safer mixing procedures; however, it is true that aqueous solution chemistry is central to laboratory chemistry. Liquid solutions are easier to store than gases and easier to mix than solids, and the amounts of substances in solution can be measured precisely. Many environmental reactions and almost all biochemical reactions occur in solution.

We know the amounts of pure substances by converting their masses into number of moles. But for dissolved substances, we need the *concentration*—the number of moles per volume of solution—to find the volume that contains a given number of moles. In this section, we first discuss *molarity,* the most common way to express concentration (Chapter 13 covers others). Then, we see how to prepare a solution of a specific molarity and how to use solutions in stoichiometric calculations.

Expressing Concentration in Terms of Molarity

A solution consists of a smaller quantity of one substance, the **solute,** dissolved in a larger quantity of another, the **solvent.** When it dissolves, the solute's chemical entities become evenly dispersed throughout the solvent. The **concentration** of a solution is often expressed as *the quantity of solute dissolved in a given quantity of solution.*

Concentration is an *intensive* property (like density or temperature; Section 1.5) and thus is independent of the solution volume: a 50-L tank of a solution has the *same concentration* (solute quantity/solution quantity) as a 50-mL beaker of the solution. **Molarity (M)** expresses the concentration in units of *moles of solute per liter of solution:*

$$\text{Molarity} = \frac{\text{moles of solute}}{\text{liters of solution}} \quad \text{or} \quad M = \frac{\text{mol solute}}{\text{L soln}} \qquad (3.9)$$

Sample Problem 3.22 — Calculating the Molarity of a Solution

Problem Glycine has the simplest structure of the 20 amino acids that make up proteins. What is the molarity of a solution that contains 0.715 mol of glycine in 495 mL?

Plan The molarity is the number of moles of solute in each liter of solution. We divide the number of moles (0.715 mol) by the volume (495 mL) and convert the volume to liters to find the molarity (see the road map).

Solution $$\text{Molarity} = \frac{0.715 \text{ mol glycine}}{495 \text{ mL soln}} \times \frac{1000 \text{ mL}}{1 \text{ L}} = \boxed{1.44\ M \text{ glycine}}$$

Check A quick look at the math shows about 0.7 mol of glycine in about 0.5 L of solution, so the concentration should be about 1.4 mol/L, or 1.4 M.

Follow-Up Problem 3.22 How many moles of KI are in 84 mL of 0.50 M KI? Include a road map that shows how you planned the solution.

Road Map

> Amount (mol) of glycine
>
> ↓ divide by volume (mL)
>
> Concentration (mol/mL) of glycine
>
> ↓ 10^3 mL = 1 L
>
> Molarity (mol/L) of glycine

Amount-Mass-Number Conversions Involving Solutions

Like many intensive properties, molarity can be used as a *conversion factor* between volume (L) of solution and amount (mol) of solute, from which we can find the mass or the number of entities of solute (Figure 3.13), as applied in Sample Problem 3.23.

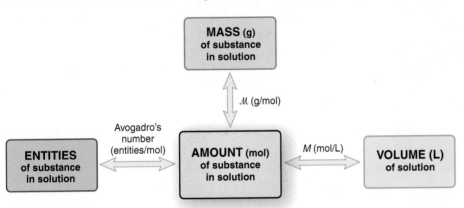

Figure 3.13 Summary of amount-mass-number relationships in solution. The amount (mol) of a substance in solution is related to the volume (L) of solution through the molarity (M; mol/L). As always, convert the given quantity to amount (mol) first.

Sample Problem 3.23 — Calculating Mass of Solute in a Given Volume of Solution

Problem Biochemists often study reactions in solutions containing phosphate ion, commonly found in cells. How many grams of solute are in 1.75 L of 0.460 M sodium hydrogen phosphate?

Plan We need the mass (g) of solute, so we multiply the known solution volume (1.75 L) by the known molarity (0.460 M) to find the amount (mol) of solute and convert it to mass (g) using the solute's molar mass (see the road map).

Solution Calculating amount (mol) of solute in solution:

$$\text{Amount (mol) of Na}_2\text{HPO}_4 = 1.75 \text{ L soln} \times \frac{0.460 \text{ mol Na}_2\text{HPO}_4}{1 \text{ L soln}} = 0.805 \text{ mol Na}_2\text{HPO}_4$$

Converting from amount (mol) of solute to mass (g):

$$\text{Mass (g) Na}_2\text{HPO}_4 = 0.805 \text{ mol Na}_2\text{HPO}_4 \times \frac{141.96 \text{ g Na}_2\text{HPO}_4}{1 \text{ mol Na}_2\text{HPO}_4} = \boxed{114 \text{ g Na}_2\text{HPO}_4}$$

Check The answer seems to be correct: ~1.8 L of 0.5 mol/L solution contains 0.9 mol, and 150 g/mol × 0.9 mol = 135 g, which is close to 114 g of solute.

Follow-Up Problem 3.23 In biochemistry laboratories, solutions of sucrose (table sugar, $C_{12}H_{22}O_{11}$) are used in high-speed centrifuges to separate the parts of a biological cell. How many liters of 3.30 M sucrose contain 135 g of solute? Include a road map that shows how you planned the solution.

Road Map

> Volume (L) of solution
>
> ↓ multiply by M (mol/L)
>
> Amount (mol) of solute
>
> ↓ multiply by $\mathcal{M}$ (g/mol)
>
> Mass (g) of solute

Preparing and Diluting Molar Solutions

Notice that the volume term in the denominator of the molarity expression in Equation 3.9 is the *solution* volume, **not** the *solvent* volume. This means that you *cannot* dissolve 1 mol of solute in 1 L of solvent to make a 1 *M* solution. Because the solute volume adds to the solvent volume, the total volume (solute + solvent) would be *more* than 1 L, so the concentration would be *less* than 1 *M*.

Step 2

Step 3

Step 4

Figure 3.14 Laboratory preparation of molar solutions.

Preparing a Solution Correctly preparing a solution of a solid solute requires four steps. Let's prepare 0.500 L of 0.350 *M* nickel(II) nitrate hexahydrate [Ni(NO$_3$)$_2$·6H$_2$O]:

1. *Weigh the solid.* Calculate the mass of solid needed by converting from volume (L) to amount (mol) and then to mass (g):

$$\text{Mass (g) of solute} = 0.500 \text{ L soln} \times \frac{0.350 \text{ mol Ni(NO}_3)_2\cdot 6\text{H}_2\text{O}}{1 \text{ L soln}}$$
$$\times \frac{290.82 \text{ g Ni(NO}_3)_2\cdot 6\text{H}_2\text{O}}{1 \text{ mol Ni(NO}_3)_2\cdot 6\text{H}_2\text{O}}$$
$$= 50.9 \text{ g Ni(NO}_3)_2\cdot 6\text{H}_2\text{O}$$

2. *Transfer the solid.* We need 0.500 L of solution, so we choose a 500-mL volumetric flask, add enough distilled water to fully dissolve the solute (usually about half the final volume, or 250 mL of distilled water in this case), and transfer the solute. Wash down any solid clinging to the neck with some solvent.

3. *Dissolve the solid.* Swirl the flask until all the solute is dissolved. If necessary, wait until the solution is at room temperature. (As we discuss in Chapter 13, the solution process may be accompanied by heating or cooling.)

4. *Add solvent to the final volume.* Add distilled water to bring the solution volume to the line on the flask neck; cover and mix thoroughly again.

Figure 3.14 shows the last three steps.

Diluting a Solution A concentrated solution (higher molarity) is converted to a dilute solution (lower molarity) by adding solvent, which means the solution volume increases but the amount (mol) of solute stays the same. As a result, the dilute solution contains *fewer solute particles per unit volume* and, thus, has a lower concentration than the concentrated solution (Figure 3.15). If you need several different dilute solutions, prepare a concentrated solution *(stock solution)* and store it and dilute it as needed.

Figure 3.15 Converting a concentrated solution to a dilute solution.

Solvent added to double volume →

Concentrated solution: *More solute particles are present per unit volume.*

Dilute solution: *Fewer solute particles are present per unit volume.*

Sample Problem 3.24 **Preparing a Dilute Solution from a Concentrated Solution**

Problem Isotonic saline is 0.15 M aqueous NaCl. It simulates the total concentration of ions in many cellular fluids, and its uses range from cleaning contact lenses to washing red blood cells. How would you prepare 0.80 L of isotonic saline from a 6.0 M stock solution?

Plan To dilute a concentrated solution, we add only solvent, so the *moles of solute are the same in both solutions*. We know the volume (0.80 L) and molarity (0.15 M) of the dilute (dil) NaCl solution needed, so we find the amount (mol) of NaCl it contains. Then, we find the volume (L) of concentrated (conc; 6.0 M) NaCl solution that contains the same amount (mol). We add solvent *up to* the final volume (see the road map).

Solution Finding amount (mol) of solute in dilute solution:

$$\text{Amount (mol) of NaCl in dil soln} = 0.80 \text{ L soln} \times \frac{0.15 \text{ mol NaCl}}{1 \text{ L soln}}$$

$$= 0.12 \text{ mol NaCl}$$

Finding amount (mol) of solute in concentrated solution:

Because we add only solvent to dilute the solution,

$$\text{Amount (mol) of NaCl in dil soln} = \text{amount (mol) of NaCl in conc soln}$$

$$= 0.12 \text{ mol NaCl}$$

Finding the volume (L) of concentrated solution that contains 0.12 mol of NaCl:

$$\text{Volume (L) of conc NaCl soln} = 0.12 \text{ mol NaCl} \times \frac{1 \text{ L soln}}{6.0 \text{ mol NaCl}}$$

$$= 0.020 \text{ L soln}$$

To prepare 0.80 L of dilute solution, place 0.020 L of 6.0 M NaCl in a 1.0-L graduated cylinder, add distilled water ($\sim$780 mL) to the 0.80-L mark, and stir thoroughly.

Check The answer seems reasonable because a small volume of concentrated solution is used to prepare a large volume of dilute solution. Also, the ratio of volumes (0.020 L/0.80 L) is the same as the ratio of concentrations (0.15 M/6.0 M).

Road Map

Volume (L) of dilute solution

↓ multiply by M (mol/L) of dilute solution

Amount (mol) of NaCl in dilute solution = Amount (mol) of NaCl in concentrated solution

↓ divide by M (mol/L) of concentrated solution

Volume (L) of concentrated solution

Follow-Up Problem 3.24 A chemical engineer dilutes a stock solution of sulfuric acid by adding 25.0 m^3 of 7.50 M acid to enough water to make 500. m^3. What is the concentration of sulfuric acid in the diluted solution in g/mL?

Solving Dilution Problems To solve dilution problems and others involving a change in concentration, apply the following relationship:

$$M_{dil} \times V_{dil} = \text{amount (mol)} = M_{conc} \times V_{conc} \qquad (3.10)$$

where M and V are the molarity and volume of the *dil*ute (subscript "dil") and *conc*entrated (subscript "conc") solutions. Using the values in Sample Problem 3.24, for example, and solving Equation 3.10 for V_{conc} gives

$$V_{conc} = \frac{M_{dil} \times V_{dil}}{M_{conc}} = \frac{0.15 \, M \times 0.80 \text{ L}}{6.0 \, M}$$

$$= 0.020 \text{ L}$$

Notice that Sample Problem 3.24 had the same calculation broken into two parts:

$$V_{conc} = 0.80 \text{ L} \times \frac{0.15 \text{ mol NaCl}}{1 \text{ L}} \times \frac{1 \text{ L}}{6.0 \text{ mol NaCl}}$$

$$= 0.020 \text{ L}$$

In the next sample problem, we use a variation of this relationship, with molecular scenes showing numbers of particles, to visualize changes in concentration.

(a)

(b)

Sample Problem 3.25 **Visualizing Changes in Concentration**

Problem The top circle at left represents a unit volume of a solution. Draw a circle representing a unit volume of the solution after each of these changes:
(a) For every 1 mL of solution, 1 mL of solvent is added.
(b) One-third of the solvent is boiled off.

Plan Given the starting solution, we have to find the number of solute particles in a unit volume after each change. The number of particles per unit volume, N, is directly related to the number of moles per unit volume, M, so we can use a relationship similar to Equation 3.10 to find the number of particles. **(a)** The volume increases, so the final solution is more dilute—fewer particles per unit volume. **(b)** Some solvent is lost, so the final solution is more concentrated—more particles per unit volume.

Solution **(a)** Finding the number of particles in the dilute solution, N_{dil}:

$$N_{dil} \times V_{dil} = N_{conc} \times V_{conc}$$

thus,

$$N_{dil} = N_{conc} \times \frac{V_{conc}}{V_{dil}} = 8 \text{ particles} \times \frac{1 \text{ mL}}{2 \text{ mL}} = 4 \text{ particles}$$

(b) Finding the number of particles in the concentrated solution, N_{conc}:

$$N_{dil} \times V_{dil} = N_{conc} \times V_{conc}$$

thus,

$$N_{conc} = N_{dil} \times \frac{V_{dil}}{V_{conc}} = 8 \text{ particles} \times \frac{1 \text{ mL}}{\frac{2}{3} \text{ mL}} = 12 \text{ particles}$$

Check In (a), the volume is doubled (from 1 mL to 2 mL), so the number of particles should be halved; $\frac{1}{2}$ of 8 is 4. In (b), the volume is $\frac{2}{3}$ of the original, so the number of particles should be $\frac{3}{2}$ of the original; $\frac{3}{2}$ of 8 is 12.

Comment In (b), we assumed that only solvent boils off. This is true with nonvolatile solutes, such as ionic compounds, but in Chapter 13, we'll encounter solutions in which both solvent *and* solute are volatile.

Follow-Up Problem 3.25 The circle labeled A represents a unit volume of a solution. Explain the changes that must be made to A to obtain the unit volumes in B and C.

A   B   C

Stoichiometry of Reactions in Solution

Solving stoichiometry problems for reactions in solution requires the additional step of converting the volume of reactant or product in solution to amount (mol):

1. Balance the equation.
2. Find the amount (mol) of one substance from the volume and molarity.
3. Relate it to the stoichiometrically equivalent amount of another substance.
4. Convert to the desired units.

Sample Problem 3.26 **Calculating Quantities of Reactants and Products for a Reaction in Solution**

Problem Specialized cells in the stomach release HCl to aid digestion. If they release too much, the excess can be neutralized with an antacid. A common antacid contains magnesium hydroxide, which reacts with the acid to form water and magnesium chloride solution. As a government chemist testing commercial antacids, you use 0.10 M HCl to simulate the acid concentration in the stomach. How many liters of "stomach acid" react with a tablet containing 0.10 g of magnesium hydroxide?

Plan We are given the mass (0.10 g) of magnesium hydroxide, $Mg(OH)_2$, that reacts with the acid. We also know the acid concentration (0.10 M) and must find the acid volume. After writing the balanced equation, we convert the mass (g) of $Mg(OH)_2$ to amount (mol) and use the molar ratio to find the amount (mol) of HCl that reacts with it. Then, we use the molarity of HCl to find the volume (L) that contains this amount (see the road map).

Solution Writing the balanced equation:

$$Mg(OH)_2(s) + 2HCl(aq) \longrightarrow MgCl_2(aq) + 2H_2O(l)$$

Converting from mass (g) of $Mg(OH)_2$ to amount (mol):

$$\text{Amount (mol) of } Mg(OH)_2 = 0.10 \text{ g } \cancel{Mg(OH)_2} \times \frac{1 \text{ mol } Mg(OH)_2}{58.33 \text{ g } \cancel{Mg(OH)_2}} = 1.7 \times 10^{-3} \text{ mol } Mg(OH)_2$$

Converting from amount (mol) of $Mg(OH)_2$ to amount (mol) of HCl:

$$\text{Amount (mol) of HCl} = 1.7 \times 10^{-3} \cancel{\text{ mol } Mg(OH)_2} \times \frac{2 \text{ mol HCl}}{1 \cancel{\text{ mol } Mg(OH)_2}} = 3.4 \times 10^{-3} \text{ mol HCl}$$

Converting from amount (mol) of HCl to volume (L):

$$\text{Volume (L) of HCl} = 3.4 \times 10^{-3} \cancel{\text{ mol HCl}} \times \frac{1 \text{ L}}{0.10 \cancel{\text{ mol HCl}}} = \boxed{3.4 \times 10^{-2} \text{ L}}$$

Check The size of the answer seems reasonable: a small volume of dilute acid (0.034 L of 0.10 M) reacts with a small amount of antacid (0.0017 mol).

Comment In Chapter 4, you'll see that this equation is an oversimplification, because HCl and $MgCl_2$ exist in solution as separated ions.

Follow-Up Problem 3.26 Another active ingredient in some antacids is aluminum hydroxide. Which is more effective at neutralizing stomach acid, magnesium hydroxide or aluminum hydroxide? [*Hint:* "Effectiveness" refers to the amount of acid that reacts with a given mass of antacid. You already know the effectiveness of 0.10 g of $Mg(OH)_2$.]

Road Map

Mass (g) of $Mg(OH)_2$
↓ divide by $\mathscr{M}$ (g/mol)
Amount (mol) of $Mg(OH)_2$
↓ molar ratio
Amount (mol) of HCl
↓ divide by M (mol/L)
Volume (L) of HCl

Except for the additional step of finding amounts (mol) in solution, limiting-reactant problems for reactions in solution are handled just like other such problems.

Sample Problem 3.27 | Solving Limiting-Reactant Problems for Reactions in Solution

Problem Mercury and its compounds have uses from fillings for teeth (as a mixture with silver, copper, and tin) to the production of chlorine. Because of their toxicity, however, soluble mercury compounds, such as mercury(II) nitrate, must be removed from industrial wastewater. One removal method reacts the wastewater with sodium sulfide solution to produce solid mercury(II) sulfide and sodium nitrate solution. In a laboratory simulation, 0.050 L of 0.010 M mercury(II) nitrate reacts with 0.020 L of 0.10 M sodium sulfide.
(a) How many grams of mercury(II) sulfide form? **(b)** Write a reaction table for this process.

Plan This is a limiting-reactant problem because *the quantities of two reactants are given*. After balancing the equation, we determine the limiting reactant. From the molarity and volume of each solution, we calculate the amount (mol) of each reactant. Then, we use the molar ratio to find the amount of product (HgS) that each reactant forms. The limiting reactant forms fewer moles of HgS, which we convert to mass (g) of HgS using its molar mass (see the road map). We use the amount of HgS formed from the limiting reactant in the reaction table.

Solution **(a)** Writing the balanced equation:

$$Hg(NO_3)_2(aq) + Na_2S(aq) \longrightarrow HgS(s) + 2NaNO_3(aq)$$

Finding the amount (mol) of HgS formed from $Hg(NO_3)_2$: Combining the steps gives

$$\text{Amount (mol) of HgS} = 0.050 \cancel{\text{ L soln}} \times \frac{0.010 \cancel{\text{ mol } Hg(NO_3)_2}}{1 \cancel{\text{ L soln}}} \times \frac{1 \text{ mol HgS}}{1 \cancel{\text{ mol } Hg(NO_3)_2}}$$

$$= \mathbf{5.0 \times 10^{-4} \text{ mol HgS}}$$

Road Map

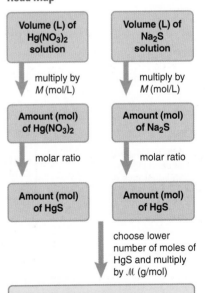

Finding the amount (mol) of HgS from Na_2S: Combining the steps gives

$$\text{Amount (mol) of HgS} = 0.020 \; \cancel{\text{L soln}} \times \frac{0.10 \; \cancel{\text{mol } Na_2S}}{1 \; \cancel{\text{L soln}}} \times \frac{1 \; \text{mol HgS}}{1 \; \cancel{\text{mol } Na_2S}} = 2.0 \times 10^{-3} \; \text{mol HgS}$$

$Hg(NO_3)_2$ is the limiting reactant because it forms fewer moles of HgS.
Converting the amount (mol) of HgS formed from $Hg(NO_3)_2$ to mass (g):

$$\text{Mass (g) of HgS} = 5.0 \times 10^{-4} \; \cancel{\text{mol HgS}} \times \frac{232.7 \; \text{g HgS}}{1 \; \cancel{\text{mol HgS}}} = \boxed{0.12 \; \text{g HgS}}$$

(b) With $Hg(NO_3)_2$ as the limiting reactant, the reaction table is

Amount (mol)	$Hg(NO_3)_2(aq)$	+	$Na_2S(aq)$	$\longrightarrow$	HgS(s)	+	$2NaNO_3(aq)$
Initial	5.0×10^{-4}		2.0×10^{-3}		0		0
Change	-5.0×10^{-4}		-5.0×10^{-4}		$+5.0 \times 10^{-4}$		$+1.0 \times 10^{-3}$
Final	0		1.5×10^{-3}		5.0×10^{-4}		1.0×10^{-3}

A large excess of Na_2S remains after the reaction. Note that the amount of $NaNO_3$ formed is twice the amount of $Hg(NO_3)_2$ consumed, as the balanced equation shows.

Check As a check on our choice of the limiting reactant, let's use the alternative method in Sample Problem 3.20 (see Comment, p. 111).
Finding amount (mol) of reactants given:

$$\text{Amount (mol) of } Hg(NO_3)_2 = 0.050 \; \cancel{\text{L soln}} \times \frac{0.010 \; \text{mol } Hg(NO_3)_2}{1 \; \cancel{\text{L soln}}} = 5.0 \times 10^{-4} \; \text{mol } Hg(NO_3)_2$$

$$\text{Amount (mol) of } Na_2S = 0.020 \; \cancel{\text{L soln}} \times \frac{0.10 \; \text{mol } Na_2S}{1 \; \cancel{\text{L soln}}} = 2.0 \times 10^{-3} \; \text{mol } Na_2S$$

The molar ratio of the reactants is 1 $Hg(NO_3)_2$/1 Na_2S. Therefore, $Hg(NO_3)_2$ is limiting because there is less of it than we would need to react with all of the available Na_2S.

Follow-Up Problem 3.27 Despite the toxicity of lead, many of its compounds are still used to make pigments. **(a)** When 268 mL of 1.50 M lead(II) acetate reacts with 130. mL of 3.40 M sodium chloride, how many grams of solid lead(II) chloride can form? (Sodium acetate solution also forms.) **(b)** Using the abbreviation "Ac" for the acetate ion, write a reaction table for the process.

Figure 3.16 An overview of amount-mass-number stoichiometric relationships.

Figure 3.16 provides a visual review of all the stoichiometric relationships we've discussed in this chapter.

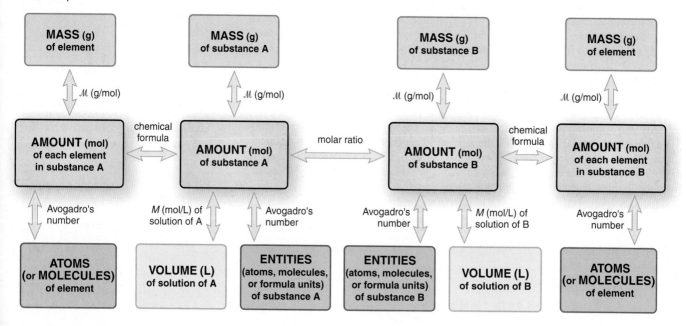

Summary of Section 3.5

- When reactions occur in solution, amounts of reactants and products are given in terms of concentration and volume.
- Molarity is the number of moles of solute dissolved in one liter of solution. A concentrated solution (higher molarity) is converted to a dilute solution (lower molarity) by adding solvent.
- By using molarity as a conversion factor, we can apply the principles of stoichiometry to reactions in solution.

CHAPTER REVIEW GUIDE

Learning Objectives   Relevant section (§) and/or sample problem (SP) numbers appear in parentheses.

Understand These Concepts

1. The definition of the mole unit (§3.1)
2. Relation between the mass of a chemical entity (in amu) and the mass of a mole of the entities (in g) (§3.1)
3. The relations among amount of substance (in mol), mass (in g), and number of chemical entities (§3.1)
4. Mole-mass-number information in a chemical formula (§3.1)
5. The difference between empirical and molecular formulas of a compound (§3.2)
6. How more than one substance can have the same empirical formula and the same molecular formula (isomers) (§3.2)
7. The importance of balancing equations for the quantitative study of chemical reactions (§3.3)
8. Mole-mass-number information in a balanced equation (§3.4)
9. The relation between amounts of reactants and amounts of products (§3.4)
10. Why one reactant limits the amount of product (§3.4)
11. The causes of lower-than-expected yields and the distinction between theoretical and actual yields (§3.4)
12. The meanings of concentration and molarity (§3.5)
13. The effect of dilution on the concentration of solute (§3.5)
14. How reactions in solution differ from reactions of pure reactants (§3.5)

Master These Skills

1. Calculating the molar mass of any substance (§3.1; SPs 3.5, 3.6)
2. Converting between amount of substance (in moles), mass (in grams), and number of chemical entities (SPs 3.1–3.5)
3. Using mass percent to find the mass of an element in a given mass of compound (SPs 3.6, 3.7)
4. Determining empirical and molecular formulas of a compound from mass percents and molar masses of elements (SPs 3.8–3.10)
5. Determining a molecular formula from combustion analysis (SP 3.11)
6. Converting a chemical statement or a molecular depiction into a balanced equation (SPs 3.12, 3.13)
7. Using stoichiometrically equivalent molar ratios to convert between amounts of reactants and products in reactions of pure and dissolved substances (SPs 3.14–3.16, 3.26)
8. Writing an overall equation from a series of equations (SP 3.17)
9. Solving limiting-reactant problems for reactions of pure and dissolved substances (SPs 3.18–3.20, 3.27)
10. Calculating percent yield (SP 3.21)
11. Calculating molarity and mass of solute in solution (SPs 3.22, 3.23)
12. Preparing a dilute solution from a concentrated one (SP 3.24)
13. Using molecular depictions to understand changes in concentration (SP 3.25)

Key Terms   Page numbers appear in parentheses.

stoichiometry (83)

Section 3.1
mole (mol) (83)
Avogadro's number (83)
molar mass ($\mathcal{M}$) (84)

Section 3.2
empirical formula (92)
molecular formula (92)

structural formula (92)
combustion analysis (95)
isomer (97)

Section 3.3
chemical equation (98)
reactant (99)
product (99)
balancing (stoichiometric) coefficient (99)

Section 3.4
overall (net) equation (106)
limiting reactant (107)
theoretical yield (112)
side reaction (112)
actual yield (112)
percent yield (% yield) (112)
green chemistry (113)

Section 3.5
solute (114)
solvent (114)
concentration (114)
molarity (M) (114)

Key Equations and Relationships   Page numbers appear in parentheses.

3.1 Number of entities in one mole (83):

1 mol contains 6.022×10^{23} entities (to 4 sf)

3.2 Converting amount (mol) to mass (g) using $\mathcal{M}$ (85):

$$\text{Mass (g)} = \text{amount (mol)} \times \frac{\text{no. of grams}}{1 \text{ mol}}$$

3.3 Converting mass (g) to amount (mol) using $1/\mathcal{M}$ (85):

$$\text{Amount (mol)} = \text{mass (g)} \times \frac{1 \text{ mol}}{\text{no. of grams}}$$

3.4 Converting amount (mol) to number of entities (85):

$$\text{No. of entities} = \text{amount (mol)} \times \frac{6.022 \times 10^{23} \text{ entities}}{1 \text{ mol}}$$

3.5 Converting number of entities to amount (mol) (85):

$$\text{Amount (mol)} = \text{no. of entities} \times \frac{1 \text{ mol}}{6.022 \times 10^{23} \text{ entities}}$$

3.6 Calculating mass % (90):

Mass % of element X

$$= \frac{\text{moles of X in formula} \times \text{molar mass of X (g/mol)}}{\text{mass (g) of 1 mol of compound}} \times 100$$

3.7 Finding the mass of an element in any mass of compound (91):

Mass of element = mass of compound

$$\times \frac{\text{mass of element in 1 mol of compound}}{\text{mass of 1 mol of compound}}$$

3.8 Calculating percent yield (112):

$$\% \text{ yield} = \frac{\text{actual yield}}{\text{theoretical yield}} \times 100$$

3.9 Defining molarity (114):

$$\text{Molarity} = \frac{\text{moles of solute}}{\text{liters of solution}} \quad \text{or} \quad M = \frac{\text{mol solute}}{\text{L soln}}$$

3.10 Diluting a concentrated solution (117):

$$M_{\text{dil}} \times V_{\text{dil}} = \text{amount (mol)} = M_{\text{conc}} \times V_{\text{conc}}$$

Brief Solutions to Follow-Up Problems

3.1

$$\text{Amount (mol) of C} = 315 \text{ mg C} \times \frac{1 \text{ g}}{10^3 \text{ mg}} \times \frac{1 \text{ mol C}}{12.01 \text{ g C}}$$
$$= 2.62 \times 10^{-2} \text{ mol C}$$

3.2

$$\text{Amount (mol) of N} = 9.72 \times 10^{21} \text{ N}_2 \text{ molecules}$$

$$\times \frac{1 \text{ mol N}_2}{6.022 \times 10^{23} \text{ N}_2 \text{ molecules}} \times \frac{2 \text{ mol N}}{1 \text{ mol N}_2}$$
$$= 3.23 \times 10^{-2} \text{ mol N}$$

3.3

$$\text{Mass (g) of Mn} = 3.22 \times 10^{20} \text{ Mn atoms}$$

$$\times \frac{1 \text{ mol Mn}}{6.022 \times 10^{23} \text{ Mn atoms}} \times \frac{54.94 \text{ g Mn}}{1 \text{ mol Mn}}$$
$$= 2.94 \times 10^{-2} \text{ g Mn}$$

3.4

$$\mathcal{M} = (1 \times \mathcal{M} \text{ of Na}) + (1 \times \mathcal{M} \text{ of F})$$
$$= 22.99 \text{ g/mol} + 19.00 \text{ g/mol} = 41.99 \text{ g/mol}$$

$$\text{Mass (g) of NaF} = 1.19 \times 10^{19} \text{ NaF formula units}$$

$$\times \frac{1 \text{ mol NaF}}{6.022 \times 10^{23} \text{ NaF formula units}}$$

$$\times \frac{41.99 \text{ g NaF}}{1 \text{ mol NaF}} = 8.30 \times 10^{-4} \text{ NaF}$$

3.5 (a) Mass (g) of P_4O_{10}

$$= 4.65 \times 10^{22} \text{ molecules } P_4O_{10}$$

$$\times \frac{1 \text{ mol } P_4O_{10}}{6.022 \times 10^{23} \text{ molecules } P_4O_{10}} \times \frac{283.88 \text{ g } P_4O_{10}}{1 \text{ mol } P_4O_{10}}$$

$$= 21.9 \text{ g } P_4O_{10}$$

(b) No. of P atoms $= 4.65 \times 10^{22} \text{ molecules } P_4O_{10}$

$$\times \frac{4 \text{ atoms P}}{1 \text{ molecule } P_4O_{10}}$$

$$= 1.86 \times 10^{23} \text{ P atoms}$$

3.6 Mass % of N $= \dfrac{2 \text{ mol N} \times \dfrac{14.01 \text{ g N}}{1 \text{ mol N}}}{80.05 \text{ g } NH_4NO_3} \times 100$

$$= 35.00 \text{ mass \% N}$$

3.7 Mass (g) of N $= 35.8 \text{ kg } NH_4NO_3 \times \dfrac{10^3 \text{ g}}{1 \text{ kg}} \times \dfrac{0.3500 \text{ g N}}{1 \text{ g } NH_4NO_3}$

$$= 1.25 \times 10^4 \text{ g N}$$

3.8 Preliminary formula: $B_{0.170}O_{0.255}$

Divide by smaller subscript: $B_{\frac{0.170}{0.170}}O_{\frac{0.255}{0.170}} = B_{1.00}O_{1.50}$

Multiply by 2: $B_{2 \times 1.00}O_{2 \times 1.50} = B_{2.00}O_{3.00} = B_2O_3$

3.9 Amount (mol) of S $= 2.88 \text{ g S} \times \dfrac{1 \text{ mol S}}{32.07 \text{ g S}} = 0.0898 \text{ mol S}$

Amount (mol) of M $= 0.0898 \text{ mol S} \times \dfrac{2 \text{ mol M}}{3 \text{ mol S}} = 0.0599 \text{ mol M}$

Molar mass of M $= \dfrac{3.12 \text{ g M}}{0.0599 \text{ mol M}} = 52.1 \text{ g/mol}$

M is chromium, and M_2S_3 is chromium(III) sulfide.

3.10 Assuming 100.00 g of compound, we have 95.21 g of C and 4.79 g of H:

Amount (mol) of C $= 95.21 \text{ g C} \times \dfrac{1 \text{ mol C}}{12.01 \text{ g C}} = 7.928 \text{ mol C}$

Similarly, there is 4.75 mol H.

Preliminary formula: $C_{7.928}H_{4.75} \approx C_{1.67}H_{1.00}$

Empirical formula: C_5H_3

Whole-number multiple $= \dfrac{252.30 \text{ g/mol}}{63.07 \text{ g/mol}} = 4$

Molecular formula: $C_{20}H_{12}$

3.11 Mass (g) of C $= 0.451 \text{ g } CO_2 \times \dfrac{12.01 \text{ g C}}{44.01 \text{ g } CO_2}$

$$= 0.123 \text{ g C}$$

Similarly, there is 0.00690 g H.

Mass (g) of Cl $= 0.250 \text{ g} - (0.123 \text{ g} + 0.00690 \text{ g}) = 0.120 \text{ g Cl}$

Amount (mol) of elements: 0.0102 mol C; 0.00685 mol H; 0.00339 mol Cl

Empirical formula: C_3H_2Cl

Whole-number multiple $= 2$

Molecular formula: $C_6H_4Cl_2$

3.12 (a) $2Na(s) + 2H_2O(l) \longrightarrow H_2(g) + 2NaOH(aq)$

(b) $2HNO_3(aq) + CaCO_3(s) \longrightarrow$
$$CO_2(g) + H_2O(l) + Ca(NO_3)_2(aq)$$

(c) $PCl_3(g) + 3HF(g) \longrightarrow PF_3(g) + 3HCl(g)$

(d) $4C_3H_5N_3O_9(l) \longrightarrow$
$$12CO_2(g) + 10H_2O(g) + 6N_2(g) + O_2(g)$$

3.13 From the depiction, we have

$$6CO + 3O_2 \longrightarrow 6CO_2$$

Or,

$$2CO(g) + O_2(g) \longrightarrow 2CO_2(g)$$

3.14

Amount (mol) of Fe

↓ molar ratio

Amount (mol) of Fe$_2$O$_3$

$Fe_2O_3(s) + 2Al(s) \longrightarrow Al_2O_3(s) + 2Fe(l)$

Amount (mol) of $Fe_2O_3 = 3.60 \times 10^3 \text{ mol Fe} \times \dfrac{1 \text{ mol } Fe_2O_3}{2 \text{ mol Fe}}$

$$= 1.80 \times 10^3 \text{ mol } Fe_2O_3$$

3.15

No. of formula units of Al$_2$O$_3$

↓ divide by Avogadro's number (formula units/mol)

Amount (mol) of Al$_2$O$_3$

↓ molar ratio

Amount (mol) of Fe

Amount (mol) of Fe $= 1.85 \times 10^{25} \text{ Al}_2\text{O}_3 \text{ f.u.}$

$$\times \frac{1 \text{ mol } Al_2O_3}{6.022 \times 10^{23} \text{ Al}_2\text{O}_3 \text{ f.u.}} \times \frac{2 \text{ mol Fe}}{1 \text{ mol } Al_2O_3}$$

$$= 61.4 \text{ mol Fe}$$

3.16

Mass (g) of Al$_2$O$_3$

↓ divide by $\mathcal{M}$ (g/mol)

Amount (mol) of Al$_2$O$_3$

↓ molar ratio

Amount (mol) of Al

↓ multiply by Avogadro's number (atoms/mol)

No. of Al atoms

No. of Al atoms $= 1.00 \text{ g } Al_2O_3 \times \dfrac{1 \text{ mol } Al_2O_3}{101.96 \text{ g } Al_2O_3}$

$$\times \frac{2 \text{ mol Al}}{1 \text{ mol } Al_2O_3} \times \frac{6.022 \times 10^{23} \text{ Al atoms}}{1 \text{ mol Al}}$$

$$= 1.18 \times 10^{22} \text{ Al atoms}$$

3.17 $\begin{aligned} 2SO_2(g) + O_2(g) &\longrightarrow 2SO_3(g) \\ 2SO_3(g) + 2H_2O(l) &\longrightarrow 2H_2SO_4(aq) \\ \hline 2SO_2(g) + O_2(g) + 2H_2O(l) &\longrightarrow 2H_2SO_4(aq) \end{aligned}$

3.18 $4AB + 2B_2 \longrightarrow 4AB_2$, or $2AB(g) + B_2(g) \longrightarrow 2AB_2(g)$

For AB: Molecules of $AB_2 = 4AB \times \dfrac{2AB_2}{2AB} = 4AB_2$

For B_2: Molecules of $AB_2 = 3B_2 \times \dfrac{2AB_2}{1B_2} = 6AB_2$

Thus, AB_2 is the limiting reactant; one B_2 molecule is in excess.

3.19

Amount (mol) of $AB_2 = 1.5 \text{ mol AB} \times \dfrac{2 \text{ mol } AB_2}{2 \text{ mol AB}} = 1.5 \text{ mol } AB_2$

Amount (mol) of $AB_2 = 1.5 \text{ mol } B_2 \times \dfrac{2 \text{ mol } AB_2}{1 \text{ mol } B_2} = 3.0 \text{ mol } AB_2$

Therefore, 1.5 mol of AB_2 can form.

3.20 $2Al(s) + 3S(s) \longrightarrow Al_2S_3(s)$

Mass (g) of Al_2S_3 formed from 10.0 g of Al

$= 10.0 \text{ g Al} \times \dfrac{1 \text{ mol Al}}{26.98 \text{ g Al}} \times \dfrac{1 \text{ mol } Al_2S_3}{2 \text{ mol Al}} \times \dfrac{150.17 \text{ g } Al_2S_3}{1 \text{ mol } Al_2S_3}$

$= 27.8 \text{ g } Al_2S_3$

Similarly, mass (g) of Al_2S_3 formed from 15.0 g of S = 23.4 g Al_2S_3. Thus, S is the limiting reactant, and 23.4 g of Al_2S_3 forms.

Mass (g) of Al in excess

$=$ total mass of Al $-$ mass of Al used

$= 10.0 \text{ g Al}$

$- \left(15.0 \text{ g S} \times \dfrac{1 \text{ mol S}}{32.07 \text{ g S}} \times \dfrac{2 \text{ mol Al}}{3 \text{ mol S}} \times \dfrac{26.98 \text{ g Al}}{1 \text{ mol Al}}\right)$

$= 1.6 \text{ g Al}$

(We would obtain the same answer if sulfur were shown more correctly as S_8.)

3.21 $CaCO_3(s) + 2HCl(aq) \longrightarrow CaCl_2(aq) + H_2O(l) + CO_2(g)$

Theoretical yield (g) of $CO_2 = 10.0 \text{ g CaCO}_3 \times \dfrac{1 \text{ mol CaCO}_3}{100.09 \text{ g CaCO}_3}$

$\times \dfrac{1 \text{ mol CO}_2}{1 \text{ mol CaCO}_3} \times \dfrac{44.01 \text{ g CO}_2}{1 \text{ mol CO}_2} = 4.40 \text{ g CO}_2$

% yield $= \dfrac{3.65 \text{ g CO}_2}{4.40 \text{ g CO}_2} \times 100 = 83.0\%$

3.22

Amount (mol) of KI $= 84 \text{ mL soln} \times \dfrac{1 \text{ L}}{10^3 \text{ mL}} \times \dfrac{0.50 \text{ mol KI}}{1 \text{ L soln}}$

$= 0.042 \text{ mol KI}$

3.23

Volume (L) of sucrose soln

$= 135 \text{ g sucrose} \times \dfrac{1 \text{ mol sucrose}}{342.30 \text{ g sucrose}} \times \dfrac{1 \text{ L soln}}{3.30 \text{ mol sucrose}}$

$= 0.120 \text{ L soln}$

3.24 M_{dil} of $H_2SO_4 = \dfrac{7.50\ M \times 25.0 \text{ m}^3}{500.\text{ m}^3} = 0.375\ M\ H_2SO_4$

Mass (g) of H_2SO_4/mL soln

$= \dfrac{0.375 \text{ mol H}_2SO_4}{1 \text{ L soln}} \times \dfrac{1 \text{ L}}{10^3 \text{ mL}} \times \dfrac{98.09 \text{ g H}_2SO_4}{1 \text{ mol H}_2SO_4}$

$= 3.68 \times 10^{-2} \text{ g/mL soln}$

3.25 To obtain B, the total volume of sol A was reduced by half:

$V_{conc} = V_{dil} \times \dfrac{N_{dil}}{N_{conc}} = 1.0 \text{ mL} \times \dfrac{6 \text{ particles}}{12 \text{ particles}} = 0.50 \text{ mL}$

To obtain C, $\frac{1}{2}$ of a volume of solvent was added for every volume of A:

$V_{dil} = V_{conc} \times \dfrac{N_{conc}}{N_{dil}} = 1.0 \text{ mL} \times \dfrac{6 \text{ particles}}{4 \text{ particles}} = 1.5 \text{ mL}$

3.26 $Al(OH)_3(s) + 3HCl(aq) \longrightarrow AlCl_3(aq) + 3H_2O(l)$

Volume (L) of HCl neutralized

$= 0.10 \text{ g Al(OH)}_3 \times \dfrac{1 \text{ mol Al(OH)}_3}{78.00 \text{ g Al(OH)}_3}$

$\times \dfrac{3 \text{ mol HCl}}{1 \text{ mol Al(OH)}_3} \times \dfrac{1 \text{ L soln}}{0.10 \text{ mol HCl}}$

$= 3.8 \times 10^{-2} \text{ L soln}$

Therefore, $Al(OH)_3$ is more effective than $Mg(OH)_2$.

3.27 (a) For $Pb(C_2H_3O_2)_2$:

Amount (mol) of $Pb(C_2H_3O_2)_2 = 0.268 \text{ L} \times \dfrac{1.50 \text{ mol Pb(C}_2H_3O_2)_2}{1 \text{ L}}$

$= 0.402 \text{ mol Pb(C}_2H_3O_2)_2$

Amount (mol) of $PbCl_2 = 0.402 \text{ mol Pb(C}_2H_3O_2)_2$

$\times \dfrac{1 \text{ mol PbCl}_2}{1 \text{ mol Pb(C}_2H_3O_2)_2} = 0.402 \text{ mol PbCl}_2$

For NaCl: Amount (mol) of NaCl $= \dfrac{3.40 \text{ mol NaCl}}{1 \text{ L}} \times 0.130 \text{ L}$

$= 0.442 \text{ mol NaCl}$

Amount (mol) of $PbCl_2 = 0.442 \text{ mol NaCl} \times \dfrac{1 \text{ mol PbCl}_2}{2 \text{ mol NaCl}}$

$= 0.221 \text{ mol PbCl}_2$

Thus, NaCl is the limiting reactant.

Mass (g) of $PbCl_2 = 0.22 \text{ mol PbCl}_2 \times \dfrac{278.1 \text{ g PbCl}_2}{1 \text{ mol PbCl}_2}$

$= 61.5 \text{ g PbCl}_2$

(b) Using "Ac" for acetate ion and with NaCl limiting:

Amount (mol)	$Pb(Ac)_2$	+	$2NaCl$	$\longrightarrow$	$PbCl_2$	+	$2NaAc$
Initial	0.402		0.442		0		0
Change	−0.221		−0.442		+0.221		+0.442
Final	0.181		0		0.221		0.442

PROBLEMS

Problems with **colored** numbers are answered in Appendix E and worked in detail in the Student Solutions Manual. Problem sections match those in the text and provide the numbers of relevant sample problems. Most offer Concept Review Questions, Skill-Building Exercises (grouped in pairs covering the same concept), and Problems in Context. The Comprehensive Problems are based on material from any section or previous chapter.

The Mole

(Sample Problems 3.1 to 3.7)

Concept Review Questions

3.1 The atomic mass of Cl is 35.45 amu, and the atomic mass of Al is 26.98 amu. What are the masses in grams of 3 mol of Al atoms and of 2 mol of Cl atoms?

3.2 (a) How many moles of C atoms are in 1 mol of sucrose ($C_{12}H_{22}O_{11}$)?
(b) How many C atoms are in 2 mol of sucrose?

3.3 Why might the expression "1 mol of chlorine" be confusing? What change would remove any uncertainty? For what other elements might a similar confusion exist? Why?

3.4 How is the molecular mass of a compound the same as the molar mass, and how is it different?

3.5 What advantage is there to using a counting unit (the mole) for amount of substance rather than a mass unit?

3.6 You need to calculate the number of P_4 molecules that can form from 2.5 g of $Ca_3(PO_4)_2$. Draw a road map for solving this and write a Plan, without doing any calculations.

3.7 Each of the following balances weighs the indicated numbers of atoms of two elements:

For each balance, which element—left, right, or neither,
(a) Has the higher molar mass?
(b) Has more atoms per gram?
(c) Has fewer atoms per gram?
(d) Has more atoms per mole?

Skill-Building Exercises (grouped in similar pairs)

3.8 Calculate the molar mass of each of the following:
(a) $Sr(OH)_2$ (b) N_2O_3 (c) $NaClO_3$ (d) Cr_2O_3

3.9 Calculate the molar mass of each of the following:
(a) $(NH_4)_3PO_4$ (b) CH_2Cl_2 (c) $CuSO_4 \cdot 5H_2O$ (d) BrF_3

3.10 Calculate the molar mass of each of the following:
(a) SnO   (b) BaF_2 (c) $Al_2(SO_4)_3$ (d) $MnCl_2$

3.11 Calculate the molar mass of each of the following:
(a) N_2O_4 (b) C_4H_9OH (c) $MgSO_4 \cdot 7H_2O$ (d) $Ca(C_2H_3O_2)_2$

3.12 Calculate each of the following quantities:
(a) Mass (g) of 0.68 mol of $KMnO_4$
(b) Amount (mol) of O atoms in 8.18 g of $Ba(NO_3)_2$
(c) Number of O atoms in 7.3×10^{-3} g of $CaSO_4 \cdot 2H_2O$

3.13 Calculate each of the following quantities:
(a) Mass (kg) of 4.6×10^{21} molecules of NO_2
(b) Amount (mol) of Cl atoms in 0.0615 g of $C_2H_4Cl_2$
(c) Number of H^- ions in 5.82 g of SrH_2

3.14 Calculate each of the following quantities:
(a) Mass (g) of 6.44×10^{-2} mol of $MnSO_4$
(b) Amount (mol) of compound in 15.8 kg of $Fe(ClO_4)_3$
(c) Number of N atoms in 92.6 mg of NH_4NO_2

3.15 Calculate each of the following quantities:
(a) Total number of ions in 38.1 g of SrF_2
(b) Mass (kg) of 3.58 mol of $CuCl_2 \cdot 2H_2O$
(c) Mass (mg) of 2.88×10^{22} formula units of $Bi(NO_3)_3 \cdot 5H_2O$

3.16 Calculate each of the following quantities:
(a) Mass (g) of 8.35 mol of copper(I) carbonate
(b) Mass (g) of 4.04×10^{20} molecules of dinitrogen pentaoxide
(c) Amount (mol) and number of formula units in 78.9 g of sodium perchlorate
(d) Number of sodium ions, perchlorate ions, chlorine atoms, and oxygen atoms in the mass of compound in part (c)

3.17 Calculate each of the following quantities:
(a) Mass (g) of 8.42 mol of chromium(III) sulfate decahydrate
(b) Mass (g) of 1.83×10^{24} molecules of dichlorine heptaoxide
(c) Amount (mol) and number of formula units in 6.2 g of lithium sulfate
(d) Number of lithium ions, sulfate ions, sulfur atoms, and oxygen atoms in the mass of compound in part (c)

3.18 Calculate each of the following:
(a) Mass % of H in ammonium bicarbonate
(b) Mass % of O in sodium dihydrogen phosphate heptahydrate

3.19 Calculate each of the following:
(a) Mass % of I in strontium periodate
(b) Mass % of Mn in potassium permanganate

3.20 Calculate each of the following:
(a) Mass fraction of C in cesium acetate
(b) Mass fraction of O in uranyl sulfate trihydrate (the uranyl ion is UO_2^{2+})

3.21 Calculate each of the following:
(a) Mass fraction of Cl in calcium chlorate
(b) Mass fraction of N in dinitrogen trioxide

Problems in Context

3.22 Oxygen is required for the metabolic combustion of foods. Calculate the number of atoms in 38.0 g of oxygen gas, the amount absorbed from the lungs at rest in about 15 min.

3.23 Cisplatin (*right*), or Platinol, is used in the treatment of certain cancers. Calculate (a) the amount (mol) of compound in 285.3 g of cisplatin; (b) the number of hydrogen atoms in 0.98 mol of cisplatin.

3.24 Allyl sulfide (*below*) gives garlic its characteristic odor. Calculate (a) the mass (g) of 2.63 mol of allyl sulfide; (b) the number of carbon atoms in 35.7 g of allyl sulfide.

3.25 Iron reacts slowly with oxygen and water to form a compound commonly called rust ($Fe_2O_3 \cdot 4H_2O$). For 45.2 kg of rust, calculate (a) moles of compound; (b) moles of Fe_2O_3; (c) grams of Fe.

3.26 Propane is widely used in liquid form as a fuel for barbecue grills and camp stoves. For 85.5 g of propane, calculate (a) moles of compound; (b) grams of carbon.

3.27 The effectiveness of a nitrogen fertilizer is determined mainly by its mass % N. Rank the following fertilizers, most effective first: potassium nitrate; ammonium nitrate; ammonium sulfate; urea, $CO(NH_2)_2$.

3.28 The mineral galena is composed of lead(II) sulfide and has an average density of 7.46 g/cm^3. (a) How many moles of lead(II) sulfide are in 1.00 ft^3 of galena? (b) How many lead atoms are in 1.00 dm^3 of galena?

3.29 Hemoglobin, a protein in red blood cells, carries O_2 from the lungs to the body's cells. Iron (as ferrous ion, Fe^{2+}) makes up 0.33 mass % of hemoglobin. If the molar mass of hemoglobin is 6.8×10^4 g/mol, how many Fe^{2+} ions are in one molecule?

Determining the Formula of an Unknown Compound
(Sample Problems 3.8 to 3.11)

Concept Review Questions

3.30 What is the difference between an empirical formula and a molecular formula? Can they ever be the same?

3.31 List three ways compositional data may be given in a problem that involves finding an empirical formula.

3.32 Which of the following sets of information allows you to obtain the molecular formula of a covalent compound? In each case that allows it, explain how you would proceed (draw a road map and write a Plan for a solution).
(a) Number of moles of each type of atom in a given sample of the compound
(b) Mass % of each element and the total number of atoms in a molecule of the compound
(c) Mass % of each element and the number of atoms of one element in a molecule of the compound
(d) Empirical formula and mass % of each element
(e) Structural formula

3.33 Is $MgCl_2$ an empirical or a molecular formula for magnesium chloride? Explain.

Skill-Building Exercises (grouped in similar pairs)

3.34 What is the empirical formula and empirical formula mass for each of the following compounds?
(a) C_2H_4 (b) $C_2H_6O_2$ (c) N_2O_5 (d) $Ba_3(PO_4)_2$ (e) Te_4I_{16}

3.35 What is the empirical formula and empirical formula mass for each of the following compounds?
(a) C_4H_8 (b) $C_3H_6O_3$ (c) P_4O_{10} (d) $Ga_2(SO_4)_3$ (e) Al_2Br_6

3.36 Give the name, empirical formula, and molar mass of the compound depicted in Figure P3.36.

3.37 Give the name, empirical formula, and molar mass of the compound depicted in Figure P3.37.

Figure P3.36   Figure P3.37

3.38 What is the molecular formula of each compound?
(a) Empirical formula CH_2 ($\mathcal{M}$ = 42.08 g/mol)
(b) Empirical formula NH_2 ($\mathcal{M}$ = 32.05 g/mol)
(c) Empirical formula NO_2 ($\mathcal{M}$ = 92.02 g/mol)
(d) Empirical formula CHN ($\mathcal{M}$ = 135.14 g/mol)

3.39 What is the molecular formula of each compound?
(a) Empirical formula CH ($\mathcal{M}$ = 78.11 g/mol)
(b) Empirical formula $C_3H_6O_2$ ($\mathcal{M}$ = 74.08 g/mol)
(c) Empirical formula HgCl ($\mathcal{M}$ = 472.1 g/mol)
(d) Empirical formula $C_7H_4O_2$ ($\mathcal{M}$ = 240.20 g/mol)

3.40 Find the empirical formula of the following compounds:
(a) 0.063 mol of chlorine atoms combined with 0.22 mol of oxygen atoms
(b) 2.45 g of silicon combined with 12.4 g of chlorine
(c) 27.3 mass % carbon and 72.7 mass % oxygen

3.41 Find the empirical formula of the following compounds:
(a) 0.039 mol of iron atoms combined with 0.052 mol of oxygen atoms
(b) 0.903 g of phosphorus combined with 6.99 g of bromine
(c) A hydrocarbon with 79.9 mass % carbon

3.42 An oxide of nitrogen contains 30.45 mass % N. (a) What is the empirical formula of the oxide? (b) If the molar mass is 90±5 g/mol, what is the molecular formula?

3.43 A chloride of silicon contains 79.1 mass % Cl. (a) What is the empirical formula of the chloride? (b) If the molar mass is 269 g/mol, what is the molecular formula?

3.44 A sample of 0.600 mol of a metal M reacts completely with excess fluorine to form 46.8 g of MF_2.
(a) How many moles of F are in the sample of MF_2 that forms?
(b) How many grams of M are in this sample of MF_2?
(c) What element is represented by the symbol M?

3.45 A 0.370-mol sample of a metal oxide (M_2O_3) weighs 55.4 g.
(a) How many moles of O are in the sample?
(b) How many grams of M are in the sample?
(c) What element is represented by the symbol M?

Problems in Context

3.46 Nicotine is a poisonous, addictive compound found in tobacco. A sample of nicotine contains 6.16 mmol of C, 8.56 mmol of H, and 1.23 mmol of N [1 mmol (1 millimole) = 10^{-3} mol]. What is the empirical formula of nicotine?

3.47 Cortisol ($\mathcal{M}$ = 362.47 g/mol) is a steroid hormone involved in protein synthesis. Medically, it has a major use in reducing inflammation from rheumatoid arthritis. Cortisol is 69.6% C, 8.34% H, and 22.1% O by mass. What is its molecular formula?

3.48 Acetaminophen (*below*) is a popular nonaspirin pain reliever. What is the mass % of each element in acetaminophen?

3.49 Menthol ($\mathcal{M}$ = 156.3 g/mol), the strong-smelling substance in many cough drops, is a compound of carbon, hydrogen, and oxygen. When 0.1595 g of menthol was burned in a combustion apparatus, 0.449 g of CO_2 and 0.184 g of H_2O formed. What is menthol's molecular formula?

Writing and Balancing Chemical Equations
(Sample Problems 3.12 and 3.13)

Concept Review Questions

3.50 What three types of information does a balanced chemical equation provide? How?

3.51 How does a balanced chemical equation apply the law of conservation of mass?

3.52 In the process of balancing the equation
$$Al + Cl_2 \longrightarrow AlCl_3$$
Student I writes: $Al + Cl_2 \longrightarrow AlCl_2$
Student II writes: $Al + Cl_2 + Cl \longrightarrow AlCl_3$
Student III writes: $2Al + 3Cl_2 \longrightarrow 2AlCl_3$
Is the approach of Student I valid? Student II? Student III? Explain.

3.53 The scenes below represent a chemical reaction between elements A (red) and B (green):

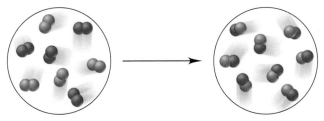

Which best represents the balanced equation for the reaction?
(a) $2A + 2B \longrightarrow A_2 + B_2$ (b) $A_2 + B_2 \longrightarrow 2AB$
(c) $B_2 + 2AB \longrightarrow 2B_2 + A_2$ (d) $4A_2 + 4B_2 \longrightarrow 8AB$

Skill-Building Exercises (grouped in similar pairs)

3.54 Write balanced equations for each of the following by inserting the correct coefficients in the blanks:
(a) __Cu(s) + __S_8(s) $\longrightarrow$ __Cu_2S(s)
(b) __P_4O_{10}(s) + __H_2O(l) $\longrightarrow$ __H_3PO_4(l)
(c) __B_2O_3(s) + __NaOH(aq) $\longrightarrow$ __Na_3BO_3(aq) + __H_2O(l)

(d) __CH_3NH_2(g) + __O_2(g) $\longrightarrow$
$\qquad$ __CO_2(g) + __H_2O(g) + __N_2(g)

3.55 Write balanced equations for each of the following by inserting the correct coefficients in the blanks:
(a) __$Cu(NO_3)_2$(aq) + __KOH(aq) $\longrightarrow$
$\qquad$ __$Cu(OH)_2$(s) + __KNO_3(aq)
(b) __BCl_3(g) + __H_2O(l) $\longrightarrow$ __H_3BO_3(s) + __HCl(g)
(c) __$CaSiO_3$(s) + __HF(g) $\longrightarrow$
$\qquad$ __SiF_4(g) + __CaF_2(s) + __H_2O(l)
(d) __$(CN)_2$(g) + __H_2O(l) $\longrightarrow$ __$H_2C_2O_4$(aq) + __NH_3(g)

3.56 Write balanced equations for each of the following by inserting the correct coefficients in the blanks:
(a) __SO_2(g) + __O_2(g) $\longrightarrow$ __SO_3(g)
(b) __Sc_2O_3(s) + __H_2O(l) $\longrightarrow$ __$Sc(OH)_3$(s)
(c) __H_3PO_4(aq) + __NaOH(aq) $\longrightarrow$
$\qquad$ __Na_2HPO_4(aq) + __H_2O(l)
(d) __$C_6H_{10}O_5$(s) + __O_2(g) $\longrightarrow$ __CO_2(g) + __H_2O(g)

3.57 Write balanced equations for each of the following by inserting the correct coefficients in the blanks:
(a) __As_4S_6(s) + __O_2(g) $\longrightarrow$ __As_4O_6(s) + __SO_2(g)
(b) __$Ca_3(PO_4)_2$(s) + __SiO_2(s) + __C(s) $\longrightarrow$
$\qquad$ __P_4(g) + __$CaSiO_3$(l) + __CO(g)
(c) __Fe(s) + __H_2O(g) $\longrightarrow$ __Fe_3O_4(s) + __H_2(g)
(d) __S_2Cl_2(l) + __NH_3(g) $\longrightarrow$
$\qquad$ __S_4N_4(s) + __S_8(s) + __NH_4Cl(s)

3.58 Convert the following into balanced equations:
(a) When gallium metal is heated in oxygen gas, it melts and forms solid gallium(III) oxide.
(b) Liquid hexane burns in oxygen gas to form carbon dioxide gas and water vapor.
(c) When solutions of calcium chloride and sodium phosphate are mixed, solid calcium phosphate forms and sodium chloride remains in solution.

3.59 Convert the following into balanced equations:
(a) When lead(II) nitrate solution is added to potassium iodide solution, solid lead(II) iodide forms and potassium nitrate solution remains.
(b) Liquid disilicon hexachloride reacts with water to form solid silicon dioxide, hydrogen chloride gas, and hydrogen gas.
(c) When nitrogen dioxide is bubbled into water, a solution of nitric acid forms and gaseous nitrogen monoxide is released.

Problem in Context

3.60 Loss of atmospheric ozone has led to an ozone "hole" over Antarctica. The loss occurs in part through three consecutive steps:
(1) Chlorine atoms react with ozone (O_3) to form chlorine monoxide and molecular oxygen.
(2) Chlorine monoxide forms ClOOCl.
(3) ClOOCl absorbs sunlight and breaks into chlorine atoms and molecular oxygen.
(a) Write a balanced equation for each step.
(b) Write an overall balanced equation for the sequence.

Calculating Quantities of Reactant and Product
(Sample Problems 3.14 to 3.21)

Concept Review Questions

3.61 What does the term *stoichiometrically equivalent molar ratio* mean, and how is it applied in solving problems?

3.62 The circle below represents a mixture of A_2 and B_2 before they react to form AB_3.

(a) What is the limiting reactant?
(b) How many molecules of product can form?

3.63 Percent yields are generally calculated from masses. Would the result be the same if amounts (mol) were used instead? Why?

Skill-Building Exercises (grouped in similar pairs)

3.64 Reactants A and B form product C. Draw a road map and write a Plan to find the mass (g) of C when 25 g of A reacts with excess B.

3.65 Reactants D and E form product F. Draw a road map and write a Plan to find the mass (g) of F when 27 g of D reacts with 31 g of E.

3.66 Chlorine gas can be made in the laboratory by the reaction of hydrochloric acid and manganese(IV) oxide:
$$4HCl(aq) + MnO_2(s) \longrightarrow MnCl_2(aq) + 2H_2O(g) + Cl_2(g)$$
When 1.82 mol of HCl reacts with excess MnO_2, how many (a) moles of Cl_2 and (b) grams of Cl_2 form?

3.67 Bismuth oxide reacts with carbon to form bismuth metal:
$$Bi_2O_3(s) + 3C(s) \longrightarrow 2Bi(s) + 3CO(g)$$
When 283 g of Bi_2O_3 reacts with excess carbon, how many (a) moles of Bi_2O_3 react and (b) moles of Bi form?

3.68 Potassium nitrate decomposes on heating, producing potassium oxide and gaseous nitrogen and oxygen:
$$4KNO_3(s) \longrightarrow 2K_2O(s) + 2N_2(g) + 5O_2(g)$$
To produce 56.6 kg of oxygen, how many (a) moles of KNO_3 and (b) grams of KNO_3 must be heated?

3.69 Chromium(III) oxide reacts with hydrogen sulfide (H_2S) gas to form chromium(III) sulfide and water:
$$Cr_2O_3(s) + 3H_2S(g) \longrightarrow Cr_2S_3(s) + 3H_2O(l)$$
To produce 421 g of Cr_2S_3, how many (a) moles of Cr_2O_3 and (b) grams of Cr_2O_3 are required?

3.70 Calculate the mass (g) of each product formed when 43.82 g of diborane (B_2H_6) reacts with excess water:
$$B_2H_6(g) + H_2O(l) \longrightarrow H_3BO_3(s) + H_2(g) \text{ [unbalanced]}$$

3.71 Calculate the mass (g) of each product formed when 174 g of silver sulfide reacts with excess hydrochloric acid:
$$Ag_2S(s) + HCl(aq) \longrightarrow AgCl(s) + H_2S(g) \text{ [unbalanced]}$$

3.72 Elemental phosphorus occurs as tetratomic molecules, P_4. What mass (g) of chlorine gas is needed to react completely with 455 g of phosphorus to form phosphorus pentachloride?

3.73 Elemental sulfur occurs as octatomic molecules, S_8. What mass (g) of fluorine gas is needed to react completely with 17.8 g of sulfur to form sulfur hexafluoride?

3.74 Solid iodine trichloride is prepared in two steps: first, a reaction between solid iodine and gaseous chlorine to form solid iodine monochloride; then, treatment with more chlorine.

(a) Write a balanced equation for each step.
(b) Write a balanced equation for the overall reaction.
(c) How many grams of iodine are needed to prepare 2.45 kg of final product?

3.75 Lead can be prepared from galena [lead(II) sulfide] by first roasting the galena in oxygen gas to form lead(II) oxide and sulfur dioxide. Heating the metal oxide with more galena forms the molten metal and more sulfur dioxide.
(a) Write a balanced equation for each step.
(b) Write an overall balanced equation for the process.
(c) How many metric tons of sulfur dioxide form for every metric ton of lead obtained?

3.76 Many metals react with oxygen gas to form the metal oxide. For example, calcium reacts as follows:
$$2Ca(s) + O_2(g) \longrightarrow 2CaO(s)$$
You wish to calculate the mass (g) of calcium oxide that can be prepared from 4.20 g of Ca and 2.80 g of O_2.
(a) What amount (mol) of CaO can be produced from the given mass of Ca?
(b) What amount (mol) of CaO can be produced from the given mass of O_2?
(c) Which is the limiting reactant?
(d) How many grams of CaO can be produced?

3.77 Metal hydrides react with water to form hydrogen gas and the metal hydroxide. For example,
$$SrH_2(s) + 2H_2O(l) \longrightarrow Sr(OH)_2(s) + 2H_2(g)$$
You wish to calculate the mass (g) of hydrogen gas that can be prepared from 5.70 g of SrH_2 and 4.75 g of H_2O.
(a) What amount (mol) of H_2 can be produced from the given mass of SrH_2?
(b) What amount (mol) of H_2 can be produced from the given mass of H_2O?
(c) Which is the limiting reactant?
(d) How many grams of H_2 can be produced?

3.78 Calculate the maximum numbers of moles and grams of iodic acid (HIO_3) that can form when 635 g of iodine trichloride reacts with 118.5 g of water:
$$ICl_3 + H_2O \longrightarrow ICl + HIO_3 + HCl \text{ [unbalanced]}$$
How many grams of the excess reactant remains?

3.79 Calculate the maximum numbers of moles and grams of H_2S that can form when 158 g of aluminum sulfide reacts with 131 g of water:
$$Al_2S_3 + H_2O \longrightarrow Al(OH)_3 + H_2S \text{ [unbalanced]}$$
How many grams of the excess reactant remain?

3.80 When 0.100 mol of carbon is burned in a closed vessel with 8.00 g of oxygen, how many grams of carbon dioxide can form? Which reactant is in excess, and how many grams of it remain after the reaction?

3.81 A mixture of 0.0375 g of hydrogen and 0.0185 mol of oxygen in a closed container is sparked to initiate a reaction. How many grams of water can form? Which reactant is in excess, and how many grams of it remain after the reaction?

3.82 Aluminum nitrite and ammonium chloride react to form aluminum chloride, nitrogen, and water. How many grams of each substance are present after 72.5 g of aluminum nitrite and 58.6 g of ammonium chloride react completely?

3.83 Calcium nitrate and ammonium fluoride react to form calcium fluoride, dinitrogen monoxide, and water vapor. How many grams of each substance are present after 16.8 g of calcium nitrate and 17.50 g of ammonium fluoride react completely?

3.84 Two successive reactions, A ⟶ B and B ⟶ C, have yields of 73% and 68%, respectively. What is the overall percent yield for conversion of A to C?

3.85 Two successive reactions, D ⟶ E and E ⟶ F, have yields of 48% and 73%, respectively. What is the overall percent yield for conversion of D to F?

3.86 What is the percent yield of a reaction in which 45.5 g of tungsten(VI) oxide (WO_3) reacts with excess hydrogen gas to produce metallic tungsten and 9.60 mL of water ($d = 1.00$ g/mL)?

3.87 What is the percent yield of a reaction in which 200. g of phosphorus trichloride reacts with excess water to form 128 g of HCl and aqueous phosphorous acid (H_3PO_3)?

3.88 When 20.5 g of methane and 45.0 g of chlorine gas undergo a reaction that has a 75.0% yield, what mass (g) of chloromethane (CH_3Cl) forms? Hydrogen chloride also forms.

3.89 When 56.6 g of calcium and 30.5 g of nitrogen gas undergo a reaction that has a 93.0% yield, what mass (g) of calcium nitride forms?

Problems in Context

3.90 Cyanogen, $(CN)_2$, has been observed in the atmosphere of Titan, Saturn's largest moon, and in the gases of interstellar nebulas. On Earth, it is used as a welding gas and a fumigant. In its reaction with fluorine gas, carbon tetrafluoride and nitrogen trifluoride gases are produced. What mass (g) of carbon tetrafluoride forms when 60.0 g of each reactant is used?

3.91 Gaseous dichlorine monoxide decomposes readily to chlorine and oxygen gases. (a) Which of the following circles best depicts the product mixture after the decomposition?

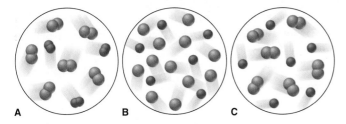

A   B   C

(b) Write the balanced equation for the decomposition.
(c) If each oxygen atom represents 0.050 mol, how many molecules of dichlorine monoxide were present before the decomposition?

3.92 An intermediate step in the production of nitric acid involves the reaction of ammonia with oxygen gas to form nitrogen monoxide and water. How many grams of nitrogen monoxide can form in the reaction of 485 g of ammonia with 792 g of oxygen?

3.93 Butane gas is compressed and used as a liquid fuel in disposable cigarette lighters and lightweight camping stoves. Suppose a lighter contains 5.50 mL of butane ($d = 0.579$ g/mL).
(a) How many grams of oxygen are needed to burn the butane completely?
(b) How many moles of H_2O form when all the butane burns?
(c) How many total molecules of gas form when the butane burns completely?

3.94 Sodium borohydride ($NaBH_4$) is used industrially in many organic syntheses. One way to prepare it is by reacting sodium hydride with gaseous diborane (B_2H_6). Assuming an 88.5% yield,

how many grams of $NaBH_4$ can be prepared by reacting 7.98 g of sodium hydride and 8.16 g of diborane?

Fundamentals of Solution Stoichiometry
(Sample Problems 3.22 to 3.27)

Concept Review Questions

3.95 Box A represents a unit volume of a solution. Choose from boxes B and C the one representing the same unit volume of solution that has (a) more solute added; (b) more solvent added; (c) higher molarity; (d) lower concentration.

A   B   C

3.96 A mathematical equation useful for dilution calculations is $M_{dil} \times V_{dil} = M_{conc} \times V_{conc}$. (a) What does each symbol mean, and why does the equation work? (b) Given the volume and molarity of a $CaCl_2$ solution, how do you determine the amount (mol) and the mass (g) of solute?

3.97 Six different aqueous solutions (with solvent molecules omitted for clarity) are represented in the beakers below, and their total volumes are noted.

(a) Which solution has the highest molarity? (b) Which solutions have the same molarity? (c) If you mix solutions A and C, does the resulting solution have a higher, a lower, or the same molarity as solution B? (d) After 50. mL of water is added to solution D, is its molarity higher, lower, or the same as the molarity of solution F after 75 mL is added to it? (e) How much solvent must be evaporated from solution E for it to have the same molarity as solution A?

3.98 Are the following instructions for diluting a 10.0 M solution to a 1.00 M solution correct: "Take 100.0 mL of the 10.0 M solution and add 900.0 mL water"? Explain.

Skill-Building Exercises (grouped in similar pairs)

3.99 Calculate each of the following quantities:
(a) Mass (g) of solute in 185.8 mL of 0.267 M calcium acetate
(b) Molarity of 500. mL of solution containing 21.1 g of potassium iodide
(c) Amount (mol) of solute in 145.6 L of 0.850 M sodium cyanide

3.100 Calculate each of the following quantities:
(a) Volume (mL) of 2.26 M potassium hydroxide that contains 8.42 g of solute
(b) Number of Cu^{2+} ions in 52 L of 2.3 M copper(II) chloride
(c) Molarity of 275 mL of solution containing 135 mmol of glucose

3.101 Calculate each of the following quantities:
(a) Mass (g) of solute needed to make 475 mL of 5.62×10^{-2} M potassium sulfate
(b) Molarity of a solution that contains 7.25 mg of calcium chloride in each milliliter
(c) Number of Mg^{2+} ions in each milliliter of 0.184 M magnesium bromide

3.102 Calculate each of the following quantities:
(a) Molarity of the solution resulting from dissolving 46.0 g of silver nitrate in enough water to give a final volume of 335 mL
(b) Volume (L) of 0.385 M manganese(II) sulfate that contains 63.0 g of solute
(c) Volume (mL) of 6.44×10^{-2} M adenosine triphosphate (ATP) that contains 1.68 mmol of ATP

3.103 Calculate each of the following quantities:
(a) Molarity of a solution prepared by diluting 37.00 mL of 0.250 M potassium chloride to 150.00 mL
(b) Molarity of a solution prepared by diluting 25.71 mL of 0.0706 M ammonium sulfate to 500.00 mL
(c) Molarity of sodium ion in a solution made by mixing 3.58 mL of 0.348 M sodium chloride with 500. mL of 6.81×10^{-2} M sodium sulfate (assume volumes are additive)

3.104 Calculate each of the following quantities:
(a) Volume (L) of 2.050 M copper(II) nitrate that must be diluted with water to prepare 750.0 mL of a 0.8543 M solution
(b) Volume (L) of 1.63 M calcium chloride that must be diluted with water to prepare 350. mL of a 2.86×10^{-2} M chloride ion solution
(c) Final volume (L) of a 0.0700 M solution prepared by diluting 18.0 mL of 0.155 M lithium carbonate with water

3.105 A sample of concentrated nitric acid has a density of 1.41 g/mL and contains 70.0% HNO_3 by mass.
(a) What mass (g) of HNO_3 is present per liter of solution?
(b) What is the molarity of the solution?

3.106 Concentrated sulfuric acid (18.3 M) has a density of 1.84 g/mL.
(a) How many moles of H_2SO_4 are in each milliliter of solution?
(b) What is the mass % of H_2SO_4 in the solution?

3.107 How many milliliters of 0.383 M HCl are needed to react with 16.2 g of $CaCO_3$?
$$2HCl(aq) + CaCO_3(s) \longrightarrow CaCl_2(aq) + CO_2(g) + H_2O(l)$$

3.108 How many grams of NaH_2PO_4 are needed to react with 43.74 mL of 0.285 M NaOH?
$$NaH_2PO_4(s) + 2NaOH(aq) \longrightarrow Na_3PO_4(aq) + 2H_2O(l)$$

3.109 How many grams of solid barium sulfate form when 35.0 mL of 0.160 M barium chloride reacts with 58.0 mL of 0.065 M sodium sulfate? Aqueous sodium chloride forms also.

3.110 How many moles of excess reactant are present when 350. mL of 0.210 M sulfuric acid reacts with 0.500 L of 0.196 M sodium hydroxide to form water and aqueous sodium sulfate?

Problems in Context

3.111 Ordinary household bleach is an aqueous solution of sodium hypochlorite. What is the molarity of a bleach solution that contains 20.5 g of sodium hypochlorite in 375 mL?

3.112 Muriatic acid, an industrial grade of concentrated HCl, is used to clean masonry and cement. Its concentration is 11.7 M.

(a) Write instructions for diluting the concentrated acid to make 3.0 gallons of 3.5 M acid for routine use (1 gal = 4 qt; 1 qt = 0.946 L). (b) How many milliliters of the muriatic acid solution contain 9.66 g of HCl?

3.113 A sample of impure magnesium was analyzed by allowing it to react with excess HCl solution:
$$Mg(s) + 2HCl(aq) \longrightarrow MgCl_2(aq) + H_2(g)$$
After 1.32 g of the impure metal was treated with 0.100 L of 0.750 M HCl, 0.0125 mol of HCl remained. Assuming the impurities do not react, what is the mass % of Mg in the sample?

Comprehensive Problems

3.114 The mole is defined in terms of the carbon-12 atom. Use the definition to find (a) the mass in grams equal to 1 atomic mass unit; (b) the ratio of the gram to the atomic mass unit.

3.115 The first sulfur-nitrogen compound was prepared in 1835 and has been used to synthesize many others. In the early 1980s, researchers made another such compound that conducts electricity like a metal. Mass spectrometry of the compound shows a molar mass of 184.27 g/mol, and analysis shows it to contain 2.288 g of S for every 1.000 g of N. What is its molecular formula?

3.116 Hydroxyapatite, $Ca_5(PO_4)_3(OH)$, is the main mineral component of dental enamel, dentin, and bone. Coating the compound on metallic implants (such as titanium alloys and stainless steels) helps the body accept the implant. When placed in bone voids, the powder encourages natural bone to grow into the void. Hydroxyapatite is prepared by adding aqueous phosphoric acid to a dilute slurry of calcium hydroxide. (a) Write a balanced equation for this preparation. (b) What mass (g) of hydroxyapatite could form from 100. g of 85% phosphoric acid and 100. g of calcium hydroxide?

3.117 Narceine is a narcotic in opium that crystallizes from solution as a hydrate that contains 10.8 mass % water and has a molar mass of 499.52 g/mol. Determine x in narceine·xH_2O.

3.118 Hydrogen-containing fuels have a "fuel value" based on their mass % H. Rank the following compounds from highest fuel value to lowest: ethane, propane, benzene, ethanol, cetyl palmitate (whale oil, $C_{32}H_{64}O_2$).

ethane   propane   benzene

ethanol

3.119 Serotonin ($\mathcal{M}$ = 176 g/mol) transmits nerve impulses between neurons. It contains 68.2% C, 6.86% H, 15.9% N, and 9.08% O by mass. What is its molecular formula?

3.120 In 1961, scientists agreed that the atomic mass unit (amu) would be defined as $\frac{1}{12}$ the mass of an atom of ^{12}C. Before then, it was defined as $\frac{1}{16}$ the *average* mass of an atom of naturally occurring oxygen (a mixture of ^{16}O, ^{17}O, and ^{18}O). The current atomic mass of oxygen is 15.9994 amu. (a) Did Avogadro's number change after the definition of an amu changed and, if so, in what direction? (b) Did the definition of the mole change? (c) Did the mass of a mole of a substance change? (d) Before 1961, was Avogadro's number 6.02×10^{23} (to three significant figures), as it is today?

3.121 Convert the following descriptions into balanced equations:
(a) In a gaseous reaction, hydrogen sulfide burns in oxygen to form sulfur dioxide and water vapor.
(b) When crystalline potassium chlorate is heated to just above its melting point, it reacts to form two different crystalline compounds, potassium chloride and potassium perchlorate.
(c) When hydrogen gas is passed over powdered iron(III) oxide, iron metal and water vapor form.
(d) The combustion of gaseous ethane in air forms carbon dioxide and water vapor.
(e) Iron(II) chloride is converted to iron(III) fluoride by treatment with chlorine trifluoride gas. Chlorine gas is also formed.

3.122 Isobutylene is a hydrocarbon used in the manufacture of synthetic rubber. When 0.847 g of isobutylene was subjected to combustion analysis, the gain in mass of the CO_2 absorber was 2.657 g and that of the H_2O absorber was 1.089 g. What is the empirical formula of isobutylene?

3.123 The multistep smelting of ferric oxide to form elemental iron occurs at high temperatures in a blast furnace. In the first step, ferric oxide reacts with carbon monoxide to form Fe_3O_4. This substance reacts with more carbon monoxide to form iron(II) oxide, which reacts with still more carbon monoxide to form molten iron. Carbon dioxide is also produced in each step. (a) Write an overall balanced equation for the iron-smelting process. (b) How many grams of carbon monoxide are required to form 45.0 metric tons of iron from ferric oxide?

3.124 One of the compounds used to increase the octane rating of gasoline is toluene (*right*). Suppose 20.0 mL of toluene ($d = 0.867$ g/mL) is consumed when a sample of gasoline burns in air.
(a) How many grams of oxygen are needed for complete combustion of the toluene? (b) How many total moles of gaseous products form? (c) How many molecules of water vapor form?

3.125 During studies of the reaction in Sample Problem 3.20,
$$2N_2H_4(l) + N_2O_4(l) \longrightarrow 3N_2(g) + 4H_2O(g)$$
a chemical engineer measured a less-than-expected yield of N_2 and discovered that the following side reaction occurs:
$$N_2H_4(l) + 2N_2O_4(l) \longrightarrow 6NO(g) + 2H_2O(g)$$
In one experiment, 10.0 g of NO formed when 100.0 g of each reactant was used. What is the highest percent yield of N_2 that can be expected?

3.126 A 0.652-g sample of a pure strontium halide reacts with excess sulfuric acid. The solid strontium sulfate formed is separated, dried, and found to weigh 0.755 g. What is the formula of the original halide?

3.127 The following circles represent a chemical reaction between AB_2 and B_2:

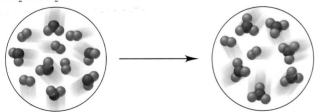

(a) Write a balanced equation for the reaction. (b) What is the limiting reactant? (c) How many moles of product can be made

from 3.0 mol of B_2 and 5.0 mol of AB_2? (d) How many moles of excess reactant remain after the reaction in part (c)?

3.128 Calculate each of the following quantities:
(a) Volume (L) of 18.0 M sulfuric acid that must be added to water to prepare 2.00 L of a 0.429 M solution
(b) Molarity of the solution obtained by diluting 80.6 mL of 0.225 M ammonium chloride to 0.250 L
(c) Volume (L) of water added to 0.130 L of 0.0372 M sodium hydroxide to obtain a 0.0100 M solution (assume the volumes are additive at these low concentrations)
(d) Mass (g) of calcium nitrate in each milliliter of a solution prepared by diluting 64.0 mL of 0.745 M calcium nitrate to a final volume of 0.100 L

3.129 Which of the following models represent compounds having the same empirical formula? What is the molecular mass of this common empirical formula?

3.130 The zirconium oxalate $K_2Zr(C_2O_4)_3(H_2C_2O_4)\cdot H_2O$ was synthesized by mixing 1.68 g of $ZrOCl_2\cdot 8H_2O$ with 5.20 g of $H_2C_2O_4\cdot 2H_2O$ and an excess of aqueous KOH. After 2 months, 1.25 g of crystalline product was obtained, along with aqueous KCl and water. Calculate the percent yield.

3.131 Seawater is approximately 4.0% by mass dissolved ions, 85% of which are from NaCl. (a) Find the mass % of NaCl in seawater. (b) Find the mass % of Na^+ ions and of Cl^- ions in seawater. (c) Find the molarity of NaCl in seawater at 15°C (d of seawater at 15°C = 1.025 g/mL).

3.132 Is each of the following statements true or false? Correct any that are false.
(a) A mole of one substance has the same number of atoms as a mole of any other substance.
(b) The theoretical yield for a reaction is based on the balanced chemical equation.
(c) A limiting-reactant problem is being stated when the available quantity of one of the reactants is given in moles.
(d) To prepare 1.00 L of 3.00 M NaCl, weigh 175.5 g of NaCl and dissolve it in 1.00 L of distilled water.
(e) The concentration of a solution is an intensive property, but the amount of solute in a solution is an extensive property.

3.133 Box A represents one unit volume of solution A. Which box—B, C, or D—represents one unit volume after adding enough solvent to solution A to (a) triple its volume; (b) double its volume; (c) quadruple its volume?

3.134 In each pair, choose the larger of the indicated quantities or state that the samples are equal:
(a) Entities: 0.4 mol of O_3 molecules or 0.4 mol of O atoms
(b) Grams: 0.4 mol of O_3 molecules or 0.4 mol of O atoms

(c) Moles: 4.0 g of N_2O_4 or 3.3 g of SO_2
(d) Grams: 0.6 mol of C_2H_4 or 0.6 mol of F_2
(e) Total ions: 2.3 mol of sodium chlorate or 2.2 mol of magnesium chloride
(f) Molecules: 1.0 g of H_2O or 1.0 g of H_2O_2
(g) Na^+ ions: 0.500 L of 0.500 M NaBr or 0.0146 kg of NaCl
(h) Grams: 6.02×10^{23} atoms of ^{235}U or 6.02×10^{23} atoms of ^{238}U

3.135 For the reaction between solid tetraphosphorus trisulfide and oxygen gas to form solid tetraphosphorus decaoxide and sulfur dioxide gas, write a balanced equation. Show the equation (see Table 3.4) in terms of (a) molecules, (b) moles, and (c) grams.

3.136 Hydrogen gas is considered a clean fuel because it produces only water vapor when it burns. If the reaction has a 98.8% yield, what mass (g) of hydrogen forms 105 kg of water?

3.137 Solar winds composed of free protons, electrons, and α particles bombard Earth constantly, knocking gas molecules out of the atmosphere. In this way, Earth loses about 3.0 kg of matter per second. It is estimated that the atmosphere will be gone in about 50 billion years. Use this estimate to calculate (a) the mass (kg) of Earth's atmosphere and (b) the amount (mol) of nitrogen, which makes up 75.5 mass % of the atmosphere.

3.138 Calculate each of the following quantities:
(a) Amount (mol) of 0.588 g of ammonium bromide
(b) Number of potassium ions in 88.5 g of potassium nitrate
(c) Mass (g) of 5.85 mol of glycerol ($C_3H_8O_3$)
(d) Volume (L) of 2.85 mol of chloroform ($CHCl_3$; $d = 1.48$ g/mL)
(e) Number of sodium ions in 2.11 mol of sodium carbonate
(f) Number of atoms in 25.0 µg of cadmium
(g) Number of atoms in 0.0015 mol of fluorine gas

3.139 Elements X (green) and Y (purple) react according to the following equation: $X_2 + 3Y_2 \longrightarrow 2XY_3$. Which molecular scene represents the product of the reaction?

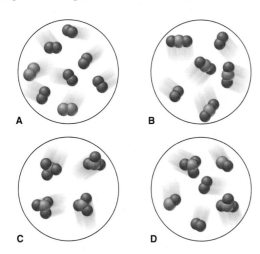

3.140 Hydrocarbon mixtures are used as fuels. (a) How many grams of $CO_2(g)$ are produced by the combustion of 200. g of a mixture that is 25.0% CH_4 and 75.0% C_3H_8 by mass? (b) A 252-g gaseous mixture of CH_4 and C_3H_8 burns in excess O_2, and 748 g of CO_2 gas is collected. What is the mass % of CH_4 in the mixture?

3.141 To 1.35 L of 0.325 M HCl, you add 3.57 L of a second HCl solution of unknown concentration. The resulting solution is 0.893 M HCl. Assuming the volumes are additive, calculate the molarity of the second HCl solution.

3.142 Nitrogen (N), phosphorus (P), and potassium (K) are the main nutrients in plant fertilizers. By industry convention, the numbers on a label refer to the mass percents of N, P_2O_5, and K_2O, in that order.

Calculate the N/P/K ratio of a 30/10/10 fertilizer in terms of moles of each element, and express it as $x/y/1.0$.

3.143 What mass percents of ammonium sulfate, ammonium hydrogen phosphate, and potassium chloride would you use to prepare 10/10/10 plant fertilizer (see Problem 3.142)?

3.144 Ferrocene, synthesized in 1951, was the first organic iron compound with Fe—C bonds. An understanding of the structure of ferrocene gave rise to new ideas about chemical bonding and led to the preparation of many useful compounds. In the combustion analysis of ferrocene, which contains only Fe, C, and H, a 0.9437-g sample produced 2.233 g of CO_2 and 0.457 g of H_2O. What is the empirical formula of ferrocene?

3.145 When carbon-containing compounds are burned in a limited amount of air, some $CO(g)$ as well as $CO_2(g)$ is produced. A gaseous product mixture is 35.0 mass % CO and 65.0 mass % CO_2. What is the mass % of C in the mixture?

3.146 Write a balanced equation for the reaction depicted below:

If each reactant molecule represents 1.25×10^{-2} mol and the reaction yield is 87%, how many grams of Si-containing product form?

3.147 Citric acid (*right*) is concentrated in citrus fruits and plays a central metabolic role in nearly every animal and plant cell. (a) What are the molar mass and formula of citric acid? (b) How many moles of citric acid are in 1.50 qt of lemon juice ($d = 1.09$ g/mL) that is 6.82% citric acid by mass?

3.148 Various nitrogen oxides, as well as sulfur oxides, contribute to acidic rainfall through complex reaction sequences. Nitrogen and oxygen combine during high-temperature combustion of fuels in air to form nitrogen monoxide gas, which reacts with more oxygen to form nitrogen dioxide gas. In contact with water vapor, nitrogen dioxide forms aqueous nitric acid and more nitrogen monoxide. (a) Write balanced equations for these reactions. (b) Use the equations to write one overall balanced equation that does *not* include nitrogen monoxide and nitrogen dioxide. (c) How many metric tons (t) of nitric acid form when 1350 t of atmospheric nitrogen is consumed (1 t = 1000 kg)?

3.149 Nitrogen monoxide reacts with elemental oxygen to form nitrogen dioxide. The scene at right represents an initial mixture of reactants. If the reaction has a 66% yield, which of the scenes below (A, B, or C) best represents the final product mixture?

3.150 Fluorine is so reactive that it forms compounds with several of the noble gases.
(a) When 0.327 g of platinum is heated in fluorine, 0.519 g of a dark red, volatile solid forms. What is its empirical formula?
(b) When 0.265 g of this red solid reacts with excess xenon gas, 0.378 g of an orange-yellow solid forms. What is the empirical formula of this compound, the first to contain a noble gas?
(c) Fluorides of xenon can be formed by direct reaction of the elements at high pressure and temperature. Under conditions that produce only the tetra- and hexafluorides, 1.85×10^{-4} mol of xenon reacted with 5.00×10^{-4} mol of fluorine, and 9.00×10^{-6} mol of xenon was found in excess. What are the mass percents of each xenon fluoride in the product mixture?

3.151 Hemoglobin is 6.0% heme ($C_{34}H_{32}FeN_4O_4$) by mass. To remove the heme, hemoglobin is treated with acetic acid and NaCl, which forms hemin ($C_{34}H_{32}N_4O_4FeCl$). A blood sample from a crime scene contains 0.65 g of hemoglobin. (a) How many grams of heme are in the sample? (b) How many moles of heme? (c) How many grams of Fe? (d) How many grams of hemin could be formed for a forensic chemist to measure?

3.152 Manganese is a key component of extremely hard steel. The element occurs naturally in many oxides. A 542.3-g sample of a manganese oxide has an Mn/O ratio of 1.00/1.42 and consists of braunite (Mn_2O_3) and manganosite (MnO). (a) How many grams of braunite and of manganosite are in the ore? (b) What is the Mn^{3+}/Mn^{2+} ratio in the ore?

3.153 The human body excretes nitrogen in the form of urea, NH_2CONH_2. The key step in its biochemical formation is the reaction of water with arginine to produce urea and ornithine:

| Arginine | Water | Urea | Ornithine |

(a) What is the mass % of nitrogen in urea, in arginine, and in ornithine? (b) How many grams of nitrogen can be excreted as urea when 135.2 g of ornithine is produced?

3.154 Aspirin (acetylsalicylic acid, $C_9H_8O_4$) is made by reacting salicylic acid ($C_7H_6O_3$) with acetic anhydride [$(CH_3CO)_2O$]:

$$C_7H_6O_3(s) + (CH_3CO)_2O(l) \longrightarrow C_9H_8O_4(s) + CH_3COOH(l)$$

In one preparation, 3.077 g of salicylic acid and 5.50 mL of acetic anhydride react to form 3.281 g of aspirin. (a) Which is the limiting reactant (d of acetic anhydride = 1.080 g/mL)? (b) What is the percent yield of this reaction? (c) What is the percent atom economy of this reaction?

3.155 The rocket fuel hydrazine (N_2H_4) is made by the three-step Raschig process, which has the following overall equation:

$$NaOCl(aq) + 2NH_3(aq) \longrightarrow N_2H_4(aq) + NaCl(aq) + H_2O(l)$$

What is the percent atom economy of this process?

3.156 Lead(II) chromate ($PbCrO_4$) is used as the yellow pigment for marking traffic lanes but is banned from house paint because of the risk of lead poisoning. It is produced from chromite ($FeCr_2O_4$), an ore of chromium:

$$4FeCr_2O_4(s) + 8K_2CO_3(aq) + 7O_2(g) \longrightarrow$$
$$2Fe_2O_3(s) + 8K_2CrO_4(aq) + 8CO_2(g)$$

Lead(II) ion then replaces the K^+ ion. If a yellow paint is to have 0.511% $PbCrO_4$ by mass, how many grams of chromite are needed per kilogram of paint?

3.157 Ethanol (CH_3CH_2OH), the intoxicant in alcoholic beverages, is also used to make other organic compounds. In concentrated sulfuric acid, ethanol forms diethyl ether and water:

$$2CH_3CH_2OH(l) \longrightarrow CH_3CH_2OCH_2CH_3(l) + H_2O(g)$$

In a side reaction, some ethanol forms ethylene and water:

$$CH_3CH_2OH(l) \longrightarrow CH_2CH_2(g) + H_2O(g)$$

(a) If 50.0 g of ethanol yields 35.9 g of diethyl ether, what is the percent yield of diethyl ether? (b) If 45.0% of the ethanol that did not produce the ether reacts by the side reaction, what mass (g) of ethylene is produced?

3.158 When powdered zinc is heated with sulfur, a violent reaction occurs, and zinc sulfide forms:

$$Zn(s) + S_8(s) \longrightarrow ZnS(s) \text{ [unbalanced]}$$

Some of the reactants also combine with oxygen in air to form zinc oxide and sulfur dioxide. When 83.2 g of Zn reacts with 52.4 g of S_8, 104.4 g of ZnS forms.
(a) What is the percent yield of ZnS?
(b) If all the remaining reactants combine with oxygen, how many grams of each of the two oxides form?

3.159 Cocaine ($C_{17}H_{21}O_4N$) is a natural substance found in coca leaves, which have been used for centuries as a local anesthetic and stimulant. Illegal cocaine arrives in the United States either as the pure compound or as the hydrochloride salt ($C_{17}H_{21}O_4NHCl$). At 25°C, the salt is very soluble in water (2.50 kg/L), but cocaine is much less so (1.70 g/L).
(a) What is the maximum mass (g) of the salt that can dissolve in 50.0 mL of water?
(b) If this solution is treated with NaOH, the salt is converted to cocaine. How much more water (L) is needed to dissolve it?

3.160 High-temperature superconducting oxides hold great promise in the utility, transportation, and computer industries.
(a) One superconductor is $La_{2-x}Sr_xCuO_4$. Calculate the molar masses of this oxide when $x = 0$, $x = 1$, and $x = 0.163$.
(b) Another common superconducting oxide is made by heating a mixture of barium carbonate, copper(II) oxide, and yttrium(III) oxide, followed by further heating in O_2:

$$4BaCO_3(s) + 6CuO(s) + Y_2O_3(s) \longrightarrow$$
$$2YBa_2Cu_3O_{6.5}(s) + 4CO_2(g)2YBa_2Cu_3O_{6.5}(s) + \tfrac{1}{2}O_2(g) \longrightarrow$$
$$2YBa_2Cu_3O_7(s)$$

When equal masses of the three reactants are heated, which reactant is limiting?
(c) After the product in part (b) is removed, what is the mass % of each reactant in the remaining solid mixture?

Three Major Classes of Chemical Reactions

Concepts and skills to review before you study this chapter

- names and formulas of compounds (Section 2.8)
- nature of ionic and covalent bonding (Section 2.7)
- amount-mass-number conversions (Section 3.1)
- molarity and amount-mass-number conversions in solution (Section 3.5)
- balancing chemical equations (Section 3.3)
- calculating quantities of reactants and products (Section 3.4)

Rapid chemical changes occur among gas molecules as sunlight bathes the atmosphere or lightning rips through a stormy sky and strikes the sea. Aqueous reactions occur unceasingly in the gigantic containers we know as oceans. And, in every cell of your body, thousands of reactions taking place right now enable you to function. Indeed, the amazing variety in nature is largely a consequence of the amazing variety of chemical reactions. With millions of reactions occurring in and around you, it would be impossible to describe them all. Fortunately, it isn't necessary because, when we survey even a small percentage of reactions, especially those in aqueous solution, a few major classes emerge.

IN THIS CHAPTER . . . We examine the underlying nature of three classes of reactions and the complex part that water plays in aqueous chemistry.
- We visualize the molecular structure of water to learn its role as solvent, how it interacts with ionic and covalent compounds, and the nature of electrolytes.
- We write ionic equations that represent the species in solution and the actual change that occurs when ionic compounds dissolve and react in water.
- We describe precipitation reactions and learn how to predict when they will occur.
- We see how acids and bases act as electrolytes and how they neutralize each other. We view acid-base reactions as proton-transfer processes and discuss how to quantify these reactions through titration.
- We examine oxidation-reduction (redox) reactions in the formation of ionic and covalent substances. We learn how to determine oxidation numbers and use them to balance redox equations and how to quantify these reactions through titration. We describe several important types of redox reactions, one of which is used to predict the relative reactivity of metals.
- An introduction to the reversible nature of all chemical change and the nature of equilibrium previews coverage of this central topic in later chapters.

4.1 • THE ROLE OF WATER AS A SOLVENT

For any reaction in solution, the solvent plays a key role that depends on its chemical nature. Some solvents passively disperse the substances into individual molecules. But water is much more active, interacting strongly with the substances and even reacting with them in some cases. Let's focus on how the water molecule interacts with both ionic and covalent solutes.

The Polar Nature of Water

On the atomic scale, water's great solvent power arises from the *uneven distribution of electron charge* and its *bent molecular shape,* which create a *polar molecule:*

1. *Uneven charge distribution.* Recall from Section 2.7 that the electrons in a covalent bond are shared between the atoms. In a bond between identical atoms—as in H_2, Cl_2, O_2—the sharing is equal and electron charge is distributed evenly between the two nuclei (symmetrical shading in the space-filling model of Figure 4.1A on the next page). In covalent bonds between different atoms, the sharing is uneven because one atom attracts the electron pair more strongly than the other atom does.

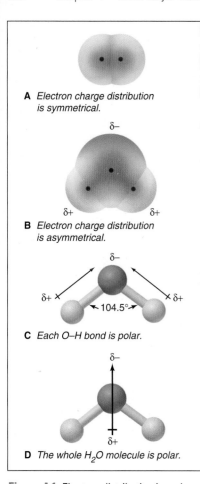

A *Electron charge distribution is symmetrical.*

B *Electron charge distribution is asymmetrical.*

104.5°

C *Each O–H bond is polar.*

D *The whole H_2O molecule is polar.*

Figure 4.1 Electron distribution in molecules of H_2 and H_2O.

For example, in each O—H bond of water, the shared electrons are closer to the O atom because an O atom attracts electrons more strongly than an H atom does. (We'll discuss the reasons in Chapter 9.) This uneven charge distribution creates a *polar bond,* one with partially charged "poles." In Figure 4.1B, the asymmetrical shading shows this distribution, and the δ symbol indicates a partial charge. The O end is partially negative, represented by red shading and δ−, and the H end is partially positive, represented by blue shading and δ+. In the ball-and-stick model of Figure 4.1C, the *polar arrow* points to the negative pole, and the tail, shaped like a plus sign, marks the positive pole.

2. *Bent molecular shape.* The sequence of the H—O—H atoms in water is not linear: the water molecule is bent with a bond angle of 104.5° (Figure 4.1C).

3. *Molecular polarity.* The combination of polar bonds and bent shape makes water a **polar molecule:** the region near the O atom is partially negative, and the region between the H atoms is partially positive (Figure 4.1D).

Ionic Compounds in Water

In this subsection, we consider two closely related aspects of aqueous solutions of ionic compounds—how they occur and how they behave. We also use a compound's formula to calculate the amount (mol) of each ion in solution.

How Ionic Compounds Dissolve: Replacement of Charge Attractions In an ionic solid, oppositely charged ions are held together by electrostatic attractions (see Figure 1.3C and Section 2.7). Water separates the ions by *replacing these attractions with stronger ones between several water molecules and each ion.* Picture a granule of a soluble ionic compound in water: the negative ends of some water molecules are attracted to the cations, and the positive ends of other water molecules are attracted to the anions (Figure 4.2). Dissolution occurs because the *attractions between each type of ion and several water molecules outweigh the attractions between the ions.* Gradually, all the ions separate (dissociate), become **solvated**—surrounded closely by solvent molecules—and then move randomly in the solution.

For an ionic compound that doesn't dissolve in water, the attraction between ions is greater than the attraction between the ions and water. Actually, these so-called insoluble substances *do* dissolve to a very small extent, usually several orders of magnitude less than so-called soluble substances. For example, NaCl (a "soluble" compound) is over 4×10^4 times more soluble than AgCl (an "insoluble" compound):

Solubility of NaCl in H_2O at 20°C = 365 g/L
Solubility of AgCl in H_2O at 20°C = 0.009 g/L

Figure 4.2 An ionic compound dissolving in water. The inset shows the polar arrow and partial charges (not shown in the rest of the scene) of each water molecule.

A *Distilled water does not conduct a current.*

B *Positive and negative ions fixed in a solid do not conduct a current.*

C *In solution, positive and negative ions move and conduct a current.*

To (+) electrode

To (−) electrode

Figure 4.3 The electrical conductivity of ionic solutions.

In Chapter 13, you'll see that dissolving involves more than a contest between the relative attractions of ions for each other or for water. It also occurs because it frees ions from the solid to disperse randomly through the solution.

How Ionic Solutions Behave: Electrolytes and Electrical Conductivity When an ionic compound dissolves, the solution's *electrical conductivity,* the flow of electric current, increases dramatically. When electrodes are immersed in distilled water (Figure 4.3A) or pushed into an ionic solid (Figure 4.3B), no current flows, as shown by the unlit bulb. But in an aqueous solution of the compound, a large current flows, as shown by the lit bulb (Figure 4.3C). Current flow implies the *movement of charged particles:* when the ionic compound dissolves, the separate solvated ions move toward the electrode of opposite charge. A substance that conducts a current when dissolved in water is an **electrolyte.** Soluble ionic compounds are *strong* electrolytes because they dissociate completely and conduct a large current.

Calculating the Amount (mol) of Ions in Solution *The formula of the soluble ionic compound tells the number of moles of the component ions in solution.* For example, the equation for dissolving KBr in water to form solvated ions is

$$KBr(s) \xrightarrow{H_2O} K^+(aq) + Br^-(aq)$$

("H$_2$O" above the arrow means that water is the solvent, not a reactant.) Note that 1 mol of KBr dissociates into 2 mol of ions—1 mol of K$^+$ and 1 mol of Br$^-$. Sample Problems 4.1 and 4.2 apply these ideas, first with molecular scenes and then in calculations.

Sample Problem 4.1 **Using Molecular Scenes to Depict an Ionic Compound in Aqueous Solution**

Problem The beakers contain aqueous solutions of the strong electrolyte potassium sulfate.
(a) Which beaker best represents the compound in solution (water molecules are not shown)?
(b) If each particle represents 0.1 mol, what is the total number of particles in solution?

A   B   C   D

Plan (a) We determine the formula and write an equation for 1 mol of compound dissociating into ions. Potassium sulfate is a strong electrolyte, so it dissociates completely, but, in general, *polyatomic ions remain intact in solution*. (b) We count the number of separate particles, and then multiply by 0.1 mol and by Avogadro's number.

Solution (a) The formula is K_2SO_4, so the equation is

$$K_2SO_4(s) \xrightarrow{H_2O} 2K^+(aq) + SO_4^{2-}(aq)$$

There are two separate 1+ particles for every 2− particle, so beaker C is best.
(b) There are 9 particles, so the total amount (mol) of particles is 0.9 mol, and we have

$$\text{No. of particles} = 0.9 \text{ mol} \times \frac{6.022 \times 10^{23} \text{ particles}}{1 \text{ mol}} = 5.420 \times 10^{23} \text{ particles}$$

Check Rounding to check the math in (b) gives $0.9 \times 6 = 5.4$, so the answer seems correct. The number of particles is an exact number since we actually counted them; thus, the answer can have as many significant figures as in Avogadro's number.

Follow-Up Problem 4.1 (a) Which strong electrolyte is dissolved in water (water molecules not shown) in the beaker at left: LiBr, Cs_2CO_3, or $BaCl_2$?
(b) If each particle represents 0.05 mol, what mass (g) of compound was dissolved?

Sample Problem 4.2 **Determining Amount (mol) of Ions in Solution**

Problem What amount (mol) of each ion is in each solution?
(a) 5.0 mol of ammonium sulfate dissolved in water
(b) 78.5 g of cesium bromide dissolved in water
(c) 7.42×10^{22} formula units of copper(II) nitrate dissolved in water
(d) 35 mL of 0.84 M zinc chloride

Plan We write an equation that shows 1 mol of compound dissociating into ions.
(a) We multiply the number of moles of ions by 5.0. (b) We first convert grams to moles. (c) We first convert formula units to moles. (d) We first convert molarity and volume to moles.

Solution (a) $(NH_4)_2SO_4(s) \xrightarrow{H_2O} 2NH_4^+(aq) + SO_4^{2-}(aq)$

Calculating amount (mol) of NH_4^+ ions:

$$\text{Amount (mol) of } NH_4^+ = 5.0 \text{ mol } (NH_4)_2SO_4 \times \frac{2 \text{ mol } NH_4^+}{1 \text{ mol } (NH_4)_2SO_4} = 10. \text{ mol } NH_4^+$$

The formula shows 1 mol of SO_4^{2-} per mole of $(NH_4)_2SO_4$, so 5.0 mol of SO_4^{2-} is also present.

(b) $CsBr(s) \xrightarrow{H_2O} Cs^+(aq) + Br^-(aq)$

Converting from mass (g) to amount (mol):

$$\text{Amount (mol) of CsBr} = 78.5 \text{ g CsBr} \times \frac{1 \text{ mol CsBr}}{212.8 \text{ g CsBr}} = 0.369 \text{ mol CsBr}$$

Thus, $\boxed{0.369 \text{ mol of } Cs^+ \text{ and } 0.369 \text{ mol of } Br^-}$ are present.

(c) $Cu(NO_3)_2(s) \xrightarrow{H_2O} Cu^{2+}(aq) + 2NO_3^-(aq)$

Converting from formula units to amount (mol):

$$\text{Amount (mol) of } Cu(NO_3)_2 = 7.42 \times 10^{22} \text{ formula units } Cu(NO_3)_2$$
$$\times \frac{1 \text{ mol } Cu(NO_3)_2}{6.022 \times 10^{23} \text{ formula units } Cu(NO_3)_2}$$
$$= 0.123 \text{ mol } Cu(NO_3)_2$$

$$\text{Amount (mol) of } NO_3^- = 0.123 \text{ mol } Cu(NO_3)_2 \times \frac{2 \text{ mol } NO_3^-}{1 \text{ mol } Cu(NO_3)_2} = \boxed{0.246 \text{ mol } NO_3^-}$$

$\boxed{0.123 \text{ mol of } Cu^{2+}}$ is also present.

(d) $ZnCl_2(aq) \longrightarrow Zn^{2+}(aq) + 2Cl^-(aq)$

Converting from volume (mL) and molarity (mol/L) to amount (mol):

$$\text{Amount (mol) of } ZnCl_2 = 35 \text{ mL} \times \frac{1 \text{ L}}{10^3 \text{ mL}} \times \frac{0.84 \text{ mol } ZnCl_2}{1 \text{ L}} = 2.9 \times 10^{-2} \text{ mol } ZnCl_2$$

$$\text{Amount (mol) of } Cl^- = 2.9 \times 10^{-2} \text{ mol } ZnCl_2 \times \frac{2 \text{ mol } Cl^-}{1 \text{ mol } ZnCl_2} = \boxed{5.8 \times 10^{-2} \text{ mol } Cl^-}$$

$\boxed{2.9 \times 10^{-2} \text{ mol of } Zn^{2+}}$ is also present.

Check Round off to check the math and see if the relative numbers of moles of ions are consistent with the formula. For instance, in (a), 10 mol NH_4^+/5.0 mol SO_4^{2-} = 2 NH_4^+/1 SO_4^{2-}, or $(NH_4)_2SO_4$. In (d), 0.029 mol Zn^{2+}/0.058 mol Cl^- = 1 Zn^{2+}/2 Cl^-, or $ZnCl_2$.

Follow-Up Problem 4.2 What amount (mol) of each ion is in each solution?
(a) 2 mol of potassium perchlorate dissolved in water
(b) 354 g of magnesium acetate dissolved in water
(c) 1.88×10^{24} formula units of ammonium chromate dissolved in water
(d) 1.32 L of 0.55 M sodium bisulfate

Covalent Compounds in Water

Water dissolves many covalent (molecular) compounds also. Table sugar (sucrose, $C_{12}H_{22}O_{11}$), beverage (grain) alcohol (ethanol, CH_3CH_2OH), and automobile antifreeze (ethylene glycol, $HOCH_2CH_2OH$) are some familiar examples. All contain their own polar bonds, which interact with the bonds of water. However, most soluble covalent substances *do not* separate into ions, but remain intact molecules. For example,

$$HOCH_2CH_2OH(l) \xrightarrow{H_2O} HOCH_2CH_2OH(aq)$$

As a result, their aqueous solutions do not conduct an electric current, and these substances are **nonelectrolytes.** (As you'll see shortly, however, a small group of H-containing molecules that act as acids in aqueous solution *do* dissociate into ions.) Many other covalent substances, such as benzene (C_6H_6) and octane (C_8H_{18}), do not contain polar bonds, and these substances do not dissolve appreciably in water.

■ Summary of Section 4.1

- Because of polar bonds and a bent shape, the water molecule is polar, and water dissolves many ionic and covalent compounds.
- When an ionic compound dissolves, the attraction between each ion and water replaces the attraction between ions. Soluble ionic compounds are electrolytes because the ions are free to move and, thus, the solution conducts electricity.

- The formula of a soluble ionic compound shows the number of moles of each ion in solution per mole of compound dissolved.
- Water dissolves many covalent substances with polar bonds. These compounds are nonelectrolytes because the molecules remain intact and, thus, the solution does not conduct electricity.

4.2 • WRITING EQUATIONS FOR AQUEOUS IONIC REACTIONS

Chemists use three types of equations to represent aqueous ionic reactions. Let's examine a reaction to see what each type shows. When solutions of silver nitrate and sodium chromate are mixed, brick-red, solid silver chromate (Ag_2CrO_4) forms. Figure 4.4 depicts the reaction at the macroscopic level *(photos)*, the atomic level *(blow-up circles)*, and the symbolic level with the three types of equations (reacting ions are in red type):

- The **molecular equation** *(top)* reveals the least about the species that are actually in solution because *it shows all the reactants and products as if they were intact, undissociated compounds.* Only the designation for solid, *(s)*, tells that a change has occurred:

$$2AgNO_3(aq) + Na_2CrO_4(aq) \longrightarrow Ag_2CrO_4(s) + 2NaNO_3(aq)$$

Figure 4.4 An aqueous ionic reaction and the three types of equations.

- The **total ionic equation** (*middle*) is much more accurate because *it shows all the soluble ionic substances dissociated into ions.* The $Ag_2CrO_4(s)$ stands out as the only undissociated substance:

$$2Ag^+(aq) + 2NO_3^-(aq) + 2Na^+(aq) + CrO_4^{2-}(aq) \longrightarrow$$
$$Ag_2CrO_4(s) + 2Na^+(aq) + 2NO_3^-(aq)$$

The charges also balance: four positive and four negative for a net zero charge on the left side, and two positive and two negative for a net zero charge on the right.

Notice that $Na^+(aq)$ and $NO_3^-(aq)$ appear unchanged on both sides of the equation. These are called **spectator ions** (shown with pale colors in the atomic-level scenes). They are not involved in the actual chemical change but are present only as part of the reactants; that is, we can't add an Ag^+ ion without also adding an anion, in this case, the NO_3^- ion.

- The **net ionic equation** (*bottom*) is very useful because *it eliminates the spectator ions and shows only the actual chemical change:*

$$2Ag^+(aq) + CrO_4^{2-}(aq) \longrightarrow Ag_2CrO_4(s)$$

The formation of solid silver chromate from silver ions and chromate ions *is* the only change. To make that point clearly, suppose we had mixed solutions of potassium chromate, $K_2CrO_4(aq)$, and silver acetate, $AgC_2H_3O_2(aq)$, instead of sodium chromate and silver nitrate. The three ionic equations would be

Molecular: $2AgC_2H_3O_2(aq) + K_2CrO_4(aq) \longrightarrow Ag_2CrO_4(s) + 2KC_2H_3O_2(aq)$

Total ionic: $2Ag^+(aq) + 2C_2H_3O_2^-(aq) + 2K^+(aq) + CrO_4^{2-}(aq) \longrightarrow$
$$Ag_2CrO_4(s) + 2K^+(aq) + 2C_2H_3O_2(aq)$$

Net ionic: $2Ag^+(aq) + CrO_4^{2-}(aq) \longrightarrow Ag_2CrO_4(s)$

Thus, the same change would have occurred, and only the spectator ions would differ—$K^+(aq)$ and $C_2H_3O_2^-(aq)$ instead of $Na^+(aq)$ and $NO_3^-(aq)$.

Next, we'll apply these types of equations to three important classes of chemical reactions—precipitation, acid-base, and oxidation-reduction.

■ Summary of Section 4.2

- A molecular equation shows all substances intact and undissociated into ions.
- A total ionic equation shows all soluble ionic compounds as separate, solvated ions. Spectator ions appear unchanged on both sides of the equation.
- A net ionic equation eliminates the spectator ions and, thus, shows only the actual chemical change.

4.3 • PRECIPITATION REACTIONS

Precipitation reactions occur commonly in both nature and commerce. Coral reefs and some gems and minerals form, in part, through this process. And the chemical industry employs precipitation methods to make several important inorganic compounds.

The Key Event: Formation of a Solid from Dissolved Ions

In a **precipitation reaction,** two soluble ionic compounds react to form an insoluble product, a **precipitate.** The reaction you saw between silver nitrate and sodium chromate is one example. Precipitates form for the same reason that some ionic compounds don't dissolve: the electrostatic attraction between the ions outweighs the tendency of the ions to remain solvated and move throughout the solution. When the two solutions are mixed, the ions collide and stay together, and a solid product "comes out of solution." Thus, the key event in a precipitation reaction is *the formation of an insoluble product through the net removal of ions from solution.* Figure 4.5 (*on the next page*) shows the process for calcium fluoride.

Figure 4.5 The precipitation of calcium fluoride. When aqueous solutions of NaF (from pipet) and $CaCl_2$ (in test tube) react, solid CaF_2 forms (water molecules are omitted for clarity).

Molecular
$$CaCl_2(aq) \quad + \quad 2NaF(aq) \quad \longrightarrow \quad CaF_2(s) + 2NaCl(aq)$$

Total ionic
$$Ca^{2+}(aq) + 2Cl^-(aq) \quad + \quad 2Na^+(aq) + 2F^-(aq) \quad \longrightarrow \quad CaF_2(s) + 2Na^+(aq) + 2Cl^-(aq)$$

Net ionic
$$Ca^{2+}(aq) \quad + \quad 2F^-(aq) \quad \longrightarrow \quad CaF_2(s)$$

Predicting Whether a Precipitate Will Form

To predict whether a precipitate will form when you mix two aqueous ionic solutions, we refer to the short list of solubility rules in Table 4.1. Let's see how to apply these rules. When sodium iodide and potassium nitrate are each dissolved in water, their solutions consist of solvated, dispersed ions:

$$NaI(s) \xrightarrow{H_2O} Na^+(aq) + I^-(aq)$$
$$KNO_3(s) \xrightarrow{H_2O} K^+(aq) + NO_3^-(aq)$$

Three steps help us predict if a precipitate forms:

1. *Note the ions in the reactants.* The reactant ions are

$$Na^+(aq) + I^-(aq) + K^+(aq) + NO_3^-(aq) \longrightarrow ?$$

2. *Consider all possible cation-anion combinations.* In addition to NaI and KNO_3, which we know are soluble, the other cation-anion combinations are $NaNO_3$ and KI.
3. *Decide whether any combination is insoluble.* According to Table 4.1, no reaction occurs because all the combinations—NaI, KNO_3, $NaNO_3$, and KI—are soluble: Rules 1 and 2 say all compounds of Group 1A(1) ions and all nitrates are soluble.

Now, what happens if we substitute a solution of lead(II) nitrate, $Pb(NO_3)_2$, for the KNO_3 solution? The reactant ions are Na^+, I^-, Pb^{2+}, and NO_3^-. In addition to the two soluble reactants, NaI and $Pb(NO_3)_2$, the other two possible cation-anion combinations are $NaNO_3$ and PbI_2. According to Table 4.1, $NaNO_3$ is soluble

Table **4.1** Solubility Rules for Ionic Compounds in Water

Soluble Ionic Compounds	Insoluble Ionic Compounds
1. All common compounds of Group 1A(1) ions (Li$^+$, Na$^+$, K$^+$, etc.) and ammonium ion (NH$_4^+$) are soluble. 2. All common nitrates (NO$_3^-$), acetates (CH$_3$COO$^-$ or C$_2$H$_3$O$_2^-$), and most perchlorates (ClO$_4^-$) are soluble. 3. All common chlorides (Cl$^-$), bromides (Br$^-$), and iodides (I$^-$) are soluble, *except* those of Ag$^+$, Pb^{2+}, Cu$^+$, and Hg$_2^{2+}$. All common fluorides (F$^-$) are soluble, *except* those of Pb^{2+} and Group 2A(2). 4. All common sulfates (SO$_4^{2-}$) are soluble, except those of Ca^{2+}, Sr^{2+}, Ba^{2+}, Ag$^+$, and Pb^{2+}.	1. All common metal hydroxides are insoluble, *except* those of Group 1A(1) and the larger members of Group 2A(2) (beginning with Ca^{2+}). 2. All common carbonates (CO$_3^{2-}$) and phosphates (PO$_4^{3-}$) are insoluble, *except* those of Group 1A(1) and NH$_4^+$. 3. All common sulfides are insoluble except those of Group 1A(1), Group 2A(2), and NH$_4^+$.

(Rule 1), but PbI$_2$ is *not* (Rule 3). The total ionic equation shows the reaction that occurs as Pb^{2+} and I$^-$ ions collide and form a precipitate:

$$2Na^+(aq) + 2I^-(aq) + Pb^{2+}(aq) + 2NO_3^-(aq) \longrightarrow 2Na^+(aq) + 2NO_3^-(aq) + PbI_2(s)$$

And the net ionic equation confirms it:

$$Pb^{2+}(aq) + 2I^-(aq) \longrightarrow PbI_2(s)$$

Metathesis Reactions The molecular equation for the reaction between Pb(NO$_3$)$_2$ and NaI shows *the ions exchanging partners* (Figure 4.6):

$$2NaI(aq) + Pb(NO_3)_2(aq) \longrightarrow PbI_2(s) + 2NaNO_3(aq)$$

Such reactions are called *double-displacement reactions,* or **metathesis** (pronounced *meh-TA-thuh-sis*) **reactions.** Several are important in industry, including the preparation of silver bromide for the manufacture of black-and-white film:

$$AgNO_3(aq) + KBr(aq) \longrightarrow AgBr(s) + KNO_3(aq)$$

The reactions that form Ag$_2$CrO$_4$ (Figure 4.4) and CaF$_2$ (Figure 4.5) are metathesis, too. Sample Problems 4.2 and 4.3 provide practice in predicting if a precipitate forms.

$$2NaI(aq) + Pb(NO_3)_2(aq) \longrightarrow$$
$$PbI_2(s) + 2NaNO_3(aq)$$

Figure 4.6 The precipitation of PbI$_2$, a metathesis reaction.

Sample Problem 4.3 | Predicting Whether a Precipitation Reaction Occurs; Writing Ionic Equations

Problem Does a reaction occur when each of these pairs of solutions is mixed? If so, write balanced molecular, total ionic, and net ionic equations, and identify the spectator ions.
(a) Potassium fluoride(*aq*) + strontium nitrate(*aq*) $\longrightarrow$
(b) Ammonium perchlorate(*aq*) + sodium bromide(*aq*) $\longrightarrow$

Plan We note the reactant ions, write the cation-anion combinations, and refer to Table 4.1 to see if any are insoluble. For the molecular equation, we predict the products and write them all as intact compounds. For the total ionic equation, we write the soluble compounds as separate ions. For the net ionic equation, we eliminate the spectator ions.

Solution (a) In addition to the reactants, the two other ion combinations are strontium fluoride and potassium nitrate. Table 4.1 shows that strontium fluoride is insoluble, so a reaction *does* occur. Writing the molecular equation:

$$2KF(aq) + Sr(NO_3)_2(aq) \longrightarrow SrF_2(s) + 2KNO_3(aq)$$

Writing the total ionic equation:

$$2K^+(aq) + 2F^-(aq) + Sr^{2+}(aq) + 2NO_3^-(aq) \longrightarrow SrF_2(s) + 2K^+(aq) + 2NO_3^-(aq)$$

Writing the net ionic equation:

$$Sr^{2+}(aq) + 2F^-(aq) \longrightarrow SrF_2(s)$$

The spectator ions are K^+ and NO_3^-.

(b) The other ion combinations are ammonium bromide and sodium perchlorate. Table 4.1 shows that all ammonium, sodium, and most perchlorate compounds are soluble, and all bromides are soluble except those of Ag^+, Pb^{2+}, Cu^+, and Hg_2^{2+}. Therefore, **no reaction occurs.** The compounds remain as solvated ions.

Follow-Up Problem 4.3 Predict whether a reaction occurs, and if so, write balanced total and net ionic equations:
(a) Iron(III) chloride(*aq*) + cesium phosphate(*aq*) $\longrightarrow$
(b) Sodium hydroxide(*aq*) + cadmium nitrate(*aq*) $\longrightarrow$
(c) Magnesium bromide(*aq*) + potassium acetate(*aq*) $\longrightarrow$
(d) Silver nitrate(*aq*) + barium chloride(*aq*) $\longrightarrow$

Sample Problem 4.4 | Using Molecular Depictions in Precipitation Reactions

Problem The molecular views below show reactant solutions for a precipitation reaction (with ions shown as colored spheres and water omitted for clarity):

(a) Which compound is dissolved in beaker A: KCl, Na_2SO_4, $MgBr_2$, or Ag_2SO_4?
(b) Which compound is dissolved in beaker B: NH_4NO_3, $MgSO_4$, $Ba(NO_3)_2$, or CaF_2?
(c) Name the precipitate and the spectator ions when solutions A and B are mixed, and write balanced molecular, total ionic, and net ionic equations for any reaction.
(d) If each particle represents 0.010 mol of ions, what is the maximum mass (g) of precipitate that can form (assuming complete reaction)?

Plan (a) and **(b)** From the depictions, we note the charge and number of each kind of ion and use Table 4.1 to determine the ion combinations that are soluble. **(c)** Once we know the combinations, Table 4.1 tells which two ions form the solid, so the other two are spectator ions. **(d)** This part is a limiting-reactant problem because the amounts of two species are involved. We count the number of each kind of ion that formed the solid. We multiply the number of each reactant ion by 0.010 mol and calculate the amount (mol) of product formed from each. Whichever ion forms less is limiting, so we use the molar mass of the precipitate to find mass (g).

Solution (a) In solution A, there are two 1+ particles for each 2− particle. Therefore, the dissolved compound cannot be KCl or $MgBr_2$. Of the remaining two choices, Ag_2SO_4 is insoluble, so the dissolved compound must be Na_2SO_4.
(b) In solution B, there are two 1− particles for each 2+ particle. Therefore, the dissolved compound cannot be NH_4NO_3 or $MgSO_4$. Of the remaining two choices, CaF_2 is insoluble, so the dissolved compound must be $Ba(NO_3)_2$.
(c) Of the two possible ion combinations, $BaSO_4$ and $NaNO_3$, $BaSO_4$ is insoluble, so Na^+ and NO_3^- are spectator ions.

Molecular: $Ba(NO_3)_2(aq) + Na_2SO_4(aq) \longrightarrow BaSO_4(s) + 2NaNO_3(aq)$

Total ionic: $Ba^{2+}(aq) + 2NO_3^-(aq) + 2Na^+(aq) + SO_4^{2-}(aq) \longrightarrow$
$$BaSO_4(s) + 2NO_3^-(aq) + 2Na^+(aq)$$

Net ionic: $Ba^{2+}(aq) + SO_4^{2-}(aq) \longrightarrow BaSO_4(s)$

(d) Finding the ion that is the limiting reactant:

For Ba^{2+}:

Amount (mol) of $BaSO_4$ = 4 ~~Ba^{2+} particles~~ $\times \dfrac{0.010 \text{ mol } Ba^{2+} \text{ ion}}{1 \text{ particle}} \times \dfrac{1 \text{ mol } BaSO_4}{1 \text{ mol } Ba^{2+} \text{ ions}}$

= 0.040 mol $BaSO_4$

For SO_4^{2-}:

$$\text{Amount (mol) of BaSO}_4 = 5 \; \text{SO}_4^{2-} \; \text{particles} \times \frac{0.010 \; \text{mol SO}_4^{2-} \; \text{ions}}{1 \; \text{particle}} \times \frac{1 \; \text{mol BaSO}_4}{1 \; \text{mol SO}_4^{2-} \; \text{ions}}$$

$$= 0.050 \; \text{mol BaSO}_4$$

Therefore, Ba^{2+} ion is the limiting reactant.

Calculating the mass (g) of product ($\mathcal{M}$ of $BaSO_4$ = 233.4 g/mol):

$$\text{Mass (g) of BaSO}_4 = 0.040 \; \text{mol BaSO}_4 \times \frac{233.4 \; \text{g BaSO}_4}{1 \; \text{mol BaSO}_4} = \boxed{9.3 \; \text{g BaSO}_4}$$

Check Counting the number of Ba^{2+} ions allows a more direct calculation for a check: four Ba^{2+} particles means the maximum mass of $BaSO_4$ that can form is

$$\text{Mass (g) of BaSO}_4 = 4 \; \text{Ba}^{2+} \text{particles} \times \frac{0.010 \; \text{mol Ba}^{2+} \text{ions}}{1 \; \text{particle}} \times \frac{1 \; \text{mol BaSO}_4}{1 \; \text{mol Ba}^{2+} \text{ions}} \times \frac{233.4 \; \text{g BaSO}_4}{1 \; \text{mol}} = 9.3 \; \text{g BaSO}_4$$

Follow-Up Problem 4.4 Molecular views of the reactant solutions for a precipitation reaction are shown below (with ions represented as spheres and water molecules omitted):

(a) Which compound is dissolved in beaker A: $Zn(NO_3)_2$, KCl, Na_2SO_4, or $PbCl_2$?
(b) Which compound is dissolved in beaker B: $(NH_4)_2SO_4$, $Cd(OH)_2$, $Ba(OH)_2$, or KNO_3?
(c) Name the precipitate and the spectator ions when solutions A and B are mixed, and write balanced molecular, total ionic, and net ionic equations for the reaction.
(d) If each particle represents 0.050 mol of ions, what is the maximum mass (g) of precipitate that can form (assuming complete reaction)?

▋Summary of Section 4.3

- In a precipitation reaction, an insoluble ionic compound forms when solutions of two soluble ones are mixed. The electrostatic attraction between certain pairs of solvated ions is strong enough to overcome the attraction of each ion for water.
- Based on a set of solubility rules, we can predict the formation of a precipitate by noting which of all possible cation-anion combinations is insoluble.

4.4 • ACID-BASE REACTIONS

Aqueous acid-base reactions occur in processes as diverse as the metabolic action of proteins, the industrial production of fertilizer, and the revitalization of lakes damaged by acid rain.

These reactions involve water as reactant or product, in addition to its common role as solvent. Of course, an **acid-base reaction** (also called a **neutralization reaction**) occurs when an acid reacts with a base, but the definitions of these terms and the scope of this reaction class have changed over the years. For our purposes at this point, we'll use definitions that apply to substances found commonly in the lab:

- An *acid is a substance that produces H^+ ions when dissolved in water.*

$$HX \xrightarrow{\text{H}_2\text{O}} H^+(aq) + X^-(aq)$$

- A *base is a substance that produces OH^- ions when dissolved in water.*

$$MOH \xrightarrow{\text{H}_2\text{O}} M^+(aq) + OH^-(aq)$$

(Other definitions are presented later in this section and in Chapter 18.)

Acids and the Solvated Proton *Acidic solutions arise when certain covalent H-containing molecules dissociate into ions in water.* In every case, these molecules contain a *polar bond to H* in which the other atom pulls much more strongly on the electron pair. A good example is HBr. The Br end of the H—Br bond is partially negative, and the H end is partially positive. When hydrogen bromide gas dissolves in water, the poles of H_2O molecules are attracted to the oppositely charged poles of the HBr. The bond breaks, with H becoming the solvated cation $H^+(aq)$ and Br becoming the solvated anion $Br^-(aq)$:

$$HBr(g) \xrightarrow{H_2O} H^+(aq) + Br^-(aq)$$

The solvated H^+ ion is a very unusual species. The H atom is a proton surrounded by an electron, so H^+ is just a proton. With a full positive charge concentrated in such a tiny volume, H^+ attracts the negative pole of water molecules so strongly that it forms a covalent bond to one of them. We can show this interaction by writing the solvated H^+ ion as an H_3O^+ ion (hydronium ion) that also is solvated:

$$HBr(g) \quad + \quad H_2O(l) \quad \longrightarrow \quad H_3O^+(aq) + \quad Br^-(aq)$$

The hydronium ion, which we write as H_3O^+ [or $(H_2O)H^+$], associates with other water molecules to give species such as $H_5O_2^+$ [or $(H_2O)_2H^+$], $H_7O_3^+$ [or $(H_2O)_3H^+$], $H_9O_4^+$ [or $(H_2O)_4H^+$], and so forth. Figure 4.7 shows $H_7O_3^+$, an H_3O^+ ion associated *(dotted lines)* with two H_2O molecules. As a general notation for these various species, we write $H^+(aq)$, but later in this chapter and in much of the text, we'll use $H_3O^+(aq)$.

Acids and Bases as Electrolytes Acids and bases are categorized in terms of their "strength," the degree to which they dissociate into ions in water (Table 4.2):

- *Strong acids and strong bases dissociate completely into ions.* Therefore, like soluble ionic compounds, they are *strong* electrolytes and conduct a large current, as shown by the brightly lit bulb (Figure 4.8A).
- *Weak acids and weak bases dissociate very little into ions.* Most of their molecules remain intact. Therefore, they are *weak* electrolytes, which means they conduct a small current (Figure 4.8B).

Because a strong acid (or strong base) dissociates completely, we can find the molarity of H^+ (or OH^-) and the amount (mol) or number of each ion in solution. (You'll see how to determine these quantities for weak acids in Chapter 18.)

Figure 4.7 The H^+ ion as a solvated hydronium ion.

Table **4.2**	Strong and Weak Acids and Bases

Acids

Strong
Hydrochloric acid, HCl
Hydrobromic acid, HBr
Hydriodic acid, HI
Nitric acid, HNO_3
Sulfuric acid, H_2SO_4
Perchloric acid, $HClO_4$

Weak (a few of many examples)
Hydrofluoric acid, HF
Phosphoric acid, H_3PO_4
Acetic acid, CH_3COOH (or $HC_2H_3O_2$)

Bases

Strong
Group 1A(1) hydroxides:
Lithium hydroxide, LiOH
Sodium hydroxide, NaOH
Potassium hydroxide, KOH
Rubidium hydroxide, RbOH
Cesium hydroxide, CsOH

Heavy Group 2A(2) hydroxides:
Calcium hydroxide, $Ca(OH)_2$
Strontium hydroxide, $Sr(OH)_2$
Barium hydroxide, $Ba(OH)_2$

Weak (one of many examples)
Ammonia, NH_3

A Strong acid (or base) = strong electrolyte

B Weak acid (or base) = weak electrolyte

Figure 4.8 Acids and bases as electrolytes.

Sample Problem 4.5 Determining the Number of H⁺ (or OH⁻) Ions in Solution

Problem Nitric acid is a major chemical in the fertilizer and explosives industries. How many $H^+(aq)$ ions are in 25.3 mL of 1.4 M nitric acid?

Plan We know the volume (25.3 mL) and molarity (1.4 M) of nitric acid, and we need the number of $H^+(aq)$. We convert from mL to L and multiply by the molarity to find the amount (mol) of acid. Table 4.2 shows that nitric acid is a strong acid, so it dissociates completely. With the formula, we write a dissociation equation, which shows the amount (mol) of H^+ ions per mole of acid. We multiply that amount by Avogadro's number to find the number of $H^+(aq)$ ions (see the road map).

Solution Finding the amount (mol) of nitric acid:

$$\text{Amount (mol) of HNO}_3 = 25.3 \text{ mL} \times \frac{1 \text{ L}}{1000 \text{ mL}} \times \frac{1.4 \text{ mol}}{1 \text{ L}} = 0.035 \text{ mol}$$

Nitric acid is HNO_3, so we have:

$$HNO_3(l) \xrightarrow{H_2O} H^+(aq) + NO_3^-(aq)$$

Finding the number of H^+ ions:

$$\text{No. of } H^+ \text{ ions} = 0.035 \text{ mol HNO}_3 \times \frac{1 \text{ mol } H^\pm}{1 \text{ mol HNO}_3} \times \frac{6.022 \times 10^{23} \text{ } H^+ \text{ ions}}{1 \text{ mol } H^\pm}$$

$$= 2.1 \times 10^{22} \text{ } H^+ \text{ ions}$$

Check The number of moles seems correct: 0.025 L × 1.4 mol/L = 0.035 mol, and multiplying by 6×10²³ ions/mol gives 2×10²² ions.

Follow-Up Problem 4.5 How many $OH^-(aq)$ ions are present in 451 mL of 1.20 M potassium hydroxide?

Road Map

Volume (mL) of HNO₃

↓ 10^3 mL = 1 L

Volume (L) of HNO₃

↓ multiply by M (mol/L)

Amount (mol) of HNO₃

↓ mol of H⁺/mol of HNO₃

Amount (mol) of H⁺ ions

↓ multiply by Avogadro's number

No. of H⁺ ions

Structural Features of Acids and Bases A key structural feature appears in common laboratory acids and bases:

- *Acids.* Strong acids, such as HNO_3 and H_2SO_4, and weak acids, such as HF and H_3PO_4, have one or more H atoms as part of their structure, which are either completely released (strong) or partially released (weak) as protons in water.
- *Bases.* Strong bases have either OH^- (e.g., NaOH) or O^{2-} (e.g., K_2O) as part of their structure. The oxide ion is not stable in water and reacts to form OH^- ion:

$$O^{2-}(s) + H_2O(l) \longrightarrow 2OH^-(aq) \quad \text{so} \quad K_2O(s) + H_2O(l) \longrightarrow 2K^+(aq) + 2OH^-(aq)$$

Weak bases, such as ammonia, do not contain OH^- ions, but, as you'll see in later chapters, they all have an electron pair on N. Weak bases produce OH^- ions in a reaction that occurs to a small extent in water:

$$NH_3(g) + H_2O(l) \rightleftharpoons NH_4^+(aq) + OH^-(aq)$$

(The reaction arrow in the preceding equation indicates that the reaction proceeds in both directions; we'll discuss this important idea further in Section 4.7.)

The Key Event: Formation of H₂O from H⁺ and OH⁻

To see the key event in acid-base reactions, we'll write the three types of aqueous ionic equations (with color) and focus on the reaction between the strong acid HCl and the strong base $Ba(OH)_2$:

- The molecular equation is

$$2HCl(aq) + Ba(OH)_2(aq) \longrightarrow BaCl_2(aq) + 2H_2O(l)$$

- HCl and $Ba(OH)_2$ dissociate completely, so the total ionic equation is

$$2H^+(aq) + 2Cl^-(aq) + Ba^{2+}(aq) + 2OH^-(aq) \longrightarrow Ba^{2+}(aq) + 2Cl^-(aq) + 2H_2O(l)$$

- In the net ionic equation, we eliminate the spectator ions, $Ba^{2+}(aq)$ and $Cl^-(aq)$:

$$2H^+(aq) + 2OH^-(aq) \longrightarrow 2H_2O(l) \quad \text{or} \quad H^+(aq) + OH^-(aq) \longrightarrow H_2O(l)$$

Thus, *the key event in aqueous reactions between a strong acid and a strong base is that an H^+ ion from the acid and an OH^- ion from the base form a water molecule.* Only the spectator ions differ from one strong acid–strong base reaction to another.

Like precipitation reactions, acid-base reactions occur through *the electrostatic attraction of ions and their removal from solution as the product.* In this case, rather than an insoluble ionic solid, the product is H_2O, which consists almost entirely of undissociated molecules. Actually, water molecules dissociate *very* slightly (which, as you'll see in Chapter 18, is very important), but the formation of water in an acid-base reaction results in an enormous net removal of H^+ and OH^- ions.

The molecular and total ionic equations above show that if you evaporate the water, the spectator ions remain: the ionic compound that results from the reaction of an acid and a base is called a **salt,** which in this case is barium chloride. Thus, in an aqueous neutralization reaction, *an acid and a base form a salt solution and water:*

$$\underset{\text{acid}}{HX(aq)} + \underset{\text{base}}{MOH(aq)} \longrightarrow \underset{\text{salt}}{MX(aq)} + \underset{\text{water}}{H_2O(l)}$$

Note that *the cation of the salt comes from the base and the anion from the acid.*

Acid-base reactions, like precipitation reactions, are metathesis (double-displacement) reactions. The reaction of aluminum hydroxide, the active ingredient in some antacids, with HCl, the major component of stomach acid, is another example:

$$3HCl(aq) + Al(OH)_3(s) \longrightarrow AlCl_3(aq) + 3H_2O(l)$$

Sample Problem 4.6 | Writing Ionic Equations for Acid-Base Reactions

Problem Write balanced molecular, total ionic, and net ionic equations for each of the following acid-base reactions and identify the spectator ions:
(a) Hydrochloric acid(*aq*) + potassium hydroxide(*aq*) $\longrightarrow$
(b) Strontium hydroxide(*aq*) + perchloric acid(*aq*) $\longrightarrow$
(c) Barium hydroxide(*aq*) + sulfuric acid(*aq*) $\longrightarrow$

Plan All are strong acids and bases (see Table 4.2), so the actual reaction is between H^+ and OH^-. The products are H_2O and a salt solution of spectator ions. In (c), we note that the salt ($BaSO_4$) is insoluble (see Table 4.1), so there are no spectator ions.

Solution (a) Writing the molecular equation:

$$HCl(aq) + KOH(aq) \longrightarrow KCl(aq) + H_2O(l)$$

Writing the total ionic equation:

$$H^+(aq) + Cl^-(aq) + K^+(aq) + OH^-(aq) \longrightarrow K^+(aq) + Cl^-(aq) + H_2O(l)$$

Writing the net ionic equation:

$$H^+(aq) + OH^-(aq) \longrightarrow H_2O(l)$$

$K^+(aq)$ and $Cl^-(aq)$ are the spectator ions.

(b) Writing the molecular equation:

$$Sr(OH)_2(aq) + 2HClO_4(aq) \longrightarrow Sr(ClO_4)_2(aq) + 2H_2O(l)$$

Writing the total ionic equation:

$$Sr^{2+}(aq) + 2OH^-(aq) + 2H^+(aq) + 2ClO_4^-(aq) \longrightarrow$$
$$Sr^{2+}(aq) + 2ClO_4^-(aq) + 2H_2O(l)$$

Writing the net ionic equation:

$$2OH^-(aq) + 2H^+(aq) \longrightarrow 2H_2O(l) \quad \text{or} \quad OH^-(aq) + H^+(aq) \longrightarrow H_2O(l)$$

$Sr^{2+}(aq)$ and $ClO_4^-(aq)$ are the spectator ions.

(c) Writing the molecular equation:

$$Ba(OH)_2(aq) + H_2SO_4(aq) \longrightarrow BaSO_4(s) + 2H_2O(l)$$

Writing the total ionic equation:

$$Ba^{2+}(aq) + 2OH^-(aq) + 2H^+(aq) + SO_4^{2-}(aq) \longrightarrow BaSO_4(s) + 2H_2O(l)$$

This is a neutralization *and* a precipitation reaction, so the net ionic equation is the same as the total ionic. There are no spectator ions.

Follow-Up Problem 4.6 Write balanced molecular, total ionic, and net ionic equations for the reaction between aqueous solutions of calcium hydroxide and nitric acid.

Proton Transfer in Acid-Base Reactions

When we take a closer look (with color) at the reaction between a strong acid and strong base, as well as several related reactions, a unifying pattern appears. Let's examine three types of reaction to gain insight about this pattern.

Reaction Between Strong Acid and Strong Base When HCl gas dissolves in water, the H^+ ion ends up bonded to a water molecule. Thus, hydrochloric acid actually consists of solvated H_3O^+ and Cl^- ions:

$$HCl(g) + H_2O(l) \longrightarrow H_3O^+(aq) + Cl^-(aq)$$

If we add NaOH solution, the total ionic equation shows that H_3O^+ *transfers a proton* to OH^- (leaving a water molecule written as H_2O, and forming a water molecule written as HOH):

$$[H_3O^+(aq) + Cl^-(aq)] + [Na^+(aq) + OH^-(aq)] \longrightarrow$$
$$H_2O(l) + Cl^-(aq) + Na^+(aq) + HOH(l)$$

with an H^+ transfer indicated from H_3O^+ to OH^-.

Without the spectator ions, the net ionic equation shows more clearly the *transfer of a proton* from H_3O^+ to OH^-:

$$H_3O^+(aq) + OH^-(aq) \longrightarrow H_2O(l) + HOH(l) \quad \text{[or } 2H_2O(l)]$$

with an H^+ transfer indicated from H_3O^+ to OH^-.

This equation is identical to the one we saw earlier (see p. 147),

$$H^+(aq) + OH^-(aq) \longrightarrow H_2O(l)$$

with the additional H_2O molecule left over from the H_3O^+. Figure 4.9 shows this process on the atomic level and also shows that, if the water is evaporated, the spectator ions, Cl^- and Na^+, crystallize as the salt NaCl.

Figure 4.9 An aqueous strong acid–strong base reaction as a proton-transfer process.

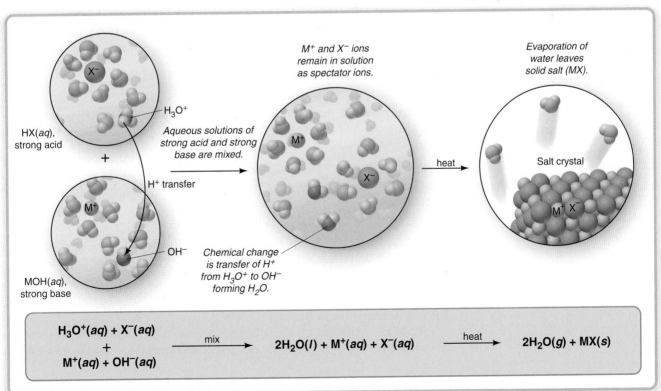

$$\begin{array}{c} H_3O^+(aq) + X^-(aq) \\ + \\ M^+(aq) + OH^-(aq) \end{array} \xrightarrow{\text{mix}} 2H_2O(l) + M^+(aq) + X^-(aq) \xrightarrow{\text{heat}} 2H_2O(g) + MX(s)$$

Thus, *an acid-base reaction is a proton-transfer process.* In the early 20th century, the chemists Johannes Brønsted and Thomas Lowry stated:

* *An acid is a molecule (or ion) that donates a proton.*
* *A base is a molecule (or ion) that accepts a proton.*

Therefore, in an aqueous reaction between strong acid and strong base, H_3O^+ *ion acts as the acid and donates a proton to* OH^- *ion, which acts as the base and accepts it.* (We discuss the Brønsted-Lowry concept thoroughly in Chapter 18.)

Gas-Forming Reactions: Acids with Carbonates (or Sulfites)

When an ionic carbonate, such as K_2CO_3, is treated with an acid, such as HCl, one of the products is carbon dioxide, as the molecular equation shows:

$$2HCl(aq) + K_2CO_3(aq) \longrightarrow 2KCl(aq) + [H_2CO_3(aq)]$$
$$[H_2CO_3(aq)] \longrightarrow H_2O(l) + CO_2(g)$$

Square brackets around a species, in this case, H_2CO_3, mean it is very unstable: H_2CO_3 decomposes immediately into water and carbon dioxide. Combining these two equations (see Sample Problem 3.17, p. 106) cancels $[H_2CO_3]$ and gives the overall equation:

$$2HCl(aq) + K_2CO_3(aq) \longrightarrow 2KCl(aq) + H_2O(l) + CO_2(g)$$

Writing the total ionic equation with H_3O^+ ions from the HCl shows the actual species in solution and the key event in a gas-forming reaction, *removal of ions from solution through formation of both a gas **and** water:*

$$2H_3O^+(aq) + 2Cl^-(aq) + 2K^+(aq) + CO_3{}^{2-}(aq) \longrightarrow$$
$$2Cl^-(aq) + 2K^+(aq) + CO_2(g) + H_2O(l) + 2H_2O(l) \quad [\text{or } 3H_2O(l)]$$

Writing the net ionic equation, with the intermediate formation of H_2CO_3, eliminates the spectator ions, Cl^- and K^+, and makes it easier to see that *proton transfer* takes place as each of the two H_3O^+ ions transfers one proton to the carbonate ion:

$$\overset{\frown \; 2H^+ \text{ transfer} \; \searrow}{2H_3O^+(aq) \; + \; CO_3{}^{2-}(aq)} \longrightarrow [H_2CO_3(aq)] + 2H_2O(l) \longrightarrow$$
$$CO_2(g) + H_2O(l) + 2H_2O(l) \quad [\text{or } 3H_2O(l)]$$

In essence, this is an acid-base reaction with carbonate ion accepting the protons and, thus, acting as the base.

Ionic sulfites react similarly to form water and gaseous SO_2; the net ionic equation, in which $SO_3{}^{2-}$ acts as the base and forms the unstable H_2SO_3, is

$$\overset{\frown \; 2H^+ \text{ transfer} \; \searrow}{2H_3O^+(aq) \; + \; SO_3{}^{2-}(aq)} \longrightarrow [H_2SO_3(aq)] + 2H_2O(l) \longrightarrow$$
$$SO_2(g) + H_2O(l) + 2H_2O(l) \quad [\text{or } 3H_2O(l)]$$

Reactions of Weak Acids with Bases

When solutions of sodium hydroxide and the weak acid acetic acid (CH_3COOH, Table 4.2) are mixed, the molecular equation is

$$CH_3COOH(aq) + NaOH(aq) \longrightarrow CH_3COONa(aq) + H_2O(l)$$

The total ionic equation is written differently for the reaction of a weak acid. Because acetic acid is weak and, thus, dissociates very little, it appears as *undissociated, intact molecules:*

$$CH_3COOH(aq) + Na^+(aq) + OH^-(aq) \longrightarrow CH_3COO^-(aq) + Na^+(aq) + H_2O(l)$$

The net ionic equation reveals that proton transfer occurs here as well, but directly from the weak acid rather than from H_3O^+:

$$\overset{\frown H^+ \text{ transfer} \searrow}{CH_3COOH(aq) \quad + \quad OH^-(aq)} \longrightarrow CH_3COO^-(aq) + H_2O(l)$$

The only spectator ion is $Na^+(aq)$.

Weak acids also react with carbonates to form CO_2, as Figure 4.10 shows for the reaction between vinegar (a 5% solution of acetic acid) and baking soda (sodium

Figure 4.10 A gas-forming reaction with a weak acid. Note that the two ionic equations include acetic acid because it does *not* dissociate appreciably into ions.

hydrogen carbonate) solution. In fact, when stomach acid (mostly HCl) builds up, your duodenum releases the hormone secretin, which stimulates your pancreas to release HCO_3^- ions that react with the excess acid in an analogous reaction.

Sample Problem 4.7 Writing Proton-Transfer Equations for Acid-Base Reactions

Problem Write balanced total and net ionic equations for the following reactions and use curved arrows to show how the proton transfer occurs. For (a), give the name and formula of the salt present when the water evaporates. For (b), note that propionic acid (CH_3CH_2COOH) is a weak acid and identify the spectator ion(s).
(a) Hydriodic acid(*aq*) + calcium hydroxide(*aq*) $\longrightarrow$
(b) Potassium hydroxide(*aq*) + propionic acid(*aq*) $\longrightarrow$

Plan **(a)** The reactants are a strong acid and a strong base (Table 4.2), so the acidic species is H_3O^+, which transfers a proton to the OH^- from the base. The products are H_2O and a solution of spectator ions that becomes a solid salt when the water evaporates.
(b) Since the acid is weak, it occurs as intact molecules in solution and transfers its proton to the OH^- from the base. The only spectator ion is the cation of the base.

Solution **(a)** Writing the total ionic equation:

$$2H_3O^+(aq) + 2I^-(aq) + Ca^{2+}(aq) + 2OH^-(aq) \longrightarrow 2I^-(aq) + Ca^{2+}(aq) + 4H_2O(l)$$

Writing the net ionic equation:

$$2H_3O^+(aq) + 2OH^-(aq) \longrightarrow 4H_2O(l) \quad \text{or} \quad H_3O^+(aq) + OH^-(aq) \longrightarrow 2H_2O(l)$$

$I^-(aq)$ and $Ca^{2+}(aq)$ are spectator ions, so the salt is calcium iodide, CaI_2.
(b) Writing the total ionic equation:

$$K^+(aq) + OH^-(aq) + CH_3CH_2COOH(aq) \longrightarrow K^+(aq) + H_2O(l) + CH_3CH_2COO^-(aq)$$

Writing the net ionic equation:

$$OH^-(aq) + CH_3CH_2COOH(aq) \longrightarrow H_2O(l) + CH_3CH_2COO^-(aq)$$

$K^+(aq)$ is the only spectator ion.

Follow-Up Problem 4.7 Write balanced total and net ionic equations for the reaction between aqueous solutions of calcium hydrogen carbonate and hydrobromic acid. Use a curved arrow in the net ionic equation to show the proton transfer. Give the name and formula of the salt that is present when the water evaporates.

Figure 4.11 An acid-base titration.

A Before titration   B Near end point   C At end point

$$H^+(aq) + X^-(aq) + M^+(aq) + OH^-(aq) \longrightarrow H_2O(l) + M^+(aq) + X^-(aq)$$

Quantifying Acid-Base Reactions by Titration

In any **titration,** *the known concentration of one solution is used to determine the unknown concentration of another.* In a typical acid-base titration, a *standardized* solution of base, one whose concentration is *known,* is added to a solution of acid whose concentration is *unknown (or vice versa).*

Figure 4.11A shows the laboratory setup for an acid-base titration with a known volume of acid and a few drops of indicator in a flask. An *acid-base indicator* is a substance whose color is different in acid than in base; the indicator used in the figure is phenolphthalein, which is pink in base and colorless in acid. (We examine indicators in Chapters 18 and 19.) Base is added from a buret, and the OH^- ions react with the H^+ ions. As the titration nears its end (Figure 4.11B), the drop of added base creates a temporary excess of OH^-, causing some indicator molecules to change to the basic color; they return to the acidic color when the flask is swirled. There are two key stages in the titration:

- The **equivalence point** occurs when *the amount (mol) of H^+ ions in the original volume of acid has reacted with the same amount (mol) of OH^- ions from the buret:*

    Amount (mol) of H^+ (originally in flask) = amount (mol) of OH^- (added from buret)
- The **end point** occurs when a tiny excess of OH^- ions changes the indicator permanently to its basic color (Figure 4.11C).

In calculations, such as in Sample Problem 4.8, we assume that this tiny excess of OH^- ions is insignificant and that *the amount of base needed to reach the end point is the same as the amount needed to reach the equivalence point.*

Sample Problem 4.8   Finding the Concentration of an Acid from a Titration

Problem To standardize an HCl solution, you put 50.00 mL of it in a flask with a few drops of indicator and put 0.1524 M NaOH in a buret. The buret reads 0.55 mL at the start and 33.87 mL at the end point. Find the molarity of the HCl solution.

Plan We have to find the molarity of the acid from the volume of acid (50.00 mL), the initial (0.55 mL) and final (33.87 mL) volumes of base, and the molarity of the base (0.1524 M). First, we balance the equation. The volume of added base is the difference in buret readings, and we use the base's molarity to calculate the amount (mol) of base. Then, we use the molar ratio from the balanced equation to find the amount (mol) of acid originally present and divide by the acid's original volume to find the molarity (see the road map).

Solution Writing the balanced equation:

$$NaOH(aq) + HCl(aq) \longrightarrow NaCl(aq) + H_2O(l)$$

Finding the volume (L) of NaOH solution added:

$$\text{Volume (L) of solution} = (33.87 \text{ mL soln} - 0.55 \text{ mL soln}) \times \frac{1 \text{ L}}{1000 \text{ mL}}$$

$$= 0.03332 \text{ L soln}$$

Finding the amount (mol) of NaOH added:

$$\text{Amount (mol) of NaOH} = 0.03332 \text{ L soln} \times \frac{0.1524 \text{ mol NaOH}}{1 \text{ L soln}}$$

$$= 5.078 \times 10^{-3} \text{ mol NaOH}$$

Finding the amount (mol) of HCl originally present: Since the molar ratio is 1/1,

$$\text{Amount (mol) of HCl} = 5.078 \times 10^{-3} \text{ mol NaOH} \times \frac{1 \text{ mol HCl}}{1 \text{ mol NaOH}} = 5.078 \times 10^{-3} \text{ mol HCl}$$

Calculating the molarity of HCl:

$$\text{Molarity of HCl} = \frac{5.078 \times 10^{-3} \text{ mol HCl}}{50.00 \text{ mL}} \times \frac{1000 \text{ mL}}{1 \text{ L}} = \boxed{0.1016 \ M \text{ HCl}}$$

Check The answer makes sense: a large volume of less concentrated acid neutralized a small volume of more concentrated base. With rounding, the numbers of moles of H^+ and OH^- are about equal: $50 \text{ mL} \times 0.1 \ M \ H^+ = 0.005 \text{ mol} = 33 \text{ mL} \times 0.15 \ M \ OH^-$.

Follow-Up Problem 4.8 What volume of $0.1292 \ M \ Ba(OH)_2$ would neutralize 50.00 mL of the HCl solution standardized in Sample Problem 4.8?

Road Map

Volume (L) of base (difference in buret readings)

↓ multiply by M (mol/L) of base

Amount (mol) of base

↓ molar ratio

Amount (mol) of acid

↓ divide by volume (L) of acid

M (mol/L) of acid

■ Summary of Section 4.4

- In an acid-base (neutralization) reaction between an acid (an H^+-yielding substance) and a base (an OH^--yielding substance), H^+ and OH^- ions form H_2O.
- Strong acids and bases dissociate completely in water (strong electrolytes); weak acids and bases dissociate slightly (weak electrolytes).
- An acid-base reaction involves the transfer of a proton from an acid (a species that donates an H^+) to a base (a species that accepts an H^+).
- A gas-forming acid-base reaction occurs when an acid transfers a proton to a carbonate (or sulfite), forming water and a gas that leaves the reaction mixture.
- Since weak acids dissociate very little, ionic equations show a weak acid as an intact molecule transferring its proton to the base.
- In a titration, the known concentration of one solution is used to determine the concentration of the other.

4.5 • OXIDATION-REDUCTION (REDOX) REACTIONS

Oxidation-reduction (redox) reactions include the formation of a compound from its elements (and the reverse process), all combustion processes, the generation of electricity in batteries, the production of cellular energy, and many others. In fact, redox reactions are so widespread that many do not occur in aqueous solution. In this section, we examine the key event in the redox process, discuss important terminology, see one way to balance redox equations, and learn how to quantify them.

The Key Event: Movement of Electrons Between Reactants

The key chemical event in an **oxidation-reduction** (or **redox**) **reaction** is the *net movement of electrons from one reactant to another*. The movement occurs from the reactant (or atom in the reactant) with *less* attraction for electrons to the reactant (or atom) with *more* attraction for electrons.

Figure 4.12 The redox process in the formation of (A) ionic and (B) covalent compounds from their elements.

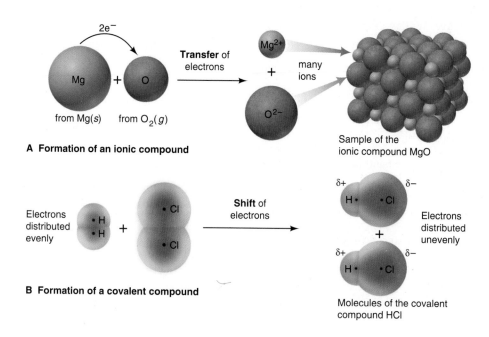

A Formation of an ionic compound

from Mg(s) from $O_2(g)$

Transfer of electrons

many ions

Sample of the ionic compound MgO

Electrons distributed evenly

Shift of electrons

Electrons distributed unevenly

B Formation of a covalent compound

Molecules of the covalent compound HCl

This process occurs in the formation of both ionic and covalent compounds:

- *Ionic compounds: transfer of electrons.* In the reaction that forms MgO from its elements (see Figure 3.7, p. 100), the balanced equation is

$$2Mg(s) + O_2(g) \longrightarrow 2MgO(s)$$

Figure 4.12A shows that each Mg atom loses two electrons and each O atom gains them. This loss and gain is a ***transfer*** *of electrons* away from each Mg atom to each O atom. The resulting Mg^{2+} and O^{2-} ions aggregate into an ionic solid.

- *Covalent compounds: shift of electrons.* During the formation of a covalent compound from its elements, there is more of a ***shift*** *of electrons* than a full transfer. Thus, *ions do not form.* Consider the formation of HCl gas:

$$H_2(g) + Cl_2(g) \longrightarrow 2HCl(g)$$

To see the electron movement, we'll compare the electron distribution in reactant and product. As Figure 4.12B shows, in H_2 and Cl_2, the electrons are shared equally between the atoms *(symmetrical shading).* Because the Cl atom attracts electrons more than the H atom, in HCl, the electrons are shared unequally *(asymmetrical shading).* Electrons shift away from H and toward Cl, so the Cl atom has more negative charge (*red* and $\delta-$) than it had in Cl_2, and the H atom has less negative charge (*blue* and $\delta+$) than it had in H_2.

Some Essential Redox Terminology

Certain key terms describe the process and explain the name of this reaction class:

- **Oxidation** is the *loss* of electrons.
- **Reduction** is the *gain* of electrons.

During the formation of MgO, Mg undergoes oxidation (loss of electrons), and O_2 undergoes reduction (gain of electrons). The loss and gain are simultaneous, but we can imagine them occurring separately:

Oxidation (electron loss by Mg): $\qquad Mg \longrightarrow Mg^{2+} + 2e^-$

Reduction (electron gain by O_2): $\frac{1}{2}O_2 + 2e^- \longrightarrow O^{2-}$

(Throughout the chapter, blue type indicates oxidation, and red type reduction.)

- The **oxidizing agent** is the species doing the oxidizing (causing the electron loss).
- The **reducing agent** is the species doing the reducing (causing the electron gain).

One reactant acts on the other. During the reaction that forms MgO, *O_2 oxidizes Mg,* so O_2 is the oxidizing agent, and *Mg reduces O_2,* so Mg is the reducing agent.

Note the give and take of electrons: O_2 takes the electrons that Mg gives up, or, put the other way around, Mg gives up the electrons that O_2 takes. This means that

- *The oxidizing agent is reduced:* it takes electrons (and, thus, gains them).
- *The reducing agent is oxidized:* it gives up electrons (and, thus, loses them).

In the formation of HCl, Cl_2 *oxidizes* H_2 (H loses some electron charge and Cl gains it), which is the same as saying that H_2 *reduces* Cl_2. The reducing agent, H_2, is oxidized, and the oxidizing agent, Cl_2, is reduced.

Using Oxidation Numbers to Monitor Electron Charge

Chemists have devised a "bookkeeping" system to monitor which atom loses electron charge and which atom gains it: each atom in a molecule (or formula unit) is assigned an **oxidation number (O.N.)**, or *oxidation state,* which is the charge the atom would have *if* electrons were transferred completely, not shared.

Each element in a binary *ionic* compound has a full charge because the atom transferred its electron(s), and so the atom's oxidation number equals the ionic charge. But, each element in a *covalent* compound (or in a polyatomic ion) has a partial charge because the electrons shifted away from one atom and toward the other. For these cases, we determine oxidation number by a set of rules (Table 4.3; you'll learn the atomic basis of the rules in Chapters 8 and 9).

An O.N. has the sign *before* the number (e.g., +2), whereas an ionic charge has the sign *after* the number (e.g., 2+). Also, unlike a unitary ionic charge, as in Na^+ or Cl^-, an O.N. of +1 or -1 retains the numeral. For example, we don't write the sodium ion as Na^{+1}, but the O.N. of the Na^+ ion is +1, not +.

Table **4.3** Rules for Assigning an Oxidation Number (O.N.)

General Rules

1. For an atom in its elemental form (Na, O_2, Cl_2, etc.): O.N. = 0
2. For a monatomic ion: O.N. = ion charge (with the sign *before* the numeral)
3. The sum of O.N. values for the atoms in a molecule or formula unit of a compound equals zero. The sum of O.N. values for the atoms in a polyatomic ion equals the ion's charge.

Rules for Specific Atoms or Periodic Table Groups

1. For Group 1A(1):	O.N. = +1 in all compounds
2. For Group 2A(2):	O.N. = +2 in all compounds
3. For hydrogen:	O.N. = +1 in combination with nonmetals
	O.N. = -1 in combination with metals and boron
4. For fluorine:	O.N. = -1 in all compounds
5. For oxygen:	O.N. = -1 in peroxides
	O.N. = -2 in all other compounds (except with F)
6. For Group 7A(17):	O.N. = -1 in combination with metals, nonmetals (except O), and other halogens lower in the group

---

Sample Problem 4.9 — Determining the Oxidation Number of Each Element in a Compound (or Ion)

Problem Determine the oxidation number (O.N.) of each element in these species:
(a) Zinc chloride **(b)** Sulfur trioxide **(c)** Nitric acid **(d)** Dichromate ion

Plan We determine the formulas and consult Table 4.3, including the general rules that the O.N. values for a compound add up to zero and those for a polyatomic ion add up to the ion's charge.

Solution (a) $ZnCl_2$. The sum of O.N.s must equal zero. The O.N. of the Zn^{2+} ion is +2, so the O.N. of each Cl^- ion is -1, for a total of -2.
(b) SO_3. The O.N. of each oxygen is -2, for a total of -6. The O.N.s must add up to zero, so the O.N. of S is +6.

(c) HNO_3. The O.N. of H is +1, so the O.N.s of the atoms in NO_3^- must add up to −1 to equal the charge of the polyatomic ion and give zero for the compound. The O.N. of each O is −2, for a total of −6. Therefore, the O.N. of N is +5.

(d) $Cr_2O_7^{2-}$. The O.N. of each O is −2, so the total for seven O atoms is −14. Therefore, each Cr must have an O.N. of +6 in order for the sum of the O.N.s to equal the charge of the ion: +12 + (−14) = −2.

Follow-Up Problem 4.9 Determine the O.N. of each element in the following:

(a) Scandium oxide (Sc_2O_3) **(b)** Gallium chloride ($GaCl_3$)
(c) Hydrogen phosphate ion **(d)** Iodine trifluoride

Using O.N.s to Identify Redox Reactions A redox reaction is defined as one in which the oxidation numbers of the species change. Sample Problem 4.10 introduces the *tie-line*, a useful device for keeping track of these changes.

Sample Problem 4.10 | **Identifying Redox Reactions**

Problem Use oxidation numbers to decide whether each of the following is a redox reaction:
(a) $CaO(s) + CO_2(g) \longrightarrow CaCO_3(s)$
(b) $4KNO_3(s) \longrightarrow 2K_2O(s) + 2N_2(g) + 5O_2(g)$
(c) $H_2SO_4(aq) + 2NaOH(aq) \longrightarrow Na_2SO_4(aq) + 2H_2O(l)$

Plan To determine whether a reaction is an oxidation-reduction process, we use Table 4.3 to assign an O.N. to each atom. If an O.N. changes during the reaction, we draw a tie-line from the atom on the left side to the one on the right and note the change.

Solution (a)

$$\overset{+2}{Ca}\overset{-2}{O}(s) + \overset{+4}{C}\overset{-2}{O_2}(g) \longrightarrow \overset{+2}{Ca}\overset{+4}{C}\overset{-2}{O_3}(s)$$

Because each atom in the product has the same O.N. that it had in the reactants, we conclude that this is *not* a redox reaction.

(b)

O.N. decreased: *reduction*

$$4\overset{+1}{K}\overset{+5}{N}\overset{-2}{O_3}(s) \longrightarrow 2\overset{+1}{K_2}\overset{-2}{O}(s) + 2\overset{0}{N_2}(g) + 5\overset{0}{O_2}(g)$$

O.N. increased: *oxidation*

In this case, the O.N. of N changes from +5 to 0, and the O.N. of O changes from −2 to 0, so this *is* a redox reaction.

(c)

$$\overset{+1}{H_2}\overset{+6}{S}\overset{-2}{O_4}(aq) + 2\overset{+1}{Na}\overset{+1}{O}\overset{-2}{H}(aq) \longrightarrow \overset{+1}{Na_2}\overset{+6}{S}\overset{-2}{O_4}(aq) + 2\overset{+1}{H_2}\overset{-2}{O}(l)$$

The O.N. values do not change, so this is *not* a redox reaction.

Comment The reaction in (c) is an acid-base reaction in which H_2SO_4 transfers two H^+ ions to two OH^- ions to form two H_2O molecules. In the net ionic equation,

$$\overset{+1}{H^+}(aq) + \overset{-2}{O}\overset{+1}{H^-}(aq) \longrightarrow \overset{+1}{H_2}\overset{-2}{O}(l)$$

we see that the O.N. values remain the same on both sides of the equation. Therefore, *an acid-base reaction is **not** a redox reaction.*

Follow-Up Problem 4.10 Use oxidation numbers to decide which, if any, of the following equations represents a redox reaction:
(a) $NCl_3(l) + 3H_2O(l) \longrightarrow NH_3(aq) + 3HOCl(aq)$
(b) $AgNO_3(aq) + NH_4I(aq) \longrightarrow AgI(s) + NH_4NO_3(aq)$
(c) $2H_2S(g) + 3O_2(g) \longrightarrow 2SO_2(g) + 2H_2O(g)$

Using O.N.s to Identify Oxidizing and Reducing Agents By assigning an oxidation number to each atom, we can see which species was oxidized and which reduced and, thus, which is the oxidizing agent and which the reducing agent:

- If an atom has a higher (more positive or less negative) O.N. in the product than it had in the reactant, the reactant that contains that atom was oxidized (lost electrons) and is the reducing agent. Thus, *oxidation is shown by an increase in O.N.*
- If an atom has a lower (more negative or less positive) O.N. in the product than it had in the reactant, the reactant that contains that atom was reduced (gained electrons) and is the oxidizing agent. Thus, *reduction is shown by a decrease in O.N.*

Sample Problem 4.11 | **Identifying Oxidizing and Reducing Agents**

Problem Identify the oxidizing agent and the reducing agent in each of the following:
(a) $2Al(s) + 3H_2SO_4(aq) \longrightarrow Al_2(SO_4)_3(aq) + 3H_2(g)$
(b) $PbO(s) + CO(g) \longrightarrow Pb(s) + CO_2(g)$
(c) $2H_2(g) + O_2(g) \longrightarrow 2H_2O(g)$

Plan We assign an O.N. to each atom (or ion). The reducing agent contains an atom that is oxidized (O.N. *increased* from left to right in the equation). The oxidizing agent contains an atom that is reduced (O.N. *decreased*). We mark the changes with tie-lines.

Solution **(a)** Assigning oxidation numbers:

$$\overset{\text{oxidation}}{\underset{\text{reduction}}{\overset{0 \quad +1 \;|-2 \quad +3 \;|-2 \quad 0}{2Al(s) + 3H_2SO_4(aq) \longrightarrow Al_2(SO_4)_3(aq) + 3H_2(g)}}}$$

with $+6$ over H_2SO_4 and $+6$ over $(SO_4)_3$.

The O.N. of Al increased from 0 to +3 (Al lost electrons), so Al was oxidized;
Al is the reducing agent.
The O.N. of H decreased from +1 to 0 (H gained electrons), so H^+ was reduced;
H_2SO_4 is the oxidizing agent.

(b) Assigning oxidation numbers:

$$\overset{\text{oxidation}}{\underset{\text{reduction}}{\overset{+2 \;|-2 \quad +2 \;|-2 \quad 0 \quad +4\;|-2}{PbO(s) + CO(g) \longrightarrow Pb(s) + CO_2(g)}}}$$

Pb decreased its O.N. from +2 to 0, so PbO was reduced; PbO is the oxidizing agent.
C increased its O.N. from +2 to +4, so CO was oxidized; CO is the reducing agent.
When a reactant (in this case, CO) becomes a product with more O atoms (CO_2), it is oxidized; when a reactant (PbO) becomes a product with fewer O atoms (Pb), it is reduced.

(c) Assigning oxidation numbers:

$$\overset{\text{oxidation}}{\underset{\text{reduction}}{\overset{0 \quad 0 \quad +1-2}{2H_2(g) + O_2(g) \longrightarrow 2H_2O(g)}}}$$

O_2 was reduced (O.N. of O decreased from 0 to −2); O_2 is the oxidizing agent.
H_2 was oxidized (O.N. of H increased from 0 to +1); H_2 is the reducing agent.
Oxygen is always the oxidizing agent in a combustion reaction.

Follow-Up Problem 4.11 Identify each oxidizing agent and each reducing agent:
(a) $2Fe(s) + 3Cl_2(g) \longrightarrow 2FeCl_3(s)$ **(b)** $2C_2H_6(g) + 7O_2(g) \longrightarrow 4CO_2(g) + 6H_2O(g)$
(c) $5CO(g) + I_2O_5(s) \longrightarrow I_2(s) + 5CO_2(g)$

Be sure to remember that *transferred electrons are never free because the reducing agent loses electrons and the oxidizing agent gains them* **simultaneously.** In other words, a complete reaction *cannot* be "an oxidation" *or* "a reduction"; it must be an oxidation-reduction. Figure 4.13 summarizes redox terminology.

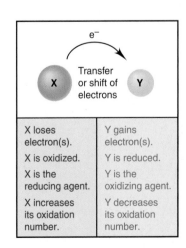

X loses electron(s).	Y gains electron(s).
X is oxidized.	Y is reduced.
X is the reducing agent.	Y is the oxidizing agent.
X increases its oxidation number.	Y decreases its oxidation number.

Figure 4.13 A summary of terminology for redox reactions.

Balancing Redox Equations

We balance a redox reaction by making sure that *the number of electrons lost by the reducing agent equals the number of electrons gained by the oxidizing agent.*

Two methods used to balance redox equations are the *oxidation number* method and the *half-reaction* method. This section describes the oxidation number method; the half-reaction method is covered in Chapter 21. (If your professor chooses to cover the half-reaction method here as well, it is easily transferable.)

The **oxidation number method** consists of five steps that use the changes in oxidation numbers to generate balancing coefficients. The first two steps are identical to those in Sample Problem 4.11:

Step 1. Assign O.N.s to all atoms.
Step 2. From the changes in O.N.s, identify the oxidized and reduced reactants.
Step 3. Compute the numbers of electrons lost in the oxidation and gained in the reduction, and draw tie-lines from the reactant atom to the product atom to show the change.
Step 4. Multiply the numbers of electrons by factor(s) that make the electrons lost equal the electrons gained, and use the factor(s) as balancing coefficients.
Step 5. Complete the balancing by inspection and add states of matter.

Sample Problem 4.12	Balancing Redox Equations by the Oxidation Number Method

Problem Use the oxidation number method to balance the following equations:
(a) $Cu(s) + HNO_3(aq) \longrightarrow Cu(NO_3)_2(aq) + NO_2(g) + H_2O(l)$
(b) $PbS(s) + O_2(g) \longrightarrow PbO(s) + SO_2(g)$

(a) Reaction of copper and nitric acid

Solution *Step 1.* Assign oxidation numbers to all atoms:

$$\overset{0}{Cu} + \overset{+1}{H}\overset{+5}{N}\overset{-2}{O_3} \longrightarrow \overset{+2}{Cu}(\overset{+5}{N}\overset{-2}{O_3})_2 + \overset{+4}{N}\overset{-2}{O_2} + \overset{+1}{H_2}\overset{-2}{O}$$

Step 2. Identify oxidized and reduced reactants. The O.N. of Cu increased from 0 (in Cu metal) to +2 (in Cu^{2+}), so Cu was oxidized. The O.N. of N decreased from +5 (in HNO_3) to +4 (in NO_2), so HNO_3 was reduced. Note that some NO_3^- also acts as a spectator ion, appearing unchanged in $Cu(NO_3)_2$.
Step 3. Compute e^- lost and e^- gained and draw tie-lines. In the oxidation, $2e^-$ were lost from Cu. In the reduction, $1e^-$ was gained by N:

loses $2e^-$

$$Cu + HNO_3 \longrightarrow Cu(NO_3)_2 + NO_2 + H_2O$$

gains $1e^-$

Step 4. Multiply by factor(s) to make e^- lost equal e^- gained, and use the factor(s) as coefficients. Cu lost $2e^-$, so the $1e^-$ gained by N should be multiplied by 2. We put the coefficient 2 before *both* NO_2 and HNO_3:

$$Cu + 2HNO_3 \longrightarrow Cu(NO_3)_2 + 2NO_2 + H_2O$$

Step 5. Complete the balancing by inspection. Balancing N atoms requires a 4 in front of HNO_3 because two additional N atoms are in the NO_3^- ions in $Cu(NO_3)_2$:

$$Cu + 4HNO_3 \longrightarrow Cu(NO_3)_2 + 2NO_2 + H_2O$$

Then, balancing H atoms requires a 2 in front of H_2O, and we add states of matter:

$$Cu(s) + 4HNO_3(aq) \longrightarrow Cu(NO_3)_2(aq) + 2NO_2(g) + 2H_2O(l)$$

Check

Reactants (1 Cu, 4 H, 4 N, 12 O) $\longrightarrow$ products [1 Cu, 4 H, (2 + 2) N, (6 + 4 + 2) O]

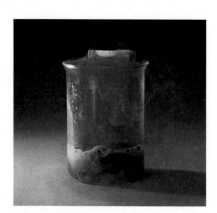

Copper in nitric acid.

Comment We often find that some of a species reacts and the rest doesn't. In this case, 2 mol of NO_3^- are reduced to NO_2, and 2 mol of NO_3^- are spectator ions.

(b) Reaction of lead(II) sulfide and oxygen

Solution *Step 1.* Assign oxidation numbers to all atoms:

$$\overset{+2}{\underset{\,}{Pb}}\overset{-2}{S} + \overset{0}{O_2} \longrightarrow \overset{+2}{\underset{\,}{Pb}}\overset{-2}{O} + \overset{+4}{\underset{\,}{S}}\overset{-2}{O_2}$$

Step 2. Identify oxidized and reduced reactants. The O.N. of S increased from −2 in PbS to +4 in SO_2, so PbS was oxidized. The O.N. of O decreased from 0 in O_2 to −2 in both PbO and SO_2, so O_2 was reduced.

Step 3. Compute e^- lost and e^- gained and draw tie-lines. In the oxidation, the S lost $6e^-$. In the reduction, each O gained $2e^-$:

$$PbS + O_2 \longrightarrow PbO + SO_2$$

loses $6e^-$ / gains $2e^-$ / gains $2e^-$

Step 4. Multiply by factor(s) to make e^- lost equal e^- gained. The S atom loses $6e^-$, and each O in O_2 gains $2e^-$, for a total gain of $4e^-$. Placing the coefficient $\frac{3}{2}$ before O_2 gives 3 O atoms that each gain $2e^-$, for a total gain of $6e^-$:

$$PbS + \tfrac{3}{2}O_2 \longrightarrow PbO + SO_2$$

Step 5. Complete the balancing by inspection. The atoms are balanced, but we multiply all coefficients by 2 to obtain integers and add states of matter:

$$2PbS(s) + 3O_2(g) \longrightarrow 2PbO(s) + 2SO_2(g)$$

Check Reactants (2 Pb, 2 S, 6 O) $\longrightarrow$ products [2 Pb, 2 S, (2 + 4) O]

Follow-Up Problem 4.12 Use the oxidation number method to balance the following equation: $K_2Cr_2O_7(aq) + HI(aq) \longrightarrow KI(aq) + CrI_3(aq) + I_2(s) + H_2O(l)$.

Quantifying Redox Reactions by Titration

In an acid-base titration, a known concentration of a base is used to find an unknown concentration of an acid (or vice versa). Similarly, in a redox titration, a known concentration of oxidizing agent is used to find an unknown concentration of reducing agent (or vice versa). This kind of titration has many applications, from measuring the iron content in drinking water to quantifying vitamin C in fruits and vegetables.

The permanganate ion, MnO_4^-, is a common oxidizing agent because it is deep purple, and so also serves as an indicator. In Figure 4.14, MnO_4^- is used to determine oxalate ion ($C_2O_4^{2-}$) concentration. As long as $C_2O_4^{2-}$ is present, it reduces the added MnO_4^- to faint pink (nearly colorless) Mn^{2+} (Figure 4.14, *left*). When all the $C_2O_4^{2-}$ has been oxidized, the next drop of MnO_4^- turns the solution light purple (Figure 4.14, *right*). This color change indicates the *end point*, which we assume is the same as the *equivalence point*, the point at which the electrons lost by the oxidized species ($C_2O_4^{2-}$) equal the electrons gained by the reduced species (MnO_4^-). We can calculate the $C_2O_4^{2-}$ concentration from the known volume of $Na_2C_2O_4$ solution and the known volume and concentration of $KMnO_4$ solution.

KMnO₄(aq)— **Before titration**   **At end point**

Na₂C₂O₄(aq)

Net ionic equation:

$$\overset{+7}{\underset{\,}{2MnO_4^-}}(aq) + 5\overset{+3}{\underset{\,}{C_2O_4^{2-}}}(aq) + 16H^+(aq) \longrightarrow 2\overset{+2}{\underset{\,}{Mn^{2+}}}(aq) + 10\overset{+4}{\underset{\,}{CO_2}}(g) + 8H_2O(l)$$

Figure 4.14 The redox titration of $C_2O_4^{2-}$ with MnO_4^-.

Sample Problem 4.13 Finding the Amount of Reducing Agent by Titration

Problem Calcium ion (Ca^{2+}) is necessary for the clotting of blood and many other physiological processes. To measure the Ca^{2+} concentration in 1.00 mL of human blood, $Na_2C_2O_4$ solution is added, which precipitates the Ca^{2+} as CaC_2O_4. This solid is dissolved in dilute H_2SO_4 to release $C_2O_4^{2-}$, and 2.05 mL of 4.88×10^{-4} M $KMnO_4$ is required to reach the end point. The balanced equation is

$$2KMnO_4(aq) + 5CaC_2O_4(s) + 8H_2SO_4(aq) \longrightarrow$$
$$2MnSO_4(aq) + K_2SO_4(aq) + 5CaSO_4(s) + 10CO_2(g) + 8H_2O(l)$$

Calculate the amount (mol) of Ca^{2+} in 1.00 mL of blood.

Road Map

Volume (mL) of $KMnO_4$ solution

$\downarrow$ 10^3 mL = 1 L

Volume (L) of $KMnO_4$ solution

$\downarrow$ multiply by M (mol/L)

Amount (mol) of $KMnO_4$

$\downarrow$ molar ratio

Amount (mol) of CaC_2O_4

$\downarrow$ ratio of elements in chemical formula

Amount (mol) of Ca^{2+}

Plan We have to find the amount (mol) of Ca^{2+} from the volume (2.05 mL) and concentration (4.88×10^{-4} M) of $KMnO_4$ used to oxidize the CaC_2O_4 precipitated from 1.00 mL of blood. We find the amount (mol) of $KMnO_4$ needed to reach the end point and use the molar ratio to find the amount (mol) of CaC_2O_4. Then we use the chemical formula, which shows 1 mol of Ca^{2+} for every mol of CaC_2O_4.

Solution Converting volume (mL) and concentration (M) to amount (mol) of $KMnO_4$:

$$\text{Amount (mol) of } KMnO_4 = 2.05 \text{ mL soln} \times \frac{1 \text{ L}}{1000 \text{ mL}} \times \frac{4.88 \times 10^{-4} \text{ mol } KMnO_4}{1 \text{ L soln}}$$
$$= 1.00 \times 10^{-6} \text{ mol } KMnO_4$$

Using the molar ratio to convert amount (mol) of $KMnO_4$ to amount (mol) of CaC_2O_4:

$$\text{Amount (mol) of } CaC_2O_4 = 1.00 \times 10^{-6} \text{ mol } KMnO_4 \times \frac{5 \text{ mol } CaC_2O_4}{2 \text{ mol } KMnO_4}$$
$$= 2.50 \times 10^{-6} \text{ mol } CaC_2O_4$$

Finding the amount (mol) of Ca^{2+}:

$$\text{Amount (mol) of } Ca^{2+} = 2.50 \times 10^{-6} \text{ mol } CaC_2O_4 \times \frac{1 \text{ mol } Ca^{2+}}{1 \text{ mol } CaC_2O_4} = \boxed{2.50 \times 10^{-6} \text{ mol } Ca^+}$$

Check A very small volume of dilute $KMnO_4$ is needed, so 10^{-6} mol of $KMnO_4$ seems reasonable. The molar ratio of CaC_2O_4 to $KMnO_4$ is 5/2, which gives 2.5×10^{-6} mol of CaC_2O_4 and thus 2.5×10^{-6} mol of Ca^{2+}.

Comment 1. When blood is donated, the receiving bag contains $Na_2C_2O_4$ solution, which precipitates the Ca^{2+} ion to prevent clotting.
2. Normal Ca^{2+} concentration in human adult blood is 9.0 to 11.5 mg Ca^{2+}/100 mL. If we multiply the amount of Ca^{2+} in 1 mL by 100 and then multiply by the molar mass of Ca (40.08 g/mol), we get 1.0×10^{-2} g, or 10.0 mg Ca^{2+} in 100 mL:

$$\text{Mass (mg) of } Ca^{2+} = \frac{2.50 \times 10^{-6} \text{ mol } Ca^{2+}}{1 \text{ mL}} \times 100 \text{ mL} \times \frac{40.08 \text{ g } Ca^{2+}}{1 \text{ mol } Ca^{2+}} \times \frac{1000 \text{ mg}}{1 \text{ g}}$$
$$= 10.0 \text{ mg } Ca^{2+}$$

Follow-Up Problem 4.13 When 2.50 mL of low-fat milk was treated with sodium oxalate and the precipitate dissolved in H_2SO_4, 6.53 mL of 4.56×10^{-3} M $KMnO_4$ was required to reach the end point. **(a)** Calculate the molarity of Ca^{2+} in the milk sample. **(b)** What is the concentration of Ca^{2+} in g/L? Is this value consistent with the typical value for milk of about 1.2 g Ca^{2+}/L?

■ Summary of Section 4.5

- When one reactant has a greater attraction for electrons than another, there is a net movement of electrons, and a redox reaction takes place. Electron gain (reduction) and electron loss (oxidation) occur simultaneously.
- Assigning oxidation numbers to all atoms in a reaction is a method for identifying a redox reaction. The species that is oxidized (contains an atom that increases in oxidation number) is the reducing agent; the species that is reduced (contains an atom that decreases in oxidation number) is the oxidizing agent.
- We balance redox reactions by keeping track of the changes in oxidation number.
- A redox titration determines the concentration of an oxidizing agent from the known concentration of the reducing agent (or vice versa).

4.6 • ELEMENTS IN REDOX REACTIONS

In many redox reactions, such as those in Sample Problems 4.11 and 4.12, *atoms occur as an element on one side of an equation and as part of a compound on the other.** One way to classify these is by comparing the *numbers* of reactants and products. With that approach, we have three types—*combination, decomposition,* and *displacement;* one other type involving elements is *combustion.* In this section, we survey each type with several examples.

Combination Redox Reactions

In a combination redox reaction, two or more reactants, at least one of which is an element, form a compound:

$$X + Y \longrightarrow Z$$

Combining Two Elements Two elements may react to form binary ionic or covalent compounds. Here are some important examples:

1. *Metal and nonmetal form an ionic compound.* Figure 4.15 shows a typical example, the reaction between the alkali metal potassium and the halogen chlorine, on the macroscopic, atomic, and symbolic levels. Note the change in oxidation numbers in the balanced equation: K is oxidized, so it is the reducing agent; Cl_2 is reduced, so it is the oxidizing agent. In fact, whenever a binary ionic compound forms from its elements, *the metal is the reducing agent and the nonmetal is the oxidizing agent.*

---

*Many other redox reactions, however, do *not* involve elements (see Sample Problem 4.13).

Figure 4.15 Combining elements to form an ionic compound: potassium metal and chlorine gas form solid potassium chloride. Darker atoms in the atomic view indicate the stoichiometry.

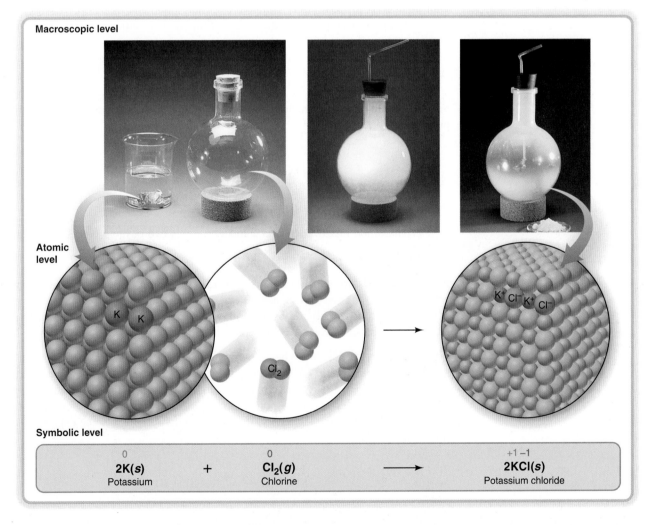

Macroscopic level

Atomic level

K   K

Cl_2

K^+ Cl^- K^+ Cl^-

Symbolic level

0		0		+1 −1
2K(s)	+	**$Cl_2(g)$**	$\longrightarrow$	**2KCl(s)**
Potassium		Chlorine		Potassium chloride

Aluminum reacts with O_2, as does nearly every metal, to form an ionic oxide:

$$\overset{0}{4Al}(s) + \overset{0}{3O_2}(g) \longrightarrow \overset{+3\ -2}{2Al_2O_3}(s)$$

The Al_2O_3 layer on the surface of an aluminum pot prevents oxygen from reacting with the next layer of Al atoms, thus protecting the metal from further oxidation.

2. *Two nonmetals form a covalent compound.* In one of thousands of examples, ammonia forms from nitrogen and hydrogen in a reaction that occurs in industry on an enormous scale:

$$\overset{0}{N_2}(g) + \overset{0}{3H_2}(g) \longrightarrow \overset{+1}{\underset{-3}{2NH_3}}(g)$$

Halogens react with many other nonmetals, as in the formation of phosphorus trichloride, a reactant in the production of pesticides and other organic compounds:

$$\overset{0}{P_4}(s) + \overset{0}{6Cl_2}(g) \longrightarrow \overset{+3}{\underset{-1}{4PCl_3}}(l)$$

Nearly every nonmetal reacts with O_2 to form a covalent oxide, as when nitrogen monoxide forms from the nitrogen and oxygen in air at the very high temperatures created by lightning and in a car's engine:

$$\overset{0}{N_2}(g) + \overset{0}{O_2}(g) \longrightarrow \overset{+2}{\underset{-2}{2NO}}(g)$$

Combining Compound and Element Many binary covalent compounds react with nonmetals to form larger compounds. Many nonmetal oxides react with additional O_2 to form "higher" oxides (those with more O atoms in each molecule). For example,

$$\overset{+2}{\underset{-2}{2NO}}(g) + \overset{0}{O_2}(g) \longrightarrow \overset{+4}{\underset{-2}{2NO_2}}(g)$$

Similarly, many nonmetal halides combine with additional halogen to form "higher" halides:

$$\overset{+3}{\underset{-1}{PCl_3}}(l) + \overset{0}{Cl_2}(g) \longrightarrow \overset{+5}{\underset{-1}{PCl_5}}(s)$$

Decomposition Redox Reactions

In a *decomposition redox reaction,* a compound forms two or more products, at least one of which is an element:

$$Z \longrightarrow X + Y$$

In any decomposition reaction, the reactant absorbs enough energy for one or more bonds to break. The energy can take several forms, but the most important are decomposition by heat (thermal) and by electricity (electrolytic). The products are either elements or elements and smaller compounds.

Thermal Decomposition When the energy absorbed is heat, the reaction is called a *thermal decomposition.* (A Greek delta, Δ, above the yield arrow indicates strong heating is required.) Many metal oxides, chlorates, and perchlorates release oxygen when strongly heated. Heating potassium chlorate is a method for forming small amounts of oxygen in the laboratory; the same reaction occurs in some explosives and fireworks:

$$\overset{+1}{\underset{}{2K}}\overset{+5}{\underset{-2}{Cl O_3}}(s) \overset{\Delta}{\longrightarrow} \overset{+1}{\underset{-1}{2KCl}}(s) + \overset{0}{3O_2}(g)$$

Figure 4.16 Decomposition of the compound mercury(II) oxide to its elements.

The decomposition of mercury(II) oxide, used by Lavoisier in his classic experiments, is shown in Figure 4.16. Notice that, in these cases, the lone reactant is the oxidizing *and* the reducing agent. For example, with the reactant HgO, the O^{2-} ion reduces the Hg^{2+} ion, and at the same time, Hg^{2+} oxidizes O^{2-}.

Electrolytic Decomposition In the process of electrolysis, a compound absorbs electrical energy and decomposes into its elements. In the early 19th century, the observation of the electrolysis of water was crucial for establishing atomic masses:

$$\overset{+1-2}{2H_2O(l)} \xrightarrow{\text{electricity}} \overset{0}{2H_2(g)} + \overset{0}{O_2(g)}$$

Many active metals, such as sodium, magnesium, and calcium, are produced industrially by electrolysis of their molten halides:

$$\overset{+2-1}{MgCl_2(l)} \xrightarrow{\text{electricity}} \overset{0}{Mg(l)} + \overset{0}{Cl_2(g)}$$

(We examine the details of electrolysis in Chapter 21 and its role in the industrial recovery of several elements in Chapter 22.)

Displacement Redox Reactions and Activity Series

In any *displacement reaction,* the number of substances on the two sides of the equation remains the same, but atoms (or ions) exchange places. There are two types:

1. In *double*-displacement (metathesis) reactions, such as precipitation and acid-base reactions (Sections 4.3 and 4.4), atoms (or ions) of two *compounds* exchange places; these reactions are *not* redox processes:

$$AB + CD \longrightarrow AC + BD$$

2. In *single*-displacement reactions, one of the substances is an *element;* therefore, *all single-displacement reactions **are** redox processes:*

$$X + YZ \longrightarrow XZ + Y$$

In solution, single-displacement reactions occur when an atom of one element displaces the ion of another: if the displacement involves metals, the atom *reduces* the

Figure 4.17 The active metal lithium displaces hydrogen from water. Only water molecules involved as products of the reaction are red and blue.

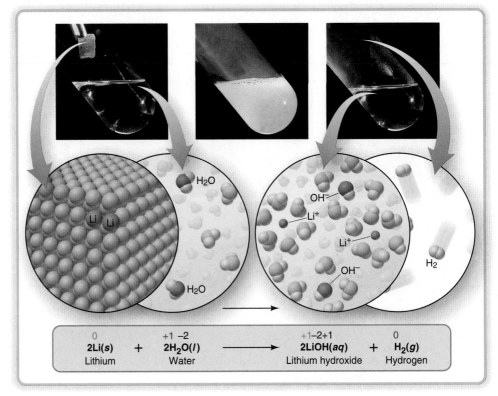

$$\underset{\substack{0 \\ \text{Lithium}}}{2\text{Li}(s)} + \underset{\substack{+1\ -2 \\ \text{Water}}}{2\text{H}_2\text{O}(l)} \longrightarrow \underset{\substack{+1-2+1 \\ \text{Lithium hydroxide}}}{2\text{LiOH}(aq)} + \underset{\substack{0 \\ \text{Hydrogen}}}{\text{H}_2(g)}$$

ion; if it involves nonmetals (specifically halogens), the atom *oxidizes* the ion. In two *activity series*—one for metals and one for halogens—the elements are ranked in order of their ability to displace hydrogen (for metals) and one another.

The Activity Series of the Metals Metals are ranked by their ability to displace H_2 from various sources and another metal from solution. In all displacements of H_2, the metal is the reducing agent (O.N. increases), and water or acid is the oxidizing agent (O.N. of H decreases). The activity series of the metals is based on these facts:

- *The most reactive metals displace H_2 from liquid water.* Group 1A(1) metals and Ca, Sr, and Ba from Group 2A(2) displace H_2 from water (Figure 4.17).
- *Slightly less reactive metals displace H_2 from steam.* Heat supplied by steam is needed for less reactive metals such as Al and Zn to displace H_2:

$$\underset{0}{2\text{Al}(s)} + \underset{+1-2}{6\text{H}_2\text{O}(g)} \xrightarrow{\Delta} \underset{+3-2}{2\text{Al(OH)}_3(s)} + \underset{0}{3\text{H}_2(g)}$$

- *Still less reactive metals displace H_2 from acids.* The higher concentration of H^+ in acid solutions is needed for even less reactive metals such as Ni and Sn to displace H_2 (Figure 4.18). For nickel, the net ionic equation is

$$\underset{0}{\text{Ni}(s)} + \underset{+1}{2\text{H}^+(aq)} \longrightarrow \underset{+2}{\text{Ni}^{2+}(aq)} + \underset{0}{\text{H}_2(g)}$$

- *The least reactive metals cannot displace H_2 from any source.* Fortunately, precious metals, such as silver, gold, and platinum, do *not* react with water or acid.
- *An atom of one metal displaces the ion of another.* Comparisons of metal reactivity show, for example, that Zn metal displaces Cu^{2+} ion from aqueous CuSO_4:

$$\underset{+2}{\text{Cu}^{2+}(aq)} + \underset{+6\ -2}{\text{SO}_4^{2-}(aq)} + \underset{0}{\text{Zn}(s)} \longrightarrow \underset{0}{\text{Cu}(s)} + \underset{+2}{\text{Zn}^{2+}(aq)} + \underset{+6\ -2}{\text{SO}_4^{2-}(aq)}$$

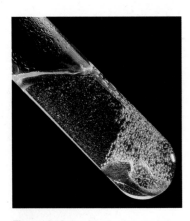

Figure 4.18 The displacement of H_2 from acid by nickel.

And Figure 4.19 shows that Cu metal displaces silver (Ag^+) ion from solution; therefore, zinc is more reactive than copper, which is more reactive than silver.

Figure 4.19 A more reactive metal (Cu) displacing the ion of a less reactive metal (Ag⁺) from solution.

Copper wire

Silver nitrate solution

Copper wire coated with silver

Copper nitrate solution

Cu^{2+}

Ag^+

Ag^+

$2e^-$

Ag atoms coating wire

Cu atoms in wire

$$\underset{+1\ +5\ -2}{2AgNO_3(aq)} + \underset{0}{Cu(s)} \longrightarrow \underset{+2\ +5\ -2}{Cu(NO_3)_2(aq)} + \underset{0}{2Ag(s)}$$

Many such reactions form the basis of the **activity series of the metals.** Note these two points from Figure 4.20:

- Elements higher on the list are stronger reducing agents than elements lower down; in other words, any metal can reduce the ions of metals below it.
- From higher to lower, a metal can displace H_2 (reduce H^+) from water, steam, acid, or not at all.

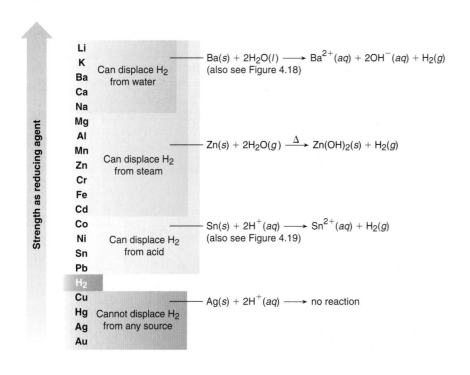

Strength as reducing agent

Li
K
Ba   **Can displace H₂ from water** ⎯⎯ $Ba(s) + 2H_2O(l) \longrightarrow Ba^{2+}(aq) + 2OH^-(aq) + H_2(g)$
Ca   (also see Figure 4.18)
Na
Mg
Al
Mn   **Can displace H₂ from steam** ⎯⎯ $Zn(s) + 2H_2O(g) \xrightarrow{\Delta} Zn(OH)_2(s) + H_2(g)$
Zn
Cr
Fe
Cd
Co
Ni   **Can displace H₂ from acid** ⎯⎯ $Sn(s) + 2H^+(aq) \longrightarrow Sn^{2+}(aq) + H_2(g)$
Sn   (also see Figure 4.19)
Pb
H₂
Cu
Hg   **Cannot displace H₂ from any source** ⎯⎯ $Ag(s) + 2H^+(aq) \longrightarrow$ no reaction
Ag
Au

Figure 4.20 The activity series of the metals. The most active metal (strongest reducing agent) is at the top, and the least active metal (weakest reducing agent) is at the bottom.

The Activity Series of the Halogens Reactivity of the elements decreases down Group 7A(17), so we have

$$F_2 > Cl_2 > Br_2 > I_2$$

A halogen higher in the group is a stronger oxidizing agent than one lower down. Thus, elemental chlorine can oxidize bromide ions (*below*) or iodide ions from solution, and elemental bromine can oxidize iodide ions:

$$\overset{-1}{2Br^-}(aq) + \overset{0}{Cl_2}(aq) \longrightarrow \overset{0}{Br_2}(aq) + \overset{-1}{2Cl^-}(aq)$$

Combustion Reactions

Combustion is the process of combining with oxygen, most commonly with the release of heat and the production of light, as in a flame. Combustion reactions are not classified by the number of reactants and products, but *all of these reactions are redox processes* because elemental oxygen is a reactant:

$$2CO(g) + O_2(g) \longrightarrow 2CO_2(g)$$

The combustion reactions that we commonly use to produce energy involve coal, petroleum, gasoline, natural gas, or wood as a reactant. These mixtures consist of substances with many C—C and C—H bonds, which break during the reaction, and each C and H atom combines with oxygen to form CO_2 and H_2O. The combustion of butane is typical:

$$2C_4H_{10}(g) + 13O_2(g) \longrightarrow 8CO_2(g) + 10H_2O(g)$$

Biological *respiration* is a multistep combustion process that occurs within our cells when we "burn" foodstuffs, such as glucose, for energy:

$$C_6H_{12}O_6(s) + 6O_2(g) \longrightarrow 6CO_2(g) + 6H_2O(g) + energy$$

Sample Problem 4.14 | **Identifying the Type of Redox Reaction**

Problem Classify each of the following redox reactions as a combination, decomposition, or displacement reaction, write a balanced molecular equation for each, as well as total and net ionic equations for part (c), and identify the oxidizing and reducing agents:
(a) Magnesium(*s*) + nitrogen(*g*) $\longrightarrow$ magnesium nitride(*s*)
(b) Hydrogen peroxide(*l*) $\longrightarrow$ water + oxygen gas
(c) Aluminum(*s*) + lead(II) nitrate(*aq*) $\longrightarrow$ aluminum nitrate(*aq*) + lead(*s*)

Plan To decide on reaction type, recall that combination reactions produce fewer products than reactants, decomposition reactions produce more products, and displacement reactions have the same number of reactants and products. The oxidation number (O.N.) becomes more positive for the reducing agent and less positive for the oxidizing agent.

Solution (a) Combination: two substances form one. This reaction occurs, along with formation of magnesium oxide, when magnesium burns in air, which is mostly N_2:

$$\overset{0}{3Mg}(s) + \overset{0}{N_2}(g) \longrightarrow \overset{+2\ -3}{Mg_3N_2}(s)$$

Mg is the reducing agent; N_2 is the oxidizing agent.

(b) Decomposition: one substance forms two. Because hydrogen peroxide is very unstable and breaks down from heat, light, or just shaking, this reaction occurs within every bottle of this common household antiseptic:

$$\overset{+1\ -1}{2H_2O_2}(l) \longrightarrow \overset{+1\ -2}{2H_2O}(l) + \overset{0}{O_2}(g)$$

H_2O_2 is both the oxidizing *and* the reducing agent. The O.N. of O in peroxides is -1. It is shown in blue *and* red because it both increases to 0 in O_2 and decreases to -2 in H_2O.

(c) Displacement: two substances form two others. As Figure 4.20 shows, Al is more active than Pb and, thus, displaces it from aqueous solution:

$$\overset{0}{2Al(s)} + \overset{+2 \ +5 \ \overset{-2}{\mid}}{3Pb(NO_3)_2(aq)} \longrightarrow \overset{+3 \ +5 \ \overset{-2}{\mid}}{2Al(NO_3)_3(aq)} + \overset{0}{3Pb(s)}$$

Al is the reducing agent; $Pb(NO_3)_2$ is the oxidizing agent.

The total ionic equation is

$$2Al(s) + 3Pb^{2+}(aq) + 6NO_3^-(aq) \longrightarrow 2Al^{3+}(aq) + 6NO_3^-(aq) + 3Pb(s)$$

The net ionic equation is

$$2Al(s) + 3Pb^{2+}(aq) \longrightarrow 2Al^{3+}(aq) + 3Pb(s)$$

Follow-Up Problem 4.14 Classify each of the following redox reactions as a combination, decomposition, or displacement reaction, write a balanced molecular equation for each, as well as total and net ionic equations for parts (b) and (c), and identify the oxidizing and reducing agents:
(a) $S_8(s) + F_2(g) \longrightarrow SF_4(g)$
(b) $CsI(aq) + Cl_2(aq) \longrightarrow CsCl(aq) + I_2(aq)$
(c) $Ni(NO_3)_2(aq) + Cr(s) \longrightarrow Ni(s) + Cr(NO_3)_3(aq)$

◼ Summary of Section 4.6

- A reaction that has an element as reactant or product is a redox reaction.
- In combination redox reactions, elements combine to form a compound, or a compound and an element combine.
- In decomposition redox reactions, compounds break down by absorption of heat or electricity into elements or into a compound and an element.
- In displacement redox reactions, one element displaces the ion of another from solution.
- Activity series rank elements in order of ability to displace each other. A more reactive metal can displace (reduce) hydrogen ion or the ion of a less reactive metal from solution. A more reactive halogen can displace (oxidize) the ion of a less reactive halogen from solution.
- Combustion releases heat through a redox reaction of a substance with O_2.

4.7 • THE REVERSIBILITY OF REACTIONS AND THE EQUILIBRIUM STATE

So far, we have viewed reactions as transformations of reactants into products that proceed until they are complete, that is, until the limiting reactant is used up. However, many reactions stop before this happens because two opposing reactions are taking place simultaneously: the forward (left-to-right) reaction continues, but the reverse (right-to-left) reaction occurs just as fast (at the same rate). At this point, *no further changes appear in the amounts of reactants or products,* and the reaction mixture has reached **dynamic equilibrium.** On the macroscopic level, the reaction is *static,* but it is *dynamic* on the molecular level.

In principle, *every reaction is reversible and will reach dynamic equilibrium if all the reactants and products are present.* Consider the reversible breakdown and formation of calcium carbonate. When heated, it breaks down to calcium oxide and carbon dioxide:

$$CaCO_3(s) \xrightarrow{\Delta} CaO(s) + CO_2(g) \text{ [breakdown]}$$

And it forms when calcium oxide and carbon dioxide react:

$$CaO(s) + CO_2(g) \longrightarrow CaCO_3(s) \text{ [formation]}$$

Let's study this process with two experiments:

1. We place $CaCO_3$ in an *open* steel container and heat it to approximately 900°C (Figure 4.21A). The $CaCO_3$ starts breaking down to CaO and CO_2, and the CO_2 escapes from the open container. The reaction goes to completion because the reverse reaction (formation) cannot occur in the absence of CO_2.

2. We perform the same experiment in a *closed* container (Figure 4.21B). The breakdown (forward reaction) starts as before, but soon the CaO and CO_2 start reacting with each other (formation). Gradually, with time, as the amounts of CaO and CO_2 increase, the formation reaction speeds up. Eventually, the reverse reaction (formation) occurs as fast as the forward reaction (breakdown), and the amounts of $CaCO_3$, CaO, and CO_2 no longer change: the system has reached a state of equilibrium. We indicate this condition with a pair of arrows pointing in opposite directions:

$$CaCO_3(s) \rightleftharpoons CaO(s) + CO_2(g)$$

In contrast to the reaction in the open container, equilibrium *is* reached because *all the substances remain in contact with each other.*

A Nonequilibrium system

B Equilibrium system

Figure 4.21 The equilibrium state. **A,** In an *open* container, $CaCO_3$ breaks down completely because CO_2 escapes. **B,** In a *closed* container, $CaCO_3$ breakdown and formation reach equilibrium.

Reaction reversibility applies to other systems as well:

1. *Weak acids in water.* Weak acids dissociate very little into ions in water because the dissociation becomes balanced by a reassociation of H_3O^+ with the anion to re-form the weak acid and water. For example, when acetic acid dissolves, some CH_3COOH molecules transfer a proton to H_2O and form H_3O^+ and CH_3COO^- ions. As more ions form, the ions react with each other more often to re-form acetic acid and water:

$$CH_3COOH(aq) + H_2O(l) \rightleftharpoons H_3O^+(aq) + CH_3COO^-(aq)$$

In fact, in 0.1 M CH_3COOH at 25°C, only about 1.3% of acid molecules are dissociated! Each weak acid dissociates to its own extent. For example, under the same conditions, propionic acid (CH_3CH_2COOH) is 1.1% dissociated, and hydrofluoric acid (HF) is 8.6% dissociated.

2. *Weak bases in water.* Similarly, the weak base ammonia reacts with water to form NH_4^+ and OH^- ions. As more ions form, they interact more often to re-form ammonia and water, and the rates of the forward and reverse reactions soon balance:

$$NH_3(aq) + H_2O(l) \rightleftharpoons NH_4^+(aq) + OH^-(aq)$$

The weak base methylamine (CH_3NH_2) reacts with water to a greater extent than ammonia does before reaching equilibrium, and the weak base aniline ($C_6H_5NH_2$) reacts to a lesser extent.

3. *Gas-forming reactions.* When an acid reacts with a carbonate, the reaction goes to completion in an open container because the CO_2 escapes. But, if the container is closed to keep the CO_2 present, the reverse reaction takes place and the mixture reaches equilibrium.

4. *Other acid-base and precipitation reactions.* These processes seem to "go to completion" because the ions become tied up in the product, either as water (acid-base) or as an insoluble solid (precipitation), and are not available to re-form reactants. In truth, though, water and ionic precipitates do dissociate to an extremely small extent, so these reactions also reach equilibrium, but the final reaction mixture consists of *almost* all product.

Thus, some reactions proceed very little before reaching equilibrium, others proceed almost to completion, and still others reach equilibrium with significant amounts of both reactants *and* products present. In Chapter 20, we'll examine the factors that determine to what extent a reaction proceeds.

Dynamic equilibrium occurs in many natural systems, from the cycling of water in the environment to the nuclear processes occurring in stars. We examine equilibrium in chemical and physical systems in Chapters 12, 13, and 17 through 21.

■ Summary of Section 4.7

- Every reaction is reversible if all the substances involved are present.
- As the amounts of products increase, the reactants begin to re-form. When the reverse reaction occurs as rapidly as the forward reaction, the amounts of the substances no longer change, and the reaction mixture has reached dynamic equilibrium.
- Weak acids and bases reach equilibrium in water with a very small proportion of their molecules dissociated.
- An aqueous ionic reaction "goes to completion" because a product is removed (gas) or products are formed that react very slightly in a reverse reaction (water or precipitate).

CHAPTER REVIEW GUIDE

Learning Objectives Relevant section (§) and/or sample problem (SP) numbers appear in parentheses.

Understand These Concepts

1. Why water is a polar molecule and how it dissociates ionic compounds into ions (§4.1)
2. The differing nature of the species present when ionic and covalent compounds dissolve in water (§4.1)
3. The distinctions among strong electrolytes, weak electrolytes, and nonelectrolytes (§4.1, §4.4)
4. The three types of equations that specify the species and the chemical change in an aqueous ionic reaction (§4.2)
5. The key event in three classes of aqueous ionic reactions (§4.3–§4.5)
6. How to decide whether a precipitation reaction occurs (§4.3)
7. The distinction between strong and weak aqueous acids and bases (§4.4)
8. How acid-base reactions are proton transfers; how carbonates (and sulfites) act as bases in gas-forming reactions (§4.4)
9. The distinction between a transfer and a shift of electrons in the formation of ionic and covalent compounds (§4.5)
10. The relation between change in oxidation number and identity of oxidizing and reducing agents (§4.5)
11. The presence of elements in combination, decomposition, and displacement redox reactions; the meaning of an activity series (§4.6)
12. The balance between forward and reverse reactions in dynamic equilibrium; why some acids and bases are weak (§4.7)

Master These Skills

1. Using molecular scenes to depict a soluble ionic compound in water (SP 4.1)
2. Using the formula of a compound to find the number of moles of ions in solution (SP 4.2)
3. Predicting whether a precipitation reaction occurs (SP 4.3)
4. Using molecular depictions to understand a precipitation reaction (SP 4.4)
5. Determining the number of H^+ (or OH^-) ions in an aqueous acid (or base) solution (SP 4.5)
6. Writing ionic equations to describe precipitation and acid-base reactions (SPs 4.3, 4.4, 4.6)
7. Writing acid-base equations as proton transfers (SP 4.7)
8. Calculating an unknown concentration from an acid-base or redox titration (SPs 4.8, 4.13)
9. Determining the oxidation number of any element in a compound (SP 4.9)
10. Identifying redox reactions from changes in O.N.s (SP 4.10)
11. Identifying the oxidizing and reducing agents in a redox reaction (SP 4.11)
12. Balancing redox reactions by the oxidation number method (SP 4.12)
13. Distinguishing among combination, decomposition, and displacement redox reactions (SP 4.14)
14. Predicting the products of a single-dissociation reaction based on an activity series (§4.6)

Key Terms   Page numbers appear in parentheses.

Section 4.1
polar molecule (136)
solvated (136)
electrolyte (137)
nonelectrolyte (139)

Section 4.2
molecular equation (140)
total ionic equation (141)
spectator ion (141)
net ionic equation (141)

Section 4.3
precipitation reaction (141)
precipitate (141)
metathesis reaction (143)

Section 4.4
acid-base (neutralization) reaction (145)
acid (145)
base (145)
salt (148)

titration (152)
equivalence point (152)
end point (152)

Section 4.5
oxidation-reduction (redox) reaction (153)
oxidation (154)
reduction (154)
oxidizing agent (154)
reducing agent (154)

oxidation number (O.N.) (or oxidation state) (155)
oxidation number method (158)

Section 4.6
activity series of the metals (165)

Section 4.7
dynamic equilibrium (167)

Brief Solutions to Follow-Up Problems

4.1 The compound is $BaCl_2$.

$$\text{Mass (g) of } BaCl_2 = 9 \text{ particles} \times \frac{0.05 \text{ mol particles}}{1 \text{ particle}}$$
$$\times \frac{1 \text{ mol } BaCl_2}{3 \text{ mol particles}} \times \frac{208.2 \text{ g } BaCl_2}{1 \text{ mol } BaCl_2}$$
$$= 31.2 \text{ g } BaCl_2$$

4.2 (a) $KClO_4(s) \xrightarrow{H_2O} K^+(aq) + ClO_4^-(aq)$;
2 mol of K^+ and 2 mol of ClO_4^-

(b) $Mg(C_2H_3O_2)_2(s) \xrightarrow{H_2O} Mg^{2+}(aq) + 2C_2H_3O_2^-(aq)$;
2.49 mol of Mg^{2+} and 4.97 mol of $C_2H_3O_2^-$

(c) $(NH_4)_2CrO_4(s) \xrightarrow{H_2O} 2NH_4^+(aq) + CrO_4^{2-}(aq)$;
6.24 mol of NH_4^+ and 3.12 mol of CrO_4^{2-}

(d) $NaHSO_4(s) \xrightarrow{H_2O} Na^+(aq) + HSO_4^-(aq)$;
0.73 mol of Na^+ and 0.73 mol of HSO_4^-

4.3 (a) $Fe^{3+}(aq) + 3Cl^-(aq) + 3Cs^+(aq) + PO_4^{3-}(aq) \longrightarrow$
$$FePO_4(s) + 3Cl^-(aq) + 3Cs^+(aq)$$

$$Fe^{3+}(aq) + PO_4^{3-}(aq) \longrightarrow FePO_4(s)$$

(b) $2Na^+(aq) + 2OH^-(aq) + Cd^{2+}(aq) + 2NO_3^-(aq) \longrightarrow$
$$2Na^+(aq) + 2NO_3^-(aq) + Cd(OH)_2(s)$$
$2OH^-(aq) + Cd^{2+}(aq) \longrightarrow Cd(OH)_2(s)$
(c) No reaction occurs
(d) $2Ag^+(aq) + 2NO_3^-(aq) + Ba^{2+}(aq) + 2Cl^-(aq) \longrightarrow$
$$2AgCl(s) + 2NO_3^-(aq) + Ba^{2+}(aq)$$
$Ag^+(aq) + Cl^-(aq) \longrightarrow AgCl(s)$

4.4 (a) Beaker A contains a solution of $Zn(NO_3)_2$.
(b) Beaker B contains a solution of $Ba(OH)_2$.
(c) The precipitate is zinc hydroxide, and the spectator ions are Ba^{2+} and NO_3^-.
Molecular: $Zn(NO_3)_2(aq) + Ba(OH)_2(aq) \longrightarrow$
$$Zn(OH)_2(s) + Ba(NO_3)_2(aq)$$
Total ionic:
$Zn^{2+}(aq) + 2NO_3^-(aq) + Ba^{2+}(aq) + 2OH^-(aq) \longrightarrow$
$$Zn(OH)_2(s) + Ba^{2+}(aq) + 2NO_3^-(aq)$$
Net ionic: $Zn^{2+}(aq) + 2OH^-(aq) \longrightarrow Zn(OH)_2(s)$
(d) The OH^- ion is limiting.
Mass (g) of $Zn(OH)_2$

$$= 6 \text{ } \cancel{OH^- \text{ particles}} \times \frac{0.050 \text{ } \cancel{\text{mol } OH^- \text{ ions}}}{1 \text{ } \cancel{OH^- \text{ particle}}}$$
$$\times \frac{1 \text{ } \cancel{\text{mol } Zn(OH)_2}}{2 \text{ } \cancel{\text{mol } OH^- \text{ ions}}} \times \frac{99.43 \text{ g } Zn(OH)_2}{1 \text{ } \cancel{\text{mol } Zn(OH)_2}}$$
$$= 15 \text{ g } Zn(OH)_2$$

4.5 No. of OH^- ions $= 451 \text{ } \cancel{mL} \times \dfrac{1 \text{ } \cancel{L}}{10^3 \text{ } \cancel{mL}}$
$$\times \frac{1.20 \text{ } \cancel{\text{mol } KOH}}{1 \text{ } \cancel{L \text{ soln}}} \times \frac{1 \text{ } \cancel{\text{mol } OH^-}}{1 \text{ } \cancel{\text{mol } KOH}}$$
$$\times \frac{6.022 \times 10^{23} \text{ } OH^- \text{ ions}}{1 \text{ } \cancel{\text{mol } OH^-}}$$
$$= 3.26 \times 10^{23} \text{ } OH^-$$

4.6 $Ca(OH)_2(aq) + 2HNO_3(aq) \longrightarrow Ca(NO_3)_2(aq) + 2H_2O(l)$
$Ca^{2+}(aq) + 2OH^-(aq) + 2H^+(aq) + 2NO_3^-(aq) \longrightarrow$
$$Ca^{2+}(aq) + 2NO_3^-(aq) + 2H_2O(l)$$
$H^+(aq) + OH^-(aq) \longrightarrow H_2O(l)$

4.7 $2H_3O^+(aq) + 2Br^-(aq) + Ca^{2+}(aq) + 2HCO_3^-(aq) \longrightarrow$
$$2CO_2(g) + 4H_2O(l) + 2Br^-(aq) + Ca^{2+}(aq)$$

or $H_3O^+(aq) + HCO_3^-(aq) \longrightarrow CO_2(g) + 2H_2O(l)$
The salt is calcium bromide, $CaBr_2$.

4.8 $Ba(OH)_2(aq) + 2HCl(aq) \longrightarrow BaCl_2(aq) + 2H_2O(l)$
Volume (L) of soln

$$= 50.00 \text{ } \cancel{mL \text{ HCl soln}} \times \frac{1 \text{ L}}{10^3 \text{ } \cancel{mL}} \times \frac{0.1016 \text{ } \cancel{\text{mol } HCl}}{1 \text{ } \cancel{L \text{ soln}}}$$
$$\times \frac{1 \text{ } \cancel{\text{mol } Ba(OH)_2}}{2 \text{ } \cancel{\text{mol } HCl}} \times \frac{1 \text{ L soln}}{0.1292 \text{ } \cancel{\text{mol } Ba(OH)_2}}$$
$$= 0.01966 \text{ L}$$

4.9 (a) O.N. of $Sc = +3$; O.N. of $O = -2$
(b) O.N. of $Ga = +3$; O.N. of $Cl = -1$
(c) O.N. of $H = +1$; O.N. of $P = +5$; O.N. of $O = -2$
(d) O.N. of $I = +3$; O.N. of $F = -1$

4.10

O.N. decreased: *reduction*

(a) $\overset{+3}{\underset{|-1}{N}}Cl_3(l) + 3\overset{+1}{\underset{|+1}{H}}_2O(l) \longrightarrow \overset{-3}{\underset{|+1}{N}}H_3(aq) + 3\overset{-2}{\underset{|+1|+1}{H}}OCl(aq)$

O.N. increased: *oxidation*

Redox; O.N. of N decreases, and O.N. of Cl increases.

(b) $\overset{+5}{\underset{+1 \text{ } |-2}{Ag}}NO_3(aq) + \overset{+1}{\underset{-3 \text{ } |-1}{NH_4}}I(aq) \longrightarrow \overset{-1}{\underset{+1|}{Ag}}I(s) + \overset{+1}{\underset{-3 \text{ } |+5 \text{ } -2}{NH_4}}NO_3(aq)$

Not redox; no changes in O.N. values.

O.N. decreased: *reduction*

(c) $2\overset{+1 \text{ } -2}{\underset{|\text{ } |}{H_2S}}(g) + 3\overset{0}{\underset{|}{O_2}}(g) \longrightarrow 2\overset{+4 -2}{\underset{|\text{ } |}{SO_2}}(g) + 2\overset{+1 \text{ } -2}{\underset{|\text{ } |}{H_2O}}(g)$

O.N. increased: *oxidation*

Redox; O.N. of S increases, and O.N. of O decreases.

4.11 (a) Fe is the reducing agent; Cl_2 is the oxidizing agent.
(b) C_2H_6 is the reducing agent; O_2 is the oxidizing agent.
(c) CO is the reducing agent; I_2O_5 is the oxidizing agent.

4.12 $K_2Cr_2O_7(aq) + 14HI(aq) \longrightarrow$
$$2KI(aq) + 2CrI_3(aq) + 3I_2(s) + 7H_2O(l)$$

4.13 (a) Amount (mol) of Ca^{2+}

$$= 6.53 \text{ } \cancel{mL \text{ soln}} \times \frac{1 \text{ } \cancel{L}}{10^3 \text{ } \cancel{mL}} \times \frac{4.56 \times 10^{-3} \text{ } \cancel{\text{mol } KMnO_4}}{1 \text{ } \cancel{L \text{ soln}}}$$
$$\times \frac{5 \text{ } \cancel{\text{mol } CaC_2O_4}}{2 \text{ } \cancel{\text{mol } KMnO_4}} \times \frac{1 \text{ mol } Ca^{2+}}{1 \text{ } \cancel{\text{mol } CaC_2O_4}}$$
$$= 7.44 \times 10^{-5} \text{ mol } Ca^{2+}$$

Molarity of $Ca^{2+} = \dfrac{7.44 \times 10^{-2} \text{ mol } Ca^{2+}}{2.50 \text{ } \cancel{mL \text{ milk}}} \times \dfrac{10^3 \text{ } \cancel{mL}}{1 \text{ L}}$
$$= 2.98 \times 10^{-2} \text{ } M \text{ } Ca^{2+}$$

(b) Conc. of Ca^{2+} (g/L) $= \dfrac{2.98 \times 10^{-2} \text{ } \cancel{\text{mol } Ca^{2+}}}{1 \text{ L}} \times \dfrac{40.08 \text{ g } Ca^{2+}}{1 \text{ } \cancel{\text{mol } Ca^{2+}}}$
$$= \frac{1.19 \text{ g } Ca^{2+}}{1 \text{ L}}$$

Yes, the calculated value is close to the typical value.

4.14 (a) Combination: $S_8(s) + 16F_2(g) \longrightarrow 8SF_4(g)$
S_8 is the reducing agent; F_2 is the oxidizing agent.
(b) Displacement:
$2CsI(aq) + Cl_2(aq) \longrightarrow 2CsCl(aq) + I_2(aq)$
$2Cs^+(aq) + 2I^-(aq) + Cl_2(aq) \longrightarrow 2Cs^+(aq) + 2Cl^-(aq) + I_2(aq)$
$2I^-(aq) + Cl_2(aq) \longrightarrow 2Cl^-(aq) + I_2(aq)$
Cl_2 is the oxidizing agent; CsI is the reducing agent.
(c) Displacement:
$3Ni(NO_3)_2(aq) + 2Cr(s) \longrightarrow 3Ni(s) + 2Cr(NO_3)_3(aq)$
$3Ni^{2+}(aq) + 6NO_3^-(aq) + 2Cr(s) \longrightarrow$
$$3Ni(s) + 2Cr^{3+}(aq) + 6NO_3^-(aq)$$
$3Ni^{2+}(aq) + 2Cr(s) \longrightarrow 3Ni(s) + 2Cr^{3+}(aq)$
Cr is the reducing agent; $Ni(NO_3)_2$ is the oxidizing agent.

PROBLEMS

Problems with **colored** numbers are answered in Appendix E and worked in detail in the Student Solutions Manual. Problem sections match those in the text and provide the numbers of relevant sample problems. Most offer Concept Review Questions, Skill-Building Exercises (grouped in pairs covering the same concept), and Problems in Context. The Comprehensive Problems are based on material from any section or previous chapter.

The Role of Water as a Solvent
(Sample Problems 4.1 and 4.2)

Concept Review Questions

4.1 What two factors cause water to be polar?

4.2 What types of substances are most likely to be soluble in water?

4.3 What must be present in an aqueous solution for it to conduct an electric current? What general classes of compounds form solutions that conduct?

4.4 What occurs on the molecular level when an ionic compound dissolves in water?

4.5 Which of the following scenes best represents how the ions occur in an aqueous solution of: (a) $CaCl_2$; (b) Li_2SO_4; (c) NH_4Br?

4.6 Which of the following scenes best represents a volume from a solution of magnesium nitrate?

= magnesium ion   = nitrate ion

4.7 Why are some ionic compounds soluble in water and others are not?

4.8 Why are some covalent compounds soluble in water and others are not?

4.9 Some covalent compounds dissociate into ions in water. What atom do these compounds have in their structures? What type of solution do they form? Name three examples of such a solution.

Skill-Building Exercises (grouped in similar pairs)

4.10 Is each of the following very soluble in water? Explain.
(a) Benzene, C_6H_6 (b) Sodium hydroxide
(c) Ethanol, CH_3CH_2OH (d) Potassium acetate

4.11 Is each of the following very soluble in water? Explain.
(a) Lithium nitrate   (b) Glycine, H_2NCH_2COOH
(c) Pentane   (d) Ethylene glycol, $HOCH_2CH_2OH$

4.12 Does an aqueous solution of each of the following conduct an electric current? Explain.
(a) Cesium bromide   (b) Hydrogen iodide

4.13 Does an aqueous solution of each of the following conduct an electric current? Explain.
(a) Potassium sulfate   (b) Sucrose, $C_{12}H_{22}O_{11}$

4.14 How many total moles of ions are released when each of the following dissolves in water?
(a) 0.32 mol of NH_4Cl (b) 25.4 g of $Ba(OH)_2 \cdot 8H_2O$
(c) 3.55×10^{19} formula units of LiCl

4.15 How many total moles of ions are released when each of the following dissolves in water?
(a) 0.805 mol of Rb_2SO_4 (b) 3.85×10^{-3} g of $Ca(NO_3)_2$
(c) 4.03×10^{19} formula units of $Sr(HCO_3)_2$

4.16 How many total moles of ions are released when each of the following dissolves in water?
(a) 0.75 mol of K_3PO_4 (b) 6.88×10^{-3} g of $NiBr_2 \cdot 3H_2O$
(c) 2.23×10^{22} formula units of $FeCl_3$

4.17 How many total moles of ions are released when each of the following dissolves in water?
(a) 0.734 mol of Na_2HPO_4 (b) 3.86 g of $CuSO_4 \cdot 5H_2O$
(c) 8.66×10^{20} formula units of $NiCl_2$

4.18 How many moles and how many ions of each type are present in each of the following?
(a) 130. mL of 0.45 M aluminum chloride
(b) 9.80 mL of a solution containing 2.59 g lithium sulfate/L
(c) 245 mL of a solution containing 3.68×10^{22} formula units of potassium bromide per liter

4.19 How many moles and how many ions of each type are present in each of the following?
(a) 88 mL of 1.75 M magnesium chloride
(b) 321 mL of a solution containing 0.22 g aluminum sulfate/L
(c) 1.65 L of a solution containing 8.83×10^{21} formula units of cesium nitrate per liter

4.20 How many moles of H^+ ions are present in the following aqueous solutions?
(a) 1.40 L of 0.25 M perchloric acid
(b) 6.8 mL of 0.92 M nitric acid
(c) 2.6 L of 0.085 M hydrochloric acid

4.21 How many moles of H^+ ions are present in the following aqueous solutions?
(a) 1.4 mL of 0.75 M hydrobromic acid
(b) 2.47 mL of 1.98 M hydriodic acid
(c) 395 mL of 0.270 M nitric acid

Problems in Context

4.22 To study a marine organism, a biologist prepares a 1.00-kg sample to simulate the ion concentrations in seawater. She mixes 26.5 g of NaCl, 2.40 g of $MgCl_2$, 3.35 g of $MgSO_4$, 1.20 g of $CaCl_2$, 1.05 g of KCl, 0.315 g of $NaHCO_3$, and 0.098 g of NaBr in distilled water. (a) If the density of the solution is 1.025 g/cm^3, what is the molarity of each ion? (b) What is the total molarity of alkali metal ions? (c) What is the total molarity of alkaline earth metal ions? (d) What is the total molarity of anions?

4.23 Water "softeners" remove metal ions such as Ca^{2+} and Fe^{3+} by replacing them with enough Na^+ ions to maintain the same number of positive charges in the solution. If 1.0×10^3 L of "hard" water is 0.015 M Ca^{2+} and 0.0010 M Fe^{3+}, how many moles of Na^+ are needed to replace these ions?

Writing Equations for Aqueous Ionic Reactions

Concept Review Questions

4.24 Which ions do not appear in a net ionic equation? Why?

4.25 Write two sets of equations (both molecular and total ionic) with different reactants that have the same net ionic equation as the following equation:

$$Ba(NO_3)_2(aq) + Na_2CO_3(aq) \longrightarrow BaCO_3(s) + 2NaNO_3(aq)$$

Precipitation Reactions

(Sample Problems 4.3 and 4.4)

Concept Review Questions

4.26 Why do some pairs of ions precipitate and others do not?

4.27 Use Table 4.1 to determine which of the following combinations leads to a precipitation reaction. How can you identify the spectator ions in the reaction?
(a) Calcium nitrate(aq) + sodium chloride(aq) $\longrightarrow$
(b) Potassium chloride(aq) + lead(II) nitrate(aq) $\longrightarrow$

4.28 The beakers represent the aqueous reaction of $AgNO_3$ and NaCl. Silver ions are gray. What colors are used to represent NO_3^-, Na^+, and Cl^-? Write molecular, total ionic, and net ionic equations for the reaction.

Skill-Building Exercises (grouped in similar pairs)

4.29 Complete the following precipitation reactions with balanced molecular, total ionic, and net ionic equations:
(a) $Hg_2(NO_3)_2(aq) + KI(aq) \longrightarrow$
(b) $FeSO_4(aq) + Sr(OH)_2(aq) \longrightarrow$

4.30 Complete the following precipitation reactions with balanced molecular, total ionic, and net ionic equations:
(a) $CaCl_2(aq) + Cs_3PO_4(aq) \longrightarrow$
(b) $Na_2S(aq) + ZnSO_4(aq) \longrightarrow$

4.31 When each of the following pairs of aqueous solutions is mixed, does a precipitation reaction occur? If so, write balanced molecular, total ionic, and net ionic equations:
(a) Sodium nitrate + copper(II) sulfate
(b) Ammonium bromide + silver nitrate

4.32 When each of the following pairs of aqueous solutions is mixed, does a precipitation reaction occur? If so, write balanced molecular, total ionic, and net ionic equations:
(a) Potassium carbonate + barium hydroxide
(b) Aluminum nitrate + sodium phosphate

4.33 When each of the following pairs of aqueous solutions is mixed, does a precipitation reaction occur? If so, write balanced molecular, total ionic, and net ionic equations.
(a) Potassium chloride + iron(III) nitrate
(b) Ammonium sulfate + barium chloride

4.34 When each of the following pairs of aqueous solutions is mixed, does a precipitation reaction occur? If so, write balanced molecular, total ionic, and net ionic equations:
(a) Sodium sulfide + nickel(II) sulfate
(b) Lead(II) nitrate + potassium bromide

4.35 If 38.5 mL of lead(II) nitrate solution reacts completely with excess sodium iodide solution to yield 0.628 g of precipitate, what is the molarity of lead(II) ion in the original solution?

4.36 If 25.0 mL of silver nitrate solution reacts with excess potassium chloride solution to yield 0.842 g of precipitate, what is the molarity of silver ion in the original solution?

4.37 With ions shown as spheres and solvent molecules omitted for clarity, the circle (*right*) illustrates the solid formed when a solution containing K^+, Mg^{2+}, Ag^+, or Pb^{2+} (*blue*) is mixed with one containing ClO_4^-, NO_3^-, or SO_4^{2-} (*yellow*). (a) Identify the solid. (b) Write a balanced net ionic equation for the reaction. (c) If each sphere represents 5.0×10^{-4} mol of ion, what mass of product forms?

4.38 The precipitation reaction between 25.0 mL of a solution containing a cation (*purple*) and 35.0 mL of a solution containing an anion (*green*) is depicted below (with ions shown as spheres and solvent molecules omitted for clarity).

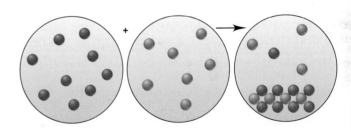

(a) Given the following choices of reactants, write balanced total ionic and net ionic equations that best represent the reaction:
(1) $KNO_3(aq) + CuCl_2(aq) \longrightarrow$
(2) $NaClO_4(aq) + CaCl_2(aq) \longrightarrow$
(3) $Li_2SO_4(aq) + AgNO_3(aq) \longrightarrow$
(4) $NH_4Br(aq) + Pb(CH_3COO)_2(aq) \longrightarrow$
(b) If each sphere represents 2.5×10^{-3} mol of ion, find the total number of ions present.
(c) What is the mass of solid formed?

4.39 A 1.50-g sample of an unknown alkali-metal carbonate was dissolved in water, and 31.10 mL of 0.350 M $CaCl_2$ was required to precipitate all the carbonate ions as $CaCO_3$. Give the name and formula of the unknown compound.

4.40 A 0.750-g sample of a compound that might be iron(II) chloride, nickel(II) chloride, or zinc chloride is dissolved in water, and 22.40 mL of 0.515 M $AgNO_3$ is required to completely precipitate all the chloride ion as AgCl. Name the compound, and write its formula.

Problems in Context

4.41 The mass percent of Cl^- in a seawater sample is determined by titrating 25.00 mL of seawater with $AgNO_3$ solution, causing a precipitation reaction. An indicator is used to detect the end point, which occurs when free Ag^+ ion is present in solution after all the Cl^- has reacted. If 53.63 mL of 0.2970 M $AgNO_3$ is required to reach the end point, what is the mass percent of Cl^- in the seawater (d of seawater = 1.024 g/mL)?

4.42 Aluminum sulfate, known as *cake alum,* has a wide range of uses, from dyeing leather and cloth to purifying sewage. In aqueous solution, it reacts with base to form a white precipitate. (a) Write balanced total and net ionic equations for its reaction with aqueous NaOH. (b) What mass of precipitate forms when 185.5 mL of 0.533 M NaOH is added to 627 mL of a solution that contains 15.8 g of aluminum sulfate per liter?

Acid-Base Reactions
(Sample Problems 4.5 to 4.8)

Concept Review Questions

4.43 Is the total ionic equation the same as the net ionic equation when $Sr(OH)_2(aq)$ and $H_2SO_4(aq)$ react? Explain.

4.44 State a general equation for a neutralization reaction.

4.45 (a) Name three common strong acids. (b) Name three common strong bases. (c) What is a characteristic behavior of a strong acid or a strong base?

4.46 (a) Name three common weak acids. (b) Name one common weak base. (c) What is the major difference between a weak acid and a strong acid or between a weak base and a strong base, and what experiment would you perform to observe it?

4.47 Do either of the following reactions go to completion? If so, what factor(s) cause(s) each to do so?
(a) $MgSO_3(s) + 2HCl(aq) \longrightarrow MgCl_2(aq) + SO_2(g) + H_2O(l)$
(b) $3Ba(OH)_2(aq) + 2H_3PO_4(aq) \longrightarrow Ba_3(PO_4)_2(s) + 6H_2O(l)$

4.48 (a) The net ionic equation for the aqueous neutralization reaction between acetic acid and sodium hydroxide is different from that for the reaction between hydrochloric acid and sodium hydroxide. Explain by writing balanced net ionic equations. (b) For a solution of acetic acid in water, list the major species in decreasing order of concentration.

Skill-Building Exercises (grouped in similar pairs)

4.49 Complete the following acid-base reactions with balanced molecular, total ionic, and net ionic equations:
(a) Potassium hydroxide(aq) + hydrobromic acid(aq) $\longrightarrow$
(b) Ammonia(aq) + hydrochloric acid(aq) $\longrightarrow$

4.50 Complete the following acid-base reactions with balanced molecular, total ionic, and net ionic equations:
(a) Cesium hydroxide(aq) + nitric acid(aq) $\longrightarrow$
(b) Calcium hydroxide(aq) + acetic acid(aq) $\longrightarrow$

4.51 Limestone (calcium carbonate) is insoluble in water but dissolves when a hydrochloric acid solution is added. Write balanced total ionic and net ionic equations, showing hydrochloric acid as it actually exists in water and the reaction as a proton-transfer process.

4.52 Zinc hydroxide is insoluble in water but dissolves when a nitric acid solution is added. Why? Write balanced total ionic and net ionic equations, showing nitric acid as it actually exists in water and the reaction as a proton-transfer process.

4.53 If 25.98 mL of 0.1180 M KOH solution reacts with 52.50 mL of CH_3COOH solution, what is the molarity of the acid solution?

4.54 If 26.25 mL of 0.1850 M NaOH solution reacts with 25.00 mL of H_2SO_4, what is the molarity of the acid solution?

Problems in Context

4.55 An auto mechanic spills 88 mL of 2.6 M H_2SO_4 solution from an auto battery. How many milliliters of 1.6 M $NaHCO_3$ must be poured on the spill to react completely with the sulfuric acid?

4.56 Sodium hydroxide is used extensively in acid-base titrations because it is a strong, inexpensive base. A sodium hydroxide solution was standardized by titrating 25.00 mL of 0.1528 M standard hydrochloric acid. The initial buret reading of the sodium hydroxide was 2.24 mL, and the final reading was 39.21 mL. What was the molarity of the base solution?

4.57 An unknown amount of acid can often be determined by adding an excess of base and then "back-titrating" the excess. A 0.3471-g sample of a mixture of oxalic acid, which has two ionizable protons, and benzoic acid, which has one, is treated with 100.0 mL of 0.1000 M NaOH. The excess NaOH is titrated with 20.00 mL of 0.2000 M HCl. Find the mass % of benzoic acid.

4.58 One of the first steps in the enrichment of uranium for use in nuclear power plants involves a displacement reaction between UO_2 and aqueous HF:

$$UO_2(s) + HF(aq) \longrightarrow UF_4(s) + H_2O(l) \text{ [unbalanced]}$$

How many liters of 2.40 M HF will react with 2.15 kg of UO_2?

4.59 A mixture of bases can sometimes be the active ingredient in antacid tablets. If 0.4826 g of a mixture of $Al(OH)_3$ and $Mg(OH)_2$ is neutralized with 17.30 mL of 1.000 M HNO_3, what is the mass % of $Al(OH)_3$ in the mixture?

Oxidation-Reduction (Redox) Reactions
(Sample Problems 4.9 to 4.13)

Concept Review Questions

4.60 Describe how to determine the oxidation number of sulfur in (a) H_2S and (b) SO_3^{2-}.

4.61 Is the following a redox reaction? Explain.
$$NH_3(aq) + HCl(aq) \longrightarrow NH_4Cl(aq)$$

4.62 Explain why an oxidizing agent undergoes reduction.

4.63 Why must every redox reaction involve an oxidizing agent and a reducing agent?

4.64 In which of the following equations does sulfuric acid act as an oxidizing agent? In which does it act as an acid? Explain.
(a) $4H^+(aq) + SO_4^{2-}(aq) + 2NaI(s) \longrightarrow$
$$2Na^+(aq) + I_2(s) + SO_2(g) + 2H_2O(l)$$
(b) $BaF_2(s) + 2H^+(aq) + SO_4^{2-}(aq) \longrightarrow 2HF(aq) + BaSO_4(s)$

4.65 Identify the oxidizing agent and the reducing agent in the following reaction, and explain your answer:
$$8NH_3(g) + 6NO_2(g) \longrightarrow 7N_2(g) + 12H_2O(l)$$

Skill-Building Exercises (grouped in similar pairs)

4.66 Give the oxidation number of carbon in the following:
(a) CF_2Cl_2 (b) $Na_2C_2O_4$ (c) HCO_3^- (d) C_2H_6

4.67 Give the oxidation number of bromine in the following:
(a) KBr   (b) BrF_3 (c) $HBrO_3$ (d) CBr_4

4.68 Give the oxidation number of nitrogen in the following:
(a) NH_2OH (b) N_2F_4 (c) NH_4^+ (d) HNO_2

4.69 Give the oxidation number of sulfur in the following:
(a) $SOCl_2$ (b) H_2S_2 (c) H_2SO_3 (d) Na_2S

4.70 Give the oxidation number of arsenic in the following:
(a) AsH_3 (b) $H_2AsO_4^-$ (c) $AsCl_3$

4.71 Give the oxidation number of phosphorus in the following:
(a) $H_2P_2O_7^{2-}$ (b) PH_4^+ (c) PCl_5

4.72 Give the oxidation number of manganese in the following:
(a) MnO_4^{2-} (b) Mn_2O_3 (c) $KMnO_4$

4.73 Give the oxidation number of chromium in the following:
(a) CrO_3 (b) $Cr_2O_7^{2-}$ (c) $Cr_2(SO_4)_3$

4.74 Identify the oxidizing and reducing agents in the following:
(a) $5H_2C_2O_4(aq) + 2MnO_4^-(aq) + 6H^+(aq) \longrightarrow$
$$2Mn^{2+}(aq) + 10CO_2(g) + 8H_2O(l)$$
(b) $3Cu(s) + 8H^+(aq) + 2NO_3^-(aq) \longrightarrow$
$$3Cu^{2+}(aq) + 2NO(g) + 4H_2O(l)$$

4.75 Identify the oxidizing and reducing agents in the following:
(a) $Sn(s) + 2H^+(aq) \longrightarrow Sn^{2+}(aq) + H_2(g)$
(b) $2H^+(aq) + H_2O_2(aq) + 2Fe^{2+}(aq) \longrightarrow$
$$2Fe^{3+}(aq) + 2H_2O(l)$$

4.76 Identify the oxidizing and reducing agents in the following:
(a) $8H^+(aq) + 6Cl^-(aq) + Sn(s) + 4NO_3^-(aq) \longrightarrow$
$$SnCl_6^{2-}(aq) + 4NO_2(g) + 4H_2O(l)$$
(b) $2MnO_4^-(aq) + 10Cl^-(aq) + 16H^+(aq) \longrightarrow$
$$5Cl_2(g) + 2Mn^{2+}(aq) + 8H_2O(l)$$

4.77 Identify the oxidizing and reducing agents in the following:
(a) $8H^+(aq) + Cr_2O_7^{2-}(aq) + 3SO_3^{2-}(aq) \longrightarrow$
$$2Cr^{3+}(aq) + 3SO_4^{2-}(aq) + 4H_2O(l)$$
(b) $NO_3^-(aq) + 4Zn(s) + 7OH^-(aq) + 6H_2O(l) \longrightarrow$
$$4Zn(OH)_4^{2-}(aq) + NH_3(aq)$$

4.78 Use the oxidation number method to balance the following equations. Identify the reducing and oxidizing agents:
(a) $HNO_3(aq) + K_2CrO_4(aq) + Fe(NO_3)_2(aq) \longrightarrow$
$$KNO_3(aq) + Fe(NO_3)_3(aq) + Cr(NO_3)_3(aq) + H_2O(l)$$
(b) $HNO_3(aq) + C_2H_6O(l) + K_2Cr_2O_7(aq) \longrightarrow$
$$KNO_3(aq) + C_2H_4O(l) + H_2O(l) + Cr(NO_3)_3(aq)$$
(c) $HCl(aq) + NH_4Cl(aq) + K_2Cr_2O_7(aq) \longrightarrow$
$$KCl(aq) + CrCl_3(aq) + N_2(g) + H_2O(l)$$
(d) $KClO_3(aq) + HBr(aq) \longrightarrow Br_2(l) + H_2O(l) + KCl(aq)$

4.79 Use the oxidation number method to balance the following equations. Identify the reducing and oxidizing agents:
(a) $HCl(aq) + FeCl_2(aq) + H_2O_2(aq) \longrightarrow FeCl_3(aq) + H_2O(l)$
(b) $I_2(s) + Na_2S_2O_3(aq) \longrightarrow Na_2S_4O_6(aq) + NaI(aq)$
(c) $HNO_3(aq) + KI(aq) \longrightarrow$
$$NO(g) + I_2(s) + H_2O(l) + KNO_3(aq)$$
(d) $PbO(s) + NH_3(aq) \longrightarrow N_2(g) + H_2O(l) + Pb(s)$

Problems in Context

4.80 The active agent in many hair bleaches is hydrogen peroxide. The amount of H_2O_2 in 14.8 g of hair bleach was determined by titration with a standard potassium permanganate solution:
$$2MnO_4^-(aq) + 5H_2O_2(aq) + 6H^+(aq) \longrightarrow$$
$$5O_2(g) + 2Mn^{2+}(aq) + 8H_2O(l)$$
(a) How many moles of MnO_4^- were required for the titration if 43.2 mL of 0.105 M $KMnO_4$ was needed to reach the end point?

(b) How many moles of H_2O_2 were present in the 14.8-g sample of bleach?
(c) How many grams of H_2O_2 were in the sample?
(d) What is the mass percent of H_2O_2 in the sample?
(e) What is the reducing agent in the redox reaction?

4.81 A person's blood alcohol (C_2H_5OH) level can be determined by titrating a sample of blood plasma with a potassium dichromate solution. The balanced equation is
$$16H^+(aq) + 2Cr_2O_7^{2-}(aq) + C_2H_5OH(aq) \longrightarrow$$
$$4Cr^{3+}(aq) + 2CO_2(g) + 11H_2O(l)$$
If 35.46 mL of 0.05961 M $Cr_2O_7^{2-}$ is required to titrate 28.00 g of plasma, what is the mass percent of alcohol in the blood?

Elements in Redox Reactions
(Sample Problem 4.14)

Concept Review Questions

4.82 Which type of redox reaction leads to each of the following?
(a) An increase in the number of substances
(b) A decrease in the number of substances
(c) No change in the number of substances

4.83 Why do decomposition redox reactions typically have compounds as reactants, whereas combination redox and displacement redox reactions have one or more elements?

4.84 Which of the types of reactions discussed in Section 4.6 commonly produce more than one compound?

4.85 Are all combustion reactions redox reactions? Explain.

4.86 Give one example of a combination reaction that is a redox reaction and another that is not a redox reaction.

Skill-Building Exercises (grouped in similar pairs)

4.87 Balance each of the following redox reactions and classify it as a combination, decomposition, or displacement reaction:
(a) $Ca(s) + H_2O(l) \longrightarrow Ca(OH)_2(aq) + H_2(g)$
(b) $NaNO_3(s) \longrightarrow NaNO_2(s) + O_2(g)$
(c) $C_2H_2(g) + H_2(g) \longrightarrow C_2H_6(g)$

4.88 Balance each of the following redox reactions and classify it as a combination, decomposition, or displacement reaction:
(a) $HI(g) \longrightarrow H_2(g) + I_2(g)$
(b) $Zn(s) + AgNO_3(aq) \longrightarrow Zn(NO_3)_2(aq) + Ag(s)$
(c) $NO(g) + O_2(g) \longrightarrow N_2O_4(l)$

4.89 Balance each of the following redox reactions and classify it as a combination, decomposition, or displacement reaction:
(a) $Sb(s) + Cl_2(g) \longrightarrow SbCl_3(s)$
(b) $AsH_3(g) \longrightarrow As(s) + H_2(g)$
(c) $Zn(s) + Fe(NO_3)_2(aq) \longrightarrow Zn(NO_3)_2(aq) + Fe(s)$

4.90 Balance each of the following redox reactions and classify it as a combination, decomposition, or displacement reaction:
(a) $Mg(s) + H_2O(g) \longrightarrow Mg(OH)_2(s) + H_2(g)$
(b) $Cr(NO_3)_3(aq) + Al(s) \longrightarrow Al(NO_3)_3(aq) + Cr(s)$
(c) $PF_3(g) + F_2(g) \longrightarrow PF_5(g)$

4.91 Predict the product(s) and write a balanced equation for each of the following redox reactions:
(a) $Sr(s) + Br_2(l) \longrightarrow$
(b) $Ag_2O(s) \overset{\Delta}{\longrightarrow}$
(c) $Mn(s) + Cu(NO_3)_2(aq) \longrightarrow$

4.92 Predict the product(s) and write a balanced equation for each of the following redox reactions:

(a) $Mg(s) + HCl(aq) \longrightarrow$

(b) $LiCl(l) \xrightarrow{\text{electricity}}$

(c) $SnCl_2(aq) + Co(s) \longrightarrow$

4.93 Predict the product(s) and write a balanced equation for each of the following redox reactions:

(a) $N_2(g) + H_2(g) \longrightarrow$

(b) $NaClO_3(s) \xrightarrow{\Delta}$

(c) $Ba(s) + H_2O(l) \longrightarrow$

4.94 Predict the product(s) and write a balanced equation for each of the following redox reactions:

(a) $Fe(s) + HClO_4(aq) \longrightarrow$

(b) $S_8(s) + O_2(g) \longrightarrow$

(c) $BaCl_2(l) \xrightarrow{\text{electricity}}$

4.95 Predict the product(s) and write a balanced equation for each of the following redox reactions:

(a) Cesium + iodine $\longrightarrow$

(b) Aluminum + aqueous manganese(II) sulfate $\longrightarrow$

(c) Sulfur dioxide + oxygen $\longrightarrow$

(d) Butane and oxygen $\longrightarrow$

(e) Write a balanced net ionic equation for (b).

4.96 Predict the product(s) and write a balanced equation for each of the following redox reactions:

(a) Pentane (C_5H_{12}) + oxygen $\longrightarrow$

(b) Phosphorus trichloride + chlorine $\longrightarrow$

(c) Zinc + hydrobromic acid $\longrightarrow$

(d) Aqueous potassium iodide + bromine $\longrightarrow$

(e) Write a balanced net ionic equation for (d).

4.97 How many grams of O_2 can be prepared from the thermal decomposition of 4.27 kg of HgO? Name and calculate the mass (in kg) of the other product.

4.98 How many grams of chlorine gas can be produced from the electrolytic decomposition of 874 g of calcium chloride? Name and calculate the mass (in g) of the other product.

4.99 In a combination reaction, 1.62 g of lithium is mixed with 6.50 g of oxygen.

(a) Which reactant is present in excess?

(b) How many moles of product are formed?

(c) After reaction, how many grams of each reactant and product are present?

4.100 In a combination reaction, 2.22 g of magnesium is heated with 3.75 g of nitrogen.

(a) Which reactant is present in excess?

(b) How many moles of product are formed?

(c) After reaction, how many grams of each reactant and product are present?

4.101 A mixture of $KClO_3$ and KCl with a mass of 0.950 g was heated to produce O_2. After heating, the mass of residue was 0.700 g. Assuming all the $KClO_3$ decomposed to KCl and O_2, calculate the mass percent of $KClO_3$ in the original mixture.

4.102 A mixture of $CaCO_3$ and CaO weighing 0.693 g was heated to produce gaseous CO_2. After heating, the remaining solid weighed 0.508 g. Assuming all the $CaCO_3$ broke down to CaO and CO_2, calculate the mass percent of $CaCO_3$ in the original mixture.

Problems in Context

4.103 Before arc welding was developed, a displacement reaction involving aluminum and iron(III) oxide was commonly used to produce molten iron (the thermite process). This reaction was used, for example, to connect sections of iron rails for train tracks. Calculate the mass of molten iron produced when 1.50 kg of aluminum reacts with 25.0 mol of iron(III) oxide.

4.104 Iron reacts rapidly with chlorine gas to form a reddish brown, ionic compound (A), which contains iron in the higher of its two common oxidation states. Strong heating decomposes compound A to compound B, another ionic compound, which contains iron in the lower of its two oxidation states. When compound A is formed by the reaction of 50.6 g of Fe and 83.8 g of Cl_2 and then heated, how much compound B forms?

The Reversibility of Reactions and the Equilibrium State

Concept Review Questions

4.105 Why is the equilibrium state called "dynamic"?

4.106 In a decomposition reaction involving a gaseous product, what must be done for the reaction to reach equilibrium?

4.107 Describe what happens on the molecular level when acetic acid dissolves in water.

4.108 When either a mixture of NO and Br_2 or pure nitrosyl bromide (NOBr) is placed in a reaction vessel, the product mixture contains NO, Br_2, and NOBr. Explain.

Problem in Context

4.109 Ammonia is produced by the millions of tons annually for use as a fertilizer. It is commonly made from N_2 and H_2 by the Haber process. Because the reaction reaches equilibrium before going completely to product, the stoichiometric amount of ammonia is not obtained. At a particular temperature and pressure, 10.0 g of H_2 reacts with 20.0 g of N_2 to form ammonia. When equilibrium is reached, 15.0 g of NH_3 has formed. (a) Calculate the percent yield. (b) How many moles of N_2 and H_2 are present at equilibrium?

Comprehensive Problems

4.110 Nutritional biochemists have known for decades that acidic foods cooked in cast-iron cookware can supply significant amounts of dietary iron (ferrous ion). (a) Write a balanced net ionic equation, with oxidation numbers, that supports this fact. (b) Measurements show an increase from 3.3 mg of iron to 49 mg of iron per $\frac{1}{2}$-cup (125-g) serving during the slow preparation of tomato sauce in a cast-iron pot. How many ferrous ions are present in a 26-oz (737-g) jar of the tomato sauce?

4.111 Limestone ($CaCO_3$) is used to remove acidic pollutants from smokestack flue gases. It is heated to form lime (CaO), which reacts with sulfur dioxide to form calcium sulfite. Assuming a 70.% yield in the overall reaction, what mass of limestone is required to remove all the sulfur dioxide formed by the combustion of 8.5×10^4 kg of coal that is 0.33 mass % sulfur?

4.112 The brewing industry uses yeast to convert glucose to ethanol. The baking industry uses the carbon dioxide produced in the same reaction to make bread rise:

$$C_6H_{12}O_6(s) \xrightarrow{\text{yeast}} 2C_2H_5OH(l) + 2CO_2(g)$$

How many grams of ethanol can be produced from 100. g of glucose? What volume of CO_2 is produced? (Assume 1 mol of gas occupies 22.4 L at the conditions used.)

4.113 A chemical engineer determines the mass percent of iron in an ore sample by converting the Fe to Fe^{2+} in acid and then titrating the Fe^{2+} with MnO_4^-. A 1.1081-g sample was dissolved in acid and then titrated with 39.32 mL of 0.03190 M $KMnO_4$. The balanced equation is

$$8H^+(aq) + 5Fe^{2+}(aq) + MnO_4^-(aq) \longrightarrow$$
$$5Fe^{3+}(aq) + Mn^{2+}(aq) + 4H_2O(l)$$

Calculate the mass percent of iron in the ore.

4.114 Mixtures of $CaCl_2$ and NaCl are used to melt ice on roads. A dissolved 1.9348-g sample of such a mixture was analyzed by using excess $Na_2C_2O_4$ to precipitate the Ca^{2+} as CaC_2O_4. The CaC_2O_4 was dissolved in sulfuric acid, and the resulting $H_2C_2O_4$ was titrated with 37.68 mL of 0.1019 M $KMnO_4$ solution.
(a) Write the balanced net ionic equation for the precipitation reaction.
(b) Write the balanced net ionic equation for the titration reaction. (See Sample Problem 4.13.)
(c) What is the oxidizing agent?
(d) What is the reducing agent?
(e) Calculate the mass percent of $CaCl_2$ in the original sample.

4.115 You are given solutions of HCl and NaOH and must determine their concentrations. You use 27.5 mL of NaOH to titrate 100. mL of HCl and 18.4 mL of NaOH to titrate 50.0 mL of 0.0782 M H_2SO_4. Find the unknown concentrations.

4.116 The flask (*right*) represents the products of the titration of 25 mL of sulfuric acid with 25 mL of sodium hydroxide.
(a) Write balanced molecular, total ionic, and net ionic equations for the reaction.
(b) If each orange sphere represents 0.010 mol of sulfate ion, how many moles of acid and of base reacted?
(c) What are the molarities of the acid and the base?

4.117 To find the mass percent of dolomite $[CaMg(CO_3)_2]$ in a soil sample, a geochemist titrates 13.86 g of soil with 33.56 mL of 0.2516 M HCl. What is the mass percent of dolomite in the soil?

4.118 On a lab exam, you have to find the concentrations of the monoprotic (one proton per molecule) acids HA and HB. You are given 43.5 mL of HA solution in one flask. A second flask contains 37.2 mL of HA, and you add enough HB solution to it to reach a final volume of 50.0 mL. You titrate the first HA solution with 87.3 mL of 0.0906 M NaOH and the mixture of HA and HB in the second flask with 96.4 mL of the NaOH solution. Calculate the molarity of the HA and HB solutions.

4.119 Nitric acid, a major industrial and laboratory acid, is produced commercially by the multistep Ostwald process, which begins with the oxidation of ammonia:

Step 1. $4NH_3(g) + 5O_2(g) \longrightarrow 4NO(g) + 6H_2O(l)$
Step 2. $2NO(g) + O_2(g) \longrightarrow 2NO_2(g)$
Step 3. $3NO_2(g) + H_2O(l) \longrightarrow 2HNO_3(l) + NO(g)$

(a) What are the oxidizing and reducing agents in each step?
(b) Assuming 100% yield in each step, what mass (in kg) of ammonia must be used to produce 3.0×10^4 kg of HNO_3?

4.120 Various data can be used to find the composition of an alloy (a metallic mixture). Show that calculating the mass % of Mg in a magnesium-aluminum alloy ($d = 2.40$ g/cm³) using each of the following pieces of data gives the same answer (within rounding): (a) a sample of the alloy has a mass of 0.263 g (d of Mg = 1.74 g/cm³; d of Al = 2.70 g/cm³); (b) an identical sample reacting with excess aqueous HCl forms 1.38×10^{-2} mol of H_2; (c) an identical sample reacting with excess O_2 forms 0.483 g of oxide.

4.121 Use the oxidation number method to balance the following equations by placing coefficients in the blanks. Identify the reducing and oxidizing agents:
(a) __KOH(aq) + __$H_2O_2(aq)$ + __$Cr(OH)_3(s)$ $\longrightarrow$
    __$K_2CrO_4(aq)$ + __$H_2O(l)$
(b) __$MnO_4^-(aq)$ + __$ClO_2^-(aq)$ + __$H_2O(l)$ $\longrightarrow$
    __$MnO_2(s)$ + __$ClO_4^-(aq)$ + __$OH^-(aq)$
(c) __$KMnO_4(aq)$ + __$Na_2SO_3(aq)$ + __$H_2O(l)$ $\longrightarrow$
    __$MnO_2(s)$ + __$Na_2SO_4(aq)$ + __$KOH(aq)$
(d) __$CrO_4^{2-}(aq)$ + __$HSnO_2^-(aq)$ + __$H_2O(l)$ $\longrightarrow$
    __$CrO_2^-(aq)$ + __$HSnO_3^-(aq)$ + __$OH^-(aq)$
(e) __$KMnO_4(aq)$ + __$NaNO_2(aq)$ + __$H_2O(l)$ $\longrightarrow$
    __$MnO_2(s)$ + __$NaNO_3(aq)$ + __$KOH(aq)$
(f) __$I^-(aq)$ + __$O_2(g)$ + __$H_2O(l)$ $\longrightarrow$ __$I_2(s)$ + __$OH^-(aq)$

4.122 In 1995, Mario Molina, Paul Crutzen, and F. Sherwood Rowland shared the Nobel Prize in chemistry for their work on atmospheric chemistry. One reaction sequence they proposed for the role of chlorine in the decomposition of stratospheric ozone (we'll see another sequence in Chapter 16) is
(1) $Cl(g) + O_3(g) \longrightarrow ClO(g) + O_2(g)$
(2) $ClO(g) + ClO(g) \longrightarrow Cl_2O_2(g)$
(3) $Cl_2O_2(g) \xrightarrow{\text{light}} 2Cl(g) + O_2(g)$
Over the tropics, O atoms are more common in the stratosphere:
(4) $ClO(g) + O(g) \longrightarrow Cl(g) + O_2(g)$
(a) Which, if any, of these are oxidation-reduction reactions?
(b) Write an overall equation combining reactions 1–3.

4.123 Sodium peroxide (Na_2O_2) is often used in self-contained breathing devices, such as those used in fire emergencies, because it reacts with exhaled CO_2 to form Na_2CO_3 and O_2. How many liters of respired air can react with 80.0 g of Na_2O_2 if each liter of respired air contains 0.0720 g of CO_2?

4.124 A student forgets to weigh a mixture of sodium bromide dihydrate and magnesium bromide hexahydrate. Upon strong heating, the sample loses 252.1 mg of water. The mixture of anhydrous salts reacts with excess $AgNO_3$ solution to form 6.00×10^{-3} mol of solid AgBr. Find the mass % of each compound in the original mixture.

4.125 A typical formulation for window glass is 75% SiO_2, 15% Na_2O, and 10.% CaO by mass. What masses of sand (SiO_2), sodium carbonate, and calcium carbonate must be combined to produce 1.00 kg of glass after carbon dioxide is driven off by thermal decomposition of the carbonates?

4.126 The quantity of dissolved oxygen (DO) in natural waters is an essential parameter for monitoring survival of most aquatic life. DO is affected by temperature and the amount of organic waste. An earlier method for determining DO involved a two-step process:

1. The water sample is treated with KI,

$$O_2(aq) + 4KI(aq) + 2H_2SO_4(aq) \longrightarrow$$
$$2I_2(aq) + 2H_2O(l) + 2K_2SO_4(aq)$$

2. The I_2 is titrated with sodium thiosulfate,

$$I_2(aq) + 2Na_2S_2O_3(aq) \longrightarrow Na_2S_4O_6(aq) + 2NaI(aq)$$

A 50.0-mL water sample is treated with KI, and then 15.75 mL of 0.0105 M $Na_2S_2O_3$ is required to reach the end point.
(a) Which substance is oxidized in step 1, and which is reduced in step 2?
(b) What mass (g) of O_2 is dissolved in the water sample?

4.127 Physicians who specialize in sports medicine routinely treat athletes and dancers. Ethyl chloride, a local anesthetic commonly used for simple injuries, is the product of the combination of ethylene with hydrogen chloride:

$$C_2H_4(g) + HCl(g) \longrightarrow C_2H_5Cl(g)$$

If 0.100 kg of C_2H_4 and 0.100 kg of HCl react: (a) How many molecules of gas (reactants plus products) are present when the reaction is complete? (b) How many moles of gas are present when half the product forms?

4.128 Thyroxine ($C_{15}H_{11}I_4NO_4$) is a hormone synthesized by the thyroid gland and used to control many metabolic functions in the body. A physiologist determines the mass percent of thyroxine in a thyroid extract by igniting 0.4332 g of extract with sodium carbonate, which converts the iodine to iodide. The iodide is dissolved in water, and bromine and hydrochloric acid are added, which convert the iodide to iodate.
(a) How many moles of iodate form per mole of thyroxine?
(b) Excess bromine is boiled off and more iodide is added, which reacts as shown in the following *unbalanced* equation:

$$IO_3^-(aq) + H^+(aq) + I^-(aq) \longrightarrow I_2(aq) + H_2O(l)$$

How many moles of iodine are produced per mole of thyroxine? (*Hint:* Be sure to balance the charges as well as the atoms.) What are the oxidizing and reducing agents in the reaction?
(c) The iodine reacts completely with 17.23 mL of 0.1000 *M* thiosulfate as shown in the following *unbalanced* equation:

$$I_2(aq) + S_2O_3^{2-}(aq) \longrightarrow I^-(aq) + S_4O_6^{2-}(aq)$$

What is the mass percent of thyroxine in the thyroid extract?

4.129 Over time, as their free fatty acid (FFA) content increases, edible fats and oils become rancid. To measure rancidity, the fat or oil is dissolved in ethanol, and any FFA present is titrated with KOH dissolved in ethanol. In a series of tests on olive oil, a stock solution of 0.050 *M* ethanolic KOH was prepared at 25°C, stored at 0°C, and then placed in a 100-mL buret to titrate oleic acid [an FFA with formula $CH_3(CH_2)_7CH=CH(CH_2)_7COOH$] in the oil. Each of four 10.00-g samples of oil took several minutes to titrate: the first required 19.60 mL, the second 19.80 mL, and the third and fourth 20.00 mL of the ethanolic KOH.
(a) What is the apparent acidity of each sample, in terms of mass % of oleic acid? (*Note:* As the ethanolic KOH warms in the buret, its volume increases by a factor of 0.00104/°C.)
(b) Is the variation in acidity a random or systematic error? Explain.
(c) What is the actual acidity? How would you demonstrate this?

4.130 A chemist mixes solid AgCl, $CuCl_2$, and $MgCl_2$ in enough water to give a final volume of 50.0 mL.
(a) With ions shown as spheres and solvent molecules omitted for clarity, which scene best represents the resulting mixture?

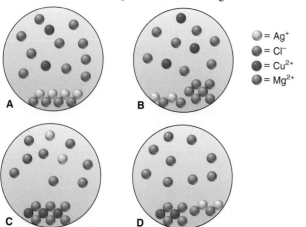

A B

C D

○ = Ag+
● = Cl−
● = Cu2+
● = Mg2+

(b) If each sphere represents $5.0×10^{-3}$ mol of ions, what is the total concentration of *dissolved* (separated) ions?
(c) What is the total mass of solid?

4.131 Calcium dihydrogen phosphate, $Ca(H_2PO_4)_2$, and sodium hydrogen carbonate, $NaHCO_3$, are ingredients of baking powder that react to produce CO_2, which causes dough or batter to rise:

$$Ca(H_2PO_4)_2(s) + NaHCO_3(s) \longrightarrow$$
$$CO_2(g) + H_2O(g) + CaHPO_4(s) + Na_2HPO_4(s)$$
$$\text{[unbalanced]}$$

If the baking powder contains 31% $NaHCO_3$ and 35% $Ca(H_2PO_4)_2$ by mass:
(a) How many moles of CO_2 are produced from 1.00 g of baking powder?
(b) If 1 mol of CO_2 occupies 37.0 L at 350°F (a typical baking temperature), what volume of CO_2 is produced from 1.00 g of baking powder?

4.132 In a titration of HNO_3, you add a few drops of phenolphthalein indicator to 50.00 mL of acid in a flask. You quickly add 20.00 mL of 0.0502 *M* NaOH but overshoot the end point, and the solution turns deep pink. Instead of starting over, you add 30.00 mL of the acid, and the solution turns colorless. Then, it takes 3.22 mL of the NaOH to reach the end point.
(a) What is the concentration of the HNO_3 solution?
(b) How many moles of NaOH were in excess after the first addition?

4.133 The active compound in Pepto-Bismol contains C, H, O, and Bi.
(a) When 0.22105 g of it was burned in excess O_2, 0.1422 g of bismuth(III) oxide, 0.1880 g of carbon dioxide, and 0.02750 g of water were formed. What is the empirical formula of this compound?
(b) Given a molar mass of 1086 g/mol, determine the molecular formula.
(c) Complete and balance the acid-base reaction between bismuth(III) hydroxide and salicylic acid ($HC_7H_5O_3$), which is used to form this compound.
(d) A dose of Pepto-Bismol contains 0.600 mg of active ingredient. If the yield of the reaction in part (c) is 88.0%, what mass (in mg) of bismuth(III) hydroxide is required to prepare one dose?

4.134 Two aqueous solutions contain the ions indicated below.

250. mL + 250. mL

● = Na+
● = CO3 2−
● = Ca2+
● = Cl−

(a) Write balanced molecular, total ionic, and net ionic equations for the reaction that occurs when the solutions are mixed.
(b) If each sphere represents 0.050 mol of ion, what mass (in g) of precipitate forms, assuming 100% yield?
(c) What is the concentration of each ion in solution after reaction?

4.135 In 1997 and 2009, at United Nations conferences on climate change, many nations agreed to expand their research efforts to develop renewable sources of carbon-based fuels. For more than a quarter century, Brazil has been engaged in a program to replace gasoline with ethanol derived from the root crop manioc (cassava).

(a) Write separate balanced equations for the complete combustion of ethanol (C_2H_5OH) and of gasoline (represented by the formula C_8H_{18}).
(b) What mass of oxygen is required to burn completely 1.00 L of a mixture that is 90.0% gasoline ($d = 0.742$ g/mL) and 10.0% ethanol ($d = 0.789$ g/mL) by volume?
(c) If 1.00 mol of O_2 occupies 22.4 L, what volume of O_2 is needed to burn 1.00 L of the mixture?
(d) Air is 20.9% O_2 by volume. What volume of air is needed to burn 1.00 L of the mixture?

4.136 In a car engine, gasoline (represented by C_8H_{18}) does not burn completely, and some CO, a toxic pollutant, forms along with CO_2 and H_2O. If 5.0% of the gasoline forms CO:
(a) What is the ratio of CO_2 to CO molecules in the exhaust?
(b) What is the mass ratio of CO_2 to CO?
(c) What percentage of the gasoline must form CO for the mass ratio of CO_2 to CO to be exactly 1/1?

4.137 The amount of ascorbic acid (vitamin C; $C_6H_8O_6$) in tablets is determined by reaction with bromine and then titration of the hydrobromic acid with standard base:

$$C_6H_8O_6(aq) + Br_2(aq) \longrightarrow C_6H_6O_6(aq) + 2HBr(aq)$$
$$HBr(aq) + NaOH(aq) \longrightarrow NaBr(aq) + H_2O(l)$$

A certain tablet is advertised as containing 500 mg of vitamin C. One tablet was dissolved in water and reacted with Br_2. The solution was then titrated with 43.20 mL of 0.1350 M NaOH. Did the tablet contain the advertised quantity of vitamin C?

4.138 In the process of *salting-in*, protein solubility in a dilute salt solution is increased by adding more salt. Because the protein solubility depends on the total ion concentration as well as the ion charge, salts containing doubly charged ions are often more effective than those containing singly charged ions.
(a) How many grams of $MgCl_2$ must dissolve to equal the ion concentration of 12.4 g of NaCl?
(b) How many grams of CaS must dissolve?
(c) Which of the three salt solutions would dissolve the most protein?

4.139 At liftoff, a space shuttle uses a solid mixture of ammonium perchlorate and aluminum powder to obtain great thrust from the volume change of solid to gas. In the presence of a catalyst, the mixture forms solid aluminum oxide and aluminum trichloride and gaseous water and nitrogen monoxide.
(a) Write a balanced equation for the reaction, and identify the reducing and oxidizing agents.
(b) How many total moles of gas (water vapor and nitrogen monoxide) are produced when 50.0 kg of ammonium perchlorate reacts with a stoichiometric amount of Al?
(c) What is the change in volume from this reaction? (d of $NH_4ClO_4 = 1.95$ g/cc, Al $= 2.70$ g/cc, $Al_2O_3 = 3.97$ g/cc, and $AlCl_3 = 2.44$ g/cc; assume 1 mol of gas occupies 22.4 L.)

4.140 A *reaction cycle* for an element is a series of reactions beginning and ending with that element. In the following copper reaction cycle, copper has either a 0 or a +2 oxidation state. Write balanced molecular and net ionic equations for each step.
(1) Copper metal reacts with aqueous bromine to produce a green-blue solution.
(2) Adding aqueous sodium hydroxide forms a blue precipitate.
(3) The precipitate is heated and turns black (water is released).
(4) The black solid dissolves in nitric acid to give a blue solution.
(5) Adding aqueous sodium phosphate forms a green precipitate.
(6) The precipitate forms a blue solution in sulfuric acid.
(7) Copper metal is recovered from the blue solution when zinc metal is added.

4.141 Two 25.0-mL aqueous solutions, labeled A and B, contain the ions indicated:

(a) If each sphere represents 1.0×10^{-3} mol of ion, will the equivalence point have been reached when all of B has been added to A?
(b) What is the molarity of B?
(c) What additional volume (mL) of B must be added to reach the equivalence point?

Gases and the Kinetic-Molecular Theory

Concepts and skills to review before you study this chapter

- physical states of matter (Section 1.1)
- SI unit conversions (Section 1.5)
- amount-mass-number conversions (Section 3.1)

Amazing as it may seem, what actually occurs when you drink through a straw is that you suck the air out of the straw and the weight of Earth's atmosphere pushes down on the liquid and forces it into your mouth! Other remarkable properties of gases are at work in the rising of a loaf of bread, the operation of a car engine, and, as we'll discuss later in the chapter, even in the act of breathing. People have been studying the behavior of gases and the other states of matter throughout history; in fact, three of the four "elements" of the ancient Greeks were air (gas), water (liquid), and earth (solid). Yet, despite millennia of observations, many questions remain. In this chapter and its companion, Chapter 12, we examine the physical states and their interrelations. Here, we highlight the gaseous state, the one we understand best.

Gases are everywhere. Our atmosphere is a colorless, odorless mixture of 18 gases, some of which—O_2, N_2, H_2O vapor, and CO_2—take part in life-sustaining cycles of redox reactions throughout the environment. And several other gases, such as chlorine and ammonia, have essential roles in industry. Yet, in this chapter, we put aside the *chemical* behavior unique to any particular gas and focus instead *on the **physical** behavior common to all gases.*

IN THIS CHAPTER . . . We explore the physical behavior of gases and the theory that explains it. In the process, we see how scientists use mathematics to model nature.

- We compare the behaviors of gases, liquids, and solids.
- We discuss laboratory methods for measuring gas pressure.
- We consider laws that describe the behavior of a gas in terms of how its volume changes with a change in (1) pressure, (2) temperature, or (3) amount. We focus on the ideal gas law, which encompasses these three laws, and apply it to solve gas law problems.
- We rearrange the ideal gas law to determine the density and molar mass of an unknown gas, the partial pressure of any gas in a mixture, and the amounts of gaseous reactants and products in a chemical change.
- We see how the kinetic-molecular theory explains the gas laws and accounts for other important behaviors of gas particles.
- We apply key ideas about gas behavior to Earth's atmosphere.
- We find that the behavior of real, not ideal, gases, especially under extreme conditions, requires refinements of the ideal gas law and the kinetic-molecular theory.

5.1 • AN OVERVIEW OF THE PHYSICAL STATES OF MATTER

Most substances can exist as a solid, a liquid, or a gas under appropriate conditions of pressure and temperature. In Chapter 1, we used the relative position and motion of the particles of a substance to distinguish how each state fills a container (see Figure 1.2, p. 6):

Figure 5.1 The three states of matter. Many pure substances, such as bromine (Br_2), can exist under appropriate conditions of pressure and temperature as a gas, liquid, or solid.

Gas: *Particles are far apart, move freely, and fill the available space.*

Liquid: *Particles are close together but move around one another.*

Solid: *Particles are close together in a regular array and do not move around one another.*

- A gas adopts the container shape and fills it, because its particles are far apart and move randomly.
- A liquid adopts the container shape to the extent of its volume, because its particles are close together but free to move around each other.
- A solid has a fixed shape regardless of the container shape, because its particles are close together and held rigidly in place.

Figure 5.1 focuses on the three states of bromine.

Several other aspects of their behaviors distinguish gases from liquids and solids:

1. *Gas volume changes significantly with pressure.* When a sample of gas is confined to a container of variable volume, such as a cylinder with a piston, *increasing* the force on the piston *decreases* the gas volume. Removing the external force allows the volume to increase again. Gases under pressure can do a lot of work: rapidly expanding compressed air in a jackhammer breaks rock and cement; compressed air in tires lifts the weight of a car. In contrast, the volume of a liquid or a solid does not change significantly under pressure.

2. *Gas volume changes significantly with temperature.* When a sample of gas is heated, it expands; when it is cooled, it shrinks. This volume change is 50 to 100 times greater for gases than for liquids or solids. The expansion that occurs when gases are rapidly heated can have dramatic effects, like lifting a rocket into space, and everyday ones, like popping corn.

3. *Gases flow very freely.* Gases flow much more freely than liquids and solids. This behavior allows gases to be transported more easily through pipes, but it also means they leak more rapidly out of small holes and cracks.

4. *Gases have relatively low densities.* Gas density is usually measured in units of grams per liter (g/L), whereas liquid and solid densities are in grams per milliliter (g/mL), about 1000 times as dense (see Table 1.5, p. 22). For example, at 20°C and normal atmospheric pressure, the density of $O_2(g)$ is 1.3 **g/L,** whereas the density of $H_2O(l)$ is 1.0 **g/mL** and the density of NaCl(s) is 2.2 **g/mL.** When a gas cools, its density *increases* because its volume *decreases*: on cooling from 20°C to 0°C, the density of $O_2(g)$ increases from 1.3 to 1.4 g/L.

5. *Gases form a solution in any proportions.* Air is a solution of 18 gases. Two liquids, however, may or may not form a solution: water and ethanol do, but water and gasoline do not. Two solids generally do not form a solution unless they are melted and mixed while liquids, then allowed to solidify (as is done to make the alloy bronze from copper and tin).

Like the way a gas completely fills a container, these macroscopic properties—changing volume with pressure or temperature, great ability to flow, low density, and ability to form solutions—arise because the particles in a gas are much farther apart than those in either a liquid or a solid.

◼ Summary of Section 5.1

- The volume of a gas can be altered significantly by changing the applied force or the temperature. Corresponding changes for liquids and solids are *much* smaller.
- Gases flow more freely and have much lower densities than liquids and solids.
- Gases mix in any proportions to form solutions; liquids and solids generally do not.
- Differences in the physical states are due to the greater average distance between particles in a gas than in a liquid or a solid.

5.2 • GAS PRESSURE AND ITS MEASUREMENT

You can blow up a balloon or pump up a tire because *a gas exerts pressure on the walls of its container.* **Pressure (P)** is defined as the force exerted per unit of surface area:

$$\text{Pressure} = \frac{\text{force}}{\text{area}}$$

Earth's gravity attracts the atmospheric gases, and they exert a force uniformly on *all* surfaces. The force, or *weight,* of these gases creates a pressure of about 14.7 pounds per square inch (lb/in^2; psi) of surface. Thus, a pressure of 14.7 lb/in^2 exists on the outside of your room (or your body), and it equals the pressure on the inside. What would happen if the pressures were *not* equal? Consider the empty can attached to a vacuum pump in Figure 5.2. With the pump off (*left*) the can maintains its shape because the pressure on the outside is equal to the pressure on the inside. With the pump on (*right*), much of the air inside is removed, decreasing the internal pressure greatly, and the pressure of the atmosphere easily crushes the can. The vacuum-filtration flasks and tubing that you may have used in the lab have thick walls that withstand the relatively higher external pressure.

Laboratory Devices for Measuring Gas Pressure

The **barometer** is used to measure atmospheric pressure. The device is still essentially the same as it was when invented in 1643 by the Italian physicist Evangelista Torricelli:

Vacuum off:
Pressure outside = pressure inside

Vacuum on:
Pressure outside >> pressure inside

Figure 5.2 Effect of atmospheric pressure on a familiar object.

Vacuum above Hg column

Pressure due to weight of mercury (P_{Hg})

Pressure due to weight of atmosphere (P_{atm})

$\Delta h = 760$ mmHg

Dish filled with Hg

Figure 5.3 A mercury barometer. The pressure of the atmosphere, P_{atm}, balances the pressure of the mercury column, P_{Hg}.

a tube about 1 m long, closed at one end, filled with mercury (atomic symbol, Hg), and inverted into a dish containing more mercury. When the tube is inverted, some of the mercury flows out into the dish, and a vacuum forms above the mercury remaining in the tube (Figure 5.3). At sea level, under ordinary atmospheric conditions, the mercury stops flowing out when the surface of the mercury in the tube is about 760 mm above the surface of the mercury in the dish. At that height, the column of mercury exerts the same pressure (weight/area) on the mercury surface in the dish as the atmosphere does: $P_{Hg} = P_{atm}$. Likewise, if you evacuate a closed tube and invert it into a dish of mercury, the atmosphere pushes the mercury up to a height of about 760 mm.

Notice that we did not specify the diameter of the barometer tube. If the mercury in a 1-cm diameter tube rises to a height of 760 mm, the mercury in a 2-cm diameter tube will rise to that height also. The *weight* of mercury is greater in the wider tube, but so is the area; thus, the *pressure*, the *ratio* of weight to area, is the same.

Because the pressure of the mercury column is directly proportional to its height, a unit commonly used for pressure is millimeters of mercury (mmHg). We discuss other units of pressure shortly. *At sea level and 0°C, normal atmospheric pressure is 760 mmHg;* at the top of Mt. Everest (elevation 29,028 ft, or 8848 m), the atmospheric pressure is only about 270 mmHg. Thus, *pressure decreases with altitude:* the column of air above the sea is taller, so it weighs more than the column of air above Mt. Everest.

Laboratory barometers contain mercury because its high density allows a barometer to be a convenient size. If a barometer contained water instead, it would have to be more than 34 ft high, because the pressure of the atmosphere equals the pressure of a column of water about 10,300 mm (almost 34 ft) high. For a given pressure, the ratio of heights (h) of the liquid columns is inversely related to the ratio of the densities (d) of the liquids:

$$\frac{h_{H_2O}}{h_{Hg}} = \frac{d_{Hg}}{d_{H_2O}}$$

Interestingly, several centuries ago, people thought a vacuum had mysterious "suction" powers, and they didn't understand why a suction pump could remove water from a well only to a depth of 34 feet. We know now, as the great 17th-century scientist Galileo explained, that a vacuum does not suck mercury up into a barometer tube, a suction pump does not suck water up from a well, the vacuum pump in Figure 5.2 does not suck in the walls of the crushed can, and the vacuum you create in a straw does not suck the drink into your mouth. Only matter—in this case, the atmospheric gases—can exert a force.

Manometers are devices used to measure the pressure of a gas in an experiment. Figure 5.4 shows two types of manometer. In the *closed-end manometer (left side),* a

Closed-end manometer

Closed end

Vacuum

Hg levels equal

Δh

Evacuated flask

P_{gas}

The Hg levels are equal because both arms of the U tube are evacuated.

A gas in the flask pushes the Hg level down in the left arm, and the difference in levels, Δh, equals the gas pressure, P_{gas}.

Open-end manometer

P_{atm} P_{atm}

Open end

Δh Δh

P_{gas} P_{gas}

When P_{gas} is less than P_{atm}, subtract Δh from P_{atm}:
$P_{gas} < P_{atm}$
$P_{gas} = P_{atm} - \Delta h$

When P_{gas} is greater than P_{atm}, add Δh to P_{atm}:
$P_{gas} > P_{atm}$
$P_{gas} = P_{atm} + \Delta h$

Figure 5.4 Two types of manometer.

mercury-filled, curved tube is *closed* at one end and attached to a flask at the other. When the flask is evacuated, the mercury levels in the two arms of the tube are the same because no gas exerts pressure on either mercury surface. When a gas is in the flask, it pushes down the mercury level in the near arm, causing the level to rise in the far arm. The *difference* in column heights (Δh) equals the gas pressure.

The *open-end manometer* (*right side* of Figure 5.4) also consists of a curved tube filled with mercury, but one end of the tube is *open* to the atmosphere and the other is connected to the gas sample. The atmosphere pushes on one mercury surface, and the gas pushes on the other. Again, Δh equals the difference between two pressures. But, when using this type of manometer, we must measure the atmospheric pressure with a barometer and either add or subtract Δh from that value.

Units of Pressure

Pressure results from a force exerted on an area. The SI unit of force is the newton (N): $1\ N = 1\ kg \cdot m/s^2$ (about the weight of an apple). The SI unit of pressure is the **pascal (Pa),** which equals a force of one newton exerted on an area of one square meter:

$$1\ Pa = 1\ N/m^2$$

A much larger unit is the **standard atmosphere (atm),** the average atmospheric pressure measured at sea level and 0°C. It is defined in terms of the pascal:

$$1\ atm = 101.325\ kilopascals\ (kPa) = 1.01325 \times 10^5\ Pa$$

Another common unit is the **millimeter of mercury (mmHg),** mentioned earlier; in honor of Torricelli, this unit has been renamed the **torr:**

$$1\ torr = 1\ mmHg = \frac{1}{760}\ atm = \frac{101.325}{760}\ kPa = 133.322\ Pa$$

The *bar* is coming into more common use in chemistry:

$$1\ bar = 1 \times 10^2\ kPa = 1 \times 10^5\ Pa$$

Despite a gradual change to SI units, many chemists still express pressure in torrs and atmospheres, so those units are used in this book, with reference to pascals and bars. Table 5.1 lists some important pressure units with the corresponding values for normal atmospheric pressure.

Table 5.1 Common Units of Pressure

Unit	Normal Atmospheric Pressure at Sea Level and 0°C
pascal (Pa); kilopascal (kPa)	1.01325×10^5 Pa; 101.325 kPa
atmosphere (atm)	1 atm*
millimeters of mercury (mmHg)	760 mmHg*
torr	760 torr*
pounds per square inch (lb/in^2 or psi)	14.7 lb/in^2
bar	1.01325 bar

*This is an exact quantity; in calculations, we use as many significant figures as necessary.

Sample Problem 5.1 | Converting Units of Pressure

Problem A geochemist heats a limestone ($CaCO_3$) sample and collects the CO_2 released in an evacuated flask attached to a closed-end manometer. After the system comes to room temperature, $\Delta h = 291.4$ mmHg. Calculate the CO_2 pressure in torrs, atmospheres, and kilopascals.

Plan The CO_2 pressure is given in units of mmHg, so we construct conversion factors from Table 5.1 to find the pressure in the other units.

Solution Converting from mmHg to torr:

$$P_{CO_2} \text{ (torr)} = 291.4 \text{ mmHg} \times \frac{1 \text{ torr}}{1 \text{ mmHg}} = \boxed{291.4 \text{ torr}}$$

Converting from torr to atm:

$$P_{CO_2} \text{ (atm)} = 291.4 \text{ torr} \times \frac{1 \text{ atm}}{760 \text{ torr}} = \boxed{0.3834 \text{ atm}}$$

Converting from atm to kPa:

$$P_{CO_2} \text{ (kPa)} = 0.3834 \text{ atm} \times \frac{101.325 \text{ kPa}}{1 \text{ atm}} = \boxed{38.85 \text{ kPa}}$$

Check There are 760 torr in 1 atm, so ~300 torr should be <0.5 atm. There are ~100 kPa in 1 atm, so <0.5 atm should be <50 kPa.

Comment 1. In the conversion from torr to atm, we retained four significant figures because this unit conversion factor involves *exact* numbers; that is, 760 torr has as many significant figures as the calculation requires (see the footnote on Table 5.1).
2. From here on, except in particularly complex situations, *unit canceling will no longer be shown.*

Follow-Up Problem 5.1 The CO_2 released from another mineral sample was collected in an evacuated flask connected to an open-end manometer. If the barometer reading is 753.6 mmHg and P_{gas} is less than P_{atm} to give a Δh of 174.0 mmHg, calculate P_{CO_2} in torrs, pascals, and lb/in^2.

■ Summary of Section 5.2

- Gases exert pressure (force/area) on all surfaces they contact.
- A barometer measures atmospheric pressure based on the height of a mercury column that the atmosphere can support (760 mmHg at sea level and 0°C).
- Closed-end and open-end manometers are used to measure the pressure of a gas sample.
- Pressure units include the atmosphere (atm), torr (identical to mmHg), and pascal (Pa, the SI unit).

5.3 • THE GAS LAWS AND THEIR EXPERIMENTAL FOUNDATIONS

The physical behavior of a sample of gas can be described completely by four variables: pressure (P), volume (V), temperature (T), and amount (number of moles, n). The variables are interdependent, which means that *any one of them can be determined by measuring the other three*. Three key relationships exist among the four gas variables—Boyle's, Charles's, and Avogadro's laws. Each of these *gas laws expresses the effect of one variable on another, with the remaining two variables held constant*. Because gas volume is so easy to measure, the laws are expressed as the effect on gas volume of a change in the pressure, temperature, or amount of the gas.

The individual gas laws are special cases of a unifying relationship called the *ideal gas law,* which quantitatively describes the behavior of an **ideal gas,** one that exhibits linear relationships among volume, pressure, temperature, and amount. Although *no ideal gas actually exists,* most simple gases, such as N_2, O_2, H_2, and the noble gases, behave nearly ideally at ordinary temperatures and pressures. We discuss the ideal gas law after the three individual laws.

The Relationship Between Volume and Pressure: Boyle's Law

Following Torricelli's invention of the barometer, the great 17th-century English chemist Robert Boyle studied the effect of pressure on the volume of a sample of gas.

1. *The experiment.* Figure 5.5 illustrates the setup Boyle might have used in his experiments (parts A and B), the data he might have collected (part C), and graphs of

Figure 5.5 Boyle's law, the relationship between the volume and pressure of a gas.

the data (parts D and E). Boyle sealed the shorter leg of a J-shaped glass tube and poured mercury into the longer open leg, thereby trapping some air (the gas in the experiment) in the shorter leg. He calculated the gas volume (V_{gas}) from the height of the trapped air and the diameter of the tube. The total pressure, P_{total}, applied to the trapped gas is the pressure of the atmosphere, P_{atm} (760 mm, measured with a barometer), plus the difference in the heights of the mercury columns (Δh) in the two legs of the J tube, 20 mm (Figure 5.5A); thus, P_{total} is 780 torr. By adding mercury, Boyle increased P_{total}, and the gas volume decreased. In Figure 5.5B, more mercury has been added to the original Δh of 20 mm, so P_{total} doubles to 1560 torr; note that V_{gas} is halved from 20 mL to 10 mL. In this way, by keeping the temperature and amount of gas constant, Boyle was able to measure the effect of the applied pressure on gas volume.

Note the following results in Figure 5.5:

- The product of corresponding P and V values is a constant (part C, rightmost column).
- V is *inversely* proportional to P (part D).
- V is *directly* proportional to $1/P$ (part E), and a plot of V versus $1/P$ is linear. This *linear relationship between two gas variables* is a hallmark of ideal gas behavior.

2. *Conclusion and statement of the law.* The generalization of Boyle's observations is known as **Boyle's law:** *at constant temperature, the volume occupied by a fixed amount of gas is **inversely** proportional to the applied (external) pressure,* or

$$V \propto \frac{1}{P} \qquad [T \text{ and } n \text{ fixed}] \qquad \text{(5.1)}$$

This relationship can also be expressed as

$$PV = \text{constant} \qquad \text{or} \qquad V = \frac{\text{constant}}{P} \qquad [T \text{ and } n \text{ fixed}]$$

That is, at fixed T and n, $\qquad P\uparrow, V\downarrow \qquad$ and $\qquad P\downarrow, V\uparrow$

The constant is the same for most simple gases under ordinary conditions. Thus, tripling the external pressure reduces the volume of a gas to a third of its initial value; halving the pressure doubles the volume; and so forth.

The wording of Boyle's law focuses on *external* pressure. But, notice that the mercury level rises as mercury is added, until the pressure of the trapped gas *on* the mercury increases enough to stop its rise. At that point, the pressure exerted *on* the gas equals the pressure exerted *by* the gas (P_{gas}). Thus, in general, if V_{gas} increases, P_{gas} decreases, and vice versa.

The Relationship Between Volume and Temperature: Charles's Law

Boyle's work showed that the pressure-volume relationship holds only at constant temperature, but why should that be so? It would take more than a century, until the work of French scientists J. A. C. Charles and J. L. Gay-Lussac, for the relationship between gas volume and temperature to be understood.

1. *The experiment.* Let's examine this relationship by measuring the volume at different temperatures of a fixed amount of a gas under constant pressure. A straight tube, closed at one end, traps a fixed amount of gas (air) under a small mercury plug. The tube is immersed in a water bath that is warmed with a heater or cooled with ice. After each change of temperature, we measure the length of the gas column, which is proportional to its volume. The total pressure exerted on the gas is constant because the mercury plug and the atmospheric pressure do not change (Figure 5.6, parts A and B).

Figure 5.6C shows some typical data. Consider the red line, which shows how the volume of 0.04 mol of gas at 1 atm pressure changes with temperature. Extrapolating that line to lower temperatures (dashed portion) shows that, in theory, the gas occupies zero volume at −273.15°C (the intercept on the temperature axis). Plots for a different amount of gas (green) or a different gas pressure (blue) have different slopes, but they all converge at −273.15°C. William Thomson (Lord Kelvin) later used this linear relation between gas volume and temperature to devise the absolute temperature scale (Section 1.5).

2. *Conclusion and statement of the law.* Above all, note that *the volume-temperature relationship is linear,* but, unlike volume and pressure, volume and temperature are *directly* proportional. This behavior is incorporated into the modern statement of the volume-temperature relationship, which is known as **Charles's law:** *at constant pressure, the volume occupied by a fixed amount of gas is **directly** proportional to its absolute (Kelvin) temperature,* or

$$V \propto T \qquad [P \text{ and } n \text{ fixed}] \tag{5.2}$$

This relationship can also be expressed as

$$\frac{V}{T} = \text{constant} \qquad \text{or} \qquad V = \text{constant} \times T \qquad [P \text{ and } n \text{ fixed}]$$

That is, at fixed P and n, $\quad T\uparrow, V\uparrow \quad$ and $\quad T\downarrow, V\downarrow$

If T increases, V increases, and vice versa. Once again, for any given P and n, the constant is the same for most simple gases under ordinary conditions.

Figure 5.6 Charles's law, the relationship between the volume and temperature of a gas.

A Ice water bath (0°C, or 273 K)

B Boiling water bath (100°C, or 373 K)

C

Absolute zero (0 K or $-273.15°C$) is the temperature at which an ideal gas would have zero volume. (Absolute zero has never been reached, but physicists have attained 10^{-9} K.) In reality, no sample of matter can have zero volume, and every real gas condenses to a liquid at some temperature higher than 0 K. Nevertheless, the linear dependence of volume on absolute temperature holds for most common gases over a wide temperature range. This dependence of gas volume on the *absolute* temperature adds a practical requirement for chemists (and chemistry students): *the Kelvin scale must be used in gas law calculations.* For instance, if the temperature changes from 200 K to 400 K, the volume of gas doubles. But, if the temperature changes from 200°C to 400°C, the volume increases by a factor of 1.42; that is,

$$\left(\frac{400°C + 273.15}{200°C + 273.15}\right) = \frac{673}{473} = 1.42$$

Other Relationships Based on Boyle's and Charles's Laws Two other important relationships arise from Boyle's and Charles's laws:

1. *The pressure-temperature relationship.* Charles's law is expressed as the effect of temperature on gas *volume* at constant pressure. But volume and pressure are interdependent, so a similar relationship can be expressed for the effect of temperature on pressure (sometimes referred to as *Amontons's law*). Measure the pressure in your car or bike tires before and after a long ride, and you'll find that it increases. Heating due to friction between the tires and the road increases the air temperature inside the tires, but since a tire's volume can't increase very much, the air pressure does. Thus, *at constant volume, the pressure exerted by a fixed amount of gas is directly proportional to the absolute temperature:*

$$P \propto T \qquad [V \text{ and } n \text{ fixed}] \tag{5.3}$$

or

$$\frac{P}{T} = \text{constant} \qquad \text{or} \qquad P = \text{constant} \times T$$

That is, at fixed V and n, $\qquad T\uparrow, P\uparrow \qquad$ and $\qquad T\downarrow, P\downarrow$

2. *The combined gas law.* Combining Boyle's and Charles's laws gives the *combined gas law,* which applies to cases when changes in *two* of the three variables (V, P, T) affect the third:

$$V \propto \frac{T}{P} \qquad \text{or} \qquad V = \text{constant} \times \frac{T}{P} \qquad \text{or} \qquad \frac{PV}{T} = \text{constant}$$

The Relationship Between Volume and Amount: Avogadro's Law

Let's see why both Boyle's and Charles's laws specify a fixed amount of gas.

1. *The experiment.* Figure 5.7 shows an experiment that involves two small test tubes, each fitted to a much larger piston-cylinder assembly. We add 0.10 mol (4.4 g) of dry ice (solid CO_2) to the first tube (A) and 0.20 mol (8.8 g) to the second tube (B). As the solid CO_2 warms to room temperature, it changes to gaseous CO_2, and the volume increases until $P_{gas} = P_{atm}$. At constant temperature, when all the solid has changed to gas, cylinder B has twice the volume of cylinder A.

Figure 5.7 The relationship between the volume and amount of a gas.

2. *Conclusion and statement of the law.* Thus, *at fixed temperature and pressure, the volume occupied by a gas is directly proportional to the amount (mol) of gas:*

$$V \propto n \qquad [P \text{ and } T \text{ fixed}] \qquad (5.4)$$

That is, as n increases, V increases, and vice versa. This relationship is also expressed as

$$\frac{V}{n} = \text{constant} \qquad \text{or} \qquad V = \text{constant} \times n$$

That is, at fixed P and T, $\qquad n\uparrow, V\uparrow \qquad$ and $\qquad n\downarrow, V\downarrow$

The constant is the same for all simple gases at ordinary temperature and pressure. This relationship is another way of expressing **Avogadro's law,** which states that *at fixed temperature and pressure, equal volumes of **any** ideal gas contain equal numbers of particles (or moles).*

Familiar Applications of the Gas Laws The gas laws apply to countless familiar phenomena. In a car engine, a reaction occurs in which fewer moles of gasoline and O_2 form more moles of CO_2 and H_2O vapor, and heat is released. The increase in n (Avogadro's law) and T (Charles's law) increases V, and the piston is pushed back. Dynamite is a solid that forms more moles of hot gases very rapidly when it reacts (Avogadro's and Charles's laws). Dough rises because yeast digests sugar, which creates bubbles of CO_2 (Avogadro's law); the dough expands more as the bread bakes in a hot oven (Charles's law).

No application of the gas laws can be more vital or familiar than breathing (Figure 5.8). When you inhale, muscles move your diaphragm down and your rib cage out (*blue*). This coordinated movement increases the volume of your lungs, which decreases the air pressure inside them (Boyle's law). The inside pressure is 1–3 torr *less* than atmospheric pressure, so air rushes in. The greater amount of air stretches the elastic tissue of the lungs and expands the volume further (Avogadro's law). The air also expands as it warms from the external temperature to your body temperature (Charles's law). When you exhale, the diaphragm moves up and the rib cage moves in, so your lung volume decreases (*red*). The inside pressure becomes 1–3 torr *more* than the outside pressure (Boyle's law), so air rushes out.

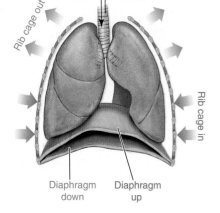

Figure 5.8 The process of breathing applies the gas laws.

Gas Behavior at Standard Conditions

To better understand the factors that influence gas behavior, chemists have assigned a baseline set of *standard conditions* called **standard temperature and pressure (STP):**

$$\text{STP:} \qquad 0°C \ (273.15 \text{ K}) \text{ and } 1 \text{ atm } (760 \text{ torr}) \qquad (5.5)$$

Under these conditions, the volume of 1 mol of an ideal gas is called the **standard molar volume:**

$$\text{Standard molar volume} = 22.4141 \text{ L or } 22.4 \text{ L } [\text{to 3 sf}] \qquad (5.6)$$

At STP, helium (He), nitrogen (N_2), oxygen (O_2), and other simple gases behave nearly ideally (Figure 5.9). Note that the mass, and thus the density (d), depend on the specific gas, but 1 mol of any of them occupies 22.4 L at STP. Figure 5.10 compares the volumes of some familiar objects with the standard molar volume of an ideal gas.

The Ideal Gas Law

Each of the three gas laws shows how one of the three other gas variables affects gas volume:

- Boyle's law focuses on pressure ($V \propto 1/P$).
- Charles's law focuses on temperature ($V \propto T$).
- Avogadro's law focuses on amount (mol) of gas ($V \propto n$).

Figure 5.9 Standard molar volume. One mole of an ideal gas occupies 22.4 L at STP (0°C and 1 atm).

Figure 5.10 The volumes of 1 mol (22.4 L) of an ideal gas and of some familiar objects: 1 gal of milk (3.79 L), a basketball (7.50 L), and 2.00 L of a carbonated drink.

By combining these individual effects, we obtain the **ideal gas law** (or *ideal gas equation*):

$$V \propto \frac{nT}{P} \quad \text{or} \quad PV \propto nT \quad \text{or} \quad \frac{PV}{nT} = R$$

where R is a proportionality constant known as the **universal gas constant.** Rearranging gives the most common form of the ideal gas law:

$$PV = nRT \qquad \text{(5.7)}$$

We obtain a value of R by measuring the volume, temperature, and pressure of a given amount of gas and substituting the values into the ideal gas law. For example, using standard conditions for the gas variables and 1 mol of gas, we have

$$R = \frac{PV}{nT} = \frac{1 \text{ atm} \times 22.4141 \text{ L}}{1 \text{ mol} \times 273.15 \text{ K}} = 0.082058 \frac{\text{atm} \cdot \text{L}}{\text{mol} \cdot \text{K}} = 0.0821 \frac{\text{atm} \cdot \text{L}}{\text{mol} \cdot \text{K}} \text{ [3 sf]} \quad \text{(5.8)}$$

This numerical value of R corresponds to P, V, and T expressed *in these units; R has a different numerical value when different units are used.* For example, on p. 209, R has the value 8.314 J/mol·K (J stands for joule, the SI unit of energy).

Figure 5.11 on the next page makes a central point: the ideal gas law *becomes* one of the individual gas laws when two of the four variables are kept constant. When initial conditions (subscript 1) change to final conditions (subscript 2), we have

$$P_1V_1 = n_1RT_1 \quad \text{and} \quad P_2V_2 = n_2RT_2$$

Thus,
$$\frac{P_1V_1}{n_1T_1} = R \quad \text{and} \quad \frac{P_2V_2}{n_2T_2} = R, \quad \text{so} \quad \frac{P_1V_1}{n_1T_1} = \frac{P_2V_2}{n_2T_2}$$

Notice that if, for example, the two variables P and T remain constant, then $P_1 = P_2$ and $T_1 = T_2$, and we obtain an expression for Avogadro's law:

$$\frac{P_1V_1}{n_1T_1} = \frac{P_2V_2}{n_2T_2} \quad \text{or} \quad \frac{V_1}{n_1} = \frac{V_2}{n_2}$$

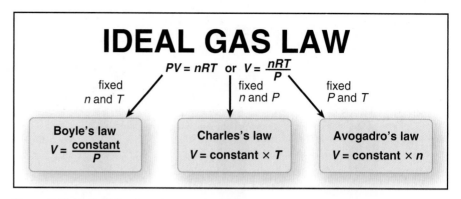

IDEAL GAS LAW

$$PV = nRT \quad \text{or} \quad V = \frac{nRT}{P}$$

fixed
n and *T*

fixed
n and *P*

fixed
P and *T*

Boyle's law
$$V = \frac{\text{constant}}{P}$$

Charles's law
$$V = \text{constant} \times T$$

Avogadro's law
$$V = \text{constant} \times n$$

Figure 5.11 The individual gas laws as special cases of the ideal gas law.

As you'll see next, you can use a similar approach to solve gas law problems. Thus, by keeping track of the initial and final values of the gas variables, you avoid the need to memorize the three individual gas laws.

Solving Gas Law Problems

Gas law problems are phrased in many ways but can usually be grouped into two types:

1. *A change in one of the four variables causes a change in another, while the two other variables remain constant.* In this type, the ideal gas law reduces to one of the individual gas laws, and you solve for the new value of the affected variable. Units must be consistent and *T* must always be in kelvins, but *R* is not involved. Sample Problems 5.2 to 5.4 and 5.6 are of this type. [A variation on this type involves the combined gas law (p. 189) when simultaneous changes in two of the variables cause a change in a third.]

2. *One variable is unknown, but the other three are known and no change occurs.* In this type, exemplified by Sample Problem 5.5, you apply the ideal gas law directly to find the unknown, and the units must conform to those in *R*.

Solving these problems requires a systematic approach:

- Summarize the changing gas variables—knowns and unknown—and those held constant.
- Convert units, if necessary.
- Rearrange the ideal gas law to obtain the needed relationship of variables, and solve for the unknown.

Road Map

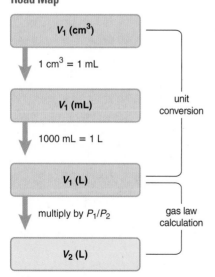

V_1 (cm³)

1 cm³ = 1 mL

V_1 (mL)

1000 mL = 1 L

V_1 (L)

multiply by P_1/P_2

V_2 (L)

unit conversion

gas law calculation

Sample Problem 5.2   **Applying the Volume-Pressure Relationship**

Problem Boyle's apprentice finds that the air trapped in a J tube occupies 24.8 cm³ at 1.12 atm. By adding mercury to the tube, he increases the pressure on the trapped air to 2.64 atm. Assuming constant temperature, what is the new volume of air (in L)?

Plan We must find the final volume (V_2) in liters, given the initial volume (V_1), initial pressure (P_1), and final pressure (P_2). The temperature and amount of gas are fixed. We convert the units of V_1 from cm³ to mL and then to L, rearrange the ideal gas law to the appropriate form, and solve for V_2. (Note that the road map has two parts.)

Solution Summarizing the gas variables:

$$P_1 = 1.12 \text{ atm} \qquad\qquad P_2 = 2.64 \text{ atm}$$
$$V_1 = 24.8 \text{ cm}^3 \text{ (convert to L)} \quad V_2 = \text{unknown} \qquad T \text{ and } n \text{ remain constant}$$

Converting V_1 from cm³ to L:

$$V_1 = 24.8 \text{ cm}^3 \times \frac{1 \text{ mL}}{1 \text{ cm}^3} \times \frac{1 \text{ L}}{1000 \text{ mL}} = 0.0248 \text{ L}$$

Rearranging the ideal gas law and solving for V_2: At fixed n and T, we have

$$\frac{P_1V_1}{n_1T_1} = \frac{P_2V_2}{n_2T_2} \quad \text{or} \quad P_1V_1 = P_2V_2$$

$$V_2 = V_1 \times \frac{P_1}{P_2} = 0.0248 \text{ L} \times \frac{1.12 \text{ atm}}{2.64 \text{ atm}} = \boxed{0.0105 \text{ L}}$$

Check The relative values of P and V can help us check the math: P more than doubled, so V_2 should be less than $\frac{1}{2}V_1$ ($0.0105/0.0248 < \frac{1}{2}$).

Comment Predicting the direction of the change provides another check on the problem setup: Since P increases, V will decrease; thus, V_2 should be less than V_1. To make $V_2 < V_1$, we must multiply V_1 by a number *less than* 1. This means the ratio of pressures must be *less than* 1, so the larger pressure (P_2) must be in the denominator, or P_1/P_2.

Follow-Up Problem 5.2 A sample of argon gas occupies 105 mL at 0.871 atm. If the temperature remains constant, what is the volume (in L) at 26.3 kPa?

Sample Problem 5.3 Applying the Pressure-Temperature Relationship

Problem A steel tank used for fuel delivery is fitted with a safety valve that opens if the internal pressure exceeds 1.00×10^3 torr. It is filled with methane at 23°C and 0.991 atm and placed in boiling water 100.°C. Will the safety valve open?

Plan The question "Will the safety valve open?" translates to "Is P_2 greater than 1.00×10^3 torr at T_2?" Thus, P_2 is the unknown, and T_1, T_2, and P_1 are given, with V (steel tank) and n fixed. We convert both T values to kelvins and P_1 to torrs in order to compare P_2 with the safety-limit pressure. We rearrange the ideal gas law and solve for P_2.

Solution Summarizing the gas variables:

$$P_1 = 0.991 \text{ atm (convert to torr)} \qquad P_2 = \text{unknown}$$
$$T_1 = 23°C \text{ (convert to K)} \qquad T_2 = 100.°C \text{ (convert to K)}$$
$$V \text{ and } n \text{ remain constant}$$

Converting T from °C to K:

$$T_1 \text{ (K)} = 23°C + 273.15 = 296 \text{ K} \qquad T_2 \text{ (K)} = 100.°C + 273.15 = 373 \text{ K}$$

Converting P from atm to torr:

$$P_1 \text{ (torr)} = 0.991 \text{ atm} \times \frac{760 \text{ torr}}{1 \text{ atm}} = 753 \text{ torr}$$

Rearranging the ideal gas law and solving for P_2: At fixed n and V, we have

$$\frac{P_1V_1}{n_1T_1} = \frac{P_2V_2}{n_2T_2} \quad \text{or} \quad \frac{P_1}{T_1} = \frac{P_2}{T_2}$$

$$P_2 = P_1 \times \frac{T_2}{T_1} = 753 \text{ torr} \times \frac{373 \text{ K}}{296 \text{ K}} = 949 \text{ torr}$$

P_2 is less than 1.00×10^3 torr, so the valve will *not* open.

Check Let's predict the change to check the math: Because $T_2 > T_1$, we expect $P_2 > P_1$. Thus, the temperature ratio should be >1 (T_2 in the numerator). The T ratio is about 1.25 (373/296), so the P ratio should also be about 1.25 (950/750 ≈ 1.25).

Follow-Up Problem 5.3 An engineer pumps air at 0°C into a newly designed piston-cylinder assembly. The volume measures 6.83 cm³. At what temperature (in K) will the volume be 9.75 cm³?

Road Map

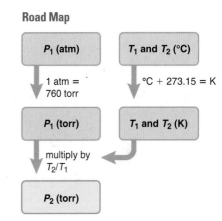

P_1 (atm)

T_1 and T_2 (°C)

1 atm = 760 torr

°C + 273.15 = K

P_1 (torr)

T_1 and T_2 (K)

multiply by T_2/T_1

P_2 (torr)

Sample Problem 5.4 | Applying the Volume-Amount Relationship

Problem A scale model of a blimp rises when it is filled with helium to a volume of 55.0 dm³. When 1.10 mol of He is added to the blimp, the volume is 26.2 dm³. How many more grams of He must be added to make it rise? Assume constant T and P.

Plan We are given the initial amount of helium (n_1), the initial volume of the blimp (V_1), and the volume needed for it to rise (V_2), and we need the additional mass of helium to make it rise. So we first need to find n_2. We rearrange the ideal gas law to the appropriate form, solve for n_2, subtract n_1 to find the additional amount ($n_{add'l}$), and then convert moles to grams.

Road Map

n_1 (mol) of He

↓ multiply by V_2/V_1

n_2 (mol) of He

↓ subtract n_1

$n_{add'l}$ (mol) of He

↓ multiply by $\mathcal{M}$ (g/mol)

Mass (g) of He

Solution Summarizing the gas variables:

$$n_1 = 1.10 \text{ mol} \qquad n_2 = \text{unknown (find, and then subtract } n_1)$$
$$V_1 = 26.2 \text{ dm}^3 \qquad V_2 = 55.0 \text{ dm}^3$$
$$P \text{ and } T \text{ remain constant}$$

Rearranging the ideal gas law and solving for n_2: At fixed P and T, we have

$$\frac{P_T V_1}{n_1 T_T} = \frac{P_2 V_2}{n_2 T_2} \qquad \text{or} \qquad \frac{V_1}{n_1} = \frac{V_2}{n_2}$$

$$n_2 = n_1 \times \frac{V_2}{V_1} = 1.10 \text{ mol He} \times \frac{55.0 \text{ dm}^3}{26.2 \text{ dm}^3}$$

$$= 2.31 \text{ mol He}$$

Finding the additional amount of He:

$$n_{add'l} = n_2 - n_1 = 2.31 \text{ mol He} - 1.10 \text{ mol He}$$

$$= 1.21 \text{ mol He}$$

Converting amount (mol) of He to mass (g):

$$\text{Mass (g) of He} = 1.21 \text{ mol He} \times \frac{4.003 \text{ g He}}{1 \text{ mol He}}$$

$$= \boxed{4.84 \text{ g He}}$$

Check We predict that $n_2 > n_1$ because $V_2 > V_1$: since V_2 is about twice V_1 ($55/26 \approx 2$), n_2 should be about twice n_1 ($2.3/1.1 \approx 2$). Since $n_2 > n_1$, we were right to multiply n_1 by a number >1 (that is, V_2/V_1). About 1.2 mol × 4 g/mol ≈ 4.8 g.

Comment 1. A different sequence of steps will give you the same answer: first find the additional volume ($V_{add'l} = V_2 - V_1$), and then solve directly for $n_{add'l}$. Try it for yourself.
2. You saw that Charles's law ($V \propto T$ at fixed P and n) becomes a similar relationship between P and T at fixed V and n. The follow-up problem demonstrates that Avogadro's law ($V \propto n$ at fixed P and T) becomes a similar relationship at fixed V and T.

Follow-Up Problem 5.4 A rigid plastic container holds 35.0 g of ethylene gas (C_2H_4) at a pressure of 793 torr. What is the pressure if 5.0 g of ethylene is removed at constant temperature?

Sample Problem 5.5 | Solving for an Unknown Gas Variable at Fixed Conditions

Problem A steel tank has a volume of 438 L and is filled with 0.885 kg of O_2. Calculate the pressure of O_2 at 21°C.

Plan We are given V, T, and the mass of O_2, and we must find P. Since conditions are not changing, we apply the ideal gas law without rearranging it. We use the given V in liters, convert T to kelvins and mass (kg) of O_2 to amount (mol), and solve for P.

Solution Summarizing the gas variables:

$V = 438$ L $T = 21°C$ (convert to K)
$n = 0.885$ kg O_2 (convert to mol) $P = $ unknown

Converting T from °C to K:

$$T\,(K) = 21°C + 273.15 = 294\ K$$

Converting from mass (g) of O_2 to amount (mol):

$$n = \text{mol of } O_2 = 0.885 \text{ kg } O_2 \times \frac{1000\ g}{1\ kg} \times \frac{1\ \text{mol } O_2}{32.00\ g\ O_2} = 27.7 \text{ mol } O_2$$

Solving for P (note the unit canceling here):

$$P = \frac{nRT}{V} = \frac{27.7\ \cancel{\text{mol}} \times 0.0821\ \frac{\text{atm} \cdot \cancel{L}}{\cancel{\text{mol}} \cdot \cancel{K}} \times 294\ \cancel{K}}{438\ \cancel{L}}$$

$$= \boxed{1.53 \text{ atm}}$$

Check The amount of O_2 seems correct: ~900 g/(30 g/mol) = 30 mol. To check the approximate size of the final calculation, round off the values, including that for R:

$$P = \frac{30 \text{ mol } O_2 \times 0.1\ \frac{\text{atm} \cdot L}{\text{mol} \cdot K} \times 300\ K}{450\ L} = 2 \text{ atm}$$

which is reasonably close to 1.53 atm.

Follow-Up Problem 5.5 The tank in the sample problem develops a slow leak that is discovered and sealed. The new pressure is 1.37 atm. How many grams of O_2 remain?

Finally, in a picture problem, we apply the gas laws to determine the balanced equation for a gaseous reaction.

Sample Problem 5.6 | Using Gas Laws to Determine a Balanced Equation

Problem The piston-cylinder below is depicted before and after a gaseous reaction that is carried out in it at constant pressure: the temperature is 150 K before and 300 K after the reaction. (Assume the cylinder is insulated.)

Which of the following balanced equations describes the reaction?
(1) $A_2(g) + B_2(g) \longrightarrow 2AB(g)$ (2) $2AB(g) + B_2(g) \longrightarrow 2AB_2(g)$
(3) $A(g) + B_2(g) \longrightarrow AB_2(g)$ (4) $2AB_2(g) \longrightarrow A_2(g) + 2B_2(g)$

Plan We are shown a depiction of the volume and temperature of a gas mixture before and after a reaction and must deduce the balanced equation. The problem says that P is constant, and the picture shows that, when T doubles, V stays the same. If n were also constant, Charles's law tells us that V should double when T doubles. But, since V does not change, n cannot be constant. From Avogadro's law, the only way to maintain V constant, with P constant and T doubling, is for n to be halved. So we examine the four balanced equations and count the number of moles on each side to see in which equation n is halved.

Solution In equation (1), n does not change, so doubling T would double V.
In equation (2), n decreases from 3 mol to 2 mol, so doubling T would increase V by one-third.
In equation (3), n decreases from 2 mol to 1 mol. Doubling T would exactly balance the decrease from halving n, so V would stay the same.
In equation (4), n increases, so doubling T would more than double V.
Therefore, equation (3) is correct:

$$A(g) + B_2(g) \longrightarrow AB_2(g)$$

Follow-Up Problem 5.6 The piston-cylinder below shows the volumes of a gaseous reaction mixture before and after a reaction that takes place at constant pressure and an initial temperature of $-73°C$.

If the *unbalanced* equation is $CD(g) \longrightarrow C_2(g) + D_2(g)$, what is the final temperature (in °C)?

▮ Summary of Section 5.3

- Four interdependent variables define the physical behavior of an ideal gas: volume (V), pressure (P), temperature (T), and amount (number of moles, n).
- Most simple gases display nearly ideal behavior at ordinary temperatures and pressures.
- Boyle's, Charles's, and Avogadro's laws refer to the linear relationships between the volume of a gas and the pressure, temperature, and amount of gas, respectively.
- At STP (0°C and 1 atm), 1 mol of an ideal gas occupies 22.4 L.
- The ideal gas law incorporates the individual gas laws into one equation: $PV = nRT$, where R is the universal gas constant.

5.4 • REARRANGEMENTS OF THE IDEAL GAS LAW

In this section, we mathematically rearrange the ideal gas law to find gas density, molar mass, the partial pressure of each gas in a mixture, and the amount of gaseous reactant or product in a reaction.

The Density of a Gas

One mole of any gas behaving ideally occupies the same volume at a given temperature and pressure, so differences in gas density ($d = m/V$) depend on differences in molar mass (see Figure 5.9, p. 191). For example, at STP, 1 mol of O_2 occupies the same volume as 1 mol of N_2; however, O_2 is denser because each O_2 molecule has a greater mass (32.00 amu) than each N_2 molecule (28.02 amu). Thus, d of O_2 is $\dfrac{32.00}{28.02} \times d$ of N_2.

We can rearrange the ideal gas law to calculate the density of a gas from its molar mass. Recall that the number of moles (n) is the mass (m) divided by the molar mass ($\mathcal{M}$), $n = m/\mathcal{M}$. Substituting for n in the ideal gas law gives

$$PV = \frac{m}{\mathcal{M}}RT$$

Rearranging to isolate m/V gives

$$\frac{m}{V} = d = \frac{\mathcal{M} \times P}{RT} \tag{5.9}$$

Two important ideas are expressed by Equation 5.9:

- *The density of a gas is directly proportional to its molar mass.* The volume of a given amount of a heavier gas equals the volume of the same amount of a lighter gas (Avogadro's law), so the density of the heavier gas is higher (as you just saw for O_2 and N_2).
- *The density of a gas is inversely proportional to the temperature.* As the volume of a gas increases with temperature (Charles's law), the same mass occupies more space, so the density of the gas is lower.

We use Equation 5.9 to find the density of a gas at any temperature and pressure near standard conditions.

Sample Problem 5.7   Calculating Gas Density

Problem To apply a green chemistry approach, a chemical engineer uses waste CO_2 from a manufacturing process, instead of chlorofluorocarbons, as a "blowing agent" in the production of polystyrene. Find the density (in g/L) of CO_2 and the number of molecules per liter **(a)** at STP (0°C and 1 atm) and **(b)** at room conditions (20.°C and 1.00 atm).

Plan We must find the density (*d*) and the number of molecules of CO_2, given two sets of *P* and *T* data. We find $\mathcal{M}$, convert *T* to kelvins, and calculate *d* with Equation 5.9. Then we convert the mass per liter to molecules per liter with Avogadro's number.

Solution **(a)** Density and molecules per liter of CO_2 at STP. Summary of gas properties:

$$T = 0°C + 273.15 = 273 \text{ K} \qquad P = 1 \text{ atm} \qquad \mathcal{M} \text{ of } CO_2 = 44.01 \text{ g/mol}$$

Calculating density (note the unit canceling here):

$$d = \frac{\mathcal{M} \times P}{RT} = \frac{44.01 \text{ g/mol} \times 1.00 \text{ atm}}{0.0821 \dfrac{\text{atm·L}}{\text{mol·K}} \times 273 \text{ K}} = \boxed{1.96 \text{ g/L}}$$

Converting from mass/L to molecules/L:

$$\text{Molecules } CO_2/\text{L} = \frac{1.96 \text{ g } CO_2}{1 \text{ L}} \times \frac{1 \text{ mol } CO_2}{44.01 \text{ g } CO_2} \times \frac{6.022 \times 10^{23} \text{ molecules } CO_2}{1 \text{ mol } CO_2}$$

$$= \boxed{2.68 \times 10^{22} \text{ molecules } CO_2/\text{L}}$$

(b) Density and molecules of CO_2 per liter at room conditions. Summary of gas properties:

$$T = 20.°C + 273.15 = 293 \text{ K} \qquad P = 1.00 \text{ atm} \qquad \mathcal{M} \text{ of } CO_2 = 44.01 \text{ g/mol}$$

Calculating density:

$$d = \frac{\mathcal{M} \times P}{RT} = \frac{44.01 \text{ g/mol} \times 1.00 \text{ atm}}{0.0821 \dfrac{\text{atm·L}}{\text{mol·K}} \times 293 \text{ K}} = \boxed{1.83 \text{ g/L}}$$

Converting from mass/L to molecules/L:

$$\text{Molecules } CO_2/\text{L} = \frac{1.83 \text{ g } CO_2}{1 \text{ L}} \times \frac{1 \text{ mol } CO_2}{44.01 \text{ g } CO_2} \times \frac{6.022 \times 10^{23} \text{ molecules } CO_2}{1 \text{ mol } CO_2}$$

$$= \boxed{2.50 \times 10^{22} \text{ molecules } CO_2/\text{L}}$$

Check Round off to check the density values; for example, in (a), at STP:

$$\frac{50 \text{ g/mol} \times 1 \text{ atm}}{0.1 \dfrac{\text{atm·L}}{\text{mol·K}} \times 250 \text{ K}} = 2 \text{ g/L} \approx 1.96 \text{ g/L}$$

At the higher temperature in (b), the density should decrease, which can happen only if there are fewer molecules per liter, so the answer is reasonable.

Comment 1. An *alternative approach* for finding the density of most simple gases, but *at STP only,* is to divide the molar mass by the standard molar volume, 22.4 L:

$$d = \frac{\mathcal{M}}{V} = \frac{44.01 \text{ g/mol}}{22.4 \text{ L/mol}} = 1.96 \text{ g/L}$$

Once you know the density at one temperature (0°C), you can find it at any other temperature with the following relationship: $d_1/d_2 = T_2/T_1$.

2. Note that we have different numbers of significant figures for the pressure values. In (a), "1 atm" is part of the definition of STP, so it is an exact number. In (b), we specified "1.00 atm" to allow three significant figures in the answer.

Follow-Up Problem 5.7 Compare the density of CO_2 at 0°C and 380. torr with its density at STP.

Gas Density and the Human Condition A few applications demonstrate the wide-ranging relevance of gas density:

- *Engineering.* Architectural designers and heating engineers place heating ducts near the floor so that the warmer, and thus less dense, air coming from the ducts will rise and mix with the cooler room air.
  - *Safety and air pollution.* In the absence of mixing, a less dense gas will lie above a more dense one. Fire extinguishers that release CO_2 are effective because this gas is heavier than air: it sinks onto the fire and keeps more O_2 from reaching the fuel. The dense gases in smog that blankets urban centers, such as Mexico City, Los Angeles, and Beijing, contribute to respiratory illnesses.
  - *Toxic releases.* During World War I, poisonous phosgene gas ($COCl_2$) was used against ground troops because it was dense enough to sink into their trenches. In 1984, the accidental release of poisonous methylisocyanate gas from a Union Carbide plant in India killed thousands of people as it blanketed nearby neighborhoods. In 1986, CO_2 released naturally from Lake Nyos in Cameroon suffocated thousands of people as it flowed down valleys into villages. Some paleontologists suggest that the release of CO_2 from volcanic lakes may have contributed to widespread dying off of dinosaurs.
- *Ballooning.* When the gas in a hot-air balloon is heated, its volume increases and the balloon inflates. Further heating causes some of the gas to escape. Thus, the gas density decreases and the balloon rises. In 1783, Jacques Charles (of Charles's law) made one of the first balloon flights, and 20 years later, Joseph Gay-Lussac (who studied the pressure-temperature relationship) set a solo altitude record that held for 50 years.

The Molar Mass of a Gas

Through another rearrangement of the ideal gas law, we can determine the molar mass of an unknown gas or a volatile liquid (one that is easily vaporized):

$$n = \frac{m}{\mathcal{M}} = \frac{PV}{RT} \qquad \text{so} \qquad \mathcal{M} = \frac{mRT}{PV} \qquad \text{(5.10)}$$

Notice that this equation is just a rearrangement of Equation 5.9.

Sample Problem 5.8 | **Finding the Molar Mass of a Volatile Liquid**

Problem An organic chemist isolates a colorless liquid from a petroleum sample. She places the liquid in a preweighed flask and puts the flask in boiling water, which vaporizes the liquid and fills the flask with gas. She closes the flask and reweighs it. She obtains the following data:

Volume (V) of flask = 213 mL	T = 100.0°C	P = 754 torr
Mass of flask + gas = 78.416 g	Mass of flask = 77.834 g	

Calculate the molar mass of the liquid.

Plan We are given V, T, P, and mass data and must find the molar mass ($\mathcal{M}$) of the liquid. We convert V to liters, T to kelvins, and P to atmospheres, find the mass of gas by subtracting the mass of the flask from the mass of the flask plus gas, and use Equation 5.10 to calculate $\mathcal{M}$.

Solution Summarizing and converting the gas variables:

$$V\ (L) = 213\ \text{mL} \times \frac{1\ L}{1000\ \text{mL}} = 0.213\ L \qquad T\ (K) = 100.0°C + 273.15 = 373.2\ K$$

$$P\ (\text{atm}) = 754\ \text{torr} \times \frac{1\ \text{atm}}{760\ \text{torr}} = 0.992\ \text{atm} \qquad m = 78.416\ g - 77.834\ g = 0.582\ g$$

Calculating $\mathcal{M}$:

$$\mathcal{M} = \frac{mRT}{PV} = \frac{0.582\ g \times 0.0821\ \dfrac{\text{atm·L}}{\text{mol·K}} \times 373.2\ K}{0.992\ \text{atm} \times 0.213\ L} = \boxed{84.4\ \text{g/mol}}$$

Check Rounding to check the arithmetic, we have

$$\frac{0.6\ g \times 0.08\ \dfrac{\text{atm·L}}{\text{mol·K}} \times 375\ K}{1\ \text{atm} \times 0.2\ L} = 90\ \text{g/mol} \qquad \text{(which is close to 84.4 g/mol)}$$

Follow-Up Problem 5.8 An empty 149-mL flask weighs 68.322 g before a sample of volatile liquid is added. The flask is then placed in a hot (95.0°C) water bath; the barometric pressure is 740. torr. The liquid vaporizes and the gas fills the flask. After cooling, flask and condensed liquid together weigh 68.697 g. What is the molar mass of the liquid?

The Partial Pressure of Each Gas in a Mixture of Gases

The gas behaviors we've discussed so far were observed in experiments with air, which is a mixture of gases; thus, the ideal gas law holds for virtually any gas at ordinary conditions, whether pure or a mixture, because

- Gases mix homogeneously (form a solution) in any proportions.
- Each gas in a mixture behaves as if it were the only gas present (assuming no chemical interactions).

Dalton's Law of Partial Pressures The second point above was discovered by John Dalton during his lifelong study of humidity. He observed that when water vapor is added to dry air, the total air pressure increases by the pressure of the water vapor:

$$P_{\text{humid air}} = P_{\text{dry air}} + P_{\text{added water vapor}}$$

He concluded that each gas in the mixture exerts a **partial pressure** equal to the pressure it would exert *by itself.* Stated as **Dalton's law of partial pressures,** his discovery was that *in a mixture of unreacting gases, the total pressure is the sum of the partial pressures of the individual gases:*

$$P_{\text{total}} = P_1 + P_2 + P_3 + \cdots \qquad (5.11)$$

As an example, suppose we have a tank of fixed volume that contains nitrogen gas at a certain pressure, and we introduce a sample of hydrogen gas into the tank. Each gas behaves independently, so we can write an ideal gas law expression for each:

$$P_{N_2} = \frac{n_{N_2}RT}{V} \qquad \text{and} \qquad P_{H_2} = \frac{n_{H_2}RT}{V}$$

Because each gas occupies the same total volume and is at the same temperature, the pressure of each gas depends only on its amount, n. Thus, the total pressure is

$$P_{\text{total}} = P_{N_2} + P_{H_2} = \frac{n_{N_2}RT}{V} + \frac{n_{H_2}RT}{V} = \frac{(n_{N_2} + n_{H_2})RT}{V} = \frac{n_{\text{total}}RT}{V}$$

where $n_{\text{total}} = n_{N_2} + n_{H_2}$.

Each component in a mixture contributes a fraction of the total number of moles in the mixture; this portion is the **mole fraction (X)** of that component. Multiplying X by 100 gives the mole percent. The sum of the mole fractions of all components must be 1, and the sum of the mole percents must be 100%. For N_2 in our mixture, the mole fraction is

$$X_{N_2} = \frac{n_{N_2}}{n_{total}} = \frac{n_{N_2}}{n_{N_2} + n_{H_2}}$$

If the total pressure is due to the total number of moles, the partial pressure of gas A is the total pressure multiplied by the mole fraction of A, X_A:

$$P_A = X_A \times P_{total} \tag{5.12}$$

Equation 5.12 is a very useful result. To see that it is valid for the mixture of N_2 and H_2, we recall that $X_{N_2} + X_{H_2} = 1$; then we obtain

$$P_{total} = P_{N_2} + P_{H_2} = (X_{N_2} \times P_{total}) + (X_{H_2} \times P_{total}) = (X_{N_2} + X_{H_2})P_{total} = 1 \times P_{total}$$

Sample Problem 5.9 | Applying Dalton's Law of Partial Pressures

Problem In a study of O_2 uptake by muscle at high altitude, a physiologist prepares an atmosphere consisting of 79 mole % N_2, 17 mole % $^{16}O_2$, and 4.0 mole % $^{18}O_2$. (The isotope ^{18}O will be measured to determine O_2 uptake.) The total pressure is 0.75 atm to simulate high altitude. Calculate the mole fraction and partial pressure of $^{18}O_2$ in the mixture.

Plan We must find $X_{^{18}O_2}$ and $P_{^{18}O_2}$ from P_{total} (0.75 atm) and the mole % of $^{18}O_2$ (4.0). Dividing the mole % by 100 gives the mole fraction, $X_{^{18}O_2}$. Then, using Equation 5.12, we multiply $X_{^{18}O_2}$ by P_{total} to find $P_{^{18}O_2}$.

Solution Calculating the mole fraction of $^{18}O_2$:

$$X_{^{18}O_2} = \frac{4.0 \text{ mol } \% \ ^{18}O_2}{100} = \boxed{0.040}$$

Solving for the partial pressure of $^{18}O_2$:

$$P_{^{18}O_2} = X_{^{18}O_2} \times P_{total} = 0.040 \times 0.75 \text{ atm} = \boxed{0.030 \text{ atm}}$$

Check $X_{^{18}O_2}$ is small because the mole % is small, so $P_{^{18}O_2}$ should be small also.

Comment At high altitudes, specialized brain cells that are sensitive to O_2 and CO_2 levels in the blood trigger an increase in rate and depth of breathing for several days, until a person becomes acclimated.

Follow-Up Problem 5.9 To prevent the presence of air, noble gases are placed over highly reactive chemicals to act as inert "blanketing" gases. A chemical engineer places a mixture of noble gases consisting of 5.50 g of He, 15.0 g of Ne, and 35.0 g of Kr in a piston-cylinder assembly at STP. Calculate the partial pressure of each gas.

Road Map

Mole % of $^{18}O_2$

↓ divide by 100

Mole fraction, $X_{^{18}O_2}$

↓ multiply by P_{total}

Partial pressure, $P_{^{18}O_2}$

Table 5.2 Vapor Pressure of Water (P_{H_2O}) at Different T

T (°C)	P_{H_2O} (torr)	T (°C)	P_{H_2O} (torr)
0	4.6	40	55.3
5	6.5	45	71.9
10	9.2	50	92.5
12	10.5	55	118.0
14	12.0	60	149.4
16	13.6	65	187.5
18	15.5	70	233.7
20	17.5	75	289.1
22	19.8	80	355.1
24	22.4	85	433.6
26	25.2	90	525.8
28	28.3	95	633.9
30	31.8	100	760.0
35	42.2		

Collecting a Gas over Water Whenever a gas is in contact with water, some of the water vaporizes into the gas. The water vapor that mixes with the gas contributes the *vapor pressure*, a portion of the total pressure that depends only on the water temperature (Table 5.2). A common use of the law of partial pressures is to determine the yield of a water-insoluble gas formed in a reaction: the gaseous product bubbles through water, some water vaporizes into the bubbles, and the mixture of product gas and water vapor is collected into an inverted container (Figure 5.12).

To determine the yield, we look up the vapor pressure (P_{H_2O}) at the temperature of the experiment in Table 5.2 and subtract it from the total gas pressure (P_{total}, corrected for barometric pressure) to get the partial pressure of the gaseous product (P_{gas}). With V and T known, we can calculate the amount of product.

The vapor pressure (P_{H_2O}) adds to P_{gas} to give P_{total}. Here, the water level in the vessel is above the level in the beaker, so $P_{total} < P_{atm}$.

Molecules of H_2O enter bubbles of gas.

Water-insoluble gaseous product bubbles through water into collection vessel.

P_{total}

P_{atm}

After all the gas has been collected, P_{total} is made equal to P_{atm} by adjusting the height of the collection vessel until the water level in it equals the level in the beaker.

P_{total} P_{atm}

$$P_{total} = \frac{P_{gas}}{P_{H_2O}}$$

P_{total} equals P_{gas} plus P_{H_2O} at the temperature of the experiment. Therefore, $P_{gas} = P_{total} - P_{H_2O}$.

Figure 5.12 Collecting a water-insoluble gaseous product and determining its pressure.

Sample Problem 5.10 | Calculating the Amount of Gas Collected over Water

Problem Acetylene (C_2H_2), an important fuel in welding, is produced in the laboratory when calcium carbide (CaC_2) reacts with water:

$$CaC_2(s) + 2H_2O(l) \longrightarrow C_2H_2(g) + Ca(OH)_2(aq)$$

For a sample of acetylene collected over water, total gas pressure (adjusted to barometric pressure) is 738 torr and the volume is 523 mL. At the temperature of the gas (23°C), the vapor pressure of water is 21 torr. How many grams of acetylene are collected?

Plan In order to find the mass of C_2H_2, we first need to find the number of moles of C_2H_2, $n_{C_2H_2}$, which we can obtain from the ideal gas law by calculating $P_{C_2H_2}$. The barometer reading gives us P_{total}, which is the sum of $P_{C_2H_2}$ and P_{H_2O}, and we are given P_{H_2O}, so we subtract to find $P_{C_2H_2}$. We are also given V and T, so we convert to consistent units, and find $n_{C_2H_2}$ from the ideal gas law. Then we convert moles to grams using the molar mass from the formula, as shown in the road map.

Road Map

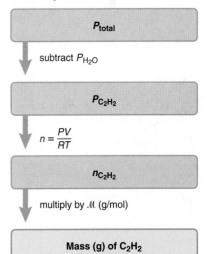

P_{total}

subtract P_{H_2O}

$P_{C_2H_2}$

$n = \dfrac{PV}{RT}$

$n_{C_2H_2}$

multiply by $\mathcal{M}$ (g/mol)

Mass (g) of C_2H_2

Solution Summarizing and converting the gas variables:

$$P_{C_2H_2} \text{ (torr)} = P_{total} - P_{H_2O} = 738 \text{ torr} - 21 \text{ torr} = 717 \text{ torr}$$

$$P_{C_2H_2} \text{ (atm)} = 717 \text{ torr} \times \frac{1 \text{ atm}}{760 \text{ torr}} = 0.943 \text{ atm}$$

$$V \text{ (L)} = 523 \text{ mL} \times \frac{1 \text{ L}}{1000 \text{ mL}} = 0.523 \text{ L}$$

$$T \text{ (K)} = 23°C + 273.15 = 296 \text{ K}$$

$$n_{C_2H_2} = \text{unknown}$$

Solving for $n_{C_2H_2}$:

$$n_{C_2H_2} = \frac{PV}{RT} = \frac{0.943 \text{ atm} \times 0.523 \text{ L}}{0.0821 \dfrac{\text{atm}\cdot\text{L}}{\text{mol}\cdot\text{K}} \times 296 \text{ K}} = 0.0203 \text{ mol}$$

Converting $n_{C_2H_2}$ to mass (g):

$$\text{Mass (g) of } C_2H_2 = 0.0203 \text{ mol } C_2H_2 \times \frac{26.04 \text{ g } C_2H_2}{1 \text{ mol } C_2H_2}$$

$$= \boxed{0.529 \text{ g } C_2H_2}$$

Check Rounding to one significant figure, a quick arithmetic check for n gives

$$n \approx \frac{1 \text{ atm} \times 0.5 \text{ L}}{0.08 \frac{\text{atm·L}}{\text{mol·K}} \times 300 \text{ K}} = 0.02 \text{ mol} \approx 0.0203 \text{ mol}$$

Comment The C_2^{2-} ion (called the *carbide*, or *acetylide, ion*) is an interesting anion. It is simply $^-C\equiv C^-$, which acts as a base in water, removing an H^+ ion from two H_2O molecules to form acetylene, $H-C\equiv C-H$.

Follow-Up Problem 5.10 A small piece of zinc reacts with dilute HCl to form H_2, which is collected over water at 16°C into a large flask. The total pressure is adjusted to barometric pressure (752 torr), and the volume is 1495 mL. Use Table 5.2 to help calculate the partial pressure and mass of H_2.

The Ideal Gas Law and Reaction Stoichiometry

As you saw in Chapters 3 and 4, and in the preceding discussion of collecting a gas over water, many reactions involve gases as reactants or products. From the balanced equation for such a reaction, you can calculate the amounts (mol) of reactants and products and convert these quantities into masses or numbers of molecules. Figure 5.13 shows how you use the ideal gas law to convert between gas variables (P, T, and V) and amounts (mol) of gaseous reactants and products. In effect, you combine a gas law problem with a stoichiometry problem, as you'll see in Sample Problems 5.11 and 5.12.

Figure 5.13 The relationships among the amount (mol, n) of gaseous reactant (or product) and the gas pressure (P), volume (V), and temperature (T).

Road Map

| Sample Problem 5.11 | Using Gas Variables to Find Amounts of Reactants or Products I |

Problem Engineers use copper in absorbent beds to react with and remove oxygen impurities in ethylene used to make polyethylene. The beds are regenerated when hot H_2 reduces the copper(II) oxide, forming the pure metal and H_2O. On a laboratory scale, what volume of H_2 at 765 torr and 225°C is needed to reduce 35.5 g of copper(II) oxide?

Plan This is a stoichiometry *and* gas law problem. To find V_{H_2}, we first need n_{H_2}. We write and balance the equation. Next, we convert the given mass (35.5 g) of copper(II) oxide, CuO, to amount (mol) and use the molar ratio to find amount (mol) of H_2 needed (stoichiometry portion). Then, we use the ideal gas law to convert moles of H_2 to liters (gas law portion). A road map is shown, but you are familiar with all the steps.

Solution Writing the balanced equation:

$$CuO(s) + H_2(g) \longrightarrow Cu(s) + H_2O(g)$$

Calculating n_{H_2}:

$$n_{H_2} = 35.5 \text{ g CuO} \times \frac{1 \text{ mol CuO}}{79.55 \text{ g CuO}} \times \frac{1 \text{ mol } H_2}{1 \text{ mol CuO}} = 0.446 \text{ mol } H_2$$

Summarizing and converting other gas variables:

$$V = \text{unknown} \qquad P \text{ (atm)} = 765 \text{ torr} \times \frac{1 \text{ atm}}{760 \text{ torr}} = 1.01 \text{ atm}$$

$$T \text{ (K)} = 225°C + 273.15 = 498 \text{ K}$$

Solving for V_{H_2}:

$$V = \frac{nRT}{P} = \frac{0.446 \text{ mol} \times 0.0821 \frac{\text{atm·L}}{\text{mol·K}} \times 498 \text{ K}}{1.01 \text{ atm}} = \boxed{18.1 \text{ L}}$$

Check One way to check the answer is to compare it with the molar volume of an ideal gas at STP (22.4 L at 273.15 K and 1 atm). One mole of H_2 at STP occupies about 22 L, so less than 0.5 mol occupies less than 11 L. T is less than twice 273 K, so V should be less than twice 11 L.

Comment The main point here is that the stoichiometry provides one gas variable (n), two more are given, and the ideal gas law is used to find the fourth.

Follow-Up Problem 5.11 Sulfuric acid reacts with sodium chloride to form aqueous sodium sulfate and hydrogen chloride gas. How many milliliters of gas form at STP when 0.117 kg of sodium chloride reacts with excess sulfuric acid?

Sample Problem 5.12   **Using Gas Variables to Find Amounts of Reactants or Products II**

Problem The alkali metals [Group 1A(1)] react with the halogens [Group 7A(17)] to form ionic metal halides. What mass of potassium chloride forms when 5.25 L of chlorine gas at 0.950 atm and 293 K reacts with 17.0 g of potassium (*see photo*)?

Plan The amounts of two reactants are given, so this is a limiting-reactant problem. The only difference between this and previous limiting-reactant problems (see Sample Problem 3.20, p. 111) is that here we use the ideal gas law to find the amount (n) of gaseous reactant from the known V, P, and T. We first write the balanced equation and then use it to find the limiting reactant and the amount and mass of product.

Solution Writing the balanced equation:

$$2K(s) + Cl_2(g) \longrightarrow 2KCl(s)$$

Summarizing the gas variables:

$$P = 0.950 \text{ atm} \qquad V = 5.25 \text{ L}$$
$$T = 293 \text{ K} \qquad n = \text{unknown}$$

Chlorine gas reacting with potassium.

Solving for n_{Cl_2}:

$$n_{Cl_2} = \frac{PV}{RT} = \frac{0.950 \text{ atm} \times 5.25 \text{ L}}{0.0821 \frac{\text{atm·L}}{\text{mol·K}} \times 293 \text{ K}} = 0.207 \text{ mol}$$

Converting from mass (g) of potassium (K) to amount (mol):

$$\text{Amount (mol) of K} = 17.0 \text{ g K} \times \frac{1 \text{ mol K}}{39.10 \text{ g K}} = 0.435 \text{ mol K}$$

Determining the limiting reactant: If Cl_2 is limiting,

$$\text{Amount (mol) of KCl} = 0.207 \text{ mol Cl}_2 \times \frac{2 \text{ mol KCl}}{1 \text{ mol Cl}_2} = 0.414 \text{ mol KCl}$$

If K is limiting,

$$\text{Amount (mol) of KCl} = 0.435 \text{ mol K} \times \frac{2 \text{ mol KCl}}{2 \text{ mol K}} = 0.435 \text{ mol KCl}$$

Cl_2 is the limiting reactant because it forms less KCl.
Converting from amount (mol) of KCl to mass (g):

$$\text{Mass (g) of KCl} = 0.414 \text{ mol KCl} \times \frac{74.55 \text{ g KCl}}{1 \text{ mol KCl}} = \boxed{30.9 \text{ g KCl}}$$

Check The gas law calculation seems correct. At STP, 22 L of Cl_2 gas contains about 1 mol, so a 5-L volume will contain a bit less than 0.25 mol of Cl_2. Moreover, since P (in numerator) is slightly lower than STP, and T (in denominator) is slightly higher than STP, these should lower the calculated n further below the ideal value. The mass of KCl seems correct: less than 0.5 mol of KCl gives $<$0.5 mol $\times$ $\mathcal{M}$ (~75 g/mol), and 30.9 g $<$ 0.5 mol $\times$ 75 g/mol.

Follow-Up Problem 5.12 Ammonia and hydrogen chloride gases react to form solid ammonium chloride. A 10.0-L reaction flask contains ammonia at 0.452 atm and 22°C, and 155 mL of hydrogen chloride gas at 7.50 atm and 271 K is introduced. After the reaction occurs and the temperature returns to 22°C, what is the pressure inside the flask? (Neglect the volume of the solid product.)

■ Summary of Section 5.4

- Gas density is inversely related to temperature: higher T causes lower d, and vice versa. At the same P and T, gases with larger $\mathcal{M}$ have higher d.
- In a mixture of gases, each component contributes its partial pressure to the total pressure (Dalton's law of partial pressures). The mole fraction of each component is the ratio of its partial pressure to the total pressure.
- When a gaseous reaction product is collected by bubbling it through water, the total pressure is the sum of the gas pressure and the vapor pressure of water at the given temperature.
- By converting the variables P, V, and T for a gaseous reactant (or product) to amount (n, mol), we can solve stoichiometry problems for gaseous reactions.

5.5 • THE KINETIC-MOLECULAR THEORY: A MODEL FOR GAS BEHAVIOR

The **kinetic-molecular theory** is the model that accounts for macroscopic gas behavior at the level of individual particles (atoms or molecules). Developed by some of the great scientists of the 19th century, most notably James Clerk Maxwell and Ludwig Boltzmann, the theory was able to explain the gas laws that some of the great scientists of the 18th century had arrived at empirically. The theory draws quantitative conclusions based on a few postulates (assumptions), but our discussion will be largely qualitative.

How the Kinetic-Molecular Theory Explains the Gas Laws

Let's address some questions the theory must answer, then state the postulates, and draw conclusions that explain the gas laws and related phenomena.

Questions Concerning Gas Behavior Observing gas behavior at the macroscopic level, we must derive a molecular model that explains it:

1. *Origin of pressure.* Pressure is a measure of the force a gas exerts on a surface. How do individual gas particles create this force?
2. *Boyle's law (V ∝ 1/P).* A change in gas pressure in one direction causes a change in gas volume in the other. What happens to the particles when external pressure compresses the gas volume? And why aren't liquids and solids compressible?
3. *Dalton's law (P$_{total}$ = P$_1$ + P$_2$ + P$_3$ + ⋯).* The pressure of a gas mixture is the sum of the pressures of the individual gases. Why does each gas contribute to the total pressure in proportion to its number of particles?
4. *Charles's law (V ∝ T).* A change in temperature causes a corresponding change in volume. What effect does higher temperature have on gas particles that increases gas volume? This question raises a more fundamental one: what does temperature measure on the molecular scale?
5. *Avogadro's law (V ∝ n).* Gas volume depends on the number of moles present, not on the chemical nature of the gas. But shouldn't 1 mol of heavier particles exert more pressure, and thus take up more space, than 1 mol of lighter ones?

Postulates of the Kinetic-Molecular Theory The theory is based on three postulates:

Postulate 1. *Particle volume.* A gas consists of a large collection of individual particles with empty space between them. The volume of each particle is so small compared with the volume of the whole sample that it is assumed to be zero; each particle is essentially a point of mass.

Postulate 2. *Particle motion.* The particles are in constant, random, straight-line motion, except when they collide with the container walls or with each other.

Postulate 3. *Particle collisions.* The collisions are *elastic,* which means that, like minute billiard balls, the colliding molecules exchange energy but do not lose any energy through friction. Thus, *their total kinetic energy (E_k) is constant.* Between collisions, the molecules do not influence each other by attractive or repulsive forces.

Imagine what a sample of gas in a container looks like. Countless minute particles move in every direction, smashing into the container walls and each other. Any given particle changes its speed often—at one moment standing still from a head-on collision and the next moment zooming away from a smash on the side.

In the sample as a whole, *each particle has a molecular speed (u); most are moving near the most probable speed, but some are much faster and others much slower.* Figure 5.14 depicts this distribution of molecular speeds for N_2 gas at three temperatures.

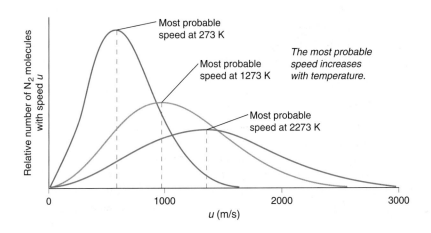

Figure 5.14 Distribution of molecular speeds for N_2 at three temperatures.

Note that the curves flatten and spread at higher temperatures and that the *most probable speed (the peak of each curve) increases as the temperature increases.* This increase occurs because the average kinetic energy of the molecules, which is related to the most probable speed, is proportional to the absolute temperature: $\overline{E_k} \propto T$, or $\overline{E_k} = c \times T$, where $\overline{E_k}$ is the average kinetic energy of the molecules (an overbar indicates the average value of a quantity) and c is a constant that is the same for any gas. (We'll return to this equation shortly.) Thus, a major conclusion based on the distribution of speeds, which arises directly from postulate 3, is that *at a given temperature, all gases have the same average kinetic energy.*

A Molecular View of the Gas Laws Let's keep visualizing gas particles in a container to see how the theory explains the macroscopic behavior of gases and answers the questions we posed above:

1. *Origin of pressure* (Figure 5.15). From postulates 1 and 2, each gas particle (point of mass) colliding with the container walls (and bottom of piston) exerts a force. Countless collisions over the inner surface of the container result in a pressure. The greater the number of particles, the more frequently they collide with the container, and so the greater the pressure.

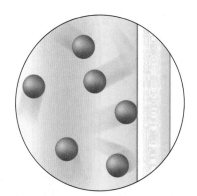

Figure 5.15 Pressure arises from countless collisions between gas particles and walls.

2. *Boyle's law* ($V \propto 1/P$) (Figure 5.16). The particles in a gas are points of mass with empty space between them (postulate 1). Before any change in pressure, the pressure exerted *by* the gas (P_{gas}) equals the pressure exerted *on* the gas (P_{ext}), and there is some average distance (d_1) between the particles and the container walls. As P_{ext} increases at constant temperature, the average distance (d_2) between the particles and the walls decreases (that is, $d_2 < d_1$), and so the sample volume decreases. Collisions of the particles with the walls become more frequent over the shorter average distance, which causes P_{gas} to increase until it again equals P_{ext}. The fact that liquids and solids cannot be compressed implies there is little, if any, free space between their particles.

Figure 5.16 A molecular view of Boyle's law.

At any T,
$P_{gas} = P_{ext}$
as particles hit the walls from an average distance, d_1.

P_{ext} increases, T and n fixed

Higher P_{ext} causes lower V, which results in more collisions, because particles hit the walls from a shorter average distance ($d_2 < d_1$). As a result, $P_{gas} = P_{ext}$ again.

3. *Dalton's law of partial pressures* ($P_{total} = P_A + P_B$) (Figure 5.17). Adding a given amount (mol) of gas A to a given amount of gas B causes an increase in the total number of particles, in proportion to the particles of A added. This increase causes a corresponding increase in the total number of collisions with the walls per second (postulate 2), which causes a corresponding increase in the total pressure of the gas mixture (P_{total}). Each gas exerts a fraction of P_{total} in proportion to its fraction of the total number of particles (or equivalently, its fraction of the total number of moles, that is, the mole fraction).

Figure 5.17 A molecular view of Dalton's law.

When gases A and B are separate, each exerts the total pressure in its own container.

Gas A

Gas B

Stopcock opened, piston depressed at fixed T

Mixture of A and B

When gas A is mixed with gas B, $P_{total} = P_A + P_B$ and the numbers of collisions of particles of each gas with the container walls are in proportion to the amount (mol) of that gas.

Closed

Open

$P_A = P_{total}$
$= 1.0$ atm
$n_A = 0.60$ mol

$P_B = P_{total}$
$= 0.50$ atm
$n_B = 0.30$ mol

$P_{total} = P_A + P_B = 1.5$ atm
$n_{total} = 0.90$ mol
$X_A = 0.67$ mol $X_B = 0.33$ mol

4. *Charles's law* ($V \propto T$) (Figure 5.18). At some starting temperature, T_1, the external (atmospheric) pressure (P_{atm}) equals the pressure of the gas (P_{gas}). When the gas is heated and the temperature increases to T_2, the most probable molecular speed and the average kinetic energy increase (postulate 3). Thus, the particles hit the walls more frequently *and* more energetically. This change temporarily increases P_{gas}. As a result, the piston moves up, which increases the volume and lowers the collision frequency until P_{atm} and P_{gas} are again equal.

Figure 5.18 A molecular view of Charles's law.

At T_1, P_{gas} = P_{atm}.

Higher T increases collision frequency, so P_{gas} > P_{atm}.

Thus, V increases until P_{gas} = P_{atm} at T_2.

5. *Avogadro's law ($V \propto n$)* (Figure 5.19). At some starting amount, n_1, of gas, P_{atm} equals P_{gas}. When more gas is added from the attached tank, the amount increases to n_2. Thus, more particles hit the walls more frequently, which temporarily increases P_{gas}. As a result, the piston moves up, which increases the volume and lowers the collision frequency until P_{atm} and P_{gas} are again equal.

Figure 5.19 A molecular view of Avogadro's law.

For a given amount, n_1, of gas, P_{gas} = P_{atm}.

When gas is added to reach n_2 the collision frequency of the particles increases, so P_{gas} > P_{atm}.

As a result, V increases until P_{gas} = P_{atm} again.

The Central Importance of Kinetic Energy Recall from Chapter 1 that the kinetic energy of an object is the energy associated with its motion. It is key to explaining some implications of Avogadro's law and, most importantly, the meaning of temperature.

1. *Implications of Avogadro's law.* As we just saw, Avogadro's law says that, at any given T and P, the volume of a gas depends only on the number of moles—that is, number of particles—in the sample. The law doesn't mention the chemical nature of the gas, so equal numbers of particles of any two gases, say O_2 and H_2, should occupy the same volume. But, why don't the heavier O_2 molecules exert more pressure on the container walls, and thus take up more volume, than the lighter H_2 molecules? To answer this, we'll show one way to express kinetic energy mathematically:

$$E_k = \tfrac{1}{2} \text{mass} \times \text{speed}^2$$

This equation says that, for a given E_k, an object's mass and speed are inversely related, which means that *a heavier object moving slower can have the same kinetic energy as a lighter object moving faster*. Figure 5.20 on the next page shows that, for several gases, *the most probable speed (top of each curve) increases as the molar mass (number in parentheses) decreases*.

As we saw earlier, postulate 3 of the kinetic-molecular theory directly implies that, at a given T, all gases have the same average kinetic energy. From Figure 5.20, we see

Figure 5.20 The relationship between molar mass and molecular speed. At a given temperature, gases with lower molar masses (numbers in parentheses) have higher most probable speeds (peak of each curve).

that O_2 molecules move more slowly, on average, than H_2 molecules. With their higher most probable speed, H_2 molecules collide with the walls of a container more often than O_2 molecules do, but their lower mass means that each collision has less force. Therefore, at a given T, equimolar samples of H_2 and O_2 (or any other gas) exert the same pressure and, thus, occupy the same volume because, on average, *their molecules hit the walls with the same kinetic energy.*

2. *The meaning of temperature.* Closely related to these ideas is the central relation between kinetic energy and temperature. Earlier we said that the average kinetic energy of the particles ($\overline{E_k}$) equals the absolute temperature times a constant; that is, $\overline{E_k} = c \times T$. Using definitions of velocity, momentum, force, and pressure, we can also express this relationship by the following equation:

$$\overline{E_k} = \tfrac{3}{2}\left(\frac{R}{N_A}\right)T$$

where R is the gas constant and N_A is the symbol for Avogadro's number. This equation makes the essential point that *temperature is a **measure** of the average kinetic energy of the particles:* as T increases, $\overline{E_k}$ increases, and vice versa. Temperature is an intensive property (Section 1.5), so it is not related to the *total* energy of motion of the particles, which depends on the size of the sample, but to the *average* energy.

Thus, for example, in the macroscopic world, we heat a beaker of water over a flame and see the mercury rise inside a thermometer we put in the beaker. We see this because, in the molecular world, kinetic energy transfers, in turn, from higher energy gas particles in the flame to lower energy particles in the beaker glass, the water molecules, the particles in the thermometer glass, and the atoms of mercury.

Root-Mean-Square Speed Finally, let's derive an expression for the speed of a gas particle that has the average kinetic energy of the particles in a sample. From the general expression for kinetic energy of an object,

$$E_k = \tfrac{1}{2}\text{mass} \times \text{speed}^2$$

the average kinetic energy of each particle in a large population is

$$\overline{E_k} = \tfrac{1}{2}m\overline{u^2}$$

where m is the particle's mass (atomic or molecular) and $\overline{u^2}$ is the average of the squares of the molecular speeds. Setting this expression for average kinetic energy equal to the earlier one gives

$$\tfrac{1}{2}m\overline{u^2} = \tfrac{3}{2}\left(\frac{R}{N_A}\right)T$$

Multiplying through by Avogadro's number, N_A, gives the average kinetic energy for a mole of gas particles:

$$\tfrac{1}{2}N_A\, m\overline{u^2} = \tfrac{3}{2}RT$$

Avogadro's number times the molecular mass, $N_A \times m$, is the molar mass, $\mathcal{M}$, and solving for $\overline{u^2}$, we have

$$\overline{u^2} = \frac{3RT}{\mathcal{M}}$$

The square root of $\overline{u^2}$ is the root-mean-square speed, or **rms speed (u_{rms}):** *a particle moving at this speed has the average kinetic energy.** That is, taking the square root of both sides of the previous equation gives

$$u_{rms} = \sqrt{\frac{3RT}{M}} \qquad (5.13)$$

where R is the gas constant, T is the absolute temperature, and M is the molar mass. (Because we want u in m/s and R includes the joule, which has units of kg·m²/s², we use the value 8.314 J/mol·K for R and express M in kg/mol.)

Thus, as an example, the root-mean-square speed of an O_2 molecule ($M = 3.200 \times 10^{-2}$ kg/mol) at room temperature (20°C, or 293 K) in the air you're breathing right now is

$$u_{rms} = \sqrt{\frac{3RT}{M}} = \sqrt{\frac{3(8.314 \text{ J/mol·K})(293 \text{ K})}{3.200 \times 10^{-2} \text{ kg/mol}}}$$

$$= \sqrt{\frac{3(8.314 \text{ kg·m}^2/\text{s}^2/\text{mol·K})(293 \text{ K})}{3.200 \times 10^{-2} \text{ kg/mol}}}$$

$$= 478 \text{ m/s (about 1070 mi/hr)}$$

Effusion and Diffusion

The movement of a gas into a vacuum and the movement of gases through one another are phenomena with some vital applications.

The Process of Effusion One of the early triumphs of the kinetic-molecular theory was an explanation of **effusion,** the process by which a gas escapes through a tiny hole in its container into an evacuated space. In 1846, Thomas Graham studied the effusion rate of a gas, the number of molecules escaping per unit time, and found that it was inversely proportional to the square root of the gas density. But, density is directly related to molar mass, so **Graham's law of effusion** is stated as follows: *the rate of effusion of a gas is inversely proportional to the square root of its molar mass,* or

$$\text{Rate of effusion} \propto \frac{1}{\sqrt{M}}$$

Figure 5.21 Effusion. Lighter (*black*) particles effuse faster than heavier (*red*) particles.

Argon (Ar) is lighter than krypton (Kr), so it effuses faster, assuming equal pressures of the two gases (Figure 5.21). Thus, the ratio of the rates is

$$\frac{\text{Rate}_{Ar}}{\text{Rate}_{Kr}} = \frac{\sqrt{M_{Kr}}}{\sqrt{M_{Ar}}} \quad \text{or, in general,} \quad \frac{\text{Rate}_A}{\text{Rate}_B} = \frac{\sqrt{M_B}}{\sqrt{M_A}} = \sqrt{\frac{M_B}{M_A}} \qquad (5.14)$$

The kinetic-molecular theory explains that, at a given temperature and pressure, *the gas with the lower molar mass effuses faster because the rms speed of its molecules is higher; therefore, more molecules reach the hole and escape per unit time.*

Sample Problem 5.13   **Applying Graham's Law of Effusion**

Problem A mixture of helium (He) and methane (CH_4) is placed in an effusion apparatus. Calculate the ratio of their effusion rates.

Plan The effusion rate is inversely proportional to $\sqrt{M}$, so we find the molar mass of each substance from the formula and take its square root. The inverse of the ratio of the square roots is the ratio of the effusion rates.

Solution

$$M \text{ of } CH_4 = 16.04 \text{ g/mol} \qquad M \text{ of He} = 4.003 \text{ g/mol}$$

---

*The rms speed, u_{rms}, is proportional to, but slightly higher than, the most probable speed; for an ideal gas, $u_{rms} = 1.09 \times$ average speed.

Calculating the ratio of the effusion rates:

$$\frac{Rate_{He}}{Rate_{CH_4}} = \sqrt{\frac{\mathcal{M}_{CH_4}}{\mathcal{M}_{He}}} = \sqrt{\frac{16.04 \text{ g/mol}}{4.003 \text{ g/mol}}} = \sqrt{4.007} = \boxed{2.002}$$

Check A ratio >1 makes sense because the lighter He should effuse faster than the heavier CH_4. Because the molar mass of CH_4 is about four times the molar mass of He, He should effuse about twice as fast as CH_4 ($\sqrt{4}$).

Follow-Up Problem 5.13 If it takes 1.25 min for 0.010 mol of He to effuse, how long will it take for the same amount of ethane (C_2H_6) to effuse?

Applications of Effusion The process of effusion has two important uses.

1. *Determination of molar mass.* We can also use Graham's law to *determine the molar mass of an unknown gas.* By comparing the effusion rate of gas X with that of a known gas, such as He, we can solve for the molar mass of X:

$$\frac{Rate_X}{Rate_{He}} = \sqrt{\frac{\mathcal{M}_{He}}{\mathcal{M}_X}}$$

Squaring both sides and solving for the molar mass of X gives

$$\mathcal{M}_X = \mathcal{M}_{He} \times \left(\frac{rate_{He}}{rate_X}\right)^2$$

2. *Preparation of nuclear fuel.* By far the most important application of Graham's law is in the preparation of fuel for nuclear energy reactors. The process of *isotope enrichment* increases the proportion of fissionable, but rarer, ^{235}U (only 0.7% by mass of naturally occurring uranium) to the nonfissionable, more abundant ^{238}U (99.3% by mass). Because the two isotopes have identical chemical properties, they are extremely difficult to separate chemically. But, one way to separate them takes advantage of a difference in a physical property—the effusion rate of gaseous compounds. Uranium ore is treated with fluorine to yield a gaseous mixture of $^{238}UF_6$ and $^{235}UF_6$ that is pumped through a series of chambers separated by porous barriers. Molecules of $^{235}UF_6$ are slightly lighter ($\mathcal{M} = 349.03$) than molecules of $^{238}UF_6$ ($\mathcal{M} = 352.04$), so they move slightly faster and effuse through each barrier 1.0043 times faster. Many passes must be made, each one increasing the fraction of $^{235}UF_6$, until the mixture obtained is 3–5% by mass $^{235}UF_6$. This process was developed during the latter years of World War II and produced enough ^{235}U for two of the world's first atomic bombs. Today, a less expensive centrifuge process is used more often. The ability to enrich uranium has become a key international concern, as more countries aspire to develop nuclear energy and nuclear arms.

The Process of Diffusion Closely related to effusion is the process of gaseous **diffusion,** the movement of one gas through another. Diffusion rates are also described generally by Graham's law:

$$\text{Rate of diffusion} \propto \frac{1}{\sqrt{\mathcal{M}}}$$

For two gases at equal pressures, such as NH_3 and HCl, moving through another gas or a mixture of gases, such as air, we find

$$\frac{Rate_{NH_3}}{Rate_{HCl}} = \sqrt{\frac{\mathcal{M}_{HCl}}{\mathcal{M}_{NH_3}}}$$

The reason for this dependence on molar mass is the same as for effusion rates: *lighter molecules have higher average speeds than heavier molecules, so they move farther in a given time.*

If gas molecules move at hundreds of meters per second (see Figure 5.14), why does it take a second or two after you open a bottle of perfume to smell it? Although convection plays an important role in this process, another reason for the time lag is

Figure 5.22 Diffusion of gases. When different gases (*black*, from the left, and *green,* from the right) move through each other, they mix. For simplicity, the complex path of only one black particle is shown (in *red*). In reality, all the particles have similar paths.

that a gas particle does not travel very far before it collides with another particle (Figure 5.22). Thus, a perfume molecule travels slowly because it collides with countless molecules in the air. The presence of so many other particles means that *diffusion rates are much lower than effusion rates.* Imagine how much quicker you can walk through an empty room than through a room crowded with other moving people.

Diffusion also occurs when a gas enters a liquid (and even to a small extent a solid). However, the average distances between molecules are so much shorter in a liquid that collisions are much more frequent; thus, diffusion of a gas through a liquid is *much* slower than through a gas. Nevertheless, this type of diffusion is a vital process in biological systems, for example, in the movement of O_2 from lungs to blood.

The Chaotic World of Gases: Mean Free Path and Collision Frequency

Refinements of the basic kinetic-molecular theory provide a view into the chaotic molecular world of gases. Try to visualize an "average" N_2 molecule in the room you are in now. It is continually changing speed as it collides with other molecules—at one instant, going 2500 mi/h, and at another, standing still. But these extreme speeds are *much* less likely than the most probable one and those near it (see Figure 5.14). At 20°C and 1 atm pressure, the N_2 molecule is hurtling at an average speed of 470 m/s (rms speed = 510 m/s), or nearly 1100 mi/h!

Mean Free Path From a particle's diameter, we can obtain the **mean free path,** the average distance it travels between collisions at a given temperature and pressure. An N_2 molecule (3.7×10^{-10} m in diameter) has a mean free path of 6.6×10^{-8} m, which means it travels an average of 180 molecular diameters before smashing into a fellow traveler. (An N_2 molecule the size of a billiard ball would travel an average of about 30 ft before hitting another.) Therefore, even though gas molecules are *not* points of mass, it is still valid to assume that a gas sample *is* nearly all empty space. Mean free path is a key factor in the rate of diffusion and the rate of heat flow through a gas.

Collision Frequency Divide the most probable speed (meters per second) by the mean free path (meters per collision) and you obtain the **collision frequency,** the average number of collisions per second that each particle undergoes. As you can see, the N_2 molecule experiences, on average, an enormous number of collisions every second: ●

$$\text{Collision frequency} = \frac{4.7 \times 10^2 \text{ m/s}}{6.6 \times 10^{-8} \text{ m/collision}} = 7.0 \times 10^9 \text{ collision/s}$$

Distribution of speed (and kinetic energy) and collision frequency are essential ideas for understanding the speed of a reaction, as you'll see in Chapter 16. As the Chemical Connections essay shows, many of the concepts we've discussed so far apply directly to our planet's atmosphere.

● **Danger in a Molecular Amusement Park** To really appreciate the astounding events in the molecular world, let's use a two-dimensional analogy to compare the moving N_2 molecule with a bumper car you are driving in an enormous amusement park ride. To match the collision frequency of the N_2 molecule, you would need to be traveling 2.8 billion mi/s (4.5 billion km/s, much faster than the speed of light!) and would smash into another bumper car every 700 yd (640 m).

| How Do the Gas Laws Apply
to Earth's Atmosphere?

An **atmosphere** is the envelope of gases that extends continuously from a planet's surface outward, thinning gradually until it is identical with outer space. A sample of clean, dry air at sea level on Earth contains 18 gases (Table B5.1). Under standard conditions, they behave nearly ideally, so volume percent equals mole percent (Avogadro's law), and the mole fraction of a component relates directly to its partial pressure (Dalton's law). Let's see how the gas laws and kinetic-molecular theory apply to our atmosphere, first with regard to variations in pressure and temperature, and then as explanations of some very familiar phenomena.

Table B5.1	Composition of Clean, Dry Air at Sea Level
Component	**Mole Fraction**
Nitrogen (N_2)	0.78084
Oxygen (O_2)	0.20946
Argon (Ar)	0.00934
Carbon dioxide (CO_2)	0.00933
Neon (Ne)	1.818×10^{-5}
Helium (He)	5.24×10^{-6}
Methane (CH_4)	2×10^{-6}
Krypton (Kr)	1.14×10^{-6}
Hydrogen (H_2)	5×10^{-7}
Dinitrogen monoxide (N_2O)	5×10^{-7}
Carbon monoxide (CO)	1×10^{-7}
Xenon (Xe)	8×10^{-8}
Ozone (O_3)	2×10^{-8}
Ammonia (NH_3)	6×10^{-9}
Nitrogen dioxide (NO_2)	6×10^{-9}
Nitrogen monoxide (NO)	6×10^{-10}
Sulfur dioxide (SO_2)	2×10^{-10}
Hydrogen sulfide (H_2S)	2×10^{-10}

The Smooth Variation in Pressure with Altitude

Because gases are compressible (Boyle's law), the pressure of the atmosphere *increases* smoothly as we approach Earth's surface, with a more rapid increase at lower altitudes (Figure B5.1, *left*). No boundary delineates the beginning of the atmosphere from the end of outer space, but the densities and compositions are identical at an altitude of about 10,000 km (6000 mi). Yet, about 99% of the atmosphere's mass lies within 30 km (almost 19 mi) of the surface, and 75% lies within the lowest 11 km (almost 7 mi).

The Zig-Zag Variation in Temperature with Altitude

Unlike pressure, temperature does *not* change smoothly with altitude above Earth's surface. The atmosphere is classified into regions based on the direction of temperature change, and we'll start at the surface (Figure B5.1, *right*).

1. *The troposphere.* In the troposphere, which extends from the surface to between 7 km (23,000 ft) at the poles and 17 km (60,000 ft) at the equator, the temperature *drops* 7°C per kilometer to −55°C (218 K). This region contains about 80% of the total mass of the atmosphere, with 50% of the mass in the lower 5.6 km (18,500 ft). All weather occurs in this region, and nearly all, except supersonic, aircraft fly here.

2. *The stratosphere and the ozone layer.* In the stratosphere, the temperature *rises* from −55°C to about 7°C (280 K) at 50 km. This rise is due to a variety of complex reactions, mostly involving ozone, and is caused by the absorption of solar radiation. Most high-energy radiation is absorbed by upper levels of the atmosphere, but some that reaches the stratosphere breaks O_2 into O atoms. The energetic O atoms collide with more O_2 to form ozone (O_3), another molecular form of oxygen:

$$O_2(g) \xrightarrow{\text{high-energy radiation}} 2O(g)$$

$$M + O(g) + O_2(g) \longrightarrow O_3(g) + M + heat$$

where M is any particle that can carry away excess energy. This reaction releases heat, which is why stratospheric temperatures increase with altitude. Over 90% of atmospheric ozone remains in a thin layer within the stratosphere, its thickness varying both geographically (greatest at the poles) and seasonally (greatest in spring in the Northern Hemisphere and in fall in the Southern). Stratospheric ozone is vital to life because it absorbs over 95% of the harmful ultraviolet (UV) solar radiation that would otherwise reach the surface. In Chapter 16, we'll discuss the destructive effect of certain industrial chemicals on the ozone layer.

3. *The mesosphere.* In the mesosphere, the temperature *drops* again to −93°C (180 K) at around 80 km.

4. *The outer atmosphere.* Within the *thermosphere,* which extends to around 500 km, the temperature *rises* again, but varies between 700 and 2000 K, depending on the intensity of solar radiation and sunspot activity. The *exosphere,* the outermost region, maintains these temperatures and merges with outer space.

What does it actually mean to have a temperature of 2000 K at 500 km (300 mi) above Earth's surface? Would a piece of iron (melting point = 1808 K) glow red-hot within a minute or so and melt in the thermosphere, as it does if heated to 2000 K in the troposphere? The answer involves the relation between temperature and the time it takes to transfer kinetic energy. Our use of the words "hot" and "cold" refers to measurements near the surface. There, the collision frequency of gas particles with a thermometer is enormous, and so the transfer of their kinetic energy is very fast. But, at an altitude of 500 km, where the density of gas particles is a million times *less,* collision frequency is extremely low, and a thermometer, or any object, experiences *very slow transfer of kinetic energy.* Thus, the object would not become "hot" in the usual sense in any reasonable time. But the high-energy solar radiation that *is* transferred to the few particles present in these regions makes their average kinetic energy extremely high, as indicated by the high absolute temperature.

Figure B5.1 Variations in pressure and temperature with altitude in Earth's atmosphere.

Convection in the Lower Atmosphere

Why must you take more breaths per minute on a high mountaintop than at sea level? Because at the higher elevation, there is a smaller *amount* of O_2 in each breath. However, the *proportion* (mole percent) of O_2 throughout the lower atmosphere remains about 21%. This uniform composition arises from *vertical (convective) mixing,* and the gas laws explain how it occurs.

Let's follow an air mass from ground level, as solar heating of Earth's surface warms it. The warmer air mass expands (Charles's law), which makes it less dense, so it rises. As it does so, the pressure on it decreases, making it expand further (Boyle's law). Pushing against the surrounding air requires energy, so the temperature of the air mass decreases and thus the air mass shrinks slightly (Charles's law). But, as its temperature drops, its water vapor condenses (or solidifies), and these changes of state release heat; therefore, the air mass becomes warmer and rises further. Meanwhile, the cooler, and thus denser, air that was above it sinks, becomes warmer through contact with the surface, and goes through the same process as the first air mass. As a result of this vertical mixing, the composition of the lower atmosphere remains uniform.

Warm air rising from the ground, called a *thermal,* is used by soaring birds and glider pilots to stay aloft. Convection helps clean the air in urban areas, because the rising air carries up pollutants, which are dispersed by winds. Under certain conditions, however, a warm air mass remains stationary over a cool one. The resulting *temperature inversion* blocks normal convection, and harmful pollutants build up, causing severe health problems.

Problems

B5.1 Suggest a reason why supersonic aircraft are kept well below their maximum speeds until they reach their highest altitudes.

B5.2 Gases behave nearly ideally under Earth's conditions. Elsewhere in the Solar System, however, conditions are very different. On which would you expect atmospheric gases to deviate most from ideal behavior, Saturn (4×10^6 atm and 130 K) or Venus (90 atm and 730 K)? Explain.

B5.3 What is the volume percent and partial pressure (in torr) of argon in a sample of dry air at sea level?

B5.4 Earth's atmosphere is estimated to have a mass of 5.14×10^{15} t (1 t = 1000 kg).
(a) If the average molar mass of air is 28.8 g/mol, how many moles of gas are in the atmosphere?
(b) How many liters would the atmosphere occupy at 25°C and 1 atm?

◼ Summary of Section 5.5

- The kinetic-molecular theory postulates that gas particles have no volume, move in straight-line paths between elastic (energy-conserving) collisions, and have average kinetic energies proportional to the absolute temperature of the gas.
- This theory explains the gas laws in terms of changes in distances between particles and the container walls, changes in molecular speed, and the energy of collisions.
- Temperature is a measure of the average kinetic energy of the particles.
- Effusion and diffusion rates are *inversely* proportional to the square root of the molar mass (Graham's law) because they are *directly* proportional to molecular speed.
- Molecular motion is characterized by a temperature-dependent, most probable speed (within a range of speeds), which affects mean free path and collision frequency.
- The atmosphere is a complex mixture of gases that exhibits variations in pressure and temperature with altitude. High temperatures in the upper atmosphere result from absorption of high-energy solar radiation. The lower atmosphere has a uniform composition as a result of convective mixing.

5.6 • REAL GASES: DEVIATIONS FROM IDEAL BEHAVIOR

A fundamental principle of science is that simpler models are more useful than complex ones, as long as they explain the data. With only a few postulates, the kinetic-molecular theory explains the behavior of most gases under ordinary conditions. But, two of the postulates are useful approximations that do not reflect reality:

1. *Gas particles are **not** points of mass* but have volumes determined by the sizes of their atoms and the lengths and directions of their bonds.
2. *Attractive and repulsive forces **do** exist among gas particles* because atoms contain charged subatomic particles and many bonds are polar. (As you'll see in Chapter 12, such forces lead to changes of physical state.)

These two features cause deviations from ideal behavior under *extreme conditions of low temperature and high pressure*. These deviations mean that we must alter the simple model and the ideal gas law to predict the behavior of real gases.

Effects of Extreme Conditions on Gas Behavior

At ordinary conditions—relatively high temperatures and low pressures—most real gases exhibit nearly ideal behavior. Yet, even at STP (0°C and 1 atm), gases deviate *slightly* from ideal behavior. Table 5.3 shows that the standard molar volumes of several gases, when measured to five significant figures, do not equal the ideal value. Note that the deviations increase as the boiling point rises.

The phenomena that cause slight deviations under standard conditions exert more influence as temperature decreases and pressure increases. Figure 5.23 shows a plot of PV/RT versus external pressure (P_{ext}) for 1 mol of several real gases and an ideal gas. The PV/RT values range from normal (at $P_{ext} = 1$ atm, $PV/RT = 1$) to very high (at $P_{ext} \approx 1000$ atm, $PV/RT \approx 1.6$ to 2.3). For the *ideal* gas, PV/RT is 1 at any P_{ext}.

The PV/RT curve for methane (CH_4) is typical of most gases: it decreases *below* the ideal value at moderately high P_{ext} and then rises *above* the ideal value as P_{ext} increases to very high values. This shape arises from two overlapping effects:

- At moderately high P_{ext}, PV/RT values are lower than ideal values (less than 1) because of *interparticle attractions*.
- At very high P_{ext}, PV/RT values are greater than ideal values (more than 1) because of *particle volume*.

Let's examine these effects on the molecular level:

1. *Effect of interparticle attractions.* Interparticle attractions occur between separate atoms or molecules and are caused by imbalances in electron distributions. They are important only over *very* short distances and are *much* weaker than the covalent bonding forces that hold a molecule together. At normal P_{ext}, the spaces between the particles are so large that attractions are negligible and the gas behaves nearly ideally.

Table 5.3 Molar Volume of Some Common Gases at STP (0°C and 1 atm)		
Gas	**Molar Volume (L/mol)**	**Boiling Point (°C)**
He	22.435	−268.9
H$_2$	22.432	−252.8
Ne	22.422	−246.1
Ideal gas	**22.414**	—
Ar	22.397	−185.9
N$_2$	22.396	−195.8
O$_2$	22.390	−183.0
CO	22.388	−191.5
Cl$_2$	22.184	−34.0
NH$_3$	22.079	−33.4

The horizontal line shows that, for 1 mol of ideal gas, $PV/RT = 1$ at all P_{ext}. At very high P_{ext}, real gases deviate significantly from ideal behavior, but small deviations appear even at ordinary pressures (expanded portion).

As P_{ext} rises, the volume of the sample decreases and the particles get closer together, so interparticle attractions have a greater effect. As a particle approaches the container wall under these higher pressures, nearby particles attract it, which lessens the force of its impact (Figure 5.24). *Repeated throughout the sample, this effect results in decreased gas pressure and, thus, a smaller numerator in PV/RT.* Similarly, lowering the temperature slows the particles, so they attract each other for a longer time.

Figure 5.24 The effect of interparticle attractions on measured gas pressure.

At ordinary P_{ext}, particles are too far apart to interact.

At moderately high P_{ext}, particles are close enough to interact.

Interparticle attractions (red arrows) lower the force of collisions with the container wall.

2. *Effect of particle volume.* At normal P_{ext}, the space between particles (free volume) is enormous compared with the volume of the particles *themselves* (particle volume); thus, the free volume is essentially equal to V, the container volume in PV/RT. At *moderately* high P_{ext} and as free volume decreases, the particle volume makes up an increasing proportion of the container volume (Figure 5.25). At *extremely* high pressures, the space taken up by the particles themselves makes the free volume significantly *less* than the container volume. Nevertheless, we continue to use the container volume for V in PV/RT, which causes the numerator, and thus the ratio, to become

Figure 5.25 The effect of particle volume on measured gas volume.

At ordinary P_{ext}, free volume ≈ container volume because particle volume is an insignificant portion of container volume.

At very high P_{ext}, free volume < container volume because particle volume becomes a significant portion of container volume.

artificially high. This particle volume effect increases as P_{ext} increases, eventually outweighing the effect of interparticle attractions and causing PV/RT to rise above the ideal value.

In Figure 5.23, note that the H_2 and He curves do not show the typical dip at moderate pressures. These gases consist of particles with such weak interparticle attractions that the particle volume effect predominates at all pressures.

The van der Waals Equation: Adjusting the Ideal Gas Law

To describe real gas behavior more accurately, we need to adjust the ideal gas equation in two ways:

1. Adjust P *up* by adding a factor that accounts for interparticle attractions.
2. Adjust V *down* by subtracting a factor that accounts for particle volume.

In 1873, Johannes van der Waals revised the ideal gas equation to account for the behavior of real gases. The **van der Waals equation** for n moles of a real gas is

$$\left(P + \frac{n^2a}{V^2}\right)(V - nb) = nRT \qquad (5.15)$$

adjusts P up   adjusts V down

where P is the measured pressure, V is the known container volume, n and T have their usual meanings, and a and b are **van der Waals constants,** experimentally determined and specific for a given gas (Table 5.4). The constant a depends on the number and distribution of electrons, which relates to the complexity of a particle and the strength of its interparticle attractions. The constant b relates to particle volume. For instance, CO_2 is both more complex and larger than H_2, and the values of their constants reflect this.

Here is a typical application of the van der Waals equation. A 1.98-L vessel contains 215 g (4.89 mol) of dry ice. After standing at 26°C (299 K), the $CO_2(s)$ changes to $CO_2(g)$. The pressure is measured (P_{real}) and then calculated by the ideal gas law (P_{IGL}) and, using the appropriate values of a and b, by the van der Waals equation (P_{VDW}). The results are revealing:

$$P_{real} = 44.8 \text{ atm} \qquad P_{IGL} = 60.6 \text{ atm} \qquad P_{VDW} = 45.9 \text{ atm}$$

Comparing the real value with each calculated value shows that P_{IGL} is 35.3% greater than P_{real}, but P_{VDW} is only 2.5% greater than P_{real}. At these conditions, CO_2 deviates so much from ideal behavior that the ideal gas law is not very useful.

A key point to realize: According to kinetic-molecular theory, the constants a and b are zero for an ideal gas because the gas particles do not attract each other and have no volume. Yet, even in a real gas at ordinary pressures, the particles are very far apart. This large average interparticle distance has two consequences:

- Attractive forces are miniscule, so $P + \dfrac{n^2a}{V^2} \approx P$.

- The particle volume is a minute fraction of the container volume, so $V - nb \approx V$.

Therefore, *at ordinary conditions, the van der Waals equation **becomes** the ideal gas equation.*

Table 5.4 Van der Waals Constants for Some Common Gases

Gas	$a\left(\dfrac{atm \cdot L^2}{mol^2}\right)$	$b\left(\dfrac{L}{mol}\right)$
He	0.034	0.0237
Ne	0.211	0.0171
Ar	1.35	0.0322
Kr	2.32	0.0398
Xe	4.19	0.0511
H_2	0.244	0.0266
N_2	1.39	0.0391
O_2	1.36	0.0318
Cl_2	6.49	0.0562
CH_4	2.25	0.0428
CO	1.45	0.0395
CO_2	3.59	0.0427
NH_3	4.17	0.0371
H_2O	5.46	0.0305

Summary of Section 5.6

- At very high P or low T, all gases deviate significantly from ideal behavior.
- As external pressure increases, most real gases exhibit first a lower and then a higher PV/RT; for 1 mol of an ideal gas, this ratio remains constant at 1.
- The deviations from ideal behavior are due to (1) attractions between particles, which lower the pressure (and decrease PV/RT), and (2) the volume of the particles themselves, which takes up an increasingly larger fraction of the container volume (and increases PV/RT).
- The van der Waals equation includes constants specific for a given gas to correct for deviations from ideal behavior. At ordinary P and T, the van der Waals equation reduces to the ideal gas equation.

CHAPTER REVIEW GUIDE

Learning Objectives
Relevant section (§) and/or sample problem (SP) numbers appear in parentheses.

Understand These Concepts

1. How gases differ in their macroscopic properties from liquids and solids (§5.1)
2. The meaning of pressure and the operation of a barometer and a manometer (§5.2)
3. The relations among gas variables expressed by Boyle's, Charles's, and Avogadro's laws (§5.3)
4. How the individual gas laws are incorporated into the ideal gas law (§5.3)
5. How the ideal gas law can be used to study gas density, molar mass, and amounts of gases in reactions (§5.4)
6. The relation between the density and the temperature of a gas (§5.4)
7. The meaning of Dalton's law and the relation between partial pressure and mole fraction of a gas; how Dalton's law applies to collecting a gas over water (§5.4)
8. How the postulates of the kinetic-molecular theory are applied to explain the origin of pressure and the gas laws (§5.5)
9. The relations among molecular speed, average kinetic energy, and temperature (§5.5)
10. The meanings of *effusion* and *diffusion* and how their rates are related to molar mass (§5.5)
11. The relations among mean free path, molecular speed, and collision frequency (§5.5)
12. Why intermolecular attractions and molecular volume cause gases to deviate from ideal behavior at low temperatures and high pressures (§5.6)
13. How the van der Waals equation corrects the ideal gas law for extreme conditions (§5.6)

Master These Skills

1. Interconverting among the units of pressure (atm, mmHg, torr, pascal, lb/in^2) (SP 5.1)
2. Reducing the ideal gas law to the individual gas laws (SPs 5.2–5.5)
3. Applying gas laws to choose the correct chemical equation (SP 5.6)
4. Rearranging the ideal gas law to calculate gas density (SP 5.7) and molar mass of a volatile liquid (SP 5.8)
5. Calculating the mole fraction and the partial pressure of a gas (SP 5.9)
6. Using the vapor pressure of water to correct for the amount of a gas collected over water (SP 5.10)
7. Applying stoichiometry and gas laws to calculate amounts of reactants and products (SPs 5.11, 5.12)
8. Using Graham's law to solve problems of gaseous effusion (SP 5.13)

Key Terms
Page numbers appear in parentheses.

Section 5.2
pressure (*P*) (183)
barometer (183)
manometer (184)
pascal (Pa) (185)
standard atmosphere (atm) (185)
millimeter of mercury (mmHg) (185)
torr (185)

Section 5.3
ideal gas (186)
Boyle's law (187)
Charles's law (188)
Avogadro's law (190)
standard temperature and pressure (STP) (190)
standard molar volume (190)
ideal gas law (191)
universal gas constant (*R*) (191)

Section 5.4
partial pressure (199)
Dalton's law of partial pressures (199)
mole fraction (*X*) (200)

Section 5.5
kinetic-molecular theory (204)
rms speed (*u*$_{rms}$) (209)
effusion (209)
Graham's law of effusion (209)

diffusion (210)
mean free path (211)
collision frequency (211)
atmosphere (212)

Section 5.6
van der Waals equation (216)
van der Waals constants (216)

Key Equations and Relationships
Page numbers appear in parentheses.

5.1 Expressing the volume-pressure relationship (Boyle's law) (187):

$$V \propto \frac{1}{P} \quad \text{or} \quad PV = \text{constant} \quad [T \text{ and } n \text{ fixed}]$$

5.2 Expressing the volume-temperature relationship (Charles's law) (188):

$$V \propto T \quad \text{or} \quad \frac{V}{T} = \text{constant} \quad [P \text{ and } n \text{ fixed}]$$

5.3 Expressing the pressure-temperature relationship (Amontons's law) (189):

$$P \propto T \quad \text{or} \quad \frac{P}{T} = \text{constant} \quad [V \text{ and } n \text{ fixed}]$$

5.4 Expressing the volume-amount relationship (Avogadro's law) (190):

$$V \propto n \quad \text{or} \quad \frac{V}{n} = \text{constant} \quad [P \text{ and } T \text{ fixed}]$$

5.5 Defining standard temperature and pressure (190):

STP: 0°C (273.15 K) and 1 atm (760 torr)

5.6 Defining the volume of 1 mol of an ideal gas at STP (190):

Standard molar volume = 22.4141 L = 22.4 L [3 sf]

5.7 Relating volume to pressure, temperature, and amount (ideal gas law) (191):

$$PV = nRT \qquad \text{and} \qquad \frac{P_1V_1}{n_1T_1} = \frac{P_2V_2}{n_2T_2}$$

5.8 Calculating the value of R (191):

$$R = \frac{PV}{nT} = \frac{1 \text{ atm} \times 22.4141 \text{ L}}{1 \text{ mol} \times 273.15 \text{ K}}$$

$$= 0.082058 \frac{\text{atm·L}}{\text{mol·K}} = 0.0821 \frac{\text{atm·L}}{\text{mol·K}} \qquad \text{[3 sf]}$$

5.9 Rearranging the ideal gas law to find gas density (196):

$$PV = \frac{m}{\mathcal{M}} RT$$

so

$$\frac{m}{V} = d = \frac{\mathcal{M} \times P}{RT}$$

5.10 Rearranging the ideal gas law to find molar mass (198):

$$n = \frac{m}{\mathcal{M}} = \frac{PV}{RT} \qquad \text{so} \qquad \mathcal{M} = \frac{mRT}{PV}$$

5.11 Relating the total pressure of a gas mixture to the partial pressures of the components (Dalton's law of partial pressures) (199):

$$P_{\text{total}} = P_1 + P_2 + P_3 + \cdots$$

5.12 Relating partial pressure to mole fraction (200):

$$P_A = X_A \times P_{\text{total}}$$

5.13 Defining rms speed as a function of molar mass and temperature (209):

$$u_{\text{rms}} = \sqrt{\frac{3RT}{\mathcal{M}}}$$

5.14 Applying Graham's law of effusion (209):

$$\frac{\text{Rate}_A}{\text{Rate}_B} = \frac{\sqrt{\mathcal{M}_B}}{\sqrt{\mathcal{M}_A}} = \sqrt{\frac{\mathcal{M}_B}{\mathcal{M}_A}}$$

5.15 Applying the van der Waals equation to find the pressure or volume of a gas under extreme conditions (216):

$$\left(P + \frac{n^2a}{V^2}\right)(V - nb) = nRT$$

Brief Solutions to Follow-Up Problems

5.1 P_{CO_2} (torr) = (753.6 mmHg − 174.0 mmHg) $\times \dfrac{1 \text{ torr}}{1 \text{ mmHg}}$

= 579.6 torr

P_{CO_2} (Pa) = 579.6 torr $\times \dfrac{1 \text{ atm}}{760 \text{ torr}} \times \dfrac{1.01325 \times 10^5 \text{ Pa}}{1 \text{ atm}}$

= 7.727 × 10⁴ Pa

P_{CO_2} (lb/in²) = 579.6 torr $\times \dfrac{1 \text{ atm}}{760 \text{ torr}} \times \dfrac{14.7 \text{ lb/in}^2}{1 \text{ atm}}$

= 11.2 lb/in²

5.2 P_2(atm) = 26.3 kPa $\times \dfrac{1 \text{ atm}}{101.325 \text{ kPa}}$ = 0.260 atm

V_2(L) = 105 mL $\times \dfrac{1 \text{ L}}{1000 \text{ mL}} \times \dfrac{0.871 \text{ atm}}{0.260 \text{ atm}}$ = 0.352 L

5.3 T_2 (K) = 273 K $\times \dfrac{9.75 \text{ cm}^3}{6.83 \text{ cm}^3}$ = 390. K

5.4 P_2 (torr) = 793 torr $\times \dfrac{35.0 \text{ g} - 5.0 \text{ g}}{35.0 \text{ g}}$ = 680. torr

(There is no need to convert mass to moles because the ratio of masses equals the ratio of moles.)

5.5 $n = \dfrac{PV}{RT} = \dfrac{1.37 \text{ atm} \times 438 \text{ L}}{0.0821 \dfrac{\text{atm·L}}{\text{mol·K}} \times 294 \text{ K}}$ = 24.9 mol O₂

Mass (g) of O₂ = 24.9 mol O₂ $\times \dfrac{32.00 \text{ g O}_2}{1 \text{ mol O}_2}$ = 7.97 × 10² g O₂

5.6 The balanced equation is 2CD(g) ⟶ C₂(g) + D₂(g), so n does not change. Therefore, given constant P, the temperature, T, must double: $T_1 = -73°C + 273.15 = 200$ K; so $T_2 = 400$ K, or 400 K − 273.15 = 127°C.

5.7 d (at 0°C and 380 torr) = $\dfrac{44.01 \text{ g/mol} \times \dfrac{380 \text{ torr}}{760 \text{ torr/atm}}}{0.0821 \dfrac{\text{atm·L}}{\text{mol·K}} \times 273 \text{ K}}$

= 0.982 g/L

The density is lower at the smaller P because V is larger. In this case, d is lowered by one-half because P is one-half as much.

5.8

$$\mathcal{M} = \frac{(68.697 \text{ g} - 68.322 \text{ g}) \times 0.0821 \dfrac{\text{atm·L}}{\text{mol·K}} \times (273.15 + 95.0) \text{ K}}{\dfrac{740. \text{ torr}}{760 \text{ torr/atm}} \times \dfrac{149 \text{ mL}}{1000 \text{ mL/L}}}$$

= 78.1 g/mol

5.9 $n_{total} = \left(5.50 \text{ g He} \times \dfrac{1 \text{ mol He}}{4.003 \text{ g He}}\right)$

$\qquad + \left(15.0 \text{ g Ne} \times \dfrac{1 \text{ mol Ne}}{20.18 \text{ g Ne}}\right)$

$\qquad + \left(35.0 \text{ g Kr} \times \dfrac{1 \text{ mol Kr}}{83.80 \text{ g Kr}}\right)$

$\qquad = 2.53 \text{ mol}$

$P_{He} = \left(\dfrac{5.50 \text{ g He} \times \dfrac{1 \text{ mol He}}{4.003 \text{ g He}}}{2.53 \text{ mol}}\right) \times 1 \text{ atm} = 0.543 \text{ atm}$

$P_{Ne} = 0.294 \text{ atm} \qquad P_{Kr} = 0.165 \text{ atm}$

5.10 $P_{H_2} = 752 \text{ torr} - 13.6 \text{ torr} = 738 \text{ torr}$

$\text{Mass (g) of } H_2 = \left(\dfrac{\dfrac{738 \text{ torr}}{760 \text{ torr/atm}} \times 1.495 \text{ L}}{0.0821 \dfrac{\text{atm·L}}{\text{mol·K}} \times 289 \text{ K}}\right) \times \dfrac{2.016 \text{ g } H_2}{1 \text{ mol } H_2}$

$\qquad = 0.123 \text{ g } H_2$

5.11 $H_2SO_4(aq) + 2NaCl(s) \longrightarrow Na_2SO_4(aq) + 2HCl(g)$

$n_{HCl} = 0.117 \text{ kg NaCl} \times \dfrac{10^3 \text{ g}}{1 \text{ kg}} \times \dfrac{1 \text{ mol NaCl}}{58.44 \text{ g NaCl}} \times \dfrac{2 \text{ mol HCl}}{2 \text{ mol NaCl}}$

$\qquad = 2.00 \text{ mol HCl}$

At STP, $V \text{ (mL)} = 2.00 \text{ mol} \times \dfrac{22.4 \text{ L}}{1 \text{ mol}} \times \dfrac{10^3 \text{ mL}}{1 \text{ L}}$

$\qquad = 4.48 \times 10^4 \text{ mL}$

5.12 $NH_3(g) + HCl(g) \longrightarrow NH_4Cl(s)$

$n_{NH_3} = 0.187 \text{ mol and } n_{HCl} = 0.0522 \text{ mol}$; thus, HCl is the limiting reactant.

n_{NH_3} after reaction

$\qquad = 0.187 \text{ mol } NH_3 - \left(0.0522 \text{ mol HCl} \times \dfrac{1 \text{ mol } NH_3}{1 \text{ mol HCl}}\right)$

$\qquad = 0.135 \text{ mol } NH_3$

$P = \dfrac{0.135 \text{ mol} \times 0.0821 \dfrac{\text{atm·L}}{\text{mol·K}} \times 295 \text{ K}}{10.0 \text{ L}} = 0.327 \text{ atm}$

5.13 $\dfrac{\text{Rate of He}}{\text{Rate of } C_2H_6} = \sqrt{\dfrac{30.07 \text{ g/mol}}{4.003 \text{ g/mol}}} = 2.741$

Time for C_2H_6 to effuse $= 1.25 \text{ min} \times 2.741 = 3.43 \text{ min}$

PROBLEMS

Problems with **colored** numbers are answered in Appendix E and worked in detail in the Student Solutions Manual. Problem sections match those in the text and provide the numbers of relevant sample problems. Most offer Concept Review Questions, Skill-Building Exercises (grouped in pairs covering the same concept), and Problems in Context. The Comprehensive Problems are based on material from any section or previous chapter.

An Overview of the Physical States of Matter

Concept Review Questions

5.1 How does a sample of gas differ in its behavior from a sample of liquid in each of the following situations?
(a) The sample is transferred from one container to a larger one.
(b) The sample is heated in an expandable container, but no change of state occurs.
(c) The sample is placed in a cylinder with a piston, and an external force is applied.

5.2 Are the particles in a gas farther apart or closer together than the particles in a liquid? Use your answer to explain each of the following general observations:
(a) Gases are more compressible than liquids.
(b) Gases have lower viscosities than liquids.
(c) After thorough stirring, all gas mixtures are solutions.
(d) The density of a substance in the gas state is lower than in the liquid state.

Gas Pressure and Its Measurement
(Sample Problem 5.1)

Concept Review Questions

5.3 How does a barometer work? Is the column of mercury in a barometer shorter when it is on a mountaintop or at sea level? Explain.

5.4 How can a unit of length such as millimeter of mercury (mmHg) be used as a unit of pressure, which has the dimensions of force per unit area?

5.5 In a closed-end manometer, the mercury level in the arm attached to the flask can never be higher than the mercury level in the other arm, whereas in an open-end manometer, it *can* be higher. Explain.

Skill-Building Exercises (grouped in similar pairs)

5.6 On a cool, rainy day, the barometric pressure is 730 mmHg. Calculate the barometric pressure in centimeters of water (cmH$_2$O) (*d* of Hg = 13.5 g/mL; *d* of H$_2$O = 1.00 g/mL).

5.7 A long glass tube, sealed at one end, has an inner diameter of 10.0 mm. The tube is filled with water and inverted into a pail of water. If the atmospheric pressure is 755 mmHg, how high (in mmH$_2$O) is the column of water in the tube (*d* of Hg = 13.5 g/mL; *d* of H$_2$O = 1.00 g/mL)?

5.8 Convert the following:
(a) 0.745 atm to mmHg   (b) 992 torr to bar
(c) 365 kPa to atm   (d) 804 mmHg to kPa

5.9 Convert the following:
(a) 76.8 cmHg to atm   (b) 27.5 atm to kPa
(c) 6.50 atm to bar   (d) 0.937 kPa to torr

5.10 In Figure P5.10, what is the pressure of the gas in the flask (in atm) if the barometer reads 738.5 torr?

5.11 In Figure P5.11, what is the pressure of the gas in the flask (in kPa) if the barometer reads 765.2 mmHg?

Figure P5.10   **Figure P5.11**

5.12 If the sample flask in Figure P5.12 is open to the air, what is the atmospheric pressure (in atm)?

5.13 What is the pressure (in Pa) of the gas in the flask in Figure P5.13?

Figure P5.12   **Figure P5.13**

Problems in Context

5.14 Convert each of the pressures described below to atm:
(a) At the peak of Mt. Everest, atmospheric pressure is only 2.75×10^2 mmHg.
(b) A cyclist fills her bike tires to 86 psi.
(c) The surface of Venus has an atmospheric pressure of 9.15×10^6 Pa.
(d) At 100 ft below sea level, a scuba diver experiences a pressure of 2.54×10^4 torr.

5.15 The gravitational force exerted by an object is given by $F = mg$, where F is the force in newtons, m is the mass in kilograms, and g is the acceleration due to gravity (9.81 m/s²).
(a) Use the definition of the pascal to calculate the mass (in kg) of the atmosphere above 1 m² of ocean.
(b) Osmium ($Z = 76$) is a transition metal in Group 8B(8) and has the highest density of any element (22.6 g/mL). If an osmium column is 1 m² in area, how high must it be for its pressure to equal atmospheric pressure? [Use the answer from part (a) in your calculation.]

The Gas Laws and Their Experimental Foundations
(Sample Problems 5.2 to 5.6)

Concept Review Questions

5.16 A student states Boyle's law as follows: "The volume of a gas is inversely proportional to its pressure." How is this statement incomplete? Give a correct statement of Boyle's law.

5.17 In the following relationships, which quantities are variables and which are fixed: (a) Charles's law; (b) Avogadro's law; (c) Amontons's law?

5.18 Boyle's law relates gas volume to pressure, and Avogadro's law relates gas volume to amount (mol). State a relationship between gas pressure and amount (mol).

5.19 Each of the following processes caused the gas volume to double, as shown. For each process, tell how the remaining gas variable changed or state that it remained fixed:
(a) T doubles at fixed P.
(b) T and n are fixed.
(c) At fixed T, the reaction is $CD_2(g) \longrightarrow C(g) + D_2(g)$.
(d) At fixed P, the reaction is $A_2(g) + B_2(g) \longrightarrow 2AB(g)$.

Skill-Building Exercises (grouped in similar pairs)

5.20 What is the effect of the following on the volume of 1 mol of an ideal gas?
(a) The pressure is tripled (at constant T).
(b) The absolute temperature is increased by a factor of 3.0 (at constant P).
(c) Three more moles of the gas are added (at constant P and T).

5.21 What is the effect of the following on the volume of 1 mol of an ideal gas?
(a) The pressure is reduced by a factor of 4 (at constant T).
(b) The pressure changes from 760 torr to 202 kPa, and the temperature changes from 37°C to 155 K.
(c) The temperature changes from 305 K to 32°C, and the pressure changes from 2 atm to 101 kPa.

5.22 What is the effect of the following on the volume of 1 mol of an ideal gas?
(a) Temperature decreases from 800 K to 400 K (at constant P).
(b) Temperature increases from 250°C to 500°C (at constant P).
(c) Pressure increases from 2 atm to 6 atm (at constant T).

5.23 What is the effect of the following on the volume of 1 mol of an ideal gas?
(a) Half the gas escapes (at constant P and T).
(b) The initial pressure is 722 torr, and the final pressure is 0.950 atm; the initial temperature is 32°F, and the final temperature is 273 K.
(c) Both the pressure and temperature decrease to one-fourth of their initial values.

5.24 A sample of sulfur hexafluoride gas occupies 9.10 L at 198°C. Assuming that the pressure remains constant, what temperature (in °C) is needed to reduce the volume to 2.50 L?

5.25 A 93-L sample of dry air cools from 145°C to −22°C while the pressure is maintained at 2.85 atm. What is the final volume?

5.26 A sample of Freon-12 (CF_2Cl_2) occupies 25.5 L at 298 K and 153.3 kPa. Find its volume at STP.

5.27 A sample of carbon monoxide occupies 3.65 L at 298 K and 745 torr. Find its volume at −14°C and 367 torr.

5.28 A sample of chlorine gas is confined in a 5.0-L container at 328 torr and 37°C. How many moles of gas are in the sample?

5.29 If 1.47×10^{-3} mol of argon occupies a 75.0-mL container at 26°C, what is the pressure (in torr)?

5.30 You have 357 mL of chlorine trifluoride gas at 699 mmHg and 45°C. What is the mass (in g) of the sample?

5.31 A 75.0-g sample of dinitrogen monoxide is confined in a 3.1-L vessel. What is the pressure (in atm) at 115°C?

Problems in Context

5.32 In preparation for a demonstration, your professor brings a 1.5-L bottle of sulfur dioxide into the lecture hall before class to allow the gas to reach room temperature. If the pressure gauge reads 85 psi and the temperature in the hall is 23°C, how many moles of sulfur dioxide are in the bottle? (*Hint:* The gauge reads zero when 14.7 psi of gas remains.)

5.33 A gas-filled weather balloon with a volume of 65.0 L is released at sea-level conditions of 745 torr and 25°C. The balloon can expand to a maximum volume of 835 L. When the balloon rises to an altitude at which the temperature is −5°C and the pressure is 0.066 atm, will it reach its maximum volume?

Rearrangements of the Ideal Gas Law
(Sample Problems 5.7 to 5.12)

Concept Review Questions

5.34 Why is moist air less dense than dry air?

5.35 To collect a beaker of H_2 gas by displacing the air already in the beaker, would you hold the beaker upright or inverted? Why? How would you hold the beaker to collect CO_2?

5.36 Why can we use a gas mixture, such as air, to study the general behavior of an ideal gas under ordinary conditions?

5.37 How does the partial pressure of gas A in a mixture compare to its mole fraction in the mixture? Explain.

5.38 The scene at right represents a portion of a mixture of four gases A (*purple*), B (*black*), C (*green*), and D_2 (*orange*).
(a) Which has the highest partial pressure?
(b) Which has the lowest partial pressure?
(c) If the total pressure is 0.75 atm, what is the partial pressure of D_2?

Skill-Building Exercises (grouped in similar pairs)

5.39 What is the density of Xe gas at STP?

5.40 Find the density of Freon-11 ($CFCl_3$) at 120°C and 1.5 atm.

5.41 How many moles of gaseous arsine (AsH_3) occupy 0.0400 L at STP? What is the density of gaseous arsine?

5.42 The density of a noble gas is 2.71 g/L at 3.00 atm and 0°C. Identify the gas.

5.43 Calculate the molar mass of a gas at 388 torr and 45°C if 206 ng occupies 0.206 µL.

5.44 When an evacuated 63.8-mL glass bulb is filled with a gas at 22°C and 747 mmHg, the bulb gains 0.103 g in mass. Is the gas N_2, Ne, or Ar?

5.45 After 0.600 L of Ar at 1.20 atm and 227°C is mixed with 0.200 L of O_2 at 501 torr and 127°C in a 400-mL flask at 27°C, what is the pressure in the flask?

5.46 A 355-mL container holds 0.146 g of Ne and an unknown amount of Ar at 35°C and a total pressure of 626 mmHg. Calculate the number of moles of Ar present.

5.47 How many grams of phosphorus react with 35.5 L of O_2 at STP to form tetraphosphorus decaoxide?

$$P_4(s) + 5O_2(g) \longrightarrow P_4O_{10}(s)$$

5.48 How many grams of potassium chlorate decompose to potassium chloride and 638 mL of O_2 at 128°C and 752 torr?

$$2KClO_3(s) \longrightarrow 2KCl(s) + 3O_2(g)$$

5.49 How many grams of phosphine (PH_3) can form when 37.5 g of phosphorus and 83.0 L of hydrogen gas react at STP?

$$P_4(s) + H_2(g) \longrightarrow PH_3(g) \quad [\text{unbalanced}]$$

5.50 When 35.6 L of ammonia and 40.5 L of oxygen gas at STP burn, nitrogen monoxide and water form. After the products return to STP, how many grams of nitrogen monoxide are present?

$$NH_3(g) + O_2(g) \longrightarrow NO(g) + H_2O(l) \quad [\text{unbalanced}]$$

5.51 Aluminum reacts with excess hydrochloric acid to form aqueous aluminum chloride and 35.8 mL of hydrogen gas over water at 27°C and 751 mmHg. How many grams of aluminum reacted?

5.52 How many liters of hydrogen gas are collected over water at 18°C and 725 mmHg when 0.84 g of lithium reacts with water? Aqueous lithium hydroxide also forms.

Problems in Context

5.53 The air in a hot-air balloon at 744 torr is heated from 17°C to 60.0°C. Assuming that the amount (mol) of air and the pressure remain constant, what is the density of the air at each temperature? (The average molar mass of air is 28.8 g/mol.)

5.54 On a certain winter day in Utah, the average atmospheric pressure is 650. torr. What is the molar density (in mol/L) of the air if the temperature is −25°C?

5.55 A sample of a liquid hydrocarbon known to consist of molecules with five carbon atoms is vaporized in a 0.204-L flask by immersion in a water bath at 101°C. The barometric pressure is 767 torr, and the remaining gas weighs 0.482 g. What is the molecular formula of the hydrocarbon?

5.56 A sample of air contains 78.08% nitrogen, 20.94% oxygen, 0.05% carbon dioxide, and 0.93% argon, by volume. How many molecules of each gas are present in 1.00 L of the sample at 25°C and 1.00 atm?

5.57 An environmental chemist sampling industrial exhaust gases from a coal-burning plant collects a CO_2-SO_2-H_2O mixture in a 21-L steel tank until the pressure reaches 850. torr at 45°C.
(a) How many moles of gas are collected?

(b) If the SO_2 concentration in the mixture is 7.95×10^3 parts per million by volume (ppmv), what is its partial pressure? [*Hint:* ppmv = (volume of component/volume of mixture) × 10^6.]

5.58 "Strike anywhere" matches contain the compound tetraphosphorus trisulfide, which burns to form tetraphosphorus decaoxide and sulfur dioxide gas. How many milliliters of sulfur dioxide, measured at 725 torr and 32°C, can be produced from burning 0.800 g of tetraphosphorus trisulfide?

5.59 Freon-12 (CF_2Cl_2), widely used as a refrigerant and aerosol propellant, is a dangerous air pollutant. In the troposphere, it traps heat 25 times as effectively as CO_2, and in the stratosphere, it participates in the breakdown of ozone. Freon-12 is prepared industrially by reaction of gaseous carbon tetrachloride with hydrogen fluoride. Hydrogen chloride gas also forms. How many grams of carbon tetrachloride are required for the production of 16.0 dm^3 of Freon-12 at 27°C and 1.20 atm?

5.60 Xenon hexafluoride was one of the first noble gas compounds synthesized. The solid reacts rapidly with the silicon dioxide in glass or quartz containers to form liquid $XeOF_4$ and gaseous silicon tetrafluoride. What is the pressure in a 1.00-L container at 25°C after 2.00 g of xenon hexafluoride reacts? (Assume that silicon tetrafluoride is the only gas present and that it occupies the entire volume.)

5.61 In the four cylinder-piston assemblies below, the reactant in the left cylinder is about to undergo a reaction at constant *T* and *P*:

2.0 L   **A**   1.0 L   **B**   1.0 L   **C**   1.0 L

Which of the other three depictions best represents the products of the reaction?

5.62 Roasting galena [lead(II) sulfide] is a step in the industrial isolation of lead. How many liters of sulfur dioxide, measured at STP, are produced by the reaction of 3.75 kg of galena with 228 L of oxygen gas at 220°C and 2.0 atm? Lead(II) oxide also forms.

5.63 In one of his most critical studies into the nature of combustion, Lavoisier heated mercury(II) oxide and isolated elemental mercury and oxygen gas. If 40.0 g of mercury(II) oxide is heated in a 502-mL vessel and 20.0% (by mass) decomposes, what is the pressure (in atm) of the oxygen that forms at 25.0°C? (Assume that the gas occupies the entire volume.)

The Kinetic-Molecular Theory: A Model for Gas Behavior
(Sample Problem 5.13)

Concept Review Questions

5.64 Use the kinetic-molecular theory to explain the change in gas pressure that results from warming a sample of gas.

5.65 How does the kinetic-molecular theory explain why 1 mol of krypton and 1 mol of helium have the same volume at STP?

5.66 Is the rate of effusion of a gas higher than, lower than, or equal to its rate of diffusion? Explain. For two gases with molecules of approximately the same size, is the ratio of their effusion rates higher than, lower than, or equal to the ratio of their diffusion rates? Explain.

5.67 Consider two 1-L samples of gas: one is H_2 and the other is O_2. Both are at 1 atm and 25°C. How do the samples compare in terms of (a) mass, (b) density, (c) mean free path, (d) average molecular kinetic energy, (e) average molecular speed, and (f) time for a given fraction of molecules to effuse?

5.68 Three 5-L flasks, fixed with pressure gauges and small valves, each contain 4 g of gas at 273 K. Flask A contains H_2, flask B contains He, and flask C contains CH_4. Rank the flask contents in terms of (a) pressure, (b) average molecular kinetic energy, (c) diffusion rate after the valve is opened, (d) total kinetic energy of the molecules, (e) density, and (f) collision frequency.

Skill-Building Exercises (grouped in similar pairs)

5.69 What is the ratio of effusion rates for the lightest gas, H_2, and the heaviest known gas, UF_6?

5.70 What is the ratio of effusion rates for O_2 and Kr?

5.71 The graph below shows the distribution of molecular speeds for argon and helium at the same temperature.

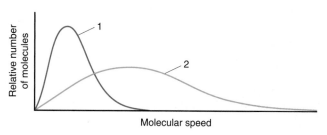

(a) Does curve 1 or 2 better represent the behavior of argon?
(b) Which curve represents the gas that effuses more slowly?
(c) Which curve more closely represents the behavior of fluorine gas? Explain.

5.72 The graph below shows the distribution of molecular speeds for a gas at two different temperatures.

(a) Does curve 1 or 2 better represent the behavior of the gas at the lower temperature?
(b) Which curve represents the gas when it has a higher $\overline{E_k}$?
(c) Which curve is consistent with a higher diffusion rate?

5.73 At a given pressure and temperature, it takes 4.85 min for a 1.5-L sample of He to effuse through a membrane. How long does it take for 1.5 L of F_2 to effuse under the same conditions?

5.74 A sample of an unknown gas effuses in 11.1 min. An equal volume of H_2 in the same apparatus under the same conditions effuses in 2.42 min. What is the molar mass of the unknown gas?

Problems in Context

5.75 White phosphorus melts and then vaporizes at high temperature. The gas effuses at a rate that is 0.404 times that of neon in the same apparatus under the same conditions. How many atoms are in a molecule of gaseous white phosphorus?

5.76 Helium (He) is the lightest noble gas component of air, and xenon (Xe) is the heaviest. [For this problem, use $R = 8.314$ J/(mol·K) and $\mathcal{M}$ in kg/mol.] (a) Find the rms speed of He in winter (0.°C) and in summer (30.°C). (b) Compare the rms speed of He with that of Xe at 30.°C. (c) Find the average kinetic energy per mole of He and of Xe at 30.°C. (d) Find the average kinetic energy per molecule of He at 30.°C.

5.77 A mixture of gaseous disulfur difluoride, dinitrogen tetrafluoride, and sulfur tetrafluoride is placed in an effusion apparatus. (a) Rank the gases in order of increasing effusion rate. (b) Find the ratio of effusion rates of disulfur difluoride and dinitrogen tetrafluoride. (c) If gas X is added, and it effuses at 0.935 times the rate of sulfur tetrafluoride, find the molar mass of X.

Real Gases: Deviations from Ideal Behavior

Skill-Building Exercises (grouped in similar pairs)

5.78 Do interparticle attractions cause negative or positive deviations from the *PV/RT* ratio of an ideal gas? Use Table 5.3 to rank Kr, CO_2, and N_2 in order of increasing magnitude of these deviations.

5.79 Does particle volume cause negative or positive deviations from the *PV/RT* ratio of an ideal gas? Use Table 5.3 to rank Cl_2, H_2, and O_2 in order of increasing magnitude of these deviations.

5.80 Does N_2 behave more ideally at 1 atm or at 500 atm? Explain.

5.81 Does SF_6 (boiling point = 16°C at 1 atm) behave more ideally at 150°C or at 20°C? Explain.

Comprehensive Problems

5.82 An "empty" gasoline can with dimensions 15.0 cm by 40.0 cm by 12.5 cm is attached to a vacuum pump and evacuated. If the atmospheric pressure is 14.7 lb/in², what is the total force (in pounds) on the outside of the can?

5.83 Hemoglobin is the protein that transports O_2 through the blood from the lungs to the rest of the body. In doing so, each molecule of hemoglobin combines with four molecules of O_2. If 1.00 g of hemoglobin combines with 1.53 mL of O_2 at 37°C and 743 torr, what is the molar mass of hemoglobin?

5.84 A baker uses sodium hydrogen carbonate (baking soda) as the leavening agent in a banana-nut quickbread. The baking soda decomposes in either of two possible reactions:

(1) $2NaHCO_3(s) \longrightarrow Na_2CO_3(s) + H_2O(l) + CO_2(g)$

(2) $NaHCO_3(s) + H^+(aq) \longrightarrow H_2O(l) + CO_2(g) + Na^+(aq)$

Calculate the volume (in mL) of CO_2 that forms at 200.°C and 0.975 atm per gram of $NaHCO_3$ by each of the reaction processes.

5.85 A weather balloon containing 600. L of He is released near the equator at 1.01 atm and 305 K. It rises to a point where conditions are 0.489 atm and 218 K and eventually lands in the northern hemisphere under conditions of 1.01 atm and 250 K. If one-fourth of the helium leaked out during this journey, what is the volume (in L) of the balloon at landing?

5.86 Chlorine is produced from sodium chloride by the electrochemical chlor-alkali process. During the process, the chlorine is collected in a container that is isolated from the other products to prevent unwanted (and explosive) reactions. If a 15.50-L container holds 0.5950 kg of Cl_2 gas at 225°C, calculate:

(a) P_{IGL} (b) $P_{VDW}\left(\text{use } R = 0.08206 \dfrac{\text{atm·L}}{\text{mol·K}}\right)$

5.87 In a certain experiment, magnesium boride (Mg_3B_2) reacted with acid to form a mixture of four boron hydrides (B_xH_y), three as liquids (labeled I, II, and III) and one as a gas (IV).
(a) When a 0.1000-g sample of each liquid was transferred to an evacuated 750.0-mL container and volatilized at 70.00°C, sample I had a pressure of 0.05951 atm; sample II, 0.07045 atm; and sample III, 0.05767 atm. What is the molar mass of each liquid?
(b) Boron is 85.63% by mass in sample I, 81.10% in II, and 82.98% in III. What is the molecular formula of each sample?
(c) Sample IV was found to be 78.14% boron. Its rate of effusion was compared to that of sulfur dioxide; under identical conditions, 350.0 mL of sample IV effused in 12.00 min and 250.0 mL of sulfur dioxide effused in 13.04 min. What is the molecular formula of sample IV?

5.88 Three equal volumes of gas mixtures, all at the same *T*, are depicted below (with gas A *red*, gas B *green*, and gas C *blue*):

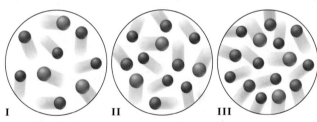

(a) Which sample, if any, has the highest partial pressure of A?
(b) Which sample, if any, has the lowest partial pressure of B?
(c) In which sample, if any, do the gas particles have the highest average kinetic energy?

5.89 Will the volume of a gas increase, decrease, or remain unchanged for each of the following sets of changes?
(a) The pressure is decreased from 2 atm to 1 atm, while the temperature is decreased from 200°C to 100°C.
(b) The pressure is increased from 1 atm to 3 atm, while the temperature is increased from 100°C to 300°C.
(c) The pressure is increased from 3 atm to 6 atm, while the temperature is increased from −73°C to 127°C.
(d) The pressure is increased from 0.2 atm to 0.4 atm, while the temperature is decreased from 300°C to 150°C.

5.90 When air is inhaled, it enters the alveoli of the lungs, and varying amounts of the component gases exchange with dissolved gases in the blood. The resulting alveolar gas mixture is quite different from the atmospheric mixture. The following table presents selected data on the composition and partial pressure of four gases in the atmosphere and in the alveoli:

Gas	Atmosphere (sea level)		Alveoli	
	Mole %	Partial Pressure (torr)	Mole %	Partial Pressure (torr)
N_2	78.6	—	—	569
O_2	20.9	—	—	104
CO_2	00.04	—	—	40
H_2O	00.46	—	—	47

If the total pressure of each gas mixture is 1.00 atm, calculate:
(a) The partial pressure (in torr) of each gas in the atmosphere
(b) The mole % of each gas in the alveoli
(c) The number of O_2 molecules in 0.50 L of alveolar air (volume of an average breath of a person at rest) at 37°C

5.91 Radon (Rn) is the heaviest, and only radioactive, member of Group 8A(18) (noble gases). It is a product of the disintegration of heavier radioactive nuclei found in minute concentrations in many common rocks used for building and construction. In recent years, health concerns about the cancers caused from inhaled residential radon have grown. If 1.0×10^{15} atoms of radium (Ra) produce an average of 1.373×10^4 atoms of Rn per second, how many liters of Rn, measured at STP, are produced per day by 1.0 g of Ra?

5.92 At 1450. mmHg and 286 K, a skin diver exhales a 208-mL bubble of air that is 77% N_2, 17% O_2, and 6.0% CO_2 by volume.
(a) How many milliliters would the volume of the bubble be if it were exhaled at the surface at 1 atm and 298 K?
(b) How many moles of N_2 are in the bubble?

5.93 Nitrogen dioxide is used industrially to produce nitric acid, but it contributes to acid rain and photochemical smog. What volume (in L) of nitrogen dioxide is formed at 735 torr and 28.2°C by reacting 4.95 cm³ of copper ($d = 8.95$ g/cm³) with 230.0 mL of nitric acid ($d = 1.42$ g/cm³, 68.0% HNO_3 by mass)?

$$Cu(s) + 4HNO_3(aq) \longrightarrow Cu(NO_3)_2(aq) + 2NO_2(g) + 2H_2O(l)$$

5.94 In the average adult male, the residual volume (RV) of the lungs, the volume of air remaining after a forced exhalation, is 1200 mL. (a) How many moles of air are present in the RV at 1.0 atm and 37°C? (b) How many molecules of gas are present under these conditions?

5.95 In a bromine-producing plant, how many liters of gaseous elemental bromine at 300°C and 0.855 atm are formed by the reaction of 275 g of sodium bromide and 175.6 g of sodium bromate in aqueous acid solution? (Assume no Br_2 dissolves.)

$$5NaBr(aq) + NaBrO_3(aq) + 3H_2SO_4(aq) \longrightarrow \\ 3Br_2(g) + 3Na_2SO_4(aq) + 3H_2O(g)$$

5.96 In a collision of sufficient force, automobile air bags respond by electrically triggering the explosive decomposition of sodium azide (NaN_3) to its elements. A 50.0-g sample of sodium azide was decomposed, and the nitrogen gas generated was collected over water at 26°C. The total pressure was 745.5 mmHg. How many liters of dry N_2 were generated?

5.97 An anesthetic gas contains 64.81% carbon, 13.60% hydrogen, and 21.59% oxygen, by mass. If 2.00 L of the gas at 25°C and 0.420 atm weighs 2.57 g, what is the molecular formula of the anesthetic?

5.98 Aluminum chloride is easily vaporized above 180°C. The gas escapes through a pinhole 0.122 times as fast as helium at the same conditions of temperature and pressure in the same apparatus. What is the molecular formula of aluminum chloride gas?

5.99 (a) What is the total volume (in L) of gaseous *products,* measured at 350°C and 735 torr, when an automobile engine burns 100. g of C_8H_{18} (a typical component of gasoline)?
(b) For part (a), the source of O_2 is air, which is 78% N_2, 21% O_2, and 1.0% Ar by volume. Assuming all the O_2 reacts, but no N_2 or Ar does, what is the total volume (in L) of gaseous *exhaust?*

5.100 An atmospheric chemist studying the pollutant SO_2 places a mixture of SO_2 and O_2 in a 2.00-L container at 800. K and 1.90 atm. When the reaction occurs, gaseous SO_3 forms, and the pressure falls to 1.65 atm. How many moles of SO_3 form?

5.101 The thermal decomposition of ethylene occurs during the compound's transit in pipelines and during the formation of polyethylene. The decomposition reaction is

$$CH_2{=}CH_2(g) \longrightarrow CH_4(g) + C(graphite)$$

If the decomposition begins at 10°C and 50.0 atm with a gas density of 0.215 g/mL and the temperature increases by 950 K,
(a) What is the final pressure of the confined gas (ignore the volume of graphite and use the van der Waals equation)?
(b) How does the PV/RT value of CH_4 compare to that in Figure 5.23? Explain.

5.102 Ammonium nitrate, a common fertilizer, was used by terrorists in the tragic explosion in Oklahoma City in 1995. How many liters of gas at 307°C and 1.00 atm are formed by the explosive decomposition of 15.0 kg of ammonium nitrate to nitrogen, oxygen, and water vapor?

5.103 An environmental engineer analyzes a sample of air contaminated with sulfur dioxide. To a 500.-mL sample at 700. torr and 38°C, she adds 20.00 mL of 0.01017 M aqueous iodine, which reacts as follows:

$$SO_2(g) + I_2(aq) + H_2O(l) \longrightarrow \\ HSO_4^-(aq) + I^-(aq) + H^+(aq) \quad \text{[unbalanced]}$$

Excess I_2 reacts with 11.37 mL of 0.0105 M sodium thiosulfate:

$$I_2(aq) + S_2O_3^{2-}(aq) \longrightarrow I^-(aq) + S_4O_6^{2-}(aq) \quad \text{[unbalanced]}$$

What is the volume % of SO_2 in the air sample?

5.104 Canadian chemists have developed a modern variation of the 1899 Mond process for preparing extremely pure metallic nickel. A sample of impure nickel reacts with carbon monoxide at 50°C to form gaseous nickel carbonyl, $Ni(CO)_4$.
(a) How many grams of nickel can be converted to the carbonyl with 3.55 m³ of CO at 100.7 kPa?
(b) The carbonyl is then decomposed at 21 atm and 155°C to pure (>99.95%) nickel. How many grams of nickel are obtained per cubic meter of the carbonyl?
(c) The released carbon monoxide is cooled and collected for reuse by passing it through water at 35°C. If the barometric pressure is 769 torr, what volume (in m³) of CO is formed per cubic meter of carbonyl?

5.105 Analysis of a newly discovered gaseous silicon-fluorine compound shows that it contains 33.01 mass % silicon. At 27°C, 2.60 g of the compound exerts a pressure of 1.50 atm in a 0.250-L vessel. What is the molecular formula of the compound?

5.106 A gaseous organic compound containing only carbon, hydrogen, and nitrogen is burned in oxygen gas, and the volume of each reactant and product is measured under the same conditions of temperature and pressure. Reaction of four volumes of the compound produces four volumes of CO_2, two volumes of N_2, and ten volumes of water vapor. (a) How many volumes of O_2 were required? (b) What is the empirical formula of the compound?

5.107 Containers A, B, and C are attached by closed stopcocks of negligible volume.

If each particle shown in the picture represents 10^6 particles, (a) How many blue particles and black particles are in B after the stopcocks are opened and the system reaches equilibrium? (b) How many blue particles and black particles are in A after the stopcocks are opened and the system reaches equilibrium? (c) If the pressure in C, P_C, is 750 torr before the stopcocks are opened, what is P_C afterward? (d) What is P_B afterward?

5.108 Combustible vapor-air mixtures are flammable over a limited range of concentrations. The minimum volume % of vapor that gives a combustible mixture is called the *lower flammable limit* (LFL). Generally, the LFL is about half the stoichiometric mixture, the concentration required for complete combustion of the vapor in air. (a) If oxygen is 20.9 vol % of air, estimate the LFL for *n*-hexane, C_6H_{14}. (b) What volume (in mL) of *n*-hexane ($d = 0.660$ g/cm^3) is required to produce a flammable mixture of hexane in 1.000 m^3 of air at STP?

5.109 By what factor would a scuba diver's lungs expand if she ascended rapidly to the surface from a depth of 125 ft without inhaling or exhaling? If an expansion factor greater than 1.5 causes lung rupture, how far could she safely ascend from 125 ft without breathing? Assume constant temperature (d of seawater = 1.04 g/mL; d of Hg = 13.5 g/mL).

5.110 When 15.0 g of fluorite (CaF_2) reacts with excess sulfuric acid, hydrogen fluoride gas is collected at 744 torr and 25.5°C. Solid calcium sulfate is the other product. What gas temperature is required to store the gas in an 8.63-L container at 875 torr?

5.111 Dilute aqueous hydrogen peroxide is used as a bleaching agent and for disinfecting surfaces and small cuts. Its concentration is sometimes given as a certain number of "volumes hydrogen peroxide," which refers to the number of volumes of O_2 gas, measured at STP, that a given volume of hydrogen peroxide solution will release when it decomposes to O_2 and liquid H_2O. How many grams of hydrogen peroxide are in 0.100 L of "20 volumes hydrogen peroxide" solution?

5.112 At a height of 300 km above Earth's surface, an astronaut finds that the atmospheric pressure is about 10^{-8} mmHg and the temperature is 500 K. How many molecules of gas are there per milliliter at this altitude?

5.113 (a) What is the rms speed of O_2 at STP? (b) If the mean free path of O_2 molecules at STP is 6.33×10^{-8} m, what is their collision frequency? [Use $R = 8.314$ J/(mol·K) and $\mathcal{M}$ in kg/mol.]

5.114 Acrylic acid (CH_2=CHCOOH) is used to prepare polymers, adhesives, and paints. The first step in making acrylic acid involves the vapor-phase oxidation of propylene (CH_2=CHCH$_3$) to acrolein (CH_2=CHCHO). This step is carried out at 330°C and 2.5 atm in a large bundle of tubes around which circulates a heat-transfer agent. The reactants spend an average of 1.8 s in the tubes, which have a void space of 100 ft^3. How many pounds of propylene must be added per hour in a mixture whose mole fractions are 0.07 propylene, 0.35 steam, and 0.58 air?

5.115 Standard conditions are based on relevant environmental conditions. If normal average surface temperature and pressure on Venus are 730. K and 90 atm, respectively, what is the standard molar volume of an ideal gas on Venus?

5.116 A barometer tube is 1.00×10^2 cm long and has a cross-sectional area of 1.20 cm^2. The height of the mercury column is 74.0 cm, and the temperature is 24°C. A small amount of N_2 is introduced into the evacuated space above the mercury, which causes the mercury level to drop to a height of 64.0 cm. How many grams of N_2 were introduced?

5.117 What is the molarity of the cleaning solution formed when 10.0 L of ammonia gas at 33°C and 735 torr dissolves in enough water to give a final volume of 0.750 L?

5.118 The Hawaiian volcano Kilauea emits an average of 1.5×10^3 m^3 of gas each day, when corrected to 298 K and 1.00 atm. The mixture contains gases that contribute to global warming and acid rain, and some are toxic. An atmospheric chemist analyzes a sample and finds the following mole fractions: 0.4896 CO_2, 0.0146 CO, 0.3710 H_2O, 0.1185 SO_2, 0.0003 S_2, 0.0047 H_2, 0.0008 HCl, and 0.0003 H_2S. How many metric tons (t) of each gas are emitted per year (1 t = 1000 kg)?

5.119 To study a key fuel-cell reaction, a chemical engineer has 20.0-L tanks of H_2 and of O_2 and wants to use up both tanks to form 28.0 mol of water at 23.8°C. (a) Use the ideal gas law to find the pressure needed in each tank. (b) Use the van der Waals equation to find the pressure needed in each tank. (c) Compare the results from the two equations.

5.120 For each of the following, which shows the greater deviation from ideal behavior at the same set of conditions? Explain.
(a) Argon or xenon   (b) Water vapor or neon
(c) Mercury vapor or radon   (d) Water vapor or methane

5.121 How many liters of gaseous hydrogen bromide at 29°C and 0.965 atm will a chemist need if she wishes to prepare 3.50 L of 1.20 *M* hydrobromic acid?

5.122 A mixture consisting of 7.0 g of CO and 10.0 g of SO_2, two atmospheric pollutants, has a pressure of 0.33 atm when placed in a sealed container. What is the partial pressure of CO?

5.123 Sulfur dioxide is used to make sulfuric acid. One method of producing it is by roasting mineral sulfides, for example,

$$FeS_2(s) + O_2(g) \xrightarrow{\Delta} SO_2(g) + Fe_2O_3(s) \quad [\text{unbalanced}]$$

A production error leads to the sulfide being placed in a 950-L vessel with insufficient oxygen. Initially, the partial pressure of O_2 is 0.64 atm, and the total pressure is 1.05 atm, with the balance due to N_2. The reaction is run until 85% of the O_2 is consumed, and the vessel is then cooled to its initial temperature. What is the total pressure and the partial pressure of each gas in the vessel?

5.124 A mixture of CO_2 and Kr weighs 35.0 g and exerts a pressure of 0.708 atm in its container. Since Kr is expensive, you wish to recover it from the mixture. After the CO_2 is completely removed by absorption with NaOH(s), the pressure in the container is 0.250 atm. How many grams of CO_2 were originally present? How many grams of Kr can you recover?

5.125 When a car accelerates quickly, the passengers feel a force that presses them back into their seats, but a balloon filled with helium floats forward. Why?

5.126 Gases such as CO are gradually oxidized in the atmosphere, not by O_2 but by the hydroxyl radical, ·OH, a species with one fewer electron than a hydroxide ion. At night, the ·OH concentration is nearly zero, but it increases to 2.5×10^{12} molecules/m^3 in polluted air during the day. At daytime conditions of 1.00 atm and 22°C, what is the partial pressure and mole percent of ·OH in air?

5.127 Aqueous sulfurous acid (H_2SO_3) was made by dissolving 0.200 L of sulfur dioxide gas at 19°C and 745 mmHg in water to yield 500.0 mL of solution. The acid solution required 10.0 mL of sodium hydroxide solution to reach the titration end point. What was the molarity of the sodium hydroxide solution?

5.128 In the 19th century, J. B. A. Dumas devised a method for finding the molar mass of a volatile liquid from the volume, temperature, pressure, and mass of its vapor. He placed a sample of such a liquid in a flask that was closed with a stopper fitted with a narrow tube, immersed the flask in a hot water bath to vaporize the liquid, and then cooled the flask. Find the molar mass of a volatile liquid from the following:
Mass of empty flask = 65.347 g
Mass of flask filled with water at 25°C = 327.4 g
Density of water at 25°C = 0.997 g/mL
Mass of flask plus condensed unknown liquid = 65.739 g
Barometric pressure = 101.2 kPa
Temperature of water bath = 99.8°C

5.129 During World War II, a portable source of hydrogen gas was needed for weather balloons, and solid metal hydrides were the most convenient form. Many metal hydrides react with water to generate the metal hydroxide and hydrogen. Two candidates were lithium hydride and magnesium hydride. What volume (in L) of gas is formed from 1.00 lb of each hydride reacting with excess water at 750. torr and 27°C?

5.130 The lunar surface reaches 370 K at midday. The atmosphere consists of neon, argon, and helium at a total pressure of only 2×10^{-14} atm. Calculate the rms speed of each component in the lunar atmosphere. [Use $R = 8.314$ J/(mol·K) and $\mathcal{M}$ in kg/mol.]

5.131 A person inhales air richer in O_2 and exhales air richer in CO_2 and water vapor. During each hour of sleep, a person exhales a total of about 300 L of this CO_2-enriched and H_2O-enriched air. (a) If the partial pressures of CO_2 and H_2O in exhaled air are each 30.0 torr at 37.0°C, calculate the mass (g) of CO_2 and of H_2O exhaled in 1 h of sleep. (b) How many grams of body mass does the person lose in an 8-h sleep if all the CO_2 and H_2O exhaled come from the metabolism of glucose?

$$C_6H_{12}O_6(s) + 6O_2(g) \longrightarrow 6CO_2(g) + 6H_2O(g)$$

5.132 Popcorn pops because the horny endosperm, a tough, elastic material, resists gas pressure within the heated kernel until it reaches explosive force. A 0.25-mL kernel has a water content of 1.6% by mass, and the water vapor reaches 170°C and 9.0 atm before the kernel ruptures. Assume that water vapor can occupy 75% of the kernel's volume. (a) What is the mass (in g) of the kernel? (b) How many milliliters would this amount of water vapor occupy at 25°C and 1.00 atm?

5.133 Sulfur dioxide emissions from coal-burning power plants are removed by *flue-gas desulfurization*. The flue gas passes through a scrubber, and a slurry of wet calcium carbonate reacts with it to form carbon dioxide and calcium sulfite. The calcium sulfite then reacts with oxygen to form calcium sulfate, which is sold as gypsum. (a) If the sulfur dioxide concentration is 1000 times higher than its mole fraction in clean dry air (2×10^{-10}), how much calcium sulfate (kg) can be made from scrubbing 4 GL of flue gas (1 GL = 1×10^9 L)? A state-of-the-art scrubber removes at least 95% of the sulfur dioxide. (b) If the mole fraction of oxygen in air is 0.209, what volume (L) of air at 1.00 atm and 25°C is needed to react with all the calcium sulfite?

5.134 Many water treatment plants use chlorine gas to kill microorganisms before the water is released for residential use. A plant engineer has to maintain the chlorine pressure in a tank below the 85.0-atm rating and, to be safe, decides to fill the tank to 80.0% of this maximum pressure. (a) How many moles of Cl_2 gas can be kept in an 850.-L tank at 298 K if she uses the ideal gas law in the calculation? (b) What is the tank pressure if she uses the van der Waals equation for this amount of gas? (c) Did the engineer fill the tank to the desired pressure?

5.135 At 10.0°C and 102.5 kPa, the density of dry air is 1.26 g/L. What is the average "molar mass" of dry air at these conditions?

5.136 In A, the picture shows a cylinder with 0.1 mol of a gas that behaves ideally. Choose the cylinder (B, C, or D) that correctly represents the volume of the gas after each of the following changes. If none of the cylinders is correct, specify "none."
(a) P is doubled at fixed n and T.
(b) T is reduced from 400 K to 200 K at fixed n and P.
(c) T is increased from 100°C to 200°C at fixed n and P.
(d) 0.1 mol of gas is added at fixed P and T.
(e) 0.1 mol of gas is added and P is doubled at fixed T.

5.137 Ammonia is essential to so many industries that, on a molar basis, it is the most heavily produced substance in the world. Calculate P_{IGL} and P_{VDW} (in atm) of 51.1 g of ammonia in a 3.000-L container at 0°C and 400.°C, the industrial temperature. (See Table 5.4 for the values of the van der Waals constants.)

5.138 A 6.0-L flask contains a mixture of methane (CH_4), argon, and helium at 45°C and 1.75 atm. If the mole fractions of helium and argon are 0.25 and 0.35, respectively, how many molecules of methane are present?

5.139 A large portion of metabolic energy arises from the biological combustion of glucose:

$$C_6H_{12}O_6(s) + 6O_2(g) \longrightarrow 6CO_2(g) + 6H_2O(g)$$

(a) If this reaction is carried out in an expandable container at 37°C and 780. torr, what volume of CO_2 is produced from 20.0 g of glucose and excess O_2? (b) If the reaction is carried out at the same conditions with the stoichiometric amount of O_2, what is the partial pressure of each gas when the reaction is 50% complete (10.0 g of glucose remains)?

5.140 What is the average kinetic energy and rms speed of N_2 molecules at STP? Compare these values with those of H_2 molecules at STP. [Use $R = 8.314$ J/(mol·K) and $\mathcal{M}$ in kg/mol.]

5.141 According to government standards, the *8-h threshold limit value* is 5000 ppmv for CO_2 and 0.1 ppmv for Br_2 (1 ppmv is 1 part by volume in 10^6 parts by volume). Exposure to either gas for 8 h above these limits is unsafe. At STP, which of the following would be unsafe for 8 h of exposure?
(a) Air with a partial pressure of 0.2 torr of Br_2
(b) Air with a partial pressure of 0.2 torr of CO_2
(c) 1000 L of air containing 0.0004 g of Br_2 gas
(d) 1000 L of air containing 2.8×10^{22} molecules of CO_2

5.142 One way to prevent emission of the pollutant NO from industrial plants is by a catalyzed reaction with NH_3:

$$4NH_3(g) + 4NO(g) + O_2(g) \xrightarrow{\text{catalyst}} 4N_2(g) + 6H_2O(g)$$

(a) If the NO has a partial pressure of 4.5×10^{-5} atm in the flue gas, how many liters of NH_3 are needed per liter of flue gas at 1.00 atm? (b) If the reaction takes place at 1.00 atm and 365°C, how many grams of NH_3 are needed per kL of flue gas?

5.143 An equimolar mixture of Ne and Xe is accidentally placed in a container that has a tiny leak. After a short while, a very small proportion of the mixture has escaped. What is the mole fraction of Ne in the effusing gas?

5.144 From the relative rates of effusion of $^{235}UF_6$ and $^{238}UF_6$, find the number of steps needed to produce a sample of the enriched fuel used in many nuclear reactors, which is 3.0 mole % ^{235}U. The natural abundance of ^{235}U is 0.72%.

5.145 A slight deviation from ideal behavior exists even at normal conditions. If it behaved ideally, 1 mol of CO would occupy 22.414 L and exert 1 atm pressure at 273.15 K. Calculate P_{VDW} for 1.000 mol of CO at 273.15 K. $\left(\text{Use } R = 0.08206 \dfrac{\text{atm·L}}{\text{mol·K}}.\right)$

5.146 In preparation for a combustion demonstration, a professor fills a balloon with equal molar amounts of H_2 and O_2, but the demonstration has to be postponed until the next day. During the night, both gases leak through pores in the balloon. If 35% of the H_2 leaks, what is the O_2/H_2 ratio in the balloon the next day?

5.147 Phosphorus trichloride is important in the manufacture of insecticides, fuel additives, and flame retardants. Phosphorus has only one naturally occurring isotope, ^{31}P, whereas chlorine has two, ^{35}Cl (75%) and ^{37}Cl (25%). (a) What different molecular masses (in amu) can be found for PCl_3? (b) Which is the most abundant? (c) What is the ratio of the effusion rates of the heaviest and the lightest PCl_3 molecules?

5.148 A truck tire has a volume of 218 L and is filled with air to 35.0 psi at 295 K. After a drive, the air heats up to 318 K. (a) If the tire volume is constant, what is the pressure (in psi)? (b) If the tire volume increases 2.0%, what is the pressure (in psi)? (c) If the tire leaks 1.5 g of air per minute and the temperature is constant, how many minutes will it take for the tire to reach the original pressure of 35.0 psi ($\mathcal{M}$ of air = 28.8 g/mol)?

5.149 Allotropes are different molecular forms of an element, such as dioxygen (O_2) and ozone (O_3). (a) What is the density of each oxygen allotrope at 0°C and 760 torr? (b) Calculate the ratio of densities, d_{O_3}/d_{O_2}, and explain the significance of this number.

5.150 When gaseous F_2 and solid I_2 are heated to high temperatures, the I_2 sublimes and gaseous iodine heptafluoride forms. If 350. torr of F_2 and 2.50 g of solid I_2 are put into a 2.50-L container at 250. K and the container is heated to 550. K, what is the final pressure (in torr)? What is the partial pressure of I_2 gas?

Thermochemistry: Energy Flow and Chemical Change

Concepts and skills to review before you study this chapter

- energy and its interconversion (Section 1.1)
- distinction between heat and temperature (Section 1.5)
- nature of chemical bonding (Section 2.7)
- calculations of reaction stoichiometry (Section 3.4)
- properties of the gaseous state (Section 5.1)
- relation between kinetic energy and temperature (Section 5.5)

All matter contains energy, so *whenever matter undergoes a change, the quantity of energy that the matter contains also changes*. When a burning candle melts a piece of ice, both chemical and physical changes occur. In the chemical change, the higher energy reactants (wax and O_2) form lower energy products (CO_2 and H_2O), and the difference in energy is *released* as heat and light. Then, during the physical change, some of that heat is *absorbed* when lower energy ice becomes higher energy water. In a thunderstorm, the changes in energy are reversed: lower energy N_2 and O_2 *absorb* energy from lightning to form higher energy NO, and higher energy water vapor *releases* energy as it condenses to lower energy liquid water that falls as rain.

This interplay of matter and energy is profoundly important and has an enormous impact on society. On an everyday level, many familiar materials release, absorb, or alter the flow of energy. Fuels such as oil and wood release energy to warm our homes or power our vehicles. Fertilizers help crops convert solar energy into food. Metal wires increase the flow of electrical energy, and polymer fibers in winter clothing limit the flow of thermal energy away from our bodies.

Thermodynamics is the study of energy and its transformations, and two chapters in this text address this central topic. Our focus here is on **thermochemistry,** the branch of thermodynamics that deals with heat in chemical and physical change. In Chapter 20, we consider the fundamental question of *why* reactions occur.

IN THIS CHAPTER . . . We see how heat, or thermal energy, flows when matter changes, how to measure the quantity of heat for a given change, and how to determine the heat flow accompanying any reaction.

- We see that energy always flows between a system and its surroundings in the form of heat or work, so the total energy is conserved.
- We discuss the units of energy and show that the total size of an energy change does not depend on how the change occurs.
- We identify the heat of a reaction in an open container as a change in enthalpy, which can be negative (exothermic reaction) or positive (endothermic reaction).
- We describe how a calorimeter measures heat and how the quantity of heat in a reaction is proportional to the amounts of substances.
- We define standard conditions to compare enthalpies of reactions and see how to obtain the change in enthalpy for any reaction.
- We discuss some current and future energy sources and describe the critical relation between energy demand and climate change.

6.1 • FORMS OF ENERGY AND THEIR INTERCONVERSION

In Chapter 1, we saw that all energy is either potential or kinetic, and that these forms are interconvertible. An object has potential energy by virtue of its position and kinetic energy by virtue of its motion. Let's re-examine these ideas by considering a weight raised above the ground. As your muscles or a motor raise the weight, its potential energy increases; this energy is converted to kinetic energy as the weight falls (see Figure 1.3, p. 9). When it hits the ground, some of that kinetic energy appears as *work* done when the weight moves the soil and pebbles slightly, and some appears as *heat* when it warms them slightly. Thus, in this situation, *potential energy is converted to kinetic energy, which appears as work and heat.*

Several other forms of energy—solar, electrical, nuclear, and chemical—are examples of potential and kinetic energy on the atomic scale. No matter what the form of energy or the situation, *when energy is transferred from one object to another, it appears as work and/or heat.* In this section, we examine this idea in terms of the release or absorption of energy during a chemical or physical change.

Defining the System and Its Surroundings

In any thermodynamic study, including measuring a change in energy, the first step is to define the **system**—the part of the universe we are focusing on. And the moment we define the system, everything else is defined as the **surroundings.**

Figure 6.1 shows a typical chemical system—the contents of a flask; the flask itself, other equipment, and perhaps the rest of the laboratory are the surroundings. In principle, the rest of the universe is the surroundings, but in practice, we consider only the parts that are relevant to the system: it's not likely that a thunderstorm in central Asia or a methane blizzard on Neptune will affect the contents of the flask, but the temperature and pressure of the lab might. Thus, the experimenter defines the system and the relevant surroundings. An astronomer defines a galaxy as the system and nearby galaxies as the surroundings; a microbiologist defines a given cell as the system and neighboring cells and the extracellular fluid as the surroundings; and so forth.

Figure 6.1 A chemical system and its surroundings.

Energy Transfer to and from a System

Each particle in a system has potential energy and kinetic energy, and the sum of all these energies is the **internal energy, E,** of the system (some texts use the symbol U). When the reactants in a chemical system change to products, the system's internal energy has changed. This change, ΔE, is the difference between the internal energy *after* the change (E_{final}) and *before* the change ($E_{initial}$):

$$\Delta E = E_{final} - E_{initial} = E_{products} - E_{reactants} \qquad (6.1)$$

where Δ (Greek *delta*) means "change (or difference) in" and refers to the *final state* **minus** *the initial state.* Thus, ΔE is the final quantity of energy of the system **minus** the initial quantity.

Because the universe consists of only system and surroundings, *a change in the energy of the system must be accompanied by an **equal** and **opposite** change in the energy of the surroundings.* In an *energy diagram,* the final and initial states are horizontal lines along a vertical energy axis, with ΔE the difference in the heights of the lines. A system can change its internal energy in one of two ways:

* By releasing some energy in a transfer *to* the surroundings (Figure 6.2A):

$$E_{final} < E_{initial} \qquad \text{so} \qquad \Delta E < 0$$

* By absorbing some energy in a transfer *from* the surroundings (Figure 6.2B):

$$E_{final} > E_{initial} \qquad \text{so} \qquad \Delta E > 0$$

Thus, ΔE is a *transfer* of energy from system to surroundings, or vice versa.

Heat and Work: Two Forms of Energy Transfer

Energy transferred from system to surroundings or vice versa appears in two forms:

1. *Heat.* **Heat** or *thermal energy* (symbolized by q) is the energy transferred as a result of a difference in temperature between the system and the surroundings. For example, energy in the form of heat is transferred from hot soup (system) to the bowl, air, and table (surroundings) because they are at a lower temperature.

A Energy of system decreases. **B** Energy of system increases.

Figure 6.2 Energy diagrams for the transfer of internal energy (E) between a system and its surroundings. A, When the system releases energy, ΔE ($E_{final} - E_{initial}$) is negative. **B,** When the system absorbs energy, ΔE ($E_{final} - E_{initial}$) is positive. (The vertical yellow arrow always has its tail at the initial state.)

2. *Work.* All other forms of energy transfer involve some type of **work (*w*),** the energy transferred when an object is moved by a force. When you (system) kick a football, energy is transferred as work because the force of the kick moves the ball and air (surroundings). When you pump up a ball, energy is transferred as work because the added air (system) exerts a force on the inner wall of the ball (surroundings) and moves it outward.

The total change in a system's internal energy is the sum of the energy transferred as heat and/or work:

$$\Delta E = q + w \qquad (6.2)$$

The values of q and w (and, therefore, of ΔE) can have either a positive or negative sign. *We define the sign of the energy change from the **system's** perspective:*

- Energy transferred *into* the system is *positive* because the *system ends up with more energy.*
- Energy transferred *out from* the system is *negative,* because the *system ends up with less* energy.

Innumerable combinations of heat and/or work can change a system's internal energy. In the rest of this subsection, we'll examine the four simplest cases—two that involve only heat and two that involve only work.

Energy Transferred as Heat Only For a system that transfers energy only as heat (q) and does no work ($w = 0$), we have, from Equation 6.2, $\Delta E = q + 0 = q$. There are two ways this transfer can happen:

1. *Heat flowing **out** from a system.* Suppose hot water is the system, and the beaker holding it and the rest of the lab are the surroundings. The water transfers energy as heat outward until the temperature of the water and the surroundings are equal. Since heat flows *out* from the system, the final energy of the system is less than the initial energy. Heat was released, so *q is negative,* and therefore ΔE *is negative* (Figure 6.3A).

2. *Heat flowing **into** a system.* If the system consists of ice water, the surroundings transfer energy as heat *into* the system, once again until the ice melts and the temperature of the water and the surroundings become equal. In this case, heat flows *in,* so the final energy of the system is higher than its initial energy. Heat was absorbed, so *q is positive,* and therefore ΔE *is positive* (Figure 6.3B). ●

● **Thermodynamics in the Kitchen** A new view of two familiar kitchen appliances can clarify the sign of q. The air in a refrigerator (surroundings) has a lower temperature than a newly added piece of food (system), so the food releases energy as heat to the refrigerator air, $q < 0$. The air in a hot oven (surroundings) has a higher temperature than a newly added piece of food (system), so the food absorbs energy as heat from the oven air, $q > 0$.

A Energy released as heat. **B** Energy absorbed as heat.

Figure 6.3 The two cases where energy is transferred as heat only. A, The system releases heat. **B,** The system absorbs heat.

A Energy released as work.   **B Energy absorbed as work.**

Figure 6.4 The two cases where energy is transferred as work only. **A,** The system does work *on* the surroundings. **B,** The system has work done on it *by* the surroundings.

Energy Transferred as Work Only For a system that transfers energy only as work, $q = 0$; therefore, $\Delta E = 0 + w = w$. There are two ways this transfer can happen:

1. *Work done **by** a system* (Figure 6.4A). Consider an aqueous reaction of a gray metal (for example, Zn) and a strong acid (for example, HCl) that takes place in a nearly evacuated (narrow P_{sys} arrow), insulated container attached to a piston-cylinder assembly and that has a gas (e.g., H_2) as one of the products. (The container is insulated so that heat does not flow.) We define the system as the reaction mixture, and the container, piston-cylinder, outside air, and so forth as the surroundings. In the initial state, the internal energy is the energy of the reactants, and in the final state, it is the energy of the products. As the gas forms, it pushes back the piston. Thus, energy is transferred as work done *by* the system *on* the surroundings. Since the system releases energy as work, *w is negative;* the final energy of the system is less than the initial energy, so ΔE is negative.*

2. *Work done **on** a system* (Figure 6.4B). Suppose that, after the reaction is over, we increase the pressure of the surroundings (wider P_{surr} arrow) so that the piston moves in. Energy is transferred as work done *by* the surroundings *on* the system, so *w is positive.* The final energy of the system is greater than the initial energy, so ΔE *is positive.*

Table 6.1 summarizes the sign conventions for q and w and their effect on the sign of ΔE.

---

*The system shown in Figure 6.4A is not doing very useful work because it just pushes back the piston and outside air. But, if the reaction mixture is gasoline and oxygen and the surroundings are an automobile engine, much of the internal energy is transferred as the work done to move a car.

Table **6.1** The Sign Conventions* for q, w, and ΔE			
q	$+$ w	$=$	ΔE
$+$	$+$		$+$
$+$	$-$		Depends on the sizes of q and w
$-$	$+$		Depends on the sizes of q and w
$-$	$-$		$-$

*For q: + means system *absorbs* heat; − means system *releases* heat.
*For w: + means work done *on* system; − means work done *by* system.

The Law of Energy Conservation

As you've seen, when a system absorbs energy, the surroundings release it, and when a system releases energy, the surroundings absorb it. Energy transferred between system and surroundings can be in the form of heat and/or various types of work—mechanical, electrical, radiant, chemical, and so forth.

Indeed, energy is often converted from one form to another during transfers. For example, when gasoline burns in a car engine, the reaction releases energy that is transferred as heat and work. The heat warms the car parts, passenger compartment, and surrounding air. The work is done when mechanical energy turns the car's wheels and belts. That energy is converted into the electrical energy of the sound system, the radiant energy of the headlights, the chemical energy of the battery, and so forth. The sum of all these forms equals the change in energy between reactants and products as the gasoline is burned.

Complex biological processes exhibit the same general pattern. During photosynthesis, green plants convert solar energy into the chemical energy of the bonds in starch and O_2; when you digest starch, the bonds in the compound are converted into the muscular (mechanical) energy needed to run a marathon.

The most important point to realize in these, and all other situations, is that the energy changes form but does not simply appear or disappear—energy cannot be created or destroyed. Put another way, *energy is conserved: the total energy of the system plus the surroundings remains constant.* The **law of conservation of energy,** also known as the **first law of thermodynamics,** restates this basic observation: *the total energy of the universe is constant.* It is expressed mathematically as

$$\Delta E_{universe} = \Delta E_{system} + \Delta E_{surroundings} = 0 \tag{6.3}$$

This law applies, as far as we know, to all systems, from a burning match to continental drift, from the pumping of your heart to the formation of the Solar System.

Units of Energy

The SI unit of energy is the **joule (J),** a derived unit composed of three base units:

$$1 \text{ J} = 1 \text{ kg·m}^2/\text{s}^2$$

Both heat and work are expressed in joules. Let's see why the joule is the unit for work. The work (w) done on a mass is the force (F) times the distance (d) that the mass moves: $w = F \times d$. A *force* changes the velocity of a mass over time; that is, a force *accelerates* a mass. Velocity has units of meters per second (m/s), so acceleration (a) has units of meters per second per second (m/s²). Force, therefore, has units of mass (m, in kilograms) times acceleration:

$$F = m \times a \quad \text{has units of} \quad \text{kg·m/s}^2$$

Therefore, $\quad w = F \times d \quad$ has units of $\quad (\text{kg·m/s}^2) \times \text{m} = \text{kg·m}^2/\text{s}^2 = \text{J}$

The **calorie (cal)** is an older unit defined originally as the quantity of energy needed to raise the temperature of 1 g of water by 1°C (from 14.5°C to 15.5°C). The calorie is now defined in terms of the joule:

$$1 \text{ cal} \equiv 4.184 \text{ J} \quad \text{or} \quad 1 \text{ J} = \frac{1}{4.184} \text{ cal} = 0.2390 \text{ cal}$$

Since the quantities of energy involved in chemical reactions are usually quite large, chemists use the kilojoule (kJ), or, in earlier sources, the kilocalorie (kcal):

$$1 \text{ kJ} = 1000 \text{ J} = 0.2390 \text{ kcal} = 239.0 \text{ cal}$$

The nutritional Calorie (note the capital C), the unit that shows the energy available from food, is actually a kilocalorie.

The *British thermal unit (Btu),* a unit that you may have seen used for the energy output of appliances, is the quantity of energy required to raise the temperature of 1 lb of water by 1°F; *1 Btu is equivalent to 1055 J.* In general, the SI unit (J or kJ) is used in this text. Some interesting quantities of energy appear in Figure 6.5.

10^{24} J —
Daily solar energy falling on Earth

10^{21} J —
Energy of a strong earthquake

10^{18} J —
Daily electrical output of Hoover Dam

10^{15} J —
1000 tons of coal burned

10^{12} J —
1 ton of TNT exploded

10^{9} J —
1 kilowatt-hour of electrical energy

10^{6} J —
Combustion of 1 mol of glucose

10^{3} J —

10^{0} J — 1 calorie (4.184 J)

10^{-3} J —

10^{-6} J —

10^{-9} J —
Heat absorbed during division of one bacterial cell

10^{-12} J —
Energy from fission of one ^{235}U atom

10^{-15} J —

10^{-18} J —

10^{-21} J —
Average kinetic energy of a molecule in air at 300 K

Figure 6.5 Some quantities of energy. The vertical scale is exponential.

Sample Problem 6.1 | Determining the Change in Internal Energy of a System

Problem When gasoline burns in a car engine, the heat released causes the products CO_2 and H_2O to expand, which pushes the pistons outward. Excess heat is removed by the car's radiator. If the expanding gases do 451 J of work on the pistons and the system releases 325 J to the surroundings as heat, calculate the change in energy (ΔE) in J, kJ, and kcal.

Plan We must define system and surroundings to choose signs for q and w, and then we calculate ΔE with Equation 6.2. The system is the reactants and products, and the surroundings are the pistons, the radiator, and the rest of the car. Heat is released by the system, so q is negative. Work is done by the system to push the pistons outward, so w is also negative. We obtain the answer in J and then convert it to kJ and kcal.

Solution Calculating ΔE (from Equation 6.2) in J:

$$q = -325 \text{ J}$$
$$w = -451 \text{ J}$$
$$\Delta E = q + w = -325 \text{ J} + (-451 \text{ J}) = \boxed{-776 \text{ J}}$$

Converting from J to kJ:

$$\Delta E = -776 \text{ J} \times \frac{1 \text{ kJ}}{1000 \text{ J}} = \boxed{-0.776 \text{ kJ}}$$

Converting from kJ to kcal:

$$\Delta E = -0.776 \text{ kJ} \times \frac{1 \text{ kcal}}{4.184 \text{ kJ}} = \boxed{-0.185 \text{ kcal}}$$

Check The answer is reasonable: combustion of gasoline releases energy from the system, so $E_{final} < E_{initial}$ and ΔE should be negative. Rounding shows that, since 4 kJ ≈ 1 kcal, nearly 0.8 kJ should be nearly 0.2 kcal.

Follow-Up Problem 6.1 In a reaction, gaseous reactants form a liquid product. The heat absorbed by the surroundings is 26.0 kcal, and the work done on the system is 15.0 Btu. Calculate ΔE (in kJ).

State Functions and the Path Independence of the Energy Change

The internal energy (E) of a system is called a **state function,** a property dependent only on the *current* state of the system (its composition, volume, pressure, and temperature), *not* on the path the system takes to reach that state. The energy change of a system can occur by countless combinations of heat (q) and/or work (w). However, because E is a state function, the overall ΔE is the same no matter what the specific combination may be. That is, ΔE does **not** depend on how the change takes place, but only on the **difference** between the final and initial states.

As an example, let's define a system in its initial state as 1 mol of octane (a component of gasoline) together with enough O_2 to burn it. In its final state, the system is the CO_2 and H_2O that form:

$$C_8H_{18}(l) + \tfrac{25}{2}O_2(g) \longrightarrow 8CO_2(g) + 9H_2O(g)$$

initial state ($E_{initial}$)   final state (E_{final})

Energy is transferred *out* from the system as heat and/or work, so ΔE is negative. Figure 6.6 shows just two of the many ways the change can occur. If we burn the octane in an open container (*left*), ΔE is transferred almost completely as heat (with a small amount of work done to push back the atmosphere). If we burn it in a car engine (*right*), a much larger portion (~30%) of ΔE is transferred as work that moves the car, with the rest released as heat that warms the car, exhaust gases, and surrounding air. If we burn the octane in a lawn mower or a plane, ΔE appears as other combinations of work and heat. Thus, q and w are *not* state functions because their values *do* depend on the path the system takes, but ΔE (the *sum* of q and w) *does* not. ●

● **Your Personal Financial State Function** The *balance* in your checkbook is a state function of your personal financial system. You can open a new checking account with a birthday gift of $50, or you can open one with a deposit of a $100 paycheck and then write two $25 checks. The two paths to the balance are different, but the balance (current state) is the same.

Pressure (P), volume (V), and temperature (T) are some other state functions. Path independence means that *changes in state functions—ΔE, ΔP, ΔV, and ΔT—depend only on the initial and final states.*

■ Summary of Section 6.1

- Internal energy (E) is transferred as heat (q) when system and surroundings are at different temperatures or as work (w) when an object is moved by a force.
- Heat or work absorbed by a system ($q > 0$; $w > 0$) increases its E; heat or work released by the system ($q < 0$; $w < 0$) decreases its E. The change in the internal energy is the sum of the heat and work: $\Delta E = q + w$. Heat and work are measured in joules (J).
- Energy is always conserved: it can change from one form to another and move into or out of the system, but the total quantity of energy in the universe (system *plus* surroundings) is constant.
- The internal energy of a system is a state function and, thus, is independent of how the system attained that energy; therefore, the same overall ΔE can occur through any combination of q and w.

6.2 • ENTHALPY: CHEMICAL CHANGE AT CONSTANT PRESSURE

Most physical and chemical changes occur at nearly constant atmospheric pressure—a reaction in an open flask, the freezing of a lake, a biochemical process in an organism. In this section, we discuss *enthalpy,* a thermodynamic variable that relates directly to energy changes at constant pressure.

The Meaning of Enthalpy

To determine ΔE, we must measure both heat and work. The two most important types of chemical work are electrical work, done by moving charged particles (Chapter 21), and **pressure-volume work (PV work),** the mechanical work done when the volume of the system changes in the presence of an external pressure (P). The quantity of PV work equals P times the change in volume (ΔV, or $V_{final} - V_{initial}$). In an open flask (or in a cylinder with a weightless, frictionless piston) (Figure 6.7), a system of an expanding gas does PV work *on* the surroundings, so it has a negative sign:

$$w = -P\Delta V \qquad (6.4)$$

For reactions *at constant pressure,* a thermodynamic variable called **enthalpy (H)** eliminates the need to measure PV work. The enthalpy of a system is defined as the internal energy *plus* the product of the pressure and volume:

$$H = E + PV$$

The **change in enthalpy (ΔH)** is the change in internal energy *plus* the product of the pressure, which is constant, and the change in volume (ΔV):

$$\Delta H = \Delta E + P\Delta V \qquad (6.5)$$

Figure 6.7 Pressure-volume work. An expanding gas pushing back the atmosphere does PV work ($w = -P\Delta V$).

Combining Equations 6.2 ($\Delta E = q + w$) and 6.4 ($w = -P\Delta V$) gives

$$\Delta E = q + w = q + (-P\Delta V) = q - P\Delta V$$

At constant pressure, we denote q as q_P, giving $\Delta E = q_P - P\Delta V$, which we can use to solve for q_P:

$$q_P = \Delta E + P\Delta V$$

Notice that the right sides of this equation and of Equation 6.5 are the same:

$$q_P = \Delta E + P\Delta V = \Delta H \qquad (6.6)$$

Thus, *the change in enthalpy equals the heat absorbed or released at **constant** pressure.* For most changes occurring at constant pressure, ΔH is more relevant than ΔE and easier to obtain: *to find ΔH, measure q_P.* We discuss the laboratory method in Section 6.3.

Comparing ΔE and ΔH

Knowing the *enthalpy* change of a system tells us a lot about its *energy* change as well. In fact, because many reactions involve little (if any) PV work, most (or all) of the energy change occurs as a transfer of heat. Here are three cases:

1. *Reactions that do not involve gases.* Gases do not appear in precipitation, many acid-base, many redox reactions, and so forth. For example,

$$2KOH(aq) + H_2SO_4(aq) \longrightarrow K_2SO_4(aq) + 2H_2O(l)$$

   Because liquids and solids undergo *very* small volume changes, $\Delta V \approx 0$; thus $P\Delta V \approx 0$ and $\Delta H \approx \Delta E$.

2. *Reactions in which the amount (mol) of gas does **not** change.* When the total amount of gaseous reactants equals the total amount of gaseous products, the volume is constant, $\Delta V = 0$, so $P\Delta V = 0$ and $\Delta H = \Delta E$. For example,

$$N_2(g) + O_2(g) \longrightarrow 2NO(g)$$

3. *Reactions in which the amount (mol) of gas **does** change.* In these cases, $P\Delta V \neq 0$. However, q_P is usually *much* larger than $P\Delta V$, so ΔH is still very close to ΔE. For instance, in the combustion of H_2, 3 mol of gas yields 2 mol of gas:

$$2H_2(g) + O_2(g) \longrightarrow 2H_2O(g)$$

   In this reaction, $\Delta H = -483.6$ kJ and $P\Delta V = -2.5$ kJ, so (from Equation 6.5),

$$\Delta H = \Delta E + P\Delta V \quad \text{and} \quad \Delta E = \Delta H - P\Delta V = -483.6 \text{ kJ} - (-2.5 \text{ kJ}) = -481.1 \text{ kJ}$$

   Since most of ΔE occurs as energy transferred as heat, $\Delta H \approx \Delta E$.

Thus, *for most reactions, ΔH equals, or is very close to, ΔE.*

Exothermic and Endothermic Processes

Because H is a combination of the three state functions E, P, and V, it is also a state function. Therefore, ΔH equals H_{final} *minus* $H_{initial}$. For a reaction, H_{final} is $H_{products}$ and $H_{initial}$ is $H_{reactants}$, so the enthalpy change of a reaction is

$$\Delta H = H_{final} - H_{initial} = H_{products} - H_{reactants}$$

Since $H_{products}$ can be either more or less than $H_{reactants}$, the *sign* of ΔH indicates whether heat is absorbed or released during the reaction. We determine the sign of ΔH *by imagining the heat as "reactant" or "product."* The two possibilities are

1. *Exothermic process.* An **exothermic** ("heat out") **process** *releases* heat and results in a *decrease* in the enthalpy of the system:

$$\text{Exothermic:} \quad H_{products} < H_{reactants} \quad \text{so} \quad \Delta H < 0$$

For example, when methane burns in air, heat flows *out of* the system into the surroundings, so we show it as a product:

$$CH_4(g) + 2O_2(g) \longrightarrow CO_2(g) + 2H_2O(g) + heat$$

A Exothermic process   **B** Endothermic process

Figure 6.8 Enthalpy diagrams for exothermic and endothermic processes. **A,** The combustion of methane is exothermic: $\Delta H < 0$. **B,** The melting of ice is endothermic: $\Delta H > 0$.

The reactants (1 mol of CH_4 and 2 mol of O_2) release heat during the reaction, so they originally had more enthalpy than the products (1 mol of CO_2 and 2 mol of H_2O):

$$H_{reactants} > H_{products} \quad \text{so} \quad \Delta H \, (H_{products} - H_{reactants}) < 0$$

This exothermic change is shown in the **enthalpy diagram** in Figure 6.8A.

2. *Endothermic process.* An **endothermic** ("heat in") **process** *absorbs* heat and results in an *increase* in the enthalpy of the system:

$$\text{Endothermic:} \quad H_{products} > H_{reactants} \quad \text{so} \quad \Delta H > 0$$

When ice melts, for instance, heat flows *into* the ice from the surroundings, so we show the heat as a reactant:

$$heat + H_2O(s) \longrightarrow H_2O(l)$$

Because heat is absorbed, the enthalpy of the product (water) must be higher than that of the reactant (ice):

$$H_{water} > H_{ice} \quad \text{so} \quad \Delta H \, (H_{water} - H_{ice}) > 0$$

This endothermic change is shown in Figure 6.8B. (In general, the value of an enthalpy change is determined with reactants and products at the same temperature.)

Sample Problem 6.2 **Drawing Enthalpy Diagrams and Determining the Sign of ΔH**

Problem In each of the following cases, determine the sign of ΔH, state whether the reaction is exothermic or endothermic, and draw an enthalpy diagram:
(a) $H_2(g) + \frac{1}{2}O_2(g) \longrightarrow H_2O(l) + 285.8 \text{ kJ}$
(b) $40.7 \text{ kJ} + H_2O(l) \longrightarrow H_2O(g)$

Plan From each equation, we note whether heat is a "product" (exothermic; $\Delta H < 0$) or a "reactant" (endothermic; $\Delta H > 0$). For exothermic reactions, reactants are above products on the enthalpy diagram; for endothermic reactions, reactants are below products. The ΔH arrow *always* points from reactants to products.

Solution (a) Heat is a product (on the right), so $\boxed{\Delta H < 0}$ and the reaction is exothermic. The enthalpy diagram appears in the margin (*top*).
(b) Heat is a reactant (on the left), so $\boxed{\Delta H > 0}$ and the reaction is endothermic. The enthalpy diagram appears in the margin (*bottom*).

Check Substances that are on the same side of the equation as the heat have less enthalpy than substances on the other side, so make sure those substances are placed on the lower line of the diagram.

Follow-Up Problem 6.2 When nitroglycerine decomposes, the reaction creates a violent explosion and releases $5.72 \times 10^3 \text{ kJ}$ of heat per mole:

$$C_3H_5(NO_3)_3(l) \longrightarrow 3CO_2(g) + \tfrac{5}{2}H_2O(g) + \tfrac{1}{4}O_2(g) + \tfrac{3}{2}N_2(g)$$

Is the decomposition of nitroglycerine exothermic or endothermic? Draw an enthalpy diagram for the process.

■ Summary of Section 6.2

- Enthalpy (H) is a state function, so any change in enthalpy (ΔH) is independent of how the change occurred. At constant P, the value of ΔH equals $\Delta E + PV$ work, which occurs when the volume of the system changes in the presence of an external pressure.
- ΔH equals q_P, the heat released or absorbed during a chemical or physical change that takes place at constant pressure.
- In most cases, ΔH is equal, or very close, to ΔE.
- A change that releases heat is exothermic ($\Delta H < 0$); a change that absorbs heat is endothermic ($\Delta H > 0$).

6.3 • CALORIMETRY: MEASURING THE HEAT OF A CHEMICAL OR PHYSICAL CHANGE

Data about energy content and usage are everywhere, from the caloric value of a slice of bread to the gas mileage of a new car. In this section, we consider the basic ideas behind how these values are determined.

Specific Heat Capacity

To find the energy change during a process, we measure the quantity of heat released or absorbed by relating it to the change in temperature. You know from everyday experience that the more you heat an object, the higher its temperature, and the more you cool it, the lower its temperature; in other words, the quantity of heat (q) absorbed or released by an object is proportional to its temperature change:

$$q \propto \Delta T \quad \text{or} \quad q = \text{constant} \times \Delta T \quad \text{or} \quad \frac{q}{\Delta T} = \text{constant}$$

What you might not know is that the temperature change depends on the object. Every object has its own **heat capacity,** the quantity of heat required to change its temperature by 1 K. Heat capacity is the proportionality constant in the preceding equation:

$$\text{Heat capacity} = \frac{q}{\Delta T} \quad [\text{in units of J/K}]$$

A related property is **specific heat capacity (c),** the quantity of heat required to change the temperature of 1 *gram* of an object by 1 K:

$$\text{Specific heat capacity } (c) = \frac{q}{\text{mass} \times \Delta T} \quad [\text{in units of J/g·K}]$$

If we know c of the object being heated (or cooled), we can measure the mass and the temperature change and calculate the heat absorbed (or released):

$$q = c \times \text{mass} \times \Delta T \tag{6.7}$$

Equation 6.7 says that when an object gets hotter, that is, when ΔT ($T_{final} - T_{initial}$) is positive, $q > 0$ (the sample absorbs heat). And when an object gets cooler, that is, when ΔT is negative, $q < 0$ (the sample releases heat). Table 6.2 lists the specific heat capacities of some representative substances and materials. Notice that metals have relatively low values of c and water has a very high value: for instance, it takes over 30 times as much energy to increase the temperature of a gram of water by 1 K as it does a gram of gold!

Closely related to the specific heat capacity (but reserved for substances) is the **molar heat capacity (C;** note the capital letter), the quantity of heat required to change the temperature of 1 *mole* of a substance by 1 K:

$$\text{Molar heat capacity } (C) = \frac{q}{\text{amount (mol)} \times \Delta T} \quad [\text{in units of J/mol·K}]$$

Table 6.2 Specific Heat Capacities (c) of Some Elements, Compounds, and Materials

Substance	c (J/g·K)*
Elements	
Aluminum, Al	0.900
Graphite, C	0.711
Iron, Fe	0.450
Copper, Cu	0.387
Gold, Au	0.129
Compounds	
Water, $H_2O(l)$	4.184
Ethyl alcohol, $C_2H_5OH(l)$	2.46
Ethylene glycol, $(CH_2OH)_2(l)$	2.42
Carbon tetrachloride, $CCl_4(l)$	0.862
Solid Materials	
Wood	1.76
Cement	0.88
Glass	0.84
Granite	0.79
Steel	0.45

*At 298 K (25°C)

To find C of liquid H_2O, we multiply c of liquid H_2O (4.184 J/g·K) by the molar mass of H_2O (18.02 g/mol):

$$C \text{ of } H_2O(l) = 4.184 \, \frac{J}{g \cdot K} \times \frac{18.02 \text{ g}}{1 \text{ mol}} = 75.40 \, \frac{J}{mol \cdot K}$$

Liquid water has a *very* high specific heat capacity (~4.2 J/g·K), about six times that of rock (~0.7 J/g·K). If Earth had no oceans (*see margin*), it would take one-sixth as much energy for the Sun to heat the rocky surface, and the surface would give off six times as much heat after sundown. Days would be scorching and nights frigid.

What if Earth had no oceans?

Sample Problem 6.3 | Finding the Quantity of Heat from a Temperature Change

Problem A layer of copper welded to the bottom of a skillet weighs 125 g. How much heat is needed to raise the temperature of the copper layer from 25°C to 300.°C? The specific heat capacity (c) of Cu is given in Table 6.2.

Plan We know the mass (125 g) and c (0.387 J/g·K) of Cu and can find ΔT in °C, which equals ΔT in K. We then use Equation 6.7 to calculate the heat.

Solution Calculating ΔT and then q:

$$\Delta T = T_{final} - T_{initial} = 300.°C - 25°C = 275°C = 275 \text{ K}$$

$$q = c \times \text{mass (g)} \times \Delta T = 0.387 \text{ J/g·K} \times 125 \text{ g} \times 275 \text{ K} = \boxed{1.33 \times 10^4 \text{ J}}$$

Check Heat is absorbed by the copper bottom (system), so q is positive. Rounding shows the arithmetic is reasonable: $q \approx 0.4 \text{ J/g·K} \times 100 \text{ g} \times 300 \text{ K} = 1.2 \times 10^4 \text{ J}$.

Follow-Up Problem 6.3 Find the heat released (in kJ) when 5.50 L of ethylene glycol (d = 1.11 g/mL; see Table 6.2) in a car radiator cools from 37.0°C to 25.0°C.

The Two Major Types of Calorimetry

How do we know the heat of an acid-base reaction or the Calories in a teaspoon of sugar? We construct "surroundings" that retain the heat as reactants change to products, and then note the temperature change. In the laboratory, these "surroundings" take the form of a **calorimeter,** a device used to measure the heat released (or absorbed) by a physical or chemical process. Let's look at two types of calorimeter—one designed to measure the heat at constant pressure and the other at constant volume.

Constant-Pressure Calorimetry For processes that take place at constant pressure, the heat transferred (q_P) is often measured in a *coffee-cup calorimeter* (Figure 6.9). This simple apparatus is often used to find the heat of an aqueous reaction or the heat accompanying the dissolving of a salt.

A coffee-cup calorimeter can also be used to find the specific heat capacity of a solid, as long as it does not react with or dissolve in water. The solid (the system) is weighed, heated to some known temperature, and added to a known mass and temperature of water (surroundings) in the calorimeter. After stirring, the final water temperature is measured, which is also the final temperature of the solid. Assuming no heat escapes the calorimeter, the heat released by the system ($-q_{sys}$, or $-q_{solid}$) is equal in magnitude but opposite in sign to the heat absorbed by the surroundings ($+q_{surr}$, or $+q_{H_2O}$):

$$-q_{solid} = q_{H_2O}$$

Substituting from Equation 6.7 on each side of this equation gives

$$-(c_{solid} \times \text{mass}_{solid} \times \Delta T_{solid}) = c_{H_2O} \times \text{mass}_{H_2O} \times \Delta T_{H_2O}$$

All the quantities are known or measured except c_{solid}:

$$c_{solid} = -\frac{c_{H_2O} \times \text{mass}_{H_2O} \times \Delta T_{H_2O}}{\text{mass}_{solid} \times \Delta T_{solid}}$$

Stirrer — Thermometer

— Cork stopper

— Nested Styrofoam cups (insulation)

— Water (surroundings)

— Sample (system)

Figure 6.9 Coffee-cup calorimeter. This device measures the heat transferred at constant pressure (q_P).

Sample Problem 6.4 Determining the Specific Heat Capacity of a Solid

Problem You heat 22.05 g of a solid in a test tube to 100.00°C and add it to 50.00 g of water in a coffee-cup calorimeter. The water temperature changes from 25.10°C to 28.49°C. Find the specific heat capacity of the solid.

Plan We are given the masses of the solid (22.05 g) and of H_2O (50.00 g), and we can find the temperature changes of the water and of the solid by subtracting the given values, always using $T_{final} - T_{initial}$. Using Equation 6.7, we set the heat released by the solid $(-q_{solid})$ equal to the heat absorbed by the water (q_{water}). The specific heat of water is known, and we solve for c_{solid}.

Solution Finding ΔT_{solid} and ΔT_{water}:

$$\Delta T_{water} = T_{final} - T_{initial} = (28.49°C - 25.10°C) = 3.39°C = 3.39 \text{ K}$$

$$\Delta T_{solid} = T_{final} - T_{initial} = (28.49°C - 100.00°C) = -71.51°C = -71.51 \text{ K}$$

Solving for c_{solid}:

$$c_{solid} = -\frac{c_{H_2O} \times \text{mass}_{H_2O} \times \Delta T_{H_2O}}{\text{mass}_{solid} \times \Delta T_{solid}} = -\frac{4.184 \text{ J/g·K} \times 50.00 \text{ g} \times 3.39 \text{ K}}{22.05 \text{ g} \times (-71.51 \text{ K})} = \boxed{0.450 \text{ J/g·K}}$$

Check Rounding gives -4 J/g·K $\times$ 50 g $\times$ 3 K/[20 g $\times (-70°C)$] = 0.4 J/g·K, so the answer seems correct.

Follow-Up Problem 6.4

A 12.18-g sample of a shiny, orange-brown metal is heated to 65.00°C in a controlled water bath. The metal is then added to 25.00 g of water in a coffee-cup calorimeter, and the water temperature changes from 25.55°C to 27.25°C. What is the unknown metal (see Table 6.2)?

In the next sample problem, the calorimeter is used to study the change in heat during an aqueous acid-base reaction. Recall that, if a reaction takes place at constant pressure, the heat of the reaction (q_{rxn}) is equal to its enthalpy change (ΔH).

Sample Problem 6.5 Determining the Enthalpy Change of an Aqueous Reaction

Problem You place 50.0 mL of 0.500 M NaOH in a coffee-cup calorimeter at 25.00°C and add 25.0 mL of 0.500 M HCl, also at 25.00°C. After stirring, the final temperature is 27.21°C. [Assume that the total volume is the sum of the individual volumes and that the final solution has the same density (1.00 g/mL) and specific heat capacity (Table 6.2) as water.] **(a)** Calculate q_{soln} (in J). **(b)** Calculate the change in enthalpy, ΔH, of the reaction (in kJ/mol of H_2O formed).

(a) Calculate q_{soln}

Plan The solution is the surroundings, and as the reaction takes place, heat flows into the solution. To find q_{soln}, we use Equation 6.7, so we need the mass of solution, the change in temperature, and the specific heat capacity. We know the solutions' volumes (25.0 mL and 50.0 mL), so we find their masses with the given density (1.00 g/mL). Then, to find q_{soln}, we multiply the total mass by the given c (4.184 J/g·K) and the change in T, which we find from $T_{final} - T_{initial}$.

Solution Finding mass_{soln} and ΔT_{soln}:

$$\text{Total mass (g) of solution} = (25.0 \text{ mL} + 50.0 \text{ mL}) \times 1.00 \text{ g/mL} = 75.0 \text{ g}$$

$$\Delta T = 27.21°C - 25.00°C = 2.21°C = 2.21 \text{ K}$$

Finding q_{soln}:

$$q_{soln} = c_{soln} \times \text{mass}_{soln} \times \Delta T_{soln} = (4.184 \text{ J/g·K})(75.0 \text{ g})(2.21 \text{ K}) = \boxed{693 \text{ J}}$$

Check Rounding to check q_{soln} gives 4 J/g·K $\times$ 75 g $\times$ 2 K = 600 J, which is close to the answer.

(b) Calculate the change in enthalpy (ΔH)

Plan To find ΔH, we write the balanced equation for the acid-base reaction and use the volumes and the concentrations (0.500 M) to find amount (mol) of each reactant (H^+ and OH^-). Since the amounts of two reactants are given, we determine which is limiting, that is, which gives less product (H_2O). The heat of the surroundings is q_{soln}, and it is the negative of the heat of the reaction (q_{rxn}), which equals ΔH. And dividing q_{rxn} by the amount (mol) of water formed gives ΔH in kJ/mol of water formed.

Solution Writing the balanced equation:

$$HCl(aq) + NaOH(aq) \longrightarrow H_2O(l) + NaCl(aq)$$

Finding amount (mol) of reactants:

Amount (mol) of HCl = 0.500 mol HCl/L × 0.0250 L = 0.0125 mol HCl

Amount (mol) of NaOH = 0.500 mol NaOH/L × 0.0500 L = 0.0250 mol NaOH

Finding the amount (mol) of product: All the coefficients in the equation are 1, which means that the amount (mol) of reactant yields that amount of product. Therefore, HCl is limiting because it yields less product: 0.0125 mol of H_2O.

Finding ΔH: Heat absorbed by the solution was released by the reaction; that is,

$$q_{soln} = -q_{rxn} = 693 \text{ J} \quad \text{so} \quad q_{rxn} = -693 \text{ J}$$

$$\Delta H \text{ (kJ/mol)} = \frac{q_{rxn}}{\text{mol } H_2O} \times \frac{1 \text{ kJ}}{1000 \text{ J}} = \frac{-693 \text{ J}}{0.0125 \text{ mol } H_2O} \times \frac{1 \text{ kJ}}{1000 \text{ J}} = \boxed{-55.4 \text{ kJ/mol } H_2O}$$

Check We check for the limiting reactant: The volume of H^+ is half the volume of OH^-, but they have the same concentration and a 1:1 stoichiometric ratio. Therefore, the amount (mol) of H^+ determines the amount of product. Rounding and taking the negative of q_{soln} to find ΔH gives −600 J/0.012 mol = −5×10⁴ J/mol, or −50 kJ/mol, so the answer seems correct.

Follow-Up Problem 6.5 After 50.0 mL of 0.500M $Ba(OH)_2$ and the same volume and concentration of HCl react in a coffee-cup calorimeter, you find q_{soln} to be 1.386 kJ. Calculate ΔH of the reaction in kJ/mol of H_2O formed.

Constant-Volume Calorimetry Constant-volume calorimetry is often carried out in a *bomb calorimeter*, a device commonly used to measure the heat of combustion reactions, such as for fuels and foods. In the coffee-cup calorimeter, we assume all the heat is absorbed by the water, but in reality, some must be absorbed by the stirrer, thermometer, and so forth. With the much more precise bomb calorimeter, the *heat capacity of the entire calorimeter* is known (or can be determined).

Figure 6.10 depicts the preweighed combustible sample in a metal-walled chamber (the bomb), which is filled with oxygen gas and immersed in an insulated water bath fitted with motorized stirrer and thermometer. A heating coil connected to an electrical source ignites the sample, and the heat released raises the temperature of the bomb, water, and other calorimeter parts. Because we know the mass of the sample and the heat capacity of the entire calorimeter, we can use the measured ΔT to calculate the heat released.

Figure 6.10 A bomb calorimeter. This device measures the heat released at constant volume (q_V). It is often used to study combustion reactions.

Note that the steel bomb is tightly sealed, not open to the atmosphere as is the coffee cup, so the pressure is *not* constant. And the volume of the bomb is fixed, so $\Delta V = 0$, and thus $P\Delta V = 0$. Thus, the energy change measured is the *heat released at constant volume* (q_V), which equals ΔE, not ΔH:

$$\Delta E = q + w = q_V + 0 = q_V$$

Recall from Section 6.2, however, that even though the number of moles of gas may change, $P\Delta V$ is usually *much* less than ΔE, so ΔH is very close to ΔE. For example, ΔH is only 0.5% larger than ΔE for the combustion of H_2 and only 0.2% smaller than ΔE for the combustion of octane.

Sample Problem 6.6 Calculating the Heat of a Combustion Reaction

Problem A manufacturer claims that its new dietetic dessert has "fewer than 10 Calories per serving." To test the claim, a chemist at the Department of Consumer Affairs places one serving in a bomb calorimeter and burns it in O_2. The initial temperature is 21.862°C and the temperature rises to 26.799°C. If the heat capacity of the calorimeter is 8.151 kJ/K, is the manufacturer's claim correct?

Plan When the dessert (system) burns, the heat released is absorbed by the calorimeter:

$$-q_{system} = q_{calorimeter}$$

The claim is correct if the heat of the system is less than 10 Calories. To find the heat, we multiply the given heat capacity of the calorimeter (8.151 kJ/K) by ΔT and then convert to Calories.

Solution Finding ΔT:

$$\Delta T = T_{final} - T_{initial} = 26.799°C - 21.862°C = 4.937°C = 4.937\ K$$

Calculating the heat absorbed by the calorimeter:

$$q_{calorimeter} = \text{heat capacity} \times \Delta T = 8.151\ \text{kJ/K} \times 4.937\ \text{K} = 40.24\ \text{kJ}$$

Recall that 1 Calorie = 1 kcal = 4.184 kJ. Therefore, 10 Calories = 41.84 kJ, so the claim is correct.

Check A quick math check shows that the answer is reasonable: 8 kJ/K × 5 K = 40 kJ.

Follow-Up Problem 6.6 A chemist burns 0.8650 g of graphite (a form of carbon) in a new bomb calorimeter, and CO_2 forms. If 393.5 kJ of heat is released per mole of graphite and ΔT is 2.613 K, what is the heat capacity of the bomb calorimeter?

▌ Summary of Section 6.3

- We calculate ΔH of a process by measuring the energy transferred as heat at constant pressure (q_P). To do this, we determine ΔT and multiply it by the mass of the substance and by its specific heat capacity (c), which is the quantity of energy needed to raise the temperature of 1 g of the substance by 1 K.
- Calorimeters measure the heat released (or absorbed) during a process either at constant pressure (coffee cup; $q_P = \Delta H$) or at constant volume (bomb; $q_V = \Delta E$).

6.4 • STOICHIOMETRY OF THERMOCHEMICAL EQUATIONS

A **thermochemical equation** is a balanced equation that includes the enthalpy change of the reaction (ΔH). Keep in mind that a given ΔH refers only to the *amounts (mol) of substances **and** their states of matter in that equation*. The enthalpy change of any process has two aspects:

- *Sign.* The sign of ΔH depends on whether the reaction is exothermic ($-$) or endothermic ($+$). A forward reaction has the *opposite* sign of the reverse reaction.
  Decomposition of 2 mol of water to its elements (endothermic):

$$2H_2O(l) \longrightarrow 2H_2(g) + O_2(g) \qquad \Delta H = 572\ \text{kJ}$$

Formation of 2 mol of water from its elements (exothermic):

$$2H_2(g) + O_2(g) \longrightarrow 2H_2O(l) \quad \Delta H = -572 \text{ kJ}$$

- *Magnitude.* The magnitude of ΔH is *proportional to the amount of substance.* Formation of 1 mol of water from its elements (half the preceding amount):

$$H_2(g) + \tfrac{1}{2}O_2(g) \longrightarrow H_2O(l) \quad \Delta H = -286 \text{ kJ}$$

Two key points to understand about thermochemical equations are as follows:

1. *Balancing coefficients.* When necessary, we use fractional coefficients to balance an equation, because we are specifying the magnitude of ΔH for a *particular amount,* often 1 mol, *of substance:*

$$\tfrac{1}{8}S_8(s) + O_2(g) \longrightarrow SO_2(g) \quad \Delta H = -296.8 \text{ kJ}$$

2. *Thermochemical equivalence.* For a *particular reaction,* a certain amount of substance is thermochemically equivalent to a certain quantity of energy. Some examples from the previous two reactions are

296.8 kJ is thermochemically equivalent to $\tfrac{1}{8}$ mol of $S_8(s)$
286 kJ is thermochemically equivalent to $\tfrac{1}{2}$ mol of $O_2(g)$
286 kJ is thermochemically equivalent to 1 mol of $H_2O(l)$

Just as we use stoichiometrically equivalent molar ratios to find amounts of substances, we use thermochemically equivalent quantities to find the ΔH of a reaction for a given amount of substance. Also, just as we use molar mass (in g/mol) to convert an amount (mol) of a substance to mass (g), we use the ΔH (in kJ/mol) to convert an amount of a substance to an equivalent quantity of heat (in kJ). Figure 6.11 shows this new relationship, and Sample Problem 6.7 applies it.

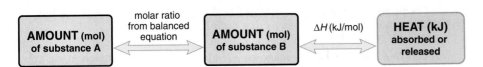

Figure 6.11 The relationship between amount (mol) of substance and the energy (kJ) transferred as heat during a reaction.

Sample Problem 6.7 | **Using the Enthalpy Change of a Reaction (ΔH) to Find Amounts of Substance**

Problem The major source of aluminum in the world is bauxite (mostly aluminum oxide). Its thermal decomposition can be written as

$$Al_2O_3(s) \xrightarrow{\Delta} 2Al(s) + \tfrac{3}{2}O_2(g) \quad \Delta H = 1676 \text{ kJ}$$

If aluminum is produced this way (see Comment), how many grams of aluminum can form when 1.000×10^3 kJ of heat is transferred?

Plan From the balanced equation and the enthalpy change, we see that 2 mol of Al forms when 1676 kJ of heat is absorbed. With this equivalent quantity, we convert the given number of kJ to amount (mol) formed and then convert amount to mass (g).

Solution Combining steps to convert from heat transferred to mass of Al:

$$\text{Mass (g) of Al} = (1.000 \times 10^3 \text{ kJ}) \times \frac{2 \text{ mol Al}}{1676 \text{ kJ}} \times \frac{26.98 \text{ g Al}}{1 \text{ mol Al}} = \boxed{32.20 \text{ g Al}}$$

Check The mass of aluminum seems correct: ~1700 kJ forms about 2 mol of Al (54 g), so 1000 kJ should form a bit more than half that amount (27 g).

Comment In practice, aluminum is not obtained by heating bauxite but by supplying electrical energy (as you'll see in Chapter 22). Because H is a state function, however, the total energy required for the change, ΔH, is the same no matter how it occurs.

Road Map

Follow-Up Problem 6.7 Hydrogenation reactions, in which H_2 and an "unsaturated" organic compound combine, are used in the food, fuel, and polymer industries. In the simplest case, ethene (C_2H_4) and H_2 form ethane (C_2H_6). If 137 kJ is given off per mole of C_2H_4 reacting, how much heat is released when 15.0 kg of C_2H_6 forms?

◼ Summary of Section 6.4

- A thermochemical equation shows a balanced reaction *and* its ΔH value. The sign of ΔH for a forward reaction is opposite that for the reverse reaction. The magnitude of ΔH is specific for the given equation.
- The amount of a substance and the quantity of heat specified by the balanced equation are thermochemically equivalent and act as conversion factors to find the quantity of heat transferred when any amount of the substance reacts.

6.5 • HESS'S LAW: FINDING ΔH OF ANY REACTION

In some cases, a reaction is difficult, even impossible, to carry out individually: it may be part of a complex biochemical process, or take place under extreme conditions, or require a change in conditions to occur. Even if we can't run a reaction in the lab, we can still find its enthalpy change. In fact, the state-function property of enthalpy (H) allows us to find ΔH of *any* reaction for which we can write an equation.

This application is based on **Hess's law:** *the enthalpy change of an overall process is the sum of the enthalpy changes of its individual steps:*

$$\Delta H_{\text{overall}} = \Delta H_1 + \Delta H_2 + \cdots + \Delta H_n \qquad (6.8)$$

This law follows from the fact that ΔH for a process depends only on the difference between the final and initial states. We apply Hess's law by

- Imagining that an overall reaction occurs through a series of individual reaction steps, whether or not it actually does. Adding the steps must give the overall reaction.
- Choosing individual reaction steps that each has a known ΔH.
- Adding the known ΔH values for the steps to get the unknown ΔH of the overall reaction. We can also find an unknown ΔH of any step by subtraction, if we know the ΔH values for the overall reaction and all the other steps.

Let's apply Hess's law to the oxidation of sulfur to sulfur trioxide, the key change in the industrial production of sulfuric acid and in the formation of acid rain. (To introduce this approach, we'll use S as the formula for sulfur, rather than the more correct S_8.) When we burn S in an excess of O_2, sulfur dioxide (SO_2) forms, *not* sulfur trioxide (SO_3) (Equation 1). After a change in conditions, we add more O_2 and oxidize SO_2 to SO_3 (Equation 2). Thus, we cannot put S and O_2 in a calorimeter and find ΔH for the overall reaction of S to SO_3 (Equation 3). But, we *can* find it with Hess's law. The three equations are

$$\text{Equation 1:} \quad S(s) + O_2(g) \longrightarrow SO_2(g) \qquad \Delta H_1 = -296.8 \text{ kJ}$$
$$\text{Equation 2:} \quad 2SO_2(g) + O_2(g) \longrightarrow 2SO_3(g) \qquad \Delta H_2 = -198.4 \text{ kJ}$$
$$\text{Equation 3:} \quad S(s) + \tfrac{3}{2}O_2(g) \longrightarrow SO_3(g) \qquad \Delta H_3 = ?$$

If we can manipulate Equation 1 and/or Equation 2, *along with their ΔH value(s),* so the equations add up to Equation 3, their ΔH values will add up to the unknown ΔH_3.

First, we identify our "target" equation, the one whose ΔH we want to find, and note the amount (mol) of each reactant and product; our "target" is Equation 3. Then, we manipulate Equations 1 and/or 2 to make them add up to Equation 3:

- Equations 3 and 1 have the same amount of S, so we don't change Equation 1.
- Equation 3 has half as much SO_3 as Equation 2, so we multiply Equation 2, *and* ΔH_2, by $\tfrac{1}{2}$; that is, we always treat the equation and its ΔH value the same.
- With the targeted amounts of reactants and products present, we add Equation 1 to the halved Equation 2 and cancel terms that appear on both sides:

$$\text{Equation 1:} \qquad\qquad\qquad S(s) + O_2(g) \longrightarrow SO_2(g) \qquad \Delta H_1 = -296.8 \text{ kJ}$$
$$\tfrac{1}{2}(\text{Equation 2}): \qquad\qquad SO_2(g) + \tfrac{1}{2}O_2(g) \longrightarrow SO_3(g) \quad \tfrac{1}{2}(\Delta H_2) = -99.2 \text{ kJ}$$

$$\text{Equation 3:} \; S(s) + O_2(g) + \cancel{SO_2(g)} + \tfrac{1}{2}O_2(g) \longrightarrow \cancel{SO_2(g)} + SO_3(g)$$

or,
$$S(s) + \tfrac{3}{2}O_2(g) \longrightarrow SO_3(g) \qquad \Delta H_3 = -396.0 \text{ kJ}$$

Because ΔH depends only on the difference between H_{final} and $H_{initial}$, Hess's law tells us that the difference between the enthalpies of the reactants (1 mol of S and $\frac{3}{2}$ mol of O_2) and the product (1 mol of SO_3) is the same, whether S is oxidized directly to SO_3 (impossible) or through the intermediate formation of SO_2 (actual).

To summarize, calculating an unknown ΔH involves three steps:

1. Identify the target equation, the step whose ΔH is unknown, and note the amount (mol) of each reactant and product.
2. Manipulate each equation with known ΔH values so that the target amount (mol) of each substance is on the correct side of the equation. Remember to:
   - Change the sign of ΔH when you reverse an equation.
   - Multiply amount (mol) and ΔH by the same factor.
3. Add the manipulated equations and their resulting ΔH values to get the target equation and its ΔH. All substances except those in the target equation must cancel.

Sample Problem 6.8 | Using Hess's Law to Calculate an Unknown ΔH

Problem Two pollutants that form in auto exhaust are CO and NO. An environmental chemist must convert these pollutants to less harmful gases through the following:

$$CO(g) + NO(g) \longrightarrow CO_2(g) + \tfrac{1}{2}N_2(g) \quad \Delta H = ?$$

Given the following information, calculate the unknown ΔH:

Equation A: $CO(g) + \tfrac{1}{2}O_2(g) \longrightarrow CO_2(g) \quad \Delta H = -283.0 \text{ kJ}$

Equation B: $N_2(g) + O_2(g) \longrightarrow 2NO(g) \quad \Delta H = 180.6 \text{ kJ}$

Plan We note the amount (mol) of each substance and on which side each appears in the target equation. We manipulate Equations A and/or B *and* their ΔH values as needed and add them together to obtain the target equation and the unknown ΔH.

Solution Noting substances in the target equation: For reactants, there are 1 mol of CO and of NO; for products, there are 1 mol of CO_2 and $\frac{1}{2}$ mol of N_2. Manipulating the given equations:

- Equation A has the same amounts of CO and CO_2 on the same sides of the arrow as in the target, so we leave it as written.
- Equation B has twice as much N_2 and NO as the target, and they are on the opposite sides in the target. Thus, we reverse Equation B, change the sign of its ΔH, and multiply both by $\frac{1}{2}$:

$$\tfrac{1}{2}[2NO(g) \longrightarrow N_2(g) + O_2(g)] \quad \Delta H = -\tfrac{1}{2}(\Delta H) = -\tfrac{1}{2}(180.6 \text{ kJ})$$

or $NO(g) \longrightarrow \tfrac{1}{2}N_2(g) + \tfrac{1}{2}O_2(g) \quad \Delta H = -90.3 \text{ kJ}$

Adding the manipulated equations to obtain the target equation:

Equation A: $CO(g) + \tfrac{1}{2}\cancel{O_2(g)} \longrightarrow CO_2(g) \quad\quad \Delta H = -283.0 \text{ kJ}$

$\tfrac{1}{2}$(Equation B reversed) $NO(g) \longrightarrow \tfrac{1}{2}N_2(g) + \tfrac{1}{2}\cancel{O_2(g)} \quad \Delta H = -90.3 \text{ kJ}$

Target equation: $CO(g) + NO(g) \longrightarrow CO_2(g) + \tfrac{1}{2}N_2(g) \quad \Delta H = -373.3 \text{ kJ}$

Check Obtaining the desired target equation is a sufficient check. Be sure to remember to change the *sign* of ΔH for any equation you reverse.

Follow-Up Problem 6.8 Nitrogen oxides undergo many reactions in the environment and in industry. Given the following information, calculate ΔH for the overall equation, $2NO_2(g) + \tfrac{1}{2}O_2(g) \longrightarrow N_2O_5(s)$:

$$N_2O_5(s) \longrightarrow 2NO(g) + \tfrac{3}{2}O_2(g) \quad \Delta H = 223.7 \text{ kJ}$$

$$NO(g) + \tfrac{1}{2}O_2(g) \longrightarrow NO_2(g) \quad \Delta H = -57.1 \text{ kJ}$$

■ Summary of Section 6.5

- Because H is a state function, we can use Hess's law to determine ΔH of any reaction by assuming that it is the sum of other reactions.
- After manipulating the equations of those reactions and their ΔH values to match the substances in the target equation, we add the manipulated ΔH values to find the unknown ΔH.

Table 6.3 Selected Standard Enthalpies of Formation at 25°C (298 K)	
Formula	ΔH°_f (kJ/mol)
Calcium	
Ca(s)	0
CaO(s)	−635.1
CaCO₃(s)	−1206.9
Carbon	
C(graphite)	0
C(diamond)	1.9
CO(g)	−110.5
CO₂(g)	−393.5
CH₄(g)	−74.9
CH₃OH(l)	−238.6
HCN(g)	135
CS₂(l)	87.9
Chlorine	
Cl(g)	121.0
Cl₂(g)	0
HCl(g)	−92.3
Hydrogen	
H(g)	218.0
H₂(g)	0
Nitrogen	
N₂(g)	0
NH₃(g)	−45.9
NO(g)	90.3
Oxygen	
O₂(g)	0
O₃(g)	143
H₂O(g)	−241.8
H₂O(l)	−285.8
Silver	
Ag(s)	0
AgCl(s)	−127.0
Sodium	
Na(s)	0
Na(g)	107.8
NaCl(s)	−411.1
Sulfur	
S₈(rhombic)	0
S₈(monoclinic)	0.3
SO₂(g)	−296.8
SO₃(g)	−396.0

6.6 • STANDARD ENTHALPIES OF REACTION (ΔH°_{rxn})

In this section, we see how Hess's law is used to determine the ΔH values of an enormous number of reactions. Thermodynamic variables, such as ΔH, vary somewhat with conditions. Therefore, in order to study and compare reactions, chemists have established a set of specific conditions called **standard states:**

- For a *gas,* the standard state is 1 atm* and ideal behavior.
- For a substance in *aqueous solution,* the standard state is 1 *M* concentration.
- For a *pure substance* (element or compound), the standard state is usually the most stable form of the substance at 1 atm and the temperature of interest. In this text (and in most thermodynamic tables), that temperature is usually 25°C (298 K).

The standard-state symbol (shown as a degree sign) indicates that the variable has been measured with *all the substances in their standard states.* For example, when the enthalpy change of a reaction is measured at the standard state, it is the **standard enthalpy of reaction, ΔH°_{rxn}** (also called *standard heat of reaction;* "rxn" stands for reaction).

Formation Equations and Their Standard Enthalpy Changes

In a **formation equation,** 1 mol of a compound forms from its elements. The **standard enthalpy of formation (ΔH°_f;** or *standard heat of formation*) is the enthalpy change for the formation equation when all the substances are in their standard states. For instance, the formation equation for methane (CH₄) is

$$C(graphite) + 2H_2(g) \longrightarrow CH_4(g) \quad \Delta H^\circ_f = -74.9 \text{ kJ}$$

Fractional coefficients are often used with reactants to obtain 1 mol of the product:

$$Na(s) + \tfrac{1}{2}Cl_2(g) \longrightarrow NaCl(s) \quad \Delta H^\circ_f = -411.1 \text{ kJ}$$

$$2C(graphite) + 3H_2(g) + \tfrac{1}{2}O_2(g) \longrightarrow C_2H_5OH(l) \quad \Delta H^\circ_f = -277.6 \text{ kJ}$$

Standard enthalpies of formation have been tabulated for many substances. Table 6.3 shows several, and a much more extensive table appears in Appendix B. The values in Table 6.3 make two points:

1. *For an element in its standard state,* $\Delta H^\circ_f = 0$.
   - The standard state for metals, like sodium, is the solid ($\Delta H^\circ_f = 0$); it takes 107.8 kJ of heat to form 1 mol of gaseous Na ($\Delta H^\circ_f = 107.8$ kJ/mol).
   - The standard state for molecular elements, such as the halogens, is the molecular form, not separate atoms: for Cl₂, $\Delta H^\circ_f = 0$, but for Cl, $\Delta H^\circ_f = 121.0$ kJ/mol.
   - Some elements exist in different forms (called *allotropes;* Chapter 14), but only one is the standard state. The standard state of carbon is graphite ($\Delta H^\circ_f = 0$), not diamond ($\Delta H^\circ_f = 1.9$ kJ/mol), the standard state of oxygen is O₂ ($\Delta H^\circ_f = 0$), not ozone (O₃; $\Delta H^\circ_f = 143$ kJ/mol), and the standard state of sulfur is S₈ in its rhombic crystal form ($\Delta H^\circ_f = 0$), not in its monoclinic form ($\Delta H^\circ_f = 0.3$ kJ/mol).

2. *Most compounds have a negative* ΔH°_f. That is, most compounds have exothermic formation reactions: *under standard conditions, heat is released when most compounds form from their elements.*

Sample Problem 6.9 Writing Formation Equations

Problem Write a balanced formation equation for each of the following and include the value of ΔH°_f:
(a) AgCl(s)   **(b)** CaCO₃(s)   **(c)** HCN(g)

Plan We write the elements as the reactants and 1 mol of the compound as the product, being sure all substances are in their standard states. Then, we balance the equations and find the ΔH°_f values in Table 6.3 or Appendix B.

---

*The definition of the standard state for gases has been changed to 1 bar, a slightly lower pressure than the 1 atm standard on which the data in this book are based (1 atm = 101.3 kPa = 1.013 bar). For most purposes, this makes very little difference in the standard enthalpy values.

Solution (a) $Ag(s) + \frac{1}{2}Cl_2(g) \longrightarrow AgCl(s)$ $\Delta H^\circ_f = -127.0$ kJ

(b) $Ca(s) + C(graphite) + \frac{3}{2}O_2(g) \longrightarrow CaCO_3(s)$ $\Delta H^\circ_f = -1206.9$ kJ

(c) $\frac{1}{2}H_2(g) + C(graphite) + \frac{1}{2}N_2(g) \longrightarrow HCN(g)$ $\Delta H^\circ_f = 135$ kJ

Follow-Up Problem 6.9 Write a balanced formation equation for each of the following and include its ΔH°_f: **(a)** $CH_3OH(l)$, **(b)** $CaO(s)$, **(c)** $CS_2(l)$.

Determining ΔH°_{rxn} from ΔH°_f Values for Reactants and Products

We can use ΔH°_f values to determine ΔH°_{rxn} for any reaction. By applying Hess's law, we can imagine the reaction occurring in two steps (Figure 6.12):

Step 1. Each reactant decomposes to its elements. This is the *reverse* of the formation reaction for the *reactant*, so the standard enthalpy change is $-\Delta H^\circ_f$.

Step 2. Each product forms from its elements. This step *is* the formation reaction for the *product*, so the standard enthalpy change is ΔH°_f.

Figure 6.12 The two-step process for determining ΔH°_{rxn} from ΔH°_f values.

$$\Delta H^\circ_{rxn} = \Sigma m\Delta H^\circ_{f(products)} - \Sigma n\Delta H^\circ_{f(reactants)}$$

According to Hess's law, we add the enthalpy changes for these steps to obtain the overall enthalpy change for the reaction (ΔH°_{rxn}). Suppose we want ΔH°_{rxn} for

$$TiCl_4(l) + 2H_2O(g) \longrightarrow TiO_2(s) + 4HCl(g)$$

We write this equation as though it were the sum of four individual equations, one for each compound. The first two show step 1, the decomposition of the reactants to their elements (*reverse* of their formation); the second two show step 2, the formation of the products from their elements:

$$TiCl_4(l) \longrightarrow Ti(s) + 2Cl_2(g) \qquad -\Delta H^\circ_f[TiCl_4(l)]$$
$$2H_2O(g) \longrightarrow 2H_2(g) + O_2(g) \qquad -2\Delta H^\circ_f[H_2O(g)]$$
$$Ti(s) + O_2(g) \longrightarrow TiO_2(s) \qquad \Delta H^\circ_f[TiO_2(s)]$$
$$2H_2(g) + 2Cl_2(g) \longrightarrow 4HCl(g) \qquad 4\Delta H^\circ_f[HCl(g)]$$

$TiCl_4(l) + 2H_2O(g) + \cancel{Ti(s)} + \cancel{O_2(g)} + \cancel{2H_2(g)} + \cancel{2Cl_2(g)} \longrightarrow$

$\qquad\qquad \cancel{Ti(s)} + \cancel{2Cl_2(g)} + \cancel{2H_2(g)} + \cancel{O_2(g)} + TiO_2(s) + 4HCl(g)$

or $TiCl_4(l) + 2H_2O(g) \longrightarrow TiO_2(s) + 4HCl(g)$

It's important to realize that when titanium(IV) chloride and water react, the reactants don't *actually* decompose to their elements, which then recombine to form the products. But the great usefulness of Hess's law and the state-function concept is that ΔH°_{rxn} is the difference between two state functions, $H^\circ_{products}$ minus $H^\circ_{reactants}$, so it doesn't matter how the reaction *actually* occurs. We add the individual enthalpy changes to find ΔH°_{rxn}:

$$\Delta H^\circ_{rxn} = \Delta H^\circ_f[TiO_2(s)] + 4\Delta H^\circ_f[HCl(g)] + \{-\Delta H^\circ_f[TiCl_4(l)]\} + \{-2\Delta H^\circ_f[H_2O(g)]\}$$
$$= \underbrace{\{\Delta H^\circ_f[TiO_2(s)] + 4\Delta H^\circ_f[HCl(g)]\}}_{\text{Products}} - \underbrace{\{\Delta H^\circ_f[TiCl_4(l)] + 2\Delta H^\circ_f[H_2O(g)]\}}_{\text{Reactants}}$$

The arithmetic in this case gives $\Delta H^{\circ}_{rxn} = -25.39$ kJ, but more importantly, when we generalize the pattern, we see that *the standard enthalpy of reaction is the sum of the standard enthalpies of formation of the **products** minus the sum of the standard enthalpies of formation of the **reactants*** (see Figure 6.12):

$$\Delta H^{\circ}_{rxn} = \Sigma m \Delta H^{\circ}_{f(products)} - \Sigma n \Delta H^{\circ}_{f(reactants)} \qquad (6.9)$$

where Σ means "sum of," and m and n are the amounts (mol) of the products and reactants given by the coefficients in the balanced equation.

Sample Problem 6.10   **Calculating ΔH°_{rxn} from ΔH°_{f} Values**

Problem Nitric acid is used to make many products, including fertilizers, dyes, and explosives. The first step in its production is the oxidation of ammonia:

$$4NH_3(g) + 5O_2(g) \longrightarrow 4NO(g) + 6H_2O(g)$$

Calculate ΔH°_{rxn} from ΔH°_{f} values.

Plan We use values from Table 6.3 (or Appendix B) and apply Equation 6.9.

Solution Calculating ΔH°_{rxn}:

$$
\begin{aligned}
\Delta H^{\circ}_{rxn} &= \Sigma m \Delta H^{\circ}_{f(products)} - \Sigma n \Delta H^{\circ}_{f(reactants)} \\
&= \{4\Delta H^{\circ}_{f}[NO(g)] + 6\Delta H^{\circ}_{f}[H_2O(g)]\} - \{4\Delta H^{\circ}_{f}[NH_3(g)] + 5\Delta H^{\circ}_{f}[O_2(g)]\} \\
&= (4\ \text{mol})(90.3\ \text{kJ/mol}) + (6\ \text{mol})(-241.8\ \text{kJ/mol}) \\
&\quad -[(4\ \text{mol})(-45.9\ \text{kJ/mol}) + (5\ \text{mol})(0\ \text{kJ/mol})] \\
&= 361\ \text{kJ} - 1451\ \text{kJ} + 184\ \text{kJ} - 0\ \text{kJ} = \boxed{-906\ \text{kJ}}
\end{aligned}
$$

Check We write formation equations, with ΔH°_{f} values for the amounts of each compound, in the correct direction (forward for products and reverse for reactants) and find the sum:

$4NH_3(g) \longrightarrow 2N_2(g) + 6H_2(g)$	$-4\Delta H^{\circ}_{f} = -4(-45.9\ \text{kJ}) =$	$184\ \text{kJ}$
$2N_2(g) + 2O_2(g) \longrightarrow 4NO(g)$	$4\Delta H^{\circ}_{f} = \quad 4(90.3\ \text{kJ}) =$	$361\ \text{kJ}$
$6H_2(g) + 3O_2(g) \longrightarrow 6H_2O(g)$	$6\Delta H^{\circ}_{f} = 6(-241.8\ \text{kJ}) =$	$-1451\ \text{kJ}$
$4NH_3(g) + 5O_2(g) \longrightarrow 4NO(g) + 6H_2O(g)$	$\Delta H^{\circ}_{rxn} =$	$-906\ \text{kJ}$

Comment In this problem, we know the individual ΔH°_{f} values and find the sum, ΔH°_{rxn}. In the follow-up problem, we know the sum and want to find one of the ΔH°_{f} values.

Follow-Up Problem 6.10 Use the following to find ΔH°_{f} of methanol [$CH_3OH(l)$]:

$$CH_3OH(l) + \tfrac{3}{2}O_2(g) \longrightarrow CO_2(g) + 2H_2O(g) \quad \Delta H^{\circ}_{rxn} = -638.5\ \text{kJ}$$
$$\Delta H^{\circ}_{f}\ \text{of}\ CO_2(g) = -393.5\ \text{kJ/mol}$$
$$\Delta H^{\circ}_{f}\ \text{of}\ H_2O(g) = -241.8\ \text{kJ/mol}$$

The Chemical Connections essay applies ideas from this chapter to new approaches for energy utilization.

▌Summary of Section 6.6

- Standard states are a set of specific conditions used for determining thermodynamic variables for all substances.
- When 1 mol of a compound forms from its elements with all substances in their standard states, the enthalpy change is the standard enthalpy of formation, ΔH°_{f}.
- Hess's law allows us to picture a reaction as the decomposition of the reactants to their elements followed by the formation of the products from their elements.
- We use tabulated ΔH°_{f} values to find ΔH°_{rxn} or use known ΔH°_{rxn} and ΔH°_{f} values to find an unknown ΔH°_{f}.
- Because of major concerns about climate change, chemists are developing energy alternatives, including coal and biomass conversion, hydrogen fuel, and noncombustible energy sources.

Out of necessity, we must rethink our global use of energy. The dwindling supplies of our most common fuels and the environmental impact of their combustion products threaten human well-being and the survival of many other species. Energy production presents scientists, engineers, and political leaders with some of the greatest challenges of our time.

A changeover in energy sources from wood to coal and then petroleum took place over the past century. The **fossil fuels**—coal, petroleum, and natural gas—remain our major sources, but they are *nonrenewable* because natural processes form them many orders of magnitude slower than we consume them. In the United States, ongoing research seeks new approaches to using coal and nuclear energy, and utilizing *renewable* sources—biomass, hydrogen, sunlight, wind, geothermal heat, and tides—is the subject of intensive efforts as well.

In this discussion, we focus on converting coal and biomass to cleaner fuels, understanding the effect of carbon-based fuels on climate, developing hydrogen as a fuel, utilizing solar energy, and conserving energy.

Converting Coal to Cleaner Fuels

U.S. reserves of coal are enormous, but the burning of coal, in addition to forming CO_2, produces SO_2 and particulates, and releases mercury. Exposure to SO_2 and particulates causes respiratory disease, and SO_2 can be oxidized to H_2SO_4, the key component of acid rain (Chapter 19). The trace amounts of Hg, a neurotoxin, spread as Hg vapor and bioaccumulate in fish.

Two processes reduce the amounts of SO_2:

Desulfurization. The removal of sulfur dioxide from flue gases is done with devices called *scrubbers* that heat powdered limestone ($CaCO_3$) or spray lime-water slurries [$Ca(OH)_2$]:

$$CaCO_3(s) + SO_2(g) \xrightarrow{\Delta} CaSO_3(s) + CO_2(g)$$
$$2CaSO_3(s) + O_2(g) + 4H_2O(l) \longrightarrow 2CaSO_4 \cdot 2H_2O(s; gypsum)$$
$$2Ca(OH)_2(aq) + 2SO_2(g) + O_2(g) + 2H_2O(l) \longrightarrow$$
$$2CaSO_4 \cdot 2H_2O(s)$$

A wallboard (drywall) plant built next to the power plant sells the gypsum (1 ton per customer each year); about 20% of the drywall produced each year is made with synthetic gypsum.

Gasification. In **coal gasification,** solid coal is converted to sulfur-free gaseous fuels. In this process, the sulfur in the coal is reduced to H_2S, which is removed through an acid-base reaction with a base, such as ethanolamine ($HOCH_2CH_2NH_2$). The resulting salt is heated to release H_2S, which is converted to elemental sulfur by the Claus process (Chapter 22) and sold. Several reactions yield mixtures with increasing fuel value, that is, with a lower C/H ratio:

- Pulverized coal reacts with limited O_2 and water at 800–1500°C to form approximately a 2/1 mixture of CO/H$_2$.
- Alternatively, in the *water-gas reaction* (or *steam-carbon reaction*), an exothermic oxidation of C to CO is followed by the endothermic reaction of C with steam to form a nearly 1/1 mixture of CO/H$_2$ called *water gas:*

$$C(s) + \tfrac{1}{2}O_2(g) \longrightarrow CO(g) \qquad \Delta H^\circ_{rxn} = -110 \text{ kJ}$$
$$C(s) + H_2O(g) \longrightarrow CO(g) + H_2(g) \qquad \Delta H^\circ_{rxn} = 131 \text{ kJ}$$

However, water gas has a much lower fuel value than methane (CH_4). For example, a mixture of 0.5 mol of CO and 0.5 mol of H_2 releases about one-third as much energy as 1.0 mol of methane ($\Delta H = -802$ kJ/mol):

$$\tfrac{1}{2}H_2(g) + \tfrac{1}{4}O_2(g) \longrightarrow \tfrac{1}{2}H_2O(g) \qquad \Delta H^\circ_{rxn} = -121 \text{ kJ}$$
$$\tfrac{1}{2}CO(g) + \tfrac{1}{4}O_2(g) \longrightarrow \tfrac{1}{2}CO_2(g) \qquad \Delta H^\circ_{rxn} = -142 \text{ kJ}$$
$$\tfrac{1}{2}H_2(g) + \tfrac{1}{2}CO(g) + \tfrac{1}{2}O_2(g) \longrightarrow \tfrac{1}{2}H_2O(g) + \tfrac{1}{2}CO_2(g)$$
$$\Delta H^\circ_{rxn} = -263 \text{ kJ}$$

- In the *CO-shift* (or *water-gas shift*) reaction, the H_2 content of water gas is increased to produce synthesis gas (*syngas*):

$$CO(g) + H_2O(g) \longrightarrow CO_2(g) + H_2(g) \quad \Delta H^\circ_{rxn} = -41 \text{ kJ}$$

- To produce CH_4, a syngas that is a 3/1 mixture of H_2/CO from which the CO_2 has been removed, is employed:

$$CO(g) + 3H_2(g) \longrightarrow CH_4(g) + H_2O(g) \quad \Delta H^\circ_{rxn} = -206 \text{ kJ}$$

Drying the product gives **synthetic natural gas (SNG).**

Syngas is used is some newer methods as well. In *integrated gasification combined cycle (IGCC),* electricity is produced in two ways—when syngas is burned in a combustion turbine and when the hot product gases generate steam to power a steam turbine. In the *Fischer-Tropsch process,* syngas is used to form liquid hydrocarbon fuels that have higher molar masses than methane:

$$nCO(g) + (2n + 1)H_2(g) \longrightarrow C_nH_{2n+2}(l) + nH_2O(g)$$

Converting Biomass to Fuels

Nearly half the world's people rely on wood for energy. In principle, wood is renewable, but widespread deforestation has resulted from its use for fuel, lumber, and paper. Therefore, great emphasis has been placed on **biomass conversion** of vegetable and animal waste. In one process, chemical and/or microbial methods convert vegetable (sugarcane, corn, switchgrass) and tree waste into fuel, mainly ethanol (C_2H_5OH). In the United States, ethanol is mixed with gasoline to form *gasohol;* in Brazil, it substitutes directly for gasoline.

Methanogenesis forms methane by anaerobic (oxygen-free) biodegradation of organic sources such as manure and vegetable waste or wastewater. China's biogas-generating facilities apply this technique, and similar ones in the U.S. use garbage and sewage. In addition to producing methane, the process yields residues that improve soil; it also prevents the wastes from polluting natural waters.

Another biomass conversion process changes vegetable oils (soybean, cottonseed, sunflower, canola, and even used cooking oil) into a mixture called *biodiesel,* whose combustion produces less CO, SO_2, and particulate matter than fossil-fuel-based diesel. The CO_2 produced in combustion of biodiesel has minimal impact on the net atmospheric amount because the carbon is taken up by the plants grown as sources of the vegetable oils.

The Greenhouse Effect and Global Warming

Combustion of all carbon-based fuels releases CO_2, and over the past two decades, it has become clear that the atmospheric build-up of this gas from our increased use of these fuels is changing the climate. Throughout Earth's history, CO_2 has played a key

(continued)

temperature-regulating role in the atmosphere. Much of the sunlight that shines on Earth is absorbed by the land and oceans and converted to heat (IR radiation; Figure B6.1). Like the glass of a greenhouse, CO_2 does not absorb visible light from the Sun, but it absorbs and re-emits some of the heat radiating from Earth's surface and, thus, helps warm the atmosphere. This process is called the *natural greenhouse effect* (Figure B6.1, *left*).

Over several billion years, due to the spread of plant life, which uses CO_2 in photosynthesis, the amount of CO_2 originally present (from volcanic activity) decreased to 0.028% by volume. With this amount, Earth's average temperature was about 14°C (57°F); without CO_2, it would be –17°C (2°F)! However, as a result of intensive use of fossil fuels for the past 150 years, this amount increased to 0.039%. Thus, although the same quantity of solar energy passes through the atmosphere, more is being trapped as heat, which has created an *enhanced greenhouse effect* that is changing the climate through *global warming* (Figure B6.1, *right*). Based on current trends, CO_2 amounts will increase to between 0.049% and 0.126% by 2100 (Figure B6.2).

If this projected increase in CO_2 occurs, two closely related questions arise: (1) How much will the temperature rise? (2) How will this rise affect life on Earth? Despite constantly improving models, answers are difficult to obtain. Natural fluctuations in temperature must be taken into account, as well as cyclic changes in solar activity. Moreover, as the amount of CO_2 increases from fossil-fuel burning, so do the amounts of particulate matter and SO_2, which may block sunlight and have a cooling effect. Water vapor also traps heat, and as temperatures rise, more water evaporates. The increased amounts of water vapor may thicken the cloud cover and lead to cooling as well.

Despite such opposing factors, all of the best models predict net warming, and scientists are observing the effects. The average temperature has increased by 0.6±0.2°C since the late 19th century and 0.2–0.3°C over the past 25 years. Globally, the decade from 2001 to 2010 was the warmest on record. Snow cover and glacial size in the northern hemisphere and floating ice in the Arctic Ocean have decreased dramatically. Antarctica is also experiencing widespread breakup of icebound regions. Globally, sea level has risen an average of 17 cm (6.7 in) over the past century, and flooding and other extreme weather events have increased.

Fifteen years ago, the best models predicted a temperature rise of 1.0–3.5°C; today, their predictions are more than 50% higher. Such increases would alter rainfall patterns and crop yields throughout the world and increase sea level as much as 1 meter, thus flooding regions such as the Netherlands, half of Florida, much of southern Asia, coastal New England and New York, and many Pacific island nations. To make matters worse, as we burn fossil fuels that *release* CO_2, we cut down forests that *absorb* it.

In addition to ways to reduce fossil-fuel consumption, researchers are studying methods of *carbon capture and storage (CCS)*, including *CO_2 sequestration,* both naturally by maintaining forests and jungles and industrially by liquefying CO_2 formed and either burying it underground or using it to produce mineral carbonates.

The 1997 United Nations Conference on Climate Change in Kyoto, Japan, created a treaty with legally binding targets to limit greenhouse gases. It was ratified by 189 countries, but not by the United States, the largest emitter. The 2009 conference in Copenhagen, Denmark, was attended by representatives from 192 countries (including the U.S.), but did not result in legally binding emission targets or financial commitments.

Figure B6.1 The trapping of heat by the atmosphere. Of the total sunlight reaching Earth, some is reflected and some is absorbed and converted to IR radiation (heat). Some heat emitted by the surface is trapped by atmospheric CO_2, creating a *natural* greenhouse effect (*left*) that has been essential to life. But, largely as a result of human activity in the past 150 years, and especially the past several decades, the buildup of CO_2 and several other greenhouse gases (*pie chart*) has created an *enhanced* greenhouse effect (*right*).

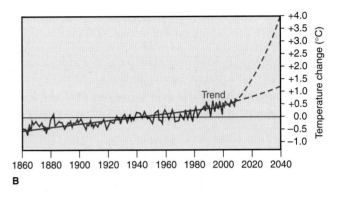

Figure B6.2 Evidence for the enhanced greenhouse effect. **A,** Since the mid-19th century, atmospheric CO_2 has increased. **B,** Since the mid-19th century, average global temperature has risen 0.6°C. (Zero is the average from 1957 to 1970.) The projections in the graphs (*dashed lines*) assume that current fossil fuel consumption and deforestation continue (*upper line*) or slow (*lower line*).

Hydrogen

The use of H_2 as an energy source holds great promise but presents several problems. The simplest element and most plentiful gas in the universe always occurs on Earth in compounds, most importantly with oxygen in water and carbon in hydrocarbons. Once freed, however, H_2 is an excellent energy source because of several properties:

- It has the highest energy content per *mass* unit of any fuel—nearly three times as much as gasoline.
- Its energy content per *volume* unit is low at STP but increases greatly when the H_2 is liquefied under extremely high *P* and low *T*.
- Its combustion does not produce CO_2, particulates, or sulfur oxides. It is such a clean energy source that H_2-fuel cells operate electrical systems aboard the space shuttles, and the crews drink the pure water product.

A hydrogen-based economy is the dream of many because, even though combustion of H_2 ($\Delta H^\circ_{rxn} = -242$ kJ/mol) produces less than one-third as much energy per mole as combustion of CH_4 ($\Delta H^\circ_{rxn} = -802$ kJ/mol), it yields nonpolluting water vapor. The keys to realizing the dream, however, involve major improvements in both production of H_2 and its transportation and storage.

Production of H_2. Hydrogen is produced by a number of methods, some more widely used than others.

- *Fossil-fuel byproduct.* In the United States today, almost all H_2 is produced by the *steam-reforming process,* in which methane or natural gas is treated with steam in high-temperature reactions (Chapter 22).
- *Electrolysis of liquid water.* Formation of H_2 from the decomposition of liquid water is endothermic ($\Delta H^\circ_{rxn} = 286$ kJ/mol), and most direct methods that utilize electricity are costly. However, energy from flowing water, wind, and geothermal sources can provide the needed electricity. An exciting new *photoelectrochemical approach* uses a photovoltaic panel coupled to an electrolysis unit: the energy of sunlight powers the decomposition of water.
- *Biological methods.* Green algae and cyanobacteria store the energy of sunlight in the form of starch or glycogen for their own metabolism. Under certain conditions, however, these

microbes can be made to produce H_2 gas instead of these large organic molecules. For example, eliminating sulfur from the diet of green algae activates a long dormant gene and the cells produce H_2. But, major improvements in yields are needed to make this method cost-effective.

Transportation and storage of H_2. The absence of an infrastructure for transporting and storing large quantities of hydrogen is still a roadblock to realizing a hydrogen-based economy. Currently, the cost of energy to cool and compress the gas to liquefy it is very high. Hydrogen is carried in pipelines, but its ability to escape through metals and make them brittle requires more expensive piping. Storage in the form of solid metal hydrides has been explored, but heating the hydrides to release the stored hydrogen requires energy. Use of H_2 in fuel cells is a major area of electrochemical research (Chapter 21). Tests are underway to commercialize fuel-cell technology using the hydrogen that is a byproduct of the petrochemical and coal industries.

Solar Energy

The Sun's energy drives global winds and ocean currents, the cycle of evaporation and condensation, and many biological processes, especially photosynthesis. More energy falls on Earth's surface as sunlight in 1 h [1.2×10^5 TW (terawatts); 1 TW $= 1 \times 10^{12}$ W] than is used in all human activity in 1 year. Solar energy is, however, a dilute source (only 1 kW/m² at noon); in 1 h, about 600–1000 TW strikes land at sites suitable for collecting. Nevertheless, covering 0.16% of that land with today's photovoltaic systems would provide 20 TW/h, equivalent to the output of 20,000 nuclear power plants producing 1 GW (gigawatt) each. Clearly, solar energy is the largest carbon-free option among renewable sources.

Three important ways to utilize solar energy are with electronic materials, biomass, and thermal systems:

Electronic materials. A **photovoltaic cell** converts sunlight directly into electricity by employing certain combinations of elements (usually metalloids; we discuss the behavior of elements with *semiconductor* properties in Chapter 12). Early cells relied primarily on crystalline silicon, but their *yield,* the proportion of electrical energy produced relative to the radiant energy supplied, was only about 10%. More recent devices have achieved much higher yields by using thin films of polycrystalline materials that

(continued)

251

incorporate combinations of other elements, such as cadmium telluride (CdTe cells, 16%), gallium arsenide (GaAs cells, 18%), and copper indium gallium selenide (CIGS cells, 20%). And ongoing research on nanometer-sized semiconductor devices, called *quantum dots,* suggests yields as high as 70%.

Biomass. Solar energy is used to convert CO_2 and water via photosynthesis to plant material (carbohydrate) and oxygen. Plant biomass can be burned directly as a fuel or converted to other fuels, such as ethanol or hydrogen (see p. 249).

Thermal systems. The operation of a photovoltaic cell creates a buildup of heat, which lowers its efficiency. A *photovoltaic thermal (PVT) hybrid cell* thus combines such a cell with conductive metal piping (filled with water or antifreeze) that transfers the heat from the cell to a domestic hot-water system.

Because sunlight is typically available only 6 to 8 hours a day and is greatly reduced in cloudy weather, another thermal system focuses on storing solar energy during the day and releasing it at night. When an ionic hydrate, such as $Na_2SO_4 \cdot 10H_2O$, is warmed by sunlight to over 32°C, the 3 mol of ions dissolve in the 10 mol of water in an endothermic process:

$$Na_2SO_4(aq) \cdot 10H_2O(s) \xrightarrow{\geq 32°C} Na_2SO_4(aq) \quad \Delta H°_{rxn} = 354 \text{ kJ}$$

When cooled below 32°C after sunset, the solution recrystallizes, releasing the absorbed energy for heating:

$$Na_2SO_4(aq) \xrightarrow{\leq 32°C} Na_2SO_4(aq) \cdot 10H_2O(s) \quad \Delta H°_{rxn} = -354 \text{ kJ}$$

Unfortunately, as of the end of the first decade of the 21st century, solar energy is not yet competitive with highly subsidized fossil fuels. Nevertheless, changes in economic policy as well as improvements in photovoltaic technology and biomass processing should greatly increase solar energy's contribution to a carbon-free energy future.

Nuclear Energy
Despite ongoing problems with disposal of radioactive waste, energy from nuclear *fission*—the splitting of large, unstable atomic nuclei—is used extensively, especially in France and other parts of northern Europe. Nuclear *fusion*—the combining of small atomic nuclei—avoids the problems of fission but has been achieved so far only with a net consumption of power. (We'll discuss these processes in detail in Chapter 24.)

Energy Conservation: More from Less
All systems, whether organisms or factories, waste energy, which is, in effect, a waste of fuel. For example, the production of one aluminum beverage can requires energy equivalent to burning 0.25 L of gasoline. Energy conservation lowers costs, extends our fuel supply, and reduces the effects of climate change. Following are three examples of conservation.

Passive solar design. Heating and cooling costs can be reduced by as much as 50% when buildings are constructed with large windows and materials that absorb the Sun's heat in the day and release it slowly at night.

Residential heating systems. A high-efficiency gas-burning furnace channels hot waste gases through a system of baffles to transfer more heat to the room and then to an attached domestic hot-water system. While moving through the system, the gases cool to 100°C, so the water vapor condenses, thus releasing about 10% more heat:

$$CH_4(g) + 2O_2(g) \longrightarrow CO_2(g) + 2H_2O(g) \quad \Delta H°_{rxn} = -802 \text{ kJ}$$
$$\underline{2H_2O(g) \longrightarrow 2H_2O(l) \qquad\qquad\qquad \Delta H°_{rxn} = -88 \text{ kJ}}$$
$$CH_4(g) + 2O_2(g) \longrightarrow CO_2(g) + 2H_2O(l) \quad \Delta H°_{rxn} = -890 \text{ kJ}$$

Modern lighting. Incandescent bulbs give off light when the material in their filament reaches a high temperature. They are very inefficient because less than 7% of the electrical energy is converted to light, the rest being wasted as heat. *Compact fluorescent lamps (CFLs)* have an efficiency of about 18% and are having a major economic impact: in many parts of Europe, incandescent bulbs are no longer sold. *Light-emitting diodes (LEDs)* are even more efficient (about 30%) and are already being used in car indicator lamps and tail lights. Light-emitting devices based on organic semiconductors (OLEDs) are used in flat-panel displays, and recent use of Al-In-Ga-P materials and Ga and In nitrides in LEDs has increased brightness and improved color richness. Over 20% of electricity generated in the U.S. is used for lighting, and burning of fossil fuels in power plants creates smog, particulates, and CO_2. By 2020, use of these devices for lighting can cut electricity usage by 50%, eliminating the emission of 2.8×10^7 metric tons of carbon per year.

Engineers and chemists will continue to explore alternatives for energy production and use, but a more hopeful energy future ultimately depends on our dedication to conserving planetary resources.

Problems

B6.1 To make use of an ionic hydrate for storing solar energy, you place 500.0 kg of sodium sulfate decahydrate on your house roof. Assuming complete reaction and 100% efficiency of heat transfer, how much heat (in kJ) is released to your house at night?

B6.2 In one step of coal gasification, coal reacts with superheated steam:

$$C(coal) + H_2O(g) \longrightarrow CO(g) + H_2(g) \quad \Delta H°_{rxn} = 129.7 \text{ kJ}$$

(a) Use this reaction and the following two to write an overall reaction for the production of methane:

$$CO(g) + H_2O(g) \longrightarrow CO_2(g) + H_2(g) \qquad \Delta H°_{rxn} = -41 \text{ kJ}$$
$$CO(g) + 3H_2(g) \longrightarrow CH_4(g) + H_2O(g) \quad \Delta H°_{rxn} = -206 \text{ kJ}$$

(b) Calculate $\Delta H°_{rxn}$ for this overall change.

(c) Using the value from part (b) and a calculated value of $\Delta H°_{rxn}$ for the combustion of methane, find the total ΔH for gasifying 1.00 kg of coal and burning the methane formed (assume water forms as a gas and M of coal = 12.00 g/mol).

CHAPTER REVIEW GUIDE

Understand These Concepts

1. The distinction between a system and its surroundings (§6.1)
2. The transfer of energy to or from a system as heat and/or work (§6.1)
3. The relation of internal energy change, heat, and work (§6.1)
4. The meaning of energy conservation (§6.1)
5. The meaning of a state function and why ΔE is constant even though q and w vary (§6.1)
6. The meaning of enthalpy and the relation between ΔE and ΔH (§6.2)
7. The meaning of ΔH and the distinction between exothermic and endothermic reactions (§6.2)
8. The relation between specific heat capacity and heat (§6.3)
9. How constant-pressure (coffee-cup) and constant-volume (bomb) calorimeters work (§6.3)
10. The relation between ΔH and amount of substance (§6.4)
11. The calculation of ΔH values with Hess's law (§6.5)
12. The meaning of a formation equation and the standard enthalpy of formation (§6.6)
13. How a reaction can be viewed as the decomposition of reactants followed by the formation of products (§6.6)

Master These Skills

1. Determining the change in a system's internal energy in different units (SP 6.1)
2. Drawing enthalpy diagrams for chemical and physical changes (SP 6.2)
3. Solving problems involving specific heat capacity and heat transferred in a reaction (SPs 6.3–6.6)
4. Relating the heat transferred in a reaction to the amounts of substances changing (SP 6.7)
5. Using Hess's law to find an unknown ΔH (SP 6.8)
6. Writing formation equations and using ΔH_f° values to find ΔH_{rxn}° (SPs 6.9, 6.10)

thermodynamics (229)
thermochemistry (229)

Section 6.1
system (230)
surroundings (230)
internal energy (E) (230)
heat (q) (230)
work (w) (231)
law of conservation of energy (first law of thermodynamics) (233)
joule (J) (233)

calorie (cal) (233)
state function (234)

Section 6.2
pressure-volume work (PV work) (235)
enthalpy (H) (235)
change in enthalpy (ΔH) (235)
exothermic process (236)
enthalpy diagram (237)
endothermic process (237)

Section 6.3
heat capacity (238)
specific heat capacity (c) (238)
molar heat capacity (C) (238)
calorimeter (239)

Section 6.4
thermochemical equation (242)

Section 6.5
Hess's law (244)

Section 6.6
standard state (246)
standard enthalpy of reaction (ΔH_{rxn}°) (246)
formation equation (246)
standard enthalpy of formation (ΔH_f°) (246)
fossil fuel (249)
coal gasification (249)
synthetic natural gas (SNG) (249)
biomass conversion (249)
methanogenesis (249)
photovoltaic cell (251)

6.1 Defining the change in internal energy (230):
$$\Delta E = E_{final} - E_{initial} = E_{products} - E_{reactants}$$
6.2 Expressing the change in internal energy in terms of heat and work (231):
$$\Delta E = q + w$$
6.3 Stating the first law of thermodynamics (law of conservation of energy) (233):
$$\Delta E_{universe} = \Delta E_{system} + \Delta E_{surroundings} = 0$$
6.4 Determining the work due to a change in volume at constant pressure (PV work) (235):
$$w = -P\Delta V$$
6.5 Relating the enthalpy change to the internal energy change at constant pressure (235):
$$\Delta H = \Delta E + P\Delta V$$

6.6 Identifying the enthalpy change with the heat absorbed or released at constant pressure (236):
$$q_P = \Delta E + P\Delta V = \Delta H$$
6.7 Calculating the heat absorbed or released when a substance undergoes a temperature change or a reaction occurs (238):
$$q = c \times mass \times \Delta T$$
6.8 Calculating the overall enthalpy change of a reaction (Hess's law) (244):
$$\Delta H_{overall} = \Delta H_1 + \Delta H_2 + \cdots + \Delta H_n$$
6.9 Calculating the standard enthalpy of reaction (248):
$$\Delta H_{rxn}^\circ = \Sigma m\Delta H_{f(products)}^\circ - \Sigma n\Delta H_{f(reactants)}^\circ$$

Brief Solutions to Follow-Up Problems

6.1 $\Delta E = q + w$

$$= \left(-26.0 \text{ kcal} \times \frac{4.184 \text{ kJ}}{1 \text{ kcal}}\right) + \left(15.0 \text{ Btu} \times \frac{1.055 \text{ kJ}}{1 \text{ Btu}}\right)$$

$$= -93 \text{ kJ}$$

6.2 The reaction is exothermic.

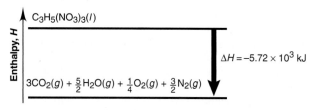

6.3 $\Delta T = 25.0°C - 37.0°C = -12.0°C = -12.0 \text{ K}$

$$\text{Mass (g)} = 1.11 \text{ g/mL} \times \frac{1000 \text{ mL}}{1 \text{ L}} \times 5.50 \text{ L} = 6.10 \times 10^3 \text{ g}$$

$q = c \times \text{mass} \times \Delta T$

$$= (2.42 \text{ J/g·K})\left(\frac{1 \text{ kJ}}{1000 \text{ J}}\right)(6.10 \times 10^3 \text{ g})(-12.0 \text{ K}) = -177 \text{ kJ}$$

6.4 $c_{\text{solid}} = -\dfrac{4.184 \text{ J/g·K} \times 25.00 \text{ g} \times 1.70 \text{ K}}{12.18 \text{ g} \times (-37.75 \text{ K})} = 0.387 \text{ J/g·K}$

From Table 6.2, the metal is copper.

6.5 $2HCl(aq) + Ba(OH)_2(aq) \longrightarrow 2H_2O(l) + BaCl_2(aq)$

Amount (mol) of HCl = 0.500 mol HCl/L × 0.0500 L = 0.0250 mol HCl

Similarly, we have 0.0250 mol $BaCl_2$.

Finding the limiting reactant from the balanced equation:

$$\text{Amount (mol) of } H_2O = 0.0250 \text{ mol HCl} \times \frac{2 \text{ mol } H_2O}{2 \text{ mol HCl}}$$

$$= 0.0250 \text{ mol } H_2O$$

$$\text{Amount (mol) of } H_2O = 0.0250 \text{ mol Ba(OH)}_2 \times \frac{2 \text{ mol } H_2O}{1 \text{ mol Ba(OH)}_2}$$

$$= 0.0500 \text{ mol } H_2O$$

Thus, HCl is limiting.

$$\Delta H \text{ (kJ/mol } H_2O) = \frac{q_{\text{rxn}}}{\text{mol } H_2O} = \frac{-1.386 \text{ kJ}}{0.0250 \text{ mol } H_2O}$$

$$= -55.4 \text{ kJ/mol } H_2O$$

6.6

$$-q_{\text{sample}} = q_{\text{calorimeter}}$$

$$-(0.8650 \text{ g C})\left(\frac{1 \text{ mol C}}{12.01 \text{ g C}}\right)(-393.5 \text{ kJ/mol C}) = (2.613 \text{ K})x$$

$$x = 10.85 \text{ kJ/K}$$

6.7 $C_2H_4(g) + H_2(g) \longrightarrow C_2H_6(g) + 137 \text{ kJ}$

$$\text{Heat (kJ)} = 15.0 \text{ kg} \times \frac{1000 \text{ g}}{1 \text{ kg}} \times \frac{1 \text{ mol } C_2H_6}{30.07 \text{ g } C_2H_6} \times \frac{137 \text{ kJ}}{1 \text{ mol}}$$

$$= 6.83 \times 10^4 \text{ kJ}$$

6.8

$$2NO(g) + \tfrac{3}{2}O_2(g) \longrightarrow N_2O_5(s) \qquad \Delta H = -223.7 \text{ kJ}$$

$$\underline{2NO_2(g) \longrightarrow 2NO(g) + O_2(g) \quad \Delta H = 114.2 \text{ kJ}}$$

$$\cancel{2NO(g)} + \tfrac{1}{2}\cancel{\tfrac{3}{}}O_2(g) + 2NO_2(g) \longrightarrow$$

$$N_2O_5(s) + \cancel{2NO(g)} + \cancel{O_2(g)}$$

$$2NO_2(g) + \tfrac{1}{2}O_2(g) \longrightarrow N_2O_5(s) \qquad \Delta H = -109.5 \text{ kJ}$$

6.9 (a) $C(\text{graphite}) + 2H_2(g) + \tfrac{1}{2}O_2(g) \longrightarrow CH_3OH(l)$

$$\Delta H_f^\circ = -238.6 \text{ kJ}$$

(b) $Ca(s) + \tfrac{1}{2}O_2(g) \longrightarrow CaO(s) \quad \Delta H_f^\circ = -635.1 \text{ kJ}$

(c) $C(\text{graphite}) + \tfrac{1}{4}S_8(\text{rhombic}) \longrightarrow CS_2(l) \quad \Delta H_f^\circ = 87.9 \text{ kJ}$

6.10 ΔH_f° of $CH_3OH(l)$

$$= -\Delta H_{\text{rxn}}^\circ + 2\Delta H_f^\circ[H_2O(g)] + \Delta H_f^\circ[CO_2(g)]$$

$$= 638.5 \text{ kJ} + (2 \text{ mol})(-241.8 \text{ kJ/mol})$$

$$+ (1 \text{ mol})(-393.5 \text{ kJ/mol})$$

$$= -238.6 \text{ kJ}$$

PROBLEMS

Problems with **colored** numbers are answered in Appendix E and worked in detail in the Student Solutions Manual. Problem sections match those in the text and provide the numbers of relevant sample problems. Most offer Concept Review Questions, Skill-Building Exercises (grouped in pairs covering the same concept), and Problems in Context. The Comprehensive Problems are based on material from any section or previous chapter.

Forms of Energy and Their Interconversion
(Sample Problem 6.1)

Concept Review Questions

6.1 Why do heat (q) and work (w) have positive values when entering a system and negative values when leaving?

6.2 If you feel warm after exercising, have you increased the internal energy of your body? Explain.

6.3 An *adiabatic* process is one that involves no heat transfer. What is the relationship between work and the change in internal energy in an adiabatic process?

6.4 State two ways that you increase the internal energy of your body and two ways that you decrease it.

6.5 Name a common device used to accomplish each change:
(a) Electrical energy to thermal energy
(b) Electrical energy to sound energy
(c) Electrical energy to light energy
(d) Mechanical energy to electrical energy
(e) Chemical energy to electrical energy

6.6 In winter, an electric heater uses a certain amount of electrical energy to heat a room to 20°C. In summer, an air conditioner uses the same amount of electrical energy to cool the room to 20°C. Is the change in internal energy of the heater larger, smaller, or the same as that of the air conditioner? Explain.

6.7 You lift your textbook and drop it onto a desk. Describe the energy transformations (from one form to another) that occur, moving backward in time from a moment after impact.

Skill-Building Exercises (grouped in similar pairs)

6.8 A system receives 425 J of heat from and delivers 425 J of work to its surroundings. What is the change in internal energy of the system (in J)?

6.9 A system conducts 255 cal of heat to the surroundings and delivers 428 cal of work. What is the change in internal energy of the system (in cal)?

6.10 What is the change in internal energy (in J) of a system that releases 675 J of thermal energy to its surroundings and has 530 cal of work done on it?

6.11 What is the change in internal energy (in J) of a system that absorbs 0.615 kJ of heat from its surroundings and has 0.247 kcal of work done on it?

6.12 Complete combustion of 2.0 metric tons of coal to gaseous carbon dioxide releases 6.6×10^{10} J of heat. Convert this energy to (a) kilojoules; (b) kilocalories; (c) British thermal units.

6.13 Thermal decomposition of 5.0 metric tons of limestone to lime and carbon dioxide absorbs 9.0×10^6 kJ of heat. Convert this energy to (a) joules; (b) calories; (c) British thermal units.

Problems in Context
6.14 The nutritional calorie (Calorie) is equivalent to 1 kcal. One pound of body fat is equivalent to about 4.1×10^3 Calories. Express this quantity of energy in joules and kilojoules.

6.15 If an athlete expends 1950 kJ/h, how long does it take her to work off 1.0 lb of body fat? (See Problem 6.14.)

Enthalpy: Chemical Change at Constant Pressure
(Sample Problem 6.2)

Concept Review Questions
6.16 Why is the work done when a system expands against a constant external pressure assigned a negative sign?

6.17 Why is it often more convenient to measure ΔH than ΔE?

6.18 "Hot packs" used by skiers use the crystallization of sodium acetate from a concentrated solution. What is the sign of ΔH for this crystallization? Is the reaction exothermic or endothermic?

6.19 Classify the following processes as exothermic or endothermic: (a) freezing of water; (b) boiling of water; (c) digestion of food; (d) a person running; (e) a person growing; (f) wood being chopped; (g) heating with a furnace.

6.20 What are the two main components of the internal energy of a substance? On what are they based?

6.21 For each process, state whether ΔH is less than (more negative), equal to, or greater than ΔE of the system. Explain.
(a) An ideal gas is cooled at constant pressure.
(b) A gas mixture reacts exothermically at fixed volume.
(c) A solid reacts exothermically to yield a mixture of gases in a container of variable volume.

Skill-Building Exercises (grouped in similar pairs)
6.22 Draw an enthalpy diagram for a general exothermic reaction; label the axis, reactants, products, and ΔH with its sign.

6.23 Draw an enthalpy diagram for a general endothermic reaction; label the axis, reactants, products, and ΔH with its sign.

6.24 Write a balanced equation and draw an approximate enthalpy diagram for: (a) combustion of 1 mol of ethane; (b) freezing of liquid water.

6.25 Write a balanced equation and draw an approximate enthalpy diagram for (a) formation of 1 mol of sodium chloride from its elements (heat is released); (b) vaporization of liquid benzene.

6.26 Write a balanced equation and draw an approximate enthalpy diagram for (a) combustion of 1 mol of liquid methanol (CH_3OH); (b) formation of 1 mol of NO_2 from its elements (heat is absorbed).

6.27 Write a balanced equation and draw an approximate enthalpy diagram for (a) sublimation of dry ice [conversion of $CO_2(s)$ directly to $CO_2(g)$]; (b) reaction of 1 mol of SO_2 with O_2.

6.28 The circles represent a phase change at constant temperature:

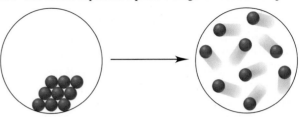

Is the value of each of the following positive (+), negative (−), or zero: (a) q_{sys}; (b) ΔE_{sys}; (c) ΔE_{univ}?

6.29 The scenes below represent a physical change taking place in a piston-cylinder assembly:

(a) Is w_{sys} +, −, or 0? (b) Is ΔH_{sys} +, −, or 0? (c) Can you determine whether ΔE_{surr} is +, −, or 0? Explain.

Calorimetry: Measuring the Heat of a Chemical or Physical Change
(Sample Problems 6.3 to 6.6)

Concept Review Questions
6.30 Which is larger, the specific heat capacity or the molar heat capacity of a substance? Explain.

6.31 What data do you need to determine the specific heat capacity of a substance?

6.32 Is the specific heat capacity of a substance an intensive or extensive property? Explain.

6.33 Distinguish between specific heat capacity, molar heat capacity, and heat capacity.

6.34 Both a coffee-cup calorimeter and a bomb calorimeter can be used to measure the heat transferred in a reaction. Which measures ΔE and which measures ΔH? Explain.

Skill-Building Exercises (grouped in similar pairs)
6.35 Find q when 22.0 g of water is heated from 25.0°C to 100.°C.

6.36 Calculate q when 0.10 g of ice is cooled from 10.°C to −75°C ($c_{ice} = 2.087$ J/g·K).

6.37 A 295-g aluminum engine part at an initial temperature of 13.00°C absorbs 75.0 kJ of heat. What is the final temperature of the part (c of Al = 0.900 J/g·K)?

6.38 A 27.7-g sample of the radiator coolant ethylene glycol releases 688 J of heat. What was the initial temperature of the sample if the final temperature is 32.5°C (c of ethylene glycol = 2.42 J/g·K)?

6.39 Two iron bolts of equal mass—one at 100.°C, the other at 55°C—are placed in an insulated container. Assuming the heat capacity of the container is negligible, what is the final temperature inside the container (c of iron = 0.450 J/g·K)?

6.40 One piece of copper jewelry at 105°C has twice the mass of another piece at 45°C. Both are placed in a calorimeter of negligible heat capacity. What is the final temperature inside the calorimeter (c of copper = 0.387 J/g·K)?

6.41 When 155 mL of water at 26°C is mixed with 75 mL of water at 85°C, what is the final temperature? (Assume that no heat is released to the surroundings; d of water is 1.00 g/mL.)

6.42 An unknown volume of water at 18.2°C is added to 24.4 mL of water at 35.0°C. If the final temperature is 23.5°C, what was the unknown volume? (Assume that no heat is released to the surroundings; d of water is 1.00 g/mL.)

6.43 A 455-g piece of copper tubing is heated to 89.5°C and placed in an insulated vessel containing 159 g of water at 22.8°C. Assuming no loss of water and a heat capacity of 10.0 J/K for the vessel, what is the final temperature (c of copper = 0.387 J/g·K)?

6.44 A 30.5-g sample of an alloy at 93.0°C is placed into 50.0 g of water at 22.0°C in an insulated coffee cup with a heat capacity of 9.2 J/K. If the final temperature of the system is 31.1°C, what is the specific heat capacity of the alloy?

Problems in Context

6.45 High-purity benzoic acid (C_6H_5COOH; ΔH for combustion = −3227 kJ/mol) is used to calibrate bomb calorimeters. A 1.221-g sample burns in a calorimeter (heat capacity = 1365 J/°C) that contains 1.200 kg of water. What is the temperature change?

6.46 Two aircraft rivets, one iron and the other copper, are placed in a calorimeter that has an initial temperature of 20.°C. The data for the rivets are as follows:

	Iron	Copper
Mass (g)	30.0	20.0
Initial T (°C)	0.0	100.0
c (J/g·K)	0.450	0.387

(a) Will heat flow from Fe to Cu or from Cu to Fe?
(b) What other information is needed to correct any measurements in an actual experiment?
(c) What is the maximum final temperature of the system (assuming the heat capacity of the calorimeter is negligible)?

6.47 A chemical engineer placed 1.520 g of a hydrocarbon in the bomb of a calorimeter (see Figure 6.10, p. 241). The bomb was immersed in 2.550 L of water and the sample was burned. The water temperature rose from 20.00°C to 23.55°C. If the calorimeter (excluding the water) had a heat capacity of 403 J/K, what was the heat released (q_V) per gram of hydrocarbon?

6.48 When 25.0 mL of 0.500 M H_2SO_4 is added to 25.0 mL of 1.00 M KOH in a coffee-cup calorimeter at 23.50°C, the temperature rises to 30.17°C. Calculate ΔH of this reaction. (Assume the total volume is the sum of the volumes and the density and specific heat capacity of the solution are the same as for water.)

Stoichiometry of Thermochemical Equations

(Sample Problem 6.7)

Concept Review Questions

6.49 Does a negative ΔH mean that the heat should be treated as a reactant or as a product?

6.50 Would you expect $O_2(g) \longrightarrow 2O(g)$ to have a positive or a negative ΔH? Explain.

6.51 Is ΔH positive or negative when 1 mol of water vapor condenses to liquid water? Why? How does this value compare with ΔH for the vaporization of 2 mol of liquid water to water vapor?

Skill-Building Exercises (grouped in similar pairs)

6.52 Consider the following balanced thermochemical equation for a reaction sometimes used for H_2S production:

$$\tfrac{1}{8}S_8(s) + H_2(g) \longrightarrow H_2S(g) \quad \Delta H = -20.2 \text{ kJ}$$

(a) Is this an exothermic or endothermic reaction?
(b) What is ΔH for the reverse reaction?
(c) What is ΔH when 2.6 mol of S_8 reacts?
(d) What is ΔH when 25.0 g of S_8 reacts?

6.53 Consider the following balanced thermochemical equation for the decomposition of the mineral magnesite:

$$MgCO_3(s) \longrightarrow MgO(s) + CO_2(g) \quad \Delta H = 117.3 \text{ kJ}$$

(a) Is heat absorbed or released in the reaction?
(b) What is ΔH for the reverse reaction?
(c) What is ΔH when 5.35 mol of CO_2 reacts with excess MgO?
(d) What is ΔH when 35.5 g of CO_2 reacts with excess MgO?

6.54 When 1 mol of NO(g) forms from its elements, 90.29 kJ of heat is absorbed. (a) Write a balanced thermochemical equation. (b) What is ΔH when 3.50 g of NO decomposes to its elements?

6.55 When 1 mol of KBr(s) decomposes to its elements, 394 kJ of heat is absorbed. (a) Write a balanced thermochemical equation. (b) What is ΔH when 10.0 kg of KBr forms from its elements?

Problems in Context

6.56 Liquid hydrogen peroxide, an oxidizing agent in many rocket fuel mixtures, releases oxygen gas on decomposition:

$$2H_2O_2(l) \longrightarrow 2H_2O(l) + O_2(g) \quad \Delta H = -196.1 \text{ kJ}$$

How much heat is released when 652 kg of H_2O_2 decomposes?

6.57 Compounds of boron and hydrogen are remarkable for their unusual bonding (described in Section 14.5) and also for their reactivity. With the more reactive halogens, for example, diborane (B_2H_6) forms trihalides even at low temperatures:

$$B_2H_6(g) + 6Cl_2(g) \longrightarrow 2BCl_3(g) + 6HCl(g)$$
$$\Delta H = -755.4 \text{ kJ}$$

What is ΔH per kilogram of diborane that reacts?

6.58 Deterioration of buildings, bridges, and other structures through the rusting of iron costs millions of dollars a day. The actual process requires water, but a simplified equation is

$$4Fe(s) + 3O_2(g) \longrightarrow 2Fe_2O_3(s) \quad \Delta H = -1.65 \times 10^3 \text{ kJ}$$

(a) How much heat is released when 0.250 kg of iron rusts?
(b) How much rust forms when 4.85×10^3 kJ of heat is released?

6.59 A mercury mirror forms inside a test tube as a result of the thermal decomposition of mercury(II) oxide:

$$2HgO(s) \longrightarrow 2Hg(l) + O_2(g) \quad \Delta H = 181.6 \text{ kJ}$$

(a) How much heat is absorbed to decompose 555 g of the oxide?
(b) If 275 kJ of heat is absorbed, how many grams of Hg form?

6.60 Most ethylene (C_2H_4), the starting material for producing polyethylene, comes from petroleum processing. It also occurs naturally as a fruit-ripening hormone and as a component of natural gas. (a) The heat transferred during combustion of C_2H_4 is −1411 kJ/mol. Write a balanced thermochemical equation. (b) How many grams of C_2H_4 must burn to give 70.0 kJ of heat?

6.61 Sucrose ($C_{12}H_{22}O_{11}$, table sugar) is oxidized in the body by O_2 via a complex set of reactions that produces $CO_2(g)$ and $H_2O(g)$ and releases 5.64×10^3 kJ/mol of sucrose. (a) Write a balanced thermochemical equation for the overall process. (b) How much heat is released per gram of sucrose oxidized?

Hess's Law: Finding ΔH of Any Reaction
(Sample Problem 6.8)

Concept Review Questions
6.62 Express Hess's law in your own words.

6.63 What is the main application of Hess's law?

6.64 When carbon burns in a deficiency of O_2, a mixture of CO and CO_2 forms. Carbon burns in excess O_2 to form only CO_2, and CO burns in excess O_2 to form only CO_2. Use ΔH values of the latter two reactions (from Appendix B) to calculate ΔH for

$$C(graphite) + \tfrac{1}{2}O_2(g) \longrightarrow CO(g)$$

Skill-Building Exercises (grouped in similar pairs)
6.65 Calculate ΔH for

$$Ca(s) + \tfrac{1}{2}O_2(g) + CO_2(g) \longrightarrow CaCO_3(s)$$

given the following reactions:

$$Ca(s) + \tfrac{1}{2}O_2(g) \longrightarrow CaO(s) \qquad \Delta H = -635.1 \text{ kJ}$$
$$CaCO_3(s) \longrightarrow CaO(s) + CO_2(g) \qquad \Delta H = 178.3 \text{ kJ}$$

6.66 Calculate ΔH for

$$2NOCl(g) \longrightarrow N_2(g) + O_2(g) + Cl_2(g)$$

given the following reactions:

$$\tfrac{1}{2}N_2(g) + \tfrac{1}{2}O_2(g) \longrightarrow NO(g) \qquad \Delta H = 90.3 \text{ kJ}$$
$$NO(g) + \tfrac{1}{2}Cl_2(g) \longrightarrow NOCl(g) \qquad \Delta H = -38.6 \text{ kJ}$$

6.67 Write the balanced overall equation (equation 3) for the following process, calculate $\Delta H_{overall}$, and match the number of each equation with the letter of the appropriate arrow in Figure P6.67:

(1) $N_2(g) + O_2(g) \longrightarrow 2NO(g) \qquad\qquad \Delta H = 180.6 \text{ kJ}$
(2) $2NO(g) + O_2(g) \longrightarrow 2NO_2(g) \qquad\quad \Delta H = -114.2 \text{ kJ}$
(3) $ \Delta H_{overall} = ?$

6.68 Write the balanced overall equation (equation 3) for the following process, calculate $\Delta H_{overall}$, and match the number of each equation with the letter of the appropriate arrow in Figure P6.68:

(1) $P_4(s) + 6Cl_2(g) \longrightarrow 4PCl_3(g) \qquad\quad \Delta H = -1148 \text{ kJ}$
(2) $4PCl_3(g) + 4Cl_2(g) \longrightarrow 4PCl_5(g) \qquad \Delta H = -460 \text{ kJ}$
(3) $ \Delta H_{overall} = ?$

Figure P6.67

Figure P6.68

6.69 At a given set of conditions, 241.8 kJ of heat is given off when 1 mol of $H_2O(g)$ forms from its elements. Under the same conditions, 285.8 kJ is given off when 1 mol of $H_2O(l)$ forms from its elements. Find ΔH for the vaporization of water at these conditions.

6.70 When 1 mol of $CS_2(l)$ forms from its elements at 1 atm and 25°C, 89.7 kJ of heat is absorbed, and it takes 27.7 kJ to vaporize 1 mol of the liquid. How much heat is absorbed when 1 mol of $CS_2(g)$ forms from its elements at these conditions?

Problems in Context
6.71 Diamond and graphite are two crystalline forms of carbon. At 1 atm and 25°C, diamond changes to graphite so slowly that the enthalpy change of the process must be obtained indirectly. Using equations from the numbered list below, determine ΔH for

$$C(diamond) \longrightarrow C(graphite)$$

(1) $C(diamond) + O_2(g) \longrightarrow CO_2(g) \quad \Delta H = -395.4 \text{ kJ}$
(2) $2CO_2(g) \longrightarrow 2CO(g) + O_2(g) \qquad\ \Delta H = 566.0 \text{ kJ}$
(3) $C(graphite) + O_2(g) \longrightarrow CO_2(g) \quad \Delta H = -393.5 \text{ kJ}$
(4) $2CO(g) \longrightarrow C(graphite) + CO_2(g) \ \Delta H = -172.5 \text{ kJ}$

Standard Enthalpies of Reaction (ΔH°_{rxn})
(Sample Problems 6.9 and 6.10)

Concept Review Questions
6.72 What is the difference between the standard enthalpy of formation and the standard enthalpy of reaction?

6.73 How are ΔH°_f values used to calculate ΔH°_{rxn}?

6.74 Make any changes needed in each of the following equations to make the enthalpy change equal to ΔH°_f for the compound:
(a) $Cl(g) + Na(s) \longrightarrow NaCl(s)$
(b) $H_2O(g) \longrightarrow 2H(g) + \tfrac{1}{2}O_2(g)$
(c) $\tfrac{1}{2}N_2(g) + \tfrac{3}{2}H_2(g) \longrightarrow NH_3(g)$

Skill-Building Exercises (grouped in similar pairs)
6.75 Use Table 6.3 or Appendix B to write a balanced formation equation at standard conditions for each of the following compounds: (a) $CaCl_2$; (b) $NaHCO_3$; (c) CCl_4; (d) HNO_3.

6.76 Use Table 6.3 or Appendix B to write a balanced formation equation at standard conditions for each of the following compounds: (a) HI; (b) SiF_4; (c) O_3; (d) $Ca_3(PO_4)_2$.

6.77 Calculate ΔH°_{rxn} for each of the following:
(a) $2H_2S(g) + 3O_2(g) \longrightarrow 2SO_2(g) + 2H_2O(g)$
(b) $CH_4(g) + Cl_2(g) \longrightarrow CCl_4(l) + HCl(g)$ [unbalanced]

6.78 Calculate ΔH°_{rxn} for each of the following:
(a) $SiO_2(s) + 4HF(g) \longrightarrow SiF_4(g) + 2H_2O(l)$
(b) $C_2H_6(g) + O_2(g) \longrightarrow CO_2(g) + H_2O(g)$ [unbalanced]

6.79 Copper(I) oxide can be oxidized to copper(II) oxide:

$$Cu_2O(s) + \tfrac{1}{2}O_2(g) \longrightarrow 2CuO(s) \quad \Delta H^\circ_{rxn} = -146.0 \text{ kJ}$$

Given ΔH°_f of $Cu_2O(s) = -168.6$ kJ/mol, find ΔH°_f of $CuO(s)$.

6.80 Acetylene burns in air by the following equation:

$$C_2H_2(g) + \tfrac{5}{2}O_2(g) \longrightarrow 2CO_2(g) + H_2O(g)$$
$$\Delta H^\circ_{rxn} = -1255.8 \text{ kJ}$$

Given ΔH°_f of $CO_2(g) = -393.5$ kJ/mol and ΔH°_f of $H_2O(g) = -241.8$ kJ/mol, find ΔH°_f of $C_2H_2(g)$.

Problems in Context
6.81 The common lead-acid car battery produces a large burst of current, even at low temperatures, and is rechargeable. The reaction that occurs while recharging a "dead" battery is

$$2PbSO_4(s) + 2H_2O(l) \longrightarrow Pb(s) + PbO_2(s) + 2H_2SO_4(l)$$

(a) Use ΔH°_f values from Appendix B to calculate ΔH°_{rxn}.
(b) Use the following equations to check your answer to part (a):

(1) $Pb(s) + PbO_2(s) + 2SO_3(g) \longrightarrow 2PbSO_4(s)$

$$\Delta H°_{rxn} = -768 \text{ kJ}$$

(2) $SO_3(g) + H_2O(l) \longrightarrow H_2SO_4(l)$ $\Delta H°_{rxn} = -132 \text{ kJ}$

Comprehensive Problems

6.82 Stearic acid ($C_{18}H_{36}O_2$) is a fatty acid, a molecule with a long hydrocarbon chain and an organic acid group (COOH) at the end. It is used to make cosmetics, ointments, soaps, and candles and is found in animal tissue as part of many saturated fats. In fact, when you eat meat, you are ingesting some fats containing stearic acid. (a) Write a balanced equation for the combustion of stearic acid to gaseous products. (b) Calculate $\Delta H°_{rxn}$ for this combustion ($\Delta H°_f$ of $C_{18}H_{36}O_2 = -948 \text{ kJ/mol}$). (c) Calculate the heat (q) released in kJ and kcal when 1.00 g of stearic acid is burned completely. (d) A candy bar contains 11.0 g of fat and 100. Cal from fat; is this consistent with your answer for part (c)?

6.83 Diluting sulfuric acid with water is highly exothermic:

$$H_2SO_4(l) \xrightarrow{H_2O} H_2SO_4(aq) + heat$$

(a) Use Appendix B to find $\Delta H°_{rxn}$ for diluting 1.00 mol of $H_2SO_4(l)$ ($d = 1.83 \text{ g/mL}$) to 1 L of 1.00 M $H_2SO_4(aq)$ ($d = 1.060 \text{ g/mL}$). (b) Suppose you carry out the dilution in a calorimeter. The initial T is 25.0°C, and the specific heat capacity of the final solution is 3.50 J/g·K. What is the final T? (c) Use the ideas of density and heat capacity to explain why you should add acid to water rather than water to acid.

6.84 A balloonist begins a trip in a helium-filled balloon in early morning when the temperature is 15°C. By mid-afternoon, the temperature is 30.°C. Assuming the pressure remains at 1.00 atm, for each mole of helium, calculate the following:
(a) The initial and final volumes
(b) The change in internal energy, ΔE (*Hint:* Helium behaves like an ideal gas, so $E = \frac{3}{2}nRT$. Be sure the units of R are consistent with those of E.)
(c) The work (w) done by the helium (in J)
(d) The heat (q) transferred (in J)
(e) ΔH for the process (in J)
(f) Explain the relationship between the answers to parts (d) and (e).

6.85 In winemaking, the sugars in grapes undergo *fermentation* by yeast to yield CH_3CH_2OH and CO_2. During cellular *respiration* (combustion), sugar and ethanol yield water vapor and CO_2.
(a) Using $C_6H_{12}O_6$ for sugar, calculate $\Delta H°_{rxn}$ of fermentation and of respiration.
(b) Write a combustion reaction for ethanol. Which has a higher $\Delta H°_{rxn}$ for combustion per mole of C, sugar or ethanol?

6.86 Three of the reactions that occur when the paraffin of a candle (typical formula $C_{21}H_{44}$) burns are as follows:
(1) Complete combustion forms CO_2 and water vapor.
(2) Incomplete combustion forms CO and water vapor.
(3) Some wax is oxidized to elemental C (soot) and water vapor.
(a) Find $\Delta H°_{rxn}$ of each reaction ($\Delta H°_f$ of $C_{21}H_{44} = -476 \text{ kJ/mol}$; use graphite for elemental carbon).
(b) Find q (in kJ) when a 254-g candle burns completely.
(c) Find q (in kJ) when 8.00% by mass of the candle burns incompletely and 5.00% by mass of it undergoes soot formation.

6.87 Ethylene oxide (EO) is prepared by the vapor-phase oxidation of ethylene. Its main uses are in the preparation of the antifreeze ethylene glycol and in the production of poly(ethylene terephtha-

late), which is used to make beverage bottles and fibers. Pure EO vapor can decompose explosively:

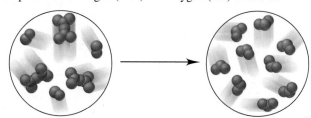

Liquid EO has $\Delta H°_f = -77.4 \text{ kJ/mol}$ and $\Delta H°$ for its vaporization = 569.4 J/g. (a) Calculate $\Delta H°_{rxn}$ for the gas-phase reaction. (b) External heating causes the vapor to decompose at 10 bar and 93°C in a distillation column. What is the final temperature if the average specific heat capacity of the products is 2.5 J/g·°C?

6.88 The following scenes represent a gaseous reaction between compounds of nitrogen (blue) and oxygen (red) at 298 K:

(a) Write a balanced equation and use Appendix B to calculate $\Delta H°_{rxn}$.
(b) If each molecule of product represents 1.50×10^{-2} mol, what quantity of heat (in J) is released or absorbed?

6.89 Isooctane (C_8H_{18}; $d = 0.692 \text{ g/mL}$) is used as the fuel in a test of a new automobile drive train.
(a) How much energy (in kJ) is released by combustion of 20.4 gal of isooctane to gases ($\Delta H°_{rxn} = -5.44 \times 10^3 \text{ kJ/mol}$)?
(b) The energy delivered to the wheels at 65 mph is 5.5×10^4 kJ/h. Assuming *all* the energy is transferred as work to the wheels, how far (in km) can the car travel on the 20.4 gal of fuel?
(c) If the actual range is 455 miles, explain your answer to (b).

6.90 Four 50.-g samples of different colorless liquids are placed in beakers at $T_{initial} = 25.00°C$. Each liquid is heated until 450. J of heat has been absorbed; T_{final} is shown on each beaker below. Rank the liquids in order of increasing specific heat capacity.

27.15°C	35.59°C	28.96°C	30.29°C
A	B	C	D

6.91 Reaction of gaseous ClF with F_2 yields liquid ClF_3, an important fluorinating agent. Use the following thermochemical equations to calculate $\Delta H°_{rxn}$ for this reaction:
(1) $2ClF(g) + O_2(g) \longrightarrow Cl_2O(g) + OF_2(g)$ $\Delta H°_{rxn} = 167.5 \text{ kJ}$
(2) $2F_2(g) + O_2(g) \longrightarrow 2OF_2(g)$ $\Delta H°_{rxn} = -43.5 \text{ kJ}$
(3) $2ClF_3(l) + 2O_2(g) \longrightarrow Cl_2O(g) + 3OF_2(g)$

$$\Delta H°_{rxn} = 394.1 \text{ kJ}$$

6.92 Silver bromide is used to coat ordinary black-and-white photographic film, while high-speed film uses silver iodide.
(a) When 50.0 mL of 5.0 g/L $AgNO_3$ is added to a coffee-cup calorimeter containing 50.0 mL of 5.0 g/L NaI, with both solutions at 25°C, what mass of AgI forms?
(b) Use Appendix B to find $\Delta H°_{rxn}$.
(c) What is ΔT_{soln} (assuming the volumes are additive and the solution has the density and specific heat capacity of water)?

6.93 The calorie (4.184 J) is defined as the quantity of energy needed to raise the temperature of 1.00 g of liquid water 1.00°C. The British thermal unit (Btu) is defined as the quantity of energy needed to raise the temperature of 1.00 lb of liquid water 1.00°F.
(a) How many joules are in 1.00 Btu (1 lb = 453.6 g; 1.0°C = 1.8°F)?
(b) The *therm* is a unit of energy consumption and is defined as 100,000 Btu. How many joules are in 1.00 therm?
(c) How many moles of methane must be burned to give 1.00 therm of energy? (Assume water forms as a gas.)
(d) If natural gas costs $0.66 per therm, what is the cost per mole of methane? (Assume natural gas is pure methane.)
(e) How much would it cost to warm 318 gal of water in a hot tub from 15.0°C to 42.0°C by burning methane (1 gal = 3.78 L)?

6.94 When organic matter decomposes under oxygen-free (anaerobic) conditions, methane is one of the products. Thus, enormous deposits of natural gas, which is almost entirely methane, serve as a major source of fuel for home and industry.
(a) Known deposits of natural gas can produce 5600 EJ of energy (1 EJ = 10^{18} J). Current total global energy usage is 4.0×10^2 EJ per year. Find the mass (in kg) of known deposits of natural gas (ΔH°_{rxn} for the combustion of CH_4 = −802 kJ/mol).
(b) At current rates of usage, for how many years could these deposits supply the world's total energy needs?
(c) What volume (in ft^3) of natural gas, measured at STP, is required to heat 1.00 qt of water from 25.0°C to 100.0°C (*d* of H_2O = 1.00 g/mL; *d* of CH_4 at STP = 0.72 g/L)?
(d) The fission of 1 mol of uranium (about 4×10^{-4} ft^3) in a nuclear reactor produces 2×10^{13} J. What volume (in ft^3) of natural gas would produce the same amount of energy?

6.95 A reaction takes place in a steel vessel within a chamber filled with argon gas. Shown below are molecular views of the argon adjacent to the surface of the reaction vessel before and after the reaction. Was the reaction exothermic or endothermic? Explain.

Before reaction → After reaction

6.96 An aqueous waste stream with a maximum concentration of 0.50 *M* H_2SO_4 (*d* = 1.030 g/mL at 25°C) is neutralized by controlled addition of 40% NaOH (*d* = 1.430 g/L) before it goes to the process sewer and then to the chemical plant waste treatment facility. A safety review finds that the waste stream could meet a small stream of an immiscible organic compound, which could form a flammable vapor in air at 40.°C. The maximum temperature reached by the NaOH solution and the waste stream is 31°C. Could the temperature increase due to the heat transferred by the neutralization cause the organic vapor to explode? Assume the specific heat capacity of each solution is 4.184 J/g·K.

6.97 Kerosene, a common space-heater fuel, is a mixture of hydrocarbons whose "average" formula is $C_{12}H_{26}$.
(a) Write a balanced equation, using the simplest whole-number coefficients, for the complete combustion of kerosene to gases.
(b) If ΔH°_{rxn} = -1.50×10^4 kJ for the combustion equation as written in part (a), determine ΔH°_f of kerosene.
(c) Calculate the heat released by combustion of 0.50 gal of kerosene (*d* of kerosene = 0.749 g/mL).

(d) How many gallons of kerosene must be burned for a kerosene furnace to produce 1250. Btu (1 Btu = 1.055 kJ)?

6.98 Silicon tetrachloride is produced annually on the multikiloton scale and used in making transistor-grade silicon. It can be produced directly from the elements (reaction 1) or, more cheaply, by heating sand and graphite with chlorine gas (reaction 2). If water is present in reaction 2, some tetrachloride may be lost in an unwanted side reaction (reaction 3):
(1) $Si(s) + 2Cl_2(g) \longrightarrow SiCl_4(g)$
(2) $SiO_2(s) + 2C(graphite) + 2Cl_2(g) \longrightarrow SiCl_4(g) + 2CO(g)$
(3) $SiCl_4(g) + 2H_2O(g) \longrightarrow SiO_2(s) + 4HCl(g)$
$$\Delta H^{\circ}_{rxn} = -139.5 \text{ kJ}$$
(a) Use reaction 3 to calculate the standard enthalpies of reaction of reactions 1 and 2. (b) What is the standard enthalpy of reaction for a fourth reaction that is the sum of reactions 2 and 3?

6.99 One mole of nitrogen gas confined within a cylinder by a piston is heated from 0°C to 819°C at 1.00 atm.
(a) Calculate the work done by the expanding gas in joules (1 J = 9.87×10^{-3} atm·L). Assume all the energy is used to do work.
(b) What would be the temperature change if the gas were heated using the same amount of energy in a container of fixed volume? (Assume the specific heat capacity of N_2 is 1.00 J/g·K.)

6.100 The chemistry of nitrogen oxides is very versatile. Given the following reactions and their standard enthalpy changes,

(1) $NO(g) + NO_2(g) \longrightarrow N_2O_3(g)$	ΔH°_{rxn} =	−39.8 kJ
(2) $NO(g) + NO_2(g) + O_2(g) \longrightarrow N_2O_5(g)$	ΔH°_{rxn} =	−112.5 kJ
(3) $2NO_2(g) \longrightarrow N_2O_4(g)$	ΔH°_{rxn} =	−57.2 kJ
(4) $2NO(g) + O_2(g) \longrightarrow 2NO_2(g)$	ΔH°_{rxn} =	−114.2 kJ
(5) $N_2O_5(s) \longrightarrow N_2O_5(g)$	ΔH°_{rxn} =	54.1 kJ

calculate the standard enthalpy of reaction for
$$N_2O_3(g) + N_2O_5(s) \longrightarrow 2N_2O_4(g)$$

6.101 Electric generating plants transport large amounts of hot water through metal pipes, and oxygen dissolved in the water can cause a major corrosion problem. Hydrazine (N_2H_4) added to the water avoids the problem by reacting with the oxygen:
$$N_2H_4(aq) + O_2(g) \longrightarrow N_2(g) + 2H_2O(l)$$
About 4×10^7 kg of hydrazine is produced every year by reacting ammonia with sodium hypochlorite in the *Raschig process:*
$$2NH_3(aq) + NaOCl(aq) \longrightarrow N_2H_4(aq) + NaCl(aq) + H_2O(l)$$
$$\Delta H^{\circ}_{rxn} = -151 \text{ kJ}$$
(a) If ΔH°_f of NaOCl(aq) = −346 kJ/mol, find ΔH°_f of $N_2H_4(aq)$.
(b) What is the heat released when aqueous N_2H_4 is added to 5.00×10^3 L of water that is 2.50×10^{-4} *M* O_2?

6.102 Liquid methanol (CH_3OH) can be used as an alternative fuel in pickup and SUV engines. An industrial method for preparing it involves the catalytic hydrogenation of carbon monoxide:
$$CO(g) + 2H_2(g) \xrightarrow{\text{catalyst}} CH_3OH(l)$$
How much heat (in kJ) is released when 15.0 L of CO at 85°C and 112 kPa reacts with 18.5 L of H_2 at 75°C and 744 torr?

6.103 (a) How much heat is released when 25.0 g of methane burns in excess O_2 to form gaseous CO_2 and H_2O?
(b) Calculate the temperature of the product mixture if the methane and air are both at an initial temperature of 0.0°C. Assume a stoichiometric ratio of methane to oxygen from the air, with air being 21% O_2 by volume (*c* of CO_2 = 57.2 J/mol·K; *c* of $H_2O(g)$ = 36.0 J/mol·K; *c* of N_2 = 30.5 J/mol·K).

Quantum Theory and Atomic Structure

Concepts and skills to review before you study this chapter

- discovery of the electron and atomic nucleus (Section 2.4)
- major features of atomic structure (Section 2.5)
- changes in the energy state of a system (Section 6.1)

Over a few remarkable decades—from around 1890 to 1930—a number of revolutions took place in Western science and culture. ● One concerned our view of matter and energy, and you demonstrate it with every flick of a light switch (*photo*). That new view is essential for understanding TV screens, fireworks, and neon signs, not to mention the structure of the atom! But revolutions in science are not the violent upheavals of political overthrow. Flaws appear in a model due to conflicting evidence, a startling discovery widens the flaws into cracks, and the theoretical structure crumbles. Then, new insight, verified by experiment, builds a model more consistent with reality. So it was when Lavoisier's theory of combustion overthrew the phlogiston model, when Dalton's atomic theory established the idea of individual units of matter, and when Rutherford's model substituted nuclear atoms for "billiard balls" or "plum puddings." You will see this process unfold again as we discuss the development of modern atomic theory.

IN THIS CHAPTER . . . We discuss quantum mechanics, the theory that explains the fundamental nature of energy and matter and accounts for atomic structure.

- We consider the classical distinction between the wave properties of energy and the particle properties of matter.
- We then examine two observations—blackbody radiation and the photoelectric effect—whose explanations led to a *quantized*, or particulate, model of light.
- We see that light emitted by excited atoms—an *atomic spectrum*—suggests an atom with distinct energy levels, and we apply spectra to chemical analysis.
- We see how wave-particle duality, which shows that matter and energy have similar properties, and the uncertainty principle, which proposes that electron behavior can never be known exactly, led to the current model of the H atom.
- We present quantum numbers, which specify the size, shape, and orientation of atomic orbitals, the regions an electron occupies in the H atom. (In Chapter 8, we'll examine quantum numbers for atoms with more than one electron.)

● **A Time of Revolution** Here are some of the revolutionary discoveries and events witnessed by the Western world during those decades:

1895	Röntgen: discovery of x-rays
1896	Becquerel: discovery of radioactivity
1897	Thomson: discovery of the electron
1900	Freud: theory of the unconscious
1900	Planck: quantum theory
1901	Marconi: invention of the radio
1903	Wright brothers: flight of a plane
1905	Ford: assembly line to build cars
1905	Rutherford: radioactivity explained
1905	Einstein: relativity/photon theories
1906	St. Denis: modern dance
1908	Matisse/Picasso: modern art
1909	Schoenberg/Berg: modern music
1911	Rutherford: nuclear model
1913	Bohr: atomic spectra and new model
1914–1918:	World War I
1923	Compton: photon momentum
1924	De Broglie: wave theory of matter
1926	Schrödinger: wave equation
1927	Heisenberg: uncertainty principle

7.1 • THE NATURE OF LIGHT

Visible light, x-rays, and microwaves are some of the types of **electromagnetic radiation** (also called *electromagnetic energy* or *radiant energy*). All electromagnetic radiation consists of energy propagated by electric and magnetic fields that increase and decrease in intensity as they move through space. This *classical wave model* explains why rainbows form, how magnifying glasses work, and many other familiar observations. But, it cannot explain observations on the very *un*familiar atomic scale. In this section, we describe some properties of electromagnetic radiation and note how they are distinguished from the properties of matter. But, then, we see that some other properties blur that distinction and require a new model to explain them.

The Wave Nature of Light

The wave properties of electromagnetic radiation are described by three variables and one constant (Figure 7.1, *next page*):

1. *Frequency* (v, Greek *nu*). The **frequency** of a wave is the number of cycles it undergoes per second, expressed by the unit 1/second [s^{-1}; also called a *hertz* (Hz)].

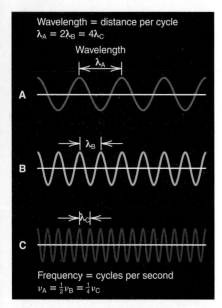

Figure 7.1 The reciprocal relationship of frequency and wavelength.

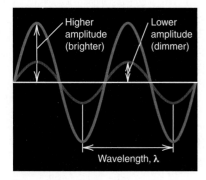

Figure 7.2 Differing amplitude (brightness, or intensity) of a wave.

2. *Wavelength* (λ, Greek *lambda*). The **wavelength** is the distance between any point on a wave and the corresponding point on the next crest (or trough) of the wave, that is, the distance the wave travels during one cycle. Wavelength has units of meters or, for very short wavelengths, nanometers (nm, 10^{-9} m), picometers (pm, 10^{-12} m), or the non-SI unit angstroms (Å, 10^{-10} m).

3. *Speed.* The speed of a wave is the distance it moves per unit time (meters per second), the product of its frequency (cycles per second) and wavelength (meters per cycle):

$$\text{Units for speed of wave:} \quad \frac{\text{cycles}}{\text{s}} \times \frac{\text{m}}{\text{cycle}} = \frac{\text{m}}{\text{s}}$$

In a vacuum, electromagnetic radiation moves at 2.99792458×10^8 m/s (3.00×10^8 m/s to three significant figures), a *physical constant* called the **speed of light** (*c*):

$$c = \nu \times \lambda \tag{7.1}$$

Since the product of ν and λ is a constant, they have a reciprocal relationship— *radiation with a high frequency has a short wavelength, and vice versa*:

$$\nu \uparrow \lambda \downarrow \quad \text{and} \quad \nu \downarrow \lambda \uparrow$$

4. *Amplitude.* The **amplitude** of a wave is the height of the crest (or depth of the trough). For an electromagnetic wave, the amplitude is related to the *intensity* of the radiation, or its brightness in the case of visible light. Light of a particular color has a specific frequency (and thus, wavelength) but, as Figure 7.2 shows, it can be dimmer (lower amplitude, less intense) or brighter (higher amplitude, more intense).

The Electromagnetic Spectrum Visible light represents a small region of the **electromagnetic spectrum** (Figure 7.3). *All waves in the spectrum travel at the same speed through a vacuum but differ in frequency and, therefore, wavelength.*

The spectrum is a *continuum of radiant energy,* so each region meets the next. For instance, the **infrared (IR)** region meets the *microwave* region on one end and the *visible* region on the other. We perceive different wavelengths (or frequencies) of visible light as colors, from red ($\lambda \approx 750$ nm) to violet ($\lambda \approx 400$ nm). Light of a single wavelength is called *monochromatic* (Greek, "one color"), whereas light of many wavelengths is *polychromatic*. White light is polychromatic. The region adjacent to visible light on the short-wavelength end consists of **ultraviolet (UV)** radiation (also called *ultraviolet light*). Still shorter wavelengths (higher frequencies) make up the x-ray and gamma (γ) ray regions.

Some types of electromagnetic radiation are utilized by familiar devices; for example, long-wavelength, low-frequency radiation is used by microwave ovens, radios, and cell phones. But electromagnetic emissions are everywhere: coming from

Figure 7.3 Regions of the electromagnetic spectrum. The visible region is expanded (and the scale made linear) to show the component colors.

human artifacts such as lightbulbs, x-ray equipment, and car motors, and from natural sources such as the Sun, lightning, radioactivity, and even the glow of fireflies! Our knowledge of the universe comes from radiation entering our eyes and our light, x-ray, and radio telescopes.

Sample Problem 7.1 | Interconverting Wavelength and Frequency

Problem A dental hygienist uses x-rays ($\lambda = 1.00$ Å) to take a series of dental radiographs while the patient listens to a radio station ($\lambda = 325$ cm) and looks out the window at the blue sky ($\lambda = 473$ nm). What is the frequency (in s^{-1}) of the electromagnetic radiation from each source? (Assume that the radiation travels at the speed of light, 3.00×10^8 m/s.)

Plan We are given the wavelengths, so we use Equation 7.1 to find the frequencies. However, we must first convert the wavelengths to meters because c has units of m/s.

Solution For the x-rays: Converting from angstroms to meters,

$$\lambda = 1.00 \text{ Å} \times \frac{10^{-10} \text{ m}}{1 \text{ Å}} = 1.00 \times 10^{-10} \text{ m}$$

Calculating the frequency:

$$\nu = \frac{c}{\lambda} = \frac{3.00 \times 10^8 \text{ m/s}}{1.00 \times 10^{-10} \text{ m}} = \boxed{3.00 \times 10^{18} \text{ s}^{-1}}$$

For the radio signal: Combining steps to calculate the frequency,

$$\nu = \frac{c}{\lambda} = \frac{3.00 \times 10^8 \text{ m/s}}{325 \text{ cm} \times \dfrac{10^{-2} \text{ m}}{1 \text{ cm}}} = \boxed{9.23 \times 10^7 \text{ s}^{-1}}$$

For the blue sky: Combining steps to calculate the frequency,

$$\nu = \frac{c}{\lambda} = \frac{3.00 \times 10^8 \text{ m/s}}{473 \text{ nm} \times \dfrac{10^{-9} \text{ m}}{1 \text{ nm}}} = \boxed{6.34 \times 10^{14} \text{ s}^{-1}}$$

Check The orders of magnitude are correct for the regions of the electromagnetic spectrum (see Figure 7.3): x-rays (10^{19} to 10^{16} s^{-1}), radio waves (10^9 to 10^4 s^{-1}), and visible light (7.5×10^{14} to 4.0×10^{14} s^{-1}).

Comment The radio station here is broadcasting at 92.3×10^6 s^{-1}, or 92.3 million Hz (92.3 MHz), about midway in the FM range.

Follow-Up Problem 7.1 Some diamonds appear yellow because they contain nitrogen compounds that absorb purple light of frequency 7.23×10^{14} Hz. Calculate the wavelength (in nm and Å) of the absorbed light.

Road Map

Wavelength (given units)

1 Å $= 10^{-10}$ m
1 cm $= 10^{-2}$ m
1 nm $= 10^{-9}$ m

Wavelength (m)

$\nu = \dfrac{c}{\lambda}$

Frequency (s^{-1}, or Hz)

The Classical Distinction Between Energy and Matter In our everyday world, matter comes in chunks you can hold and weigh, and you can change the quantity of matter piece by piece. In contrast, energy is "massless," and its quantity can change continuously. Matter moves in specific paths, whereas radiant energy (light) travels in diffuse waves. Let's examine some distinctions between the behavior of waves of energy and particles of matter.

1. *Refraction and dispersion.* Light of a given wavelength travels at different speeds through various transparent media—vacuum, air, water, quartz, and so forth. Therefore, when a light wave passes from one medium into another, the speed of the wave changes. Figure 7.4A on the next page shows the phenomenon known as **refraction.** If the wave strikes the boundary between media, say, between air and water, at an angle other than 90°, the change in speed causes a change in direction, and the wave continues at a different angle. The angle of refraction depends on the two media and the wavelength of the light. In the related process of *dispersion,* white light separates (disperses) into its component colors when it passes through a prism (or other refracting object) because each incoming wave is refracted at a slightly different angle.

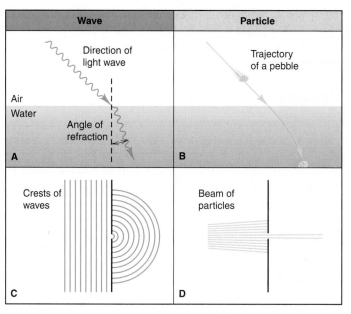

Wave	Particle
Direction of light wave	Trajectory of a pebble
Air	
Water	
Angle of refraction	
A	**B**
Crests of waves	Beam of particles
C	**D**

Figure 7.4 Different behaviors of waves and particles. A, Refraction: The speed of a light wave passing between media changes immediately, which bends its path. **B,** The speed of a particle continues changing gradually. **C,** Diffraction: A wave bends around both edges of a small opening, forming a semicircular wave. **D,** Particles either enter a small opening or not.

How does wave theory explain rainbows?

In contrast to a wave of light, a particle of matter, like a pebble, does not undergo refraction. If you throw a pebble through the air into a pond, it continues to slow down gradually along a curved path after entering the water (Figure 7.4B).

Two of many familiar applications of refraction and dispersion involve rainbows and diamonds. You see a rainbow when sunlight entering the near surface of a droplet is dispersed and reflected off the far surface. Red light is bent least, so it appears higher in the sky and violet lower *(see photo).* A diamond's color sparkles because its facets disperse and reflect the incoming light.

2. *Diffraction and interference.* When a wave strikes the edge of an object, it bends around it in a phenomenon called **diffraction.** If the wave passes through a slit about as wide as its wavelength, it bends around both edges of the slit and forms a semicircular wave on the other side of the opening (Figure 7.4C).

In contrast, when you throw a collection of particles, like a handful of sand, at a small opening, some particles hit the edge, while others go through the opening and continue in a narrower group (Figure 7.4D).

When waves of light pass through two adjacent slits, the nearby emerging circular waves interact through the process of *interference.* If the crests of the waves coincide *(in phase),* they interfere *constructively*—the amplitudes add together to form a brighter region. If crests coincide with troughs *(out of phase),* they interfere *destructively*—the amplitudes cancel to form a darker region. The result is a *diffraction pattern* (Figure 7.5).

In contrast, particles passing through adjacent openings continue in straight paths, some colliding and moving at different angles.

The Particle Nature of Light

Three observations involving matter and light confounded physicists at the turn of the 20th century: blackbody radiation, the photoelectric effect, and atomic spectra. Explaining these phenomena required a radically new picture of energy. We discuss the first two of them here and the third in Section 7.2.

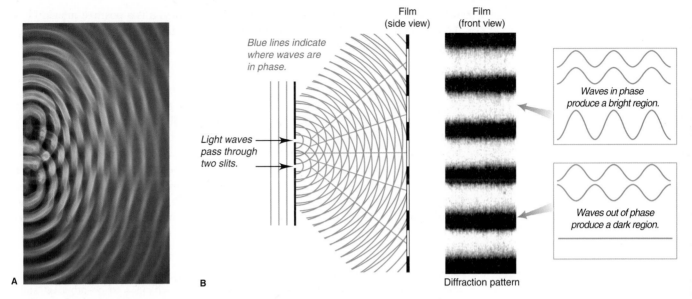

Figure 7.5 Formation of a diffraction pattern. **A,** Constructive interference and destructive interference occur as water waves pass through two adjacent slits. **B,** Light waves passing through two slits also emerge as circular waves and create a diffraction pattern.

Blackbody Radiation and the Quantum Theory of Energy The first of the puzzling observations involved the light given off by an object being heated.

- *Observation: blackbody radiation.* When a solid object is heated to about 1000 K, it begins to emit visible light, as you can see in the red glow of smoldering coal (Figure 7.6A). At about 1500 K, the light is brighter and more orange, like that from an electric heating coil (Figure 7.6B). At temperatures greater than 2000 K, the light is still brighter and whiter, like that emitted by the filament of a lightbulb (Figure 7.6C). These changes in intensity and wavelength of emitted light as an object is heated are characteristic of *blackbody radiation,* light given off by a hot *blackbody.** All attempts to account for these changes by applying classical electromagnetic theory failed.

- *Explanation: the quantum theory.* In 1900, the German physicist Max Planck (1858–1947) developed a formula that fit the data perfectly. To find a physical explanation for his formula, Planck assumed, in a self-proclaimed "act of despair," that the hot, glowing object could emit (or absorb) only *certain* quantities of energy:

$$E = nh\nu$$

---

*A blackbody is an idealized object that absorbs all the radiation incident on it. A hollow cube with a small hole in one wall approximates a blackbody.

A Smoldering coal

B Electric heating element

C Lightbulb filament

Figure 7.6 Familiar examples of light emission related to blackbody radiation.

where E is the energy of the radiation, ν is its frequency, n is a positive integer (1, 2, 3, and so on) called a **quantum number,** and h is **Planck's constant.** With energy in joules (J) and frequency in s^{-1}, h has units of J·s:

$$h = 6.62606876 \times 10^{-34} \text{ J·s} = 6.626 \times 10^{-34} \text{ J·s} \quad \text{(4 sf)}$$

Since the hot object emits only certain quantities of energy, and the energy must be emitted by the object's atoms, this means that each atom *emits* only certain quantities of energy. It follows, then, that each atom *has* only certain quantities of energy. Thus, the energy of an atom is *quantized:* it occurs in fixed quantities, rather than being continuous. Each change in an atom's energy occurs when the atom absorbs or emits one or more "packets," or definite amounts, of energy. Each energy packet is called a **quantum** ("fixed quantity"; plural, *quanta*). A quantum of energy is equal to $h\nu$. Thus, *an atom changes its energy state by emitting (or absorbing) one or more quanta,* and the energy of the emitted (or absorbed) radiation is equal to the *difference in the atom's energy states:*

$$\Delta E_{\text{atom}} = E_{\text{emitted (or absorbed) radiation}} = \Delta n h\nu$$

Because the atom can change its energy only by integer multiples of $h\nu$, the smallest change occurs when an atom in a given energy state changes to an adjacent state, that is, when $\Delta n = 1$:

$$\Delta E = h\nu \qquad (7.2)$$

The Photoelectric Effect and the Photon Theory of Light Despite the idea of quantization, physicists still pictured energy as traveling in waves. But, the wave model could not explain the second confusing observation, the flow of current when light strikes a metal.

- *Observation: the **photoelectric effect.*** When monochromatic light of sufficient frequency shines on a metal plate, a current flows (Figure 7.7). It was thought that the current arises because light transfers energy that frees electrons from the metal surface. However, the effect had two confusing features, the presence of a threshold frequency and the absence of a time lag:
    1. *Presence of a threshold frequency.* For current to flow, the light shining on the metal must have a minimum, or threshold, *frequency,* and different metals have different minimum frequencies. But, the wave theory associates the energy of light with its *amplitude* (intensity), not its frequency (color). Thus, the theory predicts that an electron would break free when it absorbed enough energy from light of *any* color.
    2. *Absence of a time lag.* Current flows the moment light of the minimum frequency shines on the metal, regardless of the light's intensity. But the wave theory predicts that with dim light there would be a time lag before the current flows, because the electrons would have to absorb enough energy to break free.

- *Explanation: the photon theory.* Building on Planck's ideas, Einstein proposed that light itself is particulate, quantized into tiny "bundles" of energy, later called **photons.** Each atom changes its energy, ΔE_{atom}, when it absorbs or emits one photon, one "particle" of light, whose energy is related to its *frequency,* not its amplitude:

$$E_{\text{photon}} = h\nu = \Delta E_{\text{atom}}$$

Let's see how the photon theory explains the two features of the photoelectric effect:

1. *Why there is a threshold frequency.* A beam of light consists of an enormous number of photons. The intensity (brightness) is related to the *number* of photons, but *not* to the energy of each. Therefore, a photon of a certain *minimum* energy must be absorbed to free an electron from the surface (see Figure 7.7). Since energy depends on frequency ($h\nu$), the theory predicts a threshold frequency.
2. *Why there is no time lag.* An electron breaks free when it absorbs a photon of *enough* energy; it cannot break free by "saving up" energy from several photons, each having less than the minimum energy. The current is weak in dim light because fewer photons of enough energy can free fewer electrons per unit time, but some current flows *as soon as* light of sufficient energy (frequency) strikes the metal. ●

Incoming light strikes the metal surface.

Evacuated tube

$h\nu$

Freed electrons travel to the electrode and produce a current.

e⁻

Metal plate

Positive electrode

Current meter

Battery

Figure 7.7 The photoelectric effect.

● **Ping-Pong Photons** This analogy helps explain why light of *insufficient* energy *cannot* free an electron from the metal surface. If one Ping-Pong ball doesn't have enough energy to knock a book off a shelf, neither does a series of Ping-Pong balls, because the book can't save up the energy from the individual impacts. But one baseball traveling at the same speed does have enough energy.

Sample Problem 7.2	Calculating the Energy of Radiation from Its Wavelength

Problem A student uses a microwave oven to heat a meal. The wavelength of the radiation is 1.20 cm. What is the energy of one photon of this microwave radiation?

Plan We know λ in centimeters (1.20 cm) so we convert to meters, find the frequency with Equation 7.1, and then find the energy of one photon with Equation 7.2.

Solution Combining steps to find the energy of a photon:

$$E = h\nu = \frac{hc}{\lambda} = \frac{(6.626 \times 10^{-34} \text{ J·s})(3.00 \times 10^8 \text{ m/s})}{(1.20 \text{ cm})\left(\dfrac{10^{-2} \text{ m}}{1 \text{ cm}}\right)} = \boxed{1.66 \times 10^{-23} \text{ J}}$$

Check Checking the order of magnitude gives

$$\frac{10^{-33} \text{ J·s} \times 10^8 \text{ m/s}}{10^{-2} \text{ m}} = 10^{-23} \text{ J}$$

Follow-Up Problem 7.2 Calculate the energy of one photon of **(a)** ultraviolet light ($\lambda = 1 \times 10^{-8}$ m); **(b)** visible light ($\lambda = 5 \times 10^{-7}$ m); and **(c)** infrared light ($\lambda = 1 \times 10^{-4}$ m). What do the answers indicate about the relationship between the wavelength and energy of light?

■ Summary of Section 7.1

- Electromagnetic radiation travels in waves characterized by a given wavelength (λ) and frequency (ν).
- Electromagnetic waves travel through a vacuum at the speed of light, c (3.00×10^8 m/s), which equals $\nu \times \lambda$. Therefore, wavelength and frequency have a reciprocal relationship.
- The intensity (brightness) of light is related to the amplitude of its waves.
- The electromagnetic spectrum ranges from very long radio waves to very short gamma rays and includes the visible region between wavelengths 750 nm (red) and 400 nm (violet).
- Refraction (change in a wave's speed when entering a different medium) and diffraction (bend of a wave around an edge of an object) indicate that energy is wavelike, with properties distinct from those of particles of mass.
- Blackbody radiation and the photoelectric effect, however, are consistent with energy occurring in discrete packets, like particles.
- Light exists as photons (quanta) whose energy is proportional to the frequency.
- According to quantum theory, an atom has only certain quantities of energy ($E = nh\nu$), and it can change its energy only by absorbing or emitting a photon whose energy equals the change in the atom's energy.

7.2 • ATOMIC SPECTRA

The third confusing observation about matter and energy involved the light emitted when an element is vaporized and then excited electrically. In this section, we discuss the nature of that light and see why it created a problem for the existing atomic model and how a new model solved the problem.

Line Spectra and the Rydberg Equation

When light from electrically excited gaseous atoms passes through a slit and is refracted by a prism, it does not create a *continuous spectrum,* or rainbow, as sunlight does. Instead, it creates a **line spectrum,** a series of fine lines at specific frequencies separated by black spaces. Figure 7.8A on the next page shows the apparatus and the line spectrum of atomic hydrogen. Figure 7.8B shows that each spectrum is *characteristic* of the element producing it.

Figure 7.8 The line spectra of several elements. **A,** The line spectrum of atomic hydrogen. **B,** Unlike the continuous spectrum of white light, emission spectra of elements, such as mercury and strontium, appear as characteristic series of colored lines.

Features of the Rydberg Equation Spectroscopists studying atomic hydrogen identified several series of spectral lines in different regions of the electromagnetic spectrum. Figure 7.9 shows three of them. Using data, not theory, the Swedish physicist Johannes Rydberg developed a relationship, called the *Rydberg equation,* that predicted the position and wavelength of any line in a given series:

$$\frac{1}{\lambda} = R\left(\frac{1}{n_1^2} - \frac{1}{n_2^2}\right) \tag{7.3}$$

where λ is the wavelength of the line, n_1 and n_2 are positive integers with $n_2 > n_1$, and R is the Rydberg constant (1.096776×10^7 m^{-1}). For the visible series, $n_1 = 2$:

$$\frac{1}{\lambda} = R\left(\frac{1}{2^2} - \frac{1}{n_2^2}\right), \quad \text{with } n_2 = 3, 4, 5, \ldots$$

(Problems 7.23 and 7.24 are two of several that apply the Rydberg equation.)

Figure 7.9 Three series of spectral lines of atomic hydrogen.

Problems with Rutherford's Nuclear Model Almost as soon as Rutherford proposed his nuclear model (described in Chapter 2), a major problem arose. A positive nucleus and a negative electron attract each other, and for them to stay apart, the kinetic energy of the electron's motion must counterbalance the potential energy of attraction. However, the laws of classical physics say that a negative particle moving in a curved path around a positive particle *must* emit radiation and thus lose energy. If the orbiting electrons behaved in that way, they would spiral into the nucleus, and all atoms would collapse! The laws of classical physics also say that the frequency of the emitted radiation should change smoothly as the negative particle spirals inward and, thus, create a continuous spectrum, not a line spectrum. The behavior of subatomic particles seemed to violate real-world experience and accepted principles.

The Bohr Model of the Hydrogen Atom

Two years after the nuclear model was proposed, Niels Bohr (1885–1962), a young Danish physicist working in Rutherford's laboratory, suggested a model for the H atom that *did* predict the existence of line spectra.

Postulates of the Model In his model, Bohr used Planck's and Einstein's ideas about quantized energy and proposed three postulates:

1. *The H atom has only certain energy levels,* which Bohr called **stationary states.** Each state is associated with a fixed circular orbit of the electron around the nucleus. The higher the energy level, the farther the orbit is from the nucleus.
2. *The atom does **not** radiate energy while in one of its stationary states.* Even though it violates principles of classical physics, the atom does not change energy while the electron moves *within* an orbit.
3. *The atom changes to another stationary state* (the electron moves to another orbit) *only by absorbing or emitting a photon. The energy of the photon (hν) equals the difference in the energies of the two states:*

$$E_{\text{photon}} = \Delta E_{\text{atom}} = E_{\text{final}} - E_{\text{initial}} = h\nu$$

Features of the Model The model has several key features:

- *Quantum numbers and electron orbit.* The quantum number n is a positive integer (1, 2, 3, . . .) associated with the radius of an electron orbit, which is directly related to the electron's energy: *the lower the n value, the smaller the radius of the orbit, and the lower the energy level.*
- *Ground state.* When the electron is in the first orbit ($n = 1$), it is closest to the nucleus, and the H atom is in its lowest (first) energy level, called the **ground state.**
- *Excited states.* If the electron is in any orbit farther from the nucleus, the atom is in an **excited state.** With the electron in the second orbit ($n = 2$), the atom is in the first excited state; when it's in the third orbit ($n = 3$), the atom is in the second excited state, and so forth.
- *Absorption.* If an H atom *absorbs* a photon whose energy equals the *difference* between lower and higher energy levels, the electron moves to the outer (higher energy) orbit.
- *Emission.* If an H atom in a higher energy level (electron in farther orbit) returns to a lower energy level (electron in closer orbit), the atom *emits* a photon whose energy equals the difference between the two levels. Figure 7.10 shows an analogy that illustrates absorption and emission.

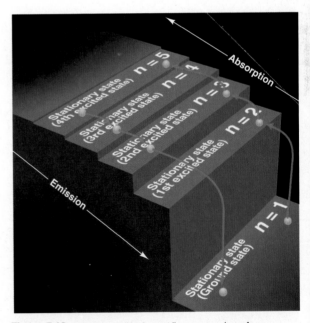

Figure 7.10 A quantum "staircase" as an analogy for atomic energy levels. Note that the electron can move up or down one or more steps at a time but cannot lie *between* steps.

How the Model Explains Line Spectra A spectral line results because a photon of specific energy (and thus frequency) is *emitted*. The emission occurs when the electron moves to an orbit closer to the nucleus as the atom's energy changes from a higher state to a lower one. Therefore, *an atomic spectrum is not continuous because the atom's energy is not continuous, but rather has only certain states.*

Figure 7.11A shows how Bohr's model accounts for three series of spectral lines of hydrogen. When a sample of gaseous H atoms is excited, the atoms absorb different quantities of energy. Each atom has one electron, but there are so many atoms in the whole sample that all the energy levels (orbits) have electrons. When electrons drop from outer orbits to the $n = 3$ orbit (second excited state), the emitted photons create the *infrared* series of lines. The *visible* series arises when electrons drop to the $n = 2$ orbit (first excited state), and the *ultraviolet* series arises when electrons drop to the $n = 1$ orbit (ground state). Figure 7.11B shows how the specific lines in the ultraviolet series appear.

Limitations of the Model Despite its great success in accounting for the spectral lines of the H atom, the Bohr model failed to predict the spectrum of any other atom. The reason is that it is a *one-electron model:* it works beautifully for the H atom and for other one-electron species, such as He^+ ($Z = 2$), Li^{2+} ($Z = 3$), and Be^{3+} ($Z = 4$). It fails completely for atoms with more than one electron because the electron-electron repulsions and additional nucleus-electron attractions that are present create much more complex interactions. But, even more fundamentally, as we'll see in Section 7.4, *electrons do not move in fixed, defined orbits.* Even though, as a picture of the atom, the Bohr model is incorrect, we still use the terms "ground state" and "excited state" and retain the central idea that *the energy of an atom occurs in discrete levels and it changes energy by absorbing or emitting a photon of specific energy.*

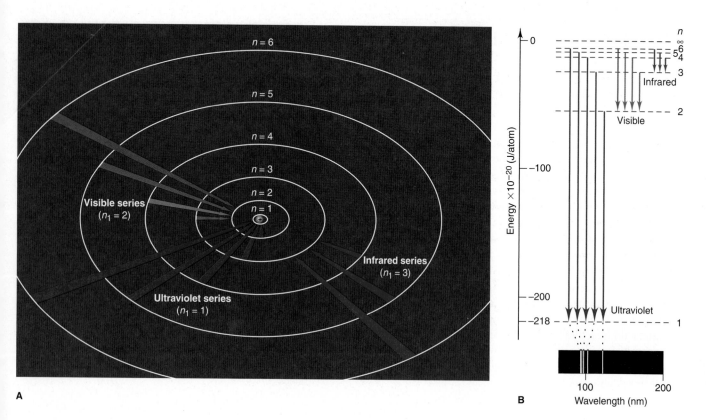

Figure 7.11 The Bohr explanation of three series of spectral lines emitted by the H atom. **A,** In a given series, the outer electron drops to the same inner orbit (the same value of n_1 in the Rydberg equation). **B,** An energy diagram shows how the ultraviolet series arises.

The Energy Levels of the Hydrogen Atom

Bohr's work leads to an equation for calculating the energy levels of an atom:

$$E = -2.18 \times 10^{-18} \text{ J} \left(\frac{Z^2}{n^2} \right)$$

where Z is the charge of the nucleus. For the H atom, $Z = 1$, so we have

$$E = -2.18 \times 10^{-18} \text{ J} \left(\frac{1^2}{n^2} \right) = -2.18 \times 10^{-18} \text{ J} \left(\frac{1}{n^2} \right)$$

Therefore, the energy of the ground state ($n = 1$) of the H atom is

$$E = -2.18 \times 10^{-18} \text{ J} \left(\frac{1}{1^2} \right) = -2.18 \times 10^{-18} \text{ J}$$

The negative sign for the energy (also used on the axis in Figure 7.11B) appears because we *define* the zero point of the atom's energy when *the electron is completely removed from the nucleus.* Thus, $E = 0$ when $n = \infty$, so $E < 0$ for any smaller n. ●

● **A tabletop analogy for defining the energy of a system.** If you define the zero point of your textbook's potential energy when the book is on a table, the energy is negative when it's on the floor.

Applying Bohr's Equation for the Energy Levels of an Atom We can use the equation for the energy levels in several ways:

1. *Finding the difference in energy between two levels.* By subtracting the initial energy level of the atom from its final energy level, we find the change in energy when the electron moves between the two levels:

$$\Delta E = E_{\text{final}} - E_{\text{initial}} = -2.18 \times 10^{-18} \text{ J} \left(\frac{1}{n_{\text{final}}^2} - \frac{1}{n_{\text{initial}}^2} \right) \qquad \textbf{(7.4)}$$

Note that, since n is in the denominator,
- *When the atom emits energy,* the electron moves closer to the nucleus ($n_{\text{final}} < n_{\text{initial}}$), so the atom's final energy is a *larger* negative number and ΔE is negative.
- *When the atom absorbs energy,* the electron moves away from the nucleus ($n_{\text{final}} > n_{\text{initial}}$), so the atom's final energy is a *smaller* negative number and ΔE is positive. (Analogously, in Chapter 6, you saw that, when the system releases heat, ΔH is negative, and when it absorbs heat, ΔH is positive.)

2. *Finding the energy needed to ionize the H atom.* We can also find the energy needed to remove the electron completely, that is, find ΔE for the following change:

$$\text{H}(g) \longrightarrow \text{H}^+(g) + \text{e}^-$$

We substitute $n_{\text{final}} = \infty$ and $n_{\text{initial}} = 1$ into Equation 7.4 and obtain

$$\Delta E = E_{\text{final}} - E_{\text{initial}} = -2.18 \times 10^{-18} \text{ J} \left(\frac{1}{\infty^2} - \frac{1}{1^2} \right)$$

$$= -2.18 \times 10^{-18} \text{ J} (0 - 1) = 2.18 \times 10^{-18} \text{ J}$$

Energy must be *absorbed* to remove the electron from the nucleus, so ΔE is positive.

The *ionization energy* of hydrogen is the energy required to form 1 mol of gaseous H^+ ions from 1 mol of gaseous H atoms. Thus, for 1 mol of H atoms,

$$\Delta E = \left(2.18 \times 10^{-18} \frac{\text{J}}{\text{atom}} \right) \left(6.022 \times 10^{23} \frac{\text{atoms}}{\text{mol}} \right) \left(\frac{1 \text{ kJ}}{10^3 \text{ J}} \right) = 1.31 \times 10^3 \text{ kJ/mol}$$

Ionization energy is a key atomic property, and we'll return to it in Chapter 8.

3. *Finding the wavelength of a spectral line.* Once we know ΔE from Equation 7.4, we find the wavelengths of the spectral lines of the H atom by combining the relation between frequency and wavelength (Equation 7.1) with Planck's expression for the change in energy of an atom (Equation 7.2) and solving for λ:

$$\Delta E = h\nu = \frac{hc}{\lambda} \quad \text{or} \quad \lambda = \frac{hc}{\Delta E}$$

In Sample Problem 7.3, we find the energy change when an H atom absorbs a photon.

Sample Problem 7.3   Determining ΔE and λ of an Electron Transition

Problem A hydrogen atom absorbs a photon of UV light (see Figure 7.11), and its electron enters the $n = 4$ energy level. Calculate (a) the change in energy of the atom and (b) the wavelength (in nm) of the photon.

Plan (a) The H atom absorbs energy, so $E_{final} > E_{initial}$. We are given $n_{final} = 4$, and Figure 7.11 shows that $n_{initial} = 1$ because a UV photon is absorbed. We apply Equation 7.4 to find ΔE. (b) Once we know ΔE, we find the frequency with Equation 7.2 and the wavelength (in m) with Equation 7.1. Then we convert from meters to nanometers.

Solution (a) Substituting the known values into Equation 7.4:

$$\Delta E = -2.18\times10^{-18}\ \text{J} \left(\frac{1}{n_{final}^2} - \frac{1}{n_{initial}^2} \right)$$

$$= -2.18\times10^{-18}\ \text{J} \left(\frac{1}{4^2} - \frac{1}{1^2} \right) = -2.18\times10^{-18}\ \text{J} \left(\frac{1}{16} - \frac{1}{1} \right)$$

$$= 2.04\times10^{-18}\ \text{J}$$

(b) Using Equations 7.2 and 7.1 to solve for λ:

$$\Delta E = h\nu = \frac{hc}{\lambda}$$

therefore,

$$\lambda = \frac{hc}{\Delta E} = \frac{(6.626\times10^{-34}\ \text{J·s})(3.00\times10^8\ \text{m/s})}{2.04\times10^{-18}\ \text{J}} = 9.74\times10^{-8}\ \text{m}$$

Converting m to nm:

$$\lambda = 9.74\times10^{-8}\ \text{m} \times \frac{1\ \text{nm}}{10^{-9}\ \text{m}} = 97.4\ \text{nm}$$

Check (a) The energy change is positive, which is consistent with absorption. (b) The wavelength is within the UV region (about 10–380 nm).

Comment In the follow-up problem, note that if ΔE is negative (the atom loses energy), we use its absolute value, $|\Delta E|$, because λ must have a positive value.

Follow-Up Problem 7.3 A hydrogen atom with its electron in the $n = 6$ energy level emits a photon of IR light. Calculate (a) the change in energy of the atom and (b) the wavelength (in Å) of the photon.

Spectrometric analysis of the H atom led to the Bohr model, the first step toward our current model of the atom. From its use by 19th-century chemists as a means of identifying elements and compounds, spectrometry has developed into a major tool of modern chemistry (see Tools of the Laboratory).

Summary of Section 7.2

- Unlike sunlight, light emitted by electrically excited atoms of elements appears as separate spectral lines.
- Spectroscopists use an empirical formula (the Rydberg equation) to determine the wavelength of a spectral line. Atomic hydrogen displays several series of spectral lines.
- To explain the existence of line spectra, Bohr proposed that an electron moves in fixed orbits. It moves from one orbit to another when the atom absorbs or emits a photon whose energy equals the difference in energy levels (orbits).
- Bohr's model predicts only the spectrum of the H atom and other one-electron species. Despite this, Bohr was correct that an atom's energy is quantized.
- Spectrometry is an instrumental technique that uses emission and absorption spectra to identify substances and measure their concentrations.

TOOLS OF THE LABORATORY | Spectrometry in Chemical Analysis

The use of spectral data to identify and quantify substances is essential to modern chemical analysis. The terms *spectroscopy* and **spectrometry** refer to a large group of instrumental techniques that obtain spectra to gather data on a substance's atomic and molecular energy levels.

Types of Spectra

Emission and absorption spectra are two important types:

1. An **emission spectrum,** such as the H atom line spectrum, occurs when atoms in an excited state *emit* photons as they return to a lower energy state. Some elements produce an intense spectral line (or several closely spaced ones) that is evidence of their presence. **Flame tests,** performed by placing a granule of an ionic compound or a drop of its solution in a flame, rely on these intense emissions (Figure B7.1, part A), and some colors of

Figure B7.2 Emission and absorption spectra of sodium atoms. The wavelengths of the bright emission lines correspond to those of the dark absorption lines because both are created by the same energy change: $\Delta E_{emission} = -\Delta E_{absorption}$. (Only the two most intense lines in the Na spectra are shown.)

fireworks are due to the same elements (Figure B7.1, part B). The colors of sodium-vapor and mercury-vapor streetlamps are due to intense emissions lines in these elements' spectra.

2. An **absorption spectrum** is produced when atoms *absorb* photons of certain wavelengths and become excited. When white light passes through sodium vapor, for example, the absorption spectrum shows dark lines at the same wavelengths as the yellow-orange lines in sodium's emission spectrum (Figure B7.2).

Basic Instrumentation

Instruments based on absorption spectra are much more common than those based on emission spectra because many substances absorb relatively few wavelengths so their spectra are more characteristic, and absorption is less destructive of fragile molecules.

Design differences depend on the region of the electromagnetic spectrum used to irradiate the sample, but all modern spectrometers have components that perform the same basic functions (Figure B7.3). (We discuss infrared spectroscopy and nuclear magnetic resonance spectroscopy in later chapters.)

Figure B7.1 Flame tests and fireworks. **A,** The flame's color is due to intense emission by the element of light of a particular wavelength. **B,** Fireworks display emissions similar to those seen in flame tests.

(continued)

Source produces radiation in the region of interest. In most cases, the source emits many wavelengths.

Lenses/slits/collimators narrow and align the beam.

Monochromator (wavelength selector) disperses the incoming radiation into its component wavelengths.

Sample in the compartment absorbs a characteristic amount of incoming wavelength.

Detector converts the transmitted radiation into an amplified electrical signal.

Computer converts the signal into displayed data.

Figure B7.3 Components of a typical spectrometer.

Identifying and Quantifying a Substance

In chemical analysis, spectra are used to identify a substance and/or quantify the amount in a sample. Visible light is often used for colored substances, because they absorb only some of the wavelengths. A leaf looks green, for example, because its chlorophyll absorbs red and blue light strongly but green light weakly, so most of the green light is reflected.

Figure B7.4 shows the visible absorption spectrum of chlorophyll *a* in ether solution. The shape of the curve and the wavelengths of the major peaks are characteristic of chlorophyll *a*. The curve varies in height because chlorophyll *a* absorbs light of different wavelengths to different extents. The absorptions appear as broad bands, rather than as the distinct lines seen on absorption spectra of elements, because there are greater numbers and types of energy levels within a molecule and between molecules and solvent.

In addition to identifying a substance, a spectrometer can be used to measure its concentration because *absorbance,* the quantity of light of a given wavelength absorbed by a substance, is *proportional to the number of molecules.* Suppose you want to determine the concentration of chlorophyll *a* in a leaf extract. You select a strongly absorbed wavelength from the compound's spectrum (such as 663 nm in Figure B7.4, part A), measure the absorbance of the *unknown* solution, and compare it with the absorbances of a series of solutions of *known* concentration (Figure B7.4, part B).

Problems

B7.1 The sodium salt of 2-quinizarinsulfonic acid forms a complex with Al^{3+} that absorbs strongly at 560 nm. (a) Use the data below to draw a plot of absorbance vs. concentration of the complex in solution and find the slope and *y*-intercept:

Concentration (*M*)	Absorbance (560 nm)
1.0×10^{-5}	0.131
1.5×10^{-5}	0.201
2.0×10^{-5}	0.265
2.5×10^{-5}	0.329
3.0×10^{-5}	0.396

(b) When 20.0 mL of a solution of this complex is diluted with water to 150. mL, its absorbance is 0.236. Find the concentrations of the diluted solution and of the original solution.

B7.2 In fireworks displays, flame tests, and other emission events, light of a given wavelength often indicates the presence of a particular element or ion. What are the frequency and color of the light associated with each of the following?
(a) Li, λ = 671 nm
(b) Cs^+, λ = 453 nm
(c) Na, λ = 589 nm

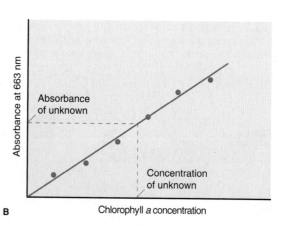

Figure B7.4 Measuring chlorophyll *a* concentration in leaf extract. **A,** The spectrometer is set to measure the strong absorption at 663 nm in the chlorophyll *a* spectrum. **B,** The absorbance from the leaf extract is compared to a series of known standards.

7.3 • THE WAVE-PARTICLE DUALITY OF MATTER AND ENERGY

The year 1905 was a busy one for Albert Einstein. He had just presented the photon theory and explained the photoelectric effect. A friend remembered him in his small apartment, rocking his baby in its carriage with one hand, while scribbling with the other ideas for a new branch of physics—the theory of relativity. One of its revelations was that *matter and energy are alternate forms of the same entity.* This idea is embodied in his famous equation $E = mc^2$, relating the quantity of energy equivalent to a given mass. Some results that showed energy to be particle-like had to coexist with others that showed matter to be wavelike. These remarkable ideas are the key to understanding our modern atomic model.

The Wave Nature of Electrons and the Particle Nature of Photons

Bohr's model was a perfect case of fitting theory to data: he *assumed* that an atom has only certain energy levels in order to *explain* line spectra. However, Bohr had no theoretical basis for the assumption. Several breakthroughs in the early 1920s provided that basis and blurred the distinction between matter (chunky and massive) and energy (diffuse and massless).

The Wave Nature of Electrons Attempting to explain why an atom has fixed energy levels, a French physics student, Louis de Broglie, considered other systems that display only certain allowed motions, such as the vibrations of a plucked guitar string. Figure 7.12 shows that, because the end of the string is fixed, only certain vibrational frequencies (and wavelengths) are allowable to create a note. De Broglie proposed that *if energy is particle-like, perhaps matter is wavelike.* He reasoned that *if electrons have wavelike motion* in orbits of fixed radii, they would have only certain allowable frequencies and energies.

Figure 7.12 Wave motion in restricted systems. A, One half-wavelength ($\lambda/2$) is the "quantum" of the guitar string's vibration. With string length L fixed by a finger on the fret, allowed vibrations occur when L is a whole-number multiple (n) of $\lambda/2$. **B,** In a circular electron orbit, only whole numbers of wavelengths are allowed ($n = 3$ and $n = 5$ are shown). A wave with a fractional number of wavelengths (such as $n = 3\frac{1}{3}$) is "forbidden" because it dies out through overlap of crests and troughs.

Combining the equations for mass-energy equivalence ($E = mc^2$) and energy of a photon ($E = h\nu = hc/\lambda$), de Broglie derived an equation for the wavelength of any particle of mass m—whether planet, baseball, or electron—moving at speed u:

$$\lambda = \frac{h}{mu} \tag{7.5}$$

According to this equation for the **de Broglie wavelength,** *matter behaves as though it moves in a wave.* An object's wavelength is *inversely* proportional to its mass, so heavy objects such as planets and baseballs have wavelengths *many* orders of magnitude smaller than the object itself (Table 7.1).

Table 7.1   The de Broglie Wavelengths of Several Objects

Substance	Mass (g)	Speed (m/s)	λ (m)
Slow electron	9×10^{-28}	1.0	7×10^{-4}
Fast electron	9×10^{-28}	5.9×10^{6}	1×10^{-10}
Alpha particle	6.6×10^{-24}	1.5×10^{7}	7×10^{-15}
1-gram mass	1.0	0.01	7×10^{-29}
Baseball	142	40.0	1×10^{-34}
Earth	6.0×10^{27}	3.0×10^{4}	4×10^{-63}

Sample Problem 7.4   Calculating the de Broglie Wavelength of an Electron

Problem Find the de Broglie wavelength of an electron with a speed of 1.00×10^6 m/s (electron mass = 9.11×10^{-31} kg; $h = 6.626 \times 10^{-34}$ kg·m²/s).

Plan We know the speed (1.00×10^6 m/s) and mass (9.11×10^{-31} kg) of the electron, so we substitute these into Equation 7.5 to find λ.

Solution

$$\lambda = \frac{h}{mu} = \frac{6.626 \times 10^{-34} \text{ kg·m}^2/\text{s}}{(9.11 \times 10^{-31} \text{ kg})(1.00 \times 10^6 \text{ m/s})} = 7.27 \times 10^{-10} \text{ m}$$

Check The order of magnitude and units seem correct:

$$\lambda \approx \frac{10^{-33} \text{ kg·m}^2/\text{s}}{(10^{-30} \text{ kg})(10^6 \text{ m/s})} = 10^{-9} \text{ m}$$

Comment As you'll see in the upcoming discussion, such fast-moving electrons, with wavelengths in the range of atomic sizes, exhibit remarkable properties.

Follow-Up Problem 7.4 What is the speed of an electron that has a de Broglie wavelength of 100. nm?

Figure 7.13 Diffraction patterns of aluminum with x-rays (*top*) and electrons (*bottom*).

If electrons travel in waves, they should exhibit diffraction and interference. A fast-moving electron has a wavelength of about 10^{-10} m, so a beam of such electrons should be diffracted by the spaces between atoms in a crystal—about 10^{-10} m. In 1927, C. Davisson and L. Germer guided a beam of x-rays and then a beam of electrons at a nickel crystal and obtained two diffraction patterns; Figure 7.13 shows these patterns for aluminum. Thus, electrons—particles with mass and charge—create diffraction patterns, just as electromagnetic waves do.

A major application of electrons traveling in waves is the *electron microscope.* Its great advantage over light microscopes is that high-speed electrons have much smaller wavelengths than visible light, which allow much higher resolution. A transmission electron microscope focuses a beam of electrons through a lens, and the beam then passes through a thin section of the specimen to a second and then third lens. In this instrument, these "lenses" are electromagnetic fields, which can result in up to 200,000-fold magnification. In a scanning electron microscope, the beam scans the specimen, knocking electrons from it that create a current, which generates an image that looks like the object's surface (Figure 7.14).

The Particle Nature of Photons If electrons have properties of energy, do photons have properties of matter? The de Broglie equation suggests that we can calculate the momentum (p), the product of mass and speed, for a photon. Substituting the speed of light (c) for speed u in Equation 7.5 and solving for p gives

$$\lambda = \frac{h}{mc} = \frac{h}{p} \quad \text{and} \quad p = \frac{h}{\lambda}$$

The inverse relationship between p and λ in this equation means that shorter wavelength (higher energy) photons have greater momentum. Thus, a decrease in a photon's momentum should appear as an increase in its wavelength. In 1923, Arthur Compton directed a beam of x-ray photons at graphite and observed an increase in the wavelength of the reflected photons. Thus, just as billiard balls transfer momentum when they collide, the photons transferred momentum to the electrons in the carbon atoms of the graphite. In this experiment, photons behaved as particles.

Wave-Particle Duality Classical experiments had shown matter to be particle-like and energy to be wavelike. But, results on the atomic scale show electrons moving in waves and photons having momentum. Thus, every property of matter was also a property of energy. The truth is that *both* matter and energy show *both* behaviors: each possesses both "faces." In some experiments, we observe one face; in other experiments, we observe the other face. Our everyday distinction between matter and energy is meaningful in the macroscopic world, *not* in the atomic world. The distinction is in our minds and the limited definitions we have created, not inherent in nature. This dual character of matter and energy is known as the **wave-particle duality.** Figure 7.15 summarizes the theories and observations that led to this new understanding.

Figure 7.14 False-color scanning electron micrograph of blood cells (x1200).

Figure 7.15 Major observations and theories leading from classical theory to quantum theory.

Heisenberg's Uncertainty Principle

In classical physics, a moving particle has a definite location at any instant, whereas a wave is spread out in space. If an electron has the properties of *both* a particle and a wave, can we determine its position in the atom? In 1927, the German physicist Werner Heisenberg postulated the **uncertainty principle,** which states that it is impossible to know simultaneously the position *and* momentum (mass times speed) of a particle. For a particle with constant mass *m*, the principle is expressed mathematically as

$$\Delta x \cdot m\Delta u \geq \frac{h}{4\pi} \tag{7.6}$$

where Δx is the uncertainty in position, Δu is the uncertainty in speed, and h is Planck's constant. The more accurately we know the position of the particle (smaller Δx), the less accurately we know its speed (larger Δu), and vice versa. The best-case scenario is that we know the product of these uncertainties, which is equal to $h/4\pi$.

For a macroscopic object like a baseball, Δx and Δu are insignificant because the mass is enormous compared with $h/4\pi$. Thus, by knowing the position and speed of a pitched baseball, we can use the laws of motion to predict its trajectory and whether it will be a ball or a strike. However, using the position and speed of an electron to find its trajectory is a very different proposition, as Sample Problem 7.5 demonstrates.

Sample Problem 7.5 **Applying the Uncertainty Principle**

Problem An electron moving near an atomic nucleus has a speed of 6×10^6 m/s $\pm$ 1%. What is the uncertainty in its position (Δx)?

Plan The uncertainty in the speed (Δu) is given as 1%, so we multiply u (6×10^6 m/s) by 0.01 to calculate the value of Δu, substitute it into Equation 7.6, and solve for the uncertainty in position (Δx).

Solution Finding the uncertainty in speed, Δu:

$$\Delta u = 1\% \text{ of } u = 0.01(6\times10^6 \text{ m/s}) = 6\times10^4 \text{ m/s}$$

Calculating the uncertainty in position, Δx:

$$\Delta x \cdot m\Delta u \geq \frac{h}{4\pi}$$

Thus,

$$\Delta x \geq \frac{h}{4\pi \, m\Delta u} \geq \frac{6.626\times10^{-34} \text{ kg}\cdot\text{m}^2/\text{s}}{4\pi (9.11\times10^{-31} \text{ kg})(6\times10^4 \text{ m/s})} \geq \boxed{1\times10^{-9} \text{ m}}$$

Check Be sure to round off and check the order of magnitude of the answer:

$$\Delta x \geq \frac{10^{-33} \text{ kg}\cdot\text{m}^2/\text{s}}{(10^1)(10^{-30} \text{ kg})(10^5 \text{ m/s})} = 10^{-9} \text{ m}$$

Comment The uncertainty in the electron's position is about 10 times greater than the diameter of the entire atom (10^{-10} m)! Therefore, we have no precise idea where in the atom the electron is located. In the follow-up problem, you'll see if an umpire has any better idea about the position of a baseball.

Follow-Up Problem 7.5 How accurately can an umpire know the position of a baseball (mass = 0.142 kg) moving at 100.0 mi/h $\pm$ 1.00% (44.7 m/s $\pm$ 1.00%)?

▮ Summary of Section 7.3

- As a result of Planck's quantum theory and Einstein's theory of relativity, we no longer view matter and energy as distinct entities.
- The de Broglie wavelength is based on the idea that an electron (or any object) has wavelike motion. Allowed atomic energy levels are related to allowed wavelengths of the electron's motion.
- Electrons exhibit diffraction, just as light waves do, and photons exhibit transfer of momentum, just as objects do. This wave-particle duality of matter and energy is observable only on the atomic scale.
- According to the uncertainty principle, we can never know the position and speed of an electron simultaneously.

7.4 • THE QUANTUM-MECHANICAL MODEL OF THE ATOM

Acceptance of the dual nature of matter and energy and of the uncertainty principle culminated in the field of **quantum mechanics,** which examines the wave nature of objects on the atomic scale. In 1926, Erwin Schrödinger derived an equation that is the basis for the *quantum-mechanical model* of the H atom. The model describes an atom with specific quantities of energy that result from allowed frequencies of its electron's wavelike motion. The electron's position can only be known within a certain probability. Key features of the model are described in the following subsections.

The Atomic Orbital and the Probable Location of the Electron

Two central aspects of the quantum-mechanical model concern the atomic orbital and the electron's probable location.

The Schrödinger Equation and the Atomic Orbital The electron's matter-wave occupies the space near the nucleus and is continuously influenced by it. The **Schrödinger equation** is quite complex but can be represented in simpler form as

$$\mathcal{H}\psi = E\psi$$

where E is the energy of the atom. The symbol ψ (Greek *psi,* pronounced "sigh") is called a **wave function** (or **atomic orbital**), a mathematical description of the electron's matter-wave in three dimensions. The symbol $\mathcal{H}$, called the Hamiltonian operator, represents a set of mathematical operations that, when carried out with a particular ψ, yields one of the allowed energy states of the atom.* Thus, *each solution of the equation gives an energy state associated with a given atomic orbital.*

An important point to keep in mind throughout this discussion is that an "orbital" in the quantum-mechanical model *bears no resemblance* to an "orbit" in the Bohr model: an *orbit* is an electron's actual path around the nucleus, whereas an *orbital* is a mathematical function that describes the electron's matter-wave but has no physical meaning.

The Probable Location of the Electron While we cannot know *exactly* where the electron is at any moment, we can know where it *probably* is, that is, where it spends most of its time. We get this information by squaring the wave function. Thus, even

---

*The complete form of the Schrödinger equation in terms of the three linear axes is

$$\left[-\frac{h^2}{8\pi^2 m_e}\left(\frac{d^2}{dx^2} + \frac{d^2}{dy^2} + \frac{d^2}{dz^2} \right) + V(x, y, z) \right]\psi(x, y, z) = E\psi(x, y, z)$$

where ψ is the wave function; m_e is the electron's mass; E is the total quantized energy of the atomic system; and V is the potential energy at point (x, y, z).

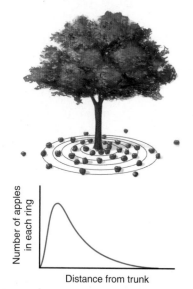

A Radial Probability Distribution of Apples An analogy might clarify why the curve in the radial probability distribution plot peaks and then falls off. Picture fallen apples around the base of an apple tree: the density of apples is greatest near the trunk and decreases with distance. Divide the ground under the tree into foot-wide concentric rings and collect the apples within each ring. Apple density is greatest in the first ring, but the area of the second ring is larger, and so it contains a greater *total* number of apples. Farther out near the edge of the tree, rings have more area but lower apple "density," so the total number of apples decreases. A plot of "number of apples in each ring" vs. "distance from trunk" shows a peak at some distance close to the trunk, as in Figure 7.16D.

though ψ has no physical meaning, ψ² does and is called the *probability density,* a measure of the probability of finding the electron in some tiny volume of the atom. We depict the electron's probable location in several ways, which we'll look at first for the H atom's *ground state:*

1. *Probability of the electron being in some tiny volume of the atom.* For each energy level, we can create an *electron probability density diagram,* or more simply, an **electron density diagram.** The value of ψ² for a given volume is shown with dots: the greater the density of dots, the higher the probability of finding the electron in that volume. Note, that for the ground state of the H atom, *the electron probability density decreases with distance from the nucleus along a line, r* (Figure 7.16A).

These diagrams are also called **electron cloud depictions** because, if we *could* take a time-exposure photograph of the electron in wavelike motion around the nucleus, it would appear as a "cloud" of positions. The electron cloud is an *imaginary* picture of the electron changing its position rapidly over time; it does *not* mean that an electron is a diffuse cloud of charge.

Figure 7.16B shows a plot of ψ² vs. *r.* Due to the thickness of the printed line, the curve appears to touch the axis; however, in the blow-up circle, we see that *the probability of the electron being far from the nucleus is very small, but not zero.*

2. *Total probability density at some distance from the nucleus.* To find *radial probability distribution,* that is, the *total* probability of finding the electron at some distance *r* from the nucleus, we first mentally divide the volume around the nucleus into thin, concentric, spherical layers, like the layers of an onion (shown in cross section in Figure 7.16C). Then, we find the *sum of ψ² values* in each layer to see which is most likely to contain the electron.

The falloff in probability density with distance has an important effect. Near the nucleus, *the volume of each layer increases faster than its density of dots decreases.* The result of these opposing effects is that the *total* probability peaks in a layer *near,* but not *at,* the nucleus. For example, the total probability in the second layer is higher than in the first, but this result disappears with greater distance. Figure 7.16D shows this result as a **radial probability distribution plot.**

3. *Probability contour and the size of the atom.* How far away from the nucleus can we find the electron? This is the same as asking "How big is the H atom?" Recall from Figure 7.16B that the probability of finding the electron far from the nucleus

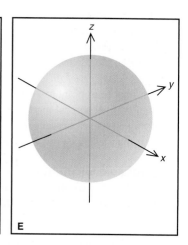

Figure 7.16 Electron probability density in the ground-state H atom. **A,** In the electron density diagram, the density of dots represents the probability of the electron within a tiny volume and decreases with distance, *r,* from the nucleus. **B,** The probability density (ψ²) decreases with *r* but does not reach zero (*blow-up circle*). **C,** Count-

ing dots within each layer gives the total probability of the electron being in that layer. **D,** A radial probability distribution plot shows that total electron density peaks *near,* but not *at,* the nucleus. **E,** A 90% probability contour for the ground state of the H atom.

is not zero. Therefore, we *cannot* assign a definite volume to an atom. However, we can visualize an atom with a 90% **probability contour**: the electron is somewhere within that volume 90% of the time (Figure 7.16E).

As you'll see later in this section, each atomic orbital has a distinctive radial probability distribution and 90% probability contour.

Quantum Numbers of an Atomic Orbital

An atomic orbital is specified by three quantum numbers (Table 7.2) that are part of the solution of the Schrödinger equation and indicate the size, shape, and orientation in space of the orbital.*

1. The **principal quantum number (*n*)** *is a positive integer* (1, 2, 3, and so forth). It indicates the relative *size* of the orbital and therefore the relative *distance from the nucleus* of the peak in the radial probability distribution plot. The principal quantum number specifies the *energy level* of the H atom: *the higher the n value, the higher the energy level.* When the electron occupies an orbital with *n* = 1, the H atom is in its ground state and has its lowest energy. When the electron occupies an orbital with *n* = 2 (first excited state), the atom has more energy.

2. The **angular momentum quantum number (*l*)** *is an integer from 0 to n* − 1. It is related to the *shape* of the orbital. Note that the principal quantum number sets a limit on the angular momentum quantum number: *n* limits *l*. For an orbital with *n* = 1, *l* can have only one value, 0. For orbitals with *n* = 2, *l* can have two values, 0 or 1. For orbitals with *n* = 3, *l* can have three values, 0, 1, or 2; and so forth. Thus, the number of possible *l* values equals the value of *n*.

3. The **magnetic quantum number (*m$_l$*)** *is an integer from* −*l through 0 to* +*l*. It prescribes the three-dimensional *orientation* of the orbital in the space around the nucleus. The angular momentum quantum number sets a limit on the magnetic quantum number: *l* limits *m$_l$*. An orbital with *l* = 0 can have only *m$_l$* = 0. However, an orbital with *l* = 1 can have one of three *m$_l$* values, −1, 0, or +1; that is, there are three possible orbitals with *l* = 1, each with its own orientation. Note that the number of *m$_l$* values *equals* 2*l* + 1, which is the number of orbitals for a given *l*. The total number of *m$_l$* values, that is, the total number of orbitals, for a given *n* value is *n^2*.

---

*For ease in discussion, chemists often refer to the size, shape, and orientation of an "atomic orbital," although we really mean the size, shape, and orientation of an "atomic orbital's radial probability distribution."

Table 7.2 The Hierarchy of Quantum Numbers for Atomic Orbitals

Name, Symbol (Property)	Allowed Values	Quantum Numbers
Principal, *n* (size, energy)	Positive integer (1, 2, 3, ...)	1 2 3
Angular momentum, *l* (shape)	0 to *n* − 1	0 0 1 0 1 2
Magnetic, *m$_l$* (orientation)	−*l*, . . ., 0, . . ., +*l*	0 0 −1 0 +1 0 −1 0 +1 −2 −1 0 +1 +2

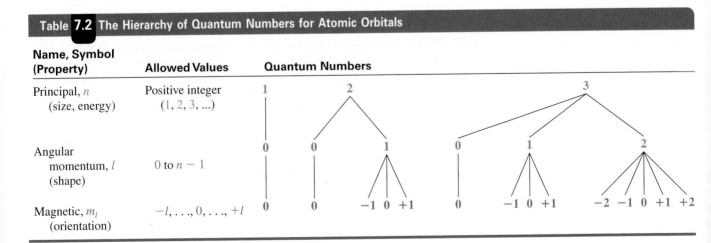

Sample Problem 7.6 · Determining Quantum Numbers for an Energy Level

Problem What values of the angular momentum (l) and magnetic (m_l) quantum numbers are allowed for a principal quantum number (n) of 3? How many orbitals are allowed?

Plan We determine allowable quantum numbers with the rules from the text: l values are integers from 0 to $n - 1$, and m_l values are integers from $-l$ to 0 to $+l$. One m_l value is assigned to each orbital, so the number of m_l values gives the number of orbitals.

Solution Determining l values: for $n = 3$, $l = 0, 1, 2$.

Determining m_l for each l value:

$$\text{For } l = 0, \quad m_l = 0$$
$$\text{For } l = 1, \quad m_l = -1, 0, +1$$
$$\text{For } l = 2, \quad m_l = -2, -1, 0, +1, +2$$

There are nine m_l values, so there are nine orbitals with $n = 3$.

Check Table 7.2 shows that we are correct. As we saw, the total number of orbitals for a given n value is n^2, and for $n = 3$, $n^2 = 9$.

Follow-Up Problem 7.6 What are the possible l and m_l values for $n = 4$?

Quantum Numbers and Energy Levels

The energy states and orbitals of the atom are described with specific terms and are associated with one or more quantum numbers:

1. *Level.* The atom's energy **levels,** or *shells,* are given by the n value: the smaller the n value, the lower the energy level and the greater the probability that the electron is closer to the nucleus.

2. *Sublevel.* The atom's levels are divided into **sublevels,** or *subshells,* that are given by the l value. Each designates the orbital shape with a letter:

$l = 0$ is an s sublevel.
$l = 1$ is a p sublevel.
$l = 2$ is a d sublevel.
$l = 3$ is an f sublevel.

(The letters derive from names of spectroscopic lines: *s*harp, *p*rincipal, *d*iffuse, and *f*undamental.) Sublevels with l values greater than 3 are designated by consecutive letters after f: g sublevel, h sublevel, and so on. A sublevel is named with its n value and letter designation; for example, the sublevel (subshell) with $n = 2$ and $l = 0$ is called the 2s sublevel. We discuss orbital shapes below.

3. *Orbital.* Each combination of n, l, and m_l specifies the size (energy), shape, and spatial orientation of one of the atom's orbitals. We know the quantum numbers of the orbitals in a sublevel from the sublevel name and the quantum-number hierarchy. For example, any orbital in the 2s sublevel has $n = 2$ and $l = 0$, and given that l value, it can have only $m_l = 0$; thus, the 2s sublevel has only one orbital. Any orbital in the 3p sublevel has $n = 3$ and $l = 1$, and given that l value, one orbital has $m_l = -1$, another has $m_l = 0$, and a third has $m_l = +1$; thus, the 3p sublevel has three orbitals.

<table>
<tr><td>**Sample Problem 7.7**</td><td>**Determining Sublevel Names and Orbital Quantum Numbers**</td></tr>
</table>

Problem Give the name, magnetic quantum numbers, and number of orbitals for each sublevel with the given n and l quantum numbers:
(a) $n = 3, l = 2$
(b) $n = 2, l = 0$
(c) $n = 5, l = 1$
(d) $n = 4, l = 3$

Plan We name the sublevel (subshell) with the n value and the letter designation of the l value. From the l value, we find the number of possible m_l values, which equals the number of orbitals in that sublevel.

Solution

n	l	Sublevel Name	Possible m_l Values	No. of Orbitals
(a) 3	2	$3d$	$-2, -1, 0, +1, +2$	5
(b) 2	0	$2s$	0	1
(c) 5	1	$5p$	$-1, 0, +1$	3
(d) 4	3	$4f$	$-3, -2, -1, 0, +1, +2, +3$	7

Check Check the number of orbitals in each sublevel using

$$\text{No. of orbitals} = \text{no. of } m_l \text{ values} = 2l + 1$$

Follow-Up Problem 7.7 What are the n, l, and possible m_l values for the $2p$ and $5f$ sublevels?

<table>
<tr><td>**Sample Problem 7.8**</td><td>**Identifying Incorrect Quantum Numbers**</td></tr>
</table>

Problem What is wrong with each of the following quantum number designations and/or sublevel names?

n	l	m_l	Name
(a) 1	1	0	$1p$
(b) 4	3	+1	$4d$
(c) 3	1	-2	$3p$

Solution **(a)** A sublevel with $n = 1$ can have only $l = 0$, not $l = 1$. The only possible sublevel name is $1s$.
(b) A sublevel with $l = 3$ is an f sublevel, not a d sublevel. The name should be $4f$.
(c) A sublevel with $l = 1$ can have only $-1, 0,$ or $+1$ for m_l, not -2.

Check Check that l is always less than n, and m_l is always $\geq -l$ and $\leq +l$.

Follow-Up Problem 7.8 Supply the missing quantum numbers and sublevel names.

n	l	m_l	Name
(a) ?	?	0	$4p$
(b) 2	1	0	?
(c) 3	2	-2	?
(d) ?	?	?	$2s$

Shapes of Atomic Orbitals

Each sublevel of the H atom consists of a set of orbitals with characteristic shapes. As you'll see in Chapter 8, orbitals for the other atoms have similar shapes.

The *s* Orbital An orbital with $l = 0$ has a *spherical* shape with the nucleus at its center and is called an *s* orbital. Because a sphere has only one orientation, an *s* orbital has only one m_l value: for any *s* orbital, $m_l = 0$.

1. *The 1s orbital* holds the electron in the H atom's ground state. *The electron probability density is highest at the nucleus.* Figure 7.17A shows this graphically (*top*), and an electron density *relief map (inset)* depicts the graph's curve in three dimensions. Note the quarter-section of a three-dimensional electron cloud depiction (*middle*) has the darkest shading at the nucleus. For reasons discussed earlier (see Figure 7.16D and the margin note, p. 280), the radial probability distribution plot

Figure 7.17 The 1s, 2s, and 3s orbitals. For each of the *s* orbitals, a plot of probability density vs. distance (*top*, with the relief map, *inset*, showing the plot in three dimensions) lies above a quarter section of an electron cloud depiction of the 90% probability contour (*middle*), which lies above a radial probability distribution plot (*bottom*). **A,** The 1s orbital. **B,** The 2s orbital. **C,** The 3s orbital.

(*bottom*) is highest slightly out from the nucleus. Both plots fall off smoothly with distance.

2. *The 2s orbital* (Figure 7.17B) has two regions of higher electron density. The radial probability distribution (Figure 7.17B, *bottom*) of the more distant region is *higher* than that of the closer one because the sum of ψ^2 for it is taken over a much larger volume. Between the two regions is a spherical **node,** where the probability of finding the electron drops to zero ($\psi^2 = 0$ at the node, analogous to zero amplitude of a wave exactly between the peak and trough). Because the 2s orbital is larger than the 1s, an electron in the 2s spends more time farther from the nucleus (in the larger of the two regions) than it does when it occupies the 1s.

3. *The 3s orbital* (Figure 7.17C) has three regions of high electron density and two nodes. Here again, the highest radial probability is at the greatest distance from the nucleus. This pattern of more nodes and higher probability with distance from the nucleus continues with the 4s, 5s, and so forth.

The *p* Orbital   An orbital with $l = 1$ is called a ***p* orbital** and has two regions (lobes) of high probability, one on *either side* of the nucleus (Figure 7.18). The *nucleus lies at the nodal plane* of this dumbbell-shaped orbital. Since the maximum value of l is $n - 1$, only levels with $n = 2$ or higher have a *p* orbital: the lowest energy *p* orbital (the one closest to the nucleus) is the 2p. One *p* orbital consists of *two* lobes, and the electron spends *equal* time in both. Similar to the pattern for s orbitals, a 3p orbital is larger than a 2p, a 4p is larger than a 3p, and so forth.

Unlike s orbitals, p orbitals *have* different spatial orientations. The three possible m_l values of -1, 0, and $+1$ refer to three *mutually perpendicular* orientations; that is, while identical in size, shape, and energy, the three *p* orbitals differ in orientation. We associate *p* orbitals with the *x*, *y*, and *z* axes: the p_x orbital lies along the *x* axis, the p_y along the *y* axis, and the p_z along the *z* axis. (There is no relationship between a particular axis and a given m_l value.)

A

Figure 7.18 The 2p orbitals. A, A radial probability distribution plot of the 2p orbital shows a peak much farther from the nucleus than for the 1s. **B,** Cross section of an electron cloud depiction of the 90% probability contour of the $2p_z$ orbital shows a nodal plane. **C,** An accurate representation of the $2p_z$ probability contour. **D,** The stylized depiction of the 2p probability contour used in the text. **E,** The three (stylized) 2p orbitals occupy mutually perpendicular regions of space, contributing to the atom's overall spherical shape.

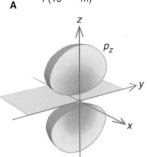

B Cross section of electron cloud depiction

C Accurate probability contour

D Stylized probability contour

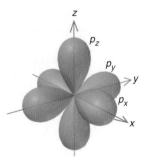

E The three *p* orbitals

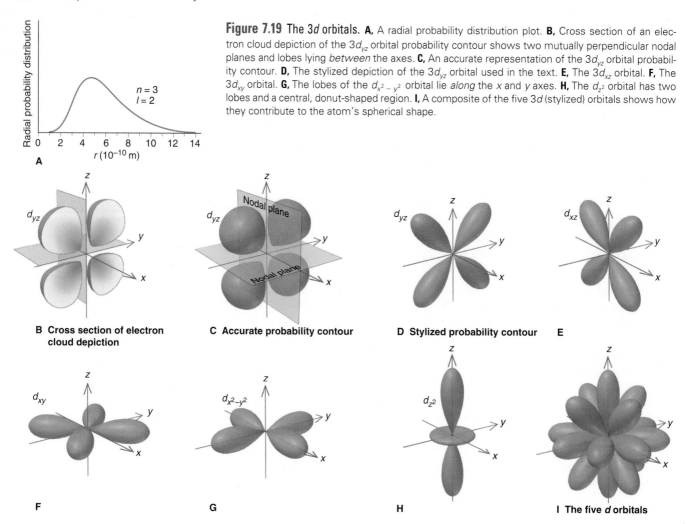

Figure 7.19 The 3d orbitals. **A,** A radial probability distribution plot. **B,** Cross section of an electron cloud depiction of the 3d_{yz} orbital probability contour shows two mutually perpendicular nodal planes and lobes lying *between* the axes. **C,** An accurate representation of the 3d_{yz} orbital probability contour. **D,** The stylized depiction of the 3d_{yz} orbital used in the text. **E,** The 3d_{xz} orbital. **F,** The 3d_{xy} orbital. **G,** The lobes of the $d_{x^2-y^2}$ orbital lie *along* the x and y axes. **H,** The d_{z^2} orbital has two lobes and a central, donut-shaped region. **I,** A composite of the five 3d (stylized) orbitals shows how they contribute to the atom's spherical shape.

B Cross section of electron cloud depiction

C Accurate probability contour

D Stylized probability contour E

F

G

H

I The five d orbitals

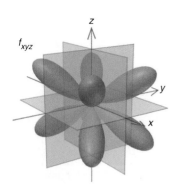

Figure 7.20 The 4f_{xyz} orbital, one of the seven 4f orbitals.

The d Orbital An orbital with $l = 2$ is called a **d orbital.** There are five possible m_l values for $l = 2$: -2, -1, 0, $+1$, and $+2$. Thus, a d orbital has any one of five orientations (Figure 7.19). Four of the five d orbitals have four lobes (a cloverleaf shape) with two mutually perpendicular nodal planes between them and the nucleus at the junction of the lobes (Figure 7.19C). (The orientation of the nodal planes always lies between the orbital lobes.) Three of these orbitals lie in the *xy, xz,* and *yz* planes, with their lobes *between* the axes, and are called the d_{xy}, d_{xz}, and d_{yz} orbitals. A fourth, the $d_{x^2-y^2}$ orbital, also lies in the *xy* plane, but its lobes are *along* the axes. The fifth d orbital, the d_{z^2}, has two major lobes *along* the z axis, and a donut-shaped region girdles the center. An electron in a d orbital spends equal time in all of its lobes.

In keeping with the quantum-number hierarchy, a d orbital ($l = 2$) must have a principal quantum number of $n = 3$ or higher, so 3d is the lowest energy d sublevel. Orbitals in the 4d sublevel are larger (extend farther from the nucleus) than the 3d, and the 5d are larger still.

Orbitals with Higher l Values Orbitals with $l = 3$ are f orbitals and have a principal quantum number of at least $n = 4$. Figure 7.20 shows one of the seven f orbitals ($2l + 1 = 7$); each f orbital has a complex, multilobed shape with several nodal planes. Orbitals with $l = 4$ are g orbitals, but they play no known role in chemical bonding.

The Special Case of Energy Levels in the H Atom

With regard to energy levels and sublevels, the H atom is a special case. When an H atom gains energy, its electron occupies an orbital of higher n value, which is (on average) farther from the nucleus. But, because it has just one electron, *hydrogen is the only atom whose energy state depends completely on the principal quantum number, n*. As you'll see in Chapter 8, because of additional nucleus-electron attractions and electron-electron repulsions, the energy states of all other atoms depend on the *n and l* values of the occupied orbitals. Thus, *for the H atom only*, all four $n = 2$ orbitals (one 2s and three 2p) have the same energy, all nine $n = 3$ orbitals (one 3s, three 3p, and five 3d) have the same energy (Figure 7.21), and so forth.

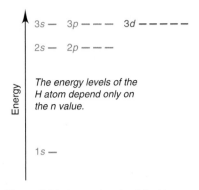

The energy levels of the H atom depend only on the n value.

Figure 7.21 Energy levels of the H atom.

■ Summary of Section 7.4

- The atomic orbital (ψ, wave function) is a mathematical description of the electron's wavelike behavior in an atom. The Schrödinger equation converts each allowed wave function to one of the atom's energy states.
- The probability density of finding the electron at a particular location is represented by ψ^2. For a given energy level, an electron density diagram and a radial probability distribution plot show how the electron occupies the space near the nucleus.
- An atomic orbital is described by three quantum numbers: size (n), shape (l), and orientation (m_l): n limits l to $n - 1$ values, and l limits m_l to $2l + 1$ values.
- An energy level has sublevels with the same n value; a sublevel has orbitals with the same n and l values but differing m_l values.
- A sublevel with $l = 0$ has a spherical (s) orbital; a sublevel with $l = 1$ has three, two-lobed (p) orbitals; and a sublevel with $l = 2$ has five multilobed (d) orbitals.
- In the special case of the H atom, the energy levels depend only on the n value.

CHAPTER REVIEW GUIDE

Learning Objectives   Relevant section (§) and/or sample problem (SP) numbers appear in parentheses.

Understand These Concepts

1. The wave characteristics of light (the interrelations of frequency, wavelength, and speed; the meaning of amplitude) and the general regions of the electromagnetic spectrum (§7.1)
2. How particles and waves differ in terms of the phenomena of refraction, diffraction, and interference (§7.1)
3. The quantization of energy and how an atom changes its energy by emitting or absorbing quanta of radiation (§7.1)
4. How the photon theory explains the photoelectric effect (§7.1)
5. How Bohr's theory explained the line spectra of the H atom; why the theory is wrong and which ideas we retain (§7.2)
6. The wave-particle duality of matter and energy and the relevant theories and experiments that led to it (de Broglie wavelength, electron diffraction, and photon momentum) (§7.3)
7. The meaning of the uncertainty principle and how uncertainty limits our knowledge of electron properties (§7.3)
8. The distinction between ψ (wave function, or atomic orbital) and ψ^2 (probability density) (§7.4)
9. How electron density diagrams and radial probability distribution plots depict the electron's location within the atom (§7.4)

10. The hierarchy of the quantum numbers that describe the size (n, energy), shape (l), and orientation (m_l) of an orbital (§7.4)
11. The distinction between energy level (shell), sublevel (subshell), and orbital (§7.4)
12. The shapes of s, p, and d orbitals (§7.4)

Master These Skills

1. Interconverting wavelength and frequency (SP 7.1)
2. Calculating the energy of a photon from its wavelength (SP 7.2)
3. Finding the energy change and wavelength of the photon absorbed or emitted when an H atom changes its energy level (SP 7.3)
4. Applying de Broglie's equation to find the wavelength of an electron (SP 7.4)
5. Applying the uncertainty principle to see that the location and speed of a particle cannot be determined simultaneously (SP 7.5)
6. Determining quantum numbers and sublevel designations (SPs 7.6–7.8)

Key Equations and Relationships Page numbers appear in parentheses.

7.1 Relating the speed of light to its frequency and wavelength (262):

$$c = v \times \lambda$$

7.2 Determining the smallest change in an atom's energy (266):

$$\Delta E = hv$$

7.3 Calculating the wavelength of any line in the H atom spectrum (Rydberg equation) (268):

$$\frac{1}{\lambda} = R\left(\frac{1}{n_1^2} - \frac{1}{n_2^2}\right)$$

where n_1 and n_2 are positive integers and $n_2 > n_1$

7.4 Finding the difference between two energy levels in the H atom (271):

$$\Delta E = E_{\text{final}} - E_{\text{initial}} = -2.18\times10^{-18} \text{ J} \left(\frac{1}{n_{\text{final}}^2} - \frac{1}{n_{\text{initial}}^2}\right)$$

7.5 Calculating the wavelength of any moving particle (de Broglie wavelength) (276):

$$\lambda = \frac{h}{mu}$$

7.6 Finding the uncertainty in position or speed of a particle (Heisenberg's uncertainty principle) (278):

$$\Delta x \cdot m\Delta u \geq \frac{h}{4\pi}$$

Brief Solutions to Follow-Up Problems

7.1 $\lambda \text{ (nm)} = \dfrac{3.00\times10^8 \text{ m/s}}{7.23\times10^{14} \text{ s}^{-1}} \times \dfrac{10^9 \text{ nm}}{1 \text{ m}} = 415 \text{ nm}$

$\lambda \text{ (Å)} = 415 \text{ nm} \times \dfrac{10 \text{ Å}}{1 \text{ nm}} = 4150 \text{ Å}$

7.2 (a) UV: $E = hc/\lambda$

$= \dfrac{(6.626\times10^{-34} \text{ J·s})(3.00\times10^8 \text{ m/s})}{1\times10^{-8} \text{ m}}$

$= 2\times10^{-17} \text{ J}$

(b) Visible: $E = 4\times10^{-19}$ J; (c) IR: $E = 2\times10^{-21}$ J
As λ increases, E decreases.

7.3 (a) With $n_{\text{final}} = 3$ for an IR photon:

$\Delta E = -2.18\times10^{-18} \text{ J} \left(\dfrac{1}{n_{\text{final}}^2} - \dfrac{1}{n_{\text{initial}}^2}\right)$

$= -2.18\times10^{-18} \text{ J} \left(\dfrac{1}{3^2} - \dfrac{1}{6^2}\right)$

$= -2.18\times10^{-18} \text{ J} \left(\dfrac{1}{9} - \dfrac{1}{36}\right) = -1.82\times10^{-19} \text{ J}$

(b) $\lambda = \dfrac{hc}{|\Delta E|} = \dfrac{(6.626\times10^{-34} \text{ J·s})(3.00\times10^8 \text{ m/s})}{1.82\times10^{-19} \text{ J}} \times \dfrac{1 \text{ Å}}{10^{-10} \text{ m}}$

$= 1.09\times10^4 \text{ Å}$

7.4 $u = \dfrac{h}{m\lambda} = \dfrac{6.626\times10^{-34} \text{ kg·m}^2\text{/s}}{(9.11\times10^{-31} \text{ kg})\left(100 \text{ nm} \times \dfrac{1 \text{ m}}{10^9 \text{ nm}}\right)}$

$= 7.27\times10^3 \text{ m/s}$

7.5 $\Delta x \geq \dfrac{6.626\times10^{-34} \text{ kg·m}^2\text{/s}}{4\pi \,(0.142 \text{ kg})(0.447 \text{ m/s})} \geq 8.31\times10^{-34} \text{ m}$

7.6 $n = 4$, so $l = 0, 1, 2, 3$. In addition to the nine m_l values in Sample Problem 7.6 there are those for $l = 3$:
$$m_l = -3, -2, -1, 0, +1, +2, +3$$

7.7 For 2p: $n = 2$, $l = 1$, $m_l = -1, 0, +1$
For 5f: $n = 5$, $l = 3$, $m_l = -3, -2, -1, 0, +1, +2, +3$

7.8 (a) $n = 4$, $l = 1$; (b) name is 2p; (c) name is 3d; (d) $n = 2$, $l = 0$, $m_l = 0$

PROBLEMS

Problems with **colored** numbers are answered in Appendix E and worked in detail in the Student Solutions Manual. Problem sections match those in the text and provide numbers of relevant sample problems. Most offer Concept Review Questions, Skill-Building Exercises (grouped in pairs covering the same concept), and Problems in Context. Comprehensive Problems are based on material from any section or previous chapter.

The Nature of Light
(Sample Problems 7.1 and 7.2)

Concept Review Questions

7.1 In what ways are microwave and ultraviolet radiation the same? In what ways are they different?

7.2 Consider the following types of electromagnetic radiation:
(1) Microwave   (2) Ultraviolet   (3) Radio waves
(4) Infrared   (5) X-ray   (6) Visible
(a) Arrange them in order of increasing wavelength.
(b) Arrange them in order of increasing frequency.
(c) Arrange them in order of increasing energy.

7.3 Define each of the following wave phenomena, and give an example of where each occurs: (a) refraction; (b) diffraction; (c) dispersion; (d) interference.

7.4 In the 17th century, Newton proposed that light was a stream of particles. The wave-particle debate continued for over 250 years until Planck and Einstein presented their ideas. Give two pieces of evidence for the wave model and two for the particle model.

7.5 Portions of electromagnetic waves A, B, and C are represented below (not drawn to scale):

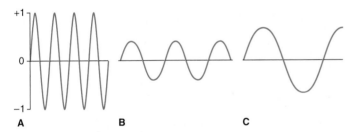

Rank them in order of (a) increasing frequency; (b) increasing energy; (c) increasing amplitude. (d) If wave B just barely fails to cause a current when shining on a metal, is wave A or C more likely to do so? (e) If wave B represents visible radiation, is wave A or C more likely to be IR radiation?

7.6 What new idea about light did Einstein use to explain the photoelectric effect? Why does the photoelectric effect exhibit a threshold frequency but not a time lag?

Skill-Building Exercises (grouped in similar pairs)

7.7 An AM station broadcasts rock music at "950 on your radio dial." Units for AM frequencies are given in kilohertz (kHz). Find the wavelength of the station's radio waves in meters (m), nanometers (nm), and angstroms (Å).

7.8 An FM station broadcasts music at 93.5 MHz (megahertz, or 10^6 Hz). Find the wavelength (in m, nm, and Å) of these waves.

7.9 A radio wave has a frequency of 3.8×10^{10} Hz. What is the energy (in J) of one photon of this radiation?

7.10 An x-ray has a wavelength of 1.3 Å. Calculate the energy (in J) of one photon of this radiation.

7.11 Rank these photons in terms of increasing energy: (a) blue ($\lambda = 453$ nm); (b) red ($\lambda = 660$ nm); (c) yellow ($\lambda = 595$ nm).

7.12 Rank these photons in terms of decreasing energy: (a) IR ($\nu = 6.5 \times 10^{13}$ s^{-1}); (b) microwave ($\nu = 9.8 \times 10^{11}$ s^{-1}); (c) UV ($\nu = 8.0 \times 10^{15}$ s^{-1}).

Problems in Context

7.13 Police often monitor traffic with "K-band" radar guns, which operate in the microwave region at 22.235 GHz (1 GHz $= 10^9$ Hz). Find the wavelength (in nm and Å) of this radiation.

7.14 Covalent bonds in a molecule absorb radiation in the IR region and vibrate at characteristic frequencies.
(a) The C—O bond absorbs radiation of wavelength 9.6 μm. What frequency (in s^{-1}) corresponds to that wavelength?
(b) The H—Cl bond has a frequency of vibration of 8.652×10^{13} Hz. What wavelength (in μm) corresponds to that frequency?

7.15 Cobalt-60 is a radioactive isotope used to treat cancers. A gamma ray emitted by this isotope has an energy of 1.33 MeV (million electron volts; 1 eV $= 1.602 \times 10^{-19}$ J). What is the frequency (in Hz) and the wavelength (in m) of this gamma ray?

7.16 (a) Ozone formation in the upper atmosphere starts when oxygen molecules absorb UV radiation of wavelengths ≤ 242 nm. Find the frequency and energy of the least energetic of these photons. (b) Ozone absorbs radiation of wavelengths 2200–2900 Å, thus protecting organisms from this radiation. Find the frequency and energy of the most energetic of these photons.

Atomic Spectra
(Sample Problem 7.3)

Concept Review Questions

7.17 How is n_1 in the Rydberg equation (Equation 7.3) related to the quantum number n in the Bohr model?

7.18 What key assumption of Bohr's model would a "Solar System" model of the atom violate? What was the theoretical basis for this assumption?

7.19 Distinguish between an absorption spectrum and an emission spectrum. With which did Bohr work?

7.20 Which of these electron transitions correspond to absorption of energy and which to emission?
(a) $n = 2$ to $n = 4$ (b) $n = 3$ to $n = 1$
(c) $n = 5$ to $n = 2$ (d) $n = 3$ to $n = 4$

7.21 Why couldn't the Bohr model predict spectra for atoms other than hydrogen?

7.22 The H atom and the Be^{3+} ion each have one electron. Would you expect the Bohr model to predict their spectra accurately? Would you expect their spectra to be identical? Explain.

Skill-Building Exercises (grouped in similar pairs)

7.23 Use the Rydberg equation to find the wavelength (in nm) of the photon emitted when an H atom undergoes a transition from $n = 5$ to $n = 2$.

7.24 Use the Rydberg equation to find the wavelength (in Å) of the photon absorbed when an H atom undergoes a transition from $n = 1$ to $n = 3$.

7.25 What is the wavelength (in nm) of the least energetic spectral line in the infrared series of the H atom?

7.26 What is the wavelength (in nm) of the least energetic spectral line in the visible series of the H atom?

7.27 Calculate the energy difference (ΔE) for the transition in Problem 7.23 for 1 mol of H atoms.

7.28 Calculate the energy difference (ΔE) for the transition in Problem 7.24 for 1 mol of H atoms.

7.29 Arrange the following H atom electron transitions in order of *increasing* frequency of the photon absorbed or emitted:
(a) $n = 2$ to $n = 4$ (b) $n = 2$ to $n = 1$
(c) $n = 2$ to $n = 5$ (d) $n = 4$ to $n = 3$

7.30 Arrange the following H atom electron transitions in order of *decreasing* wavelength of the photon absorbed or emitted:
(a) $n = 2$ to $n = \infty$ (b) $n = 4$ to $n = 20$
(c) $n = 3$ to $n = 10$ (d) $n = 2$ to $n = 1$

7.31 The electron in a ground-state H atom absorbs a photon of wavelength 97.20 nm. To what energy level does it move?

7.32 An electron in the $n = 5$ level of an H atom emits a photon of wavelength 1281 nm. To what energy level does it move?

Problems in Context

7.33 In addition to continuous radiation, fluorescent lamps emit some visible lines from mercury. A prominent line has a wavelength of 436 nm. What is the energy (in J) of one photon of it?

7.34 A Bohr-model representation of the H atom is shown below with several electron transitions depicted by arrows:

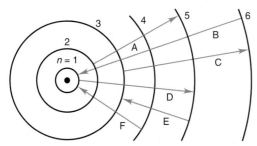

(a) Which transitions are absorptions and which are emissions?
(b) Rank the emissions in terms of increasing energy. (c) Rank the absorptions in terms of increasing wavelength of light absorbed.

The Wave-Particle Duality of Matter and Energy
(Sample Problems 7.4 and 7.5)

Concept Review Questions

7.35 In what sense is the wave motion of a guitar string analogous to the motion of an electron in an atom?

7.36 What experimental support did de Broglie's concept receive?

7.37 If particles have wavelike motion, why don't we observe that motion in the macroscopic world?

7.38 Why can't we overcome the uncertainty predicted by Heisenberg's principle by building more precise instruments to reduce the error in measurements below the $h/4\pi$ limit?

Skill-Building Exercises (grouped in similar pairs)

7.39 A 232-lb fullback runs 40 yd at 19.8 ± 0.1 mi/h.
(a) What is his de Broglie wavelength (in meters)?
(b) What is the uncertainty in his position?

7.40 An alpha particle (mass = 6.6×10^{-24} g) emitted by a radium isotope travels at $3.4 \times 10^7 \pm 0.1 \times 10^7$ mi/h.
(a) What is its de Broglie wavelength (in meters)?
(b) What is the uncertainty in its position?

7.41 How fast must a 56.5-g tennis ball travel to have a de Broglie wavelength equal to that of a photon of green light (5400 Å)?

7.42 How fast must a 142-g baseball travel to have a de Broglie wavelength equal to that of an x-ray photon with $\lambda = 100.$ pm?

7.43 A sodium flame has a characteristic yellow color due to emissions of wavelength 589 nm. What is the mass equivalence of one photon of this wavelength (1 J = 1 kg·m²/s²)?

7.44 A lithium flame has a characteristic red color due to emissions of wavelength 671 nm. What is the mass equivalence of 1 mol of photons of this wavelength (1 J = 1 kg·m²/s²)?

The Quantum-Mechanical Model of the Atom
(Sample Problems 7.6 to 7.8)

Concept Review Questions

7.45 What physical meaning is attributed to ψ^2?

7.46 What does "electron density in a tiny volume of space" mean?

7.47 Explain what it means for the peak in the radial probability distribution plot for the $n = 1$ level of an H atom to be at 0.529 Å. Is the probability of finding an electron at 0.529 Å from the nucleus greater for the 1s or the 2s orbital?

7.48 What feature of an orbital is related to each of the following?
(a) Principal quantum number (n)
(b) Angular momentum quantum number (l)
(c) Magnetic quantum number (m_l)

Skill-Building Exercises (grouped in similar pairs)

7.49 How many orbitals in an atom can have each of the following designations: (a) 1s; (b) 4d; (c) 3p; (d) $n = 3$?

7.50 How many orbitals in an atom can have each of the following designations: (a) 5f; (b) 4p; (c) 5d; (d) $n = 2$?

7.51 Give all possible m_l values for orbitals that have each of the following: (a) $l = 2$; (b) $n = 1$; (c) $n = 4, l = 3$.

7.52 Give all possible m_l values for orbitals that have each of the following: (a) $l = 3$; (b) $n = 2$; (c) $n = 6, l = 1$.

7.53 Draw 90% probability contours (with axes) for each of the following orbitals: (a) s; (b) p_x.

7.54 Draw 90% probability contours (with axes) for each of the following orbitals: (a) p_z; (b) d_{xy}.

7.55 For each of the following, give the sublevel designation, the allowable m_l values, and the number of orbitals:
(a) $n = 4, l = 2$ (b) $n = 5, l = 1$ (c) $n = 6, l = 3$

7.56 For each of the following, give the sublevel designation, the allowable m_l values, and the number of orbitals:
(a) $n = 2, l = 0$ (b) $n = 3, l = 2$ (c) $n = 5, l = 1$

7.57 For each of the following sublevels, give the n and l values and the number of orbitals: (a) 5s; (b) 3p; (c) 4f.

7.58 For each of the following sublevels, give the n and l values and the number of orbitals: (a) 6g; (b) 4s; (c) 3d.

7.59 Are the following combinations allowed? If not, show two ways to correct them:
(a) $n = 2; l = 0; m_l = -1$ (b) $n = 4; l = 3; m_l = -1$
(c) $n = 3; l = 1; m_l = 0$ (d) $n = 5; l = 2; m_l = +3$

7.60 Are the following combinations allowed? If not, show two ways to correct them:
(a) $n = 1; l = 0; m_l = 0$ (b) $n = 2; l = 2; m_l = +1$
(c) $n = 7; l = 1; m_l = +2$ (d) $n = 3; l = 1; m_l = -2$

Comprehensive Problems

7.61 The orange color of carrots and orange peel is due mostly to β-carotene, an organic compound insoluble in water but soluble in benzene and chloroform. Describe an experiment to determine the concentration of β-carotene in the oil from orange peel.

7.62 The quantum-mechanical treatment of the H atom gives the energy, E, of the electron as a function of n:

$$E = -\frac{h^2}{8\pi^2 m_e a_0^2 n^2} \qquad (n = 1, 2, 3, \ldots)$$

where h is Planck's constant, m_e is the electron mass, and a_0 is 52.92×10^{-12} m.
(a) Write the expression in the form $E = -(\text{constant})(1/n^2)$, evaluate the constant (in J), and compare it with the corresponding expression from Bohr's theory.
(b) Use the expression to find ΔE between $n = 2$ and $n = 3$.
(c) Calculate the wavelength of the photon that corresponds to this energy change.

7.63 The photoelectric effect is illustrated in a plot of the kinetic energies of electrons ejected from the surface of potassium metal or silver metal at different frequencies of incident light.

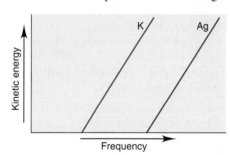

(a) Why don't the lines begin at the origin? (b) Why don't the lines begin at the same point? (c) From which metal will light of shorter wavelength eject an electron? (d) Why are the slopes equal?

7.64 The optic nerve needs a minimum of 2.0×10^{-17} J of energy to trigger a series of impulses that eventually reach the brain.
(a) How many photons of red light (700. nm) are needed? (b) How many photons of blue light (475 nm)?

7.65 One reason carbon monoxide (CO) is toxic is that it binds to the blood protein hemoglobin more strongly than oxygen does. The bond between hemoglobin and CO absorbs radiation of 1953 cm^{-1}. (The units are the reciprocal of the wavelength in centimeters.) Calculate the wavelength (in nm and Å) and the frequency (in Hz) of the absorbed radiation.

7.66 A metal ion M^{n+} has a single electron. The highest energy line in its emission spectrum has a frequency of 2.961×10^{16} Hz. Identify the ion.

7.67 Compare the wavelengths of an electron (mass = 9.11×10^{-31} kg) and a proton (mass = 1.67×10^{-27} kg), each having (a) a speed of 3.4×10^6 m/s; (b) a kinetic energy of 2.7×10^{-15} J.

7.68 Five lines in the H atom spectrum have these wavelengths (in Å): (a) 1212.7; (b) 4340.5; (c) 4861.3; (d) 6562.8; (e) 10,938. Three lines result from transitions to $n_{final} = 2$ (visible series). The other two result from transitions in different series, one with $n_{final} = 1$ and the other with $n_{final} = 3$. Identify $n_{initial}$ for each line.

7.69 In his explanation of the threshold frequency in the photoelectric effect, Einstein reasoned that the absorbed photon must have a minimum energy to dislodge an electron from the metal surface. This energy is called the *work function* (φ) of that metal. What is the longest wavelength of radiation (in nm) that could cause the photoelectric effect in each of these metals: (a) calcium, φ = 4.60×10^{-19} J; (b) titanium, φ = 6.94×10^{-19} J; (c) sodium, φ = 4.41×10^{-19} J?

7.70 Refractometry is based on the difference in the speed of light through a substance (v) and through a vacuum (c). In the procedure, light of known wavelength passes through a fixed thickness of the substance at a known temperature. The index of refraction equals c/v. Using yellow light ($\lambda = 589$ nm) at 20°C, for example, the index of refraction of water is 1.33 and that of diamond is 2.42. Calculate the speed of light in (a) water and (b) diamond.

7.71 A laser (*light amplification by stimulated emission of radiation*) provides nearly monochromatic high-intensity light. Lasers are used in eye surgery, CD/DVD players, basic research, and many other areas. Some dye lasers can be "tuned" to emit a desired wavelength. Fill in the blanks in the following table of the properties of some common lasers:

Type	λ (nm)	v (s^{-1})	E (J)	Color
He-Ne	632.8	?	?	?
Ar	?	6.148×10^{14}	?	?
Ar-Kr	?	?	3.499×10^{-19}	?
Dye	663.7	?	?	?

7.72 The following combinations are not allowed. If n and m_l are correct, change the l value to create an allowable combination:
(a) $n = 3; l = 0; m_l = -1$ (b) $n = 3; l = 3; m_l = +1$
(c) $n = 7; l = 2; m_l = +3$ (d) $n = 4; l = 1; m_l = -2$

7.73 A ground-state H atom absorbs a photon of wavelength 94.91 nm, and its electron attains a higher energy level. The atom then emits two photons: one of wavelength 1281 nm to reach an intermediate energy level, and a second to return to the ground state.
(a) What higher level did the electron reach?
(b) What intermediate level did the electron reach?
(c) What was the wavelength of the second photon emitted?

7.74 Ground-state ionization energies of some one-electron species are

$$H = 1.31\times10^3 \text{ kJ/mol} \qquad He^+ = 5.24\times10^3 \text{ kJ/mol}$$
$$Li^{2+} = 1.18\times10^4 \text{ kJ/mol}$$

(a) Write a general expression for the ionization energy of any one-electron species. (b) Use your expression to calculate the ionization energy of B^{4+}. (c) What is the minimum wavelength required to remove the electron from the $n = 3$ level of He^+? (d) What is the minimum wavelength required to remove the electron from the $n = 2$ level of Be^{3+}?

7.75 Use the relative size of the $3s$ orbital below to answer the following questions about orbitals A–D.

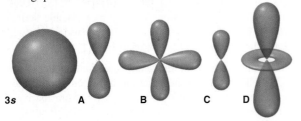

3s   **A**   **B**   **C**   **D**

(a) Which orbital has the highest value of n? (b) Which orbital(s) have a value of $l = 1$? $l = 2$? (c) How many other orbitals with the same value of n have the same shape as orbital B? Orbital C? (d) Which orbital has the highest energy? Lowest energy?

7.76 In the course of developing his model, Bohr arrived at the following formula for the radius of the electron's orbit: $r_n = n^2h^2\epsilon_0/\pi m_e e^2$, where m_e is the electron mass, e is its charge, and ϵ_0 is a constant related to charge attraction in a vacuum. Given that $m_e = 9.109\times10^{-31}$ kg, $e = 1.602\times10^{-19}$ C, and $\epsilon_0 = 8.854\times10^{-12}$ $C^2/J\cdot m$, calculate the following:
(a) The radius of the first ($n = 1$) orbit in the H atom
(b) The radius of the tenth ($n = 10$) orbit in the H atom

7.77 (a) Find the Bohr radius of an electron in the $n = 3$ orbit of an H atom (see Problem 7.76). (b) What is the energy (in J) of the atom in part (a)? (c) What is the energy of an Li^{2+} ion with its electron in the $n = 3$ orbit? (d) Why are the answers to (b) and (c) different?

7.78 Enormous numbers of microwave photons are needed to warm macroscopic samples of matter. A portion of soup containing 252 g of water is heated in a microwave oven from 20.°C to 98°C, with radiation of wavelength 1.55×10^{-2} m. How many photons are absorbed by the water in the soup?

7.79 The quantum-mechanical treatment of the hydrogen atom gives this expression for the wave function, ψ, of the $1s$ orbital:

$$\psi = \frac{1}{\sqrt{\pi}}\left(\frac{1}{a_0}\right)^{3/2}e^{-r/a_0}$$

where r is the distance from the nucleus and a_0 is 52.92 pm. The probability of finding the electron in a tiny volume at distance r from the nucleus is proportional to ψ^2. The total probability of finding the electron at all points at distance r from the nucleus is proportional to $4\pi r^2\psi^2$. Calculate the values (to three significant figures) of ψ, ψ^2, and $4\pi r^2\psi^2$ to fill in the following table and sketch a plot of each set of values versus r. Compare the latter two plots with those in Figure 7.17A, p. 284:

r (pm)	ψ (pm$^{-3/2}$)	ψ^2 (pm^{-3})	$4\pi r^2\psi^2$ (pm^{-1})
0			
50			
100			
200			

7.80 Lines in one spectral series can overlap lines in another. (a) Does the range of wavelengths in the $n_1 = 1$ series for the H atom overlap the range in the $n_1 = 2$ series? (b) Does the range in the $n_1 = 3$ series overlap the range in the $n_1 = 4$ series? (c) How many lines in the $n_1 = 4$ series lie in the range of the $n_1 = 5$ series? (d) What does this overlap imply about the H atom line spectrum at longer wavelengths?

7.81 The following values are the only energy levels of a hypothetical one-electron atom:

$E_6 = -2\times10^{-19}$ J	$E_5 = -7\times10^{-19}$ J
$E_4 = -11\times10^{-19}$ J	$E_3 = -15\times10^{-19}$ J
$E_2 = -17\times10^{-19}$ J	$E_1 = -20\times10^{-19}$ J

(a) If the electron were in the $n = 3$ level, what would be the highest frequency (and minimum wavelength) of radiation that could be emitted? (b) What is the ionization energy (in kJ/mol) of the atom in its ground state? (c) If the electron were in the $n = 4$ level, what would be the shortest wavelength (in nm) of radiation that could be absorbed without causing ionization?

7.82 Photoelectron spectroscopy applies the principle of the photoelectric effect to study orbital energies of atoms and molecules. High-energy radiation (usually UV or x-ray) is absorbed by a sample and an electron is ejected. The orbital energy can be calculated from the known energy of the radiation and the measured energy of the electron lost. The following energy differences were determined for several electron transitions:

$\Delta E_{2\longrightarrow1} = 4.098\times10^{-17}$ J $\qquad \Delta E_{3\longrightarrow1} = 4.854\times10^{-17}$ J
$\Delta E_{5\longrightarrow1} = 5.242\times10^{-17}$ J $\qquad \Delta E_{4\longrightarrow2} = 1.024\times10^{-17}$ J

Calculate ΔE and λ of a photon emitted in the following transitions: (a) level 3 $\longrightarrow$ 2; (b) level 4 $\longrightarrow$ 1; (c) level 5 $\longrightarrow$ 4.

7.83 Horticulturists know that, for many plants, dark green leaves are associated with low light levels and pale green with high levels. (a) Use the photon theory to explain this behavior. (b) What change in leaf composition might account for this difference?

7.84 In order to comply with the requirement that energy be conserved, Einstein showed in the photoelectric effect that the energy of a photon ($h\nu$) absorbed by a metal is the sum of the work function (ϕ), the minimum energy needed to dislodge an electron from the metal's surface, and the kinetic energy (E_k) of the electron: $h\nu = \phi + E_k$. When light of wavelength 358.1 nm falls on the surface of potassium metal, the speed (u) of the dislodged electron is 6.40×10^5 m/s. (a) What is E_k ($\frac{1}{2}mu^2$) of the dislodged electron? (b) What is ϕ (in J) of potassium?

7.85 For any microscope, the smallest object observable is one-half the wavelength of the radiation used. For example, the smallest object observable with light of 400 nm is 2×10^{-7} m. (a) What is the smallest object observable with an electron microscope using electrons moving at 5.5×10^4 m/s? (b) At 3.0×10^7 m/s?

7.86 In fireworks, the heat of the reaction of an oxidizing agent, such as $KClO_4$, with an organic compound excites certain salts, which emit specific colors. Strontium salts have an intense emission at 641 nm, and barium salts have one at 493 nm. (a) What colors do these emissions produce? (b) What is the energy (in kJ) of these emissions for 5.00 g each of the chloride salts of Sr and Ba? (Assume that all the heat produced is converted to emitted light.)

7.87 Atomic hydrogen produces several series of spectral lines. Each series fits the Rydberg equation with its own particular n_1 value. Calculate the value of n_1 (by trial and error if necessary) that would produce a series of lines in which:
(a) The *highest* energy line has a wavelength of 3282 nm.
(b) The *lowest* energy line has a wavelength of 7460 nm.

7.88 Fish-liver oil is a good source of vitamin A, whose concentration is measured spectrometrically at a wavelength of 329 nm.
(a) Suggest a reason for using this wavelength.
(b) In what region of the spectrum does this wavelength lie?
(c) When 0.1232 g of fish-liver oil is dissolved in 500. mL of solvent, the absorbance is 0.724 units. When 1.67×10^{-3} g of vitamin A is dissolved in 250. mL of solvent, the absorbance is 1.018 units. Calculate the vitamin A concentration in the fish-liver oil.

7.89 Many calculators use photocells as their energy source. Find the maximum wavelength needed to remove an electron from silver ($\phi = 7.59 \times 10^{-19}$ J). Is silver a good choice for a photocell that uses visible light? [The concept of the work function (ϕ) is explained in Problem 7.69.]

7.90 In a game of "Clue," Ms. White is killed in the conservatory. A spectrometer in each room records who is present to help find the murderer. For example, if someone wearing yellow is in a room, light at 580 nm is reflected. The suspects are Col. Mustard, Prof. Plum, Mr. Green, Ms. Peacock (blue), and Ms. Scarlet. At the time of the murder, the spectrometer in the dining room shows a reflection at 520 nm, those in the lounge and study record lower frequencies, and the one in the library records the shortest possible wavelength. Who killed Ms. White? Explain.

7.91 Technetium (Tc; $Z = 43$) is a synthetic element used as a radioactive tracer in medical studies. A Tc atom emits a beta particle (electron) with a kinetic energy (E_k) of 4.71×10^{-15} J. What is the de Broglie wavelength of this electron ($E_k = \frac{1}{2}mv^2$)?

7.92 Electric power is measured in watts (1 W = 1 J/s). About 95% of the power output of an incandescent bulb is converted to heat and 5% to light. If 10% of that light shines on your chemistry text, how many photons per second shine on the book from a 75-W bulb? (Assume the photons have a wavelength of 550 nm.)

7.93 The flame tests for sodium and potassium are based on the emissions at 589 nm and 404 nm, respectively. When both elements are present, the Na^+ emission is so strong that the K^+ emission can only be seen by looking through a cobalt-glass filter. (a) What are the colors of these Na^+ and K^+ emissions?

(b) What does the cobalt-glass filter do? (c) Why is $KClO_4$ used as an oxidizing agent in fireworks rather than $NaClO_4$?

7.94 The net change during photosynthesis involves CO_2 and H_2O forming glucose ($C_6H_{12}O_6$) and O_2. Chlorophyll absorbs light in the 600–700 nm region.
(a) Write a balanced thermochemical equation for formation of 1.00 mol of glucose.
(b) What is the minimum number of photons with $\lambda = 680.$ nm needed to form 1.00 mol of glucose?

7.95 Only certain transitions are allowed from one energy level to another. In one-electron species, the change in l of an allowed transition is ± 1. For example, a $3p$ electron can move to a $2s$ orbital but not to a $2p$. Thus, in the UV series, where $n_{final} = 1$, allowed transitions can start in a p orbital ($l = 1$) of $n = 2$ or higher, not in an s ($l = 0$) or d ($l = 2$) orbital of $n = 2$ or higher. From what orbital do each of the allowed transitions start for the first four emission lines in the visible series ($n_{final} = 2$)?

7.96 The discharge of phosphate in detergents to the environment has led to imbalances in the life cycle of freshwater lakes. A chemist uses a spectrometric method to measure total phosphate and obtains the following data for known standards:

Absorbance (880 nm)	Concentration (mol/L)
0	0.0×10^{-5}
0.10	2.5×10^{-5}
0.16	3.2×10^{-5}
0.20	4.4×10^{-5}
0.25	5.6×10^{-5}
0.38	8.4×10^{-5}
0.48	10.5×10^{-5}
0.62	13.8×10^{-5}
0.76	17.0×10^{-5}
0.88	19.4×10^{-5}

(a) Draw a curve of absorbance vs. phosphate concentration.
(b) If a sample of lake water has an absorbance of 0.55, what is its phosphate concentration?

Electron Configuration and Chemical Periodicity

Concepts and skills to review before you study this chapter

- format of the periodic table (Section 2.6)
- characteristics of metals and nonmetals (Section 2.6)
- attractions, repulsions, and Coulomb's law (Section 2.7)
- characteristics of acids and bases (Section 4.4)
- rules for assigning quantum numbers (Section 7.4)

We have become expert at measuring recurring patterns in nature—day and night, the seasons, solar and lunar eclipses, even the swirl in a shell or the rhythm of a heartbeat. Elements exhibit recurring patterns in properties because their atoms do, and we can measure these patterns, too.

The outpouring of scientific creativity by early 20th-century physicists that led to the new quantum-mechanical model of the atom was preceded by countless hours of laboratory work by 19th-century chemists who were exploring the nature of electrolytes, the kinetic-molecular theory, and chemical thermodynamics. The fields of organic chemistry and biochemistry were born in the 19th century, as were the fertilizer, explosives, glassmaking, soapmaking, bleaching, and dyestuff industries. And, for the first time, chemistry became a subject in universities in Europe and America.

Condensed from all these efforts, an enormous body of facts emerged about the elements, which became organized into the periodic table:

- *The original periodic table.* In 1870, the Russian chemist Dmitri Mendeleev arranged the 65 elements known at the time into a table and summarized their behavior in the **periodic law:** when arranged by *atomic mass,* the elements exhibit a periodic recurrence of similar properties. Mendeleev left blank spaces in his table and was even able to *predict* the properties of several elements, for example, germanium, that were not discovered until later.
- *The modern periodic table.* Today's table *(inside front cover)* includes 52 elements not known in 1870 and, most importantly, arranges the elements by *atomic number* (number of protons) *not* atomic mass. This change is based on the work of the British physicist Henry G. J. Moseley, who obtained x-ray spectra of various metals by bombarding the metals with electrons. Moseley found that the largest x-ray peak for each metal was related to the nuclear charge, which increased by 1 for each successive element.

The great test for the new atomic model was to answer one of the central questions in chemistry: *why* do the elements behave as they do? Or, rephrasing to fit the main topic of this chapter, how does the **electron configuration** of an element—*the distribution of electrons within the levels and sublevels of its atoms*—relate to its chemical and physical properties?

IN THIS CHAPTER . . . We explore recurring patterns of electron distributions in atoms to see how they account for the recurring behavior of the elements.
- We describe a new quantum number and a restriction on the number of electrons in an orbital, which allows us to define a unique set of quantum numbers for each electron in an atom of any element.
- We explore electrostatic effects that lead to splitting of atomic energy levels into sublevels and give rise to the order in which orbitals fill with electrons. This filling order correlates with the order of elements in the periodic table.
- We examine the reasons for periodic trends in three atomic properties.
- We see how these trends account for chemical reactivity with regard to metallic and redox behavior, oxide acidity, ion formation, and magnetic behavior.

8.1 • CHARACTERISTICS OF MANY-ELECTRON ATOMS

The Schrödinger equation (introduced in Chapter 7) does not give *exact* solutions for the energy levels of *many-electron atoms,* those with more than one electron—that is, all atoms except hydrogen. However, unlike the Bohr model, it gives excellent *approximate* solutions. Three additional features become important in many-electron atoms: (1) a fourth quantum number, (2) a limit on the number of electrons in an orbital, and (3) a splitting of energy levels into sublevels.

The Electron-Spin Quantum Number

The three quantum numbers n, l, and m_l describe the size (energy), shape, and orientation, respectively, of an atomic orbital. An additional quantum number describes a property called *spin*, which is a property of the electron and not the orbital.

When a beam of atoms that have one or more lone electrons passes through a nonuniform magnetic field (created by magnet faces with different shapes), it splits into two beams; Figure 8.1 shows this for a beam of H atoms. Each electron behaves like a spinning charge and generates a tiny magnetic field, which can have one of two values of *spin*. The two electron fields have opposing directions, so half of the electrons are *attracted* by the large external magnetic field while the other half are *repelled* by it.

Figure 8.1 **The effect of electron spin.** A beam of H atoms splits because each atom's electron has one of the two possible values of spin.

Corresponding to the two directions of the electron's field, the **spin quantum number (m_s)** has two possible values, $+\frac{1}{2}$ or $-\frac{1}{2}$. Thus, *each electron in an atom is described completely by a set of **four** quantum numbers: the first three describe its orbital, and the fourth describes its spin.* The quantum numbers are summarized in Table 8.1.

Now we can write a set of four quantum numbers for any electron in the ground state of any atom. For example, the set of quantum numbers for the lone electron in hydrogen (H; $Z = 1$) is $n = 1$, $l = 0$, $m_l = 0$, and $m_s = +\frac{1}{2}$. (The spin quantum number could just as well have been $-\frac{1}{2}$, but by convention, we assign $+\frac{1}{2}$ to the first electron in an orbital.)

Table **8.1** Summary of Quantum Numbers of Electrons in Atoms			
Name	**Symbol**	**Permitted Values**	**Property**
Principal	n	Positive integers (1, 2, 3, . . .)	Orbital energy (size)
Angular momentum	l	Integers from 0 to $n - 1$	Orbital shape (the l values 0, 1, 2, and 3 correspond to s, p, d, and f orbitals, respectively.)
Magnetic	m_l	Integers from $-l$ to 0 to $+l$	Orbital orientation
Spin	m_s	$+\frac{1}{2}$ or $-\frac{1}{2}$	Direction of e^- spin

The Exclusion Principle

The element after hydrogen is helium (He; $Z = 2$), the first with atoms having more than one electron. The first electron in the He ground state has the same set of quantum numbers as the electron in the H atom, but the second He electron does not. Based on observations of excited states, the Austrian physicist Wolfgang Pauli formulated the **exclusion principle:** *no two electrons in the same atom can have the same four quantum numbers.* Therefore, the second He electron occupies the same orbital as the first but has an opposite spin: $n = 1$, $l = 0$, $m_l = 0$, and $m_s = -\frac{1}{2}$. ●

The major consequence of the exclusion principle is that *an atomic orbital can hold a maximum of two electrons and they must have opposing spins.* We say that the 1s orbital in He is *filled* and that the electrons have *paired spins.* Thus, a beam of He atoms is not split in an experiment like that in Figure 8.1.

Electrostatic Effects and Energy-Level Splitting

Electrostatic effects—attraction of opposite charges and repulsion of like charges—play a major role in determining the energy states of many-electron atoms. Unlike the H atom, in which there is only the attraction between nucleus and electron and the energy state is determined *only* by the *n* value, the energy states of many-electron atoms are also affected by electron-electron repulsions. You'll see shortly how these additional interactions give rise to *the splitting of energy levels into sublevels of differing energies: the energy of an orbital in a many-electron atom depends mostly on its n value (size) and to a lesser extent on its l value (shape).*

Our first encounter with energy-level splitting occurs with lithium (Li; $Z = 3$). The first two electrons of Li fill its 1s orbital, so the third Li electron must go into the $n = 2$ level. But, this level has 2s *and* 2p sublevels: which does the third electron enter? For reasons we discuss below, the 2s is lower in energy than the 2p, so the ground state of Li has its third electron in the 2s.

This energy difference arises from three factors—*nuclear attraction, electron repulsions,* and *orbital shape* (i.e., radial probability distribution). Their interplay leads to two phenomena—*shielding* and *penetration*—that occur in all atoms *except* hydrogen. [In the following discussion, keep in mind that more energy is needed to remove an electron from a more stable (lower energy) sublevel than from a less stable (higher energy) sublevel.]

The Effect of Nuclear Charge (Z) on Sublevel Energy Higher charges interact more strongly than lower charges (Coulomb's law, Section 2.7). Therefore, *a higher nuclear charge increases nucleus-electron attractions and, thus, lowers sublevel energy (stabilizes the atom).* We see this effect by comparing the 1s sublevel energies of three species with one electron—H atom ($Z = 1$), He$^+$ ion ($Z = 2$), and Li^{2+} ion ($Z = 3$). Figure 8.2 shows that the 1s sublevel in H is the least stable (highest energy), so the least energy is needed to remove its electron; and the 1s sublevel in Li^{2+} is the most stable, so the most energy is needed to remove its electron.

Shielding: The Effect of Electron Repulsions on Sublevel Energy In many-electron atoms, each electron "feels" not only the attraction to the nucleus but also repulsions from other electrons. Repulsions counteract the nuclear attraction somewhat, making each electron easier to remove by, in effect, helping to push it away. We speak of each electron "shielding" the other electrons to some extent from the nuclear charge. **Shielding** (also called *screening*) reduces the full nuclear charge to an **effective nuclear charge (Z_{eff}),** the nuclear charge an electron *actually experiences, and this lower nuclear charge makes the electron easier to remove.*

1. *Shielding by other electrons in a given energy level.* Electrons in the *same* energy level shield each other somewhat. Compare the He atom and He$^+$ ion: both have a 2+ nuclear charge, but He has two electrons in the 1s sublevel and He$^+$ has

Figure 8.2 The effect of nuclear charge on sublevel energy. Greater nuclear charge lowers sublevel energy (to a more negative number), which makes the electron harder to remove. (The strength of attraction is indicated by the thickness of the black arrows.)

Figure 8.3 Shielding and energy levels.
A, Within an energy level, each electron shields *(red arrows)* other electrons from the full nuclear charge *(black arrows)*, so they experience a lower Z_{eff}. **B,** Inner electrons shield outer electrons *much* more effectively than electrons in the same energy level.

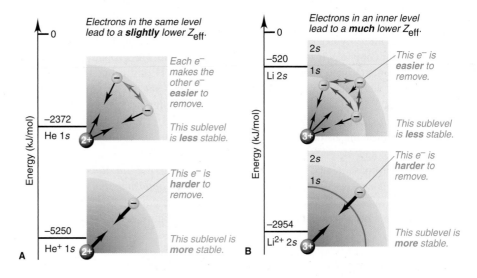

only one (Figure 8.3A). It takes less than half as much energy to remove an electron from He (2372 kJ/mol) than from He$^+$ (5250 kJ/mol) because the second electron in He repels the first, in effect causing a lower Z_{eff}.

2. *Shielding by electrons in inner energy levels.* Because inner electrons spend nearly all their time *between* the outer electrons and the nucleus, they cause a *much* lower Z_{eff} than do electrons in the same level. We can see this by comparing two atomic systems with the same nucleus, one *with* inner electrons and the other *without*. The ground-state Li atom has two inner ($1s$) electrons and one outer ($2s$) electron, while the Li^{2+} ion has only one electron, which occupies the $2s$ orbital in the first excited state (Figure 8.3B). It takes about one-sixth as much energy to remove the $2s$ electron from the Li atom (520 kJ/mol) as it takes to remove it from the Li^{2+} ion (2954 kJ/mol), because the *inner electrons shield very effectively*.

Penetration: The Effect of Orbital Shape on Sublevel Energy To see why the third Li electron occupies the $2s$ sublevel rather than the $2p$, we have to consider orbital shapes, that is, radial probability distributions (Figure 8.4). A $2p$ orbital *(orange curve)* is slightly closer to the nucleus, on average, than the major portion of the $2s$ orbital *(blue curve)*. But a small portion of the $2s$ radial probability distribution peaks within the $1s$ region. Thus, an electron in the $2s$ orbital spends part of its time "penetrating" very close to the nucleus. **Penetration** has two effects:

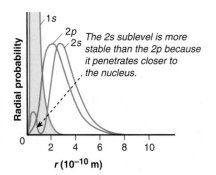

The 2s sublevel is more stable than the 2p because it penetrates closer to the nucleus.

Figure 8.4 Penetration and sublevel energy.

- It *increases the nuclear attraction* for a $2s$ electron over that for a $2p$ electron.
- It *decreases the shielding* of a $2s$ electron by the $1s$ electrons.

Thus, since it takes more energy to remove a $2s$ electron (520 kJ/mol) than a $2p$ (341 kJ/mol), the $2s$ sublevel is lower in energy than the $2p$.

Splitting of Levels into Sublevels In general, *penetration and the resulting effects on shielding cause an energy level to split into sublevels of differing energy.* The lower the l value of a sublevel, the more its electrons penetrate, and so the greater their attraction to the nucleus. Therefore, *for a given n value, a lower l value indicates a more stable (lower energy) sublevel:*

$$\text{Order of sublevel energies: } s < p < d < f \qquad \textbf{(8.1)}$$

Thus, the $2s$ ($l = 0$) is lower in energy than the $2p$ ($l = 1$), the $3p$ ($l = 1$) is lower than the $3d$ ($l = 2$), and so forth.

Figure 8.5 shows the general energy order of levels (n value) and how they are split into sublevels (l values) of differing energies. (Compare this with the H atom energy levels in Figure 7.21, p. 287.) Next, we'll use this energy order to construct a periodic table of ground-state atoms.

■ Summary of Section 8.1

- Identifying electrons in many-electron atoms requires four quantum numbers: three (n, l, m_l) describe the orbital, and a fourth (m_s) describes electron spin.
- The exclusion principle requires each electron to have a unique set of four quantum numbers; therefore, an orbital can hold no more than two electrons, and their spins must be paired (opposite).
- Electrostatic interactions determine sublevel energies as follows:
  1. Greater nuclear charge lowers sublevel energy, making electrons harder to remove.
  2. Electron-electron repulsions raise sublevel energy, making electrons easier to remove. Repulsions shield electrons from the full nuclear charge, reducing it to an effective nuclear charge, Z_{eff}. Inner electrons shield outer electrons very effectively.
  3. Penetration makes an electron harder to remove because nuclear attraction increases and shielding decreases. As a result, an energy level is split into sublevels with the energy order $s < p < d < f$.

8.2 • THE QUANTUM-MECHANICAL MODEL AND THE PERIODIC TABLE

Quantum mechanics provides the theoretical foundation for the experimentally based periodic table. In this section, we fill the table by determining the ground-state electron configuration of each element—*the lowest-energy distribution of electrons in the sublevels of its atoms*. Note especially the *recurring pattern in electron configurations, which is the basis for recurring patterns in chemical behavior*.

A useful way to determine electron configurations is based on the **aufbau principle** (German *aufbauen*, "to build up"). We start at the beginning of the periodic table and add one proton to the nucleus and one electron to the *lowest energy sublevel available*. (Of course, one or more neutrons are also added to the nucleus.)

There are two common ways to indicate the distribution of electrons:

- *The electron configuration.* This shorthand notation consists of the principal energy level (n value), the letter designation of the sublevel (l value), and the number of electrons (#) in the sublevel, written as a superscript: $nl^{\#}$.
- *The orbital diagram.* An **orbital diagram** consists of a box (or circle, or just a line) for each orbital in a given energy level, grouped by sublevel (with nl designation shown beneath), with an arrow representing an electron *and* its spin: ↑ is $+\frac{1}{2}$ and ↓ is $-\frac{1}{2}$. (Throughout the text, orbital occupancy is also indicated by color intensity: no color is empty, pale color is half-filled, and full color is filled.)

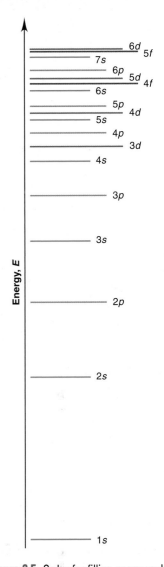

Figure 8.5 Order for filling energy sublevels with electrons. In general, energies of sublevels increase with the principal quantum number n ($1 < 2 < 3$, etc.) and the angular momentum quantum number l ($s < p < d < f$). As n increases, some sublevels overlap; for example, the $4s$ sublevel is lower in energy than the $3d$. (Line color indicates sublevel type.)

Building Up Period 1

Let's begin by applying the aufbau principle to Period 1, whose ground-state elements have only the $n = 1$ level and, thus, only the $1s$ sublevel, which consists of only the $1s$ orbital. We'll also assign a set of four quantum numbers to each element's *last added* electron.

1. *Hydrogen.* For the electron in H, as you've seen, the set of quantum numbers is H ($Z = 1$): $n = 1$, $l = 0$, $m_l = 0$, $m_s = +\frac{1}{2}$. The electron configuration (spoken "one-ess-one") and orbital diagram are

$$\text{H } (Z = 1) \quad 1s^1 \quad \boxed{\uparrow}$$
$$1s$$

2. *Helium.* Recall that the first electron in He has the same quantum numbers as the electron in H, but the second He electron has opposing spin (exclusion principle) He ($Z = 2$): $n = 1$, $l = 0$, $m_l = 0$, $m_s = -\frac{1}{2}$. The electron configuration (spoken "one-ess-two," *not* "one-ess-squared") and orbital diagram are

$$\text{He } (Z = 2) \quad 1s^2 \quad \boxed{\uparrow\downarrow}$$
$$1s$$

Figure 8.6 A vertical orbital diagram for the Li ground state.

Building Up Period 2

The exclusion principle says an orbital can hold no more than two electrons. Therefore, with He, the $1s$ orbital, the $1s$ sublevel, the $n = 1$ level, and Period 1 are filled. Filling the $n = 2$ level builds up Period 2 and begins with the $2s$ sublevel, which is the next lowest in energy (see Figure 8.4) and consists of only the $2s$ orbital. When the $2s$ sublevel is filled, we proceed to fill the $2p$.

1. *Lithium.* The first two electrons in Li fill the $1s$ sublevel, and the last added Li electron has quantum numbers $n = 2$, $l = 0$, $m_l = 0$, $m_s = +\frac{1}{2}$. The electron configuration and orbital diagram are

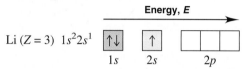

(Note that a complete orbital diagram shows all the orbitals for the given n value, whether or not they are occupied.) To save space on a page, orbital diagrams are written horizontally, with *the sublevel energy increasing left to right.* But Figure 8.6 highlights the energy increase with a vertical orbital diagram for lithium.

2. *Beryllium.* The $2s$ orbital is only half-filled in Li, and the fourth electron of beryllium fills it with the electron's spin paired: $n = 2$, $l = 0$, $m_l = 0$, $m_s = -\frac{1}{2}$.

$$\text{Be } (Z = 4) \quad 1s^2 2s^2$$

3. *Boron.* The next lowest energy sublevel is the $2p$. A p sublevel has $l = 1$, so the m_l (orientation) values can be -1, 0, or $+1$. The three orbitals in the $2p$ sublevel have *equal energy* (same n and l values), which means that the fifth electron of boron can go into *any one of the 2p orbitals.* For convenience, let's label the boxes from left to right: -1, 0, $+1$. By convention, we start on the left and place the fifth electron in the $m_l = -1$ orbital: $n = 2$, $l = 1$, $m_l = -1$, $m_s = +\frac{1}{2}$.

$$\text{B } (Z = 5) \quad 1s^2 2s^2 2p^1$$

4. *Carbon.* To minimize electron-electron repulsions, the sixth electron of carbon enters one of the *unoccupied* $2p$ orbitals; by convention, we place it in the $m_l = 0$ orbital. Experiment shows that the spin of this electron is *parallel* to (the same as) the spin of the other $2p$ electron. This result exemplifies **Hund's rule:** *when orbitals of equal energy are available, the electron configuration of lowest energy has the maximum number of unpaired electrons with parallel spins.* Thus, the sixth electron has $n = 2$, $l = 1$, $m_l = 0$, and $m_s = +\frac{1}{2}$.

$$\text{C } (Z = 6) \quad 1s^2 2s^2 2p^2$$

5. *Nitrogen.* Based on Hund's rule, nitrogen's seventh electron enters the last empty $2p$ orbital, with its spin parallel to the other two: $n = 2$, $l = 1$, $m_l = +1$, $m_s = +\frac{1}{2}$.

$$\text{N } (Z = 7) \quad 1s^2 2s^2 2p^3$$

6. *Oxygen.* The eighth electron in oxygen must enter one of the three half-filled $2p$ orbitals and "pair up" with (oppose the spin of) the electron present. We place the electron in a half-filled $2p$ orbital: $n = 2$, $l = 1$, $m_l = -1$, $m_s = -\frac{1}{2}$.

$$\text{O } (Z = 8) \quad 1s^2 2s^2 2p^4$$

7. *Fluorine.* Fluorine's ninth electron enters the next of the two remaining half-filled $2p$ orbitals: $n = 2, l = 1, m_l = 0, m_s = -\frac{1}{2}$.

F $(Z = 9)$ $1s^2 2s^2 2p^5$

$\uparrow\downarrow$	$\uparrow\downarrow$	$\uparrow\downarrow$ $\uparrow\downarrow$ $\uparrow$
$1s$	$2s$	$2p$

8. *Neon.* Only one unfilled $2p$ orbital remains, so the tenth electron of neon occupies it: $n = 2, l = 1, m_l = +1, m_s = -\frac{1}{2}$. With neon, the $n = 2$ level is filled.

Ne $(Z = 10)$ $1s^2 2s^2 2p^6$

$\uparrow\downarrow$	$\uparrow\downarrow$	$\uparrow\downarrow$ $\uparrow\downarrow$ $\uparrow\downarrow$
$1s$	$2s$	$2p$

Sample Problem 8.1 Determining Quantum Numbers from Orbital Diagrams

Problem Use the orbital diagram shown above to write the set of quantum numbers for the third electron and the set for the eighth electron of the F atom.

Plan Referring to the orbital diagram, we identify the electron of interest and note its level (n), sublevel (l), orbital (m_l), and spin (m_s).

Solution The third electron is in the $2s$ orbital. The upward arrow indicates a spin of $+\frac{1}{2}$:

$$n = 2, l = 0, m_l = 0, m_s = +\frac{1}{2}$$

The eighth electron is in the first $2p$ orbital, which is designated $m_l = -1$, and has a downward arrow:

$$n = 2, l = 1, m_l = -1, m_s = -\frac{1}{2}$$

Follow-Up Problem 8.1 Use the periodic table to identify the element with the electron configuration $1s^2 2s^2 2p^4$. Write its orbital diagram and the set of quantum numbers for its sixth electron.

With our attention on these notations, it's easy to forget that atoms are real objects and electrons occupy volumes with specific shapes and orientations. Figure 8.7 shows orbital contours for the first 10 elements arranged in periodic table format.

Even now, we can make an important correlation: *elements in the same group have similar outer electron configurations and similar patterns of reactivity.* As an example, helium (He) and neon (Ne) in Group 8A(18) both have filled outer sublevels—$1s^2$ for helium and $2s^2 2p^6$ for neon—and neither element forms compounds. Filled outer sublevels make elements much more stable and unreactive.

Figure 8.7 Depicting orbital occupancy for the first 10 elements. In addition to atomic number, atomic symbol, and ground-state electron configuration, each box shows the probability contours of the atom's orbitals. Orbital occupancy is indicated by lighter shading for half-filled (one e⁻) orbitals and darker shading for filled (two e⁻) orbitals.

Table 8.2 **Partial Orbital Diagrams and Electron Configurations* for the Elements in Period 3**

Atomic Number	Element	Partial Orbital Diagram (3s and 3p Sublevels Only)	Full Electron Configuration†	Condensed Electron Configuration
11	Na	$3s$ ↑ $3p$ □□□	$[1s^22s^22p^6]\,3s^1$	$[\text{Ne}]\,3s^1$
12	Mg	↑↓ □□□	$[1s^22s^22p^6]\,3s^2$	$[\text{Ne}]\,3s^2$
13	Al	↑↓ ↑□□	$[1s^22s^22p^6]\,3s^23p^1$	$[\text{Ne}]\,3s^23p^1$
14	Si	↑↓ ↑↑□	$[1s^22s^22p^6]\,3s^23p^2$	$[\text{Ne}]\,3s^23p^2$
15	P	↑↓ ↑↑↑	$[1s^22s^22p^6]\,3s^23p^3$	$[\text{Ne}]\,3s^23p^3$
16	S	↑↓ ↑↓↑↑	$[1s^22s^22p^6]\,3s^23p^4$	$[\text{Ne}]\,3s^23p^4$
17	Cl	↑↓ ↑↓↑↓↑	$[1s^22s^22p^6]\,3s^23p^5$	$[\text{Ne}]\,3s^23p^5$
18	Ar	↑↓ ↑↓↑↓↑↓	$[1s^22s^22p^6]\,3s^23p^6$	$[\text{Ne}]\,3s^23p^6$

*Colored type indicates the sublevel to which the last electron is added.
†The full configuration is not usually written with square brackets; they are included here to show how the [Ne] designation arises.

Building Up Period 3

The Period 3 elements, Na through Ar, lie directly under the Period 2 elements, Li through Ne. That is, even though the $n = 3$ level splits into 3s, 3p, and 3d sublevels, Period 3 fills only 3s and 3p; as you'll see shortly, the 3d is filled in Period 4. Table 8.2 introduces two ways to present electron distributions more concisely:

- *Partial orbital diagrams* show only the sublevels being filled, here the 3s and 3p.
- *Condensed electron configurations (rightmost column)* have the element symbol of the previous noble gas in brackets, to stand for its configuration, followed by the electron configuration of filled inner sublevels and the energy level being filled. For example, the condensed electron configuration of sulfur is [Ne] $3s^23p^4$, where [Ne] stands for $1s^22s^22p^6$.

In Na (the second alkali metal) and Mg (the second alkaline earth metal), electrons are added to the 3s sublevel, which contains only the 3s orbital; this is directly comparable to the filling of the 2s sublevel in Li and Be in Period 2. Then, in the same way as the 2p orbitals of B, C, and N in Period 2 are half-filled, the last electrons added to Al, Si, and P in Period 3 half-fill successive 3p orbitals with spins parallel (Hund's rule). The last electrons added to S, Cl, and Ar then successively pair up to fill those 3p orbitals, which fills the 3p sublevel.

Similar Electron Configurations Within Groups

One of the central points in chemistry is that *similar outer electron configurations correlate with similar chemical behavior.* Figure 8.8 shows the condensed electron configurations of the first 18 elements. Note the similarity within each group. Here are examples from three of the groups:

- In Group 1A(1), Li and Na have the outer electron configuration ns^1 (where n is the quantum number of the highest energy level), as do the other alkali metals (K, Rb, Cs, and Fr). All are highly reactive metals whose atoms lose the outer electron when they form ionic compounds with nonmetals, and all react vigorously with water to displace H_2 (Figure 8.9A).
- In Group 7A(17), F and Cl have the outer electron configuration ns^2np^5, as do the other halogens (Br, I, and At). All are reactive nonmetals that occur as diatomic

Figure 8.8 Condensed electron configurations in the first three periods. Elements in a group have similar outer electron configurations (*color*).

molecules (X_2), and all form ionic compounds with metals (KX, MgX_2) in which the ion charge is $1-$ (Figure 8.9B), covalent compounds with hydrogen (HX) that yield acidic solutions in water, and covalent compounds with carbon (CX_4).

• In Group 8A(18), He has the electron configuration ns^2, and all the other elements in the group have the outer configuration ns^2np^6. Consistent with their *filled* energy levels, all the members are very unreactive monatomic gases.

To summarize the major connection between quantum mechanics and chemical periodicity: *sublevels are filled in order of increasing energy, which leads to outer electron configurations that recur periodically, which leads to chemical properties that recur periodically.*

A

B

Figure 8.9 Similar reactivities in a group. **A,** Potassium reacting with water. **B,** Chlorine reacting with potassium.

Building Up Period 4: The First Transition Series

Period 4 contains the first series of **transition elements,** those in which *d* orbitals are being filled. Let's examine three factors that affect the filling pattern in a period with a transition series.

1. *Effects of shielding and penetration on sublevel energy.* The 3*d* sublevel is filled in Period 4, but *the 4s sublevel is filled first.* This switch in filling order is due to shielding and penetration effects. Based on the 3*d* radial probability distribution (see Figure 7.19, p. 286), a 3*d* electron spends most of the time outside the filled inner $n = 1$ and $n = 2$ levels, so it is shielded very effectively from the nuclear charge. However, the outermost 4*s* electron penetrates close to the nucleus part of the time, so it is subject to a greater attraction. As a result, the 4*s* orbital is slightly *lower* in energy than the 3*d* and fills first. In any period, *the ns sublevel fills before the*

$(n-1)d$ *sublevel.* Other variations in the filling pattern occur at higher values of n because sublevel energies become very close together (see Figure 8.5).

2. *Filling the 4s and 3d sublevels.* Table 8.3 shows the partial orbital diagrams and full and condensed electron configurations for the 18 elements in Period 4. The first two elements, K and Ca, are the next alkali and alkaline earth metals, respectively; the last electron of K half-fills and that of Ca fills the $4s$ sublevel. The last electron of scandium (Sc; $Z = 21$), the first transition element, occupies any one of the five $3d$ orbitals because they are equal in energy; Sc has the electron configuration [Ar] $4s^23d^1$. Filling of the $3d$ orbitals proceeds one electron at a time, as with the p orbitals, except in two cases, chromium (Cr; $Z = 24$) and copper (Cu; $Z = 29$), discussed next.

3. *Stability of half-filled and filled sublevels.* Vanadium (V; $Z = 23$) has three half-filled d orbitals ([Ar] $4s^23d^3$). However, the last electron of the next element, Cr, does not enter a fourth empty d orbital to give [Ar] $4s^23d^4$; instead, Cr has one electron in the $4s$ sublevel and five in the $3d$ sublevel, making both sublevels half filled: [Ar] $4s^13d^5$ (*see margin*). In the next element, manganese (Mn; $Z = 25$), the $4s$ sublevel is filled again ([Ar] $4s^23d^5$).

Cr ($Z = 24$)   [Ar] $4s^13d^5$

4s   3d   4p

Table 8.3 Partial Orbital Diagrams and Electron Configurations* for the Elements in Period 4

Atomic Number	Element	Partial Orbital Diagram (4s, 3d, and 4p Sublevels Only)			Full Electron Configuration	Condensed Electron Configuration
		4s	3d	4p		
19	K	↑			$1s^22s^22p^63s^23p^64s^1$	[Ar] $4s^1$
20	Ca	↑↓			$1s^22s^22p^63s^23p^64s^2$	[Ar] $4s^2$
21	Sc	↑↓	↑		$1s^22s^22p^63s^23p^64s^23d^1$	[Ar] $4s^23d^1$
22	Ti	↑↓	↑ ↑		$1s^22s^22p^63s^23p^64s^23d^2$	[Ar] $4s^23d^2$
23	V	↑↓	↑ ↑ ↑		$1s^22s^22p^63s^23p^64s^23d^3$	[Ar] $4s^23d^3$
24	Cr	↑	↑ ↑ ↑ ↑ ↑		$1s^22s^22p^63s^23p^64s^13d^5$	[Ar] $4s^13d^5$
25	Mn	↑↓	↑ ↑ ↑ ↑ ↑		$1s^22s^22p^63s^23p^64s^23d^5$	[Ar] $4s^23d^5$
26	Fe	↑↓	↑↓ ↑ ↑ ↑ ↑		$1s^22s^22p^63s^23p^64s^23d^6$	[Ar] $4s^23d^6$
27	Co	↑↓	↑↓ ↑↓ ↑ ↑ ↑		$1s^22s^22p^63s^23p^64s^23d^7$	[Ar] $4s^23d^7$
28	Ni	↑↓	↑↓ ↑↓ ↑↓ ↑ ↑		$1s^22s^22p^63s^23p^64s^23d^8$	[Ar] $4s^23d^8$
29	Cu	↑	↑↓ ↑↓ ↑↓ ↑↓ ↑↓		$1s^22s^22p^63s^23p^64s^13d^{10}$	[Ar] $4s^13d^{10}$
30	Zn	↑↓	↑↓ ↑↓ ↑↓ ↑↓ ↑↓		$1s^22s^22p^63s^23p^64s^23d^{10}$	[Ar] $4s^23d^{10}$
31	Ga	↑↓	↑↓ ↑↓ ↑↓ ↑↓ ↑↓	↑	$1s^22s^22p^63s^23p^64s^23d^{10}4p^1$	[Ar] $4s^23d^{10}4p^1$
32	Ge	↑↓	↑↓ ↑↓ ↑↓ ↑↓ ↑↓	↑ ↑	$1s^22s^22p^63s^23p^64s^23d^{10}4p^2$	[Ar] $4s^23d^{10}4p^2$
33	As	↑↓	↑↓ ↑↓ ↑↓ ↑↓ ↑↓	↑ ↑ ↑	$1s^22s^22p^63s^23p^64s^23d^{10}4p^3$	[Ar] $4s^23d^{10}4p^3$
34	Se	↑↓	↑↓ ↑↓ ↑↓ ↑↓ ↑↓	↑↓ ↑ ↑	$1s^22s^22p^63s^23p^64s^23d^{10}4p^4$	[Ar] $4s^23d^{10}4p^4$
35	Br	↑↓	↑↓ ↑↓ ↑↓ ↑↓ ↑↓	↑↓ ↑↓ ↑	$1s^22s^22p^63s^23p^64s^23d^{10}4p^5$	[Ar] $4s^23d^{10}4p^5$
36	Kr	↑↓	↑↓ ↑↓ ↑↓ ↑↓ ↑↓	↑↓ ↑↓ ↑↓	$1s^22s^22p^63s^23p^64s^23d^{10}4p^6$	[Ar] $4s^23d^{10}4p^6$

*Colored type indicates sublevel(s) whose occupancy changes when the last electron is added.

Because it follows nickel (Ni; [Ar] $4s^23d^8$), copper would be expected to have the configuration [Ar] $4s^23d^9$. Instead, the $4s$ sublevel of Cu is *half-filled* with 1 electron, and the $3d$ sublevel is *filled* with 10 (*see margin*). From these two exceptions, Cr and Cu, we conclude that *half-filled and filled sublevels are unexpectedly stable (low in energy);* we see this pattern with many other elements.

With zinc (Zn; $Z = 30$), the $4s$ sublevel is filled ([Ar] $4s^23d^{10}$), and the first transition series ends. The $4p$ sublevel is filled by the next six elements, and Period 4 ends with the noble gas krypton (Kr; $Z = 36$).

Cu ($Z = 29$)   [Ar] $4s^13d^{10}$

↑	↑↓	↑↓	↑↓	↑↓	↑↓			

4s   3d   4p

General Principles of Electron Configurations

Figure 8.10 shows the partial (highest energy sublevels being filled) ground-state electron configurations of the 117 known elements. Let's highlight some key relationships among them.

Similar Outer Electron Configurations Within a Group Among the main-group elements (A groups)—the *s*-block and *p*-block elements—outer electron configurations within a group are identical. Some variations in the transition elements (B groups, *d* block) and inner transition elements (*f* block) occur, as we'll see.

Orbital Filling Order When the elements are "built up" by filling levels and sublevels in order of increasing energy, we obtain the sequence in the periodic table. Reading the table from left to right, like words on a page, gives the energy order

Figure 8.10 A periodic table of partial ground-state electron configurations.

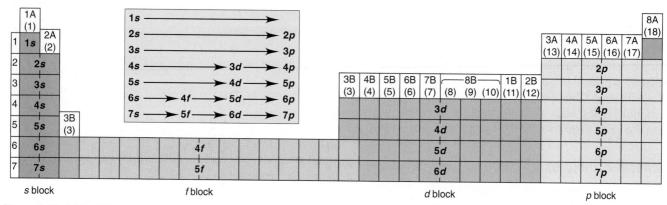

Figure 8.11 Orbital filling and the periodic table. This form of the periodic table shows the sublevel blocks. *Pale green inset:* A summary of the sublevel filling order.

● Aid to memorizing sublevel filling order. List the sublevels as shown, and read from 1s, following the direction of the arrows. Note that the
- *n* value is constant horizontally
- *l* value is constant vertically
- *n* + *l* is constant diagonally

of levels and sublevels (Figure 8.11); the margin note is a memory aid for sublevel filling order when a periodic table is not available. ●

Categories of Electrons Atoms have three categories of electrons:

1. **Inner (core) electrons** are those an atom has in common with the previous noble gas and any *completed* transition series. They fill all the *lower energy levels* of an atom.
2. **Outer electrons** are those in the *highest energy level* (highest *n* value). They spend most of their time farthest from the nucleus.
3. **Valence electrons** are those involved in forming compounds:
   - For main-group elements, the *valence electrons **are** the outer electrons.*
   - For transition elements, in addition to the outer *ns* electrons, the $(n - 1)d$ electrons are also valence electrons, though the metals Fe ($Z = 26$) through Zn ($Z = 30$) may use only a few, if any, of their *d* electrons in bonding.

Group and Period Numbers Key information is embedded in the periodic table:

- Among the main-group elements (A groups), *the A number equals the number of outer electrons* (those with the highest *n*); thus, chlorine (Cl; Group **7A**) has 7 outer electrons, and so forth.
- *The period number is the n value of the highest energy level.*
- For an energy level, the *n* value squared (n^2) is the number of *orbitals*, and $2n^2$ is the maximum number of *electrons* (or elements). For example, consider the $n = 3$ level. The number of orbitals is $n^2 = 9$: one 3*s*, three 3*p*, and five 3*d*. The number of electrons is $2n^2 = 18$: two 3*s* and six 3*p* electrons for the eight elements of Period 3, and ten 3*d* electrons for the ten transition elements of Period 4.

Intervening Series: Transition and Inner Transition Elements

As Figure 8.11 shows, the *d* block and *f* block occur between the main-group *s* and *p* blocks.

1. *Transition series.* Periods 4, 5, 6, and 7 incorporate the 3*d, 4d, 5d,* and 6*d* sublevels, respectively. As you've seen, the general pattern is that the $(n - 1)d$ sublevel is filled between the *ns* and *np* sublevels. Thus, in Period 5, the filling order is 5*s*, then 4*d*, and then 5*p*.

2. *Inner transition series.* In Period 6, the first of two series of **inner transition elements,** those in which *f* orbitals are being filled, appears (Figure 8.11). The *f* orbitals have *l* = 3, so the possible m_l values are $-3, -2, -1, 0, +1, +2,$ and $+3$; that is, there are seven *f* orbitals, for a total of 14 elements in *each* of the two inner transition series:
   - The Period 6 inner transition series, called the **lanthanides** (or **rare earths**), occurs after lanthanum (La; $Z = 57$), and the 4*f* orbitals are filled.
   - The Period 7 inner transition series, called the **actinides,** occurs after actinium (Ac; $Z = 89$), and the 5*f* orbitals are filled.

Thus, in Periods 6 and 7, the filling sequence is

ns, first of the $(n - 1)d$, all $(n - 2)f$, remainder of the $(n - 1)d$, and *np*

Period 6 ends with the 6*p* sublevel. Period 7 is incomplete because only five elements with 7*p* electrons are known at this time; element 117 has not yet been synthesized.

3. *Irregular filling patterns.* Irregularities in the filling pattern, such as those for Cr and Cu in Period 4, occur in the *d* and *f* blocks because the sublevel energies in these larger atoms differ very little. Even though occasional deviations occur in the *d* block, the sum of *ns* electrons and $(n - 1)d$ electrons always equals the new group number (in parentheses). For instance, despite variations in Group 6B(**6**)—Cr, Mo, W, and Sg—the sum of *ns* and $(n - 1)d$ electrons is 6; for Group 8B(**10**)—Ni, Pd, Pt, and Ds—the sum is 10.

Sample Problem 8.2 | Determining Electron Configurations

Problem Using the periodic table (not Figure 8.10 or Table 8.3) and assuming a regular filling pattern, give the full and condensed electron configurations, partial orbital diagrams showing valence electrons only, and number of inner electrons for the following elements:
(a) Potassium (K; *Z* = 19)   **(b)** Technetium (Tc; *Z* = 43)   **(c)** Lead (Pb; *Z* = 82)

Plan The atomic number tells us the number of electrons, and the periodic table shows the order for filling sublevels. In the partial orbital diagrams, we include all electrons added after the previous noble gas *except* those in *filled* inner sublevels. The number of inner electrons is the sum of those in the previous noble gas and in filled *d* and *f* sublevels.

Solution (a) For K (*Z* = 19), the full electron configuration is $1s^2 2s^2 2p^6 3s^2 3p^6 4s^1$.
The condensed configuration is $[Ar] 4s^1$.
The partial orbital diagram showing valence electrons is

K is a main-group element in Group 1A(1) and Period 4, so there are 18 inner electrons.
(b) For Tc (*Z* = 43), assuming the expected pattern, the full electron configuration is
$1s^2 2s^2 2p^6 3s^2 3p^6 4s^2 3d^{10} 4p^6 5s^2 4d^5$.
The condensed electron configuration is $[Kr] 5s^2 4d^5$.
The partial orbital diagram showing valence electrons is

Tc is a transition element in Group 7B(7) and Period 5, so there are 36 inner electrons.
(c) For Pb (*Z* = 82), the full electron configuration is
$1s^2 2s^2 2p^6 3s^2 3p^6 4s^2 3d^{10} 4p^6 5s^2 4d^{10} 5p^6 6s^2 4f^{14} 5d^{10} 6p^2$.

The condensed electron configuration is $[Xe] 6s^2 4f^{14} 5d^{10} 6p^2$.
The partial orbital diagram showing valence electrons (no filled inner sublevels) is

Pb is a main-group element in Group 4A(14) and Period 6, so there are 54 (in Xe) + 14 (in the 4*f* sublevel) + 10 (in the 5*d* sublevel) = 78 inner electrons.

Check Be sure that the sum of the superscripts (numbers of electrons) in the full electron configuration equals the atomic number and that the number of *valence* electrons in the condensed configuration equals the number of electrons in the partial orbital diagram.

Follow-Up Problem 8.2 Without referring to Table 8.3 or Figure 8.10, give full and condensed electron configurations, partial orbital diagrams showing valence electrons only, and the number of inner electrons for the following elements:
(a) Ni (*Z* = 28)   **(b)** Sr (*Z* = 38)   **(c)** Po (*Z* = 84)

▪ Summary of Section 8.2

- By the aufbau principle, one electron is added to an atom of each successive element in accord with the exclusion principle (no two electrons can have the same set of quantum numbers) and Hund's rule (orbitals of equal energy become half-filled, with electron spins parallel, before any pairing of spins occurs).
- The elements of a group have similar outer electron configurations and similar chemical behavior.
- For the main-group elements, valence electrons (those involved in reactions) are in the outer (highest energy) level only. For transition elements, $(n - 1)d$ electrons are also considered valence electrons.
- Because of shielding of d electrons by electrons in inner sublevels and penetration by the ns electron, the $(n - 1)d$ sublevel fills after the ns and before the np sublevels.
- In Periods 6 and 7, $(n - 2)f$ orbitals fill between the first and second $(n - 1)d$ orbitals.

8.3 • TRENDS IN THREE ATOMIC PROPERTIES

In this section, we focus on three atomic properties directly influenced by electron configuration and effective nuclear charge: atomic size, ionization energy, and electron affinity. Most importantly, these properties are *periodic*, which means they generally exhibit consistent changes, or *trends*, within a group or period.

Trends in Atomic Size

Recall from Chapter 7 that we often represent atoms with spherical contours in which the electrons spend 90% of their time. We *define* **atomic size** (the extent of the contour) in terms of how closely one atom lies next to another. But, in practice, as we discuss in Chapter 12, we measure the distance between atomic nuclei in a sample of an element and divide that distance in half. Because atoms do not have hard surfaces, the size of an atom in a given compound depends somewhat on the atoms near it. In other words, *atomic size varies slightly from substance to substance.*

Figure 8.12 shows two common definitions of atomic size:

1. **Metallic radius.** Used mostly for *metals*, it is one-half the shortest distance between nuclei of adjacent, individual atoms in a crystal of the element (Figure 8.12A).
2. **Covalent radius.** Used for elements occurring as molecules, mostly *nonmetals*, it is one-half the shortest distance between nuclei of bonded atoms (Figure 8.12B).

Radii measured for some elements are used to determine the radii of other elements from distances between atoms in compounds. For instance, in a carbon-chlorine compound, the distance between nuclei in a C—Cl bond is 177 pm. Using the known covalent radius of Cl (100 pm), we find the covalent radius of C (177 pm − 100 pm = 77 pm) (Figure 8.12C).

Main-Group Elements Figure 8.13 shows the atomic radii of the main-group elements and most of the transition elements. Among the main-group elements, atomic size varies within both groups and periods as a result of two opposing influences:

1. *Changes in n.* As the principal quantum number (n) increases, the probability that outer electrons spend most of their time farther from the nucleus increases as well; thus, atomic size increases.
2. *Changes in Z_{eff}.* As the effective nuclear charge (Z_{eff}) increases, outer electrons are pulled closer to the nucleus; thus, atomic size decreases.

The net effect of these influences depends on how effectively the inner electrons shield the increasing nuclear charge:

1. *Down a group, n dominates.* As we move down a main group, each member has *one more level of inner electrons that shield the outer electrons very effectively.* Even though additional protons do moderately increase Z_{eff} for the outer electrons, the atoms get larger as a result of the increasing n value:

*Atomic radius generally **increases** down a group.*

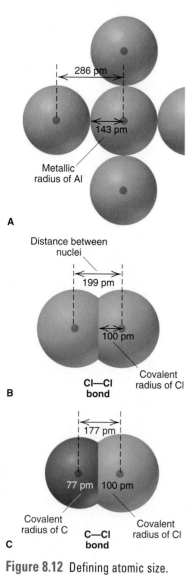

Figure 8.12 Defining atomic size.
A, The metallic radius of aluminum. **B,** The covalent radius of chlorine. **C,** Known covalent radii and distances between nuclei can be used to find unknown radii.

(Labels in figure:)
286 pm
143 pm
Metallic radius of Al
A

Distance between nuclei
199 pm
100 pm
Covalent radius of Cl
Cl—Cl bond
B

177 pm
77 pm   100 pm
Covalent radius of C
C—Cl bond
Covalent radius of Cl
C

2. *Across a period, Z_{eff} dominates.* Across a period from left to right, electrons are added to the *same* outer level, so the shielding by inner electrons does not change. Despite greater electron repulsions, outer electrons shield each other only slightly, so Z_{eff} rises significantly, and the outer electrons are pulled closer to the nucleus:

*Atomic radius generally **decreases** across a period.*

Transition Elements As Figure 8.13 shows, size trends are *not* as consistent for the transition elements:

1. *Down a transition group, n increases,* but shielding by an additional level of inner electrons results in only a small size increase from Period 4 to 5 and none from 5 to 6.

2. *Across a transition series,* atomic size shrinks through the first two or three elements because of the increasing nuclear charge. But, from then on, *size remains relatively constant* because shielding by the inner *d* electrons counteracts the increase in Z_{eff}. Thus, for example, in Period 4, the third transition element, vanadium (V; $Z = 23$), has the same radius as the last, zinc (Zn; $Z = 30$). This pattern also appears in Periods 5 and 6 in the transition and both inner transition series.

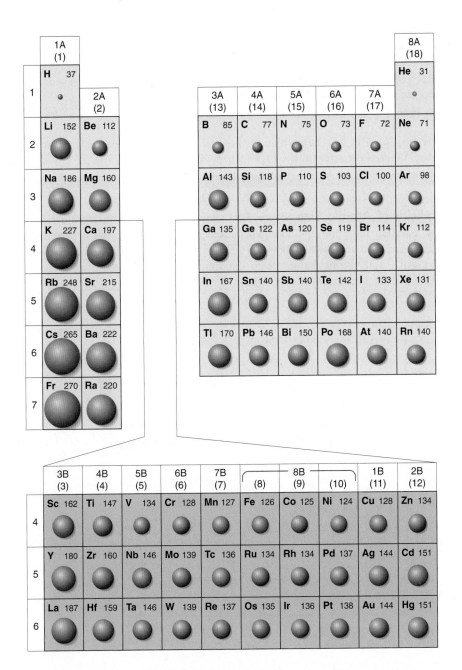

Figure 8.13 Atomic radii of the main-group and transition elements. Atomic radii (in picometers) are shown for the main-group elements (*tan*) and the transition elements (*blue*). (Values for the noble gases are calculated.)

3. *A transition series affects atomic size in neighboring main groups.* Shielding by *d* electrons causes a *major size decrease from Group 2A(2) to Group 3A(13)* in Periods 4 through 6. Because the *np* sublevel has more penetration than the $(n-1)d$, the first *np* electron [added in Group 3A(13)] "feels" a much greater Z_{eff}, due to all the protons added in the intervening transition elements. The greatest decrease occurs in Period 4: calcium (Ca; $Z = 20$) in Group 2A(2) is nearly 50% larger than gallium (Ga; $Z = 31$) in 3A(13). In fact, *d*-orbital shielding causes gallium to be slightly *smaller* than aluminum (Al; $Z = 13$), the element above it!

Sample Problem 8.3 | **Ranking Elements by Atomic Size**

Problem Using only the periodic table (not Figure 8.13), rank each set of main-group elements in order of *decreasing* atomic size:
(a) Ca, Mg, Sr   **(b)** K, Ga, Ca   **(c)** Br, Rb, Kr   **(d)** Sr, Ca, Rb

Plan To rank the elements by atomic size, we find them in the periodic table. They are main-group elements, so size increases down a group and decreases across a period.

Solution **(a)** Sr > Ca > Mg. These three elements are in Group 2A(2), and size decreases up the group.
(b) K > Ca > Ga. These three elements are in Period 4, and size decreases across a period.
(c) Rb > Br > Kr. Rb is largest because it has one more energy level (Period 5) and is farthest to the left. Kr is smaller than Br because Kr is farther to the right in Period 4.
(d) Rb > Sr > Ca. Ca is smallest because it has one fewer energy level. Sr is smaller than Rb because it is farther to the right.

Check From Figure 8.13, we see that the rankings are correct.

Follow-Up Problem 8.3 Using only the periodic table, rank the elements in each set in order of *increasing* size: **(a)** Se, Br, Cl; **(b)** I, Xe, Ba.

Periodicity of Atomic Size Figure 8.14 shows the variation in atomic size with atomic number. Note the up-and-down pattern as size drops across a period to the noble gas (*purple*) and then leaps up to the alkali metal (*brown*) that begins the next period. Also note the deviations from the smooth size decrease in each transition (*blue*) and inner transition (*green*) series.

Figure 8.14 Periodicity of atomic radius.

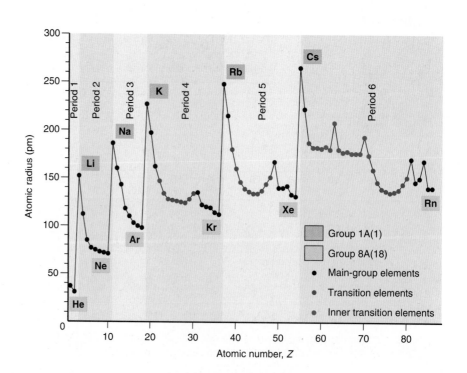

Trends in Ionization Energy

The **ionization energy (IE)** is the energy required for the *complete removal* of 1 mol of electrons from 1 mol of gaseous atoms or ions. Pulling an electron away from a nucleus *requires* energy to overcome their electrostatic attraction. Because energy flows *into* the system, the ionization energy is always positive (like ΔH of an endothermic reaction). (Chapter 7 viewed the ionization energy of the H atom as the energy difference between $n = 1$ and $n = \infty$, where the electron is completely removed.) The ionization energy is a key factor in an element's reactivity:

- *Atoms with a low IE tend to form cations during reactions.*
- *Atoms with a high IE (except the noble gases) tend to form anions.*

Many-electron atoms can lose more than one electron. The *first* ionization energy (IE_1) removes an outermost electron (highest energy sublevel) from a gaseous atom:

$$\text{Atom}(g) \longrightarrow \text{ion}^+(g) + e^- \qquad \Delta E = IE_1 > 0 \qquad \textbf{(8.2)}$$

The *second* ionization energy (IE_2) removes a second electron. Since this electron is pulled away from a positive ion, IE_2 is always larger than IE_1:

$$\text{Ion}^+(g) \longrightarrow \text{ion}^{2+}(g) + e^- \qquad \Delta E = IE_2 \ (\text{always} > IE_1)$$

Periodicity of First Ionization Energy Figure 8.15 shows the variation in first ionization energy with atomic number. This up-and-down pattern—IE_1 rising across a period to the noble gas (*purple*) and then dropping down to the next alkali metal (*brown*)—is the *inverse* of the variation in atomic size (Figure 8.14): *as size decreases, it takes more energy to remove an electron because the nucleus is closer, so IE₁ increases.*

Let's examine the group and period trends and their exceptions:

1. *Down a group.* As we move *down* a main group, the n value increases, so atomic size does as well. As the distance from nucleus to outer electron increases, their attraction lessens, so the electron is easier to remove (Figure 8.16, *next page*):

*Ionization energy generally **decreases** down a group.*

The only significant exception occurs in Group 3A(13): IE_1 decreases from boron (B) to aluminum (Al), but not for the rest of the group. Filling the transition series in Periods 4, 5, and 6 causes a much higher Z_{eff} and an unusually small change in size, so outer electrons in the larger Group 3A members are held tighter.

Figure 8.15 Periodicity of first ionization energy (IE_1). This trend is the *inverse* of the trend in atomic size (see Figure 8.14).

Figure 8.16 First ionization energies of the main-group elements.

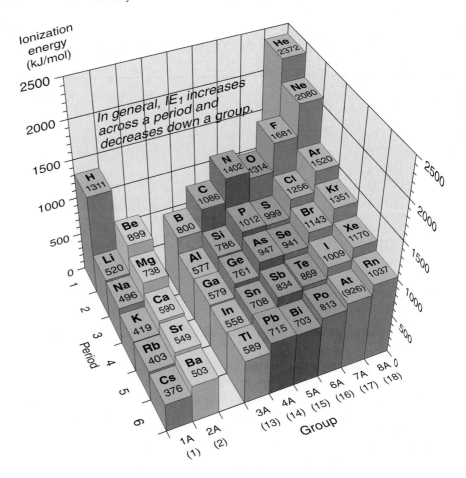

2. *Across a period.* As we move left to right across a period, Z_{eff} increases and atomic size decreases. The attraction between nucleus and outer electron increases, so the electron is harder to remove:

> *Ionization energy generally **increases** across a period.*

There are two exceptions to the otherwise smooth increase in IE_1 across periods:

- In Periods 2 and 3, there are dips at the Group 3A(13) elements, B and Al. These elements have the first np electrons, which are removed more easily because the resulting ion has a filled (stable) ns sublevel.
- In Periods 2 and 3, once again, there are dips at the Group 6A(16) elements, O and S. These elements have a fourth np electron, the first to pair up with another np electron, and electron-electron repulsions raise the orbital energy. The fourth np electron is easier to remove because doing so relieves the repulsions and leaves a half-filled (stable) np sublevel.

Sample Problem 8.4 | **Ranking Elements by First Ionization Energy**

Problem Using the periodic table only, rank the elements in each set in order of *decreasing* IE_1: **(a)** Kr, He, Ar; **(b)** Sb, Te, Sn; **(c)** K, Ca, Rb; **(d)** I, Xe, Cs.

Plan We find the elements in the periodic table and then apply the general trends of decreasing IE_1 down a group and increasing IE_1 across a period.

Solution **(a)** He > Ar > Kr. These are in Group 8A(18), and IE_1 decreases down a group.

(b) Te > Sb > Sn. These are in Period 5, and IE_1 increases across a period.

(c) Ca > K > Rb. IE_1 of K is larger than IE_1 of Rb because K is higher in Group 1A(1). IE_1 of Ca is larger than IE_1 of K because Ca is farther to the right in Period 4.

(d) Xe > I > Cs. IE_1 of I is smaller than IE_1 of Xe because I is farther to the left. IE_1 of I is larger than IE_1 of Cs because I is farther to the right and in the previous period.

Check Because trends in IE_1 are generally the opposite of the trends in size, you can rank the elements by size and check that you obtain the reverse order.

Follow-Up Problem 8.4 Rank the elements in each set in order of *increasing* IE_1: **(a)** Sb, Sn, I; **(b)** Sr, Ca, Ba.

Ionization energy (MJ/mol)

IE_3 14.85

Core e^- is removed.

IE_2 1.76

IE_1 0.90

Figure 8.17 The first three ionization energies of beryllium. Beryllium has two valence electrons, so IE_3 is much larger than IE_2.

Successive Ionization Energies For a given element, IE_1, IE_2, and so on, increase because each electron is pulled away from a species with a higher positive charge. This increase includes an enormous jump *after* the outer (valence) electrons have been removed because *much* more energy is needed to remove an inner (core) electron (Figure 8.17).

Table 8.4 shows successive ionization energies for Period 2 and the first element in Period 3. Move across the values for any element, and you reach a point that separates relatively low from relatively high IE values *(shaded area)*. For example, follow the values for boron (B): IE_1 (0.80 MJ) is lower than IE_2 (2.43 MJ), which is lower than IE_3 (3.66 MJ), which is *much* lower than IE_4 (25.02 MJ). From this jump, we know that boron has three electrons in the highest energy level ($1s^22s^22p^1$). Because they are so difficult to remove, *core electrons are not involved in reactions.*

Sample Problem 8.5 | Identifying an Element from Its Ionization Energies

Problem Name the Period 3 element with the following ionization energies (kJ/mol), and write its full electron configuration:

IE_1	IE_2	IE_3	IE_4	IE_5	IE_6
1012	1903	2910	4956	6278	22,230

Plan We look for a large jump in the IE values, which occurs after all valence electrons have been removed. Then we refer to the periodic table to find the Period 3 element with this number of valence electrons and write its electron configuration.

Solution The large jump occurs after IE_5, indicating that the element has five valence electrons and, thus, is in Group 5A(15). This Period 3 element is phosphorus (P; $Z = 15$). Its electron configuration is $1s^22s^22p^63s^23p^3$.

Follow-Up Problem 8.5 Element Q is in Period 3 and has the following ionization energies (in kJ/mol):

IE_1	IE_2	IE_3	IE_4	IE_5	IE_6
577	1816	2744	11,576	14,829	18,375

Name element Q, and write its full electron configuration.

Table 8.4 Successive Ionization Energies of the Elements Lithium Through Sodium

Z	Element	Number of Valence Electrons	Ionization Energy (MJ/mol)*									
			IE_1	IE_2	IE_3	IE_4	IE_5	IE_6	IE_7	IE_8	IE_9	IE_{10}
3	Li	1	0.52	7.30	11.81							
4	Be	2	0.90	1.76	14.85	21.01		CORE ELECTRONS				
5	B	3	0.80	2.43	3.66	25.02	32.82					
6	C	4	1.09	2.35	4.62	6.22	37.83	47.28				
7	N	5	1.40	2.86	4.58	7.48	9.44	53.27	64.36			
8	O	6	1.31	3.39	5.30	7.47	10.98	13.33	71.33	84.08		
9	F	7	1.68	3.37	6.05	8.41	11.02	15.16	17.87	92.04	106.43	
10	Ne	8	2.08	3.95	6.12	9.37	12.18	15.24	20.00	23.07	115.38	131.43
11	Na	1	0.50	4.56	6.91	9.54	13.35	16.61	20.11	25.49	28.93	141.37

*MJ/mol, or megajoules per mole = 10^3 kJ/mol.

Trends in Electron Affinity

The **electron affinity (EA)** is the energy change (kJ/mol) accompanying the *addition* of 1 mol of electrons to 1 mol of gaseous atoms or ions. The *first electron affinity* (EA_1) refers to the formation of 1 mol of monovalent (1−) gaseous anions:

$$\text{Atom}(g) + e^- \longrightarrow \text{ion}^-(g) \qquad \Delta E = EA_1$$

As with ionization energy, there is a first electron affinity, a second, and so forth. The first electron is *attracted* by the atom's nucleus, so in most cases, EA_1 *is negative* (energy is released), analogous to the negative ΔH for an exothermic reaction.* But, the second electron affinity (EA_2) is always positive because energy must be *absorbed* to overcome electrostatic repulsions and add another electron to a negative ion.

Factors other than Z_{eff} and atomic size affect electron affinities, so trends are not regular, as are those for size and IE_1. The many exceptions arise from changes in sublevel energy and electron-electron repulsion:

- *Down a group.* We might expect a smooth decrease (smaller negative number) down a group because size increases, and the nucleus is farther away from an electron being added. But only Group 1A(1) exhibits this behavior (Figure 8.18).

- *Across a period.* We might expect a regular increase (larger negative number) across a period because size decreases, and higher Z_{eff} should attract the electron being added more strongly. There is an overall left-to-right increase, but it is not at all regular.

1A (1)	2A (2)		3A (13)	4A (14)	5A (15)	6A (16)	7A (17)	8A (18)
H −72.8								**He** (0.0)
Li −59.6	**Be** ≤0		**B** −26.7	**C** −122	**N** +7	**O** −141	**F** −328	**Ne** (+29)
Na −52.9	**Mg** ≤0		**Al** −42.5	**Si** −134	**P** −72.0	**S** −200	**Cl** −349	**Ar** (+35)
K −48.4	**Ca** −2.37		**Ga** −28.9	**Ge** −119	**As** −78.2	**Se** −195	**Br** −325	**Kr** (+39)
Rb −46.9	**Sr** −5.03		**In** −28.9	**Sn** −107	**Sb** −103	**Te** −190	**I** −295	**Xe** (+41)
Cs −45.5	**Ba** −13.95		**Tl** −19.3	**Pb** −35.1	**Bi** −91.3	**Po** −183	**At** −270	**Rn** (+41)

Figure 8.18 Electron affinities of the main-group elements (in kJ/mol). Values for Group 8A(18) are estimates, which is indicated by parentheses.

Despite these irregularities, relative values of IE and EA show three general behavior patterns:

1. *Reactive nonmetals.* Members of Group 6A(16) and especially Group 7A(17) (the halogens) have high IEs and highly negative (exothermic) EAs: these elements lose electrons with difficulty but attract them strongly. Therefore, *in their ionic compounds, they form negative ions.*

2. *Reactive metals.* Members of Groups 1A(1) and 2A(2) have low IEs and slightly negative (exothermic) EAs: they lose electrons easily but attract them weakly, if at all. Therefore, *in their ionic compounds, they form positive ions.*

3. *Noble gases.* Members of Group 8A(18) have very high IEs and slightly positive (endothermic) EAs: *they tend **not** to lose or gain electrons.* In fact, only the larger members of the group (Kr, Xe, and Rn) form compounds at all.

Summary of Section 8.3

- Trends in three atomic properties are summarized in Figure 8.19.
- Atomic size (half the distance between nuclei of adjacent atoms) increases down a main group and decreases across a period. In a transition series, size remains relatively constant.
- First ionization energy (the energy required to remove the outermost electron from a mole of gaseous atoms) is inversely related to atomic size: IE_1 decreases down a main group and increases across a period.
- Successive ionization energies of an element show a very large increase after all valence electrons have been removed, because the first inner (core) electron is in an orbital of much lower energy and so is held very tightly.
- Electron affinity (the energy involved in adding an electron to a mole of gaseous atoms) shows many variations from expected trends.
- Based on the relative sizes of IEs and EAs, Group 1A(1) and 2A(2) elements tend to form cations and Group 6A(16) and 7A(17) elements tend to form anions in ionic compounds. Group 8A(18) elements are very unreactive.

Figure 8.19 Trends in three atomic properties. For electron affinity, the dashed arrows indicate that there are numerous exceptions to expected trends.

---

*Some tables of EA_1 list them as positive values because energy would be *absorbed* to remove an electron from the anion.

8.4 • ATOMIC PROPERTIES AND CHEMICAL REACTIVITY

All physical and chemical behaviors of the elements and their compounds are based on electron configuration and effective nuclear charge. In this section, you'll see how atomic properties determine metallic behavior and the properties of ions.

Trends in Metallic Behavior

The three general classes of elements have distinguishing properties:

- *Metals,* found in the left and lower three-quarters of the periodic table, are typically shiny solids, have moderate to high melting points, are good conductors of heat and electricity, can be machined into wires and sheets, and lose electrons to nonmetals.
- *Nonmetals,* found in the upper right quarter of the table, are typically not shiny, have relatively low melting points, are poor conductors, are mostly crumbly solids or gases, and tend to gain electrons from metals.
- *Metalloids,* found between the other two classes, have intermediate properties.

Thus, *metallic behavior decreases left-to-right across a period and increases down a group in the periodic table* (Figure 8.20).

Remember, though, that some elements don't fit these categories: as graphite, nonmetallic carbon is a good electrical conductor; the nonmetal iodine is shiny; metallic gallium melts in your hand; mercury is a liquid; and iron is brittle. Despite such exceptions, in this discussion, we'll make several generalizations about metallic behavior and its applications to redox behavior and the acid-base properties of oxides.

Figure 8.20 Trends in metallic behavior. (Hydrogen appears next to helium.)

Relative Tendency to Lose or Gain Electrons Metals tend to lose electrons to nonmetals during reactions:

1. *Down a main group.* The increase in metallic behavior down a group is consistent with an increase in size and a decrease in IE and is most obvious in groups with more than one class of element, such as Group 5A(15) (Figure 8.21, *vertical*): *elements at the top can form anions, and*

those at the bottom can form cations. Nitrogen (N) is a gaseous nonmetal, and phosphorus (P) is a soft nonmetal; both occur occasionally as 3− anions in their compounds. Arsenic (As) and antimony (Sb) are metalloids, with Sb the more metallic, and neither forms ions readily. Bismuth (Bi) is a typical metal, forming a 3+ cation in its mostly ionic compounds. Groups 3A(13), 4A(14), and 6A(16) show a similar trend. But even in Group 2A(2), which contains only metals, the tendency to form cations increases down the group: beryllium (Be) forms covalent compounds with nonmetals, whereas all compounds of barium (Ba) are ionic.

2. *Across a period.* The decrease in metallic behavior across a period is consistent with a decrease in size, an increase in IE, and a more favorable (more negative) EA. Consider Period 3 (Figure 8.21, *horizontal*): *elements at the left tend to form cations, and those at the right tend to form anions.* Sodium and magnesium are metals that occur as Na^+ and Mg^{2+} in seawater, minerals, and organisms. Aluminum is metallic physically and occurs as Al^{3+} in some compounds, but it bonds covalently in most others. Silicon (Si) is a shiny metalloid that does not occur as

Group 5A(15)

Atomic number
Atomic symbol
First ionization energy (kJ/mol)

Period 3					
11 Na 496	12 Mg 738	13 Al 577	14 Si 786	15 P 1012	16 S 999	17 Cl 1256

7 N 1402

33 As 947

51 Sb 834

83 Bi 703

Figure 8.21 Metallic behavior in Group 5A(15) and Period 3. Moving down from N to Bi, there is an *increase* in metallic behavior. Moving across from Na to Cl, there is a *decrease* in metallic behavior.

Figure 8.22 Highest and lowest O.N.s of reactive main-group elements.

a monatomic ion. Phosphorus is a white, waxy nonmetal that occurs rarely as P^{3-}, whereas crumbly, yellow sulfur forms S^{2-} in many compounds, and gaseous, yellow-green chlorine occurs in nature almost always as Cl^-.

Redox Behavior of the Main-Group Elements Closely related to an element's tendency to lose or gain electrons is its redox behavior—that is, whether it behaves as an oxidizing or reducing agent and the associated changes in its oxidation number (O.N.). You can find the highest and lowest oxidation numbers of many main-group elements from the periodic table (Figure 8.22):

- For most elements, the A-group number is the *highest* oxidation number (always positive) of any element in the group. The exceptions are O and F (see Table 4.3).
- For nonmetals and some metalloids, the A-group number minus 8 is the *lowest* oxidation number (always negative) of any element in the group.

For example, the highest oxidation number of S (Group 6A) is +6, as in SF_6, and the lowest is $6 - 8$, or -2, as in FeS and other metal sulfides.

Redox behavior is closely related to atomic properties:

- With their low IEs and small EAs, the members of Groups 1A(1) and 2A(2) lose electrons readily, so they are *strong reducing agents* and become oxidized.
- With their high IEs and large EAs, nonmetals in Groups 6A(16) and 7A(17) gain electrons readily, so they are *strong oxidizing agents* and become reduced.

Acid-Base Behavior of Oxides Metals are also distinguished from nonmetals by the acid-base behavior of their oxides in water:

- Most main-group metals *transfer* electrons to oxygen, so their *oxides are ionic. In water, these oxides act as bases,* producing OH^- ions from O^{2-} and reacting with acids. Calcium oxide is an example (Figure 8.23, *left*).
- Nonmetals *share* electrons with oxygen, so *nonmetal oxides are covalent. They react with water to form acids,* producing H^+ ions and reacting with bases. Tetraphosphorus decaoxide is an example (Figure 8.23, *right*).

Some metals and many metalloids form oxides that are **amphoteric:** they can act as acids *or* bases in water.

Figure 8.24 shows the acid-base behavior of some common oxides of elements in Group 5A(15) and Period 3 with a gradient from blue (basic) to red (acidic):

1. *As elements become more metallic down a group (larger size and smaller IE), their oxides become more basic.* In Group 5A(15), dinitrogen pentaoxide, N_2O_5, forms the strong acid HNO_3:

$$N_2O_5(s) + H_2O(l) \longrightarrow 2HNO_3(aq)$$

Tetraphosphorus decaoxide, P_4O_{10}, forms the weaker acid H_3PO_4:

$$P_4O_{10}(s) + 6H_2O(l) \longrightarrow 4H_3PO_4(aq)$$

The oxide of the metalloid arsenic is weakly acidic, whereas that of the metalloid antimony is weakly basic. Bismuth, the most metallic of the group, forms a basic oxide that is insoluble in water but reacts with acid to yield a salt and water:

$$Bi_2O_3(s) + 6HNO_3(aq) \longrightarrow 2Bi(NO_3)_3(aq) + 3H_2O(l)$$

Figure 8.23 Oxide acidity. In water, metal oxides are basic (*left*), and nonmetal oxides are acidic (*right*). The colors are due to the presence of acid-base indicators.

Figure 8.24 Acid-base behavior of some element oxides.

2. *As the elements become less metallic across a period (smaller size and higher IE), their oxides become more acidic.* In Period 3, Na_2O and MgO are strongly basic, and amphoteric aluminum oxide (Al_2O_3) reacts with acid or with base:

$$Al_2O_3(s) + 6HCl(aq) \longrightarrow 2AlCl_3(aq) + 3H_2O(l)$$
$$Al_2O_3(s) + 2NaOH(aq) + 3H_2O(l) \longrightarrow 2NaAl(OH)_4(aq)$$

Silicon dioxide is weakly acidic, forming a salt and water with base:

$$SiO_2(s) + 2NaOH(aq) \longrightarrow Na_2SiO_3(aq) + H_2O(l)$$

The common oxides of phosphorus, sulfur, and chlorine form acids of increasing strength: H_3PO_4, H_2SO_4, and $HClO_4$.

Properties of Monatomic Ions

So far we have focused on the reactants—the atoms—in the process of electron loss and gain. Now we focus on the products—the ions—considering their electron configurations, magnetic properties, and sizes.

Electron Configurations of Main-Group Ions Why does an ion have a particular charge: Na^+ not Na^{2+}, or F^- not F^{2-}? Why do some metals form two ions, such as Sn^{2+} and Sn^{4+}? The answer relates to the location of the element in the periodic table and the energy associated with losing or gaining electrons:

   1. *Ions with a noble gas configuration.* Atoms of the noble gases have very low reactivity because their highest energy level is *filled* (ns^2np^6). Thus, *when elements at either end of a period form ions, they attain a filled outer level—a noble gas configuration.* These elements lie on either side of Group 8A(18), and their ions are **isoelectronic** (Greek *iso*, "same") with the nearest noble gas (Figure 8.25; see also Figure 2.13, p. 57).

• Elements in Groups 1A(1) and 2A(2) *lose* electrons and become isoelectronic with the *previous* noble gas. The Na^+ ion, for example, is isoelectronic with neon (Ne):

$$Na(1s^22s^22p^63s^1) \longrightarrow e^- + Na^+([He]2s^22p^6) \text{ [isoelectronic with Ne}([He]2s^22p^6)]$$

• Elements in Groups 6A(16) and 7A(17) *gain* electrons and become isoelectronic with the *next* noble gas. The Br^- ion, for example, is isoelectronic with krypton (Kr):

$$Br ([Ar] 4s^23d^{10}4p^5) + e^- \longrightarrow Br^- ([Ar] 4s^23d^{10}4p^6)$$
$$\text{[isoelectronic with Kr } ([Ar] 4s^23d^{10}4p^6)]$$

   The energy needed to remove electrons from metals or add them to nonmetals determines the charges of the resulting ions:

• *Cations.* Removing another electron from Na^+ or from Mg^{2+} means removing a core electron, which requires too much energy: thus, $NaCl_2$ and MgF_3 do *not* exist.

• *Anions.* Similarly, adding another electron to F^- or to O^{2-} means putting it into the next higher energy level ($n = 3$). With 10 electrons ($1s^22s^22p^6$) acting as inner electrons, the nuclear charge would be shielded very effectively, and adding an outer electron would require too much energy: thus, we never see Na_2F or Mg_3O_2.

   2. *Ions without a noble gas configuration.* Except for aluminum, the metals of Groups 3A(13) to 5A(15) do not form ions with noble gas configurations. Instead, they form cations with two different stable configurations:

• *Pseudo–noble gas configuration.* If the metal atom empties its highest energy level, it attains the stability of empty *ns* and *np* sublevels and filled inner ($n - 1$)*d* sublevel. This ($n - 1$)d^{10} configuration is called a **pseudo–noble gas configuration.** For example, tin (Sn; Z = 50) loses four electrons to form the tin(IV) ion (Sn^{4+}), which has empty 5*s* and 5*p* sublevels and a filled inner 4*d* sublevel:

$$Sn ([Kr] 5s^24d^{10}5p^2) \longrightarrow Sn^{4+} ([Kr] 4d^{10}) + 4e^-$$

• *Inert pair configuration.* Alternatively, the metal atom loses just its *np* electrons and attains a stable configuration with filled *ns* and ($n - 1$)*d* sublevels. The retained ns^2 electrons are sometimes called an *inert pair.* For example, in the more

Figure 8.25 Main-group elements whose ions have noble gas electron configurations.

common tin(II) ion (Sn^{2+}), the atom loses the two $5p$ electrons and has filled $5s$ and $4d$ sublevels:

$$Sn\ ([Kr]\ 5s^24d^{10}5p^2) \longrightarrow Sn^{2+}\ ([Kr]\ 5s^24d^{10}) + 2e^-$$

Thallium, lead, and bismuth, the largest and, thus, most metallic members of Groups 3A(13) to 5A(15), form ions that retain the ns^2 pair: Tl^+, Pb^{2+}, and Bi^{3+}.

Once again, energy considerations explain these configurations. It would be energetically impossible for metals in Groups 3A(13) to 5A(15) to achieve noble gas configurations: tin, for example, would have to lose 14 electrons—ten $4d$ in addition to the two $5p$ and two $5s$—to be isoelectronic with krypton (Kr; $Z = 36$), the previous noble gas.

Sample Problem 8.6   Writing Electron Configurations of Main-Group Ions

Problem Using condensed electron configurations, write equations representing the formation of the ion(s) of the following elements:
(a) Iodine ($Z = 53$)   **(b)** Potassium ($Z = 19$)   **(c)** Indium ($Z = 49$)

Plan We identify the element's position in the periodic table and recall that
- Ions of elements in Groups 1A(1), 2A(2), 6A(16), and 7A(17) are isoelectronic with the nearest noble gas.
- Metals in Groups 3A(13) to 5A(15) lose the ns and np electrons or just the np.

Solution (a) Iodine is in Group 7A(17), so it gains one electron, and I^- is isoelectronic with xenon:

$$I\ ([Kr]\ 5s^24d^{10}5p^5) + e^- \longrightarrow I^-\ ([Kr]\ 5s^24d^{10}5p^6)\quad \text{(same as Xe)}$$

(b) Potassium is in Group 1A(1), so it loses one electron; K^+ is isoelectronic with argon:

$$K\ ([Ar]\ 4s^1) \longrightarrow K^+\ ([Ar]) + e^-$$

(c) Indium is in Group 3A(13), so it loses either three electrons to form In^{3+} (with a pseudo–noble gas configuration) or one to form In^+ (with an inert pair):

$$In\ ([Kr]\ 5s^24d^{10}5p^1) \longrightarrow In^{3+}\ ([Kr]\ 4d^{10}) + 3e^-$$

$$In\ ([Kr]\ 5s^24d^{10}5p^1) \longrightarrow In^+\ ([Kr]\ 5s^24d^{10}) + e^-$$

Check Be sure that the number of electrons in the ion's electron configuration, plus the number gained or lost to form the ion, equals Z.

Follow-Up Problem 8.6   Using condensed electron configurations, write equations representing the formation of the ion(s) of the following elements:
(a) Ba ($Z = 56$)   **(b)** O ($Z = 8$)   **(c)** Pb ($Z = 82$)

Electron Configurations of Transition Metal Ions In contrast to many main-group ions, *transition metal ions rarely attain a noble gas configuration*. Aside from the Period 4 elements scandium, which forms Sc^{3+}, and titanium, which occasionally forms Ti^{4+}, *a transition element typically forms more than one cation by losing all of its ns and some of its (n − 1)d electrons*.

The reason, once again, is that energy costs are too high. Let's consider again the filling of Period 4. At the beginning of Period 4 (the same point holds in other periods), penetration makes the $4s$ sublevel *more stable* than the $3d$. Therefore, the first and second electrons added enter the $4s$, which is the outer sublevel. But, the $3d$ is an *inner* sublevel, so as it begins to fill, its electrons are not well shielded from the increasing nuclear charge.

A *crossover in sublevel energy* results: the $3d$ becomes *more stable* than the $4s$ in the transition series (Figure 8.26). This crossover has a major effect on the formation of Period 4 transition metal ions: because the $3d$ electrons are held tightly and shield those in the outer sublevel, *the 4s electrons of a transition metal are lost **before** the*

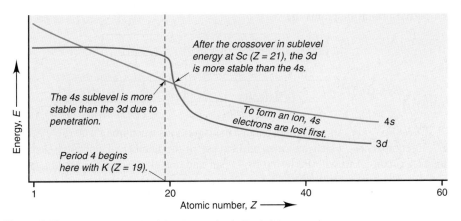

Figure 8.26 The crossover of sublevel energies in Period 4.

3d electrons. Thus, 4*s* electrons are added before 3*d* electrons to form the *atom* and are lost before them to form the *ion*, the so-called "first-in, first-out" rule.

Ion Formation: A Summary of Electron Loss or Gain

The various ways that cations form have one point in common—*outer electrons are removed first*. Here is a summary of the rules for formation of any main-group or transition metal ion:

- Main-group *s*-block metals lose all electrons with the highest *n* value.
- Main-group *p*-block metals lose *np* electrons before *ns* electrons.
- Transition (*d*-block) metals lose *ns* electrons before $(n - 1)d$ electrons.
- Nonmetals gain electrons in the *p* orbitals of highest *n* value.

Magnetic Properties of Transition Metal Ions

We learn a great deal about an element's electron configuration from atomic spectra, and magnetic studies provide additional evidence.

Recall that electron spin generates a tiny magnetic field, which causes a beam of H atoms to split in an external magnetic field (see Figure 8.1). Only a beam of a species (atoms, ions, or molecules) with one or more *unpaired* electrons will split. A beam of silver atoms (Ag; $Z = 47$) was used in the original 1921 experiment:

$$Ag\ (Z = 47)\quad [Kr]\ 5s^1 4d^{10}$$

$$\boxed{\uparrow}\quad \boxed{\uparrow\downarrow\,|\,\uparrow\downarrow\,|\,\uparrow\downarrow\,|\,\uparrow\downarrow\,|\,\uparrow\downarrow}\quad \boxed{\ \ |\ \ |\ \ }$$
$$\quad 5s\qquad\qquad 4d\qquad\qquad\qquad 5p$$

Note the unpaired 5*s* electron. A beam of cadmium atoms (Cd; $Z = 48$) is not split because their 5*s* electrons are *paired* ([Kr] $5s^2 4d^{10}$).

A species with unpaired electrons exhibits **paramagnetism:** it is attracted by an external field. A species with all of its electrons paired exhibits **diamagnetism:** it is not attracted (and is slightly repelled) by the field (Figure 8.27). Many transition metals and their compounds are paramagnetic because their atoms and ions have unpaired electrons.

Let's see three examples of how magnetic studies might provide evidence for a proposed electron configuration:

1. *The Ti^{2+} ion*. Spectral analysis of titanium metal yields the electron configuration [Ar] $4s^2 3d^2$, and experiment shows that the metal is paramagnetic, which indicates the presence of unpaired electrons. Spectral analysis shows that the Ti^{2+} ion is [Ar] $3d^2$, indicating loss of the 4*s* electrons. In support of the spectra, magnetic studies show that Ti^{2+} compounds are paramagnetic. If Ti had lost its 3*d* electrons to form Ti^{2+}, its compounds would be diamagnetic:

$$Ti\ ([Ar]\ 4s^2 3d^2) \longrightarrow Ti^{2+}\ ([Ar]\ 3d^2) + 2e^-$$

A Electromagnet

B Electromagnet

Figure 8.27 Measuring the magnetic behavior of a sample. The substance is weighed with the external magnetic field "off." **A,** If the substance is diamagnetic (has all *paired* electrons), its apparent mass is unaffected (or slightly reduced) with the field "on." **B,** If the substance is paramagnetic (has *unpaired* electrons), its apparent mass increases.

The partial orbital diagrams are

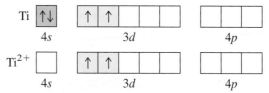

2. *The Fe^{3+} ion.* An increase in paramagnetism occurs when iron metal (Fe) becomes Fe^{3+} in compounds, which indicates an increase in the number of unpaired electrons. This fact is consistent with Fe losing its $4s$ pair and one electron of a $3d$ pair:

$$Fe\ ([Ar]\ 4s^2 3d^6) \longrightarrow Fe^{3+}\ ([Ar]\ 3d^5) + 3e^-$$

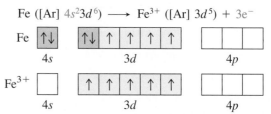

3. *The Cu^+ and Zn^{2+} ions.* Copper (Cu) metal is paramagnetic, but zinc (Zn) is diamagnetic. The Cu^+ and Zn^{2+} ions are diamagnetic, too. These observations are consistent with the ions being isoelectronic, which means $4s$ electrons were lost:

$$Cu\ ([Ar]\ 4s^1 3d^{10}) \longrightarrow Cu^+\ ([Ar]\ 3d^{10}) + e^-$$
$$Zn\ ([Ar]\ 4s^2 3d^{10}) \longrightarrow Zn^{2+}\ ([Ar]\ 3d^{10}) + 2e^-$$

Sample Problem 8.7 | **Writing Electron Configurations and Predicting Magnetic Behavior of Transition Metal Ions**

Problem Use condensed electron configurations to write an equation for the formation of each transition metal ion, and predict whether it is paramagnetic:
(a) Mn^{2+} ($Z = 25$)   **(b)** Cr^{3+} ($Z = 24$)   **(c)** Hg^{2+} ($Z = 80$)

Plan We first write the condensed electron configuration of the atom, recalling the irregularity for Cr. Then we remove electrons, beginning with ns electrons, to attain the ion charge. If unpaired electrons are present, the ion is paramagnetic.

Solution (a) $Mn\ ([Ar]\ 4s^2 3d^5) \longrightarrow Mn^{2+}\ ([Ar]\ 3d^5) + 2e^-$

There are five unpaired e^-, so Mn^{2+} is paramagnetic.

(b) $Cr\ ([Ar]\ 4s^1 3d^5) \longrightarrow Cr^{3+}\ ([Ar]\ 3d^3) + 3e^-$

There are three unpaired e^-, so Cr^{3+} is paramagnetic.

(c) $Hg\ ([Xe]\ 6s^2 4f^{14} 5d^{10}) \longrightarrow Hg^{2+}\ ([Xe]\ 4f^{14} 5d^{10}) + 2e^-$

The $4f$ and $5d$ sublevels are filled, so there are no unpaired e^-: Hg^{2+} is *not* paramagnetic.

Check We removed the ns electrons first, and the sum of the lost electrons and those in the electron configuration of the ion equals Z.

Follow-Up Problem 8.7 Write the condensed electron configuration of each transition metal ion, and predict whether it is paramagnetic:
(a) V^{3+} ($Z = 23$)   **(b)** Ni^{2+} ($Z = 28$)   **(c)** La^{3+} ($Z = 57$)

Figure 8.28 Ionic radius. Cation radius (r^+) and anion radius (r^-) together make up the distance between nuclei.

Ionic Size vs. Atomic Size The **ionic radius** is a measure of the size of an ion and is obtained from the distance between the nuclei of adjacent ions in a crystalline ionic compound (Figure 8.28). From the relation between effective nuclear charge (Z_{eff}) and atomic size, we can predict the size of an ion relative to its parent atom:

- *Cations are smaller than parent atoms.* When a cation forms, electrons are *removed from* the outer level. The resulting decrease in shielding and value of n allows the nucleus to pull the remaining electrons closer.
- *Anions are larger than parent atoms.* When an anion forms, electrons are *added to* the outer level. The increases in shielding and electron repulsions means the electrons occupy more space.

Figure 8.29 shows the radii of some main-group ions and their parent atoms:

1. *Down a group, ionic size increases* because *n* increases.
2. *Across a period,* for instance, Period 3, the pattern is complex:
   - *Among cations,* the increase in Z_{eff} from left to right makes Na^+ larger than Mg^{2+}, which is larger than Al^{3+}.
   - *From last cation to first anion,* a great jump in size occurs: we are *adding* electrons rather than removing them, so repulsions increase sharply. For instance, P^{3-} has eight more electrons than Al^{3+}.
   - *Among anions,* the increase in Z_{eff} from left to right makes P^{3-} larger than S^{2-}, which is larger than Cl^-.
   - *Within an isoelectronic series,* these factors have striking results. Within the dashed outline in Figure 8.29, the ions are isoelectronic with neon. Period 2 anions are much larger than Period 3 cations because the same number of electrons are attracted by an increasing nuclear charge. The pattern is

$$3- > 2- > 1- > 1+ > 2+ > 3+$$

3. *Cation size decreases with charge.* When a metal forms more than one cation, *the greater the ionic charge, the smaller the ionic radius.* With the two ions of iron, for example, Fe^{3+} has one fewer electron, so shielding is reduced somewhat, and the same nucleus is attracting fewer electrons. As a result, Z_{eff} increases, so Fe^{3+} is smaller than Fe^{2+}.

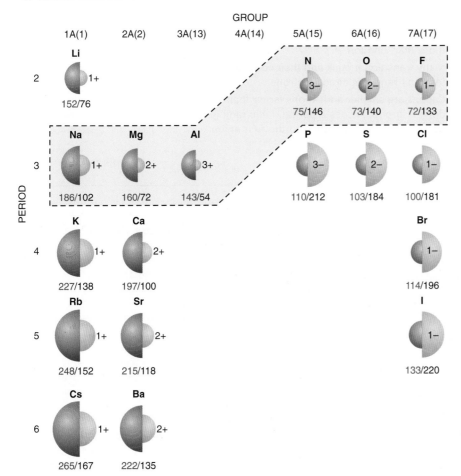

Figure 8.29 Ionic vs. atomic radii. Atomic radii (*color*) and ionic radii (*gray*) are given in picometers. Metal atoms (*blue*) form *smaller* positive ions, and nonmetal atoms (*red*) form *larger* negative ions. Ions in the dashed outline are *isoelectronic* with neon.

Sample Problem 8.8 Ranking Ions by Size

Problem Rank each set of ions in order of *decreasing* size, and explain your ranking:
(a) Ca^{2+}, Sr^{2+}, Mg^{2+} (b) K^+, S^{2-}, Cl^- (c) Au^+, Au^{3+}

Plan We find the position of each element in the periodic table and apply the ideas presented in the text.

Solution (a) Mg^{2+}, Ca^{2+}, and Sr^{2+} are all from Group 2A(2), so their sizes decrease up the group: $Sr^{2+} > Ca^{2+} > Mg^{2+}$.

(b) The ions K^+, S^{2-}, and Cl^- are isoelectronic. S^{2-} has a lower Z_{eff} than Cl^-, so it is larger. K^+ is a cation and has the highest Z_{eff}, so it is smallest: $S^{2-} > Cl^- > K^+$.

(c) Au^+ has a lower charge than Au^{3+}, so it is larger: $Au^+ > Au^{3+}$.

Follow-Up Problem 8.8 Rank the ions in each set in order of *increasing* size:
(a) Cl^-, Br^-, F^- (b) Na^+, Mg^{2+}, F^- (c) Cr^{2+}, Cr^{3+}

▮ Summary of Section 8.4

- Metallic behavior correlates with large atomic size and low ionization energy. Thus, metallic behavior increases down a group and decreases across a period.
- Elements in Groups 1A(1) and 2A(2) are strong reducing agents; nonmetals in Groups 6A(16) and 7A(17) are strong oxidizing agents.
- Within the main groups, metal oxides are basic and nonmetal oxides acidic. Thus, oxides become more acidic across a period and more basic down a group.
- Many main-group elements form ions that are isoelectronic with the nearest noble gas. Removing (or adding) more electrons than needed to attain the noble gas configuration requires a prohibitive amount of energy.
- Metals in Groups 3A(13) to 5A(15) lose either their np electrons or both their ns and np electrons.
- Transition metals lose ns electrons before $(n-1)d$ electrons and commonly form more than one ion.
- Many transition metals and their compounds are paramagnetic because their atoms (or ions) have unpaired electrons.
- Cations are smaller and anions larger than their parent atoms. Ionic radius increases down a group. Across a period, ionic radii generally decrease, but a large increase occurs from the last cation to the first anion.

CHAPTER REVIEW GUIDE

Learning Objectives   Relevant section (§) and/or sample problem (SP) numbers appear in parentheses.

Understand These Concepts

1. The meaning of the periodic law and the arrangement of elements by atomic number (Introduction)
2. The reason for the spin quantum number and its two possible values (§8.1)
3. How the exclusion principle applies to orbital filling (§8.1)
4. The effects of nuclear charge, shielding, and penetration on the splitting of energy levels; the meaning of effective nuclear charge (§8.1)
5. How the arrrangement of the periodic table is based on the order of sublevel energies (§8.2)
6. How sublevels are filled in main-group and transition elements; the importance of Hund's rule (§8.2)
7. How outer electron configuration within a group is related to chemical behavior (§8.2)
8. The distinction among inner, outer, and valence electrons (§8.2)
9. The meaning of atomic radius, ionization energy, and electron affinity (§8.3)

10. How n value and effective nuclear charge give rise to the periodic trends of atomic size and ionization energy (§8.3)
11. The importance of core electrons to the pattern of successive ionization energies (§8.3)
12. How atomic properties relate to the tendency to form ions (§8.3)
13. The general properties of metals and nonmetals (§8.4)
14. How vertical and horizontal trends in metallic behavior are related to ion formation and oxide acidity (§8.4)
15. How atomic size and IE relate to redox behavior (§8.4)
16. Why main-group ions are either isoelectronic with the nearest noble gas or have a pseudo–noble gas electron configuration (§8.4)
17. Why transition elements lose ns electrons first (§8.4)
18. The origin of paramagnetic and diamagnetic behavior (§8.4)
19. The relation between ionic and atomic size and the trends in ionic size (§8.4)

Master These Skills

1. Using orbital diagrams to determine the set of quantum numbers for any electron in an atom (SP 8.1)
2. Writing full and condensed electron configurations for an element (SP 8.2)
3. Using periodic trends to rank elements by atomic size and first ionization energy (SPs 8.3, 8.4)
4. Identifying an element from its successive ionization energies (SP 8.5)
5. Writing electron configurations of main-group and transition metal ions (SPs 8.6, 8.7)
6. Using periodic trends to rank ions by size (SP 8.8)

Key Terms Page numbers appear in parentheses.

Introduction
periodic law (295)
electron configuration (295)

Section 8.1
spin quantum number (m_s) (296)
exclusion principle (297)
shielding (297)
effective nuclear charge (Z_{eff}) (297)
penetration (298)

Section 8.2
aufbau principle (299)
orbital diagram (299)
Hund's rule (300)
transition elements (303)
inner (core) electrons (306)
outer electrons (306)
valence electrons (306)
inner transition elements (306)

lanthanides (rare earths) (306)
actinides (306)

Section 8.3
metallic radius (308)
covalent radius (308)
ionization energy (IE) (311)
electron affinity (EA) (314)

Section 8.4
amphoteric (316)
isoelectronic (317)
pseudo–noble gas configuration (317)
paramagnetism (319)
diamagnetism (319)
ionic radius (320)

Key Equations and Relationships Page numbers appear in parentheses.

8.1 Defining the energy order of sublevels in terms of the angular momentum quantum number (l value) (298):

Order of sublevel energies: $s < p < d < f$

8.2 Meaning of the first ionization energy (311):

$$\text{Atom}(g) \longrightarrow \text{ion}^+(g) + e^- \qquad \Delta E = \text{IE}_1 > 0$$

Brief Solutions to Follow-Up Problems

8.1 The element has eight electrons, so $Z = 8$: oxygen.

$$
\boxed{\uparrow\downarrow}\quad \boxed{\uparrow\downarrow}\quad \boxed{\uparrow\downarrow \;\uparrow\; \uparrow}
$$
$$
1s \qquad 2s \qquad\quad 2p
$$

Sixth electron: $n = 2, l = 1, m_l = 0, +\frac{1}{2}$

8.2 (a) For Ni, $1s^2 2s^2 2p^6 3s^2 3p^6 4s^2 3d^8$; [Ar] $4s^2 3d^8$

$$
\boxed{\uparrow\downarrow}\quad \boxed{\uparrow\downarrow\;\uparrow\downarrow\;\uparrow\downarrow\;\uparrow\;\uparrow}\quad \boxed{\;\;\;\;}
$$
$$
4s \qquad\qquad 3d \qquad\qquad 4p
$$

Ni has 18 inner electrons.

(b) For Sr, $1s^2 2s^2 2p^6 3s^2 3p^6 4s^2 3d^{10} 4p^6 5s^2$; [Kr] $5s^2$

$$
\boxed{\uparrow\downarrow}\quad \boxed{\;\;\;\;}\quad \boxed{\;\;\;\;}
$$
$$
5s \qquad\qquad 4d \qquad\qquad 5p
$$

Sr has 36 inner electrons.

(c) For Po, $1s^2 2s^2 2p^6 3s^2 3p^6 4s^2 3d^{10} 4p^6 5s^2 4d^{10} 5p^6 6s^2 4f^{14} 5d^{10} 6p^4$; [Xe] $6s^2 4f^{14} 5d^{10} 6p^4$

Po has 78 inner electrons.

8.3 (a) Cl < Br < Se; (b) Xe < I < Ba

8.4 (a) Sn < Sb < I; (b) Ba < Sr < Ca

8.5 Q is aluminum: $1s^2 2s^2 2p^6 3s^2 3p^1$

8.6 (a) Ba ([Xe] $6s^2$) $\longrightarrow$ Ba^{2+} ([Xe]) + 2e$^-$

(b) O ([He] $2s^2 2p^4$) + 2e$^-$ $\longrightarrow$ O^{2-} ([He] $2s^2 2p^6$) (same as Ne)

(c) Pb ([Xe] $6s^2 4f^{14} 5d^{10} 6p^2$) $\longrightarrow$ Pb^{2+} ([Xe] $6s^2 4f^{14} 5d^{10}$) + 2e$^-$
Pb ([Xe] $6s^2 4f^{14} 5d^{10} 6p^2$) $\longrightarrow$ Pb^{4+} ([Xe] $4f^{14} 5d^{10}$) + 4e$^-$

8.7 (a) V^{3+}: [Ar] $3d^2$; paramagnetic
(b) Ni^{2+}: [Ar] $3d^8$; paramagnetic
(c) La^{3+}: [Xe]; not paramagnetic (diamagnetic)

8.8 (a) F$^-$ < Cl$^-$ < Br$^-$
(b) Mg^{2+} < Na$^+$ < F$^-$
(c) Cr^{3+} < Cr^{2+}

PROBLEMS

Problems with **colored** numbers are answered in Appendix E and worked in detail in the Student Solutions Manual. Problem sections match those in the text and provide the numbers of relevant sample problems. Most offer Concept Review Questions, Skill-Building Exercises (grouped in pairs covering the same concept), and Problems in Context. The Comprehensive Problems are based on material from any section or previous chapter.

Introduction

Concept Review Questions

8.1 What would be your reaction to a claim that a new element had been discovered and it fit between tin (Sn) and antimony (Sb) in the periodic table?

8.2 Based on results of his study of atomic x-ray spectra, Moseley discovered a relationship that replaced atomic mass as the criterion for ordering the elements. By what criterion are the elements now ordered in the periodic table? Give an example of a sequence of element order that was confirmed by Moseley's findings.

Skill-Building Exercises (grouped in similar pairs)

8.3 Before Mendeleev published his periodic table, Döbereiner grouped elements with similar properties into "triads," in which the unknown properties of one member could be predicted by averaging known values of the properties of the others. To test this idea, predict the values of the following quantities:
(a) The atomic mass of K from the atomic masses of Na and Rb
(b) The melting point of Br_2 from the melting points of Cl_2 ($-101.0°C$) and I_2 ($113.6°C$) (actual value $= -7.2°C$)

8.4 To test Döbereiner's idea (Problem 8.3), predict:
(a) The boiling point of HBr from the boiling points of HCl ($-84.9°C$) and HI ($-35.4°C$) (actual value $= -67.0°C$)
(b) The boiling point of AsH_3 from the boiling points of PH_3 ($-87.4°C$) and SbH_3 ($-17.1°C$) (actual value $= -55°C$)

Characteristics of Many-Electron Atoms

Concept Review Questions

8.5 Summarize the rules for the allowable values of the four quantum numbers of an electron in an atom.

8.6 Which of the quantum numbers relate(s) to the electron only? Which relate(s) to the orbital?

8.7 State the exclusion principle. What does it imply about the number and spin of electrons in an atomic orbital?

8.8 What is the key distinction between sublevel energies in one-electron species, such as the H atom, and those in many-electron species, such as the C atom? What factors lead to this distinction? Would you expect the pattern of sublevel energies in Be^{3+} to be more like that in H or that in C? Explain.

8.9 Define *shielding* and *effective nuclear charge*. What is the connection between the two?

8.10 What is penetration? How is it related to shielding? Use the penetration effect to explain the difference in relative orbital energies of a $3p$ and a $3d$ electron in the same atom.

Skill-Building Exercises (grouped in similar pairs)

8.11 How many electrons in an atom can have each of the following quantum number or sublevel designations?
(a) $n = 2, l = 1$ (b) $3d$ (c) $4s$

8.12 How many electrons in an atom can have each of the following quantum number or sublevel designations?
(a) $n = 2, l = 1, m_l = 0$ (b) $5p$ (c) $n = 4, l = 3$

8.13 How many electrons in an atom can have each of the following quantum number or sublevel designations?
(a) $4p$ (b) $n = 3, l = 1, m_l = +1$ (c) $n = 5, l = 3$

8.14 How many electrons in an atom can have each of the following quantum number or sublevel designations?
(a) $2s$ (b) $n = 3, l = 2$ (c) $6d$

The Quantum-Mechanical Model and the Periodic Table
(Sample Problems 8.1 and 8.2)

Concept Review Questions

8.15 State the periodic law, and explain its relation to electron configuration. (Use Na and K in your explanation.)

8.16 State Hund's rule in your own words, and show its application in the orbital diagram of the nitrogen atom.

8.17 How does the aufbau principle, in connection with the periodic law, lead to the format of the periodic table?

8.18 For main-group elements, are outer electron configurations similar or different within a group? Within a period? Explain.

8.19 For which blocks of elements are outer electrons the same as valence electrons? For which are d electrons often included among the valence electrons?

8.20 What is the electron capacity of the nth energy level? What is the capacity of the fourth energy level?

Skill-Building Exercises (grouped in similar pairs)

8.21 Write a full set of quantum numbers for the following:
(a) The outermost electron in an Rb atom
(b) The electron gained when an S^- ion becomes an S^{2-} ion
(c) The electron lost when an Ag atom ionizes
(d) The electron gained when an F^- ion forms from an F atom

8.22 Write a full set of quantum numbers for the following:
(a) The outermost electron in an Li atom
(b) The electron gained when a Br atom becomes a Br^- ion
(c) The electron lost when a Cs atom ionizes
(d) The highest energy electron in the ground-state B atom

8.23 Write the full ground-state electron configuration for each:
(a) Rb (b) Ge (c) Ar

8.24 Write the full ground-state electron configuration for each:
(a) Br (b) Mg (c) Se

8.25 Write the full ground-state electron configuration for each:
(a) Cl (b) Si (c) Sr

8.26 Write the full ground-state electron configuration for each:
(a) S (b) Kr (c) Cs

8.27 Draw a partial (valence-level) orbital diagram, and write the condensed ground-state electron configuration for each:
(a) Ti (b) Cl (c) V

8.28 Draw a partial (valence-level) orbital diagram, and write the condensed ground-state electron configuration for each:
(a) Ba (b) Co (c) Ag

8.29 Draw a partial (valence-level) orbital diagram, and write the condensed ground-state electron configuration for each:
(a) Mn   (b) P   (c) Fe

8.30 Draw a partial (valence-level) orbital diagram, and write the condensed ground-state electron configuration for each:
(a) Ga   (b) Zn   (c) Sc

8.31 Draw the partial (valence-level) orbital diagram, and write the symbol, group number, and period number of the element:
(a) $[He] 2s^2 2p^4$ (b) $[Ne] 3s^2 3p^3$

8.32 Draw the partial (valence-level) orbital diagram, and write the symbol, group number, and period number of the element:
(a) $[Kr] 5s^2 4d^{10}$ (b) $[Ar] 4s^2 3d^8$

8.33 Draw the partial (valence-level) orbital diagram, and write the symbol, group number, and period number of the element:
(a) $[Ne] 3s^2 3p^5$ (b) $[Ar] 4s^2 3d^{10} 4p^3$

8.34 Draw the partial (valence-level) orbital diagram, and write the symbol, group number, and period number of the element:
(a) $[Ar] 4s^2 3d^5$ (b) $[Kr] 5s^2 4d^2$

8.35 From each partial (valence-level) orbital diagram, write the condensed electron configuration and group number:

8.36 From each partial (valence-level) orbital diagram, write the condensed electron configuration and group number:

(a) $5s$ $4d$ $5p$
(b) $2s$ $2p$

8.37 How many inner, outer, and valence electrons are present in an atom of each of the following elements?
(a) O   (b) Sn   (c) Ca   (d) Fe   (e) Se

8.38 How many inner, outer, and valence electrons are present in an atom of each of the following elements?
(a) Br   (b) Cs   (c) Cr   (d) Sr   (e) F

8.39 Identify each element below, and give the symbols of the other elements in its group:
(a) $[He] 2s^2 2p^1$ (b) $[Ne] 3s^2 3p^4$ (c) $[Xe] 6s^2 5d^1$

8.40 Identify each element below, and give the symbols of the other elements in its group:
(a) $[Ar] 4s^2 3d^{10} 4p^4$ (b) $[Xe] 6s^2 4f^{14} 5d^2$ (c) $[Ar] 4s^2 3d^5$

8.41 Identify each element below, and give the symbols of the other elements in its group:
(a) $[He] 2s^2 2p^2$ (b) $[Ar] 4s^2 3d^3$ (c) $[Ne] 3s^2 3p^3$

8.42 Identify each element below, and give the symbols of the other elements in its group:
(a) $[Ar] 4s^2 3d^{10} 4p^2$ (b) $[Ar] 4s^2 3d^7$ (c) $[Kr] 5s^2 4d^5$

Problems in Context

8.43 After an atom in its ground state absorbs energy, it exists in an excited state. Spectral lines are produced when the atom returns to its ground state. The yellow-orange line in the sodium spectrum, for example, is produced by the emission of energy when excited sodium atoms return to their ground state. Write the electron configuration and the orbital diagram of the first excited state of sodium. (*Hint:* The outermost electron is excited.)

8.44 One reason spectroscopists study excited states is to gain information about the energies of orbitals that are unoccupied in an atom's ground state. Each of the following electron configurations represents an atom in an excited state. Identify the element, and write its condensed ground-state configuration:
(a) $1s^2 2s^2 2p^6 3s^1 3p^1$ (b) $1s^2 2s^2 2p^6 3s^2 3p^4 4s^1$
(c) $1s^2 2s^2 2p^6 3s^2 3p^6 4s^2 3d^4 4p^1$ (d) $1s^2 2s^2 2p^5 3s^1$

Trends in Three Atomic Properties
(Sample Problems 8.3 to 8.5)

Concept Review Questions

8.45 If the exact outer limit of an isolated atom cannot be measured, what criterion can we use to determine atomic radii? What is the difference between a covalent radius and a metallic radius?

8.46 Given the following partial (valence-level) electron configurations, (a) identify each element, (b) rank the four elements in order of increasing atomic size, and (c) rank them in order of increasing ionization energy:

8.47 In what region of the periodic table will you find elements with relatively high IEs? With relatively low IEs?

8.48 (a) Why do successive IEs of a given element always increase? (b) When the difference between successive IEs of a given element is exceptionally large (for example, between IE_1 and IE_2 of K), what do we learn about its electron configuration? (c) The bars represent the relative magnitudes of the first five ionization energies of an atom:

Identify the element and write its complete electron configuration, assuming it comes from (a) Period 2; (b) Period 3; (c) Period 4.

8.49 In a plot of IE_1 for the Period 3 elements (see Figure 8.15, p. 311), why do the values for elements in Groups 3A(13) and 6A(16) drop slightly below the generally increasing trend?

8.50 Which group in the periodic table has elements with high (endothermic) IE_1 and very negative (exothermic) first electron affinities (EA_1)? Give the charge on the ions these atoms form.

8.51 The EA_2 of an oxygen atom is positive, even though its EA_1 is negative. Why does this change of sign occur? Which other elements exhibit a positive EA_2? Explain.

8.52 How does d-electron shielding influence atomic size among the Period 4 transition elements?

Skill-Building Exercises (grouped in similar pairs)

8.53 Arrange each set in order of *increasing* atomic size:
(a) Rb, K, Cs   (b) C, O, Be   (c) Cl, K, S   (d) Mg, K, Ca

8.54 Arrange each set in order of *decreasing* atomic size:
(a) Ge, Pb, Sn   (b) Sn, Te, Sr   (c) F, Ne, Na   (d) Be, Mg, Na

8.55 Arrange each set of atoms in order of *increasing* IE_1:
(a) Sr, Ca, Ba   (b) N, B, Ne   (c) Br, Rb, Se   (d) As, Sb, Sn

8.56 Arrange each set of atoms in order of *decreasing* IE_1:
(a) Na, Li, K   (b) Be, F, C   (c) Cl, Ar, Na   (d) Cl, Br, Se

8.57 Write the full electron configuration of the Period 2 element with the following successive IEs (in kJ/mol):

$IE_1 = 801$ $IE_2 = 2427$ $IE_3 = 3659$
$IE_4 = 25,022$ $IE_5 = 32,822$

8.58 Write the full electron configuration of the Period 3 element with the following successive IEs (in kJ/mol):

$IE_1 = 738$ $IE_2 = 1450$ $IE_3 = 7732$
$IE_4 = 10,539$ $IE_5 = 13,628$

8.59 Which element in each of the following sets would you expect to have the *highest* IE_2?
(a) Na, Mg, Al   (b) Na, K, Fe   (c) Sc, Be, Mg

8.60 Which element in each of the following sets would you expect to have the *lowest* IE_3?
(a) Na, Mg, Al   (b) K, Ca, Sc   (c) Li, Al, B

Atomic Properties and Chemical Reactivity
(Sample Problems 8.6 to 8.8)

Concept Review Questions

8.61 List three ways in which metals and nonmetals differ.

8.62 Summarize the trend in metallic character as a function of position in the periodic table. Is it the same as the trend in atomic size? The trend in ionization energy?

8.63 Explain the relationship between atomic size and reducing strength in Group 1A(1). Explain the relationship between IE and oxidizing strength in Group 7A(17).

8.64 Summarize the acid-base behavior of the main-group metal and nonmetal oxides in water. How does oxide acidity in water change down a group and across a period?

8.65 What ions are possible for the two largest stable elements in Group 4A(14)? How does each arise?

8.66 What is a pseudo–noble gas configuration? Give an example of one ion from Group 3A(13) that has it.

8.67 How are measurements of paramagnetism used to support electron configurations derived spectroscopically? Use Cu(I) and Cu(II) chlorides as examples.

8.68 The charges of a set of isoelectronic ions vary from 3+ to 3−. Place the ions in order of increasing size.

Skill-Building Exercises (grouped in similar pairs)

8.69 Which element would you expect to be *more* metallic?
(a) Ca or Rb   (b) Mg or Ra   (c) Br or I

8.70 Which element would you expect to be *more* metallic?
(a) S or Cl   (b) In or Al   (c) As or Br

8.71 Which element would you expect to be *less* metallic?
(a) Sb or As   (b) Si or P   (c) Be or Na

8.72 Which element would you expect to be *less* metallic?
(a) Cs or Rn   (b) Sn or Te   (c) Se or Ge

8.73 Does the reaction of a main-group nonmetal oxide in water produce an acidic or a basic solution? Write a balanced equation for the reaction of a Group 6A(16) nonmetal oxide with water.

8.74 Does the reaction of a main-group metal oxide in water produce an acidic or a basic solution? Write a balanced equation for the reaction of a Group 2A(2) oxide with water.

8.75 Write the charge and full ground-state electron configuration of the monatomic ion most likely to be formed by each:
(a) Cl   (b) Na   (c) Ca

8.76 Write the charge and full ground-state electron configuration of the monatomic ion most likely to be formed by each:
(a) Rb   (b) N   (c) Br

8.77 Write the charge and full ground-state electron configuration of the monatomic ion most likely to be formed by each:
(a) Al   (b) S   (c) Sr

8.78 Write the charge and full ground-state electron configuration of the monatomic ion most likely to be formed by each:
(a) P   (b) Mg   (c) Se

8.79 How many unpaired electrons are present in a ground-state atom from each of the following groups?
(a) 2A(2)   (b) 5A(15)   (c) 8A(18)   (d) 3A(13)

8.80 How many unpaired electrons are present in a ground-state atom from each of the following groups?
(a) 4A(14)   (b) 7A(17)   (c) 1A(1)   (d) 6A(16)

8.81 Which of these are paramagnetic in their ground state?
(a) Ga   (b) Si   (c) Be   (d) Te

8.82 Are compounds of these ground-state ions paramagnetic?
(a) Ti^{2+} (b) Zn^{2+} (c) Ca^{2+} (d) Sn^{2+}

8.83 Write the condensed ground-state electron configurations of these transition metal ions, and state which are paramagnetic:
(a) V^{3+} (b) Cd^{2+} (c) Co^{3+} (d) Ag^+

8.84 Write the condensed ground-state electron configurations of these transition metal ions, and state which are paramagnetic:
(a) Mo^{3+} (b) Au^+ (c) Mn^{2+} (d) Hf^{2+}

8.85 Palladium (Pd; $Z = 46$) is diamagnetic. Draw partial orbital diagrams to show which of the following electron configurations is consistent with this fact:
(a) [Kr] $5s^2 4d^8$ (b) [Kr] $4d^{10}$ (c) [Kr] $5s^1 4d^9$

8.86 Niobium (Nb; $Z = 41$) has an anomalous ground-state electron configuration for a Group 5B(5) element: [Kr] $5s^1 4d^4$. What is the expected electron configuration for elements in this group? Draw partial orbital diagrams to show how paramagnetic measurements could support niobium's actual configuration.

8.87 Rank the ions in each set in order of *increasing* size, and explain your ranking:
(a) Li^+, K^+, Na^+ (b) Se^{2-}, Rb^+, Br^- (c) O^{2-}, F^-, N^{3-}

8.88 Rank the ions in each set in order of *decreasing* size, and explain your ranking:
(a) Se^{2-}, S^{2-}, O^{2-} (b) Te^{2-}, Cs^+, I^- (c) Sr^{2+}, Ba^{2+}, Cs^+

Comprehensive Problems

8.89 Name the element described in each of the following:
(a) Smallest atomic radius in Group 6A(16)
(b) Largest atomic radius in Period 6
(c) Smallest metal in Period 3
(d) Highest IE_1 in Group 4A(14)
(e) Lowest IE_1 in Period 5
(f) Most metallic in Group 5A(15)
(g) Group 3A(13) element that forms the most basic oxide
(h) Period 4 element with highest energy level filled
(i) Condensed ground-state electron configuration of [Ne] $3s^2 3p^2$
(j) Condensed ground-state electron configuration of [Kr] $5s^2 4d^6$
(k) Forms 2+ ion with electron configuration [Ar] $3d^3$
(l) Period 5 element that forms 3+ ion with pseudo–noble gas configuration
(m) Period 4 transition element that forms 3+ diamagnetic ion
(n) Period 4 transition element that forms 2+ ion with a half-filled d sublevel
(o) Heaviest lanthanide
(p) Period 3 element whose 2− ion is isoelectronic with Ar
(q) Alkaline earth metal whose cation is isoelectronic with Kr
(r) Group 5A(15) metalloid with the most acidic oxide

8.90 Use electron configurations to account for the stability of the lanthanide ions Ce^{4+} and Eu^{2+}.

8.91 When a nonmetal oxide reacts with water, it forms an oxoacid with the same oxidation number as the nonmetal. Give the name and formula of the oxide used to prepare each of these oxoacids: (a) hypochlorous acid; (b) chlorous acid; (c) chloric acid; (d) perchloric acid; (e) sulfuric acid; (f) sulfurous acid; (g) nitric acid; (h) nitrous acid; (i) carbonic acid; (j) phosphoric acid.

8.92 A fundamental relationship of electrostatics states that the energy required to separate opposite charges of magnitudes Q_1 and Q_2 that are a distance d apart is proportional to $\dfrac{Q_1 \times Q_2}{d}$.
Use this relationship and any other factors to explain the following: (a) the IE_2 of He ($Z = 2$) is *more* than twice the IE_1 of H ($Z = 1$); (b) the IE_1 of He is *less* than twice the IE_1 of H.

8.93 The energy difference between the $5d$ and $6s$ sublevels in gold accounts for its color. Assuming this energy difference is about 2.7 eV (electron volt; 1 eV = 1.602×10^{-19} J), explain why gold has a warm yellow color.

8.94 Write the formula and name of the compound formed from the following ionic interactions: (a) The 2+ ion and the 1− ion are both isoelectronic with the atoms of a chemically unreactive Period 4 element. (b) The 2+ ion and the 2− ion are both isoelectronic with the Period 3 noble gas. (c) The 2+ ion is the smallest with a filled d sublevel; the anion forms from the smallest halogen. (d) The ions form from the largest and smallest ionizable atoms in Period 2.

8.95 The energy changes for many unusual reactions can be determined using Hess's law (Section 6.5).
(a) Calculate ΔE for the conversion of $F^-(g)$ into $F^+(g)$.
(b) Calculate ΔE for the conversion of $Na^+(g)$ into $Na^-(g)$.

8.96 Discuss each conclusion from a study of redox reactions:
(a) The sulfide ion functions only as a reducing agent.
(b) The sulfate ion functions only as an oxidizing agent.
(c) Sulfur dioxide functions as an oxidizing or a reducing agent.

8.97 The hot glowing gases around the Sun, the *corona*, can reach millions of degrees Celsius, high enough to remove many electrons from gaseous atoms. Iron ions with charges as high as 14+ have been observed in the corona. Which ions from Fe^+ to Fe^{14+} are paramagnetic? Which would be most strongly attracted to a magnetic field?

8.98 There are some exceptions to the trends of first and successive ionization energies. For each of the following pairs, explain which ionization energy would be higher:
(a) IE_1 of Ga or IE_1 of Ge   (b) IE_2 of Ga or IE_2 of Ge
(c) IE_3 of Ga or IE_3 of Ge   (d) IE_4 of Ga or IE_4 of Ge

8.99 Use Figure 8.16, p. 312, to find: (a) the longest wavelength of electromagnetic (EM) radiation that can ionize an alkali metal atom; (b) the longest wavelength of EM radiation that can ionize an alkaline earth metal atom; (c) the elements, other than the alkali and alkaline earth metals, that could also be ionized by the radiation of part (b); (d) the region of the EM spectrum in which these photons are found.

8.100 Rubidium and bromine atoms are depicted at right. (a) What monatomic ions do they form? (b) What electronic feature characterizes this pair of ions, and which noble gas are they related to? (c) Which pair best represents the relative ionic sizes?

A   B   C   D

8.101 Partial (valence-level) electron configurations for four different ions are shown below:

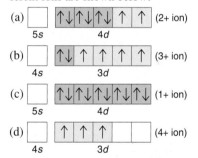

Identify the elements from which the ions are derived, and write the formula of the oxide each ion forms.

8.102 Data from the planet Zog for some main-group elements are shown below (Zoggian units are linearly related to Earth units but are not shown). Radio signals from Zog reveal that balloonium is a monatomic gas with two positive nuclear charges. Use the data to deduce the names that Earthlings give to these elements:

Name	Atomic Radius	IE_1	EA_1
Balloonium	10	339	0
Inertium	24	297	+4.1
Allotropium	34	143	−28.6
Brinium	63	70.9	−7.6
Canium	47	101	−15.3
Fertilium	25	200	0
Liquidium	38	163	−46.4
Utilium	48	82.4	−6.1
Crimsonium	72	78.4	−2.9

Models of Chemical Bonding

Concepts and skills to review before you study this chapter

- characteristics of ionic and covalent compounds; Coulomb's law (Section 2.7)
- polar covalent bonds and the polarity of water (Section 4.1)
- Hess's law, ΔH°_{rxn}, and ΔH°_f (Sections 6.5 and 6.6)
- atomic and ionic electron configurations (Sections 8.2 and 8.4)
- trends in atomic properties and metallic behavior (Sections 8.3 and 8.4)

Why do substances behave as they do? That is, why is table salt (or any other ionic substance) a hard, brittle, high-melting solid that conducts a current only when molten or dissolved in water? Why is candle wax (along with most covalent substances) low melting, soft, and nonconducting, even though diamond (and a few others of this type of covalent substance) is high melting and extremely hard? And why is copper (and most other metals) shiny, malleable, and able to conduct a current whether molten or solid? The answers lie in the *type of bonding within the substance*. In Chapter 8, we examined the properties of individual atoms and ions. But the behavior of matter really depends on how those atoms and ions bond.

IN THIS CHAPTER . . . We examine how atomic properties give rise to three models of chemical bonding—ionic, covalent, and metallic—and how each model explains the behavior of substances.

- We see how metals and nonmetals combine via three types of bonding and learn how to depict atoms and ions with Lewis symbols.
- We detail the steps in the formation of an ionic solid and focus on the importance of lattice energy.
- Covalent bonding occurs in the vast majority of compounds, so we look at how a bond forms and discuss the relations among bond order, energy, and length.
- We explore the relationship between bond energy and the enthalpy change of a reaction, with a focus on fuels and foods.
- We examine periodic trends in electronegativity and learn its role in the range of bonding, from pure covalent to ionic, and in bond polarity.
- We consider a simple bonding model that explains the properties of metals.

9.1 • ATOMIC PROPERTIES AND CHEMICAL BONDS

Before we examine the types of chemical bonding, we should start with the most fundamental question: why do atoms bond at all? In general, *bonding lowers the potential energy between positive and negative particles* (see Figure 1.3, p. 9), whether they are oppositely charged ions or nuclei and electron pairs. Just as the electron configuration and the strength of nucleus-electron attractions determine the properties of an atom, the type and strength of chemical bonds determine the properties of a substance.

Types of Bonding: Three Ways Metals and Nonmetals Combine

In general, there is a gradation from atoms of more metallic elements to atoms of more nonmetallic elements across a period *and* up a group (Figure 9.1, *next page*). Three types of bonding result from the three ways these two types of atoms can combine:

A

Figure 9.1 A comparison of metals and nonmetals. **A,** Location within the periodic table. **B,** Relative magnitudes of some atomic properties across a period.

PROPERTY	METAL ATOM	NONMETAL ATOM
Atomic size	Larger	Smaller
Z_{eff}	Lower	Higher
IE	Lower	Higher
EA	Less negative	More negative

B

1. *Metal with nonmetal: electron transfer and ionic bonding* (Figure 9.2A). We observe **ionic bonding** between atoms with large differences in their tendencies to lose or gain electrons. Such differences occur between reactive metals [Groups 1A(1) and 2A(2)] and nonmetals [Group 7A(17) and the top of Group 6A(16)]. A metal atom (low IE) loses its one or two valence electrons, and a nonmetal atom (highly negative EA) gains the electron(s). *Electron transfer* from metal to nonmetal occurs, and each atom forms an ion with a noble gas electron configuration. The electrostatic attractions between these positive and negative ions draw them into a three-dimensional array to form an ionic solid. Note that the chemical formula of an ionic compound is the *empirical formula* because it gives the cation-to-anion ratio.

2. *Nonmetal with nonmetal: electron sharing and covalent bonding* (Figure 9.2B). When two atoms differ little, or not at all, in their tendencies to lose or gain electrons, we observe *electron sharing* and **covalent bonding,** which occurs most commonly between nonmetal atoms. Each atom holds onto its own electrons tightly (high IE) and attracts other electrons (highly negative EA). The nucleus of each atom attracts the valence electrons of the other, which draws the atoms together. The shared electron pair is typically *localized* between the two atoms, linking them in a covalent bond of a particular length and strength. In most cases, separate molecules result when atoms bond covalently. Note that the chemical formula of a covalent compound is the *molecular formula* because it gives the actual numbers of atoms in each molecule.

Figure 9.2 Three models of chemical bonding.

A Ionic bonding

B Covalent bonding

C Metallic bonding

3. *Metal with metal: electron pooling and metallic bonding* (Figure 9.2C). Metal atoms are relatively large, and their few outer electrons are well shielded by filled inner levels (core electrons). Thus, they lose outer electrons easily (low IE) and do not gain them readily (slightly negative or positive EA). These properties lead metal atoms to share their valence electrons, but not by covalent bonding. In the simplest model of **metallic bonding,** the enormous number of atoms in a sample of a metal *pool* their valence electrons into a "sea" of electrons that "flows" between and around each metal-ion core (nucleus plus inner electrons), thereby attracting them together. Unlike the localized electrons in covalent bonding, electrons in metallic bonding are *delocalized,* moving freely throughout the entire piece of metal.

In the world of real substances, there are exceptions to these idealized models, so you can't always predict bond type from positions of the elements in the periodic table. As just one example, when the metal beryllium [Group 2A(2)] combines with the nonmetal chlorine [Group 7A(17)], there is more electron sharing than transferring—that is, the bonding is more covalent than ionic. Thus, just as we see gradations in atomic behavior within a group or period, we see gradations in type of bonding between atoms from different groups and periods (Figure 9.3).

Figure 9.3 Gradations in bond type among Period 3 *(black type)* and Group 4A *(red type)* elements.

Lewis Symbols and the Octet Rule

Before examining each of the models, let's learn a method for depicting the valence electrons of interacting atoms that predicts how they bond. In a **Lewis electron-dot symbol** (named for the American chemist G. N. Lewis), the element symbol represents the nucleus *and* inner electrons, and dots around the symbol represent the valence electrons (Figure 9.4). Note that the pattern of dots is the same for elements within a group.

Figure 9.4 Lewis electron-dot symbols for elements in Periods 2 and 3.

We use these steps to write the Lewis symbol for any main-group element:

1. Note its A-group number (1A to 8A), which tells the number of valence electrons.
2. Place one dot at a time on each of the four sides (top, right, bottom, left) of the element symbol.
3. Keep adding dots, pairing them, until all are used up.

The specific placement of dots is not important; that is, in addition to the one shown in Figure 9.4, the Lewis symbol for nitrogen can *also* be written as

$$\cdot\ddot{N}\colon \quad \text{or} \quad \cdot\ddot{N}\cdot \quad \text{or} \quad \colon\ddot{N}\cdot$$

The Lewis symbol provides information about an element's bonding behavior:

• For a *metal,* the *total* number of dots is the number of electrons an atom loses to form a cation.
• For a *nonmetal,* the number of *unpaired* dots equals either the number of electrons an atom *gains* to form an anion or the number it *shares* to form covalent bonds.

The Lewis symbol for carbon illustrates the last point. Rather than one pair of dots and two unpaired dots, as its electron configuration seems to call for ([He] $2s^2 2p^2$), carbon has four unpaired dots because it forms four bonds. Larger nonmetals can form as many bonds as the number of dots in their Lewis symbol (Chapter 10).

In his pioneering studies, Lewis generalized much of bonding behavior into the **octet rule:** *when atoms bond, they lose, gain, or share electrons to attain a filled outer level of eight electrons (or two, for H and Li).* The octet rule holds for nearly all of the compounds of Period 2 elements and a large number of others as well.

■ Summary of Section 9.1

- Nearly all naturally occurring substances consist of atoms or ions bonded to others. Chemical bonding allows atoms to lower their energy.
- Ionic bonding occurs when metal atoms transfer electrons to nonmetal atoms, and the resulting ions attract each other and form an ionic solid.
- Covalent bonding is most common between nonmetal atoms and usually results in individual molecules. Bonded atoms share one or more pairs of electrons that are localized between them.
- Metallic bonding occurs when many metal atoms pool their valence electrons into a delocalized electron "sea" that holds all the atoms in the sample together.
- The Lewis electron-dot symbol of a main-group atom shows valence electrons as dots surrounding the element symbol.
- The octet rule says that, when bonding, many atoms lose, gain, or share electrons to attain a filled outer level of eight (or two) electrons.

9.2 • THE IONIC BONDING MODEL

The central idea of the ionic bonding model is the *transfer of electrons from metal atoms to nonmetal atoms to form ions that attract each other into a solid compound.* In most cases, for the main groups, the ion that forms has a filled outer level of either two or eight electrons, the number in the nearest noble gas (octet rule).

The transfer of an electron from a lithium atom to a fluorine atom is depicted in three ways in Figure 9.5. In each, Li loses its single outer electron and is left with a filled $n = 1$ level (two e^-), while F gains a single electron to fill its $n = 2$ level (eight e^-). In this case, each atom is one electron away from the configuration of its nearest noble gas, so the number of electrons lost by each Li equals the number gained by each F. Therefore, equal numbers of Li^+ and F^- ions form, as the formula LiF indicates. That is, in ionic bonding, *the total number of electrons lost by the metal atom(s) equals the total number of electrons gained by the nonmetal atom(s).*

Figure 9.5 Three ways to depict electron transfer in the formation of Li^+ and F^-. The electron being transferred is shown in red.

Sample Problem 9.1 | **Depicting Ion Formation**

Problem Use partial orbital diagrams and Lewis symbols to depict the formation of Na^+ and O^{2-} ions from the atoms, and give the formula of the compound formed.

Plan First we draw the orbital diagrams and Lewis symbols for Na and O atoms. To attain filled outer levels, Na loses one electron and O gains two. To make the number of electrons lost equal the number gained, two Na atoms are needed for each O atom.

Solution

The formula is Na_2O.

Follow-Up Problem 9.1 Use condensed electron configurations and Lewis symbols to depict the formation of Mg^{2+} and Cl^- ions from the atoms, and give the formula of the compound formed.

Why Ionic Compounds Form: The Importance of Lattice Energy

You may be surprised to learn that energy is *absorbed* during electron transfer. So why does it occur? And, in view of this absorption of energy, why do ionic substances exist at all? As you'll see, the answer involves the enormous quantity of energy *released* after electron transfer, as the ions form a solid.

1. *The electron-transfer process.* Consider the electron-transfer process for the formation of lithium fluoride, which involves a gaseous Li atom losing an electron, and a gaseous F atom gaining it:

• The first ionization energy (IE_1) of Li is the energy absorbed when 1 mol of gaseous Li atoms loses 1 mol of valence electrons:

$$Li(g) \longrightarrow Li^+(g) + e^- \qquad IE_1 = 520 \text{ kJ}$$

• The first electron affinity (EA_1) of F is the energy released when 1 mol of gaseous F atoms gains 1 mol of electrons:

$$F(g) + e^- \longrightarrow F^-(g) \qquad EA_1 = -328 \text{ kJ}$$

• Taking the sum shows that electron transfer *by itself* requires energy:

$$Li(g) + F(g) \longrightarrow Li^+(g) + F^-(g) \qquad IE_1 + EA_1 = 192 \text{ kJ}$$

2. *Other steps that absorb energy.* The total energy needed prior to ion formation adds to the sum of IE_1 and EA_1: metallic lithium must be made into gaseous atoms (161 kJ/mol), and fluorine molecules must be broken into separate atoms (79.5 kJ/mol).

3. *Steps that release energy.* Despite these endothermic steps, the standard enthalpy of formation (ΔH_f°) of solid LiF is −617 kJ/mol; that is, 617 kJ is *released* when 1 mol of LiF(s) forms from its elements. Formation of LiF is typical of reactions between active metals and nonmetals: ionic solids form readily (Figure 9.6).

If the overall reaction releases energy, there must be some step that is exothermic enough to outweigh the endothermic steps. This step involves the *strong attraction between pairs of oppositely charged ions.* When 1 mol of $Li^+(g)$ and 1 mol of $F^-(g)$ form 1 mol of gaseous LiF molecules, a large quantity of heat is released:

$$Li^+(g) + F^-(g) \longrightarrow LiF(g) \qquad \Delta H^\circ = -755 \text{ kJ}$$

But, as you know, under ordinary conditions, LiF does not exist as gaseous molecules: *even more energy is released when the separate gaseous ions coalesce into a crystalline solid* because each ion attracts *several* oppositely charged ions:

$$Li^+(g) + F^-(g) \longrightarrow LiF(s) \qquad \Delta H^\circ = -1050 \text{ kJ}$$

The negative of this enthalpy change is 1050 kJ, the lattice energy of LiF. The **lattice energy** ($\Delta H_{lattice}^\circ$) is the enthalpy change that accompanies the reverse of this equation—1 mol of ionic solid separating into gaseous ions.

Determining Lattice Energy with a Born-Haber Cycle The magnitude of the lattice energy is a measure of the strength of the ionic interactions and influences macroscopic properties, such as melting point, hardness, and solubility. Despite playing this crucial role in the formation of ionic compounds, lattice energy cannot be measured directly. One way to determine it applies Hess's law (see Section 6.5) in a **Born-Haber cycle,** a series of steps from elements to ionic solid for which all the enthalpies* are known except the lattice energy.

A

B

Figure 9.6 The exothermic formation of sodium bromide. **A,** Sodium (in beaker under mineral oil) and bromine. **B,** The reaction is rapid and vigorous.

---

*Strictly speaking, ionization energy (IE) and electron affinity (EA) are internal energy changes (ΔE), not enthalpy changes (ΔH), but in these steps, $\Delta H = \Delta E$ because $\Delta V = 0$ (see Section 6.2).

Let's go through a Born-Haber cycle for the formation of lithium fluoride to calculate $\Delta H^{\circ}_{\text{lattice}}$. Figure 9.7 shows two possible paths, a direct combination reaction ($\Delta H^{\circ}_{\text{f}}$; *black arrow*) and a multistep path (*orange arrows*) in which one step is the unknown $\Delta H^{\circ}_{\text{lattice}}$. Hess's law tells us both paths involve the same overall enthalpy change:

$$\Delta H^{\circ}_{\text{f}} \text{ of LiF}(s) = \text{sum of } \Delta H^{\circ} \text{ values for multistep path}$$

Hess's law lets us choose *hypothetical* steps whose enthalpy changes we can measure, even though *they are **not** the actual steps that occur when lithium reacts with fluorine*. We identify each ΔH° by its step number in Figure 9.7:

Step 1. From solid Li to Li atoms. This step, called *atomization,* has the enthalpy change $\Delta H^{\circ}_{\text{atom}}$. It involves breaking metallic bonds, so it absorbs energy:

$$\text{Li}(s) \longrightarrow \text{Li}(g) \qquad \Delta H^{\circ}_{\text{step 1}} = \Delta H^{\circ}_{\text{atom}} = 161 \text{ kJ}$$

Step 2. From F_2 molecules to F atoms. This step involves breaking a covalent bond, so it absorbs energy; as we discuss later, this is the *bond energy* (BE) of F_2. Since we need 1 mol of F atoms to make 1 mol of LiF, we start with $\frac{1}{2}$ mol of F_2:

$$\tfrac{1}{2}\text{F}_2(g) \longrightarrow \text{F}(g) \qquad \Delta H^{\circ}_{\text{step 2}} = \tfrac{1}{2}(\text{BE of F}_2) = \tfrac{1}{2}(159 \text{ kJ}) = 79.5 \text{ kJ}$$

Step 3. From Li to Li^+. Removing the $2s$ electron from Li absorbs energy:

$$\text{Li}(g) \longrightarrow \text{Li}^+(g) + \text{e}^- \qquad \Delta H^{\circ}_{\text{step 3}} = \text{IE}_1 = 520 \text{ kJ}$$

Step 4. From F to F^-. Adding an electron to F releases energy:

$$\text{F}(g) + \text{e}^- \longrightarrow \text{F}^-(g) \qquad \Delta H^{\circ}_{\text{step 4}} = \text{EA}_1 = -328 \text{ kJ}$$

Step 5. From gaseous ions to ionic solid. Forming solid LiF from gaseous Li^+ and F^- releases a lot of energy. The enthalpy change for this step is unknown but is, by definition, the negative of the lattice energy:

$$\text{Li}^+(g) + \text{F}^-(g) \longrightarrow \text{LiF}(s) \qquad \Delta H^{\circ}_{\text{step 5}} = -\Delta H^{\circ}_{\text{lattice}} \text{ of LiF} = ?$$

The enthalpy change of the combination reaction (*black arrow*) is

$$\text{Li}(s) + \tfrac{1}{2}\text{F}_2(g) \longrightarrow \text{LiF}(s) \qquad \Delta H^{\circ}_{\text{overall}} = \Delta H^{\circ}_{\text{f}} = -617 \text{ kJ}$$

Figure 9.7 The Born-Haber cycle for lithium fluoride. The formation of LiF(s) from its elements can happen in one combination reaction (black arrow) or in five steps (orange arrows). The unknown enthalpy change is $\Delta H^{\circ}_{\text{step 5}}$ ($-\Delta H^{\circ}_{\text{lattice}}$ of LiF).

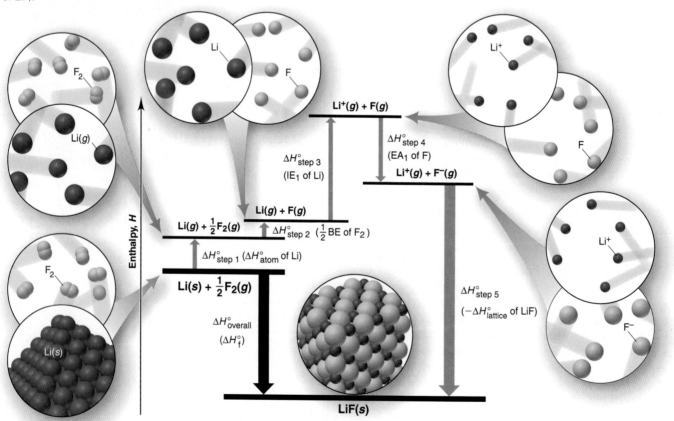

We set ΔH_f° equal to the sum of the ΔH° values for the steps and solve for $\Delta H_{lattice}^\circ$:

$$\Delta H_f^\circ = \Delta H_{step\ 1}^\circ + \Delta H_{step\ 2}^\circ + \Delta H_{step\ 3}^\circ + \Delta H_{step\ 4}^\circ + (-\Delta H_{lattice}^\circ \text{ of LiF})$$

Solving for $-\Delta H_{lattice}^\circ$ of LiF gives

$$\begin{aligned}
-\Delta H_{lattice}^\circ \text{ of LiF} &= \Delta H_f^\circ - (\Delta H_{step\ 1}^\circ + \Delta H_{step\ 2}^\circ + \Delta H_{step\ 3}^\circ + \Delta H_{step\ 4}^\circ) \\
&= -617 \text{ kJ} - [161 \text{ kJ} + 79.5 \text{ kJ} + 520 \text{ kJ} + (-328 \text{ kJ})] \\
&= -1050 \text{ kJ}
\end{aligned}$$

And changing the sign gives,

$$\Delta H_{lattice}^\circ \text{ of LiF} = -(-1050 \text{ kJ}) = 1050 \text{ kJ}$$

Note that *the lattice energy is, by far, the largest component of the multistep process.* (Problems 9.30 and 9.31 are among several that focus on Born-Haber cycles.)

The Born-Haber cycle shows that the energy *required* for elements to form ions is *supplied* by the attraction among the ions in the solid. And the "take-home lesson" is that *ionic solids exist **only** because the lattice energy far exceeds the total energy needed to form the ions.*

Periodic Trends in Lattice Energy

The lattice energy results from electrostatic interactions among ions, so its magnitude depends on ionic size, ionic charge, and ionic arrangement in the solid. Therefore, we expect to see periodic trends in lattice energy.

Explaining the Trends with Coulomb's Law Recall from Chapter 2 that **Coulomb's law** states that the electrostatic energy between particles A and B is directly proportional to the product of their charges and inversely proportional to the distance between them:

$$\text{Electrostatic energy} \propto \frac{\text{charge A} \times \text{charge B}}{\text{distance}}$$

Lattice energy is directly proportional to electrostatic energy. In an ionic solid, cations and anions lie as close to each other as possible, so the distance between them is the sum of the ionic radii (see Figure 8.28, p. 320):

$$\text{Electrostatic energy} \propto \frac{\text{cation charge} \times \text{anion charge}}{\text{cation radius} + \text{anion radius}} \propto \Delta H_{lattice}^\circ \qquad (9.1)$$

This relationship helps us explain the effects of ionic size and charge on trends in lattice energy:

1. *Effect of ionic size.* As we move down a group, ionic radii increase, so the electrostatic energy between cations and anions decreases; thus, lattice energies should decrease as well. Figure 9.8 on the next page shows that, for the alkali-metal halides, lattice energy decreases down the group whether we hold the cation constant (LiF to LiI) or the anion constant (LiF to RbF).

2. *Effect of ionic charge.* Across a period, ionic charge changes. For example, lithium fluoride and magnesium oxide have cations and anions of about equal radii (Li^+ = 76 pm and Mg^{2+} = 72 pm; F^- = 133 pm and O^{2-} = 140 pm). The major difference is between singly charged Li^+ and F^- ions and doubly charged Mg^{2+} and O^{2-} ions. The difference in the lattice energies of the two compounds is striking:

$$\Delta H_{lattice}^\circ \text{ of LiF} = 1050 \text{ kJ/mol} \qquad \text{and} \qquad \Delta H_{lattice}^\circ \text{ of MgO} = 3923 \text{ kJ/mol}$$

This nearly fourfold increase in $\Delta H_{lattice}^\circ$ reflects the fourfold increase in the product of the charges (1 $\times$ 1 vs. 2 $\times$ 2) in the numerator of Equation 9.1.

Why Does MgO Exist? We might ask how ionic solids, like MgO, with its doubly charged ions, could even form. After all, forming 1 mol of Mg^{2+} involves the sum of the first *and* second ionization energies:

$$Mg(g) \longrightarrow Mg^{2+}(g) + 2e^- \qquad \Delta H^\circ = IE_1 + IE_2 = 738 \text{ kJ} + 1450 \text{ kJ} = 2188 \text{ kJ}$$

Figure 9.8 Trends in lattice energy. The lattice energies are shown for compounds formed from a given Group 1A(1) cation *(left side)* and one of the Group 7A(17) anions *(bottom)*. LiF (smallest ions) has the highest lattice energy, and RbI (largest ions) has the lowest.

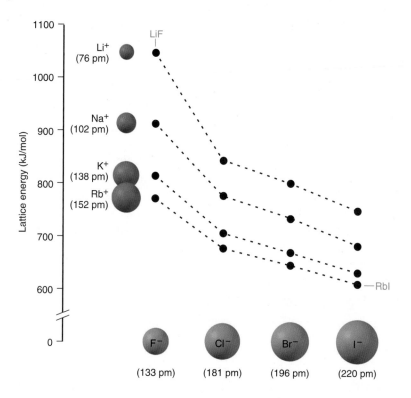

And, while forming 1 mol of O^- ions is exothermic (first electron affinity, EA_1), adding a second mole of electrons (second electron affinity, EA_2) is endothermic because the electron is added to a negative ion. The overall formation of O^{2-} ions is endothermic:

$$
\begin{array}{lll}
O(g) + e^- \longrightarrow O^-(g) & \Delta H^\circ = EA_1 & = -141 \text{ kJ} \\
O^-(g) + e^- \longrightarrow O^{2-}(g) & \Delta H^\circ = EA_2 & = 878 \text{ kJ} \\
\hline
O(g) + 2e^- \longrightarrow O^{2-}(g) & \Delta H^\circ = EA_1 + EA_2 = & 737 \text{ kJ}
\end{array}
$$

There are also the endothermic steps for converting $Mg(s)$ to $Mg(g)$ (148 kJ/mol) and breaking $\frac{1}{2}$ mol of O_2 molecules into O atoms (498 kJ/mol). Nevertheless, the 2+ and 2− ionic charges make the lattice energy so large ($\Delta H^\circ_{\text{lattice}} = 3923$ kJ/mol) that solid MgO forms readily whenever Mg burns in air ($\Delta H^\circ_f = -601$ kJ/mol).

How the Model Explains the Properties of Ionic Compounds

The central role of any model is to explain the facts. With atomic-level views, we can see how the ionic bonding model accounts for the properties of ionic solids:

1. *Physical behavior.* As a typical ionic compound, a piece of rock salt (NaCl) is *hard* (does not dent), *rigid* (does not bend), and *brittle* (cracks without deforming). These properties arise from the strong attractive forces that hold the ions *in specific positions*. Moving them out of position requires overcoming these forces, so rock salt does not dent or bend. If enough force *is* applied, ions of like charge are brought next to each other, and repulsions between them crack the sample suddenly (Figure 9.9).

Figure 9.9 Why ionic compounds crack. **A,** Ionic compounds crack when struck with enough force. **B,** When a force moves like charges near each other, repulsions cause a crack.

A

B

Figure 9.10 Electrical conductance and ion mobility.

2. *Electrical conductivity.* Ionic compounds typically *do not* conduct electricity in the solid state but *do* conduct when melted or dissolved. According to the model, the solid consists of fixed ions, but when it melts or dissolves, the ions can move and carry a current (Figure 9.10).

3. *Thermal conductivity.* Large amounts of energy would be needed to free the ions from their positions and separate them. Thus, we would expect ionic compounds to have high melting points and much higher boiling points (Table 9.1). In fact, the interionic attraction is so strong that the vapor consists of **ion pairs,** gaseous ionic molecules, rather than individual ions (Figure 9.11). In their normal state, as you know, ionic compounds are solid arrays of ions, and *no separate molecules exist.*

Table 9.1 Melting and Boiling Points of Some Ionic Compounds		
Compound	**mp (°C)**	**bp (°C)**
CsBr	636	1300
NaI	661	1304
$MgCl_2$	714	1412
KBr	734	1435
$CaCl_2$	782	>1600
NaCl	801	1413
LiF	845	1676
KF	858	1505
MgO	2852	3600

◼ Summary of Section 9.2

- In ionic bonding, a metal transfers electrons to a nonmetal, and the resulting ions attract each other to form a solid.
- Main-group elements often attain a filled outer level (either eight electrons or two) by forming ions with the electron configuration of the nearest noble gas.
- Ion formation by itself *absorbs* energy, but more than enough energy is *released* when the ions form a solid. The lattice energy, the energy required to separate the solid into gaseous ions, is the reason ionic solids exist.
- The lattice energy is determined by applying Hess's law in a Born-Haber cycle.
- Lattice energies increase with higher ionic charge and decrease with larger ionic radius.
- According to the ionic bonding model, the strong electrostatic attractions that keep ions in position explain why ionic solids are hard, conduct a current only when melted or dissolved, and have high melting and boiling points.
- Ion pairs form when an ionic compound vaporizes.

Figure 9.11 Ion pairs formed when an ionic compound vaporizes.

9.3 • THE COVALENT BONDING MODEL

Look through the *Handbook of Chemistry and Physics,* and you'll find that the number of covalent compounds dwarfs the number of ionic compounds. Molecules held together by covalent bonds range from tiny, diatomic hydrogen to biological and synthetic macromolecules with thousands of atoms. And covalent bonds occur in all polyatomic ions, too. Without doubt, *sharing electrons is the main way that atoms interact.*

The Formation of a Covalent Bond

Why does hydrogen gas consist of H_2 molecules and not separate H atoms? Figure 9.12 plots the potential energy of a system of two isolated H atoms versus the distance between their nuclei (see also Figure 2.14, p. 60). Let's start at the right end of the curve and move along it as the atoms get closer:

- *At point 1,* the atoms are far apart, and each acts as though the other were not present.
- *At point 2,* the distance between the atoms has decreased enough for each nucleus to start attracting the other atom's electron, which lowers the potential energy. As the atoms get closer, these attractions increase, but so do repulsions between the nuclei and between the electrons.
- *At point 3* (bottom of the energy "well"), the maximum attraction is achieved in the face of the increasing repulsion, and the system has its minimum energy.
- *At point 4,* if it were reached, the atoms would be too close, and the rise in potential energy from increasing repulsions would push them apart toward point 3 again.

Thus, a **covalent bond** arises from the balance between the nuclei attracting the electrons and electrons and nuclei repelling each other. (We'll return to Figure 9.12 shortly.)

   *Formation of a covalent bond always results in greater electron density **between** the nuclei.* Figure 9.13 depicts this fact with a cross section of a space-filling model (A), an *electron density contour map* (B), and an *electron density relief map* (C).

Figure 9.12 Covalent bond formation in H_2. The energy difference between points 1 and 3 is the H_2 *bond energy* (432 kJ/mol): it is released when the bond forms and absorbed to break the bond. The internuclear distance at point 3 is the H_2 *bond length* (74 pm).

Internuclear distance (pm)

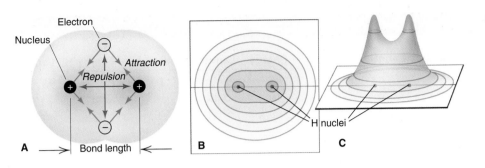

Figure 9.13 Distribution of electron density in H_2. **A,** At some distance (bond length), attractions balance repulsions. Electron density *(blue shading)* is high around and between the nuclei. **B,** Electron density doubles with each concentric curve. **C,** The highest regions of electron density are shown as peaks.

Bonding Pairs and Lone Pairs

To achieve a full outer (valence) level of electrons, *each atom in a covalent bond "counts" the shared electrons as belonging entirely to itself.* Thus, the two shared electrons in H_2 simultaneously fill the outer level of *both* H atoms, as clarified by the blue circles added below (which are *not* part of the Lewis structures). The **shared pair,** or **bonding pair,** is represented by a pair of dots or a line:

$$\text{bonding pair} \quad \text{H:H} \quad \text{or} \quad \text{H—H}$$

An outer-level electron pair that is *not* involved in bonding is called a **lone pair,** or **unshared pair.** The bonding pair in HF fills the outer level of the H atom *and,* together with three lone pairs, fills the outer level of the F atom as well:

$$\text{bonding pair} \quad \text{H:F:} \quad \text{lone pairs} \quad \text{or} \quad \text{H—F:}$$

In F_2 the bonding pair and three lone pairs fill the outer level of *each* F atom:

$$\text{:F:F:} \quad \text{or} \quad \text{:F—F:}$$

(This text generally shows bonding pairs as lines and lone pairs as dots.)

Properties of a Covalent Bond: Order, Energy, and Length

A covalent bond has three important properties that are closely related to one another and to the compound's reactivity—bond order, bond energy, and bond length.

1. *Bond order.* The **bond order** is the number of electron pairs being shared by a given pair of atoms:
- A **single bond,** as shown above in H_2, HF, or F_2, is the most common bond and consists of one bonding pair of electrons. Thus, a *single bond has a bond order of 1.*
- Many molecules (and ions) contain *multiple bonds,* in which more than one pair is shared between two atoms. Multiple bonds usually involve C, O, and/or N atoms. A **double bond** consists of two bonding electron pairs, four electrons shared between two atoms, so *the bond order is 2.* Ethylene (C_2H_4) contains a carbon-carbon double bond and four carbon-hydrogen single bonds:

$$\begin{array}{c} \text{H} \quad \text{H} \\ \text{C::C} \\ \text{H} \quad \text{H} \end{array} \quad \text{or} \quad \begin{array}{c} \text{H} \qquad \text{H} \\ \diagdown \qquad \diagup \\ \text{C}=\text{C} \\ \diagup \qquad \diagdown \\ \text{H} \qquad \text{H} \end{array}$$

Each carbon "counts" the four electrons in the double bond and the four in its two single bonds to hydrogens to attain an octet.
- A **triple bond** consists of three shared pairs: two atoms share six electrons, so *the bond order is 3.* The N_2 molecule has a triple bond, and each N atom also has a lone pair. Six shared and two unshared electrons give *each* N atom an octet:

$$\text{:N:::N:} \quad \text{or} \quad \text{:N}\equiv\text{N:}$$

2. *Bond energy.* The strength of a covalent bond depends on the magnitude of the attraction between the nuclei and shared electrons. The **bond energy (BE)** (also called *bond enthalpy* or *bond strength*) is the energy needed to overcome this attraction and is defined as the standard enthalpy change for breaking the bond in 1 mol

Table 9.2 Average Bond Energies (kJ/mol) and Bond Lengths (pm)

Bond	Energy	Length	Bond	Energy	Length	Bond	Energy	Length	Bond	Energy	Length
Single Bonds											
H—H	432	74	N—H	391	101	Si—H	323	148	S—H	347	134
H—F	565	92	N—N	160	146	Si—Si	226	234	S—S	266	204
H—Cl	427	127	N—P	209	177	Si—O	368	161	S—F	327	158
H—Br	363	141	N—O	201	144	Si—S	226	210	S—Cl	271	201
H—I	295	161	N—F	272	139	Si—F	565	156	S—Br	218	225
			N—Cl	200	191	Si—Cl	381	204	S—I	~170	234
C—H	413	109	N—Br	243	214	Si—Br	310	216			
C—C	347	154	N—I	159	222	Si—I	234	240	F—F	159	143
C—Si	301	186							F—Cl	193	166
C—N	305	147	O—H	467	96	P—H	320	142	F—Br	212	178
C—O	358	143	O—P	351	160	P—Si	213	227	F—I	263	187
C—P	264	187	O—O	204	148	P—P	200	221	Cl—Cl	243	199
C—S	259	181	O—S	265	151	P—F	490	156	Cl—Br	215	214
C—F	453	133	O—F	190	142	P—Cl	331	204	Cl—I	208	243
C—Cl	339	177	O—Cl	203	164	P—Br	272	222	Br—Br	193	228
C—Br	276	194	O—Br	234	172	P—I	184	246	Br—I	175	248
C—I	216	213	O—I	234	194				I—I	151	266
Multiple Bonds											
C=C	614	134	N=N	418	122	C≡C	839	121	N≡N	945	110
C=N	615	127	N=O	607	120	C≡N	891	115	N≡O	631	106
C=O	745	123	O_2	498	121	C≡O	1070	113			
	(799 in CO_2)										

Internuclear distance (bond length) — Covalent radius

143 pm — 72 pm — F_2

199 pm — 100 pm — Cl_2

228 pm — 114 pm — Br_2

266 pm — 133 pm — I_2

Figure 9.14 Bond length and covalent radius.

of gaseous molecules. Bond breakage is an *endothermic* process, so *bond energy is always positive:*

$$A—B(g) \longrightarrow A(g) + B(g) \qquad \Delta H^{\circ}_{\text{bond breaking}} = BE_{A—B} \text{ (always} > 0)$$

The bond energy is the difference in energy between separated and bonded atoms (the potential energy difference between points 1 and 3, the energy "well" in Figure 9.12). *The same quantity of energy absorbed to break the bond is released when the bond forms.* Bond formation is an *exothermic* process, so *the sign of its enthalpy change is always negative:*

$$A(g) + B(g) \longrightarrow A—B(g) \qquad \Delta H^{\circ}_{\text{bond forming}} = -BE_{A—B} \text{ (always} < 0)$$

Table 9.2 lists the energies of some common bonds. By definition,

- *Stronger bonds are lower in energy (have a deeper energy well).*
- *Weaker bonds are higher in energy (have a shallower energy well).*

The energy of a given bond varies slightly from molecule to molecule and even within the same molecule, so each value is an *average* bond energy.

3. *Bond length.* A covalent bond has a **bond length,** the distance between the nuclei of two bonded atoms. In Figure 9.12, bond length is the distance between the nuclei at the point of minimum energy (bottom of the well), and Table 9.2 shows the lengths of some covalent bonds. Like bond energies, these values are *average* bond lengths for a bond in different substances. Bond length is related to the sum of the radii of the bonded atoms. In fact, most atomic radii are calculated from measured bond lengths (see Figure 8.14C, p. 310). Bond lengths for a series of similar bonds, as in the halogens, increase with atomic size (Figure 9.14).

The order, energy, and length of a covalent bond are interrelated. Two nuclei are more strongly attracted to two shared pairs than to one, so double-bonded atoms are drawn closer together *and* are more difficult to pull apart than single-bonded atoms: *for a given pair of atoms, a higher bond order results in a shorter bond length and*

Table 9.3 The Relation of Bond Order, Bond Length, and Bond Energy

Bond	Bond Order	Average Bond Length (pm)	Average Bond Energy (kJ/mol)
C—O	1	143	358
C=O	2	123	745
C≡O	3	113	1070
C—C	1	154	347
C=C	2	134	614
C≡C	3	121	839
N—N	1	146	160
N=N	2	122	418
N≡N	3	110	945

a higher bond energy. Thus, as Table 9.3 shows, for a given pair of atoms, *a shorter bond is a stronger bond.*

In some cases, we can see a relation among atomic size, bond length, and bond energy by varying one of the atoms in a single bond while holding the other constant:

- *Variation within a group.* The trend in carbon-halogen single bond lengths, C—I > C—Br > C—Cl, parallels the trend in atomic size, I > Br > Cl, and is opposite to the trend in bond energy, C—Cl > C—Br > C—I.
- *Variation within a period.* Looking again at single bonds involving carbon, the trend in bond lengths, C—N > C—O > C—F, is opposite to the trend in bond energy, C—F > C—O > C—N.

Sample Problem 9.2   Comparing Bond Length and Bond Strength

Problem Without referring to Table 9.2, rank the bonds in each set in order of *decreasing* bond length and *decreasing* bond strength:
(a) S—F, S—Br, S—Cl   (b) C=O, C—O, C≡O

Plan (a) S is singly bonded to three different halogen atoms, so the bond order is the same. Bond length increases and bond strength decreases as the halogen's atomic radius increases. (b) The same two atoms are bonded, but the bond orders differ. In this case, bond strength increases and bond length decreases as bond order increases.

Solution (a) Atomic size increases down a group, so F < Cl < Br.

Bond length: S—Br > S—Cl > S—F

Bond strength: S—F > S—Cl > S—Br

(b) By ranking the bond orders, C≡O > C=O > C—O, we obtain

Bond length: C—O > C=O > C≡O

Bond strength: C≡O > C=O > C—O

Check From Table 9.2, we see that the rankings are correct.

Comment Remember that for bonds involving pairs of different atoms, as in part (a), *the relationship between length and strength holds* only *for single bonds* and not in every case, so apply it carefully.

Follow-Up Problem 9.2 Rank the bonds in each set in order of *increasing* bond length and *increasing* bond strength: (a) Si—F, Si—C, Si—O; (b) N=N, N—N, N≡N.

How the Model Explains the Properties of Covalent Substances

The covalent bonding model proposes that electron sharing between pairs of atoms leads to *strong, localized bonds.* Most, but not all, covalent substances consist of individual molecules. These *molecular* covalent substances have very different *physical* properties than *network* covalent solids because different types of forces give rise to them.

Figure 9.15 Strong forces within molecules and weak forces between them.

Strong covalent bonds *within* molecules do not break.

Gaseous phase

Liquid phase

Weak forces *between* molecules are overcome.

1. *Physical properties of molecular covalent substances.* At first glance, the model seems inconsistent with physical properties of covalent substances. Most are gases (such as methane and ammonia), liquids (such as benzene and water), or low-melting solids (such as sulfur and paraffin wax). If covalent bonds are so strong (~200 to 500 kJ/mol), why do covalent substances melt and boil at such low temperatures?

To answer this, we'll focus on two different forces: (1) *strong bonding forces* hold the atoms together within the molecule, and (2) *weak intermolecular forces* act between separate molecules in the sample. It is the weak forces *between* molecules that account for the physical properties of *molecular* covalent substances. For example, look what happens when pentane (C_5H_{12}) boils (Figure 9.15): weak forces *between* pentane molecules are overcome, not the strong C—C and C—H bonds *within* each pentane molecule.

2. *Physical properties of network covalent solids.* Some covalent substances do not consist of separate molecules. Rather, these *network covalent solids* are held together by covalent bonds *between atoms throughout the sample,* and their properties *do* reflect the strength of covalent bonds. Two examples are quartz and diamond (Figure 9.16). Quartz (SiO_2; *top*) has silicon-oxygen covalent bonds in three dimensions; no separate SiO_2 molecules exist. It is very hard and melts at 1550°C. Diamond (*bottom*) has covalent bonds connecting each carbon atom to four others. It is the hardest natural substance known and melts at around 3550°C. Thus, covalent bonds *are* strong, but most covalent substances consist of separate molecules with weak forces between them. (We discuss intermolecular forces in detail in Chapter 12.)

3. *Electrical conductivity.* An electric current is carried by either mobile electrons or mobile ions. Most covalent substances are poor electrical conductors, whether melted or dissolved, because their electrons are localized as either shared or unshared pairs, and no ions are present. The Tools of the Laboratory essay describes a tool used widely for studying the types of bonds in covalent substances.

Quartz   Silicon   Oxygen

Diamond   Carbon

Figure 9.16 Covalent bonds of network covalent solids: quartz and diamond.

Summary of Section 9.3

- A shared, localized pair of valence electrons holds the nuclei of two atoms together in a covalent bond, filling each atom's outer level.
- Bond order is the number of shared pairs between two atoms. Bond energy is the energy absorbed to separate the atoms; the same quantity of energy is released when the bond forms. Bond length is the distance between their nuclei.
- For a given pair of atoms, bond order is directly related to bond energy and inversely related to bond length.
- Molecular covalent substances are soft and low melting because of the weak forces *between* the molecules, not the strong bonding forces *within* them. Network covalent solids are hard and high melting because covalent bonds join all the atoms in the sample.
- Most covalent substances have low electrical conductivity because their electrons are localized and ions are absent.
- Atoms in a covalent bond vibrate, and the energies of these vibrations are studied with IR spectroscopy.

Infrared **(IR) spectroscopy** is an instrumental technique most often used to study covalently bonded molecules. The key components of an IR spectrometer are the same as those of other types of spectrometers (see Figure B7.3, p. 273). The source emits radiation of many wavelengths, but only those in the IR region are selected. The sample is typically a pure liquid or solid that absorbs varying amounts of certain IR wavelengths. An IR spectrum consists of peaks that indicate these various absorptions.

Molecular Vibrations and IR Absorption

An IR spectrum indicates the types of bonds in a molecule based on their vibrations. All molecules undergo movement through space, rotation around several axes, and vibrations of bonds. Consider a sample of ethane gas. The H_3C—CH_3 molecules zoom throughout the container, but let's disregard motion through space and focus on other motions. The whole molecule rotates and its two CH_3 groups rotate about the C—C bond. More important to IR spectroscopy, each pair of atoms is vibrating as though the bonds were springs. Figure B9.1 depicts the vibrations of diatomic and triatomic molecules; larger molecules vibrate in many more ways.

The energies of IR photons are in the range of these vibrational energies. *Each vibration has a frequency based on the type of motion, masses of the atoms, and strength of the bond.* The frequencies correspond to IR wavelengths between 2.5 and 25 μm. *The energy of these vibrations is quantized.* Just as an atom can absorb a photon whose energy equals the difference between *electron* energy levels, a molecule can absorb an IR photon whose energy equals the difference between *vibrational* energy levels.

IR Radiation and Global Warming

Carbon dioxide, O=C=O, is a linear molecule that bends and stretches symmetrically and asymmetrically when it absorbs IR radiation (Problem B9.2). Sunlight is absorbed by Earth's surface and re-emitted as heat, much of which is IR radiation. Atmospheric CO_2 absorbs this radiation and re-emits it, thus warming the atmosphere (see Chemical Connections, pp. 249–251).

Compound Identification

An IR spectrum can be used to identify a compound for three related reasons:

1. *Each kind of bond absorbs a specific range of wavelengths.* That is, a C—C bond absorbs a different range than does a C=C bond, a C—H bond, a C=O bond, and so forth.
2. *Different types of organic compounds have characteristic spectra.* The different groupings of atoms that define an alcohol, a carboxylic acid, an ether, and so forth (see Chapter 15) absorb differently.
3. *Each compound has a unique spectrum.* The IR spectrum acts like a fingerprint to identify the compound, because the quantity of each wavelength absorbed depends on the detailed molecular structure. For example, no other compound has the IR spectrum of acrylonitrile, a compound used to make plastics (Figure B9.2, *next page*).

DIATOMIC MOLECULE

Stretch

LINEAR TRIATOMIC MOLECULE

Stretch symmetrical

Stretch asymmetrical

Bend

NONLINEAR TRIATOMIC MOLECULE

Stretch symmetrical

Stretch asymmetrical

Bend

Figure B9.1 Vibrational motions in general diatomic and triatomic molecules.

(continued)

Figure B9.2 The infrared (IR) spectrum of acrylonitrile. In this typical IR spectrum, many absorption bands (peaks) of differing depths and sharpness appear. Most correspond to a particular type of vibration (stretch, bend, rock, wag, or twist). Some broad peaks (e.g., "combination band") represent several overlapping vibrations. The bottom axis is given as wavenumber, the inverse of wavelength, and has units of cm^{-1}. (The scale expands to the right of 2000 cm^{-1}.)

Recall from Chapter 3 that constitutional (structural) isomers have the same molecular formula but different structures. We should see very different IR spectra for the isomers diethyl ether and 2-butanol because their molecular structures are so dissimilar (Figure B9.3). But, even the very similar 1,3-dimethylbenzene and 1,4-dimethylbenzene have different spectra (Figure B9.4).

Problems

B9.1 In Figure B9.2, the peak labeled "C≡C stretch" occurs at a shorter wavelength (higher wavenumber) than that labeled "C—C stretch," as it does in the IR spectrum of any sub-

stance with those bonds. Explain the relative positions of these peaks. In what relative position along the wavelength scale of Figure B9.2 would you expect to find a peak for a C≡C stretch? Explain.

B9.2 The vibrations of a CO_2 molecule are symmetrical stretch, bend, and asymmetrical stretch (Figure B9.1), with frequencies of 4.02×10^{13} s^{-1}, 2.00×10^{13} s^{-1}, and 7.05×10^{13} s^{-1}, respectively.
(a) What wavelengths correspond to these vibrations?
(b) Calculate the energy (in J) of each vibration. Which uses the least energy?

Figure B9.3 The infrared spectra of 2-butanol (*green*) and diethyl ether (*red*).

Figure B9.4 The infrared spectra of 1,3-dimethylbenzene (*green*) and 1,4-dimethylbenzene (*red*).

9.4 • BOND ENERGY AND CHEMICAL CHANGE

The relative strengths of the bonds in reactants and products determine whether heat is released or absorbed in a chemical reaction. In Chapter 20, you'll see that the change in bond energy is one of two factors determining whether the reaction occurs at all. In this section, we'll discuss the origin of the enthalpy of reaction (ΔH_{rxn}), use bond energies to calculate it, and look at the energy available from fuels and foods.

Changes in Bond Energy: Where Does ΔH°_{rxn} Come From?

In Chapter 6, we discussed the heat involved in a chemical change but never asked a central question: where does the enthalpy of reaction (ΔH°_{rxn}) come from? For example, when 1 mol of H_2 and 1 mol of F_2 react to form 2 mol of HF at 1 atm and 298 K,

$$H_2(g) + F_2(g) \longrightarrow 2HF(g) + 546 \text{ kJ}$$

where does the 546 kJ come from? We find the answer by looking closely at the energies of the molecules involved. A system's total internal energy is composed of its kinetic energy and potential energy. Let's see how these change during the formation of HF:

• *Kinetic energy.* The most important contributions to the kinetic energy are the molecules' movements in space, rotations, and vibrations. However, since kinetic energy is proportional to temperature, which is constant at 298 K, it doesn't change during the reaction.
• *Potential energy.* The most important contributions to the potential energy are phase changes and changes in the attraction between vibrating atoms, between nucleus and electrons (and between electrons) in each atom, between protons and neutrons in each nucleus, and between nuclei and the shared electron pair in each bond. Of these, there are no phase changes, vibrational forces vary only slightly as the bonded atoms change, and forces within the atoms and nuclei don't change at all. The only significant change in potential energy comes from changes in the attraction between the nuclei and the shared electron pair—the bond energy.

Thus, our answer to "where does ΔH°_{rxn} come from?" is that it doesn't really "come from" anywhere: *the heat released or absorbed during a chemical change is due to differences between reactant bond energies and product bond energies.*

Using Bond Energies to Calculate ΔH°_{rxn}

Hess's law allows us to think of any reaction as a two-step process, whether or not it actually occurs that way:

1. *A quantity of heat is absorbed ($\Delta H^{\circ} > 0$) to break the reactant bonds and form separate atoms.*
2. *A different quantity of heat is then released ($\Delta H^{\circ} < 0$) when the atoms form product bonds.*

The sum (symbolized by Σ) of these enthalpy changes is the enthalpy of reaction, ΔH°_{rxn}:

$$\Delta H^{\circ}_{rxn} = \Sigma \Delta H^{\circ}_{\text{reactant bonds broken}} + \Sigma \Delta H^{\circ}_{\text{product bonds formed}} \qquad (9.2)$$

• In an exothermic reaction, the magnitude of $\Delta H^{\circ}_{\text{product bonds formed}}$ is *greater* than that of $\Delta H^{\circ}_{\text{reactant bonds broken}}$, so the sum, ΔH°_{rxn}, is *negative* (heat is released).
• In an endothermic reaction, the opposite situation is true, the magnitude of $\Delta H^{\circ}_{\text{product bonds formed}}$ is *smaller* than that of $\Delta H^{\circ}_{\text{reactant bonds broken}}$, so ΔH°_{rxn} is *positive* (heat is absorbed).

An equivalent form of Equation 9.2 uses bond energies:

$$\Delta H^{\circ}_{rxn} = \Sigma BE_{\text{reactant bonds broken}} - \Sigma BE_{\text{product bonds formed}}$$

(We need the minus sign because all bond energies are positive.)

Typically, only certain bonds break and form during a reaction, but with Hess' law, the following is a simpler method of calculating ΔH°_{rxn}:

1. Break **all** the reactant bonds to obtain individual atoms.
2. Use the atoms to form **all** the product bonds.
3. Add the bond energies, with appropriate signs, to obtain the enthalpy of reaction.

(This method assumes reactants and products do not change physical state; additional heat is involved when phase changes occur. We address this topic in Chapter 12.)

Let's use the method to calculate ΔH°_{rxn} for two reactions:

1. *Formation of HF.* When 1 mol of H—H bonds and 1 mol of F—F bonds absorb energy and break, the 2 mol of H atoms and 2 mol of F atoms form 2 mol of H—F bonds, which releases energy (Figure 9.17). We find the bond energy values in Table 9.2 (p. 340) and use a positive sign for bonds broken and a negative sign for bonds formed:

Bonds broken:

$$1 \times \text{H—H} = (1 \text{ mol})(432 \text{ kJ/mol}) = 432 \text{ kJ}$$
$$\underline{1 \times \text{F—F} = (1 \text{ mol})(159 \text{ kJ/mol}) = 159 \text{ kJ}}$$
$$\Sigma \Delta H^{\circ}_{\text{reactant bonds broken}} = 591 \text{ kJ}$$

Bonds formed:

$$2 \times \text{H—F} = (2 \text{ mol})(-565 \text{ kJ/mol}) = \Sigma \Delta H^{\circ}_{\text{product bonds formed}} = -1130 \text{ kJ}$$

Applying Equation 9.2 gives

$$\Delta H^{\circ}_{rxn} = \Sigma \Delta H^{\circ}_{\text{reactant bonds broken}} + \Sigma \Delta H^{\circ}_{\text{product bonds formed}}$$
$$= 591 \text{ kJ} + (-1130 \text{ kJ}) = -539 \text{ kJ}$$

The small discrepancy between this bond energy value (-539 kJ) and the value from tabulated ΔH° values (-546 kJ) is due to variations in experimental method.

2. *Combustion of CH_4.* In this more complicated reaction, all the bonds in CH_4 and O_2 break, and the atoms form all the bonds in CO_2 and H_2O (Figure 9.18). Once again, we use Table 9.2 and appropriate signs for bonds broken and bonds formed:

Bonds broken:

$$4 \times \text{C—H} = (4 \text{ mol})(413 \text{ kJ/mol}) = 1652 \text{ kJ}$$
$$\underline{2 \times \text{O}_2 = (2 \text{ mol})(498 \text{ kJ/mol}) = 996 \text{ kJ}}$$
$$\Sigma \Delta H^{\circ}_{\text{reactant bonds broken}} = 2648 \text{ kJ}$$

Bonds formed:

$$2 \times \text{C}=\text{O} = (2 \text{ mol})(-799 \text{ kJ/mol}) = -1598 \text{ kJ}$$
$$\underline{4 \times \text{O—H} = (4 \text{ mol})(-467 \text{ kJ/mol}) = -1868 \text{ kJ}}$$
$$\Sigma \Delta H^{\circ}_{\text{product bonds formed}} = -3466 \text{ kJ}$$

Applying Equation 9.2 gives

$$\Delta H^{\circ}_{rxn} = \Sigma \Delta H^{\circ}_{\text{reactant bonds broken}} + \Sigma \Delta H^{\circ}_{\text{product bonds formed}}$$
$$= 2648 \text{ kJ} + (-3466 \text{ kJ}) = -818 \text{ kJ}$$

Figure 9.17 Using bond energies to calculate ΔH°_{rxn} for HF formation.

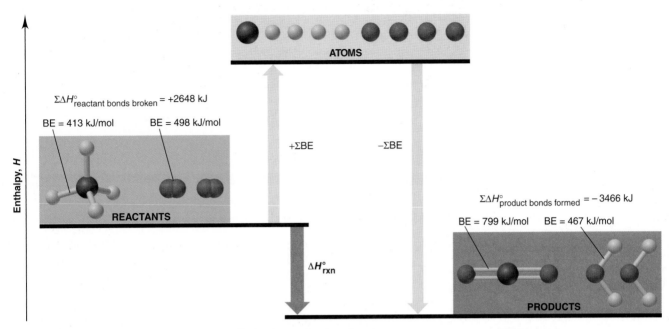

Figure 9.18 Using bond energies to calculate ΔH°_{rxn} for the combustion of methane.

In addition to variations in experimental method, there is a more basic reason for the discrepancy between the ΔH°_{rxn} obtained from bond energies (-818 kJ) and the value obtained by calorimetry (-802 kJ; Section 6.3). A bond energy is an *average* value for a given bond over many compounds. The value *in a particular substance* is usually close, but not equal, to the average. For example, the C—H bond energy of 413 kJ/mol is the average for C—H bonds in many molecules. In fact, 415 kJ is actually required to break 1 mol of C—H bonds in methane, or 1660 kJ for 4 mol of these bonds, which gives a ΔH°_{rxn} closer to the calorimetric value. Thus, it isn't surprising to find small discrepancies between ΔH°_{rxn} values obtained in different ways.

Sample Problem 9.3 Using Bond Energies to Calculate ΔH°_{rxn}

Problem Calculate ΔH°_{rxn} for the chlorination of methane to form chloroform:

$$H-\underset{\underset{H}{|}}{\overset{\overset{H}{|}}{C}}-H \ + \ 3\,Cl-Cl \ \longrightarrow \ Cl-\underset{\underset{Cl}{|}}{\overset{\overset{H}{|}}{C}}-Cl \ + \ 3\,H-Cl$$

Plan *All* the reactant bonds break, and *all* the product bonds form. We find the bond energies in Table 9.2 and substitute the two sums, with correct signs, into Equation 9.2.

Solution Finding the standard enthalpy changes for bonds broken and for bonds formed: For bonds broken, the bond energy values are

$$
\begin{aligned}
4 \times C-H &= (4\ mol)(413\ kJ/mol) = 1652\ kJ \\
3 \times Cl-Cl &= (3\ mol)(243\ kJ/mol) = 729\ kJ \\
\hline
\Sigma \Delta H^{\circ}_{bonds\ broken} &= 2381\ kJ
\end{aligned}
$$

For bonds formed, the values are

$$
\begin{aligned}
3 \times C-Cl &= (3\ mol)(-339\ kJ/mol) = -1017\ kJ \\
1 \times C-H &= (1\ mol)(-413\ kJ/mol) = -413\ kJ \\
3 \times H-Cl &= (3\ mol)(-427\ kJ/mol) = -1281\ kJ \\
\hline
\Sigma \Delta H^{\circ}_{bonds\ formed} &= -2711\ kJ
\end{aligned}
$$

Calculating ΔH°_{rxn}:

$$
\begin{aligned}
\Delta H^{\circ}_{rxn} &= \Sigma \Delta H^{\circ}_{bonds\ broken} + \Sigma \Delta H^{\circ}_{bonds\ formed} \\
&= 2381\ kJ + (-2711\ kJ) \\
&= \boxed{-330\ kJ}
\end{aligned}
$$

Check The signs of the enthalpy changes are correct: $\Sigma \Delta H^\circ_{\text{bonds broken}} > 0$, and $\Sigma \Delta H^\circ_{\text{bonds formed}} < 0$. More energy is released than absorbed, so $\Delta H^\circ_{\text{rxn}}$ is negative:

$$\sim 2400 \text{ kJ} + [\sim (-2700 \text{ kJ})] = -300 \text{ kJ}$$

Follow-Up Problem 9.3 One of the most important industrial reactions is the formation of ammonia from its elements:

$$N\equiv N \ + \ 3\ H{-}H \longrightarrow 2\ H{-}\overset{\displaystyle H}{\underset{\displaystyle |}{N}}{-}H$$

Use bond energies to calculate $\Delta H^\circ_{\text{rxn}}$.

Bond Strengths and the Heat Released from Fuels and Foods

A *fuel* is a material that reacts with atmospheric oxygen to release energy *and* is available at a reasonable cost. The most common fuels for machines are hydrocarbons and coal, and the most common ones for organisms are fats and carbohydrates. All of these fuels are composed of large organic molecules with many C—C and C—H bonds and fewer C—O and O—H bonds. According to our two-step approach, when the fuel reacts with O_2, all of the bonds break, and the C, H, and O atoms form C=O and O—H bonds in the products (CO_2 and H_2O). Because their combustion is exothermic, the total of the bond energies in the products is *greater* than the total in the reactants. *Weaker bonds (less stable, more reactive) are easier to break than stronger bonds (more stable, less reactive) because they are already higher in energy.* Therefore, the bonds in CO_2 and H_2O are stronger (lower energy, more stable) than those in gasoline (or cooking oil) and O_2 (weaker, higher energy, less stable).

Fuels with more weak bonds yield more energy than fuels with fewer weak bonds. When a hydrocarbon burns, C—C and C—H bonds break; when an alcohol burns, C—O and O—H bonds break as well. Table 9.2 (p. 340) shows that the sum for C—C and C—H bonds (760 kJ/mol) is less than the sum for C—O and O—H bonds (825 kJ/mol). Therefore, it takes more energy to break the bonds of a fuel with a lot of C—O and O—H bonds. Thus, in general, *a fuel with fewer bonds to O releases more energy* (Figure 9.19).

Both fats and carbohydrates serve as high-energy foods and consist of chains or rings of C atoms attached to H atoms, with some C—O, C=O, and O—H bonds *(shown in red below):*

Figure 9.19 Relative bond strength and energy from fuels.

Triolein, a fat

Sucrose, a carbohydrate

Carbohydrates have fewer chains of C atoms and bonds to H and more bonds to O. Fats "contain more Calories" per gram than carbohydrates because fats have fewer bonds to O (Table 9.4).

Table 9.4 Enthalpies of Reaction for Combustion of Some Foods	
Substance	ΔH_{rxn} **(kJ/g)**
Fats	
Vegetable oil	−37.0
Margarine	−30.1
Butter	−30.0
Carbohydrates	
Table sugar (sucrose)	−16.2
Brown rice	−14.9
Maple syrup	−10.4

Summary of Section 9.4

- The only component of internal energy that changes significantly during a reaction is the bond energies of reactants and products, and this change appears as the enthalpy of reaction, $\Delta H^\circ_{\text{rxn}}$.
- A reaction involves breaking reactant bonds and forming product bonds. Applying Hess's law, we use tabulated bond energies to calculate $\Delta H^\circ_{\text{rxn}}$.
- Bonds in fuels are weaker (less stable, higher energy) than bonds in the combustion products. Fuels with more weak bonds release more energy than fuels with fewer.

9.5 • BETWEEN THE EXTREMES: ELECTRONEGATIVITY AND BOND POLARITY

Scientific models are idealized descriptions of reality. The ionic and covalent bonding models portray compounds as formed by *either* complete electron transfer *or* complete electron sharing. But, in real substances, most atoms are joined by *polar covalent bonds*—partly ionic and partly covalent (Figure 9.20). In this section, we explore the "in-between" nature of these bonds and its importance in the properties of substances.

Electronegativity

Electronegativity (EN) is the relative ability of a bonded atom to attract shared electrons.* We might expect the H—F bond energy to be the average of an H—H bond (432 kJ/mol) and an F—F bond (159 kJ/mol), or 296 kJ/mol. But, the actual HF bond energy is 565 kJ/mol, or 269 kJ/mol *higher!* To explain this difference, the American chemist Linus Pauling reasoned this way: If F attracted the shared electron pair more strongly than H, that is, if F were more *electronegative* than H, the electrons would spend more time closer to F, and this unequal sharing would make the F end of the bond partially negative and the H end partially positive. The electrostatic attraction between these partial charged bond "poles" would *increase* the energy required to break the bond. From studies with many other compounds, Pauling derived a scale of *relative EN values* based on fluorine having the highest EN value, 4.0 (Figure 9.21).

*Electronegativity refers to a *bonded* atom attracting a shared pair; electron affinity refers to a gaseous atom gaining an electron to form an anion. Elements with a high EN also have a highly negative EA.

Figure 9.20 Bonding between the models. Pure ionic bonding (*top*) and pure covalent bonding (*bottom*) are far less common than polar covalent bonding (*middle*).

Figure 9.21 The Pauling electronegativity (EN) scale. The height of each post is proportional to the EN, which is shown on top. The key has several EN cutoffs. In the main groups, EN *increases* across and *decreases* down. The transition and inner transition elements show little change in EN. Here hydrogen is placed near elements with similar EN values.

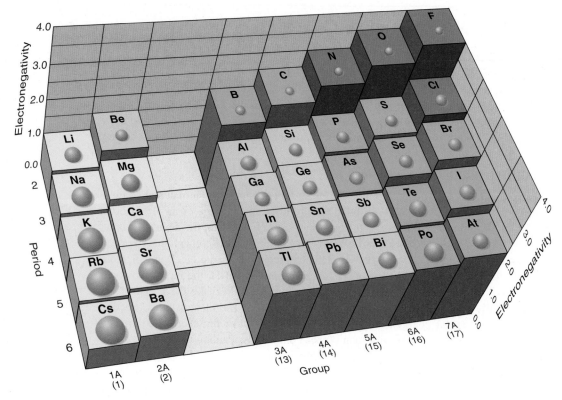

Figure 9.22 Electronegativity and atomic size.

Trends in Electronegativity In general, *electronegativity is inversely related to atomic size* because the nucleus of a smaller atom is closer to the shared pair than the nucleus of a larger atom, so it attracts the electrons more strongly (Figure 9.22):

- *Down a main group,* electronegativity (height of post) decreases as size (hemisphere on top of post) increases.
- *Across a period of main-group elements,* electronegativity increases.
- Nonmetals are *more* electronegative than metals.

The most electronegative element is fluorine, with oxygen a close second. Thus, except when it bonds with fluorine, oxygen always pulls bonding electrons toward itself. The least electronegative element (also referred to as the most *electropositive*) is francium, in the lower left corner of the periodic table, but it is radioactive and extremely rare, so for all practical purposes, cesium is the most electropositive.*

Electronegativity and Oxidation Number An important use of electronegativity is in determining an atom's oxidation number (O.N.; see Section 4.5):

1. The more electronegative atom in a bond is assigned *all* the *shared* electrons; the less electronegative atom is assigned *none.*
2. Each atom in a bond is assigned *all* of its *unshared* electrons.
3. The oxidation number is given by

$$\text{O.N.} = \text{no. of valence } e^- - (\text{no. of shared } e^- + \text{no. of unshared } e^-)$$

In HCl, for example, Cl is more electronegative than H. Cl has 7 valence electrons and is assigned 8 (2 shared + 6 unshared), so its O.N. is $7 - 8 = -1$. The H atom has 1 valence electron and is assigned none, so its O.N. is $1 - 0 = +1$.

---

*In 1934, the American physicist Robert S. Mulliken developed electronegativity values based on atomic properties: $\text{EN} = (\text{IE} - \text{EA})/2$. By this approach as well, fluorine, with a high ionization energy (IE) and a large negative electron affinity (EA), has a high EN; and cesium, with a low IE and a small EA, has a low EN.

Figure 9.23 Electron density distributions in H₂, F₂, and HF. In HF, the electron density shifts from H to F. (The electron density peak for F has been cut off to limit the figure height.)

Bond Polarity and Partial Ionic Character

Whenever atoms of different electronegativities form a bond, such as H (2.1) and F (4.0) in HF, the bonding pair is shared *unequally*. This unequal distribution of electron density results in a **polar covalent bond.** It is depicted by a polar arrow (⟶) pointing toward the partially negative pole or by δ+ and δ− symbols (see Figure 4.1):

$$\overset{\longmapsto}{H-\ddot{\underset{..}{F}}:} \quad \text{or} \quad \overset{\delta+ \quad \delta-}{H-\ddot{\underset{..}{F}}:}$$

In the H—H and F—F bonds, where the atoms are identical, the bonding pair is shared *equally,* and a **nonpolar covalent bond** results. In Figure 9.23, relief maps show the distribution of electron density in H₂, F₂, and HF.

The Importance of Electronegativity Difference (ΔEN)

The **electronegativity difference (ΔEN),** the difference between the EN values of the bonded atoms, is directly related to a bond's polarity. It ranges from 0.0 in a diatomic element, such as H₂, O₂, or Cl₂, all the way up to 3.3, the difference between the most electronegative atom, F (4.0), and the most electropositive, Cs (0.7), in the ionic compound CsF.

Another parameter closely related to ΔEN is the **partial ionic character** of a bond: *a greater ΔEN results in larger partial charges and higher partial ionic character.* Consider three Cl-containing gaseous molecules: ΔEN for LiCl(*g*) is 3.0 − 1.0 = 2.0; for HCl(*g*), it is 3.0 − 2.1 = 0.9; and for Cl₂(*g*), it is 3.0 − 3.0 = 0.0. Thus, the bond in LiCl has more ionic character than the one in HCl, which has more than the one in Cl₂.

Here are two approaches that quantify ionic character. Both use arbitrary cutoffs, which is not really consistent with the actual gradation in bonding:

1. *ΔEN range.* This approach divides bonds into mostly ionic, polar covalent, mostly covalent, and nonpolar covalent based on a range of ΔEN values (Figure 9.24).

2. *Percent ionic character.* This approach is based on the behavior of a diatomic molecule in an electric field. A plot of *percent ionic character* vs. ΔEN for several gaseous molecules shows that, as expected, *percent ionic character generally increases with ΔEN* (Figure 9.25A). A value of 50% divides ionic from covalent bonds. Note that a substance like Cl₂(*g*) has 0% ionic character, but none has 100% ionic character: *electron sharing occurs to some extent in every bond,* even in an alkali halide (Figure 9.25B).

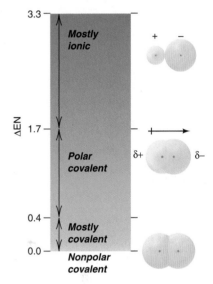

Figure 9.24 ΔEN ranges for classifying the partial ionic character of bonds.

Figure 9.25 Percent ionic character as a function of ΔEN. A, ΔEN correlates with ionic character. **B,** Even in highly ionic LiF (ΔEN = 3.0), the relief map shows some electron sharing between the ions.

A

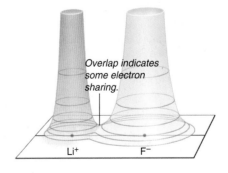

B

Sample Problem 9.4 | **Determining Bond Polarity from EN Values**

Problem (a) Use a polar arrow to indicate the polarity of each bond: N—H, F—N, I—Cl.
(b) Rank the following bonds in order of *increasing* polarity and *decreasing* percent ionic character: H—N, H—O, H—C.

Plan (a) We use Figure 9.21 to find the EN values for the atoms and point the polar arrow toward the negative end. (b) To rank the bond polarity, we determine ΔEN: the higher the value, the greater the polarity. Percent ionic character is also directly related to ΔEN (and bond polarity); it decreases in the opposite order that polarity increases.

Solution (a) The EN of N = 3.0 and the EN of H = 2.1, so $\overset{\longleftarrow^{+}}{\text{N—H}}$
The EN of F = 4.0 and the EN of N = 3.0, so $\overset{\longleftarrow^{+}}{\text{F—N}}$

The EN of I = 2.5 and the EN of Cl = 3.0, so $\overset{\overset{+}{\longrightarrow}}{\text{I—Cl}}$
(b) The ΔEN values are 0.9 for H—N, 1.4 for H—O, and 0.4 for H—C.
The order of *increasing* bond polarity is H—C < H—N < H—O.
The order of *decreasing* percent ionic character is H—O > H—N > H—C.

Check In (b), we can check the order of bond polarity using periodic trends. Each bond involves H and a Period 2 atom. Since size decreases and EN increases across a period, the polarity is greatest for the bond to O (farthest to the right in Period 2).

Comment In Chapter 10, you'll see that the bond polarity contributes to the overall polarity of the molecule, which is a major factor determining behavior.

Follow-Up Problem 9.4 Arrange each set of bonds in order of increasing polarity, and indicate bond polarity with δ+ and δ− symbols:
(a) Cl—F, Br—Cl, Cl—Cl   (b) Si—Cl, P—Cl, S—Cl, Si—Si

The Gradation in Bonding Across a Period

A metal and a nonmetal—elements from the left and right sides of the periodic table—have a relatively large ΔEN and typically form an ionic compound. Two nonmetals—both from the right side of the table—have a small ΔEN and form a covalent compound. When we combine chlorine with each of the other Period 3 elements, starting with sodium, we observe a steady decrease in ΔEN and a gradation in bond type from ionic through polar covalent to nonpolar covalent.

Figure 9.26 shows an electron density relief map of a bond in each of the common Period 3 chlorides; note the steady increase in the height of electron density *between* the peaks—the bonding region—which indicates an *increase in electron sharing*. Figure 9.27 shows samples of common Period 3 chlorides—NaCl, MgCl$_2$, AlCl$_3$, SiCl$_4$, PCl$_3$, and SCl$_2$, as well as Cl$_2$—along with the change in ΔEN and two physical properties:

- NaCl. Sodium chloride is a white (colorless) crystalline solid with a ΔEN of 2.1, a high melting point, and high electrical conductivity when molten—ionic by any criterion. However, just as for LiF (Figure 9.25B), a small but significant region of electron sharing appears in the relief map.
- MgCl$_2$. With a ΔEN of 1.8, magnesium chloride is still ionic, but it has a lower melting point and lower conductivity, as well as slightly more electron sharing.

Figure 9.26 Electron density distributions in bonds of the Period 3 chlorides. Note the steady increase in electron sharing from left to right.

Shared e⁻ density (bonding region) increases →

Figure 9.27 **Properties of the Period 3 chlorides.** As ΔEN decreases, melting point and electrical conductivity decrease because the bond type changes from ionic to polar covalent to nonpolar covalent.

- **AlCl₃.** Rather than being a three-dimensional lattice of Al³⁺ and Cl⁻ ions, aluminum chloride, with a ΔEN value of 1.5, consists of layers of highly polar Al—Cl bonds. Weak forces between layers result in a much lower melting point, and the low conductivity implies few free ions. And, electron density between the nuclei is higher.
- **SiCl₄, PCl₃, SCl₂, and Cl₂.** The trend toward more covalent bonding continues through the remaining substances. Each occurs as separate molecules, which have no conductivity and such weak forces *between* them that melting points are below 0°C. In Cl₂, the bond is nonpolar (ΔEN = 0.0). The relief maps show the increasing height of the electron density in the bonding region.

   Thus, *as ΔEN decreases, the bond becomes more covalent,* and the character of the substance changes from ionic solid to covalent gas.

◼ Summary of Section 9.5

- Electronegativity is the ability of a bonded atom to attract shared electrons, which generates opposite partial charges at the ends of the bond and contributes to the bond energy.
- Electronegativity increases across a period and decreases down a group, the reverse of the trends in atomic size.
- The larger the ΔEN for two bonded atoms, the more polar the bond is and the greater its ionic character.
- For Period 3 chlorides, there is a gradation in bond type from ionic to polar covalent to nonpolar covalent.

9.6 • AN INTRODUCTION TO METALLIC BONDING

In this section, you'll see how a simple, qualitative model for metallic bonding accounts for the properties of metals; a more detailed model is presented in Chapter 12.

The Electron-Sea Model

Metals can transfer electrons to nonmetals and form ionic solids, such as NaCl. And experiments with metals in the gas phase show that two metal atoms can even share their valence electrons to form gaseous, diatomic molecules, such as Na_2. But what holds the atoms together in a chunk of Na metal? The **electron-sea model** of metallic bonding proposes that all the metal atoms in the sample contribute their valence electrons to form a delocalized electron "sea" throughout the piece, with the metal ions (nuclei and core electrons) lying in an orderly array (see Figure 9.2C). *All the atoms in the sample share the electrons,* and the piece is held together by the mutual attraction of the metal cations for the mobile, valence electrons. Thus, bonding in metals is fundamentally different than the other two types:

- *In contrast to ionic bonding,* the metal ions are not held in place as rigidly.
- *In contrast to covalent bonding,* no particular pair of metal atoms is bonded through a localized electron pair.
- *Instead of forming compounds,* two or more metals typically form **alloys,** solid mixtures of variable composition. Alloys appear in car and airplane bodies, bridges, coins, jewelry, dental fillings, and many other familiar objects.

How the Model Explains the Properties of Metals

The physical properties of metals vary over a wide range. Two features of the electron-sea model that account for these properties are (1) the *regularity,* but not rigidity, of the metal-ion array and (2) the *number* and *mobility* of the valence electrons.

1. *Melting and boiling points.* Nearly all metals are solids with moderate to high melting points and much higher boiling points (Table 9.5). These properties are related to the energy of the metallic bonding. Melting points are only moderately high because the cations can move without breaking the attraction to the surrounding electrons. Boiling points are very high because each cation and its valence electron(s) must break away from the others. Gallium provides a striking example: it can melt in your hand (mp 29.8°C) but doesn't boil until over 2400°C.

   Periodic trends are consistent with the strength of the bonding:

- *Down a group,* melting points decrease because the larger metal ions have a weaker attraction to the electron sea.
- *Across a period,* melting points increase. Alkaline earth metals [Group 2A(2)] have higher melting points than alkali metals [Group 1A(1)] because their 2+ cations have stronger attractions to twice as many valence electrons (Figure 9.28).

Table 9.5 Melting and Boiling Points of Some Metals

Element	mp (°C)	bp (°C)
Lithium (Li)	180	1347
Tin (Sn)	232	2623
Aluminum (Al)	660	2467
Barium (Ba)	727	1850
Silver (Ag)	961	2155
Copper (Cu)	1083	2570
Uranium (U)	1130	3930

Figure 9.28 Melting points of Group 1A(1) and Group 2A(2) metals.

2. *Mechanical properties.* When a piece of metal is deformed by a hammer, the metal ions do not repel each other, but rather slide past each other through the electron sea and end up in new positions; thus metals dent and bend, as shown in Figure 9.29. Compare this behavior with the interionic repulsions that occur when an ionic solid is struck (see Figure 9.9, p. 336).

Figure 9.29 Why metals dent and bend rather than crack.

All the Group 1B(11) metals—copper, silver, and gold—are soft enough to be machined into sheets (malleable) and wires (ductile), but gold is in a class by itself. One gram of gold, about the size of a small ball-bearing, can be drawn into a wire 20 μm thick and 165 m long or hammered into a 1.0-m^2 sheet that is 230 atoms (about 70 nm) thick *(see photo)*!

How thin is gold leaf?

3. *Electrical conductivity.* Unlike ionic and covalent substances, metals are good conductors of electricity in both the solid and liquid states because of their mobile electrons. When a piece of metal wire is attached to a battery, electrons flow from one terminal into the wire, replacing the electrons that flow from the wire into the other terminal. Foreign atoms disrupt the array of metal atoms and reduce conductivity. Copper used in electrical wiring is over 99.99% pure because traces of other atoms drastically restrict electron flow.

4. *Thermal conductivity.* Mobile electrons also make metals good conductors of heat. Place your hand on a piece of metal and a piece of wood that are both at room temperature. The metal feels colder because it conducts heat away from your hand much faster than the wood. The mobile, delocalized electrons in the metal disperse the heat from your hand more quickly than the localized electron pairs in the covalent bonds of wood.

▌Summary of Section 9.6

- According to the electron-sea model, the valence electrons of the metal atoms in a sample are highly delocalized and attract all the metal cations, holding them together.

- Metals have only moderately high melting points because the metal ions remain attracted to the electron sea even if their relative positions change.

- Boiling involves complete separation of individual cations with their valence electrons from all the others, so metals have very high boiling points.

- Metals can be deformed because the electron sea prevents repulsions among the cations.

- Metals conduct electricity and heat because their electrons are mobile.

CHAPTER REVIEW GUIDE

Understand These Concepts

1. How differences in atomic properties lead to differences in bond type; the basic distinctions among the three types of bonding (§9.1)
2. The essential features of ionic bonding: electron transfer to form ions, and their electrostatic attraction to form a solid (§9.2)
3. How lattice energy is ultimately responsible for the formation of ionic compounds (§9.2)
4. How ionic compound formation is conceptualized as occurring in hypothetical steps (a Born-Haber cycle) to calculate the lattice energy (§9.2)
5. How Coulomb's law explains the periodic trends in lattice energy (§9.2)
6. Why ionic compounds are brittle and high melting and conduct electricity only when molten or dissolved in water (§9.2)
7. How nonmetal atoms form a covalent bond (§9.3)
8. How bonding and lone electron pairs fill the outer (valence) level of each atom in a molecule (§9.3)
9. The interrelationships among bond order, bond length, and bond energy (§9.3)
10. How the distinction between bonding and nonbonding forces explains the properties of covalent molecules and network covalent solids (§9.3)
11. How changes in bond strength account for the enthalpy of reaction (§9.4)

12. How a reaction can be divided conceptually into bond-breaking and bond-forming steps (§9.4)
13. The periodic trends in electronegativity and the inverse relationship of EN values to atomic sizes (§9.5)
14. How bond polarity arises from differences in the electronegativities of bonded atoms; the direction of bond polarity (§9.5)
15. The change in partial ionic character with ΔEN and the change from ionic to polar covalent to nonpolar covalent bonding across a period (§9.5)
16. The role of delocalized electrons in metallic bonding (§9.6)
17. How the electron-sea model explains why metals bend, have very high boiling points, and conduct electricity in solid or molten form (§9.6)

Master These Skills

1. Using Lewis electron-dot symbols to depict main-group atoms (§9.1)
2. Depicting the formation of ions with electron configurations, orbital diagrams, and Lewis symbols, and writing the formula of the ionic compound (SP 9.1)
3. Calculating lattice energy from the enthalpies of the steps to ionic compound formation (§9.2)
4. Ranking similar covalent bonds according to their length and strength (SP 9.2)
5. Using bond energies to calculate ΔH°_{rxn} (SP 9.3)
6. Determining bond polarity from EN values (SP 9.4)

Section 9.1
ionic bonding (330)
covalent bonding (330)
metallic bonding (331)
Lewis electron-dot symbol (331)
octet rule (331)

Section 9.2
lattice energy ($\Delta H^{\circ}_{lattice}$) (333)

Born-Haber cycle (333)
Coulomb's law (335)
ion pair (337)

Section 9.3
covalent bond (338)
bonding (shared) pair (339)
lone (unshared) pair (339)
bond order (339)
single bond (339)

double bond (339)
triple bond (339)
bond energy (BE) (339)
bond length (340)
infrared (IR) spectroscopy (343)

Section 9.5
electronegativity (EN) (349)
polar covalent bond (351)

nonpolar covalent bond (351)
electronegativity difference (ΔEN) (351)
partial ionic character (351)

Section 9.6
electron-sea model (354)
alloy (354)

9.1 Relating the energy of attraction to the lattice energy (335):

$$\text{Electrostatic energy} \propto \frac{\text{cation charge} \times \text{anion charge}}{\text{cation radius} + \text{anion radius}} \propto \Delta H^{\circ}_{lattice}$$

9.2 Calculating enthalpy of reaction from bond enthalpies or bond energies (345):

$$\Delta H^{\circ}_{rxn} = \Sigma \Delta H^{\circ}_{\text{reactant bonds broken}} + \Sigma \Delta H^{\circ}_{\text{product bonds formed}}$$

or $\quad \Delta H^{\circ}_{rxn} = \Sigma BE_{\text{reactant bonds broken}} - \Sigma BE_{\text{product bonds formed}}$

Brief Solutions to Follow-Up Problems

9.1 Mg ([Ne] $3s^2$) + 2Cl ([Ne] $3s^2 3p^5$) $\longrightarrow$

$$Mg^{2+} ([Ne]) + 2Cl^- ([Ne] 3s^2 3p^6)$$

Mg· + :C̈l: $\longrightarrow$ Mg^{2+} + 2 :C̈l:$^-$ Formula: $MgCl_2$

9.2 (a) Bond length: Si—F < Si—O < Si—C
Bond strength: Si—C < Si—O < Si—F
(b) Bond length: N≡N < N=N < N—N
Bond strength: N—N < N=N < N≡N

9.3 N≡N + 3 H—H $\longrightarrow$ 2 H—N—H with H below

$\Sigma \Delta H^\circ_{bonds\ broken} = 1\ N≡N + 3\ H—H$
$= 945\ kJ + 1296\ kJ = 2241\ kJ$
$\Sigma \Delta H^\circ_{bonds\ formed} = 6\ N—H = -2346\ kJ$
$\Delta H^\circ_{rxn} = -105\ kJ$

9.4 (a) $\overset{\delta+}{Cl}—\overset{\delta-}{Cl} < \overset{\delta+}{Br}—\overset{\delta-}{Cl} < \overset{\delta+}{Cl}—\overset{\delta-}{F}$

(b) $Si—Si < \overset{\delta+}{S}—\overset{\delta-}{Cl} < \overset{\delta+}{P}—\overset{\delta-}{Cl} < \overset{\delta+}{Si}—\overset{\delta-}{Cl}$

PROBLEMS

Problems with **colored** numbers are answered in Appendix E and worked in detail in the Student Solutions Manual. Problem sections match those in the text and provide the numbers of relevant sample problems. Most offer Concept Review Questions, Skill-Building Exercises (grouped in pairs covering the same concept), and Problems in Context. The Comprehensive Problems are based on material from any section or previous chapter.

Atomic Properties and Chemical Bonds

Concept Review Questions

9.1 In general terms, how does each of the following atomic properties influence the metallic character of the main-group elements in a period?
(a) Ionization energy
(b) Atomic radius
(c) Number of outer electrons
(d) Effective nuclear charge

9.2 Three solids are represented below. What is the predominant type of intramolecular bonding in each?

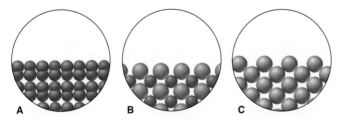

A   **B**   **C**

9.3 What is the relationship between the tendency of a main-group element to form a monatomic ion and its position in the periodic table? In what part of the table are the main-group elements that typically form cations? Anions?

Skill-Building Exercises (grouped in similar pairs)
9.4 Which member of each pair is *more* metallic?
(a) Na or Cs   (b) Mg or Rb   (c) As or N

9.5 Which member of each pair is *less* metallic?
(a) I or O   (b) Be or Ba   (c) Se or Ge

9.6 State the type of bonding—ionic, covalent, or metallic—you would expect in each: (a) CsF(*s*); (b) N_2(*g*); (c) Na(*s*).

9.7 State the type of bonding—ionic, covalent, or metallic—you would expect in each: (a) ICl_3(*g*); (b) N_2O(*g*); (c) LiCl(*s*).

9.8 State the type of bonding—ionic, covalent, or metallic—you would expect in each: (a) O_3(*g*); (b) $MgCl_2$(*s*); (c) BrO_2(*g*).

9.9 State the type of bonding—ionic, covalent, or metallic—you would expect in each: (a) Cr(*s*); (b) H_2S(*g*); (c) CaO(*s*).

9.10 Draw a Lewis electron-dot symbol for (a) Rb; (b) Si; (c) I.

9.11 Draw a Lewis electron-dot symbol for (a) Ba; (b) Kr; (c) Br.

9.12 Draw a Lewis electron-dot symbol for (a) Sr; (b) P; (c) S.

9.13 Draw a Lewis electron-dot symbol for (a) As; (b) Se; (c) Ga.

9.14 Give the group number and general electron configuration of an element with each electron-dot symbol: (a) ·Ẍ: (b) Ẋ·

9.15 Give the group number and general electron configuration of an element with each electron-dot symbol: (a) ·Ẋ: (b) ·Ẍ·

The Ionic Bonding Model
(Sample Problem 9.1)

Concept Review Questions
9.16 If energy is required to form monatomic ions from metals and nonmetals, why do ionic compounds exist?

9.17 (a) In general, how does the lattice energy of an ionic compound depend on the charges and sizes of the ions? (b) Ion arrangements of three general salts are represented below. Rank them in order of increasing lattice energy.

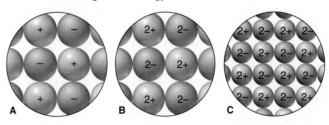

A   **B**   **C**

9.18 When gaseous Na^+ and Cl^- ions form gaseous NaCl ion pairs, 548 kJ/mol of energy is released. Why, then, does NaCl occur as a solid under ordinary conditions?

9.19 To form S^{2-} ions from gaseous sulfur atoms requires 214 kJ/mol, but these ions exist in solids such as K_2S. Explain.

Skill-Building Exercises (grouped in similar pairs)

9.20 Use condensed electron configurations and Lewis electron-dot symbols to depict the ions formed from each of the following atoms, and predict the formula of their compound:
(a) Ba and Cl   (b) Sr and O   (c) Al and F   (d) Rb and O

9.21 Use condensed electron configurations and Lewis electron-dot symbols to depict the ions formed from each of the following atoms, and predict the formula of their compound:
(a) Cs and S   (b) O and Ga   (c) N and Mg   (d) Br and Li

9.22 For each ionic compound formula, identify the main group to which X belongs: (a) XF_2; (b) MgX; (c) X_2SO_4.

9.23 For each ionic compound formula, identify the main group to which X belongs: (a) X_3PO_4; (b) $X_2(SO_4)_3$; (c) $X(NO_3)_2$.

9.24 For each ionic compound formula, identify the main group to which X belongs: (a) X_2O_3; (b) XCO_3; (c) Na_2X.

9.25 For each ionic compound formula, identify the main group to which X belongs: (a) CaX_2; (b) Al_2X_3; (c) XPO_4.

9.26 For each pair, choose the compound with the higher lattice energy, and explain your choice: (a) BaS or CsCl; (b) LiCl or CsCl.

9.27 For each pair, choose the compound with the higher lattice energy, and explain your choice: (a) CaO or CaS; (b) BaO or SrO.

9.28 For each pair, choose the compound with the lower lattice energy, and explain your choice: (a) CaS or BaS; (b) NaF or MgO.

9.29 For each pair, choose the compound with the lower lattice energy, and explain your choice: (a) NaF or NaCl; (b) K_2O or K_2S.

9.30 Use the following to calculate the $\Delta H^\circ_{lattice}$ of NaCl:

$Na(s) \longrightarrow Na(g)$	$\Delta H^\circ =$	109 kJ
$Cl_2(g) \longrightarrow 2Cl(g)$	$\Delta H^\circ =$	243 kJ
$Na(g) \longrightarrow Na^+(g) + e^-$	$\Delta H^\circ =$	496 kJ
$Cl(g) + e^- \longrightarrow Cl^-(g)$	$\Delta H^\circ =$	-349 kJ
$Na(s) + \frac{1}{2}Cl_2(g) \longrightarrow NaCl(s)$	$\Delta H^\circ =$	-411 kJ

Compared with the lattice energy of LiF (1050 kJ/mol), is the magnitude of the value for NaCl what you expected? Explain.

9.31 Use the following to calculate the $\Delta H^\circ_{lattice}$ of MgF_2:

$Mg(s) \longrightarrow Mg(g)$	$\Delta H^\circ =$	148 kJ
$F_2(g) \longrightarrow 2F(g)$	$\Delta H^\circ =$	159 kJ
$Mg(g) \longrightarrow Mg^+(g) + e^-$	$\Delta H^\circ =$	738 kJ
$Mg^+(g) \longrightarrow Mg^{2+}(g) + e^-$	$\Delta H^\circ =$	1450 kJ
$F(g) + e^- \longrightarrow F^-(g)$	$\Delta H^\circ =$	-328 kJ
$Mg(s) + F_2(g) \longrightarrow MgF_2(s)$	$\Delta H^\circ =$	-1123 kJ

Compared with the lattice energy of LiF (1050 kJ/mol) or the lattice energy you calculated for NaCl in Problem 9.30, does the relative magnitude of the value for MgF_2 surprise you? Explain.

Problems in Context

9.32 Aluminum oxide (Al_2O_3) is a widely used industrial abrasive (emery, corundum), for which the specific application depends on the hardness of the crystal. What does this hardness imply about the magnitude of the lattice energy? Would you have predicted from the chemical formula that Al_2O_3 is hard? Explain.

9.33 Born-Haber cycles were used to obtain the first reliable values for electron affinity by considering the EA value as the unknown and using a theoretically calculated value for the lattice energy. Use a Born-Haber cycle for KF and the following values to calculate a value for the electron affinity of fluorine:

$K(s) \longrightarrow K(g)$	$\Delta H^\circ =$	90 kJ
$K(g) \longrightarrow K^+(g) + e^-$	$\Delta H^\circ =$	419 kJ
$F_2(g) \longrightarrow 2F(g)$	$\Delta H^\circ =$	159 kJ
$K(s) + \frac{1}{2}F_2(g) \longrightarrow KF(s)$	$\Delta H^\circ =$	-569 kJ
$K^+(g) + F^-(g) \longrightarrow KF(s)$	$\Delta H^\circ =$	-821 kJ

The Covalent Bonding Model
(Sample Problem 9.2)

Concept Review Questions

9.34 Describe the interactions that occur between individual chlorine atoms as they approach each other and form Cl_2. What combination of forces gives rise to the energy holding the atoms together and to the final internuclear distance?

9.35 Define bond energy using the H—Cl bond as an example. When this bond breaks, is energy absorbed or released? Is the accompanying ΔH value positive or negative? How do the magnitude and sign of this ΔH value relate to the value that accompanies H—Cl bond formation?

9.36 For single bonds between similar types of atoms, how does the strength of the bond relate to the sizes of the atoms? Explain.

9.37 How does the energy of the bond between a given pair of atoms relate to the bond order? Why?

9.38 When liquid benzene (C_6H_6) boils, does the gas consist of molecules, ions, or separate atoms? Explain.

Skill-Building Exercises (grouped in similar pairs)

9.39 Using the periodic table only, arrange the members of each of the following sets in order of increasing bond *strength:*
(a) Br—Br, Cl—Cl, I—I   (b) S—H, S—Br, S—Cl
(c) C=N, C—N, C≡N

9.40 Using the periodic table only, arrange the members of each of the following sets in order of increasing bond *length:*
(a) H—F, H—I, H—Cl   (b) C—S, C=O, C—O
(c) N—H, N—S, N—O

Problem in Context

9.41 Formic acid (HCOOH; structural formula shown below) is secreted by certain species of ants when they bite.

Rank the relative strengths of (a) the C—O and C=O bonds and (b) the H—C and H—O bonds. Explain these rankings.

Bond Energy and Chemical Change
(Sample Problem 9.3)

Concept Review Questions

9.42 Write a solution Plan (without actual numbers, but including the bond energies you would use and how you would combine them algebraically) for calculating the total enthalpy change of the following reaction:

$$H_2(g) + O_2(g) \longrightarrow H_2O_2(g) \qquad (H-O-O-H)$$

9.43 The text points out that, for similar types of substances, one with weaker bonds is usually more reactive than one with stronger bonds. Why is this generally true?

9.44 Why is there a discrepancy between a heat of reaction obtained from calorimetry and one obtained from bond energies?

Skill-Building Exercises (grouped in similar pairs)

9.45 Which of the following gases would you expect to have the greater heat of reaction per mole for combustion? Why?

methane or formaldehyde

9.46 Which of the following gases would you expect to have the greater heat of reaction per mole for combustion? Why?

ethanol or methanol

9.47 Use bond energies to calculate the heat of reaction:

9.48 Use bond energies to calculate the heat of reaction:

Problems in Context

9.49 An important industrial route to extremely pure acetic acid is the reaction of methanol with carbon monoxide:

Use bond energies to calculate the enthalpy of reaction.

9.50 Sports trainers treat sprains and soreness with ethyl bromide. It is manufactured by reacting ethylene with hydrogen bromide:

Use bond energies to find the enthalpy of reaction.

Between the Extremes: Electronegativity and Bond Polarity
(Sample Problem 9.4)

Concept Review Questions

9.51 Describe the vertical and horizontal trends in electronegativity (EN) among the main-group elements. According to Pauling's

scale, what are the two most electronegative elements? The two least electronegative elements?

9.52 What is the general relationship between IE_1 and EN for the elements? Why?

9.53 Is the H—O bond in water nonpolar covalent, polar covalent, or ionic? Define each term, and explain your choice.

9.54 How does electronegativity differ from electron affinity?

9.55 How is the partial ionic character of a bond in a diatomic molecule related to ΔEN for the bonded atoms? Why?

Skill-Building Exercises (grouped in similar pairs)

9.56 Using the periodic table only, arrange the elements in each set in order of *increasing* EN: (a) S, O, Si; (b) Mg, P, As.

9.57 Using the periodic table only, arrange the elements in each set in order of *increasing* EN: (a) I, Br, N; (b) Ca, H, F.

9.58 Using the periodic table only, arrange the elements in each set in order of *decreasing* EN: (a) N, P, Si; (b) Ca, Ga, As.

9.59 Using the periodic table only, arrange the elements in each set in order of *decreasing* EN: (a) Br, Cl, P; (b) I, F, O.

9.60 Use Figure 9.21, p. 349, to indicate the polarity of each bond with a *polar arrow:* (a) N—B; (b) N—O; (c) C—S; (d) S—O; (e) N—H; (f) Cl—O.

9.61 Use Figure 9.21, p. 349, to indicate the polarity of each bond with *partial charges:* (a) Br—Cl; (b) F—Cl; (c) H—O; (d) Se—H; (e) As—H; (f) S—N.

9.62 Which is the more polar bond in each of the following pairs from Problem 9.60: (a) or (b); (c) or (d); (e) or (f)?

9.63 Which is the more polar bond in each of the following pairs from Problem 9.61: (a) or (b); (c) or (d); (e) or (f)?

9.64 Are the bonds in each of the following substances ionic, non-polar covalent, or polar covalent? Arrange the substances with polar covalent bonds in order of increasing bond polarity:
(a) S_8 (b) RbCl (c) PF_3 (d) SCl_2 (e) F_2 (f) SF_2

9.65 Are the bonds in each of the following substances ionic, non-polar covalent, or polar covalent? Arrange the substances with polar covalent bonds in order of increasing bond polarity:
(a) KCl (b) P_4 (c) BF_3 (d) SO_2 (e) Br_2 (f) NO_2

9.66 Rank the members of each set of compounds in order of *increasing* ionic character of their bonds. Use *polar arrows* to indicate the bond polarity of each:
(a) HBr, HCl, HI (b) H_2O, CH_4, HF (c) SCl_2, PCl_3, $SiCl_4$

9.67 Rank the members of each set of compounds in order of *decreasing* ionic character of their bonds. Use *partial charges* to indicate the bond polarity of each:
(a) PCl_3, PBr_3, PF_3 (b) BF_3, NF_3, CF_4 (c) SeF_4, TeF_4, BrF_3

Problem in Context

9.68 The energy of the C—C bond is 347 kJ/mol, and that of the Cl—Cl bond is 243 kJ/mol. Which of the following values might you expect for the C—Cl bond energy? Explain.
(a) 590 kJ/mol (sum of the values given)
(b) 104 kJ/mol (difference of the values given)
(c) 295 kJ/mol (average of the values given)
(d) 339 kJ/mol (greater than the average of the values given)

An Introduction to Metallic Bonding

Concept Review Questions

9.69 (a) List four physical characteristics of a solid metal. (b) List two chemical characteristics of a metallic element.

9.70 Briefly account for the following relative values:
(a) The melting points of Na and K are 89°C and 63°C, respectively.
(b) The melting points of Li and Be are 180°C and 1287°C, respectively.
(c) Li boils more than 1100°C higher than it melts.

9.71 Magnesium metal is easily deformed by an applied force, whereas magnesium fluoride is shattered. Why do these two solids behave so differently?

Comprehensive Problems

9.72 Geologists have a rule of thumb: when molten rock cools and solidifies, crystals of compounds with the smallest lattice energies appear at the bottom of the mass. Suggest a reason for this.

9.73 Acetylene gas (ethyne; HC≡CH) burns in an oxyacetylene torch to produce carbon dioxide and water vapor. The heat of reaction for the combustion of acetylene is 1259 kJ/mol. (a) Calculate the C≡C bond energy, and compare your value with that in Table 9.2, p. 340. (b) When 500.0 g of acetylene burns, how many kilojoules of heat are given off? (c) How many grams of CO_2 form? (d) How many liters of O_2 at 298 K and 18.0 atm are consumed?

9.74 Use Lewis electron-dot symbols to represent the formation of (a) BrF_3 from bromine and fluorine atoms; (b) AlF_3 from aluminum and fluorine atoms.

9.75 Even though so much energy is required to form a metal cation with a 2+ charge, the alkaline earth metals form halides with general formula MX_2, rather than MX.
(a) Use the following data to calculate the ΔH_f° of MgCl:

$Mg(s) \longrightarrow Mg(g)$	$\Delta H^\circ =$	148 kJ
$Cl_2(g) \longrightarrow 2Cl(g)$	$\Delta H^\circ =$	243 kJ
$Mg(g) \longrightarrow Mg^+(g) + e^-$	$\Delta H^\circ =$	738 kJ
$Cl(g) + e^- \longrightarrow Cl^-(g)$	$\Delta H^\circ =$	−349 kJ

$\Delta H_{lattice}^\circ$ of MgCl = 783.5 kJ/mol

(b) Is MgCl favored energetically relative to Mg and Cl_2? Explain.
(c) Use Hess's law to calculate ΔH° for the conversion of MgCl to $MgCl_2$ and Mg (ΔH_f° of $MgCl_2 = -641.6$ kJ/mol).
(d) Is MgCl favored energetically relative to $MgCl_2$? Explain.

9.76 Gases react explosively if the heat released when the reaction begins is sufficient to cause more reaction, which leads to a rapid expansion of the gases. Use bond energies to calculate ΔH° of the following reactions, and predict which occurs explosively:
(a) $H_2(g) + Cl_2(g) \longrightarrow 2HCl(g)$
(b) $H_2(g) + I_2(g) \longrightarrow 2HI(g)$
(c) $2H_2(g) + O_2(g) \longrightarrow 2H_2O(g)$

9.77 By using photons of specific wavelengths, chemists can dissociate gaseous HI to produce H atoms with certain speeds. When HI dissociates, the H atoms move away rapidly, whereas the heavier I atoms move more slowly. (a) What is the longest wavelength (in nm) that can dissociate a molecule of HI? (b) If a photon of 254 nm is used, what is the excess energy (in J) over that needed for dissociation? (c) If this excess energy is carried away by the H atom as kinetic energy, what is its speed (in m/s)?

9.78 In developing the concept of electronegativity, Pauling used the term *excess bond energy* for the difference between the actual bond energy of X—Y and the average bond energies of X—X and Y—Y (see text discussion for the case of HF). Based on the values in Figure 9.21, p. 349, which of the following substances contains bonds with no excess bond energy?
(a) PH_3 (b) CS_2 (c) BrCl   (d) BH_3 (e) Se_8

9.79 Use condensed electron configurations to predict the relative hardnesses and melting points of rubidium ($Z = 37$), vanadium ($Z = 23$), and cadmium ($Z = 48$).

9.80 Without stratospheric ozone (O_3), harmful solar radiation would cause gene alterations. Ozone forms when the bond in O_2 breaks and each O atom reacts with another O_2 molecule. It is destroyed by reaction with Cl atoms formed when the C—Cl bond in synthetic chemicals breaks. Find the wavelengths of light that can break the C—Cl bond and the bond in O_2.

9.81 "Inert" xenon actually forms many compounds, especially with highly electronegative fluorine. The ΔH_f° values for xenon difluoride, tetrafluoride, and hexafluoride are −105, −284, and −402 kJ/mol, respectively. Find the average bond energy of the Xe—F bonds in each fluoride.

9.82 The HF bond length is 92 pm, 16% shorter than the sum of the covalent radii of H (37 pm) and F (72 pm). Suggest a reason for this difference. Similar data show that the difference becomes smaller down the group, from HF to HI. Explain.

9.83 There are two main types of covalent bond breakage. In homolytic breakage (as in Table 9.2, p. 340), each atom in the bond gets one of the shared electrons. In some cases, the electronegativity of adjacent atoms affects the bond energy. In heterolytic breakage, one atom gets both electrons and the other gets none; thus, a cation and an anion form.
(a) Why is the C—C bond in H_3C—CF_3 (423 kJ/mol) stronger than that in H_3C—CH_3 (376 kJ/mol)?
(b) Use bond energy and any other data to calculate the enthalpy of reaction for the heterolytic cleavage of O_2.

9.84 Find the longest wavelengths of light that can cleave the bonds in elemental nitrogen, oxygen, and fluorine.

9.85 The work function (ϕ) of a metal is the minimum energy needed to remove an electron from its surface. (a) Is it easier to remove an electron from a gaseous silver atom or from the surface of solid silver ($\phi = 7.59\times10^{-19}$ J; IE = 731 kJ/mol)? (b) Explain the results in terms of the electron-sea model of metallic bonding.

9.86 Lattice energies can also be calculated for covalent solids using a Born-Haber cycle, and the network solid silicon dioxide has one of the highest $\Delta H_{lattice}^\circ$ values. Silicon dioxide is found in pure crystalline form as transparent rock quartz. Much harder than glass, this material was once prized for making lenses for optical devices and expensive spectacles. Use Appendix B and the following data to calculate $\Delta H_{lattice}^\circ$ of SiO_2:

$Si(s) \longrightarrow Si(g)$	$\Delta H^\circ =$	454 kJ
$Si(g) \longrightarrow Si^{4+}(g) + 4e^-$	$\Delta H^\circ =$	9949 kJ
$O_2(g) \longrightarrow 2O(g)$	$\Delta H^\circ =$	498 kJ
$O(g) + 2e^- \longrightarrow O^{2-}(g)$	$\Delta H^\circ =$	737 kJ

9.87 The average C—H bond energy in CH_4 is 415 kJ/mol. Use Table 9.2 (p. 340) and the following to calculate the average C—H bond energy in ethane (C_2H_6; C—C bond), in ethene (C_2H_4; C=C bond), and in ethyne (C_2H_2; C≡C bond):

$$C_2H_6(g) + H_2(g) \longrightarrow 2CH_4(g) \qquad \Delta H^{\circ}_{rxn} = -65.07 \text{ kJ/mol}$$

$$C_2H_4(g) + 2H_2(g) \longrightarrow 2CH_4(g) \qquad \Delta H^{\circ}_{rxn} = -202.21 \text{ kJ/mol}$$

$$C_2H_2(g) + 3H_2(g) \longrightarrow 2CH_4(g) \qquad \Delta H^{\circ}_{rxn} = -376.74 \text{ kJ/mol}$$

9.88 Carbon-carbon bonds form the "backbone" of nearly every organic and biological molecule. The average bond energy of the C—C bond is 347 kJ/mol. Calculate the frequency and wavelength of the least energetic photon that can break an average C—C bond. In what region of the electromagnetic spectrum is this radiation?

9.89 In a future hydrogen-fuel economy, the cheapest source of H_2 will certainly be water. It takes 467 kJ to produce 1 mol of H atoms from water. What is the frequency, wavelength, and minimum energy of a photon that can free an H atom from water?

9.90 Dimethyl ether (CH_3OCH_3) and ethanol (CH_3CH_2OH) are constitutional isomers (see Table 3.4, p. 103). (a) Use Table 9.2 (p. 340) to calculate ΔH°_{rxn} for the formation of each compound as a gas from methane and oxygen; water vapor also forms. (b) State which reaction is more exothermic. (c) Calculate ΔH°_{rxn} for the conversion of ethanol to dimethyl ether.

9.91 Enthalpies of reaction calculated from bond energies and from enthalpies of formation are often, but not always, close to each other.
(a) Industrial ethanol (CH_3CH_2OH) is produced by a catalytic reaction of ethylene ($CH_2{=}CH_2$) with water at high pressures and temperatures. Calculate ΔH°_{rxn} for this gas-phase hydration of ethylene to ethanol, using bond energies and then using enthalpies of formation.
(b) Ethylene glycol is produced by the catalytic oxidation of ethylene to ethylene oxide, which then reacts with water to form ethylene glycol:

$$\underset{CH_2 - CH_2}{\overset{O}{\diagup \diagdown}}(l) \; + \; H_2O(l) \longrightarrow HOCH_2CH_2OH(l)$$

The ΔH°_{rxn} for this hydrolysis step, based on enthalpies of formation, is −97 kJ/mol. Calculate ΔH°_{rxn} for the hydrolysis using bond energies.
(c) Why are the two values relatively close for the hydration in part (a) but not close for the hydrolysis in part (b)?

The Shapes of Molecules

Concepts and skills to review before you study this chapter

- electron configurations of main-group elements (Section 8.2)
- electron-dot symbols (Section 9.1)
- octet rule (Section 9.1)

- bond order, bond length, and bond energy (Sections 9.3 and 9.4)
- polar covalent bonds and bond polarity (Section 9.5)

In the everyday world, the shapes of interacting objects often reflect their function—cup and saucer, mortar and pestle, or the matching shapes of hand and glove. The same is true in the molecular world. But, with all the symbols, lines, and dots you've been seeing, it's easy to forget that every molecule has a characteristic minute architecture. Each atom, bonding pair, and lone pair has its own position relative to the others, with definite angles and distances between them that are determined by the attractive and repulsive forces governing all matter. Molecular shape plays a crucial role in the interactions of reactants, the behavior of synthetic materials, and especially in the life-sustaining processes in cells.

IN THIS CHAPTER . . . We learn how to picture molecules by applying two approaches that explain their shapes, and we examine some effects of molecular shape on physical and biochemical behavior.
- We learn how to apply the octet rule to convert a molecular formula into a flat structural formula that shows atom attachments and electron-pair locations.
- We see how electron delocalization limits our ability to depict a molecule with a single structural formula and requires us to apply the concept of resonance.
- We introduce bond angle and apply a theory that converts two-dimensional formulas into three-dimensional shapes.
- We describe five basic classes of shapes that many molecules adopt, how multiple bonds and lone pairs affect them, and how to combine smaller molecular portions into the shapes of more complex molecules.
- We discuss the relation among bond polarity, shape, and molecular polarity and the effect of polarity on behavior.
- We describe a few examples of shape influencing biological function.

10.1 • DEPICTING MOLECULES AND IONS WITH LEWIS STRUCTURES

The first step toward visualizing a molecule is to convert its molecular formula to its **Lewis structure** (or **Lewis formula***), which shows electron-dot symbols for the atoms, the bonding pairs as lines, and the lone pairs that fill each atom's outer level (valence shell) as pairs of dots.

Applying the Octet Rule to Write Lewis Structures

To write a Lewis structure, we decide on the relative placement of the atoms in the molecule or polyatomic ion and then distribute the total number of valence electrons as bonding and lone pairs. In many, but not all, cases, the octet rule (Section 9.1) guides us in distributing the electrons. We begin with species that "obey" the octet rule, in which each atom fills its outer level with eight electrons (or two for hydrogen).

*A Lewis *structure* does *not* indicate the three-dimensional shape, so it may be more correct to call it a Lewis *formula*, but we follow convention and use the term *structure*.

Figure 10.1 The steps in converting a molecular formula into a Lewis structure.

Molecules with Single Bonds Figure 10.1 lays out the steps for writing Lewis structures for species with only single bonds. Let's use nitrogen trifluoride, NF_3, to introduce the steps:

Step 1. Place the atoms relative to each other. For compounds with the general molecular formula AB_n, place the atom with the *lower group number* in the center because it needs more electrons to attain an octet; usually, this is also the atom with the *lower electronegativity.* In NF_3, the N (Group 5A; EN = 3.0) has five electrons and so needs three, whereas each F (Group 7A; EN = 4.0) has seven and needs only one; thus, N goes in the center with the three F atoms around it:

$$\begin{array}{c} F \\ \quad N \\ F \quad\quad F \end{array}$$

If the atoms have the same group number, as in SO_3, place the atom with the *higher period number* (also lower EN) in the center. H can form only one bond, so it is *never* a central atom.

Step 2. Determine the total number of valence electrons.
- For molecules, add up the valence electrons of the atoms. (Recall that the number of valence electrons equals the A-group number.) In NF_3, N has five valence electrons, and each F has seven:

$$[1 \times N(5e^-)] + [3 \times F(7e^-)] = 5e^- + 21e^- = 26 \text{ valence } e^-$$

- For polyatomic ions, *add* one e^- for each negative charge, or *subtract* one e^- for each positive charge.

Step 3. Draw a single bond from each surrounding atom to the central atom, and subtract $2e^-$ from the total for each bond to find the number of e^- remaining:

$$\begin{array}{c} F \\ | \\ F\diagup N \diagdown F \end{array}$$

$$3 \text{ N—F bonds} \times 2e^- = 6e^- \quad \text{so} \quad 26e^- - 6e^- = 20e^- \text{ remaining}$$

Step 4. Distribute the remaining electrons in pairs so that each atom ends up with $8e^-$ (or $2e^-$ for H). First, place lone pairs on the *surrounding (more electronegative) atoms* to give each an octet. If any electrons remain, place them around the central atom—each F gets 3 pairs ($3 \times 6e^- = 18e^-$) and the N gets 1 ($2e^-$), for a total of $20e^-$. Then check that each atom has $8e^-$:

$$\begin{array}{c} :\!\ddot{F}\!: \\ | \\ :\!\ddot{F}\diagup \ddot{N} \diagdown \ddot{F}\!: \end{array}$$

This is the Lewis structure for NF_3. It is a neutral species, so the total number of electrons (bonds plus lone pairs) equals the sum of the valence electrons:

$$6e^- \text{ in three bonds} + 20e^- \text{ in ten lone pairs} = 26 \text{ valence } e^-$$

If we were writing a Lewis structure for a polyatomic ion, we would also take the charge into account, as described in step 2.

Since Lewis structures do not indicate shape, an equally correct depiction of NF_3 is

$$\begin{array}{c} :\!\ddot{F}\!: \\ | \\ :\!\ddot{F}\!\!-\!\!N\!\!-\!\!\ddot{F}\!: \end{array}$$

or any other that retains the *same connections among the atoms*—a central N atom connected by single bonds to each of three surrounding F atoms.

Using these four steps, you can write a Lewis structure for any singly bonded species with a central C, N, or O atom, as well as for some species with central atoms from higher periods. In nearly all their compounds,

- Hydrogen atoms form one bond.
- Carbon atoms form four bonds.
- Nitrogen atoms form three bonds.
- Oxygen atoms form two bonds.
- Surrounding halogens form one bond; fluorine is *always* a surrounding atom.

Sample Problem 10.1 | **Writing Lewis Structures for Molecules with One Central Atom**

Problem Write a Lewis structure for CCl_2F_2, one of the compounds responsible for the depletion of stratospheric ozone.

Solution *Step 1.* Place the atoms relative to each other. In CCl_2F_2, carbon has the lowest group number and EN, so it is the central atom (*see margin*). The halogen atoms surround it, but their specific positions are not important.

Step 2. Determine the total number of valence electrons (from A-group numbers): C is in Group 4A; F and Cl are in Group 7A. Therefore, we have

$$[1 \times C(4e^-)] + [2 \times F(7e^-)] + [2 \times Cl(7e^-)] = 32 \text{ valence } e^-$$

Step 3. Draw single bonds to the central atom (*see margin*) and subtract $2e^-$ for each bond:

$$4 \text{ bonds} \times 2e^- = 8e^- \quad \text{so} \quad 32e^- - 8e^- = 24e^- \text{ remaining}$$

Step 4. Distribute the remaining electrons in pairs, beginning with the surrounding atoms, so that each atom has an octet. Each surrounding halogen gets 3 pairs (*see margin*).

Check Always check that each atom has an octet. Bonding electrons belong to each atom in the bond. The total number in bonds ($8e^-$) and lone pairs ($24e^-$) equals 32 valence e^-. As expected, C has four bonds and the surrounding halogens have one each.

Follow-Up Problem 10.1 Write a Lewis structure for **(a)** H_2S; **(b)** OF_2; **(c)** $SOCl_2$.

Step 1:

Cl
F C F
Cl

Step 3:

Cl
|
F—C—F
|
Cl

Step 4:

:Cl:
|
:F—C—F:
|
:Cl:

In molecules with two or more central atoms bonded to each other, it is usually clear which atoms are central and which surrounding.

Sample Problem 10.2 | **Writing Lewis Structures for Molecules with More Than One Central Atom**

Problem Write the Lewis structure for methanol (molecular formula CH_4O), an important industrial alcohol that can be used as a gasoline alternative in cars.

Solution *Step 1.* Place the atoms relative to each other. The H atoms can have only one bond, so C and O must be central and adjacent to each other. C has four bonds and O has two, so we arrange the H atoms accordingly (*see margin*).

Step 2. Find the sum of valence electrons (C is in Group 4A, O is in Group 6A):

$$[1 \times C(4e^-)] + [1 \times O(6e^-)] + [4 \times H(1e^-)] = 14e^-$$

Step 3. Add single bonds (*see margin*) and subtract $2e^-$ for each bond:

$$5 \text{ bonds} \times 2e^- = 10e^- \quad \text{so} \quad 14e^- - 10e^- = 4e^- \text{ remaining}$$

Step 4. Add the remaining electrons in pairs to fill each valence level. C already has an octet, and each H shares $2e^-$ with the C; so the remaining $4e^-$ form two lone pairs on O to give the Lewis structure for methanol (*see margin*).

Check Each H atom has $2e^-$, and C and O each have $8e^-$. The total number of valence electrons is $14e^-$, which equals $10e^-$ in bonds plus $4e^-$ in two lone pairs. Each H has one bond, C has four, and O has two.

Follow-Up Problem 10.2 Write a Lewis structure for **(a)** hydroxylamine (NH_3O); **(b)** dimethyl ether (C_2H_6O; no O—H bonds).

Step 1:

H
H C O H
H

Step 3:

H
|
H—C—O—H
|
H

Step 4:

H
|
H—C—Ö—H
|
H

Molecules with Multiple Bonds In most cases, if there are not enough electrons for the central atom(s) to attain an octet, a multiple bond is present, and we add the following step to the procedure for writing a Lewis structure:

Step 5. *Cases involving multiple bonds.* If a central atom does not end up with an octet, change a lone pair on a surrounding atom into another bonding pair to the central atom, thus forming a multiple bond.

Sample Problem 10.3 | **Writing Lewis Structures for Molecules with Multiple Bonds**

Problem Write Lewis structures for the following:
(a) Ethylene (C_2H_4), the most important reactant in the manufacture of polymers
(b) Nitrogen (N_2), the most abundant atmospheric gas

Plan We show the structure resulting from steps 1 to 4: placing the atoms, counting the total valence electrons, making single bonds, and distributing the remaining valence electrons in pairs to attain octets. Then we continue with step 5, if needed.

Solution (a) For C_2H_4. After steps 1 to 4, we have

$$\text{H}\backslash \quad / \text{H}$$
$$\text{C}-\ddot{\text{C}}$$
$$\text{H}/ \quad \backslash\text{H}$$

Step 5. Change a lone pair to a bonding pair. The right C has an octet, but the left C has only 6e⁻, so we change the lone pair to another bonding pair between the two C atoms:

$$\text{H}\backslash \quad / \text{H}$$
$$\text{C}=\text{C}$$
$$\text{H}/ \quad \backslash\text{H}$$

(b) For N_2. After steps 1 to 4, we have $:\ddot{\text{N}}-\ddot{\text{N}}:$
Step 5. Neither N has an octet, so we change a lone pair to a bonding pair, $:\ddot{\text{N}}=\text{N}:$
In this case, moving one lone pair to make a double bond still does not give the right N an octet, so we move a lone pair from the left N to make a triple bond, $:\text{N}\equiv\text{N}:$

Check (a) Each C has four bonds and counts the 4e⁻ in the double bond as part of its own octet. The valence electron total is 12e⁻, all in six bonds. **(b)** Each N counts the 6e⁻ in the triple bond as part of its own octet. The valence electron total is 10e⁻, which equals the electrons in three bonds and two lone pairs.

Follow-Up Problem 10.3 Write Lewis structures for **(a)** CO (the only common molecule in which C has three bonds); **(b)** HCN; **(c)** CO_2.

Resonance: Delocalized Electron-Pair Bonding

We often find that, for a molecule or polyatomic ion with *double bonds next to single bonds,* we can write more than one Lewis structure. Which, if any, is correct?

The Need for Resonance Structures To understand this issue, consider ozone (O_3), an air pollutant at ground level but an absorber of harmful ultraviolet (UV) radiation in the stratosphere. Two Lewis structures (with lettered O atoms for clarity) are

$$:\ddot{\text{O}}\diagup^{\ddot{\text{O}}}_{\text{B}}\diagdown\ddot{\text{O}}: \qquad\qquad :\ddot{\text{O}}\diagdown^{\ddot{\text{O}}}_{\text{B}}\diagup\ddot{\text{O}}:$$
$$\text{A} \qquad \text{C} \qquad\qquad\qquad \text{A} \qquad \text{C}$$
$$\text{I} \qquad\qquad\qquad\qquad\qquad \text{II}$$

In structure I, oxygen B has a double bond to oxygen A and a single bond to oxygen C. In structure II, the single and double bonds are reversed. You can rotate I to get II, so these are *not* different types of ozone molecules, but different Lewis structures for the *same* molecule.

In fact, *neither* Lewis structure depicts O_3 accurately, because the two oxygen-oxygen bonds in O_3 are actually identical in length and energy. The bonds in O_3 have properties between an O—O bond and an O=O bond, something like a "one-and-a-half" bond. The molecule is shown more correctly with two Lewis structures, called

resonance structures (or **resonance forms**), and a two-headed resonance arrow ($\longleftrightarrow$) between them. Resonance structures *have the same relative placement of atoms but different locations of bonding and lone electron pairs.* You can convert one resonance form to another by moving lone pairs to bonding positions, and vice versa:

Resonance structures are not real bonding depictions: O_3 does *not* change back and forth quickly from structure I to structure II. The actual molecule is a **resonance hybrid,** an average of the resonance forms. ●

Electron Delocalization Our need for more than one Lewis structure to depict O_3 is due to **electron-pair delocalization.** In a single, double, or triple bond, each electron pair is *localized* between the bonded atoms. In a resonance hybrid, two of the electron pairs (one bonding and one lone pair) are *delocalized:* their density is "spread" over a few adjacent atoms. (This delocalization involves just a few e⁻ pairs, so it is *much less* extensive than the electron delocalization in metals that we saw in Section 9.6.)

In O_3, the result is two identical bonds, each consisting of a single bond (the localized pair) and a *partial bond* (the contribution from one of the delocalized pairs). We draw the resonance hybrid with a curved dashed line to show the delocalized pairs:

resonance hybrid

Resonance is very common. For example, benzene (C_6H_6, *shown below*) has two important resonance forms in which alternating single and double bonds have different positions. The actual molecule is an average of the two forms with six C—C bonds and three electron pairs delocalized over all six C atoms. The delocalized pairs are often shown as a dashed circle (or simply a circle):

resonance forms

or

resonance hybrid

Fractional Bond Orders Partial bonding, as in resonance hybrids, often leads to fractional bond orders. For O_3, we have

$$\text{Bond order} = \frac{3 \text{ electron pairs}}{2 \text{ bonded-atom pairs}} = 1\tfrac{1}{2}$$

The carbon-to-carbon bond order in benzene is 9 electron pairs/6 bonded-atom pairs, or $1\tfrac{1}{2}$ also. For the carbonate ion, CO_3^{2-}, three resonance structures can be drawn. Each has 4 electron pairs shared among 3 bonded-atom pairs, so the bond order is $\tfrac{4}{3}$, or $1\tfrac{1}{3}$. One of the three resonance structures for CO_3^{2-} is

Note here (and in Sample Problem 10.4) that the Lewis structure of a polyatomic ion is written in *square brackets with the ion charge outside the brackets.*

Blue horse   Red donkey

|||

Purple mule

● **A Purple Mule, Not a Blue Horse and a Red Donkey** A mule is a genetic mix, a hybrid, of a horse and a donkey; it is not a horse one instant and a donkey the next. Similarly, the color purple is a mix of red and blue, not red one instant and blue the next. In the same sense, a resonance hybrid is one molecular species, not one resonance form this instant and another resonance form the next. The problem is that we cannot depict the actual species, the hybrid, accurately with a single Lewis structure.

Sample Problem 10.4   Writing Resonance Structures

Problem Write resonance structures for the nitrate ion, NO_3^-, and find the bond order.

Plan We write a Lewis structure, remembering to add $1e^-$ to the total number of valence electrons because of the $1-$ ionic charge. Then we move lone and bonding pairs to write other resonance forms and connect them with the resonance arrow. The bond order is the number of shared electron pairs divided by the number of atom pairs.

Solution After steps 1 to 4, we have

Step 5. Since N has only $6e^-$, we change a lone pair on one of the O atoms to a bonding pair to form a double bond, which gives each atom an octet. All the O atoms are equivalent, however, so we can move a lone pair from any one of the three and obtain three resonance structures:

The bond order is

$$\frac{\text{4 shared electron pairs}}{\text{3 bonded-atom pairs}} = 1\tfrac{1}{3}$$

Check Each structure has the same relative placement of atoms, an octet around each atom, and $24e^-$ (the sum of the valence electron total and $1e^-$ from the ionic charge, distributed in four bonds and eight lone pairs).

Comment These three resonance forms contribute equally to the resonance hybrid because all of the surrounding atoms are identical. This is not always the case, as you'll see next.

Follow-Up Problem 10.4 One of the three resonance structures for CO_3^{2-} was shown just before Sample Problem 10.4. Draw the other two.

Formal Charge: Selecting the More Important Resonance Structure

If one resonance form "looks" more like the resonance hybrid than the others, it "weights" the average in its favor. One way to select the more important resonance form is by determining each atom's **formal charge,** the charge it would have *if the bonding electrons were shared equally.* We'll examine this concept and then see how formal charge compares with oxidation number.

Determining Formal Charge An atom's formal charge is its total number of valence electrons minus *all* of its unshared valence electrons and *half* of its shared valence electrons. Thus,

> Formal charge of atom =
>   no. of valence e^- − (no. of unshared valence e^- + $\tfrac{1}{2}$ no. of shared valence e^-)   **(10.1)**

For example, in O_3, the formal charge of oxygen A in resonance form I is

$$\text{6 valence } e^- - (\text{4 unshared } e^- + \tfrac{1}{2}\text{ of 4 shared } e^-) = 6 - 4 - 2 = 0$$

The formal charges of all the atoms in the two O_3 resonance forms are

Forms I and II have the same formal charges but on different O atoms, so they contribute equally to the resonance hybrid. *Formal charges must sum to the actual charge on the species:* zero for a molecule or the ionic charge for an ion.

Note that, in I, instead of oxygen's usual two bonds, O_B has three bonds and O_C has one. Only when an atom has a zero formal charge does it have its usual number of bonds; the same holds for C in CO_3^{2-}, N in NO_3^-, and so forth.

Choosing the More Important Resonance Form

Three criteria help us choose the more important resonance structure:

- Smaller formal charges (positive *or* negative) are preferable to larger ones.
- The *same* nonzero formal charges on adjacent atoms are not preferred.
- A more negative formal charge should reside on a more electronegative atom.

As in the case of O_3, the resonance forms for CO_3^{2-}, NO_3^-, and benzene all have identical atoms surrounding the central atom(s) and, thus, have identical formal charges and are equally important contributors to the resonance hybrid. But, let's apply these criteria to the cyanate ion, NCO^-, which has two *different* atoms around the central one. Three resonance forms with formal charges are

Formal charges:
Resonance forms:

Form I is *not* an important contributor to the hybrid because it has a larger formal charge on N and a positive formal charge on the more electronegative O. Forms II and III have the same magnitude of charges, but III has a -1 charge on O, the more electronegative atom. Therefore, II and III are more important than I, and III is more important than II.

Formal Charge Versus Oxidation Number

Formal charge (used to examine resonance structures) is *not* the same as oxidation number (used to monitor redox reactions):

- For a *formal charge,* bonding electrons are *shared equally* by the atoms (as if the bonding were *nonpolar covalent*), so each atom has half of them:

$$\text{Formal charge} = \text{valence e}^- - (\text{lone pair e}^- + \tfrac{1}{2}\text{ bonding e}^-)$$

- For an *oxidation number,* bonding electrons are *transferred completely* to the more electronegative atom (as if the bonding were *pure ionic*):

$$\text{Oxidation number} = \text{valence e}^- - (\text{lone pair e}^- + \text{bonding e}^-)$$

For the three cyanate ion resonance structures,

Formal charges:
Oxidation numbers:

Notice that the oxidation numbers *do not* change from one resonance form to another (because the electronegativities *do not* change), but the formal charges *do* change (because the numbers of bonding and lone pairs *do* change).

Lewis Structures for Exceptions to the Octet Rule

The octet rule applies to most molecules (and ions) with Period 2 central atoms, but not every one, and not to many with central atoms from Period 3 and higher. Three important exceptions occur in molecules with (1) electron-deficient atoms, (2) odd-electron atoms, and (3) atoms with expanded valence shells. In this discussion, you'll also see that formal charge has limitations for selecting the best resonance form.

Molecules with Electron-Deficient Atoms

Gaseous molecules containing either beryllium or boron as the central atom are often **electron deficient:** they have *fewer* than eight electrons around the central atom. The Lewis structures, with formal charges, of gaseous beryllium chloride* and boron trifluoride are

*Even though beryllium is in Group 2A(2), most Be compounds have considerable covalent bonding. For example, molten $BeCl_2$ does not conduct electricity, indicating a lack of ions.

There are only four electrons around Be and six around B. Surrounding halogen atoms don't form multiple bonds to the central atoms to give them an octet, because the halogens are much more electronegative. Formal charges make the following structures unlikely:

(Some data for BF_3 show a shorter than expected B—F bond. Shorter bonds indicate double-bond character, so the structure with the B=F bond may be a minor contributor to a resonance hybrid.) Electron-deficient atoms often attain an octet by forming additional bonds in reactions. When BF_3 reacts with ammonia, for instance, a compound forms in which boron attains an octet:*

Molecules with Odd-Electron Atoms A few molecules contain a central atom with an odd number of valence electrons, so they cannot have all their electrons in pairs. Most have a central atom from an odd-numbered group, such as N [Group 5A(15)] or Cl [Group 7A(17)]. These are called **free radicals**, species that contain a lone (unpaired) electron, which makes them paramagnetic (Section 8.4) and extremely reactive. Free radicals are dangerous because they can bond to an H atom in a biomolecule and extract it, which forms a new free radical. This step repeats and can disrupt genes and membranes. Recent studies suggest that free radicals may be involved in cancer and even aging. Antioxidants like vitamin E interrupt free-radical proliferation.

Consider the free radical nitrogen dioxide, NO_2, a major contributor to urban smog, that is formed when the NO in auto exhaust is oxidized. NO_2 has several resonance forms. Two differ in terms of which O atom is doubly bonded, as in the case of ozone. Two others have the lone electron residing on the N or on an O, so the resonance hybrid has the lone electron delocalized over these two atoms:

Let's see if formal charge considerations help us decide where the electron resides most of the time. The form with it on the singly bonded O has zero formal charges (*right*), while the form with it on N (*left*) has some nonzero charges. Thus, based on formal charge, the form on the right is more important. But, chemical facts suggest otherwise. Free radicals often react with each other to pair their lone electrons. When two NO_2 molecules react, the lone electrons pair up to form the N—N bond in dinitrogen tetraoxide (N_2O_4) and each N attains an octet:

Thus, given the way NO_2 reacts, the lone electron may spend most of its time on N, making *that* form more important. Apparently, in this case, formal charge is not very useful for picking the most important resonance form; we'll see other cases below.

Expanded Valence Shells Many molecules (and ions) have more than eight valence electrons around the central atom. *An atom expands its valence shell to form more bonds, which releases energy.* The central atom must be large and have empty orbitals that can hold the additional pairs. Therefore, **expanded valence shells** occur only with *nonmetals from Period 3 or higher because they have d orbitals available.* Such a central atom may be bonded to more than four atoms, or to four or fewer.

---

*Reactions in which one species "donates" an electron pair to another to form a covalent bond are Lewis acid-base reactions, which we discuss fully in Chapter 18.

1. *Central atom bonded to more than four atoms.* Phosphorus pentachloride, PCl_5, is a fuming yellow-white solid used to manufacture lacquers and films. It forms when phosphorus trichloride, PCl_3, reacts with chlorine gas. The P in PCl_3 has an octet, but two more bonds to chlorine form and P expands its valence shell to 10 electrons in PCl_5. Note that when PCl_5 forms, *one* Cl—Cl bond breaks *(left side of the equation)*, and *two* P—Cl bonds form *(right side)*, for a net increase of one bond:

Sulfur hexafluoride, SF_6, a dense and inert gas, is used as an electrical insulator. Analogously to PCl_5, it forms when sulfur tetrafluoride, SF_4, reacts with F_2. The S in SF_4 already has an expanded valence shell of 10 electrons, but two more bonds to F expand the valence shell further to 12 electrons:

2. *Central atoms bonded to four or fewer atoms.* By applying the concept of formal charge, we can draw Lewis structures with expanded valence shells of central atoms bonded to *four or fewer* atoms. The S in SF_4 is one example, and others follow:

- *Sulfuric acid.* Two resonance forms of H_2SO_4, with formal charges, are

Form I obeys the octet rule, but it has several nonzero formal charges. In form II, sulfur has 12 electrons (6 bonds) around it, but all zero formal charges. Thus, based on the formal charge rules alone, II contributes more than I to the resonance hybrid. More important than whether rules are followed, form II is consistent with observation. In gaseous H_2SO_4, the two sulfur-oxygen bonds *with* an H atom attached to the O are 157 pm long, whereas the two sulfur-oxygen bonds *without* an H atom are 142 pm long. This shorter bond indicates double-bond character, and other measurements indicate greater electron density in the bonds without the attached H.

- *Sulfate ion.* When sulfuric acid loses two H^+ ions, it forms the sulfate ion, SO_4^{2-}. Measurements indicate all the bonds in SO_4^{2-} are 149 pm long, between the length of an S=O bond (~142 pm) and that of an S—O bond (~157 pm). Six of the seven resonance forms consistent with these data have an expanded valence shell and zero formal charges. Two of the six *(left)* and the one that obeys the octet rule *(right)* are

- *Two sulfur oxides.* Measurements show that the sulfur-oxygen bonds in SO_2 and SO_3 are all approximately 142 pm long, indicating S=O bonds. Lewis structures consistent with these data have zero formal charges *(two at left)*, but others *(two at right)* obey the octet rule:

3. *Limitations of Lewis structures and formal charge.* Chemistry has been a central science for well over two centuries, yet controversies often arise over interpretation of

data, even in established areas like bonding and structure. We've seen that a single Lewis structure often cannot accurately depict a molecule, so we need several resonance forms to do so.

Formal charge rules have limitations, too. They were not useful in choosing the correct location for the lone electron in NO_2. And, quantum-mechanical calculations indicate that resonance forms with expanded valence shells that have zero formal charges look *less* like the actual species than forms that follow the octet rule but have higher formal charges. Shorter bonds arise, these findings suggest, not from double-bond character, but because the higher formal charges draw the bonded atoms closer. Such considerations favor the octet-rule forms for H_2SO_4, SO_4^{2-}, SO_2, and SO_3. Thus, formal charge may be a useful tool for selecting the most important resonance form, but it is far from perfect. Nevertheless, while keeping these contrary findings in mind, we will continue to draw structures based on formal charge rules because they provide a simple approach consistent with experimental data.

Sample Problem 10.5 | **Writing Lewis Structures for Octet-Rule Exceptions**

Problem Write a Lewis structure and identify the octet-rule exception for **(a)** $SClF_5$; **(b)** H_3PO_4 (draw two resonance forms and select the more important); **(c)** $BFCl_2$.

Plan We write each Lewis structure and examine it for exceptions to the octet rule. **(a)** and **(b)** The central atoms are in Period 3, so they can have more than an octet. **(c)** The central atom is B, which can have fewer than an octet of electrons.

Solution **(a)** $SClF_5$ has an *expanded valence shell*. The Lewis structure is

(b) H_3PO_4 has two resonance forms. The structures, with formal charges, are

Structure I obeys the octet rule but has nonzero formal charges. Structure II has an expanded valence shell with zero formal charges. According to formal charge rules, structure II is the more important form.

(c) $BFCl_2$ is an *electron-deficient molecule;* B has only six electrons surrounding it:

Comment In (b), structure II is consistent with bond-length measurements, which show one shorter (152 pm) phosphorus-oxygen bond and three longer (157 pm) ones. Nevertheless, as for H_2SO_4, calculations show that structure I may be more important.

Follow-Up Problem 10.5 Write a Lewis structure with minimal formal charges for **(a)** $POCl_3$; **(b)** ClO_2; **(c)** XeF_4.

■ Summary of Section 10.1

- A stepwise process converts a molecular formula into a Lewis structure, a two-dimensional representation of a molecule (or ion) that shows the placement of atoms and distribution of valence electrons among bonding and lone pairs.
- When two or more Lewis structures can be drawn for the same relative placement of atoms, the actual structure is a hybrid of those resonance forms.

- Formal charges can be useful for choosing the more important contributor to the hybrid, but experimental data always determine the choice.
- Molecules with an electron-deficient atom (central Be or B) or an odd-electron atom (free radicals) have less than an octet around the central atom but often attain an octet in reactions.
- In a molecule (or ion) with a central atom from Period 3 or higher, that atom can have more than eight valence electrons because it is larger and has empty *d* orbitals for expanding its valence shell.

10.2 • VALENCE-SHELL ELECTRON-PAIR REPULSION (VSEPR) THEORY

Virtually every biochemical process hinges to a great extent on the shapes of interacting molecules. Every medicine you take, odor you smell, or flavor you taste depends on part or all of one molecule fitting together with another. Biologists have found that complex behaviors in many organisms, such as mating, defense, navigation, and feeding, often depend on one molecule's shape matching that of another. In this section, we discuss a model for predicting the shape of a molecule.

To obtain the molecular shape, chemists start with the Lewis structure and apply **valence-shell electron-pair repulsion (VSEPR) theory.** Its basic principle is that, *to minimize repulsions, each group of valence electrons around a central atom is located as far as possible from the others.* A "group" of electrons is any number that occupies a localized region around an atom: single bond, double bond, triple bond,* lone pair, or even lone electron. The **molecular shape** is the three-dimensional arrangement of nuclei joined by the bonding groups.

Electron-Group Arrangements and Molecular Shapes

When two, three, four, five, or six objects attached to a central point maximize the space between them, five geometric patterns result, which Figure 10.2A shows with balloons. If the objects are valence-electron groups, repulsions maximize the space each occupies around the central atom, and we obtain the five *electron-group arrangements* seen in the great majority of molecules and polyatomic ions.

Classifying Molecular Shapes The *electron-group arrangement* is defined by the bonding *and* nonbonding electron groups, but the *molecular shape* is defined by the relative positions of the nuclei, which are connected by the bonding groups only. Figure 10.2B shows the molecular shapes that occur when *all* the surrounding electron groups are *bonding* groups. When some are *nonbonding* groups, no nucleus is attached so dif-

---

*The two electron pairs in a double bond (or the three pairs in a triple bond) occupy separate orbitals, so they remain near each other and act as one electron group (see Chapter 11).

Figure 10.2 Electron-group repulsions and molecular shapes. A, Five geometric orientations arise when each balloon occupies as much space as possible. **B,** Mutually repelling bonding groups (*gray sticks*) attach a surrounding atom (*dark gray*) to the central atom (*red*). The name is the electron-group arrangement.

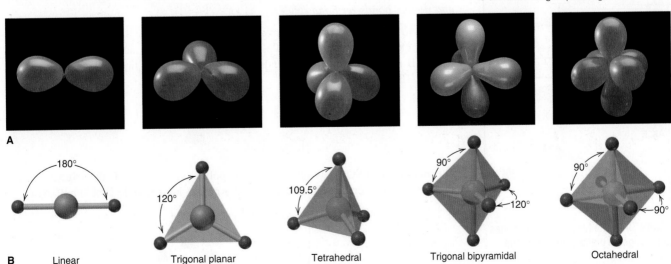

A

B   Linear   Trigonal planar   Tetrahedral   Trigonal bipyramidal   Octahedral

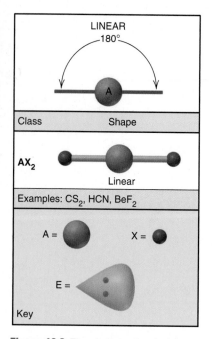

Figure 10.3 The single molecular shape of the linear electron-group arrangement. The key (*bottom*) for A, X, and E also refers to Figures 10.4, 10.5, 10.7, and 10.8.

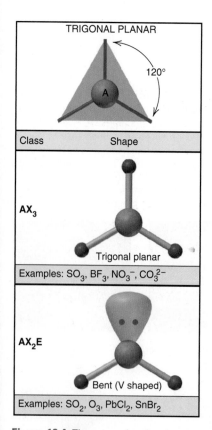

Figure 10.4 The two molecular shapes of the trigonal planar electron-group arrangement.

ferent molecular shapes occur. Thus, *the same electron-group arrangement can give rise to different molecular shapes:* some with all bonding groups (as in Figure 10.2B) and others with bonding and nonbonding groups. To classify molecular shapes, we assign each a specific AX_mE_n designation, where m and n are integers, A is the central atom, X is a surrounding atom, and E is a nonbonding valence-electron group (usually a lone pair).

The Importance of Bond Angle The **bond angle** is the angle formed by the nuclei of two surrounding atoms with the nucleus of the central atom at the vertex. The angles shown for the shapes in Figure 10.2B are *ideal* bond angles determined by basic geometry alone. We observe them when all the bonding groups are the same and connected to the same type of atom. When this is not the case, the real bond angles deviate from the ideal angles:

The Molecular Shape with Two Electron Groups (Linear Arrangement)

Two electron groups attached to a central atom point in opposite directions. This **linear arrangement** of electron groups results in a molecule with a **linear shape** and a bond angle of 180°. Figure 10.3 shows the general form (*top*) and shape (*middle*) with VSEPR shape class (AX_2), and gives the formulas of some linear molecules.

Gaseous beryllium chloride ($BeCl_2$) is a linear molecule. Recall that gaseous Be compounds are electron deficient, with two electron pairs around the central Be:

In carbon dioxide, the central C atom forms two double bonds with the O atoms:

Each double bond acts as one electron group and is 180° away from the other. The lone pairs on the O atoms of CO_2 or on the Cl atoms of $BeCl_2$ are *not* involved in the molecular shape: only electron groups around the *central* atom affect shape.

Molecular Shapes with Three Electron Groups (Trigonal Planar Arrangement)

Three electron groups around a central atom point to the corners of an equilateral triangle, which gives the **trigonal planar arrangement** and an ideal bond angle of 120° (Figure 10.4). This arrangement has two molecular shapes—one with all bonding groups and the other with one lone pair. It allows us to see *the effects of lone pairs and double bonds on bond angles*.

1. *All bonding groups: trigonal planar shape (AX_3).* Boron trifluoride (BF_3), another electron-deficient molecule, is an example. It has six electrons around the central B atom in three single bonds to F atoms. The four nuclei lie in a plane, and each F—B—F angle is 120°:

The nitrate ion (NO_3^-) is one of several polyatomic ions with the trigonal planar shape. One of three resonance forms of the nitrate ion (Sample Problem 10.4) is

The resonance hybrid has three identical bonds of bond order $1\frac{1}{3}$, so the ideal bond angle is observed.

2. One lone pair: bent or V shape (AX$_2$E). Gaseous tin(II) chloride is a molecule with a **bent shape,** or **V shape,** with three electron groups in a trigonal plane and a lone pair at one of the triangle's corners. A lone pair often has a major effect on bond angle. Because it is held by only one nucleus, a lone pair is less confined than a bonding pair and so exerts stronger repulsions. In general, *a lone pair repels bonding pairs more than bonding pairs repel each other, so it decreases the angle between bonding pairs.* Note the 95° bond angle in SnCl$_2$, which is considerably less than the ideal 120°:

Effect of Double Bonds on Bond Angle

When the surrounding atoms and electron groups are not identical, the bond angles may also be affected. Consider formaldehyde (CH$_2$O), whose uses include the manufacture of countertops and the production of methanol. Its trigonal planar shape is due to two types of surrounding atoms (O and H) and two types of electron groups (single and double bonds):

The actual H—C—H bond angle is less than the ideal 120° because *the greater electron density of a double bond repels electrons in single bonds more than the single bonds repel each other.*

Molecular Shapes with Four Electron Groups (Tetrahedral Arrangement)

Shapes based on two or three electron groups lie in a plane, but four electron groups require three dimensions to maximize separation. Consider methane, whose Lewis structure (*below, left*) shows four bonds pointing to the corners of a square, which suggests 90° bond angles. But, *Lewis structures do **not** depict shape.* In three dimensions, the four electron groups lie at the corners of a *tetrahedron,* a polyhedron with four faces made of equilateral triangles, giving bond angles of 109.5° (Figure 10.5).

A *perspective drawing* for methane (*above, middle*) indicates depth by using solid and dashed wedges for bonds out of the plane of the page. The normal bond lines (*blue*) are in the plane of the page; the solid wedge (*green*) is the bond from the C atom in the plane of the page to the H above that plane; and the dashed wedge (*red*) is the bond from the C to the H below the plane of the page. The ball-and-stick model (*above, right*) shows the tetrahedral shape more clearly.

*All molecules or ions with four electron groups around a central atom adopt the **tetrahedral arrangement**.* There are three shapes with this arrangement:

1. All bonding groups: tetrahedral shape (AX$_4$). Methane has a tetrahedral shape, a very common geometry in organic molecules. In Sample Problem 10.1, we drew the Lewis structure for CCl$_2$F$_2$, without regard to relative placement of the four halogen atoms around the carbon atom. Because Lewis structures are flat, it may seem like you can write two different ones for CCl$_2$F$_2$, but they represent the same molecule, as a twist of the wrist reveals (Figure 10.6, *next page*).

Figure 10.5 The three molecular shapes of the tetrahedral electron-group arrangement.

Figure 10.6 Lewis structures do not indicate molecular shape. In this model, Cl is green and F is yellow.

2. *One lone pair: trigonal pyramidal shape (AX₃E).* Ammonia (NH_3) is an example of a molecule with a **trigonal pyramidal shape,** a tetrahedron with one vertex "missing." Stronger repulsions by the lone pair make the H—N—H bond angle slightly less than the ideal 109.5°. The lone pair forces the N—H pairs closer to each other, and the bond angle is 107.3°. NF_3 (see page 364) also has a trigonal pyramidal shape.

Picturing shapes is a great way to visualize a reaction. For instance, when ammonia reacts with an acid, the lone pair on N forms a bond to the H^+ and yields the ammonium ion (NH_4^+), one of many tetrahedral polyatomic ions. As the lone pair becomes a bonding pair, the H—N—H angle expands from 107.3° to 109.5°:

3. *Two lone pairs: bent or V shape (AX₂E₂).* Water is the most important V-shaped molecule with the tetrahedral arrangement. [Note that, in the trigonal planar arrangement, the V shape has two bonding groups and *one* lone pair (AX₂E), and its ideal bond angle is 120°, not 109.5°.] Repulsions from two lone pairs are greater than from one, and the H—O—H bond angle is 104.5°, less than the H—N—H angle in NH_3:

Thus, for similar molecules within a given electron-group arrangement, electron-electron repulsions cause deviations from ideal bond angles in the following order:

> Lone pair–lone pair > lone pair–bonding pair > bonding pair–bonding pair   (10.2)

Molecular Shapes with Five Electron Groups (Trigonal Bipyramidal Arrangement)

All molecules with five or six electron groups have a central atom from Period 3 or higher because only those atoms have *d* orbitals available to expand the valence shell.

Relative Positions of Electron Groups Five mutually repelling electron groups form the **trigonal bipyramidal arrangement,** in which two trigonal pyramids share a common base (Figure 10.7). This is the only case in which *there are two different positions for electron groups and two ideal bond angles.* Three **equatorial groups** lie in a trigonal plane that includes the central atom, and two **axial groups** lie above and below this plane. Therefore, a 120° bond angle separates equatorial groups, and a 90° angle separates axial from equatorial groups. Two factors come into play:

- The greater the bond angle, the weaker the repulsions, so *equatorial-equatorial (120°) repulsions are weaker than axial-equatorial (90°) repulsions.*
- The stronger repulsions from lone pairs means that, when possible, *lone pairs occupy equatorial positions.*

Shapes for the Trigonal Bipyramidal Arrangement
The tendency for lone pairs to occupy equatorial positions, and thus minimize stronger axial-equatorial repulsions, governs three of the four shapes for this arrangement.

1. *All bonding groups: trigonal bipyramidal shape (AX₅).* Phosphorus pentachloride (PCl₅) has a trigonal bipyramidal shape. With five identical surrounding atoms, the bond angles are ideal:

2. *One lone pair: seesaw shape (AX₄E).* Sulfur tetrafluoride (SF₄), a strong fluorinating agent, has the **seesaw shape**; in Figure 10.7, the "seesaw" is tipped on an end. This is the first example of *lone pairs occupying equatorial positions* to minimize repulsions. The lone pair repels all four bonding pairs, reducing the bond angles to 101.5° and 86.8°:

3. *Two lone pairs: T shape (AX₃E₂).* Bromine trifluoride (BrF₃), one of many compounds with fluorine bonded to a larger halogen, has a **T shape.** Since both lone pairs occupy equatorial positions, we see a greater decrease in the axial-equatorial bond angle, down to 86.2°:

4. *Three lone pairs: linear shape (AX₂E₃).* The triiodide ion (I₃⁻), which forms when I₂ dissolves in aqueous I⁻ solution, is linear. With three equatorial lone pairs and two axial bonding pairs, the three nuclei form a straight line and a 180° X—A—X bond angle:

Figure 10.7 The four molecular shapes of the trigonal bipyramidal electron-group arrangement.

Examples: SF$_6$, IOF$_5$

Examples: BrF$_5$, TeF$_5^-$, XeOF$_4$

Examples: XeF$_4$, ICl$_4^-$

Figure 10.8 The three molecular shapes of the octahedral electron-group arrangement.

Molecular Shapes with Six Electron Groups (Octahedral Arrangement)

Six electron groups form the **octahedral arrangement.** An *octahedron* is a polyhedron with eight equilateral triangles for faces and six identical vertices (Figure 10.8). Each of the six groups points to a corner, which gives a 90° ideal bond angle.

1. *All bonding groups: octahedral shape (AX$_6$).* When seesaw-shaped SF$_4$ reacts with more F$_2$ (see pp. 371 and 377), the central S atom expands its valence shell further to form octahedral sulfur hexafluoride (SF$_6$):

2. *One lone pair: square pyramidal shape (AX$_5$E).* Iodine pentafluoride (IF$_5$) has a **square pyramidal shape.** Note that it makes no difference where one lone pair resides because all the bond angles are 90°. The lone pair reduces the bond angles to 81.9°:

3. *Two lone pairs: square planar shape (AX$_4$E$_2$).* Xenon tetrafluoride (XeF$_4$) has a **square planar shape.** To avoid stronger 90° lone pair–lone pair repulsions, two lone pairs lie *opposite* each other:

Figure 10.9 displays the shapes possible for elements in different periods, and Figure 10.10 summarizes the molecular shapes we've discussed.

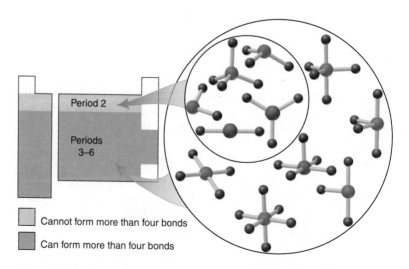

Cannot form more than four bonds

Can form more than four bonds

Figure 10.9 Molecular shapes for central atoms in Period 2 and in higher periods.

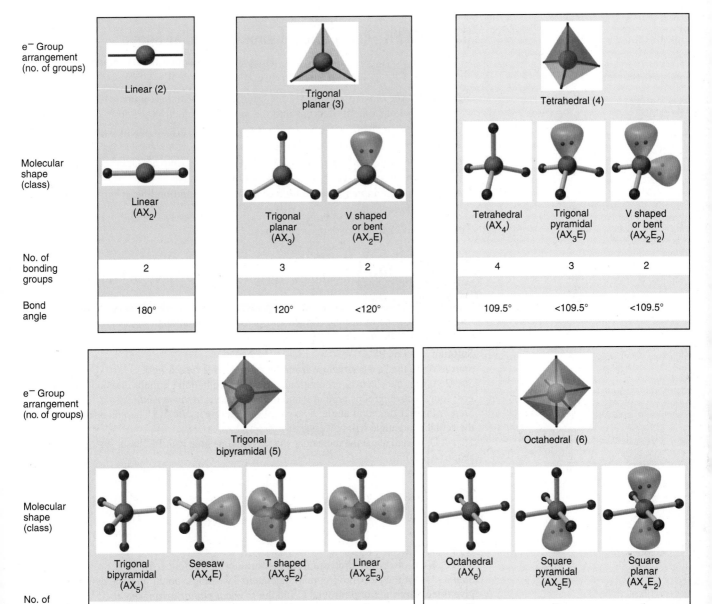

Figure 10.10 A summary of common molecular shapes with two to six electron groups.

Figure 10.11 The four steps in converting a molecular formula to a molecular shape.

Using VSEPR Theory to Determine Molecular Shape

Let's apply a stepwise method for using VSEPR theory to determine a molecular shape from a molecular formula (Figure 10.11):

Step 1. Write the Lewis structure from the molecular formula (Figure 10.1, p. 364) to see the relative placement of atoms and the number of electron groups.

Step 2. Assign an electron-group arrangement by counting *all* electron groups (bonding plus nonbonding) around the central atom.

Step 3. Predict the ideal bond angle from the electron-group arrangement and *the effect of any deviation* caused by lone pairs or double bonds.

Step 4. Draw and name the molecular shape by counting bonding groups and nonbonding groups separately.

The next two sample problems apply these steps.

Sample Problem 10.6   Examining Shapes with Two, Three, or Four Electron Groups

Problem Draw the molecular shapes and predict the bond angles (relative to the ideal angles) of **(a)** PF_3 and **(b)** $COCl_2$.

Solution (a) For PF_3.

Step 1. Write the Lewis structure from the formula (*see below, left*).

Step 2. Assign the electron-group arrangement: Three bonding groups and one lone pair give four electron groups around P and the *tetrahedral arrangement*.

Step 3. Predict the bond angle: The ideal bond angle is 109.5°. There is one lone pair, so the actual bond angle will be less than 109.5°.

Step 4. Draw and name the molecular shape: With one lone pair, PF_3 has a trigonal pyramidal shape (AX_3E):

$$:\!F\!\!-\!\!P\!\!-\!\!F\!: \quad \xrightarrow[\text{groups}]{4\ e^-} \quad \text{Tetrahedral arrangement} \quad \xrightarrow[\text{pair}]{1\ \text{lone}} \quad <109.5° \quad \xrightarrow[\text{groups}]{3\ \text{bonding}} \quad :\!F\!\cdots\!\overset{P}{\diagdown}\!F\!: \quad 96.3° \quad AX_3E$$

(b) For $COCl_2$.

Step 1. Write the Lewis structure from the formula (*see below, left*).

Step 2. Assign the electron-group arrangement: Two single bonds and one double bond give three electron groups around C and the *trigonal planar arrangement*.

Step 3. Predict the bond angles: The ideal bond angle is 120°, but the double bond between C and O will compress the Cl—C—Cl angle to less than 120°.

Step 4. Draw and name the molecular shape: With three electron groups and no lone pairs, $COCl_2$ has a trigonal planar shape (AX_3):

$$:\!\overset{\displaystyle :O:}{\underset{\displaystyle :Cl \diagup \ \diagdown Cl:}{C}} \quad \xrightarrow[\text{groups}]{3\ e^-} \quad \text{Trigonal planar arrangement} \quad \xrightarrow[\text{bond}]{1\ \text{double}} \quad \begin{array}{l} Cl\!-\!C\!=\!O >120° \\ Cl\!-\!C\!-\!Cl <120° \end{array} \quad \xrightarrow[\text{groups}]{3\ \text{bonding}} \quad :\!\overset{\displaystyle :O:}{\underset{\displaystyle :Cl \quad 111° \quad Cl:}{C}}\ 124.5° \quad AX_3$$

Check We compare the answers with the general information in Figure 10.10.

Comment Be sure the Lewis structure is correct because it determines the other steps.

Follow-Up Problem 10.6 Draw the molecular shapes and predict the bond angles (relative to the ideal angles) of **(a)** CS_2; **(b)** $PbCl_2$; **(c)** CBr_4; **(d)** SF_2.

Sample Problem 10.7 — Examining Shapes with Five or Six Electron Groups

Problem Draw the molecular shapes and predict the bond angles (relative to the ideal angles) of (a) SbF_5 and (b) BrF_5.

Plan We proceed as in Sample Problem 10.6, being sure to minimize the number of axial-equatorial repulsions.

Solution (a) For SbF_5.

Step 1. Lewis structure (*see below, left*).

Step 2. Electron-group arrangement: With five electron groups, this is the *trigonal bipyramidal* arrangement.

Step 3. Bond angles: All the groups and surrounding atoms are identical, so the bond angles are ideal: 120° between equatorial groups and 90° between axial and equatorial groups.

Step 4. Molecular shape: Five electron groups and no lone pairs give the trigonal bipyramidal shape (AX_5):

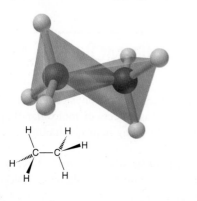

(b) For BrF_5.

Step 1. Lewis structure (*see below, left*).

Step 2. Electron-group arrangement: Six electron groups give the *octahedral* arrangement.

Step 3. Bond angles: The lone pair will make all bond angles less than the ideal 90°.

Step 4. Molecular shape: With one lone pair, BrF_5 has the square pyramidal shape (AX_5E):

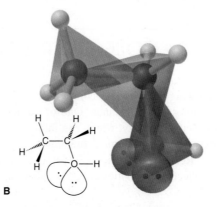

Check We compare our answers with Figure 10.10.

Comment We will also see the linear, tetrahedral, square planar, and octahedral shapes in an important group of substances, called *coordination compounds,* in Chapter 23.

Follow-Up Problem 10.7 Draw the molecular shapes and predict the bond angles (relative to the ideal angles) of (a) ICl_2^-; (b) ClF_3; (c) SOF_4.

Molecular Shapes with More Than One Central Atom

The shapes of molecules with more than one central atom are composites of the shapes around each of the atoms. Here are two examples:

1. Ethane (CH_3CH_3; molecular formula C_2H_6) is a component of natural gas. With four bonding groups and no lone pairs around the two central carbons, ethane is shaped like two overlapping tetrahedra (Figure 10.12A).

Figure 10.12 The tetrahedral shapes around the central atoms and the overall shapes of ethane (**A**) and ethanol (**B**).

A

B

2. Ethanol (CH_3CH_2OH; molecular formula C_2H_6O), the intoxicating substance in beer, wine, and whiskey, has three central atoms (Figure 10.12B). The CH_3— group is tetrahedrally shaped, and the —CH_2— group has four bonding groups around its central C atom, so it is also tetrahedrally shaped. The O atom has two bonding groups and two lone pairs around it, so the —OH group has a V shape (AX_2E_2).

Sample Problem 10.8 **Predicting Molecular Shapes with More Than One Central Atom**

Problem Determine the shape around each central atom in acetone, $(CH_3)_2CO$.

Plan There are three central C atoms, two of which are in CH_3— groups. We determine the shape around one central atom at a time.

Solution *Step 1.* Lewis structure (*see below, left*).

Step 2. Electron-group arrangement: Each CH_3— group has four electron groups around its central C, so its electron-group arrangement is *tetrahedral*. The third C atom has three electron groups around it, so it has the *trigonal planar arrangement.*

Step 3. Bond angles: The H—C—H angle in CH_3— should be near the ideal 109.5°. The C=O double bond will compress the C—C—C angle to less than the ideal 120°.

Step 4. Shapes around central atoms: With four electron groups and no lone pairs, the shape around C in each CH_3— is tetrahedral (AX_4). With three electron groups and no lone pairs, the shape around the middle C is trigonal planar (AX_3):

Follow-Up Problem 10.8 Determine the shape around each central atom and predict any deviations from ideal bond angles in the following: **(a)** H_2SO_4; **(b)** propyne (C_3H_4; there is one C≡C bond); **(c)** S_2F_2.

■ Summary of Section 10.2

- VSEPR theory proposes that each electron group (single bond, multiple bond, lone pair, or lone electron) around a central atom remains as far from the others as possible.
- Five electron-group arrangements are possible when two, three, four, five, or six electron groups surround a central atom. Each arrangement is associated with one or more molecular shapes, depending on the numbers of bonding and lone pairs.
- Ideal bond angles are based on the regular geometric arrangements. Deviations from them occur when surrounding atoms and/or electron groups are not identical.
- Lone pairs and double bonds exert stronger repulsions than single bonds.
- Shapes of larger molecules are composites of the shapes around each central atom.

10.3 • MOLECULAR SHAPE AND MOLECULAR POLARITY

Knowing the shape of its molecules is key to understanding the physical and chemical behavior of a substance. One of the most far-reaching effects of molecular shape is molecular polarity, which can influence melting and boiling points, solubility, reactivity, and even biological function.

Recall from Chapter 9 that a covalent bond is *polar* when the atoms have different electronegativities and, thus, share the electrons unequally. In diatomic molecules, such as HF, the only bond is polar, so the molecule is polar. In larger molecules, *both shape and bond polarity determine* **molecular polarity,** an imbalance of charge over the whole molecule or large portion of it. Polar molecules become oriented in an electric field, with their partially charged ends pointing toward the oppositely charged plates (Figure 10.13). **Dipole moment (μ)** is a measure of molecular polarity, given in the unit *debye* (D)* derived from SI units of charge (coulomb, C) and length (m): $1 \text{ D} = 3.34 \times 10^{-30} \text{ C·m}$.

Bond Polarity, Bond Angle, and Dipole Moment

The presence of polar bonds does not *always* result in a polar molecule; we must also consider shape and the atoms surrounding the central atom. Here are three cases:

1. *CO_2: polar bonds, nonpolar molecule.* In carbon dioxide, the electronegativity difference between C (EN = 2.5) and O (EN = 3.5) makes each C=O bond polar. But CO_2 is linear, so the bonds point 180° from each other. The two bond polarities are counterbalanced, and the molecule has *no net dipole moment* (μ = 0 D). The electron density model shows regions of high negative charge (*red*) distributed equally on either side of the central region of high positive charge (*blue*):

2. *H_2O: polar bonds, polar molecule.* Water also has two polar bonds, but it *is* polar (μ = 1.85 D). In each O—H bond, electron density is pulled from H (EN = 2.1) toward O (EN = 3.5). Bond polarities are *not* counterbalanced because the molecule is V shaped (also see Figure 4.1, p. 138). The bond polarities are partially reinforced, making the O end partially negative and the other end (the region between the H atoms) partially positive:

(The molecular polarity of water has some amazing effects, from determining the composition of the oceans to supporting life itself, as you'll see in Chapter 12.)

3. *Same shapes, different polarities.* When different molecules have the same shape, the identities of the surrounding atoms affect polarity. Carbon tetrachloride (CCl_4) and chloroform ($CHCl_3$) are tetrahedral molecules with very different polarities. In CCl_4, all the surrounding atoms are Cl atoms. Each C—Cl bond is polar (ΔEN = 0.5), but the molecule is nonpolar (μ = 0 D) because the bond polarities counterbalance each other. In $CHCl_3$, an H replaces one Cl, disrupting the balance and giving chloroform a significant dipole moment (μ = 1.01 D):

B Electric field off

C Electric field on

Figure 10.13 The orientation of polar molecules in an electric field. **A,** Space-filling (*left*) and electron-density models (*right*) of the polar HF molecule. **B,** With the external electric field off, HF molecules are oriented randomly. **C,** With the field on, the molecules, on average, become oriented.

*The unit is named for the Dutch-American scientist Peter Debye (1884–1966) who won the Nobel Prize in 1936 for contributions to the fields of molecular structure and solution behavior.

Sample Problem 10.9   Predicting the Polarity of Molecules

Problem For each of the following, use the molecular shape and EN values and trends (Figure 9.20, p. 349) to predict the direction of bond and molecular polarity, if present:
(a) Ammonia, NH_3
(b) Boron trifluoride, BF_3
(c) Carbonyl sulfide, COS (atom sequence SCO)

Plan We draw and name the molecular shape and point a polar arrow toward the atom with higher EN in each bond. If the bond polarities balance one another, the molecule is nonpolar; if they reinforce each other, we show the direction of the molecular polarity.

Solution (a) For NH_3. The molecular shape is trigonal pyramidal. N (EN = 3.0) is more electronegative than H (EN = 2.1), so the bond polarities point toward N and partially reinforce each other; thus the molecular polarity points toward N:

molecular shape

bond polarities

molecular polarity

Therefore, ammonia is polar.

(b) For BF_3. The molecular shape is trigonal planar. F (EN = 4.0) is farther to the right in Period 2 than B (EN = 2.0), so it is more electronegative; thus, each bond polarity points toward F. However, the bond angle is 120°, so the three bond polarities balance each other, and BF_3 has no molecular polarity:

molecular shape

bond polarities

no molecular polarity

Therefore, boron trifluoride is nonpolar.

(c) For COS. The molecular shape is linear. With C and S having the same EN, the C=S bond is nonpolar, but the C=O bond is quite polar (ΔEN = 1.0), so there is a net molecular polarity toward the O:

S=C=O
molecular shape

S=C=O
bond polarity

S=C=O
molecular polarity

Therefore, carbonyl sulfide is polar.

Check The electron density models confirm our conclusions. Note that, in (b), the negative (*red*) regions surround the central B (*blue*) symmetrically.

Follow-Up Problem 10.9 Show the bond polarities and molecular polarity, if any, for each of the following:
(a) Dichloromethane (CH_2Cl_2)
(b) Iodine oxide pentafluoride (IOF_5)
(c) Nitrogen tribromide (NBr_3).

The Effect of Molecular Polarity on Behavior

Earlier we mentioned that molecular polarity influences physical behavior. Let's see how a molecular property like dipole moment affects a macroscopic property like boiling point. Consider the two dichloroethylenes shown below. They have the *same* molecular formula ($C_2H_2Cl_2$) but *different* physical and chemical properties; that is, they are constitutional isomers (Section 3.3). Both molecules are planar, with a trigonal planar shape around each C atom. The *trans* isomer is nonpolar ($\mu = 0$ D) because the polar C—Cl bonds balance each other. The *cis* isomer is polar ($\mu = 1.90$ D) because the bond polarities partially reinforce each other, with the molecular polarity pointing between the Cl atoms.

A liquid boils when it forms bubbles against the atmospheric pressure. To enter the bubble, the molecules in the liquid must overcome the weak attractive forces *between* them. Because of their polarity, the *cis* molecules attract each other more strongly than the *trans* molecules do. Since more energy is needed to overcome the stronger attractions, we expect the *cis* isomer to have a higher boiling point: *cis*-1,2-dichloroethylene boils 13°C higher than *trans*-1,2-dichloroethylene.

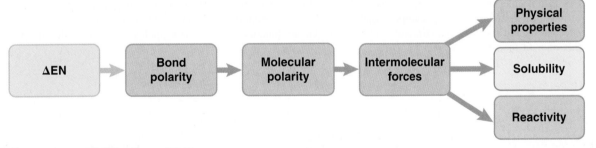

Figure 10.14 shows the chain of influences of atomic properties on the behavior of substances. We extend these relationships in Chapter 12, and the upcoming Chemical Connections essay discusses some biological effects of molecular shape and polarity.

Figure 10.14 The influence of atomic properties on macroscopic behavior.

ΔEN → **Bond polarity** → **Molecular polarity** → **Intermolecular forces** → **Physical properties** / **Solubility** / **Reactivity**

■ Summary of Section 10.3

- Bond polarity and molecular shape determine molecular polarity, which is measured as a dipole moment.
- A molecule with polar bonds is not necessarily a polar molecule. When bond polarities counterbalance each other, the molecule is nonpolar; when they reinforce each other, the molecule is polar.
- Molecular shape and polarity can affect physical properties, such as boiling point, and they play a central role in biological function.

A biological cell can be thought of as a membrane-bound sack filled with an aqueous fluid containing many molecules of various shapes. Many complex processes begin when a molecular "key" fits into a molecular "lock" with a complementary shape. Typically, the key is a small molecule circulating in cellular or other bodily fluid, and the lock, the *biological receptor*, is a large molecule often embedded in a membrane. The *receptor site* is a small region of the receptor with a shape that matches the molecular key. Thousands of molecules per second collide with the receptor site, but when one with the correct shape does, the receptor "grabs" it through intermolecular attractions, and the biological response begins.

Molecular Shape and the Sense of Smell

Molecular shapes fitting together is crucial to the sense of smell (olfaction). To have an odor, a substance must be a gas or a volatile liquid or solid and must be at least slightly soluble in the aqueous film of the nasal passages. And the odorous molecule, or a portion of it, must fit into one of the receptor sites on nerve endings in this area. When this happens, nerve impulses travel to the brain, which interprets them as a specific odor.

Over half a century ago, a new theory proposed that molecular shape (and sometimes polarity), but *not* composition, determines odor. It stated that any molecule producing one of seven primary odors—camphor-like, musky, floral, minty, ethereal, pungent, and putrid—matches a receptor site of a particular shape. Figure B10.1 shows three of the seven sites holding a molecule with that odor.

Several predictions of the theory proved to be correct:

- If different substances fit a given receptor, they have the same odor. The four molecules in Figure B10.2 fit the camphor-like receptor and smell like moth repellent.
- If different parts of a molecule fit different receptors, it has a mixed odor. Portions of benzaldehyde fit the camphor-like, floral, and minty receptors, and it smells like almonds; other molecules with this odor fit the same three receptors.

But, other predictions were not confirmed. For example, an odor predicted from the shape was often not the odor smelled. The reason is that molecules may not have the same shape in solution at the receptor as they have in the gas phase.

Evidence from the 1990s suggests that the original model is far too simple. The 2004 Nobel Prize in medicine or physiology was given to Richard Axel and Linda B. Buck for showing that olfaction involves about 1000 different receptors and molecules fitting various combinations of them produce the over 10,000 odors humans smell.

Thus, although the process is much more complex than originally thought, the central idea that odor depends on molecular shape is valid and is being actively researched in the food, cosmetics, and insecticide industries.

Biological Significance of Molecular Shape

Countless other examples show that no chemical property is more crucial to living systems than molecular shape. Here are just a few of the many biochemical processes controlled by one molecule fitting into a receptor site on another:

- Enzymes are proteins that bind cellular reactants and speed their reaction. An early step in energy metabolism involves glucose binding to the "active" site of the enzyme hexokinase (Figure B10.3).
- Nerve impulses are transmitted when small molecules released from one nerve fit into receptors on the next. Mind-altering drugs act by chemically disrupting the molecular fit at such nerve receptors in the brain.
- One type of immune response is triggered when a molecule on a bacterial surface binds to the receptors on "killer" cells in the bloodstream.
- Hormones regulate processes by fitting into and activating specific receptors on target tissues and organs.
- Genes function when certain nucleic acid molecules fit into specific regions of others.

Floral **Camphor-like** **Ethereal**

Figure B10.1 Shapes of some olfactory receptor sites.

Camphor   Hexachloroethane   Thiophosphoric acid dichloride ethylamide   Cyclooctane

Figure B10.2 Different molecules with the same odor.

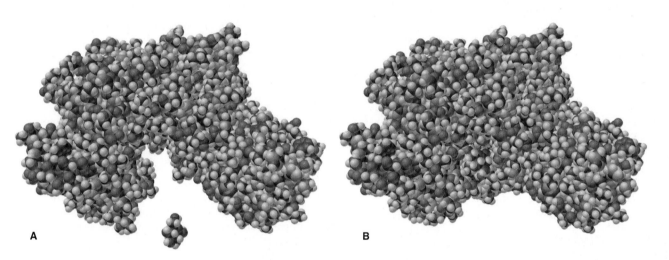

A

B

Figure B10.3 Molecular shape and enzyme action. **A,** A small sugar molecule (*bottom*) is shown near a specific region of an enzyme molecule. **B,** When the sugar lands in that region, the reaction begins.

Problems

B10.1 As you'll learn in Chapter 11, groups joined by a single bond rotate freely around the bond, but those joined by double bonds don't. Peptide bonds make up a major portion of protein chains. Determine the molecular shape around the central C and N atoms in the two resonance forms of the peptide bond:

B10.2 Lewis structures of mescaline, a hallucinogenic compound in peyote cactus, and dopamine, a neurotransmitter in the mammalian brain, are shown below. Suggest a reason for mescaline's ability to disrupt nerve impulses.

mescaline   dopamine

CHAPTER REVIEW GUIDE

Understand These Concepts

1. How Lewis structures depict the atoms, bonding pairs, and lone electron pairs in a molecule or polyatomic ion (§10.1)
2. How resonance and electron delocalization explain bond properties in many compounds with double bonds adjacent to single bonds (§10.1)
3. The meaning of formal charge and how it is used to select the most important resonance structure; the difference between formal charge and oxidation number (§10.1)
4. The octet rule and its three major exceptions—molecules with a central atom that has an electron deficiency, an odd number of electrons, or an expanded valence shell (§10.1)
5. How electron-group repulsions lead to molecular shapes (§10.2)
6. The five electron-group arrangements and their associated molecular shapes (§10.2)
7. Why double bonds and lone pairs cause deviations from ideal bond angles (§10.2)
8. How bond polarities and molecular shape combine to give a molecule polarity (§10.3)

Master These Skills

1. Using a stepwise method for writing a Lewis structure from a molecular formula (SPs 10.1–10.3, 10.5)
2. Writing resonance structures for molecules and ions (SP 10.4)
3. Calculating the formal charge of any atom in a molecule or ion (SP 10.5)
4. Predicting molecular shapes from Lewis structures (SPs 10.6–10.8)
5. Using molecular shape and electronegativity values to predict the polarity of a molecule (SP 10.9)

Section 10.1
Lewis structure (Lewis formula) (363)
resonance structure (resonance form) (367)
resonance hybrid (367)
electron-pair delocalization (367)
formal charge (368)
electron deficient (369)

free radical (370)
expanded valence shell (370)
Section 10.2
valence-shell electron-pair repulsion (VSEPR) theory (373)
molecular shape (373)
bond angle (374)
linear arrangement (374)
linear shape (374)

trigonal planar arrangement (374)
bent shape (V shape) (375)
tetrahedral arrangement (375)
trigonal pyramidal shape (376)
trigonal bipyramidal arrangement (376)
equatorial group (376)
axial group (377)

seesaw shape (377)
T shape (377)
octahedral arrangement (378)
square pyramidal shape (378)
square planar shape (378)
Section 10.3
molecular polarity (383)
dipole moment (μ) (383)

10.1 Calculating the formal charge on an atom (368):

Formal charge of atom
$$= \text{no. of valence e}^-$$
$$- (\text{no. of unshared valence e}^- + \tfrac{1}{2} \text{ no. of shared valence e}^-)$$

10.2 Ranking the effect of electron-pair repulsions on bond angle (376):
Lone pair–lone pair > lone pair–bonding pair > bonding pair–bonding pair

Brief Solutions to Follow-Up Problems

10.1 (a) H—S̈: (b) :Ö: (c) :Ö:
            |
            H
            :F̈: :F̈:

10.2 (a) H—N̈—Ö—H (b)

10.3 (a) :C≡O: (b) H—C≡N: (c) :Ö=C=Ö:

10.4

10.5 (a) (b) (c)

10.6 (a) S̈=C=S̈ (b)   V shaped, <120°
Linear, 180°

(c) (d)   Tetrahedral, 109.5°   V shaped, <109.5°

10.7

(a) Linear, 180° (b) T shaped, <90° (c) Trigonal bipyramidal
F_{eq}—S—F_{eq} angle <120°
F_{ax}—S—F_{eq} angle <90°

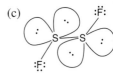

10.8 (a)   S is tetrahedral; double bonds compress O—S—O angle to <109.5°. Shape around each O in an —OH is V shape; lone pairs compress H—O—S angle to <109.5°.

(b)   (c)

Shape around C in CH_3— is tetrahedral, with angles ~109.5°; other C atoms are linear, 180°.   V shape around each S; F—S—S angle <109.5°.

10.9

(a) (b) (c)

PROBLEMS

Problems with **colored** numbers are answered in Appendix E and worked in detail in the Student Solutions Manual. Problem sections match those in the text and provide the numbers of relevant sample problems. Most offer Concept Review Questions, Skill-Building Exercises (grouped in pairs covering the same concept), and Problems in Context. The Comprehensive Problems are based on material from any section or previous chapter.

Depicting Molecules and Ions with Lewis Structures
(Sample Problems 10.1 to 10.5)

Concept Review Questions

10.1 Which of these atoms *cannot* serve as a central atom in a Lewis structure: (a) O; (b) He; (c) F; (d) H; (e) P? Explain.

10.2 When is a resonance hybrid needed to adequately depict the bonding in a molecule? Using NO_2 as an example, explain how a resonance hybrid is consistent with the actual bond length, bond strength, and bond order.

10.3 In which of these bonding patterns does X obey the octet rule?

(a) (b) (c) (d) (e) (f) (g) (h)

—Ẋ— :Ẋ— X ≡X: —Ẍ= —Ẍ= X :Ẍ:²⁻

10.4 What is required for an atom to expand its valence shell? Which of the following atoms can expand its valence shell: F, S, H, Al, Se, Cl?

Skill-Building Exercises (grouped in similar pairs)

10.5 Draw a Lewis structure for (a) SiF_4; (b) $SeCl_2$; (c) COF_2 (C is central).

10.6 Draw a Lewis structure for (a) $PH_4{}^+$; (b) C_2F_4; (c) SbH_3.

10.7 Draw a Lewis structure for (a) PF_3; (b) H_2CO_3 (both H atoms are attached to O atoms); (c) CS_2.

10.8 Draw a Lewis structure for (a) CH_4S; (b) S_2Cl_2; (c) $CHCl_3$.

10.9 Draw Lewis structures of all the important resonance forms of (a) $NO_2{}^+$; (b) NO_2F (N is central).

10.10 Draw Lewis structures of all the important resonance forms of (a) HNO_3 ($HONO_2$); (b) $HAsO_4{}^{2-}$ ($HOAsO_3{}^{2-}$).

10.11 Draw Lewis structures of all the important resonance forms of (a) $N_3{}^-$; (b) $NO_2{}^-$.

10.12 Draw Lewis structures of all the important resonance forms of (a) $HCO_2{}^-$ (H is attached to C); (b) $HBrO_4$ ($HOBrO_3$).

10.13 Draw the Lewis structure with lowest formal charges, and determine the charge of each atom in (a) IF_5; (b) AlH_4^-.

10.14 Draw the Lewis structure with lowest formal charges, and determine the charge of each atom in (a) OCS; (b) NO.

10.15 Draw the Lewis structure with lowest formal charges, and determine the charge of each atom in (a) CN^-; (b) ClO^-.

10.16 Draw the Lewis structure with lowest formal charges, and determine the charge of each atom in (a) BF_4^-; (b) ClNO.

10.17 Draw a Lewis structure for a resonance form of each ion with the lowest possible formal charges, show the charges, and give oxidation numbers of the atoms: (a) BrO_3^-; (b) SO_3^{2-}.

10.18 Draw a Lewis structure for a resonance form of each ion with the lowest possible formal charges, show the charges, and give oxidation numbers of the atoms: (a) AsO_4^{3-}; (b) ClO_2^-.

10.19 These species do not obey the octet rule. Draw a Lewis structure for each, and state the type of octet-rule exception:
(a) BH_3 (b) AsF_4^- (c) $SeCl_4$

10.20 These species do not obey the octet rule. Draw a Lewis structure for each, and state the type of octet-rule exception:
(a) PF_6^- (b) ClO_3 (c) H_3PO_3 (one P—H bond)

10.21 These species do not obey the octet rule. Draw a Lewis structure for each, and state the type of octet-rule exception:
(a) BrF_3 (b) ICl_2^- (c) BeF_2

10.22 These species do not obey the octet rule. Draw a Lewis structure for each, and state the type of octet-rule exception:
(a) O_3^- (b) XeF_2 (c) SbF_4^-

Problems in Context

10.23 Molten beryllium chloride reacts with chloride ion from molten NaCl to form the $BeCl_4^{2-}$ ion, in which the Be atom attains an octet. Show the net ionic reaction with Lewis structures.

10.24 Despite many attempts, the perbromate ion (BrO_4^-) was not prepared in the laboratory until about 1970. (In fact, articles were published explaining theoretically why it could never be prepared!) Draw a Lewis structure for BrO_4^- in which all atoms have lowest formal charges.

10.25 Cryolite (Na_3AlF_6) is an indispensable component in the electrochemical production of aluminum. Draw a Lewis structure for the AlF_6^{3-} ion.

10.26 Phosgene is a colorless, highly toxic gas that was employed against troops in World War I and it is used today as a key reactant in organic syntheses. From the following resonance structures, select the one with the lowest formal charges:

Valence-Shell Electron-Pair Repulsion (VSEPR) Theory
(Sample Problems 10.6 to 10.8)

Concept Review Questions

10.27 If you know the formula of a molecule or ion, what is the first step in predicting its shape?

10.28 In what situation is the name of the molecular shape the same as the name of the electron-group arrangement?

10.29 Which of the following numbers of electron groups can give rise to a bent (V-shaped) molecule: two, three, four, five, six? Draw an example for each case, showing the shape classification (AX_mE_n) and the ideal bond angle.

10.30 Name all the molecular shapes that have a tetrahedral electron-group arrangement.

10.31 Consider the following molecular shapes:

A   B   C   D

(a) Which has the most electron pairs (both shared and unshared) around the central atom?
(b) Which has the most unshared pairs around the central atom?
(c) Do any have only shared pairs around the central atom?

10.32 Use wedge-bond perspective drawings (if necessary) to sketch the atom positions in a general molecule of formula (not shape class) AX_n that has each of the following shapes:
(a) V shaped   (b) trigonal planar   (c) trigonal bipyramidal
(d) T shaped   (e) trigonal pyramidal   (f) square pyramidal

10.33 What would you expect to be the electron-group arrangement around atom A in each of the following cases? For each arrangement, give the ideal bond angle and the direction of any expected deviation:

(a) X—A: with X above and X below

(b) X—A≡X

(c) X=A—X with X above and X below

(d) X—Ä—X

(e) X=A=X

(f) :A with X, X, X

Skill-Building Exercises (grouped in similar pairs)

10.34 Determine the electron-group arrangement, molecular shape, and ideal bond angle(s) for each of the following:
(a) O_3 (b) H_3O^+ (c) NF_3

10.35 Determine the electron-group arrangement, molecular shape, and ideal bond angle(s) for each of the following:
(a) SO_4^{2-} (b) NO_2^- (c) PH_3

10.36 Determine the electron-group arrangement, molecular shape, and ideal bond angle(s) for each of the following:
(a) CO_3^{2-} (b) SO_2 (c) CF_4

10.37 Determine the electron-group arrangement, molecular shape, and ideal bond angle(s) for each of the following:
(a) SO_3 (b) N_2O (N is central)   (c) CH_2Cl_2

10.38 Name the shape and give the AX_mE_n classification and ideal bond angle(s) for each of the following general molecules:

(a)   (b)   (c)

10.39 Name the shape and give the AX_mE_n classification and ideal bond angle(s) for each of the following general molecules:

(a)   (b)   (c)

10.40 Determine the shape, ideal bond angle(s), and the direction of any deviation from those angles for each of the following:
(a) ClO_2^- (b) PF_5 (c) SeF_4 (d) KrF_2

10.41 Determine the shape, ideal bond angle(s), and the direction of any deviation from those angles for each of the following:
(a) ClO_3^- (b) IF_4^- (c) $SeOF_2$ (d) TeF_5^-

10.42 Determine the shape around each central atom in each molecule, and explain any deviation from ideal bond angles:
(a) CH_3OH (b) N_2O_4 (O_2NNO_2)

10.43 Determine the shape around each central atom in each molecule, and explain any deviation from ideal bond angles:
(a) H_3PO_4 (no H—P bond)   (b) CH_3—O—CH_2CH_3

10.44 Determine the shape around each central atom in each molecule, and explain any deviation from ideal bond angles:
(a) CH_3COOH (b) H_2O_2

10.45 Determine the shape around each central atom in each molecule, and explain any deviation from ideal bond angles:
(a) H_2SO_3 (no H—S bond)   (b) N_2O_3 $(ONNO_2)$

10.46 Arrange the following AF_n species in order of *increasing* F—A—F bond angles: BF_3, BeF_2, CF_4, NF_3, OF_2.

10.47 Arrange the following ACl_n species in order of *decreasing* Cl—A—Cl bond angles: SCl_2, OCl_2, PCl_3, $SiCl_4$, $SiCl_6^{2-}$.

10.48 State an ideal value for each of the bond angles in each molecule, and note where you expect deviations:

(a)   (b)   (c)

(a)
$$H—\overset{\overset{\displaystyle H}{|}}{C}=\ddot{N}—\ddot{\underset{..}{O}}—H$$

(b)
$$H—\overset{\overset{\displaystyle H}{|}}{\underset{\underset{\displaystyle H}{|}}{C}}—\ddot{\underset{..}{O}}—\overset{\overset{\displaystyle H}{|}}{C}—H$$

(c)
$$H—\ddot{\underset{..}{O}}—B—\ddot{\underset{..}{O}}—H$$ with $:\ddot{O}:$ above B and H above

10.49 State an ideal value for each of the bond angles in each molecule, and note where you expect deviations:

(a)   (b)   (c)

(a)
$$\ddot{O}=N—\ddot{\underset{..}{O}}—H$$ with $:\ddot{O}:$ below N

(b)
$$H—\overset{\overset{\displaystyle H}{|}}{\underset{\underset{\displaystyle H}{|}}{C}}—C=\ddot{O}$$ with H below

(c)
$$H—\overset{\overset{\displaystyle :O:}{\|}}{C}—\ddot{\underset{..}{O}}—H$$

Problems in Context

10.50 Because both tin and carbon are members of Group 4A(14), they form structurally similar compounds. However, tin exhibits a greater variety of structures because it forms several ionic species. Predict the shapes and ideal bond angles, including any deviations, for the following:
(a) $Sn(CH_3)_2$ (b) $SnCl_3^-$ (c) $Sn(CH_3)_4$
(d) SnF_5^- (e) SnF_6^{2-}

10.51 In the gas phase, phosphorus pentachloride exists as separate molecules. In the solid phase, however, the compound is composed of alternating PCl_4^+ and PCl_6^- ions. What change(s) in molecular shape occur(s) as PCl_5 solidifies? How does the Cl—P—Cl angle change?

Molecular Shape and Molecular Polarity
(Sample Problem 10.9)

Concept Review Questions

10.52 For molecules of general formula AX_n (where $n > 2$), how do you determine if a molecule is polar?

10.53 How can a molecule with polar covalent bonds not be polar? Give an example.

10.54 Explain in general why the shape of a biomolecule is important to its function.

Skill-Building Exercises (grouped in similar pairs)

10.55 Consider the molecules SCl_2, F_2, CS_2, CF_4, and BrCl.
(a) Which has bonds that are the most polar?
(b) Which molecules have a dipole moment?

10.56 Consider the molecules BF_3, PF_3, BrF_3, SF_4, and SF_6.
(a) Which has bonds that are the most polar?
(b) Which molecules have a dipole moment?

10.57 Which molecule in each pair has the greater dipole moment? Give the reason for your choice.
(a) SO_2 or SO_3 (b) ICl or IF
(c) SiF_4 or SF_4 (d) H_2O or H_2S

10.58 Which molecule in each pair has the greater dipole moment? Give the reason for your choice.
(a) ClO_2 or SO_2 (b) HBr or HCl
(c) $BeCl_2$ or SCl_2 (d) AsF_3 or AsF_5

Problems in Context

10.59 There are three different dichloroethylenes (molecular formula $C_2H_2Cl_2$), which we can designate X, Y, and Z. Compound X has no dipole moment, but compound Z does. Compounds X and Z each combine with hydrogen to give the same product:

$$C_2H_2Cl_2 \,(X \text{ or } Z) + H_2 \longrightarrow ClCH_2—CH_2Cl$$

What are the structures of X, Y, and Z? Would you expect compound Y to have a dipole moment?

10.60 Dinitrogen difluoride, N_2F_2, is the only stable, simple inorganic molecule with an N=N bond. The compound occurs in *cis* and *trans* forms.
(a) Draw the molecular shapes of the two forms of N_2F_2.
(b) Predict the direction of the polarity, if any, of each form.

Comprehensive Problems

10.61 In addition to ammonia, nitrogen forms three other hydrides: hydrazine (N_2H_4), diazene (N_2H_2), and tetrazene (N_4H_4).

(a) Use Lewis structures to compare the strength, length, and order of the nitrogen-nitrogen bonds in hydrazine, diazene, and N_2.
(b) Tetrazene (atom sequence H_2NNNNH_2) decomposes above 0°C to hydrazine and nitrogen gas. Draw a Lewis structure for tetrazene, and calculate $\Delta H°_{rxn}$ for this decomposition.

10.62 Draw a Lewis structure for each species: (a) PF_5; (b) CCl_4; (c) H_3O^+; (d) ICl_3; (e) BeH_2; (f) PH_2^-; (g) $GeBr_4$; (h) CH_3^-; (i) BCl_3; (j) BrF_4^+; (k) XeO_3; (l) TeF_4.

10.63 Give the molecular shape of each species in Problem 10.62.

10.64 Consider the following reaction of silicon tetrafluoride:

$$SiF_4 + F^- \longrightarrow SiF_5^-$$

(a) Which depiction below best illustrates the change in molecular shape around Si? (b) Give the name and AX_mE_n designation of each shape in the depiction chosen in part (a).

10.65 Both aluminum and iodine form chlorides, Al_2Cl_6 and I_2Cl_6, with "bridging" Cl atoms. The Lewis structures are

(a) What is the formal charge on each atom? (b) Which of these molecules has a planar shape? Explain.

10.66 The VSEPR model was developed before any xenon compounds had been prepared. Thus, these compounds provided an excellent test of the model's predictive power. What would you have predicted for the shapes of XeF_2, XeF_4, and XeF_6?

10.67 When SO_3 gains two electrons, SO_3^{2-} forms. (a) Which depiction shown below best illustrates the change in molecular shape around S? (b) Does molecular polarity change during this reaction?

10.68 The actual bond angle in NO_2 is 134.3°, and in NO_2^- it is 115.4°, although the ideal bond angle is 120° in both. Explain.

10.69 "Inert" xenon actually forms several compounds, especially with the highly electronegative elements oxygen and fluorine. The simple fluorides XeF_2, XeF_4, and XeF_6 are all formed by direct reaction of the elements. As you might expect from the size of the xenon atom, the Xe—F bond is not a strong one. Calculate the Xe—F bond energy in XeF_6, given that the enthalpy of formation is −402 kJ/mol.

10.70 Propylene oxide is used to make many products, including plastics such as polyurethane. One method for synthesizing it involves oxidizing propene with hydrogen peroxide:

$$CH_3 - CH = CH_2 + H_2O_2 \longrightarrow CH_3 - CH - CH_2 + H_2O$$

(a) What is the molecular shape and ideal bond angle around each carbon atom in propylene oxide?
(b) Predict any deviation from the ideal for the actual C—C—C bond angles (assume the three atoms in the ring form an equilateral triangle).

10.71 Chloral, $Cl_3C—CH=O$, reacts with water to form the sedative and hypnotic agent chloral hydrate, $Cl_3C—CH(OH)_2$. Draw Lewis structures for these substances, and describe the change in molecular shape, if any, that occurs around each of the carbon atoms during the reaction.

10.72 Like several other bonds, carbon-oxygen bonds have lengths and strengths that depend on the bond order. Draw Lewis structures for the following species, and arrange them in order of increasing carbon-oxygen bond length and then by increasing carbon-oxygen bond strength: (a) CO; (b) CO_3^{2-}; (c) H_2CO; (d) CH_4O; (e) HCO_3^- (H attached to O).

10.73 In the 1980s, there was an international agreement to destroy all stockpiles of mustard gas, $ClCH_2CH_2SCH_2CH_2Cl$. When this substance contacts the moisture in eyes, nasal passages, and skin, the —OH groups of water replace the Cl atoms and create high local concentrations of hydrochloric acid, which cause severe blistering and tissue destruction. Write a balanced equation for this reaction, and calculate $\Delta H°_{rxn}$.

10.74 The four bonds of carbon tetrachloride (CCl_4) are polar, but the molecule is nonpolar because the bond polarity is canceled by the symmetric tetrahedral shape. When other atoms substitute for some of the Cl atoms, the symmetry is broken and the molecule becomes polar. Use Figure 9.21 (p. 349) to rank the following molecules from the least polar to the most polar: CH_2Br_2, CF_2Cl_2, CH_2F_2, CH_2Cl_2, CBr_4, CF_2Br_2.

10.75 Ethanol (CH_3CH_2OH) is being used as a gasoline additive or alternative in many parts of the world.
(a) Use bond energies to find $\Delta H°_{rxn}$ for the combustion of gaseous ethanol. (Assume H_2O forms as a gas.)
(b) In its standard state at 25°C, ethanol is a liquid. Its vaporization requires 40.5 kJ/mol. Correct the value from part (a) to find the enthalpy of reaction for the combustion of liquid ethanol.
(c) How does the value from part (b) compare with the value you calculate from standard enthalpies of formation (Appendix B)?
(d) "Greener" methods produce ethanol from corn and other plant material, but the main industrial method involves hydrating ethylene from petroleum. Use Lewis structures and bond energies to calculate $\Delta H°_{rxn}$ for the formation of gaseous ethanol from ethylene gas with water vapor.

10.76 In the following compounds, the C atoms form a single ring. Draw a Lewis structure for each compound, identify cases for which resonance exists, and determine the carbon-carbon bond order(s): (a) C_3H_4; (b) C_3H_6; (c) C_4H_6; (d) C_4H_4; (e) C_6H_6.

10.77 An experiment requires 50.0 mL of 0.040 M NaOH for the titration of 1.00 mmol of acid. Mass analysis of the acid shows 2.24% hydrogen, 26.7% carbon, and 71.1% oxygen. Draw the Lewis structure of the acid.

10.78 A gaseous compound has a composition by mass of 24.8% carbon, 2.08% hydrogen, and 73.1% chlorine. At STP, the gas has a density of 4.3 g/L. Draw a Lewis structure that fits these facts. Would another structure be equally satisfactory? Explain.

10.79 Perchlorates are powerful oxidizing agents used in fireworks, flares, and the booster rockets of space shuttles. Lewis structures for the perchlorate ion (ClO_4^-) can be drawn with all single bonds or with one, two, or three double bonds. Draw each of these possible resonance forms, use formal charges to determine the most important, and calculate its average bond order.

10.80 Methane burns in oxygen to form carbon dioxide and water vapor. Hydrogen sulfide burns in oxygen to form sulfur dioxide and water vapor. Use bond energies (Table 9.2, p. 340) to determine the enthalpy of each reaction per mole of O_2 (assume Lewis structures with zero formal charges; BE of S=O is 552 kJ/mol).

10.81 Use Lewis structures to determine which *two* of the following are unstable: (a) SF_2; (b) SF_3; (c) SF_4; (d) SF_5; (e) SF_6.

10.82 A major short-lived, neutral species in flames is OH. (a) What is unusual about the electronic structure of OH? (b) Use the standard enthalpy of formation of OH(g) (39.0 kJ/mol) and bond energies to calculate the O—H bond energy in OH(g). (c) From the average value for the O—H bond energy in Table 9.2 (p. 340) and your value for the O—H bond energy in OH(g), find the energy needed to break the first O—H bond in water.

10.83 Pure HN_3 (atom sequence HNNN) is explosive. In aqueous solution, it is a weak acid that yields the azide ion, N_3^-. Draw resonance structures to explain why the nitrogen-nitrogen bond lengths are equal in N_3^- but unequal in HN_3.

10.84 Except for nitrogen, the elements of Group 5A(15) all form pentafluorides, and most form pentachlorides. The chlorine atoms of PCl_5 can be replaced with fluorine atoms one at a time to give, successively, PCl_4F, PCl_3F_2, ... , PF_5. (a) Given the sizes of F and Cl, would you expect the first two F substitutions to be at axial or equatorial positions? Explain. (b) Which of the five fluorine-containing molecules have no dipole moment?

10.85 Dinitrogen monoxide (N_2O) supports combustion in a manner similar to oxygen, with the nitrogen atoms forming N_2. Draw three resonance structures for N_2O (one N is central), and use formal charges to decide the relative importance of each. What correlation can you suggest between the most important structure and the observation that N_2O supports combustion?

10.86 Oxalic acid ($H_2C_2O_4$) is found in toxic concentrations in rhubarb leaves. The acid forms two ions, $HC_2O_4^-$ and $C_2O_4^{2-}$, by the sequential loss of H^+ ions. Draw Lewis structures for the three species, and comment on the relative lengths and strengths of their carbon-oxygen bonds. The connections among the atoms are shown below with single bonds only.

$$
\begin{array}{c}
\text{H—O} \qquad \text{O—H} \\
\diagdown \quad \diagup \\
\text{C—C} \\
\diagup \quad \diagdown \\
\text{O} \qquad \text{O}
\end{array}
$$

10.87 The Murchison meteorite that landed in Australia in 1969 contained 92 different amino acids, including 21 found in Earth organisms. A skeleton structure (single bonds only) of one of these extraterrestrial amino acids is shown below.

$$
\begin{array}{c}
\text{H}_3\text{N—CH—C—O} \\
\qquad | \qquad | \\
\qquad \text{CH}_2 \quad \text{O} \\
\qquad | \\
\qquad \text{CH}_3
\end{array}
$$

Draw a Lewis structure, and identify any atoms having a nonzero formal charge.

10.88 Hydrazine (N_2H_4) is used as a rocket fuel because it reacts very exothermically with oxygen to form nitrogen gas and water vapor. The heat released and the increase in number of moles of gas provide thrust. Calculate the enthalpy of reaction.

10.89 A student isolates a product with the molecular shape shown at right (F is orange). (a) If the species is a neutral compound, can the black sphere represent selenium (Se)? (b) If the species is an anion, can the black sphere represent N? (c) If the black sphere represents Br, what is the charge of the species?

10.90 When gaseous sulfur trioxide is dissolved in concentrated sulfuric acid, disulfuric acid forms:

$$SO_3(g) + H_2SO_4(l) \longrightarrow H_2S_2O_7(l)$$

Use bond energies (Table 9.2, p. 340) to determine ΔH_{rxn}°. (The S atoms in $H_2S_2O_7$ are bonded through an O atom. Assume Lewis structures with zero formal charges; BE of S=O is 552 kJ/mol.)

10.91 A molecule of formula AY_3 is found experimentally to be polar. Which molecular shapes are possible and which are impossible for AY_3?

10.92 Consider the following molecular shapes:

(a) Match each shape with one of the following species: XeF_3^+, $SbBr_3$, $GaCl_3$.
(b) Which, if any, is polar?
(c) Which has the most valence electrons around the central atom?

10.93 Hydrogen cyanide can be catalytically reduced with hydrogen to form methylamine. Use Lewis structures and bond energies to determine ΔH_{rxn}° for

$$HCN(g) + 2H_2(g) \longrightarrow CH_3NH_2(g)$$

10.94 Ethylene, C_2H_4, and tetrafluoroethylene, C_2F_4, are used to make the polymers polyethylene and polytetrafluoroethylene (Teflon), respectively.
(a) Draw the Lewis structures for C_2H_4 and C_2F_4, and give the ideal H—C—H and F—C—F bond angles.
(b) The actual H—C—H and F—C—F bond angles are 117.4° and 112.4°, respectively. Explain these deviations.

10.95 Using bond lengths in Table 9.2 (p. 340) and assuming ideal geometry, calculate each of the following distances:
(a) Between H atoms in C_2H_2
(b) Between F atoms in SF_6 (two answers)
(c) Between equatorial F atoms in PF_5

10.96 Phosphorus pentachloride, a key industrial compound with annual world production of about 2×10^7 kg, is used to make other compounds. It reacts with sulfur dioxide to produce phosphorus oxychloride ($POCl_3$) and thionyl chloride ($SOCl_2$). Draw a Lewis structure, and name the molecular shape of each product.

Theories of Covalent Bonding

Concepts and skills to review before you study this chapter

- atomic orbital shapes (Section 7.4)
- exclusion principle (Section 8.1)
- Hund's rule (Section 8.2)
- Lewis structures (Section 10.1)

- resonance in covalent bonding (Section 10.1)
- molecular shapes (Section 10.2)
- molecular polarity (Section 10.3)

All scientific models have limitations because they are simplifications of reality. The VSEPR theory, covered in Chapter 10, accounts for molecular shapes, but it doesn't explain how they arise from interactions of atomic orbitals. After all, the orbitals described in Chapter 7 aren't oriented toward the corners of, say, an octahedron, like the ones shown at left for the sulfur in SF_6. Moreover, knowing the shape doesn't help us explain the magnetic and spectral properties of molecules; only an understanding of their orbitals and energy levels can.

The two theories presented in this chapter focus on different questions and complement each other. Don't be concerned if we need several models to explain a complex phenomenon like bonding. In every science, one model may account for some aspect of a topic better than another, and several are employed to explain a wider range of phenomena.

IN THIS CHAPTER... We introduce two theories of bonding in molecules based on the interactions of the orbitals of their atoms.
- We discuss valence bond (VB) theory, which rationalizes molecular shapes through interactions of atomic orbitals during bonding to form hybrid orbitals.
- We apply VB theory to sigma and pi bonds, the two types of covalent bonds.
- We see why parts of molecules don't rotate freely around multiple bonds, which has major effects on reactivity, physical properties, and biological behavior.
- We discuss molecular orbital (MO) theory, which explains molecular energy levels and properties through formation of orbitals that spread over the whole molecule.
- We apply MO theory to understand key properties of some diatomic and simple polyatomic molecules.

11.1 • VALENCE BOND (VB) THEORY AND ORBITAL HYBRIDIZATION

What *is* a covalent bond, and what characteristic gives it strength? And how can we explain *molecular* shapes based on the interactions of *atomic* orbitals? The most useful approach for answering these questions is based on quantum mechanics (Chapter 7) and called **valence bond (VB) theory.**

The Central Themes of VB Theory

The basic principle of VB theory is that *a covalent bond forms when orbitals of two atoms overlap and a pair of electrons occupy the overlap region.* In the terminology of quantum mechanics, overlap of the two orbitals means their wave functions are *in phase* (constructive interference), so the amplitude between the nuclei increases (see Figure 7.5, p. 265). The central themes of VB theory derive from this principle:

1. *Opposing spins of the electron pair.* As the exclusion principle (Section 8.1) prescribes, the space formed by the overlapping orbitals *has a maximum capacity for two electrons that have opposite (paired) spins.* In the simplest case, a molecule of H_2 forms when the 1s orbitals of two H atoms overlap, and the electrons, with their spins paired, spend more time in the overlap region (up and down arrows in Figure 11.1).

Figure 11.1 Orbital overlap and spin pairing in H_2.

A Hydrogen fluoride, HF

B Fluorine, F₂

Figure 11.2 Orbital orientation and maximum overlap. (The $2p_x$ orbital is shown bonding; the other two $2p$ orbitals of F are omitted for clarity.)

2. Maximum overlap of bonding orbitals. Bond strength depends on the attraction between nuclei and shared electrons, so *the greater the orbital overlap, the stronger the bond.* Extent of overlap depends on orbital shape and direction. An *s* orbital is spherical, so its orientation is the same in any direction, but *p* and *d* orbitals have specified directions. Thus, a *p* or *d* orbital involved in a bond is oriented so as to maximize overlap. In HF, for example, the $1s$ orbital of H overlaps a half-filled $2p$ orbital of F *along its long axis* (Figure 11.2A). In F_2, the two half-filled $2p$ orbitals interact end to end, that is, *along the long axes* of the orbitals (Figure 11.2B).

3. Hybridization of atomic orbitals. To account for the bonding in diatomic molecules, we picture direct overlap of *s* and/or *p* orbitals of isolated atoms. But how can we account for the shape of a molecule like methane from the shapes and orientations of C and H atomic orbitals? A C atom ([He] $2s^2 2p^2$) has two valence electrons in the spherical $2s$ orbital and one each in two of the three mutually perpendicular $2p$ orbitals. If the half-filled *p* orbitals overlap the $1s$ orbitals of two H atoms, *two* C—H bonds would form with a 90° H—C—H bond angle. But methane has the formula CH_4, not CH_2, and its bond angle is 109.5°.

To explain such facts, Linus Pauling proposed that, during bonding, *the valence atomic orbitals in the isolated atoms become **different** when they are in the molecule.* Quantum-mechanical calculations show that if we mathematically "mix" certain combinations of orbitals, we form new ones whose spatial orientations *do* match the observed molecular shapes. The process of orbital mixing is called **hybridization,** and the new atomic orbitals are called **hybrid orbitals.**

4. Features of hybrid orbitals. Here are some central points about hybrid orbitals that arise during bonding:
• The *number* of hybrid orbitals formed *equals* the number of atomic orbitals mixed.
• The *type* of hybrid orbitals formed *varies* with the types of atomic orbitals mixed.
• The *shape* and *orientation* of a hybrid orbital *maximizes* overlap with the orbital of the other atom in the bond.

You can think of hybridization as a process in which atomic orbitals mix, hybrid orbitals form, they overlap other orbitals, and electrons enter the overlap region with opposing spins, thus forming stable bonds. In truth, hybridization is a concept to explain the results we calculate that predict the molecular shapes we observe.

Types of Hybrid Orbitals

We postulate the type of hybrid orbitals in a molecule *after* we observe its shape. Note that the orientations of the five types of hybrid orbitals we discuss next correspond to the five electron-group arrangements in VSEPR theory.

sp **Hybridization** When two electron groups surround the central atom, we observe a linear shape, which means the bonding orbitals must have a linear orientation.

1. Orbitals mixed and orbitals formed. VB theory proposes two *nonequivalent* orbitals of a central atom, one *s* and one *p*, mix and form two *equivalent* **sp hybrid orbitals** that are oriented 180° apart (Figure 11.3A). The shape of these hybrid orbitals, with one large and one small lobe, differs markedly from the shapes of the atomic orbitals. The orbital orientations increase electron density *in the bonding direction.*

2. Overlap of orbitals from central and surrounding atoms: BeCl₂. In beryllium chloride, the Be atom is *sp* hybridized. Figure 11.3B depicts the hybridization of Be in an orbital box diagram, and part C shows an orbital box diagram with shaded contours instead of arrows. Bond formation with Cl is shown in part D. The filled $2s$ and one of the three empty $2p$ orbitals of Be mix and form two half-filled *sp* orbitals. Two empty unhybridized $2p$ orbitals of Be lie perpendicular to each other and to the *sp* hybrids. The hybrid orbitals overlap the half-filled $3p$ orbital in each of two Cl atoms. The four electrons—two from Be and one from each Cl—appear as pairs with opposite spins in the two overlap regions. (The $3p$ and *sp* hybrid orbitals that are partially colored on the left become fully colored on the right, after the bonds form and each orbital is filled with two electrons.)

A Formation of sp hybrid orbitals

B Orbital box diagram

Isolated Be atom   Hybridized Be atom

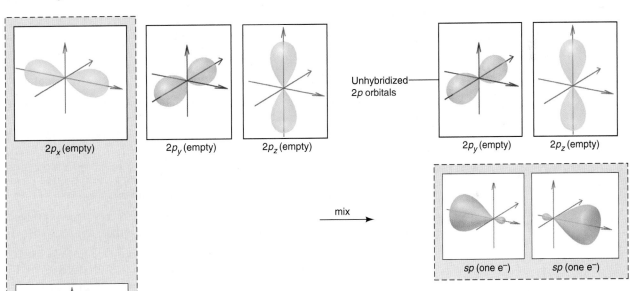

C Box diagram with orbital contours

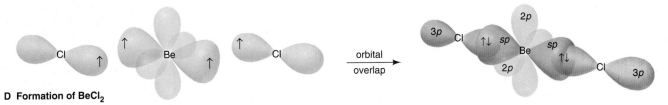

D Formation of BeCl₂

Figure 11.3 Formation and orientation of *sp* hybrid orbitals and the bonding in BeCl₂. **A,** One 2*s* and one 2*p* atomic orbital mix to form two *sp* hybrid orbitals. (The simplified hybrid orbitals at far right are used elsewhere, often even without the small lobe.) **B,** The orbital box diagram for hybridization of Be, drawn vertically. **C,** The orbital box diagram with orbital contours. **D,** Overlap of Be and Cl orbitals to form BeCl₂. (Only the Cl 3*p* orbital involved in bonding is shown.)

***sp*² Hybridization** We use this type of hybridization to rationalize the two shapes possible for the trigonal planar electron-group arrangement.

1. *Orbitals mixed and orbitals formed.* Mixing one *s* and two *p* orbitals gives three ***sp*² hybrid orbitals** that point to the corners of an equilateral triangle, their axes 120° apart. (In hybrid orbitals, unlike in electron configurations, superscripts refer to the number of *atomic orbitals* of a given type, *not* the number of *electrons* in the orbital: thus, one *s* and two *p* orbitals give s^1p^2, or sp^2.) The third 2*p* orbital remains unhybridized.

2. *Overlap of orbitals from central and surrounding atoms: BF₃.* The central B atom in BF₃ is *sp*² hybridized, with the three *sp*² orbitals in a trigonal plane and the third 2*p* orbital unhybridized and perpendicular to this plane (Figure 11.4). Each half-filled *sp*² orbital overlaps the half-filled 2*p* orbital of an F atom, and the six valence electrons—three from B and one from each of the three F atoms—form three bonding pairs.

Figure 11.4 The *sp*² hybrid orbitals in BF₃. **A,** The orbital box diagram shows the formation of three *sp*² hybrid orbitals. One 2*p* orbital is unhybridized and empty. **B,** Contour depiction of BF₃.

3. *Placement of lone pairs.* To account for other molecular shapes within a given electron-group arrangement, one or more hybrid orbitals contains a lone pair. In ozone (O₃), for example, the central O is *sp*² hybridized and a lone pair fills one of the three *sp*² orbitals.

***sp*³ Hybridization** The type of hybridization that accounts for the shape of methane applies to any species with a tetrahedral electron-group arrangement.

1. *Orbitals mixed and orbitals formed.* Mixing one *s* and three *p* orbitals gives four ***sp*³ hybrid orbitals** that point to the corners of a tetrahedron.

2. *Overlap of orbitals from central and surrounding atoms: CH₄.* The C atom in methane is *sp*³ hybridized. Its four valence electrons half-fill the four *sp*³ hybrids, which overlap the half-filled 1*s* orbitals of four H atoms to form four C—H bonds (Figure 11.5).

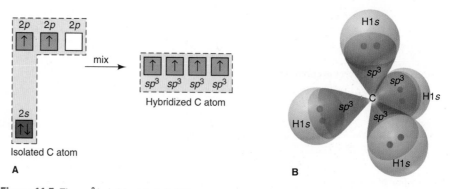

Figure 11.5 The *sp*³ hybrid orbitals in CH₄. **A,** The orbital box diagram shows formation of four *sp*³ hybrids. **B,** Contour depiction of CH₄, with electron pairs shown as dots.

Figure 11.6 The sp^3 hybrid orbitals in NH_3 and H_2O. **A,** The orbital box diagrams show sp^3 hybridization, with lone pairs filling one (NH_3) or two (H_2O) hybrid orbitals. **B,** Contour depictions.

3. *Placement of lone pairs.* The trigonal pyramidal shape of NH_3 arises when a lone pair fills any one of the four sp^3 orbitals of N, and the bent shape of H_2O arises when lone pairs fill any two of the sp^3 orbitals of O (Figure 11.6).

sp^3d Hybridization Molecules with shapes due to the trigonal bipyramidal electron-group arrangement have central atoms from Period 3 or higher. VB theory proposes that d orbitals, as well as s and p orbitals, are mixed to form hybrid orbitals.

1. *Orbitals mixed and orbitals formed.* Mixing one $3s$, the three $3p$, and one of the five $3d$ orbitals gives five **sp^3d hybrid orbitals,** which point to the corners of a trigonal bipyramid.

2. *Overlap of orbitals from central and surrounding atoms: PCl_5.* The P atom in PCl_5 is sp^3d hybridized. Each hybrid orbital overlaps a $3p$ orbital of a Cl atom, and ten valence electrons—five from P and one from each of the five Cl atoms—form five P—Cl bonds (Figure 11.7).

3. *Placement of lone pairs.* Seesaw, T-shaped, and linear molecules have lone pairs in, respectively, one, two, or three of the central atom's sp^3d orbitals.

Figure 11.7 The sp^3d hybrid orbitals in PCl_5. **A,** The orbital box diagram shows the formation of five half-filled sp^3d orbitals. Four $3d$ orbitals are unhybridized and empty. **B,** Contour depiction of PCl_5. (For clarity, unhybridized $3d$ orbitals, the other two Cl $3p$ orbitals, and the five bonding P—Cl pairs are not shown.)

Figure 11.8 The sp^3d^2 hybrid orbitals in SF_6. **A,** The orbital box diagram shows formation of six half-filled sp^3d^2 orbitals; three $3d$ orbitals remain unhybridized and empty. **B,** Contour depiction of SF_6.

sp^3d^2 Hybridization The VB model proposes that molecules with shapes having the octahedral electron-group arrangement also use d orbitals to form hybrids.

1. *Orbitals mixed and orbitals formed.* Mixing one $3s$, the three $3p$, and two $3d$ orbitals gives six **sp^3d^2 hybrid orbitals,** which point to the corners of an octahedron.

2. *Overlap of orbitals from central and surrounding atoms: SF_6.* The S atom in SF_6 is sp^3d^2 hybridized. Each half-filled hybrid orbital overlaps a half-filled $2p$ orbital of an F atom, and 12 valence electrons—six from S and one from each of the six F atoms—form six S—F bonds (Figure 11.8).

3. *Placement of lone pairs.* Square pyramidal and square planar molecules have lone pairs in one and two of the central atom's sp^3d^2 orbitals, respectively.

Table 11.1 summarizes the numbers and types of atomic orbitals that mix to form the five types of hybrid orbitals. Figure 11.9 shows three conceptual steps from a molecular formula to the hybrid orbitals in the molecule, and Sample Problem 11.1 focuses on the last step of that process.

Table **11.1** Composition and Orientation of Hybrid Orbitals					
	Linear	**Trigonal Planar**	**Tetrahedral**	**Trigonal Bipyramidal**	**Octahedral**
Atomic orbitals mixed	one s one p	one s two p	one s three p	one s three p one d	one s three p two d
Hybrid orbitals formed	two p	three sp^2	four sp^3	five sp^3d	six sp^3d^2
Unhybridized orbitals remaining	two p	one p	none	four d	three d
Orientation					

Figure 11.9 From molecular formula to hybrid orbitals. (See Figures 10.1, p. 364, and 10.10, p. 379.)

Sample Problem 11.1 Postulating Hybrid Orbitals in a Molecule

Problem Use partial orbital diagrams to describe how mixing the atomic orbitals of the central atom(s) leads to the hybrid orbitals in each of the following:
(a) Methanol, CH_3OH **(b)** Sulfur tetrafluoride, SF_4

Plan Prior to the Solution steps below, we have used the molecular formula to draw the Lewis structure and determined the electron-group arrangement of each central atom. Then, starting from there, we use Table 11.1 to postulate the type of hybrid orbitals. We write the partial orbital diagram for each central atom before and after the orbitals are hybridized.

Solution **(a)** For CH_3OH. The electron-group arrangement is tetrahedral around both the C and the O atom, so each mixed one $2s$ and three $2p$ to become sp^3 hybridized. The C atom has four half-filled sp^3 orbitals:

The O atom has two half-filled sp^3 orbitals and two filled with lone pairs:

(b) For SF_4. The electron-group arrangement is trigonal bipyramidal, so the central S atom is sp^3d hybridized, which means one $3s$, three $3p$, and one $3d$ orbital are mixed. One hybrid orbital is filled with a lone pair, and four are half-filled. Four unhybridized $3d$ orbitals remain empty:

Follow-Up Problem 11.1 Use partial orbital diagrams to show how the atomic orbitals of the central atom mix to form hybrid orbitals in **(a)** beryllium fluoride, BeF_2; **(b)** silicon tetrachloride, $SiCl_4$; **(c)** xenon tetrafluoride, XeF_4.

Limitations to the Concept of Hybridization
We rely on the VSEPR and VB theories to rationalize an observed molecular shape. In some cases, however, the theories may not be consistent with other findings.

1. *Hybridization does not apply: large nonmetal hydrides.* Consider the Lewis structure and bond angle of H_2S:

Based on VSEPR theory, we would predict that, as in H_2O, the four electron groups around H_2S point to the corners of a tetrahedron, and the two lone pairs compress the H—S—H bond angle below the ideal 109.5°. Based on VB theory, we would propose that the $3s$ and $3p$ orbitals of the S atom mix and form four sp^3 hybrids, two of which are filled with lone pairs, while the other two overlap $1s$ orbitals of two H atoms and are filled with bonding pairs.

But observation does *not* support these arguments. The bond angle of 92° is close to the 90° angle between *unhybridized p* orbitals. Similar angles occur in the hydrides of other large nonmetals of Groups 5A(15) and 6A(16). Why apply a theory if the facts don't warrant it? Real factors—bond length, atomic size, and electrostatic repulsions—influence shape. Larger atoms form longer bonds to H, which decreases repulsions; thus, overlap of *unhybridized* orbitals explains these shapes.

2. *d-Orbital hybridization is less important: rationalizing shapes with expanded valence shells.* Quantum-mechanical calculations show that *d*-orbitals have such high energies that they do not hybridize effectively with the *much* more stable *s* and *p* orbitals of a given *n* value. Thus, for example, some have proposed that SF_6 is most stable when the bonding orbitals of the central S use a combination of *sp*-hybrid orbitals and unhybridized $3p$-orbitals instead of sp^3d^2 hybrid orbitals. Others prefer explanations that involve molecular orbitals or even ionic structures. These topics are beyond the scope of this text, and while they are being actively debated, we will continue to use the traditional, though limited, approach of including *d*-orbital hybridization for molecules with expanded valence shells.

■ Summary of Section 11.1

- VB theory explains that a covalent bond forms when two atomic orbitals overlap and two electrons with paired (opposite) spins spend more time in the overlapped regions.
- To explain molecular shape, the theory proposes that, during bonding, atomic orbitals mix to form hybrid orbitals with a different shape and direction. This process gives rise to greater overlap and, thus, stronger bonds.
- Based on the observed molecular shape (and the related electron-group arrangement), we postulate the type of hybrid orbital that accounts for the shape. In many cases, especially molecules with larger central atoms, the concept of hybridization has major limitations.

11.2 • MODES OF ORBITAL OVERLAP AND THE TYPES OF COVALENT BONDS

Orbitals can overlap by two *modes*—end to end or side to side—which gives rise to two types of covalent bonds—*sigma* and *pi*. We'll use VB theory to describe the two types here and, as you'll see, they are described by molecular orbital theory as well.

Orbital Overlap in Single and Multiple Bonds

Ethane (C_2H_6), ethylene (C_2H_4), and acetylene (C_2H_2) have different shapes. Ethane is tetrahedral at both carbons with bond angles near the ideal 109.5°. Ethylene is trigonal planar at both carbons with bond angles near the ideal 120°. Acetylene is linear with bond angles of 180°:

ethane   ethylene   acetylene

In these molecules, two modes of orbital overlap result in two types of bonds.

End-to-End Overlap and Sigma (σ) Bonding

Both C atoms of ethane are sp^3 hybridized (Figure 11.10). The C—C bond arises from overlap of the end of one sp^3 orbital with the end of the other. *End-to-end* overlap forms a **sigma (σ) bond,** which has its *highest electron density along the bond axis* and is shaped like an ellipse rotated

Figure 11.10 The σ bonds in
ethane (C_2H_6). **A,** Depiction
using atomic contours. **B,** An
electron density model shows
very slightly positive (*blue*)
and negative (*red*) regions.
C, Wedge-bond perspective
drawing.

about its long axis (like a football). *All single bonds are σ bonds,* including the six C—H
bonds in ethane.

Side-to-Side Overlap and Pi (π) Bonding

For this type of bonding, we'll examine
ethylene and acetylene:

1. *In ethylene,* each C atom is sp^2 hybridized. The four valence electrons of C
half-fill the three sp^2 orbitals *and* the unhybridized $2p$ orbital, which lies perpendicular
to the sp^2 plane (Figure 11.11). Two sp^2 orbitals of each C form C—H σ bonds. The
third sp^2 orbital forms a σ bond with the other C. With the σ-bonded C atoms near
each other, their half-filled $2p$ orbitals overlap *side to side,* which forms a **pi (π) bond.**
It has *two regions (lobes) of electron density,* one above and one below the σ-bond
axis. *The two electrons in one π bond occupy both lobes. A double bond consists of
one σ bond and one π bond,* which increases electron density between the nuclei
(Figure 11.11D). The two electron pairs act as one electron group because each pair occupies a different orbital, which reduces repulsions.

Figure 11.11 The σ and π bonds in ethylene (C_2H_4). **A,** The C—C σ bond and the
four C—H σ bonds are shown with the
unhybridized $2p$ orbitals. **B,** An accurate
depiction of the $2p$ orbitals shows the
side-to-side overlap; σ bonds are shown
in ball-and-stick form. **C,** Two overlapping
regions comprise *one* π bond, which is
occupied by two electrons. **D,** With four
electrons (one σ bond and one π bond)
between the C atoms, electron density
(*red*) is higher. **E,** Wedge-bond perspective drawing.

2. *In acetylene,* each C atom is sp hybridized, and its four valence electrons half-
fill the two sp hybrids *and* the two unhybridized $2p$ orbitals (Figure 11.12). Each C
forms a C—H σ bond with one sp orbital and a C—C σ bond with the other. Side-to-
side overlap of one pair of $2p$ orbitals gives one π bond, with electron density above
and below the σ bond. Side-to-side overlap of the other pair of $2p$ orbitals gives
another π bond, 90° away from the first, with electron density in front and back of the
σ bond. The result is a *cylindrically symmetrical* H—C≡C—H molecule. Note the
greater electron density between the C atoms created by the six bonding electrons.
Any triple bond *consists of one σ and two π bonds.*

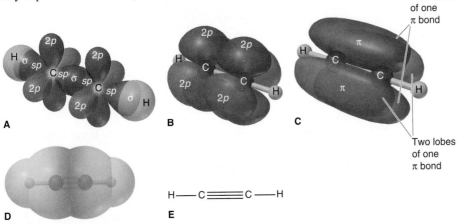

Figure 11.12 The σ bonds and π bonds
in acetylene (C_2H_2). **A,** A contour depiction shows the C—C σ bond, the two
C—H σ bonds, and two unhybridized
$2p$ orbitals (one pair is in *red* for clarity).
B, The $2p$ orbitals (accurate form) overlap
side to side; σ bonds are shown by a ball-
and-stick model. **C,** Overlapping regions
of two π bonds, one black and the other
red. **D,** The molecule has cylindrical symmetry. Six electrons (one σ bond and two
π bonds) create even higher electron
density (*red*) between the C atoms.
E, Bond-line drawing.

Mode of Overlap, Bond Strength, and Bond Order

Because orbitals overlap less side to side than end to end, a π bond is weaker than a σ bond; thus, for carbon-carbon bonds, a double bond is less than twice as strong as a single bond (Table 9.2, p. 340). Figure 11.13 shows electron density relief maps of the three types of carbon-carbon bonds; note the increasing electron density between the nuclei from single to double to triple bond.

Figure 11.13 Electron density and bond order in ethane, ethylene, and acetylene.

Lone-pair repulsions, bond polarities, and other factors affect overlap between other pairs of atoms. Nevertheless, as a rough approximation, in terms of bond order (BO), a double bond (BO = 2) is about twice as strong as a single bond (BO = 1), and a triple bond (BO = 3) is about three times as strong.

Sample Problem 11.2   Describing the Types of Bonds in Molecules

Problem Describe the types of bonds and orbitals in acetone, $(CH_3)_2CO$.

Plan We use the shape around each central atom to postulate the hybrid orbitals used and use unhybridized orbitals to form the C=O bond.

Solution The shapes are tetrahedral around each C of the two CH_3 (methyl) groups and trigonal planar around the middle C (see Sample Problem 10.8, p. 382). Thus, the middle C has three sp^2 orbitals and one unhybridized p orbital. Each of the two methyl C atoms has four sp^3 orbitals. Three of these form σ bonds with the $1s$ orbitals of H atoms; the fourth forms a σ bond with an sp^2 orbital of the middle C. Thus, two of the three sp^2 orbitals of the middle C form σ bonds to the other two C atoms.

The O atom is also sp^2 hybridized and has an unhybridized p orbital that can form a π bond. Two of the O atom's sp^2 orbitals hold lone pairs, and the third forms a σ bond with the third sp^2 orbital of the middle C atom. The unhybridized, half-filled $2p$ orbitals of C and O form a π bond. The σ and π bonds constitute the C=O bond:

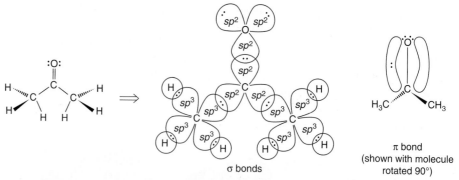

Comment Why would the O atom in acetone be hybridized? After all, it could use two perpendicular p orbitals for the σ and π bonds with C and leave the other p and the s orbital to hold the two lone pairs. Instead, having each lone pair in an sp^2 orbital oriented away from the C=O bond lowers electron-electron repulsions.

Follow-Up Problem 11.2 Describe the types of bonds and orbitals in **(a)** hydrogen cyanide, HCN, and **(b)** carbon dioxide, CO_2.

Orbital Overlap and Molecular Rotation

The type of overlap—end-to-end or side-to-side—affects rotation around the bond:

- *Sigma bond.* A σ *bond allows free rotation* because the extent of overlap is not affected. If you could hold one CH_3 group of ethane, the other CH_3 could spin without affecting the overlap of the C—C σ bond (see Figure 11.10).
- *Pi bond.* A π *bond restricts rotation* because *p* orbitals must be parallel to each other to overlap most effectively. Holding one CH_2 group in ethylene and trying to spin the other decreases the side-to-side overlap and breaks the π bond. For this reason, distinct *cis* and *trans* structures exist for compounds such as 1,2-dichloroethylene (Section 10.3). As Figure 11.14 shows, the π bond allows two *different* arrangements of atoms around the C atoms, which has a major effect on molecular polarity (see p. 385). Rotation around a triple bond is not meaningful: each triple-bonded C atom is bonded to one other group in a linear arrangement, so there can be no difference in the relative positions of attached groups.

cis-1,2-Dichloroethylene

trans-1,2-Dichloroethylene

Figure 11.14 Restricted rotation around a π bond. *Cis*- and *trans*-1,2-dichloroethylene are different molecules because the π bond restricts rotation.

■ Summary of Section 11.2

- End-to-end overlap of atomic orbitals forms a σ bond, which allows free rotation of the bonded parts of the molecule.
- Side-to-side overlap forms a π bond, which restricts rotation.
- A multiple bond consists of a σ bond and either one π bond (double bond) or two (triple bond). Multiple bonds have greater electron density between the nuclei than single bonds do and, thus, higher bond energies.

11.3 • MOLECULAR ORBITAL (MO) THEORY AND ELECTRON DELOCALIZATION

Scientists choose the model that best answers a question: VSEPR for one about molecular shape and VB theory for one about orbital overlap. But neither adequately explains magnetic and spectral properties, and both understate the importance of electron delocalization. To deal with phenomena like these, which involve molecular energy levels, chemists choose **molecular orbital (MO) theory.** The MO model is a quantum-mechanical treatment for molecules similar to the one for atoms (Chapter 8): just as an atom has atomic orbitals (AOs) of given energies and shapes that are occupied by the atom's electrons, a molecule has **molecular orbitals (MOs)** of given energies and shapes that are occupied by the molecule's electrons.

There is a key distinction between VB and MO theories:

- VB theory pictures a molecule as a group of atoms bonded through *localized* overlapping of valence-shell atomic and/or hybrid orbitals occupied by electrons.
- MO theory pictures a molecule as a collection of nuclei with orbitals *delocalized* over the whole molecule and occupied by electrons.

Despite its usefulness, MO theory has a drawback in that MOs are more difficult to visualize than the shapes of VSEPR theory or the hybrid orbitals of VB theory.

The Central Themes of MO Theory

Several key ideas of MO theory appear in its description of H_2 and other simple species: how MOs form, what their energies and shapes are, and how they fill with electrons.

Formation of Molecular Orbitals Just as we need approximations to solve the Schrödinger equation for any atom with more than one electron, we need an approximation to determine the MOs of even the simplest molecule, H_2. The approximation is

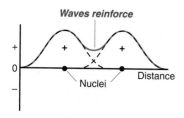

A Amplitudes of wave functions added

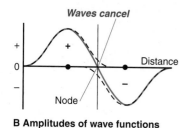

B Amplitudes of wave functions subtracted

Figure 11.15 An analogy between light waves and atomic wave functions.

to mathematically *combine* (add or subtract) AOs (atomic wave functions) of nearby atoms to form MOs (molecular wave functions). Thus, when two H nuclei lie near each other, their AOs overlap and combine in two ways:

- *Adding the wave functions together.* This combination forms a **bonding MO**, which has *a region of high electron density between the nuclei*. Additive overlap is analogous to light waves reinforcing each other, which makes the amplitude higher and the light brighter. For electron waves, the overlap *increases* the probability that the electrons are between the nuclei (Figure 11.15A).
- *Subtracting the wave functions from each other.* This combination forms an **antibonding MO**, which has *a node, a region of zero electron density, between the nuclei* (Figure 11.15B). Subtractive overlap is analogous to light waves canceling each other, causing the light to disappear. With electron waves, the probability that the electrons lie between the nuclei *decreases* to zero.

The two possible combinations for hydrogen atoms H_A and H_B are

AO of H_A + AO of H_B = bonding MO of H_2 (more e^- density between nuclei)
AO of H_A − AO of H_B = antibonding MO of H_2 (less e^- density between nuclei)

Notice that *the number of AOs combined always equals the number of MOs formed*: two H atomic orbitals combine to form two H_2 molecular orbitals.

Shape and Energy of H_2 Molecular Orbitals Bonding and antibonding MOs have different shapes and energies. Figure 11.16 shows these orbitals for H_2:

Figure 11.16 Contours and energies of H_2 bonding and antibonding MOs.

- *Bonding MO.* A bonding MO is *lower in energy* than the AOs that form it. Because it is spread mostly *between* the nuclei, nuclear repulsions decrease while nucleus-electron attractions increase. Moreover, two electrons in this MO can delocalize their charges over a larger volume than in nearby, separate AOs, which lowers electron repulsions. Because of these electrostatic effects, when electrons occupy this orbital, the H_2 molecule is *more stable* than the separate H atoms.
- *Antibonding MO.* An antibonding MO is *higher in energy* than the AOs that form it. With most of its electron density *outside* the internuclear region, it has a node between the nuclei, and nuclear repulsions increase. Therefore, when electrons occupy this orbital, the H_2 molecule is *less stable* than the separate H atoms.

Both the bonding and antibonding MOs of H_2 are **sigma (σ) MOs** because they are cylindrically symmetrical about an imaginary line between the nuclei. The bonding MO is denoted by σ_{1s}; that is, a σ MO derived from $1s$ AOs. Antibonding orbitals are denoted with a superscript star: the antibonding MO derived from $1s$ AOs is σ_{1s}^* (spoken "sigma, one ess, star").

For AOs to interact enough to form MOs, they must be similar in *energy* and *orientation*. The $1s$ orbitals of two H atoms have identical energy and orientation, so they interact strongly. We'll revisit this requirement for molecules composed of many-electron atoms.

Electrons in Molecular Orbitals Several aspects of MO theory—filling of MOs, energy-level diagrams, electron configuration, and bond order—relate to earlier ideas:

1. *Filling MOs with electrons.* Electrons enter MOs just as they do AOs:
- MOs are filled in order of increasing energy (aufbau principle).
- An MO can hold a maximum of two electrons with opposite spins (exclusion principle).
- Orbitals of equal energy are half-filled, with spins parallel, before any of them are filled (Hund's rule).

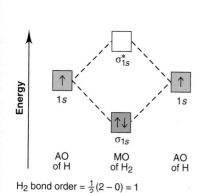

H_2 bond order = $\frac{1}{2}(2 - 0) = 1$

Figure 11.17 MO diagram for H_2.
The vertical placement of the boxes indicates relative energies. Orbital occupancy is shown with arrows and color (dark = full, pale = half-filled, none = empty).

2. *MO energy-level diagrams.* A **molecular orbital (MO) diagram** shows the relative energy and number of electrons in each MO, as well as the AOs from which they formed. In the MO diagram for H_2 (Figure 11.17), two electrons, one from the AO of each H, fill the H_2 bonding MO, while the antibonding MO remains empty.

3. *Electron configuration.* Just as we write an electron configuration for an atom, we can write one for a molecule. The symbol of each occupied MO is written in parentheses, with the number of electrons in it as a superscript outside: the electron configuration of H_2 is $(\sigma_{1s})^2$.

4. *Bond order.* In a Lewis structure, bond order is the number of electron pairs per atom-to-atom linkage. The **MO bond order** is the number of electrons in bonding MOs minus the number in antibonding MOs, divided by two:

$$\text{Bond order} = \tfrac{1}{2}[(\text{no. of } e^- \text{ in bonding MO}) - (\text{no. of } e^- \text{ in antibonding MO})] \qquad \textbf{(11.1)}$$

Here are three key points about MO bond order:

- Bond order > 0: the molecule is more stable than the separate atoms, so it *will* form. For H_2, the bond order is $\tfrac{1}{2}(2 - 0) = 1$.
- Bond order = 0: the molecule is as stable as the separate atoms, so it will *not* form (occurs when equal numbers of electrons occupy bonding and antibonding MOs).
- In general, the *higher* the bond order, the *stronger* the bond is.

Do He₂⁺ and He₂ Exist?

One of the early triumphs of MO theory was its ability to *predict* the existence of He_2^+, the helium molecule-ion, which consists of two He nuclei and three electrons. Let's use MO diagrams to see why He_2^+ exists but He_2 doesn't:

- In He_2^+, the $1s$ AOs form MOs (Figure 11.18A). The three electrons are distributed as a pair in the σ_{1s} MO and a lone electron in the σ_{1s}^* MO. The bond order is $\tfrac{1}{2}(2 - 1) = \tfrac{1}{2}$. Thus, He_2^+ has a relatively weak bond, but it should exist. Indeed, this species has been observed frequently when He atoms collide with He^+ ions. Its electron configuration is $(\sigma_{1s})^2(\sigma_{1s}^*)^1$.
- In He_2, with four electrons in the σ_{1s} and σ_{1s}^* MOs, both the bonding and antibonding orbitals are filled (Figure 11.18B). Stabilization from the electron pair in the bonding MO is canceled by destabilization from the electron pair in the antibonding MO. With a zero bond order $[\tfrac{1}{2}(2 - 2) = 0]$, we predict, and experiment has so far confirmed, that a covalent He_2 molecule does not exist.

A He₂⁺ bond order = $\tfrac{1}{2}$

B He₂ bond order = 0

Figure 11.18 MO diagrams for He₂⁺ and He₂.

Sample Problem 11.3 | Predicting Stability of Species Using MO Diagrams

Problem Use MO diagrams to find bond orders and predict whether H_2^+ and H_2^- exist. If either exists, write its electron configuration.

Plan Since the $1s$ AOs form the MOs, the MO diagrams are similar to the one for H_2. We find the number of electrons in each species and distribute them one at a time to the MOs in order of increasing energy. We obtain the bond order with Equation 11.1 and write the electron configuration as described in the text.

Solution For H_2^+. H_2 has two e^-, so H_2^+ has only one, which enters the bonding MO (*see diagram, below left*). The bond order is $\tfrac{1}{2}(1 - 0) = \tfrac{1}{2}$, so we predict that H_2^+ exists. The electron configuration is $(\sigma_{1s})^1$.

For H_2^-. H_2 has two e^-, so H_2^- has three. We place two paired e^- in the bonding MO and one unpaired e^- in the antibonding MO (*see diagram, below right*). The bond order is $\tfrac{1}{2}(2 - 1) = \tfrac{1}{2}$, so we predict that H_2^- exists. The electron configuration is $(\sigma_{1s})^2(\sigma_{1s}^*)^1$.

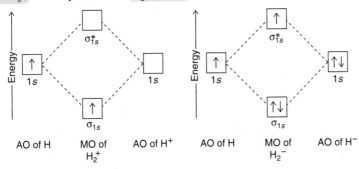

Check The number of electrons in the MOs equals the number of electrons in the AOs.

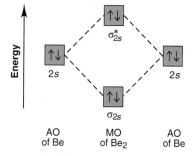

A Li$_2$ bond order = 1

B Be$_2$ bond order = 0

Figure 11.19 Bonding in *s*-block homonuclear diatomic molecules. Only outer (valence) AOs interact enough to form MOs.

Comment Both species have been detected spectroscopically, H$_2^+$ in the material around stars and H$_2^-$ in the laboratory.

Follow-Up Problem 11.3 Use an MO diagram to find the bond order and predict whether two H$^-$ ions could form H$_2^{2-}$. If it does exist, write its electron configuration.

Homonuclear Diatomic Molecules of Period 2 Elements

Homonuclear diatomic molecules are composed of two identical atoms. In addition to H$_2$ from Period 1, you're familiar with N$_2$, O$_2$, and F$_2$ from Period 2 as the elemental forms under standard conditions. Others in Period 2—Li$_2$, Be$_2$, B$_2$, C$_2$, and Ne$_2$—are observed, if at all, at high temperatures. We'll divide them into molecules from the *s* block, Groups 1A(1) and 2A(2), and the *p* block, Groups 3A(13) through 8A(18).

Bonding in the *s*-Block Homonuclear Diatomic Molecules
Both Li and Be occur as metals under normal conditions, but MO theory can examine their stability as diatomic gases, dilithium (Li$_2$) and diberyllium (Be$_2$).

These atoms have electrons in inner (1*s*) and outer (2*s*) AOs, but we ignore the inner ones because, in general, *only outer (valence) AOs interact enough to form MOs.* Like those formed from 1*s* AOs, these 2*s* AOs form σ MOs, cylindrically symmetrical around the internuclear axis.

- In Li$_2$, the two valence electrons fill the bonding (σ$_{2s}$) MO, with opposing spins, leaving the antibonding (σ$_{2s}^*$) MO empty (Figure 11.19A). The bond order is $\frac{1}{2}(2-0) = 1$. In fact, Li$_2$ *has* been observed; the electron configuration is (σ$_{2s}$)^2.
- In Be$_2$, the four valence electrons fill the σ$_{2s}$ and σ$_{2s}^*$ MOs (Figure 11.19B), giving an orbital occupancy similar to that in He$_2$. The bond order is $\frac{1}{2}(2-2) = 0$, and the ground state of Be$_2$ has never been observed.

Shape and Energy of MOs from Atomic *p*-Orbital Combinations
As we move to boron, atomic 2*p* orbitals are occupied. Recall that *p* orbitals can overlap by two modes, which correspond to two ways their wave functions combine (Figure 11.20):

- End-to-end combination gives a pair of σ MOs, the σ$_{2p}$ and σ$_{2p}^*$.
- Side-to-side combination gives a pair of **pi (π) MOs,** π$_{2p}$ and π$_{2p}^*$.

Despite the different shapes, MOs derived from *p* orbitals are like those from *s* orbitals. Bonding MOs have most of the electron density *between* the nuclei, and antibonding MOs have most *outside* the internuclear region, with a node between the nuclei.

Figure 11.20 Shapes and energies of σ and π MOs from combinations of 2*p* atomic orbitals. **A,** The *p* orbitals lying along the internuclear axis (designated *p$_x$*) overlap end to end and form σ$_{2p}$ and σ$_{2p}^*$ MOs. **B,** The *p* orbitals perpendicular to the internuclear axis overlap side to side and form two π MOs. (The *p$_y$* interactions, shown here, are the same as for the *p$_z$*, for a total of four π MOs.)

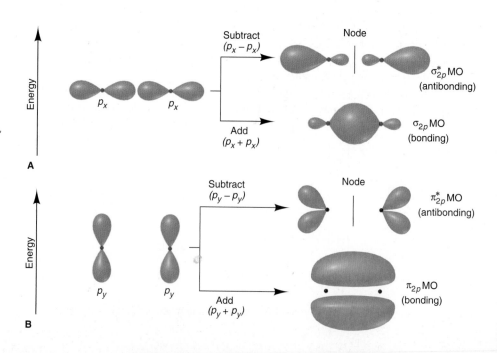

The order of energy levels for MOs, whether bonding or antibonding, is based on the order of AO energy levels *and* on the mode of the *p*-orbital overlap:

- MOs formed from 2*s* orbitals are *lower in energy* than MOs formed from 2*p* orbitals because 2*s* AOs are lower in energy than 2*p* AOs.
- Bonding MOs are *lower in energy* than antibonding MOs: σ_{2p} is lower in energy than σ_{2p}^{*} and π_{2p} is lower than π_{2p}^{*}.
- Atomic *p* orbitals overlap more extensively end to end than side to side. Thus, the σ_{2p} MO is usually lower in energy than the π_{2p} MO. We also find that the destabilizing effect of the σ_{2p}^{*} MO is greater than that of the π_{2p}^{*} MO.

Thus, the energy order for MOs derived from 2*p* orbitals is typically

$$\sigma_{2p} < \pi_{2p} < \pi_{2p}^{*} < \sigma_{2p}^{*}$$

Each atom has three mutually perpendicular 2*p* orbitals. When the six *p* orbitals in two atoms combine, the two that interact end to end form one σ and one σ* MO, and the two pairs of orbitals that interact side to side form two π MOs and two π* MOs. Placing these orientations within the energy order gives the *expected* MO diagram for the *p*-block Period 2 homonuclear diatomic molecules (Figure 11.21A).

Recall that only AOs of similar energy interact enough to form MOs. This fact leads to two energy orders:

1. ***Without s and p orbital mixing: O_2, F_2, and Ne_2.*** The order in Figure 11.21A assumes that *s* and *p* AOs are so different in energy that they do not interact; we say the orbitals do not *mix*. Lying at the right of Period 2, O, F, and Ne are relatively small. Thus, as electrons start to pair up in the half-filled 2*p* orbitals, strong repulsions raise the energy of the 2*p* orbitals high enough above the 2*s* orbitals to prevent orbital mixing.

2. ***With s and p orbital mixing: B_2, C_2, and N_2.*** B, C, and N atoms are relatively large, with 2*p* AOs only half-filled, so repulsions are weaker. As a result, orbital energies are close enough for some mixing to occur between the 2*s* of one atom and the end-on 2*p* of the other. The effect is to *lower* the energy of the σ_{2s} and σ_{2s}^{*} MOs and *raise* the energy of the σ_{2p} and σ_{2p}^{*} MOs; the π MOs are not affected. The MO diagram for B_2, C_2, and N_2 reflects this mixing (Figure 11.21B). The only difference from the MO diagram for O_2, F_2, and Ne_2 is the *reverse in energy order* of the σ_{2p} and π_{2p} MOs.

Figure 11.21 Relative MO energy levels for Period 2 homonuclear diatomic molecules. (For clarity, the MOs affected by mixing are shown in *purple.*)

Without 2*s* - 2*p* mixing

With 2*s* - 2*p* mixing

Energy

AO   MO   AO

A MO energy levels for O_2, F_2, and Ne_2

AO   MO   AO

B MO energy levels for B_2, C_2, and N_2

Figure 11.22 MO occupancy and some properties of B_2 through Ne_2. Energy order and occupancy of MOs are above bar graphs of bond energy and length, bond order, magnetic properties, and outer (valence) electron configuration.

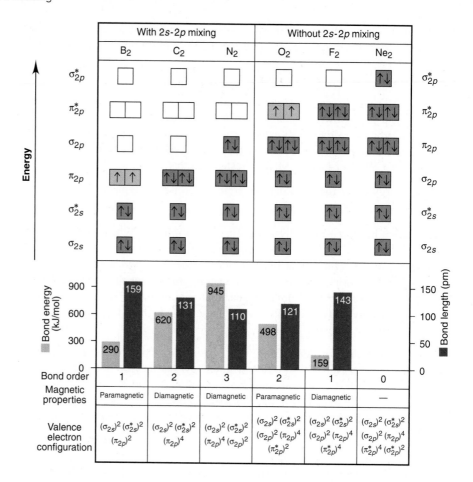

Bonding in the *p*-Block Homonuclear Diatomic Molecules

Figure 11.22 shows the MOs, electron occupancy, and some properties of B_2 through Ne_2. Note that

1. *Higher* bond order correlates with *greater* bond energy and *shorter* bond length.

2. Orbital occupancy correlates with magnetic properties. Recall from Chapter 8 that if a substance has unpaired electrons, it is *paramagnetic,* and if all electrons are paired, the substance is *diamagnetic;* the same applies to molecules. Let's examine the MO occupancy and some properties of these molecules:

- B_2. The B_2 molecule has six outer electrons: four fill the σ_{2s} and σ_{2s}^* MOs. The remaining two electrons occupy the two π_{2p} MOs, one in each orbital, in keeping with Hund's rule. With four electrons in bonding MOs and two in antibonding MOs, the bond order of B_2 is $\frac{1}{2}(4-2) = 1$. As expected from the two lone electrons, B_2 is paramagnetic.

- C_2. Two additional electrons in C_2 fill the two π_{2p} MOs. With two more bonding electrons than B_2, the bond order of C_2 is 2 and the bond is stronger and shorter. But with all the electrons paired, C_2 is diamagnetic.

- N_2. Two more electrons in N_2 fill the σ_{2p} MO, so the molecule is also diamagnetic. The bond order of 3 is consistent with the triple bond in the Lewis structure and with a stronger, shorter bond.

- O_2. With this molecule, we see the power of MO theory over VB theory and others based on electrons in localized orbitals. It is impossible to write one Lewis structure consistent with the fact that O_2 is double bonded and paramagnetic. We can write one with a double bond and paired electrons, and another with a single bond and two unpaired electrons:

$$\ddot{\text{O}}{=}\ddot{\text{O}} \quad \text{or} \quad \text{:}\dot{\text{O}}{-}\dot{\text{O}}\text{:}$$

MO theory resolves this paradox beautifully: with eight electrons in bonding MOs and four in antibonding MOs, the bond order is $\frac{1}{2}(8-4) = 2$, and it is paramagnetic because *one* electron occupies each of *two* π_{2p}^* MOs with unpaired (parallel) spins. A thin stream of liquid O_2 will remain suspended between the poles of a powerful magnet (Figure 11.23). As expected, the bond is weaker and longer than the one in N_2.

- *F_2*. Two more electrons in F_2 fill the π_{2p}^* orbitals, so it is diamagnetic. The bond has an order of 1 and is weaker and longer than the one in O_2. Note that this bond is shorter, yet about half as strong as the single bond in B_2. We might have expected it to be stronger because F is smaller than B. But 18 electrons in the smaller volume of F_2 cause greater repulsions than the 10 in B_2, so the F_2 bond is weaker.
- *Ne_2*. The final member of the Period 2 series doesn't exist for the same reason He_2 doesn't: all the MOs are filled, which gives a bond order of zero.

Figure 11.23 The paramagnetic properties of O_2.

Sample Problem 11.4 — Using MO Theory to Explain Bond Properties

Problem Explain the following data with diagrams showing the occupancy of MOs:

	N_2	N_2^+	O_2	O_2^+
Bond energy (kJ/mol)	945	841	498	623
Bond length (pm)	110	112	121	112

Plan The data show that removing an electron from each parent molecule has opposite effects: N_2^+ has a weaker, longer bond than N_2, but O_2^+ has a stronger, shorter bond than O_2. We determine the valence electrons in each species, draw the sequence of MO energy levels (showing orbital mixing in N_2 but not in O_2), and fill them with electrons. To explain the data, we calculate bond orders, which relate directly to bond energy and inversely to bond length.

Solution Determining the valence electrons:

$$N \text{ has 5 valence } e^-, \text{ so } N_2 \text{ has 10 and } N_2^+ \text{ has 9}$$
$$O \text{ has 6 valence } e^-, \text{ so } O_2 \text{ has 12 and } O_2^+ \text{ has 11}$$

Drawing and filling the MO diagrams:

Calculating bond orders:

$$\tfrac{1}{2}(8 - 2) = 3 \qquad \tfrac{1}{2}(7 - 2) = 2.5 \qquad \tfrac{1}{2}(8 - 4) = 2 \qquad \tfrac{1}{2}(8 - 3) = 2.5$$

Explaining the data:
1. When N_2 becomes N_2^+, a *bonding* electron is removed, so the bond order decreases. Thus, N_2^+ has a weaker, longer bond than N_2.
2. When O_2 becomes O_2^+, an *antibonding* electron is removed, so the bond order increases. Thus, O_2^+ has a stronger, shorter bond than O_2.

Check The answers make sense in terms of bond order, bond energy, and bond length. Check that the total number of bonding and antibonding electrons equals the number of valence electrons calculated.

Follow-Up Problem 11.4 Determine the bond orders for the following species: F_2^{2-}, F_2^-, F_2, F_2^+, F_2^{2+}. List the species in order of increasing bond energy and in order of increasing bond length.

Two Heteronuclear Diatomic Molecules: HF and NO

Heteronuclear diatomic molecules have asymmetric MO diagrams because the AOs of the *different* atoms have unequal energies. Atoms with greater effective nuclear charge (Z_{eff}) pull their electrons closer, so they have more stable (lower energy) AOs (Section 8.1) and higher EN values (Section 9.5). Let's examine the bonding in HF and NO.

Bonding in HF To form the MOs in HF, we decide which AOs will combine. The high Z_{eff} of F holds its electrons so tightly that the $1s$, $2s$, and $2p$ orbitals of F have lower energy than the $1s$ of H. The half-filled F $2p$ orbital interacts with the H $1s$ through end-on overlap, which forms σ and σ* MOs. The two filled $2p$ orbitals of F are called **nonbonding MOs.** Because they are not involved in bonding, they have the same energy as the isolated AOs (Figure 11.24A).

The bonding MO is closer in energy to the AOs of F, so the F $2p$ orbital contributes more to the HF bond than the H $1s$ does. In polar covalent molecules, *bonding MOs are closer in energy to the AOs of the more electronegative atom.* In effect, fluorine's greater electronegativity lowers the energy of the bonding MO and draws the bonding electrons closer.

Bonding in NO Nitrogen monoxide (nitric oxide) is highly reactive because of its lone electron. Two possible Lewis structures for NO, with formal charges (Section 10.1), are

$$\overset{0\ \ \ 0}{:\!\dot{N}\!=\!\ddot{O}:} \quad \text{or} \quad \overset{-1\ \ +1}{:\!\ddot{N}\!=\!\dot{O}:}$$
$$\textbf{I} \qquad\qquad \textbf{II}$$

Both structures show a double bond, but the *measured* bond energy suggests a bond order *higher* than 2. Moreover, it is not clear where the lone electron resides, although the lower formal charges for structure I suggest that it is on the N.

The MO diagram is asymmetric, with the AOs of the more electronegative O lower in energy (Figure 11.24B). When the 11 valence electrons fill the MOs of NO, the lone electron occupies one of the π^*_{2p} orbitals. Eight bonding and three antibonding electrons give a bond order of $\frac{1}{2}(8 - 3) = 2.5$, more in keeping with the data than either Lewis structure. Bonding electrons lie in MOs closer in energy to the AOs of the O atom. The $2p$ orbitals of N contribute more to the orbital that holds the lone electron, so it spends more time closer to N. (This diagram shows the energy order *with* $2s$–$2p$ mixing, as in Figure 11.21, but the result is the same as the order without mixing.)

Figure 11.24 The MO diagrams for HF and NO. **A,** In HF, the bonding MO is closer in energy to the $2p$ orbital of F. (The $2s$ AO of F is not shown.) **B,** In NO, the lone electron occupies an MO closer in energy to the $2p$ of N.

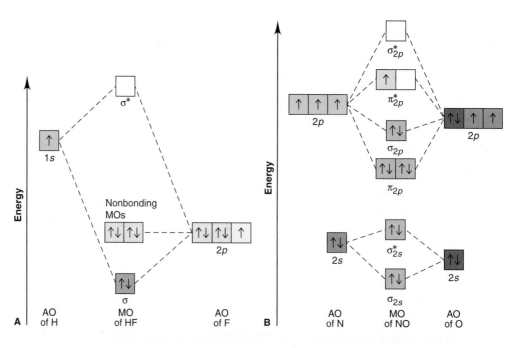

Two Polyatomic Molecules: Benzene and Ozone

The orbital shapes and MO diagrams for polyatomic molecules are too complex for a detailed treatment here. But we'll briefly discuss how the model eliminates the need for resonance forms and helps explain the effects of the absorption of energy.

Recall that we cannot draw one Lewis structure for either benzene or ozone, so we draw separate forms of a resonance hybrid. The VB model also uses resonance because it relies on *localized* bonds. In contrast, MO theory pictures a structure of delocalized σ and π MOs. Figure 11.25 shows the lowest energy π-bonding MOs in benzene and ozone. The extended areas of electron density allow delocalization of one π-bonding electron pair over the entire molecule, thus eliminating the need for separate resonance forms:

- *In benzene*, the upper and lower hexagonal lobes of this MO lie above and below the σ plane of the six C nuclei.
- *In ozone*, the two lobes of this MO extend over and under the three O nuclei.

The full MO diagrams for these molecules help us rationalize how bonding electrons in O_3 become excited and occupy empty antibonding orbitals when the molecule absorbs UV radiation in the stratosphere, and why the UV spectrum of benzene has its characteristic absorption bands.

Benzene, C_6H_6

Ozone, O_3

Figure 11.25 The lowest energy π-bonding MOs in benzene and ozone.

▌Summary of Section 11.3

- Molecular orbital (MO) theory treats a molecule as a collection of nuclei with MOs delocalized over the entire structure.
- Atomic orbitals of comparable energy can be added or subtracted to obtain bonding or antibonding MOs, respectively.
- Bonding MOs, whether σ or π, have most of the electron density between the nuclei and are lower in energy than the AOs; most of the electron density in antibonding MOs does not lie between the nuclei, so these MOs are higher in energy.
- MOs are filled in order of their energy with paired electrons having opposite spins.
- MO diagrams show energy levels and orbital occupancy. Diagrams for the Period 2 homonuclear diatomic molecules explain bond energy, bond length, and magnetic behavior.
- In heteronuclear diatomic molecules, the more electronegative atom contributes more to the bonding MOs.
- MO theory eliminates the need for resonance forms to depict larger molecules.

CHAPTER REVIEW GUIDE

Learning Objectives   Relevant section (§) and/or sample problem (SP) numbers appear in parentheses.

Understand These Concepts

1. The main ideas of valence bond theory—orbital overlap, opposing electron spins, and hybridization—as a means of rationalizing molecular shapes (§11.1)
2. How orbitals mix to form hybrid orbitals with different spatial orientations (§11.1)
3. The distinction between end-to-end and side-to-side overlap and the origin of sigma (σ) and pi (π) bonds in simple molecules (§11.2)
4. How these two modes of orbital overlap lead to single, double, and triple bonds (§11.2)
5. Why π bonding restricts rotation around double bonds (§11.2)
6. The distinction between the localized bonding of VB theory and the delocalized bonding of MO theory (§11.3)
7. How addition or subtraction of AOs forms bonding or antibonding MOs (§11.3)
8. The shapes of MOs formed from combinations of two *s* orbitals and combinations of two *p* orbitals (§11.3)
9. How MO bond order predicts the stability of molecular species (§11.3)
10. How MO theory explains the bonding and magnetic properties of homonuclear and heteronuclear diatomic molecules of Period 2 elements (§11.3)

Master These Skills

1. Using molecular shape to postulate the hybrid orbitals used by a central atom (SP 11.1)
2. Describing the types of orbitals and bonds in a molecule (SP 11.2)
3. Drawing MO diagrams, writing electron configurations, and calculating bond orders of molecular species (SP 11.3)
4. Explaining bond and magnetic properties with MO theory (SP 11.4)

Key Equations and Relationships   Page numbers appear in parentheses.

11.1 Calculating the MO bond order (407): Bond order = $\frac{1}{2}$[(no. of e⁻ in bonding MO) − (no. of e⁻ in antibonding MO)]

Brief Solutions to Follow-Up Problems

11.1 (a) Shape is linear, so Be is *sp* hybridized.

Isolated Be atom   Hybridized Be atom

(b) Shape is tetrahedral, so Si is *sp³* hybridized.

Isolated Si atom   Hybridized Si atom

(c) Shape is square planar, so Xe is *sp³d²* hybridized.

Isolated Xe atom   Hybridized Xe atom

11.2 (a) H—C≡N:

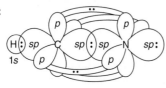

HCN is linear, so C is *sp* hybridized. N is also *sp* hybridized. One *sp* of C overlaps the 1*s* of H to form a σ bond. The other *sp* of C overlaps one *sp* of N to form a σ bond. The other *sp* of N holds a lone pair. Two unhybridized *p* orbitals of N and two of C overlap to form two π bonds.
(b) Ö=C=Ö

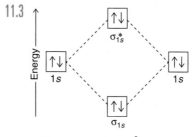

CO_2 is linear, so C is *sp* hybridized. Both O atoms are *sp²* hybridized. Each *sp* of C overlaps one *sp²* of an O to form two σ bonds. Each of the two unhybridized *p* orbitals of C forms a π bond with the unhybridized *p* of one of the two O atoms. Two *sp²* of each O hold lone pairs.

11.3

AO of H⁻   MO of H_2^{2-} AO of H⁻

Does not exist: bond order = $\frac{1}{2}(2 - 2) = 0$.

11.4 Bond orders: $F_2^{2-} = 0$; $F_2^- = \frac{1}{2}$; $F_2 = 1$; $F_2^+ = 1\frac{1}{2}$
$$F_2^{2+} = 2$$
Bond energy: $F_2^{2-} < F_2^- < F_2 < F_2^+ < F_2^{2+}$
Bond length: $F_2^{2+} < F_2^+ < F_2 < F_2^-$; F_2^{2-} does not exist

PROBLEMS

Problems with **colored** numbers are answered in Appendix E and worked in detail in the Student Solutions Manual. Problem sections match those in the text and provide the numbers of relevant sample problems. Most offer Concept Review Questions, Skill-Building Exercises (grouped in pairs covering the same concept), and Problems in Context. The Comprehensive Problems are based on material from any section or previous chapter.

Valence Bond (VB) Theory and Orbital Hybridization

(Sample Problem 11.1)

Concept Review Questions

11.1 What type of central-atom orbital hybridization corresponds to each electron-group arrangement: (a) trigonal planar; (b) octahedral; (c) linear; (d) tetrahedral; (e) trigonal bipyramidal?

11.2 What is the orbital hybridization of a central atom that has one lone pair and bonds to: (a) two other atoms; (b) three other atoms; (c) four other atoms; (d) five other atoms?

11.3 How do carbon and silicon differ with regard to the *types* of orbitals available for hybridization? Explain.

11.4 How many hybrid orbitals form when four atomic orbitals of a central atom mix? Explain.

Skill-Building Exercises (grouped in similar pairs)

11.5 Give the number and type of hybrid orbital that forms when each set of atomic orbitals mixes:
(a) two *d*, one *s*, and three *p*   (b) three *p* and one *s*

11.6 Give the number and type of hybrid orbital that forms when each set of atomic orbitals mixes:
(a) one *p* and one *s*   (b) three *p*, one *d*, and one *s*

11.7 What is the hybridization of nitrogen in each of the following: (a) NO; (b) NO_2; (c) NO_2^-?

11.8 What is the hybridization of carbon in each of the following: (a) CO_3^{2-}; (b) $C_2O_4^{2-}$; (c) NCO^-?

11.9 What is the hybridization of chlorine in each of the following: (a) ClO_2; (b) ClO_3^-; (c) ClO_4^-?

11.10 What is the hybridization of bromine in each of the following: (a) BrF_3; (b) BrO_2^-; (c) BrF_5?

11.11 Which types of atomic orbitals of the central atom mix to form hybrid orbitals in (a) $SiClH_3$; (b) CS_2; (c) SCl_3F; (d) NF_3?

11.12 Which types of atomic orbitals of the central atom mix to form hybrid orbitals in (a) Cl_2O; (b) $BrCl_3$; (c) PF_5; (d) SO_3^{2-}?

11.13 Phosphine (PH_3) reacts with borane (BH_3) as follows:

$$PH_3 + BH_3 \longrightarrow H_3P-BH_3$$

(a) Which of the illustrations below depicts the change, if any, in the orbital hybridization of P during this reaction? (b) Which depicts the change, if any, in the orbital hybridization of B?

11.14 The illustrations below depict differences in orbital hybridization of some tellurium (Te) fluorides. (a) Which depicts the difference, if any, between TeF_6 (*left*) and TeF_5^- (*right*)? (b) Which depicts the difference, if any, between TeF_4 (*left*) and TeF_6 (*right*)?

11.15 Use partial orbital diagrams to show how the atomic orbitals of the central atom lead to hybrid orbitals in (a) $GeCl_4$; (b) BCl_3; (c) CH_3^+.

11.16 Use partial orbital diagrams to show how the atomic orbitals of the central atom lead to hybrid orbitals in (a) BF_4^-; (b) PO_4^{3-}; (c) SO_3.

11.17 Use partial orbital diagrams to show how the atomic orbitals of the central atom lead to hybrid orbitals in (a) $SeCl_2$; (b) H_3O^+; (c) IF_4^-.

11.18 Use partial orbital diagrams to show how the atomic orbitals of the central atom lead to hybrid orbitals in (a) $AsCl_3$; (b) $SnCl_2$; (c) PF_6^-.

Problems in Context

11.19 Methyl isocyanate, $CH_3-\ddot{N}=C=\ddot{O}:$, is an intermediate in the manufacture of many pesticides. In 1984 a leak from a manufacturing plant resulted in the death of more than 2000 people in Bhopal, India. What are the hybridizations of the N atom and the two C atoms in methyl isocyanate? Sketch the molecular shape.

Modes of Orbital Overlap and the Types of Covalent Bonds

(Sample Problem 11.2)

Concept Review Questions

11.20 Are these statements true or false? Correct any false ones.
(a) Two σ bonds comprise a double bond.
(b) A triple bond consists of one π bond and two σ bonds.
(c) Bonds formed from atomic *s* orbitals are always σ bonds.
(d) A π bond restricts rotation about the σ-bond axis.
(e) A π bond consists of two pairs of electrons.
(f) End-to-end overlap results in a bond with electron density above and below the bond axis.

Skill-Building Exercises (grouped in similar pairs)

11.21 Describe the hybrid orbitals used by the central atom and the type(s) of bonds formed in (a) NO_3^-; (b) CS_2; (c) CH_2O.

11.22 Describe the hybrid orbitals used by the central atom and the type(s) of bonds formed in (a) O_3; (b) I_3^-; (c) $COCl_2$ (C is central).

11.23 Describe the hybrid orbitals used by the central atom(s) and the type(s) of bonds formed in (a) FNO; (b) C_2F_4; (c) $(CN)_2$.

11.24 Describe the hybrid orbitals used by the central atom(s) and the type(s) of bonds formed in (a) BrF_3; (b) $CH_3C\equiv CH$; (c) SO_2.

Problem in Context

11.25 2-Butene (CH_3CH=$CHCH_3$) is a starting material in the manufacture of lubricating oils and many other compounds. Draw two different structures for 2-butene, indicating the σ and π bonds in each.

Molecular Orbital (MO) Theory and Electron Delocalization

(Sample Problems 11.3 and 11.4)

Concept Review Questions

11.26 Two *p* orbitals from one atom and two *p* orbitals from another atom are combined to form molecular orbitals for the joined atoms. How many MOs will result from this combination? Explain.

11.27 Certain atomic orbitals on two atoms were combined to form the following MOs. Name the atomic orbitals used and the MOs formed, and explain which MO has higher energy:

11.28 How do the bonding and antibonding MOs formed from a given pair of AOs compare to each other with respect to (a) energy; (b) presence of nodes; (c) internuclear electron density?

11.29 Antibonding MOs always have at least one node. Can a bonding MO have a node? If so, draw an example.

Skill-Building Exercises (grouped in similar pairs)

11.30 How many electrons does it take to fill (a) a σ bonding MO; (b) a π antibonding MO; (c) the MOs formed from combination of the 1*s* orbitals of two atoms?

11.31 How many electrons does it take to fill (a) the MOs formed from combination of the 2*p* orbitals of two atoms; (b) a σ^*_{2p} MO; (c) the MOs formed from combination of the 2*s* orbitals of two atoms?

11.32 The molecular orbitals depicted below are derived from 2*p* atomic orbitals in F_2^+. (a) Give the orbital designations. (b) Which is occupied by at least one electron in F_2^+? (c) Which is occupied by only one electron in F_2^+?

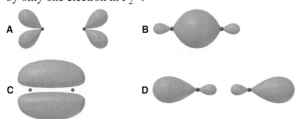

11.33 The molecular orbitals depicted below are derived from *n* = 2 atomic orbitals. (a) Give the orbital designations. (b) Which is highest in energy? (c) Lowest in energy? (d) Rank the MOs in order of increasing energy for B_2.

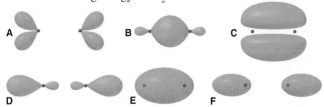

11.34 Use MO diagrams and the bond orders you obtain from them to answer: (a) Is Be_2^+ stable? (b) Is Be_2^+ diamagnetic? (c) What is the outer (valence) electron configuration of Be_2^+?

11.35 Use MO diagrams and the bond orders you obtain from them to answer: (a) Is O_2^- stable? (b) Is O_2^- paramagnetic? (c) What is the outer (valence) electron configuration of O_2^-?

11.36 Use MO diagrams to place C_2^-, C_2, and C_2^+ in order of (a) increasing bond energy; (b) increasing bond length.

11.37 Use MO diagrams to place B_2^+, B_2, and B_2^- in order of (a) decreasing bond energy; (b) decreasing bond length.

Comprehensive Problems

11.38 Predict the shape, state the hybridization of the central atom, and give the ideal bond angle(s) and any expected deviations for:
(a) BrO_3^- (b) $AsCl_4^-$ (c) SeO_4^{2-} (d) BiF_5^{2-}
(e) SbF_4^+ (f) AlF_6^{3-} (g) IF_4^+

11.39 Butadiene (*right*) is a colorless gas used to make synthetic rubber and many other compounds. (a) How many σ bonds and π bonds does the molecule have? (b) Are *cis-trans* arrangements about the double bonds possible? Explain.

11.40 Epinephrine (or adrenaline; *below*) is a naturally occurring hormone that is also manufactured commercially for use as a heart stimulant, a nasal decongestant, and a glaucoma treatment.

(a) What is the hybridization of each C, O, and N atom? (b) How many σ bonds does the molecule have? (c) How many π electrons are delocalized in the ring?

11.41 Use partial orbital diagrams to show how the atomic orbitals of the central atom lead to the hybrid orbitals in:
(a) IF_2^- (b) ICl_3 (c) $XeOF_4$ (d) BHF_2

11.42 Isoniazid (*below*) is an antibacterial agent that is very useful against many common strains of tuberculosis. (a) How many σ bonds are in the molecule? (b) What is the hybridization of each C and N atom?

11.43 Hydrazine, N_2H_4, and carbon disulfide, CS_2, form a cyclic molecule (*below*). (a) Draw Lewis structures for N_2H_4 and CS_2. (b) How do electron-group arrangement, molecular shape, and hybridization of N change when N_2H_4 reacts to form the product? (c) How do electron-group arrangement, molecular shape, and hybridization of C change when CS_2 reacts to form the product?

11.44 In each of the following equations, what hybridization change, if any, occurs for the underlined atom?
(a) $\underline{B}F_3 + NaF \longrightarrow Na^+BF_4^-$
(b) $\underline{P}Cl_3 + Cl_2 \longrightarrow PCl_5$
(c) $H\underline{C}\equiv CH + H_2 \longrightarrow H_2C$=$CH_2$
(d) $\underline{Si}F_4 + 2F^- \longrightarrow SiF_6^{2-}$
(e) $\underline{S}O_2 + \frac{1}{2}O_2 \rightarrow SO_3$

11.45 The ionosphere lies about 100 km above Earth's surface. This layer consists mostly of NO, O_2, and N_2, and photoionization creates NO^+, O_2^+, and N_2^+. (a) Use MO theory to compare the bond orders of the molecules and ions. (b) Does the magnetic behavior of each species change when its ion forms?

11.46 Glyphosate (*below*) is a common herbicide that is relatively harmless to animals but deadly to most plants. Describe the shape around and the hybridization of the P, N, and three numbered C atoms.

11.47 Tryptophan is one of the amino acids found in proteins:

(a) What is the hybridization of each of the numbered C, N, and O atoms? (b) How many σ bonds are present in tryptophan? (c) Predict the bond angles at points a, b, and c.

11.48 Some species with two oxygen atoms only are the oxygen molecule, O_2, the peroxide ion, O_2^{2-}, the superoxide ion, O_2^-, and the dioxygenyl ion, O_2^+. Draw an MO diagram for each, rank them in order of increasing bond length, and find the number of unpaired electrons in each.

11.49 Molecular nitrogen, carbon monoxide, and cyanide ion are isoelectronic. (a) Draw an MO diagram for each. (b) CO and CN^- are toxic. What property may explain why N_2 isn't?

11.50 There is concern in health-related government agencies that the American diet contains too much meat, and numerous recommendations have been made urging people to consume more fruit and vegetables. One of the richest sources of vegetable protein is soy, available in many forms. Among these is soybean curd, or tofu, which is a staple of many Asian diets. Chemists have isolated an anticancer agent called *genistein* from tofu, which may explain the much lower incidence of cancer among people in the Far East. A valid Lewis structure for genistein is

(a) Is the hybridization of each C in the right-hand ring the same? Explain. (b) Is the hybridization of the O atom in the center ring the same as that of the O atoms in OH groups? Explain. (c) How many carbon-oxygen σ bonds are there? How many carbon-oxygen π bonds? (d) Do all the lone pairs on oxygens occupy the same type of hybrid orbital? Explain.

11.51 An organic chemist synthesizes the molecule below:

11.52 Simple proteins consist of amino acids linked together in a long chain; a small portion of such a chain is

Experiment shows that rotation about the C—N bond (indicated by the arrow) is somewhat restricted. Explain with resonance structures, and show the types of bonding involved.

11.53 Sulfur forms oxides, oxoanions, and halides. What is the hybridization of the central S in SO_2, SO_3, SO_3^{2-}, SCl_4, SCl_6, and S_2Cl_2 (atom sequence Cl—S—S—Cl)?

11.54 The compound 2,6-dimethylpyrazine (*below*) gives chocolate its odor and is used in flavorings. (a) Which atomic orbitals mix to form the hybrid orbitals of N? (b) In what type of hybrid orbital do the lone pairs of N reside? (c) Is C in CH_3 hybridized the same as any C in the ring? Explain.

11.55 Acetylsalicylic acid (aspirin), the most widely used medicine in the world, has the Lewis structure shown below. (a) What is the hybridization of each C and each O atom? (b) How many localized π bonds are present? (c) How many C atoms have a trigonal planar shape around them? A tetrahedral shape?

11.56 Linoleic acid is an essential fatty acid found in many vegetable oils, such as soy, peanut, and cottonseed. A key structural feature of the molecule is the *cis* orientation around its two double bonds, where R_1 and R_2 represent two different groups that form the rest of the molecule.

(a) How many different compounds are possible, changing only the *cis-trans* arrangements around these two double bonds? (b) How many are possible for a similar compound with three double bonds?

(a) Which of the orientations of hybrid orbitals shown below are present in the molecule? (b) Are there any present that are not shown below? If so, what are they? (c) How many of each type of hybrid orbital are present?

Organic Compounds and the Atomic Properties of Carbon

Concepts and skills to review before you study this chapter

- naming straight-chain alkanes (Section 2.8)
- constitutional isomerism (Section 3.2)
- ΔEN and bond polarity (Section 9.5)
- resonance structures (Section 10.1)
- VSEPR theory (Section 10.2)
- orbital hybridization (Section 11.1)

- σ and π bonding (Section 11.2)
- intermolecular forces and synthetic and biological macromolecules (Sections 12.3, 12.7, and 13.2)
- properties of the Period 2 elements (Section 14.2)
- properties of the Group 4A(14) elements (Section 14.6)

Organic compounds occur throughout every living thing and in countless products—like jelly beans in a plastic container! Jelly beans are composed of sugars, gelatin, and starch—all organic compounds. And the plastic container is a combination of polymeric organic compounds. In fact, except for a few inorganic salts and ever-present water, nearly everything you put into or on your body—jelly beans, medicine, cosmetics, and clothing—consists of organic compounds. Organic fuels warm our homes, cook our meals, and power our vehicles. Major industries are devoted to producing organic compounds, including plastics, pharmaceuticals, and insecticides.

What *is* an organic compound? The dictionary definition is "a compound of carbon," but that definition is too general because it includes carbonates, cyanides, carbides, cyanates, and other carbon-containing ionic compounds that most chemists classify as inorganic. Here is a more specific definition: all **organic compounds** contain carbon, nearly always bonded to other carbons and hydrogen, and often to other elements.

In the early 19th century, organic compounds were usually obtained from living things, so they were thought to possess a spiritual "vital force" that made them impossible to synthesize and fundamentally different from inorganic compounds. Today, we know that *the same chemical principles govern organic and inorganic systems* because the behavior of a compound arises from the properties of its elements.

IN THIS CHAPTER . . . We apply the text's central theme to the enormous field of organic chemistry to see how the structures and reactivities of organic molecules emerge naturally from the properties of their component atoms.
- We begin by reviewing the atomic properties of carbon and seeing how they lead to the complex structures and reactivity of organic molecules.
- We then focus on writing and naming hydrocarbons as a prelude to naming other types of organic compounds.
- We classify the main types of organic reactions in terms of bond order and apply them to the functional groups that characterize families of organic compounds.
- We examine the giant organic molecules of commerce and life—synthetic and natural polymers.

15.1 • THE SPECIAL NATURE OF CARBON AND THE CHARACTERISTICS OF ORGANIC MOLECULES

Although there is nothing mystical about organic molecules, their indispensable role in biology and industry leads us to ask if carbon has some extraordinary attributes that give it a special chemical "personality." Of course, each element has its own specific properties, and carbon is no more unique than sodium, hafnium, or any other element. But the atomic properties of carbon do give it bonding capabilities beyond those of any other element, which in turn lead to the two obvious characteristics of organic molecules—structural complexity and chemical diversity.

The Structural Complexity of Organic Molecules

Most organic molecules have more complex structures than most inorganic molecules. A quick review of carbon's atomic properties and bonding behavior shows why.

Electron Configuration, Electronegativity, and Covalent Bonding Carbon forms covalent bonds in all its elemental forms and compounds, sharing electrons to attain a filled outer (valence) level. Carbon's formation of covalent bonds, rather than ionic bonds, is the result of its electron configuration and its electronegativity value:

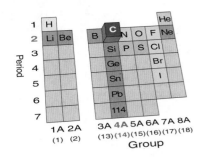

Figure 15.1 The position of carbon in the periodic table.

- Carbon's ground-state electron configuration of [He] $2s^2 2p^2$—four electrons more than He and four fewer than Ne—means that the formation of carbon ions is energetically impossible under ordinary conditions. The loss of four electrons to form the C^{4+} cation requires energy equal to the sum of IE_1 through IE_4; the gain of four electrons to form the C^{4-} anion requires the sum of EA_1 through EA_4, the last three steps of which are endothermic.
- Lying at the center of Period 2, carbon has an electronegativity (EN = 2.5) that is midway between that of the most metallic element (Li, EN = 1.0) and the most non-metallic element (F, EN = 4.0) of Period 2 (Figure 15.1).

Bond Properties, Catenation, and Molecular Shape The *number* and *strength* of carbon's bonds lead to its property of **catenation,** the ability to bond to itself, which in turn allows it to form a multitude of chemically and thermally stable chain, ring, and branched compounds. Carbon's small size and ability to form hybrid orbitals and multiple bonds increase the number of different molecules by affecting molecular shape:

- Through the process of orbital hybridization (Section 11.1), carbon forms four bonds in virtually all its compounds, and they point in as many as four different directions.
- The small size of carbon allows close approach to another atom and thus greater orbital overlap, so carbon forms relatively short, strong bonds.
- The C—C bond is short enough to allow side-to-side overlap of half-filled, unhybridized *p* orbitals and the formation of multiple bonds, which restrict rotation of attached groups (see Figure 11.14, p. 405).

Molecular Stability Although silicon and several other elements also catenate, none can form chains as stable as those of carbon. Atomic and bonding properties confer three crucial differences between C and Si chains that explain why C chains are so stable and, therefore, so common:

- *Atomic size and bond strength.* As atomic size increases down Group 4A(14), bonds between identical atoms become longer and weaker. Thus, a C—C bond (347 kJ/mol) is much stronger than an Si—Si bond (226 kJ/mol).
- *Relative enthalpies of reaction.* A C—C bond (347 kJ/mol), a C—O bond (358 kJ/mol), and a C—Cl bond (339 kJ/mol) have nearly the same energy, so relatively little heat is released when a C chain reacts and one bond replaces the other. In contrast, an Si—O bond (368 kJ/mol) or an Si—Cl bond (381 kJ/mol) is much stronger than an Si—Si bond (226 kJ/mol), so a large quantity of heat is released when an Si chain reacts.
- *Orbitals available for reaction.* Unlike C, Si has low-energy *d* orbitals that can be attacked (occupied) by the lone pairs of incoming reactants. For example, ethane (CH_3—CH_3) is stable in water and does not react in air unless sparked, whereas disilane (SiH_3—SiH_3) breaks down in water and ignites spontaneously in air.

The Chemical Diversity of Organic Molecules

In addition to their complex geometries, organic compounds are noted for their sheer number and diverse chemical behavior. Several million organic compounds are known, and thousands more are discovered or synthesized each year. This incredible diversity is also founded on atomic and bonding behavior and is due to three inter-related factors, discussed below.

Bonding to Heteroatoms Many organic compounds contain **heteroatoms,** atoms other than C or H. The most common heteroatoms are N and O, but S, P, and the halogens often occur, and organic compounds with other elements are known as well. Figure 15.2 shows that 23 different molecular structures are possible from various arrangements of four C atoms singly bonded to each other, just one O atom (either singly or doubly bonded), and the necessary number of H atoms.

Electron Density and Reactivity Most reactions start—that is, a new bond begins to form—*when a region of high electron density on one molecule meets a region of low electron density on another.* These regions may be due to the presence of a multiple bond or to the properties of carbon-heteroatom bonds. Consider the reactivities of four bonds commonly found in organic molecules:

- *The C—C bond.* When C is singly bonded to another C, as occurs in portions of nearly every organic molecule, the EN values are equal and the bond is nonpolar. Therefore, in general, *C—C bonds are unreactive.*
- *The C—H bond.* This bond, which also occurs in nearly every organic molecule, is short (109 pm) and very nearly nonpolar, with EN values of H (2.1) and C (2.5). Thus, *C—H bonds are largely unreactive.*
- *The C—O bond.* This bond, which occurs in many types of organic molecules, is highly polar ($\Delta EN = 1.0$), with the O end of the bond electron rich and the C end electron poor. As a result of this imbalance in electron density, *the C—O bond is reactive,* and, given appropriate conditions, a reaction will occur there.
- *Bonds to other heteroatoms.* Even when a carbon-heteroatom bond has a small ΔEN, such as that for C—Br ($\Delta EN = 0.3$), or none at all, as for C—S ($\Delta EN = 0$), the heteroatoms are generally large, so their bonds to carbon are long, weak, and thus *reactive.*

Importance of Functional Groups One of the most important ideas in organic chemistry is that of the **functional group,** a specific combination of bonded atoms that reacts in a *characteristic* way, no matter what molecule it occurs in. In nearly every case, *the reaction of an organic compound takes place at the functional group.* As you'll see, we often substitute a general symbol for the remainder of the organic molecule because it usually stays the same while the functional group reacts. Functional groups include carbon-carbon multiple bonds and several combinations of carbon-heteroatom bonds, and each has its own pattern of reactivity. A particular bond may be a functional group itself or *part* of one or more functional groups. For example, the C—O bond occurs in four functional groups. We will discuss the reactivity of three of these groups in this chapter:

alcohol group   carboxylic acid group   ester group

Figure 15.2 Heteroatoms and different bonding arrangements lead to great chemical diversity.

Summary of Section 15.1

- Carbon's small size, intermediate electronegativity, four valence electrons, and ability to form multiple bonds result in the structural complexity of organic compounds.
- These factors lead to carbon's ability to catenate, which creates chains, branches, and rings of C atoms. Small size and absence of *d* orbitals in its valence level lead to strong, chemically resistant bonds that point in as many as four directions from each C.
- Carbon's ability to bond to many other elements, including O and N, creating polar bonds and resulting in greater reactivity, leads to the chemical diversity of organic compounds.
- Most organic compounds contain functional groups, specific groupings of bonded atoms that react in characteristic ways.

15.2 • THE STRUCTURES AND CLASSES OF HYDROCARBONS

A fanciful, anatomical analogy can be made between an organic molecule and an animal. The carbon-carbon bonds form the skeleton: the longest continual chain is the backbone, and any branches are the limbs. Covering the skeleton is a skin of hydrogen atoms, with functional groups protruding at specific locations, like chemical fingers ready to grab an incoming reactant. In this section, we "dissect" one group of compounds down to their skeletons and see how to name and draw them.

Hydrocarbons, the simplest type of organic compound, are a large group of substances containing only H and C atoms. Some common fuels, such as natural gas and gasoline, are hydrocarbon mixtures. Some hydrocarbons, such as ethylene, acetylene, and benzene, are important *feedstocks,* precursor reactants used to make other compounds.

Carbon Skeletons and Hydrogen Skins

Let's begin by examining the possible bonding arrangements of C atoms only (leaving off the H atoms for now) in simple skeletons without multiple bonds or rings. To distinguish different skeletons, focus on the *arrangement* of C atoms (that is, the successive linkages of one to another) and keep in mind that *groups joined by a single (sigma) bond are relatively free to rotate* (Section 11.2).

Structures with one, two, or three carbons can be arranged in only one way. Whether you draw three C atoms in a line or with a bend, the arrangement is the same. Four C atoms, however, have two possible arrangements—a four-C chain or a three-C chain with a one-C branch at the central C:

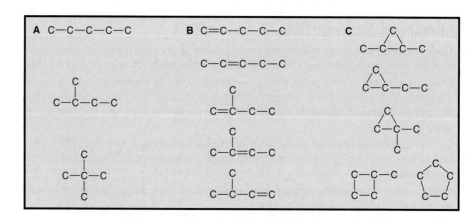

Even when we show the chains more realistically, with the bends due to the tetrahedral shape around the C atoms (as in the ball-and-stick models above), the situation is the same. Notice that if the branch is added to either end of the three-C chain, it is simply a bend in a four-C chain, *not* a different arrangement. Similarly, if the branch points down instead of up, it represents the same arrangement because groups joined by a single bond rotate.

As the total number of C atoms increases, the number of different arrangements increases as well. Five C atoms have 3 possible arrangements (Figure 15.3A); 6 C atoms can be arranged in 5 ways, 7 C atoms in 9 ways, 10 C atoms in 75 ways, and

Figure 15.3 Some five-carbon skeletons.

20 C atoms in more than 300,000 ways! If we include multiple bonds and rings, the number of arrangements increases further. For example, including one C=C bond in the five-C skeletons creates 5 more arrangements (Figure 15.3B), and including one ring creates 5 more (Figure 15.3C).

When determining the number of different skeletons for a given number of C atoms, remember that

- Each C atom can form a *maximum* of four single bonds, or two single and one double bond, or one single and one triple bond.
- The *arrangement* of C atoms determines the skeleton, so a straight chain and a bent chain represent the same skeleton.
- Groups joined by a single bond can *rotate,* so a branch pointing down is the same as one pointing up. (Recall that a double bond restricts rotation.)

If we put a hydrogen "skin" on a carbon skeleton, we obtain a hydrocarbon. Figure 15.4 shows that a skeleton has the correct number of H atoms when each C has four bonds. Sample Problem 15.1 provides practice drawing hydrocarbons.

Figure 15.4 Adding the H-atom skin to the C-atom skeleton.

A C atom single-bonded to one other atom gets three H atoms.

A C atom single-bonded to two other atoms gets two H atoms.

A C atom single-bonded to three other atoms gets one H atom.

A C atom single-bonded to four other atoms is already fully bonded (no H atoms).

A double-bonded C atom is treated as if it were bonded to two other atoms.

A double- and single-bonded C atom or a triple-bonded C atom is treated as if it were bonded to three other atoms.

Sample Problem 15.1   Drawing Hydrocarbons

Problem Draw structures that have different atom arrangements for hydrocarbons with:
(a) Six C atoms, no multiple bonds, and no rings
(b) Four C atoms, one double bond, and no rings
(c) Four C atoms, no multiple bonds, and one ring

Plan In each case, we draw the longest carbon chain first and then work down to smaller chains with branches at different points along them. The process typically involves trial and error. Then, we add H atoms to give each C a total of four bonds.

Solution **(a)** Compounds with six C atoms:

(b) Compounds with four C atoms and one double bond:

4-C chains:

3-C chain:

(c) Compounds with four C atoms and one ring:

4-C ring:

3-C ring:

Check Be sure each skeleton has the correct number of C atoms, multiple bonds, and/or rings, and no arrangements are repeated or omitted; remember a double bond counts as two bonds.

Comment Avoid some *common mistakes:*

In (a): C—C—C—C—C is the same skeleton as C—C—C—C—C

C—C—C—C is the same skeleton as C—C—C—C

In (b): C—C—C≡C is the same skeleton as C≡C—C—C

The double bond restricts rotation, so, in addition to the *cis* form shown in part (b), another possibility is the *trans* form:

(We discuss *cis* and *trans* forms fully later in this section.)

Also, avoid drawing too many bonds to one C, as here:

In (c): there are too many bonds to one C in

Follow-Up Problem 15.1 Draw all hydrocarbons that have different atom arrangements with: **(a)** Seven C atoms, no multiple bonds, and no rings (nine arrangements) **(b)** Five C atoms, one triple bond, and no rings (three arrangements)

Hydrocarbons can be classified into four main groups. In the remainder of this section, we discuss naming, as well as some structural features and physical properties of each group. Later, we'll discuss the chemical behavior of the hydrocarbons.

Alkanes: Hydrocarbons with Only Single Bonds

A hydrocarbon that contains only single bonds is an **alkane** (general formula C_nH_{2n+2}, where n is a positive integer). For example, if $n = 5$, the formula is $C_5H_{[(2\times5)+2]}$, or C_5H_{12}. The alkanes comprise a **homologous series,** one in which each member differs from the next by a —CH_2— (methylene) group. In an alkane, each C is sp^3 hybridized. Because each C is bonded to the *maximum number of other atoms* (C or H), alkanes are referred to as **saturated hydrocarbons.**

Naming Alkanes You learned the straight-chain alkanes in Section 2.8. Here we discuss general rules for naming any alkane and, by extension, other organic compounds as well. The key point is that *each chain, branch, or ring has a name based on the **number** of C atoms*. The name of a compound has three portions:

$$\text{PREFIX} + \text{ROOT} + \text{SUFFIX}$$

- *Root:* The root tells the number of C atoms in the longest *continuous* chain in the molecule. The roots for the ten smallest alkanes are shown in Table 15.1. As you can see, there are special roots for compounds with chains of one to four C atoms; roots of longer chains are based on Greek numbers.
- *Suffix:* The suffix tells the *type of organic compound* that is being named; that is, it identifies the key functional group the molecule possesses. The suffix is placed *after* the root.
- *Prefix:* Each prefix identifies a *group attached to the main chain* and the number of the carbon to which it is attached. Prefixes identifying hydrocarbon branches are the same as root names (Table 15.1) but have *-yl* as their ending. Each prefix is placed *before* the root.

For example, in the name 2-methylbutane, *2-methyl-* is the prefix (a one-carbon branch is attached to C-2 of the main chain), *-but-* is the root (the main chain has four C atoms), and *-ane* is the suffix (the compound is an alkane).

To obtain the systematic name of a compound,

1. Name the longest chain (root).
2. Add the compound type (suffix).
3. Name any branches (prefix).

Table 15.2 presents the rules for naming any organic compound and applies them to an alkane component of gasoline. Other organic compounds are named with a variety of other prefixes and suffixes (see Table 15.5, p. 592). In addition to these *systematic* names, some *common* names are still in use.

Depicting Alkanes with Formulas and Models Chemists have several ways to depict organic compounds. Expanded, condensed, and carbon-skeleton formulas are easy to draw; ball-and-stick and space-filling models show the actual shapes.

Table 15.1 Numerical Roots for Carbon Chains and Branches

Roots	Number of C Atoms
meth-	1
eth-	2
prop-	3
but-	4
pent-	5
hex-	6
hept-	7
oct-	8
non-	9
dec-	10

Table 15.2 Rules for Naming an Organic Compound

1. Naming the longest chain (root)
   (a) Find the longest *continuous* chain of C atoms.
   (b) Select the root that corresponds to the number of C atoms in this chain.

$$CH_3-CH-CH-CH_2-CH_2-CH_3$$
with CH_3 on the second carbon and CH_2-CH_3 on the third carbon

6 carbons $\Longrightarrow$ hex-

2. Naming the compound type (suffix)
   (a) For alkanes, add the suffix *-ane* to the chain root. (Other suffixes appear in Table 15.5 with their functional group and compound type.)
   (b) If the chain forms a ring, the name is preceded by *cyclo-*.

hex- + -ane $\Longrightarrow$ hexane

3. Naming the branches (prefixes) (If the compound has no branches, the name consists of the root and suffix.)
   (a) Each branch name consists of a subroot (number of C atoms) and the ending *-yl* to signify that it is not part of the main chain.
   (b) Branch names precede the chain name. When two or more branches are present, their names appear in *alphabetical* order.
   (c) To specify where the branch occurs along the chain, number the main-chain C atoms consecutively, starting at the end *closer* to a branch, to achieve the *lowest* numbers for the branches. Precede each branch name with the number of the main-chain C to which that branch is attached.

CH_3 methyl

$$CH_3-CH-CH-CH_2-CH_2-CH_3$$
with CH_2-CH_3 ethyl

ethylmethylhexane

$$CH_3-CH-CH-CH_2-CH_2-CH_3$$
numbered 1,2,3,4,5,6 with CH_3 on C-2 and CH_2-CH_3 on C-3

3-ethyl-2-methylhexane

Expanded formula	Condensed formula	Carbon-skeleton formula	Ball-and-stick model	Space-filling model

Figure 15.5 Ways of depicting the alkane 3-ethyl-2-methylhexane.

The *expanded formula* shows each atom and bond. One type of *condensed formula* groups each C atom with its H atoms. *Carbon-skeleton formulas* show only carbon-carbon bonds and appear as zig-zag lines, often with branches. *Each end or bend of a zig-zag line or branch represents a C atom attached to the number of H atoms that gives it a total of four bonds:*

propane $CH_3—CH_2—CH_3$

2,3-dimethylbutane $CH_3—CH—CH—CH_3$ (CH₃ CH₃)

Figure 15.5 shows these formulas (and models) of the compound named in Table 15.2.

Cyclic Hydrocarbons A **cyclic hydrocarbon** contains one or more rings in its structure. When a straight-chain alkane (C_nH_{2n+2}) forms a ring, two H atoms are lost as the C—C bond forms to join the two ends of the chain. Thus, *cycloalkanes* have the general formula C_nH_{2n}. Cyclic hydrocarbons are often drawn with carbon-skeleton formulas (Figure 15.6, *top row*). Except for three-carbon rings, *cycloalkanes are nonplanar,* as the models show. This structural feature arises from the tetrahedral shape around each C atom and the need to minimize electron repulsions between adjacent H atoms. As a result, orbital overlap of adjacent C atoms is maximized. The most stable form of cyclohexane is called the *chair conformation* (Figure 15.6D).

Figure 15.6 Depicting cycloalkanes.

A Cyclopropane   B Cyclobutane   C Cyclopentane   D Cyclohexane

Constitutional Isomerism and the Physical Properties of Alkanes

Recall from Section 3.2 that two or more compounds with the same molecular formula but different properties are called **isomers.** Those with *different arrangements of bonded atoms* are **constitutional** (or **structural**) **isomers;** alkanes with the same number of C atoms but different skeletons are examples. The smallest alkane to exhibit constitutional isomerism has four C atoms: two different compounds have the formula C_4H_{10} (Table 15.3). The unbranched one is butane (common name, *n*-butane; *n*- stands for "normal," or having a straight chain), and the other is 2-methylpropane (common name, *iso*butane). Similarly, three compounds have the formula C_5H_{12}. The unbranched isomer is pentane (common name, *n*-pentane); the one with a methyl group at C-2 of a four-C chain is 2-methylbutane (common name, *iso*pentane). The third isomer has two methyl branches on C-2 of a three-C chain, so its name is 2,2-dimethylpropane (common name, *neo*pentane).

Dispersion Forces and Boiling Points Because alkanes are nearly nonpolar, we expect their physical properties to be determined by dispersion forces, and the boiling points in Table 15.3 bear this out. The four-C alkanes boil lower than the five-C compounds. Moreover, within each group of isomers, the more spherical member (isobutane or neopentane) boils lower than the more elongated one (*n*-butane or *n*-pentane). As you saw in Chapter 12, this trend occurs because a spherical shape leads to less intermolecular contact, and thus lower total dispersion forces, than does an elongated shape.

   A particularly clear example of the effect of dispersion forces on physical properties occurs among the unbranched alkanes (*n*-alkanes). Among these compounds, boiling points increase steadily with chain length: the longer the chain,

Table 15.3 The Constitutional Isomers of C_4H_{10} and C_5H_{12}

Systematic Name (Common Name)	Expanded Formula	Condensed and Skeleton Formulas	Space-Filling Model	Density (g/mL)	Boiling Point (°C)
Butane (*n*-butane)		$CH_3—CH_2—CH_2—CH_3$		0.579	−0.5
2-Methylpropane (isobutane)		$CH_3—CH—CH_3$ $\quad\quad\; CH_3$		0.549	−11.6
Pentane (*n*-pentane)		$CH_3—CH_2—CH_2—CH_2—CH_3$		0.626	36.1
2-Methylbutane (isopentane)		$CH_3—CH—CH_2—CH_3$ $\quad\quad\; CH_3$		0.620	27.8
2,2-Dimethylpropane (neopentane)		$CH_3—\overset{\displaystyle CH_3}{\underset{\displaystyle CH_3}{C}}—CH_3$		0.614	9.5

		Temperature (°C)
methane (CH$_4$; $\mathcal{M}$ = 16.04)	CH$_4$	-164
ethane (C$_2$H$_6$; $\mathcal{M}$ = 30.07)	CH$_3$CH$_3$	-89
propane (C$_3$H$_8$; $\mathcal{M}$ = 44.09)	CH$_3$CH$_2$CH$_3$	-42
butane (C$_4$H$_{10}$; $\mathcal{M}$ = 58.12)	CH$_3$CH$_2$CH$_2$CH$_3$	-0.5
pentane (C$_5$H$_{12}$; $\mathcal{M}$ = 72.15)	CH$_3$CH$_2$CH$_2$CH$_2$CH$_3$	36
hexane (C$_6$H$_{14}$; $\mathcal{M}$ = 86.17)	CH$_3$CH$_2$CH$_2$CH$_2$CH$_2$CH$_3$	69
heptane (C$_7$H$_{16}$; $\mathcal{M}$ = 100.20)	CH$_3$CH$_2$CH$_2$CH$_2$CH$_2$CH$_2$CH$_3$	98
octane (C$_8$H$_{18}$; $\mathcal{M}$ = 114.22)	CH$_3$CH$_2$CH$_2$CH$_2$CH$_2$CH$_2$CH$_2$CH$_3$	126
nonane (C$_9$H$_{20}$; $\mathcal{M}$ = 128.25)	CH$_3$CH$_2$CH$_2$CH$_2$CH$_2$CH$_2$CH$_2$CH$_2$CH$_3$	151
decane (C$_{10}$H$_{22}$; $\mathcal{M}$ = 142.28)	CH$_3$CH$_2$CH$_2$CH$_2$CH$_2$CH$_2$CH$_2$CH$_2$CH$_2$CH$_3$	174

-273 -200 -100 0   100   200

Temperature (°C)

Figure 15.7 Formulas, molar masses (in g/mol), structures, and boiling points (at 1 atm pressure) of the first 10 unbranched alkanes.

the greater the intermolecular contact, the stronger the dispersion forces, and the higher the boiling point (Figure 15.7). Pentane (five C atoms) is the smallest *n*-alkane that exists as a liquid at room temperature. The solubility of alkanes, and of all hydrocarbons, is easy to predict from the like-dissolves-like rule (Section 13.1). Alkanes are miscible in each other and in other nonpolar solvents, such as benzene, but are nearly insoluble in water. The solubility of pentane in water, for example, is only 0.36 g/L at room temperature.

Chiral Molecules and Optical Isomerism

Another type of isomerism exhibited by some alkanes and many other organic (as well as some inorganic) compounds is called *stereoisomerism*. **Stereoisomers** are molecules with the same arrangement of atoms *but different orientations of groups in space.* Optical isomerism is one type of stereoisomerism: *when two objects are mirror images of each other and cannot be superimposed, they are* **optical isomers,** also called *enantiomers.* To use a familiar example, your right hand is an optical isomer of your left. Look at your right hand in a mirror: the *image* is identical to your left hand (Figure 15.8). No matter how you twist your arms around, however, your hands cannot lie on top of each other with your palms facing in the same direction and be superimposed. They are not superimposable because each is *asymmetric:* there is no plane of symmetry that divides your hand into two identical parts.

Figure 15.8 An analogy for optical isomers.

Asymmetry and Chirality An asymmetric molecule is called **chiral** (Greek *cheir,* "hand"). Typically, an organic molecule *is chiral if it contains a carbon atom that is bonded to four* **different** *groups.* This C atom is called a *chiral center,* or an asymmetric carbon. In 3-methylhexane, for example, C-3 is a chiral center, because it is bonded to four different groups: H—, CH$_3$—, CH$_3$—CH$_2$—, and CH$_3$—CH$_2$—CH$_2$— (Figure 15.9A). Like your two hands, the two forms are mirror images and cannot be superimposed on each other: when two of the groups are superimposed, the other two are opposite each other. Thus, the two forms are optical isomers. The central C atom in the amino acid alanine is also a chiral center (Figure 15.9B).

Figure 15.9 Two chiral molecules.

A Optical isomers of 3-methylhexane

B Optical isomers of alanine

Properties of Optical Isomers Unlike constitutional isomers, which have different physical properties such as boiling point, optical isomers are identical in all but two respects:

1. In their physical properties, *optical isomers differ only in the direction that each isomer rotates the plane of polarized light.* A **polarimeter** is used to measure the angle that the plane is rotated (Figure 15.10). A beam of light consists of waves that oscillate in all planes. A polarizing filter blocks all waves except those in one plane, so the light emerging through the filter is *plane-polarized*. An optical isomer is **optically active** because it rotates the plane of this polarized light. (Liquid crystal displays incorporate polarizing filters and optically active compounds; see Figure 12.44, p. 459.) The *dextrorotatory* isomer (designated *d* or +) rotates the plane of light clockwise; the *levorotatory* isomer (designated *l* or −) is the mirror image of the *d* isomer and rotates the plane counterclockwise. An equimolar mixture of the two isomers (called a *racemic mixture*) does not rotate the plane of light because the dextrorotation cancels the levorotation. The *specific rotation* is a characteristic, measurable property of an optical isomer at a certain temperature, concentration, and wavelength of light.

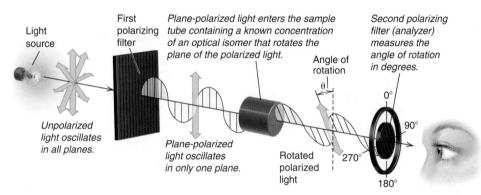

Figure 15.10 The rotation of plane-polarized light by an optically active substance.

2. In their chemical properties, *optical isomers differ only in a chiral (asymmetric) chemical environment,* one that distinguishes "right-handed" from "left-handed" molecules. As an analogy, your right hand fits well in your right glove but not in your left glove. Typically, one isomer of an optically active reactant is added to a mixture of optical isomers of another compound. The products of the reaction have different properties and can be separated.

The Role of Optical Isomerism in Organisms and Medicines Optical isomerism plays a vital role in living cells. Nearly all carbohydrates and amino acids are optically active, but only one of the isomers is biologically usable. For example, *d*-glucose is metabolized for energy, but *l*-glucose is not, and is excreted unused. Similarly, *l*-alanine is incorporated naturally into proteins, but *d*-alanine is not. An organism can utilize only one of a pair of optical isomers because of its enzymes (Section 16.7). Enzymes are proteins that speed virtually every reaction in a living cell by binding to the reactants; an enzyme distinguishes one optical isomer from another because its binding site is chiral (asymmetric) (Figure 15.11). The shape of one optical isomer fits at the binding site, but the mirror image shape of the other isomer does not fit, so it cannot bind.

Figure 15.11 The binding site of an enzyme.

Many drugs are chiral molecules. One optical isomer has certain biological activity, and the other has either a different type of activity or none at all. Naproxen (*see margin*), a pain reliever and anti-inflammatory agent, is an example: one isomer is active as an anti-arthritic agent, and the other is a potent liver toxin that must be removed from the mixture during synthesis. The notorious drug thalidomide is another example: one optical isomer is active against depression, whereas the other causes fetal mutations and deaths. Tragically, this drug was sold in the 1950s as the racemic mixture and caused limb malformations in many newborns whose mothers had it prescribed to relieve "morning sickness" during pregnancy.

Naproxen

Alkenes: Hydrocarbons with Double Bonds

A hydrocarbon that contains at least one C=C bond is called an **alkene.** With two H atoms removed to make the double bond, alkenes have the general formula C_nH_{2n}. The double-bonded C atoms are sp^2 hybridized. Because their carbon atoms are bonded to fewer than the maximum of four atoms each, alkenes are considered **unsaturated hydrocarbons.**

Alkene names differ from those of alkanes in two respects:

1. The main chain (root) *must* contain both C atoms of the double bond, even if it is not the longest chain. The chain is numbered from the end *closer* to the C=C bond, and the position of the bond is indicated by the number of the *first* C atom in it.
2. The suffix for alkenes is *-ene*.

For example, there are three four-C alkenes (C_4H_8), two unbranched and one branched (see Sample Problem 15.1b). The branched isomer is 2-methylpropene; the unbranched isomer with the C=C bond between C-1 and C-2 is 1-butene; the unbranched isomer with the C=C bond between C-2 and C-3 is 2-butene. As you'll see next, there are two isomers of 2-butene, but they are of a different sort (discussed briefly in Sections 10.3 and 11.2).

The C=C Bond and Geometric (*cis-trans*) Isomerism There are two major structural differences between alkanes and alkenes.

- Alkanes have a *tetrahedral* geometry (bond angles of ~109.5°) around each C atom, whereas the double-bonded C atoms in alkenes are *trigonal planar* (~120°).
- The C—C bond *allows* rotation of bonded groups, so the atoms in an alkane continually change their relative positions; in contrast, the π bond of the alkene C=C bond *restricts* rotation, so the relative positions of the atoms attached to the double bond are fixed.

This rotational restriction leads to another type of stereoisomerism. **Geometric isomers** (also called *cis-trans* isomers) have different orientations of groups around a double bond (or similar structural feature). Table 15.4 shows the two geometric isomers of 2-butene (also see Comment, Sample Problem 15.1). One isomer, *cis*-2-butene, has the CH_3 groups on the *same* side of the C=C bond, whereas the other isomer, *trans*-2-butene, has them on *opposite* sides of the C=C bond. In general, the *cis* isomer has the *larger portions of the main chain* (in this case, two CH_3 groups) *on the same side* of the double bond, and the *trans* isomer has them on opposite sides. For a molecule to have geometric isomers, *each C atom in the C=C bond must be bonded to two different groups.*

Like structural isomers, geometric isomers have different physical properties. Note in Table 15.4 that the two 2-butenes differ in molecular shape *and* physical properties. The *cis* isomer has a bend in the chain that the *trans* isomer lacks. In Chapters 10 and 12, you saw how such a difference affects molecular polarity and physical properties, which arise from differing strengths of intermolecular attractions.

Table 15.4 The Geometric Isomers of 2-Butene				
Systematic Name	Condensed and Skeleton Formulas	Space-Filling Model	Density (g/mL)	Boiling Point (°C)
cis-2-Butene			0.621	3.7
trans-2-Butene			0.604	0.9

Geometric Isomers and the Chemistry of Vision The difference in properties between geometric isomers has profound effects in biological systems. For example, the first step in the sequence of events that allows us to see relies on the different shapes of a pair of geometric isomers. *Retinal,* a 20-C compound consisting of a 15-C chain with five 1-C branches and 5 C=C bonds, is part of the molecule responsible for receiving light energy that is converted to electrical signals that are transmitted to the brain. There are two biologically occurring isomers of retinal, which have very different shapes. The all-*trans* isomer has a *trans* orientation around all five double bonds and is elongated. The 11-*cis* isomer has a *cis* orientation around the C=C bond between C-11 and C-12, which results in a bend in the structure at that double bond.

Certain cells of the retina are densely packed with *rhodopsin,* a large protein covalently bonded to 11-*cis* retinal. The initial chemical event in vision occurs when rhodopsin absorbs a photon of visible light. The energy range of visible photons (165–293 kJ/mol) encompasses the energy needed to break a C=C π bond (about 250 kJ/mol). Within a few millionths of a second after rhodopsin absorbs a photon, the 11-*cis* π bond of retinal breaks, the intact σ bond between C-11 and C-12 rotates, and the π bond re-forms to produce all-*trans* retinal (Figure 15.12).

Figure 15.12 The initial chemical event in vision and the change in the shape of retinal.

11-*cis* retinal

all-*trans* retinal

The rapid and significant change in shape of retinal causes the attached protein to change its shape as well, triggering a flow of ions into the retina's cells and initiating electrical impulses, which the optic nerve conducts to the brain. Meanwhile, the free all-*trans* retinal diffuses away from the protein and is changed back to the *cis* form, which then binds to the protein portion again. Because of the speed and efficiency with which light causes such a large structural change in retinal, natural selection has made it the photon absorber in organisms as different as purple bacteria, mollusks, insects, and vertebrates.

Alkynes: Hydrocarbons with Triple Bonds

Hydrocarbons that contain at least one C≡C bond are called **alkynes.** Their general formula is C_nH_{2n-2} because they have two H atoms fewer than alkenes with the same number of carbons. Because a carbon involved in a C≡C bond can bond to only one other atom, the geometry around each C atom is linear (180°): each C is *sp* hybridized. Alkynes are named in the same way as alkenes, except that the suffix is *-yne.* Because of their localized π electrons, C=C and C≡C bonds are electron rich and act as functional groups. Thus, alkenes and alkynes are much more reactive than alkanes, as we'll discuss in Section 15.4.

Sample Problem 15.2 Naming Alkanes, Alkenes, and Alkynes

Problem Give the systematic name for each of the following, indicate the chiral center in part (d), and draw two geometric isomers for part (e):

(a)

$$CH_3-\underset{\underset{CH_3}{|}}{\overset{\overset{CH_3}{|}}{C}}-CH_2-CH_3$$

(b)

$$CH_3-CH_2-\underset{\underset{\underset{CH_3}{|}}{\overset{|}{CH_2}}}{CH}-\overset{\overset{CH_3}{|}}{CH}-CH_3$$

(c)

(d)

$$CH_3-CH_2-\overset{\overset{CH_3}{|}}{CH}-CH=CH_2$$

(e)

$$CH_3-CH_2-CH=\overset{\overset{CH_3}{|}}{C}-\underset{\underset{CH_3}{|}}{CH}-CH_3$$

Plan For (a) to (c), we refer to Table 15.2, p. 577. We first name the longest chain (*root-*) and add the suffix *-ane* because there are only single bonds. Then we find the *lowest* branch numbers by counting C atoms from the end *closer* to a branch. Finally, we name each branch (*root-* + *-yl*) and put the names alphabetically before the root name. For (d) and (e), the longest chain that *includes* the multiple bond is numbered from the end closer to it. For (d), the chiral center is the C atom bonded to four different groups. In (e), the *cis* isomer has larger groups on the same side of the double bond, and the *trans* isomer has them on opposite sides.

Solution

(a)

2,2-dimethylbutane

When a type of branch appears more than once, we group the branch numbers and indicate the number of branches with a prefix, as in 2,2-*di*methyl.

(b)

hexane

$$\underset{6}{CH_3}-\underset{5}{CH_2}-\underset{4}{CH}-\underset{3}{CH}\overset{\overset{CH_3\text{ — methyl}}{}}{}(CH_3)$$
with CH_2 (2), CH_3 (1) branch

3,4-dimethylhexane

In this case, we can number the chain from either end because the branches are the same and are attached to the two central C atoms.

(c) cyclopentane

methyl
ethyl

1-ethyl-2-methylcyclopentane

We number the ring C atoms so that a branch is attached to C-1.

(d)

chiral center

3-methyl-1-pentene

(e)

$$\underset{6}{CH_3}-\underset{5}{CH_2}-\overset{H}{\underset{}{C}}=\overset{\overset{CH_3\text{ — methyl}}{}}{\underset{4}{C}}-\underset{3}{\underset{\underset{CH_3\text{—methyl}}{}}{CH}}-\underset{1}{CH_3}$$
3-hexene

cis-2,3-dimethyl-3-hexene

$$CH_3-CH_2\diagdown \overset{}{C}=\overset{\overset{CH_3}{}}{C}\diagup \underset{\underset{CH_3}{}}{CH}-CH_3$$
with H below

trans-2,3-dimethyl-3-hexene

Check A good check (and excellent practice) is to reverse the process by drawing structures for the names to see if you come up with the structures given in the problem.

Comment 1. In (b), C-3 and C-4 are chiral centers, as are C-1 and C-2 in (c). However, in (b) the molecule is not chiral: it has a plane of symmetry between C-3 and C-4, so each half of the molecule rotates light in opposite directions. **2.** Avoid these common mistakes: In (b), 2-ethyl-3-methylpentane is wrong: the longest chain is *hexane*. In (c), 1-methyl-2-ethylcyclopentane is wrong: the branch names should appear *alphabetically*.

Follow-Up Problem 15.2 Draw condensed formulas for the following compounds: **(a)** 3-ethyl-3-methyloctane; **(b)** 1-ethyl-3-propylcyclohexane (also draw a carbon-skeleton formula for this compound); **(c)** 3,3-diethyl-1-hexyne; **(d)** *trans*-3-methyl-3-heptene.

Aromatic Hydrocarbons: Cyclic Molecules with Delocalized π Electrons

Unlike the cycloalkanes, **aromatic hydrocarbons** are planar molecules, usually with one or more rings of six C atoms, and are often drawn with alternating single and double bonds. As you learned for benzene (Section 10.1), however, all the ring bonds are identical, with values of length and strength *between* those of a C—C and a C=C

Resonance forms have alternating single and double bonds.

Resonance hybrid shows the delocalized electrons as either an unbroken or a dashed circle.

or

A

σ-bond plane

delocalized π cloud

B

Figure 15.13 Representations of benzene.

bond. To indicate this, benzene is also shown as a resonance hybrid, with a circle (or dashed circle) representing the delocalized character of the π electrons (Figure 15.13A). An orbital picture shows the two lobes of the delocalized π cloud above and below the hexagonal plane of the σ-bonded C atoms (Figure 15.13B).

The systematic naming of simple aromatic compounds is quite straightforward. Usually, benzene is the parent compound, and attached groups, or *substituents,* are named as prefixes. However, many common names are still in use. For example, benzene with one methyl group attached is systematically named *methylbenzene* but is better known by its common name, *toluene.* With only one substituent present in toluene, we do not number the ring C atoms; when two or more groups are attached, however, we number in such a way that one of the groups is attached to ring C-1:

| methylbenzene (toluene) bp = 110.6°C | 1,2-dimethylbenzene (*o*-xylene) bp = 144.4°C | 1,3-dimethylbenzene (*m*-xylene) bp = 139.1°C | 1,4-dimethylbenzene (*p*-xylene) bp = 138.3°C |

In common names, the positions of two groups are indicated by *o*- (ortho) for groups on adjacent ring C atoms, *m*- (meta) for groups separated by one ring C atom, and *p*- (para) for groups on opposite ring C atoms. The dimethylbenzenes (commonly known as *xylenes*) are important solvents and feedstocks for polyester fibers and dyes. Benzene and many other aromatic hydrocarbons have been shown to have carcinogenic (cancer-causing) activity.

The number of isomers increases with more than two attached groups. For example, there are six isomers for a compound with one methyl and three nitro (—NO_2) groups attached to a benzene ring; the explosive TNT, shown below, is one of the isomers:

O_2N —— NO_2

NO_2

2,4,6-trinitromethylbenzene (trinitrotoluene, TNT)

One of the most important methods for determining the structures of organic molecules is discussed in the upcoming Tools of the Laboratory essay.

In addition to mass spectrometry (Chapter 2) and infrared (IR) spectroscopy (Chapter 9), one of the most useful tools for analyzing organic and biochemical structures is **nuclear magnetic resonance (NMR) spectroscopy,** which measures the molecular environments of certain nuclei in a molecule.

Like electrons, several types of nuclei such as ^{13}C, ^{19}F, ^{31}P, and ^{1}H can spin in either of two directions, each of which creates a tiny magnetic field. In this discussion, we focus primarily on ^{1}H-NMR spectroscopy, which examines the proton, ^{1}H, the nucleus of the most common isotope of hydrogen. Generally oriented randomly, the magnetic fields of all the protons in a sample of compound, when placed in a strong external magnetic field (B_0), become aligned either with the external field (parallel) or against it (antiparallel). Most nuclei adopt the parallel orientation, which is slightly lower in energy. The energy difference (ΔE) between the two energy states (spin states) lies in the radio-frequency (rf) region of the electromagnetic spectrum (Figure B15.1).

When a proton in the lower energy (parallel) spin state absorbs a photon in the radio-frequency region with an energy equal to ΔE, the proton "flips," in a process called *resonance,* to the higher energy (antiparallel) spin state. The system then re-emits that energy, which is detected by the rf receiver of the ^{1}H-NMR spectrometer. The ΔE between the two states depends on the *actual* magnetic field felt by each proton, which is affected by the tiny magnetic fields of the *electrons* of atoms adjacent to that proton. Thus, the ΔE required for resonance of each proton depends on the specific molecular environment of the proton—the C atoms, electronegative atoms, multiple bonds, and aromatic rings around it. The protons in different molecular environments produce different peaks in the ^{1}H-NMR spectrum.

An ^{1}H-NMR spectrum, which is unique for each compound, is a series of peaks that represents the resonance of each proton as a function of the changing magnetic field. The *chemical shift* of the protons in a given environment is where a peak appears. The chemical shifts are shown relative to that of an added standard, tetramethylsilane [$(CH_3)_4Si$, or TMS]. TMS has 12 protons bonded to four C atoms that are bonded to one Si atom in a tetrahedral arrangement, so all 12 protons are in identical environments and produce only one peak.

Figure B15.2 shows the ^{1}H-NMR spectrum of acetone. The six protons of acetone have identical environments: all six are bonded to two C atoms that are each bonded to the C atom in a C=O bond. So one peak is produced, but at a different position from the TMS peak. The spectrum of dimethoxymethane in Figure B15.3 shows *two* peaks in addition to the TMS peak since there are protons in two different environments. The taller peak is due to the six CH_3 protons, and the shorter peak is due to the two CH_2 protons. The area under each peak (given here in units of chart-paper spaces) is proportional to *the number of protons in a given environment*. Note that the area ratio is $20.3/6.8 \approx 3/1$, the same as the ratio of six CH_3 protons to two CH_2 protons. Thus by analyzing the chemical shifts and peak areas, the chemist learns the type and number of hydrogen atoms in the compound.

Figure B15.1 The basis of proton spin resonance.

Figure B15.2 The ^{1}H-NMR spectrum of acetone.

Figure B15.3 The ^{1}H-NMR spectrum of dimethoxymethane.

NMR has many applications in biochemistry and medicine. Applying the principle to imaging of organs and other body parts is known as computer-aided magnetic resonance imaging, or MRI. For example, an MRI scan of the head (Figure B15.4) can reveal a brain tumor by mapping levels of metabolic activity in different regions of the brain.

Figure B15.4 An MRI scan showing a brain tumor.

Problems

B15.1 How many peaks appear in the NMR spectrum of each isomer of C_4H_{10} and of C_5H_{12} shown in Table 15.3 (p. 579)?

B15.2 Radio-frequency radiation is used in NMR since ΔE, the energy difference between the two spin states of the proton, is very small. Calculate the ΔE (in J/mol) that corresponds to a frequency of 200. MHz.

B15.3 Consider three isomers of $C_4H_8Br_2$:

$$
\begin{array}{ccc}
\underset{\text{A}}{
\begin{array}{c}
\text{Br} \qquad\qquad \text{Br} \\
| \qquad\qquad | \\
\text{H}_2\text{C}-\text{CH}_2-\text{CH}_2-\text{CH}_2
\end{array}
} &
\underset{\text{B}}{
\begin{array}{c}
\text{CH}_3 \; \text{Br} \\
| \quad | \\
\text{H}_3\text{C}-\text{C}-\text{CH}_2 \\
| \\
\text{Br}
\end{array}
} &
\underset{\text{C}}{
\begin{array}{c}
\text{Br} \; \text{CH}_3 \text{Br} \\
| \quad | \quad | \\
\text{H}_2\text{C}-\text{C}-\text{CH}_2 \\
| \\
\text{H}
\end{array}
}
\end{array}
$$

Which of these isomers is characterized by a ^{1}H-NMR spectrum that consists of two peaks with a 3/1 ratio?

Variations on a Theme: Catenated Inorganic Hydrides

In brief discussions called Variations on a Theme found throughout this chapter, we examine similarities between organic and inorganic compounds. From this perspective, you'll see that the behavior of carbon is remarkable, but not unique, in the chemistry of the elements.

Although no other element has as many different hydrides as carbon, catenated hydrides occur for several other elements, and many ring, chain, and cage structures are known.

- *Boranes.* One such group of inorganic compounds is the boron hydrides, or boranes (Section 14.5). Although their varied shapes rival those of the hydrocarbons, the weakness of their unusual bridge bonds renders most of them thermally and chemically unstable.

- *Silanes.* An obvious structural similarity exists between alkanes and the silicon hydrides, or silanes. Silanes even have an analogous general formula (Si_nH_{2n+2}). Branched silanes are known, but no cyclic or unsaturated (containing an $Si=Si$ bond) compounds had been prepared until very recently. Unlike alkanes, silanes are unstable thermally and ignite spontaneously in air.

- *Polysulfanes.* Sulfur's ability to catenate is second only to carbon's, and many chains and rings occur among its allotropes (Section 14.8). A number of sulfur hydrides, or polysulfanes, are known. However, these molecules are unbranched chains with H atoms only at the ends ($H-S_n-H$). Like the silanes, the polysulfanes are oxidized easily and decompose readily, yielding sulfur's only stable hydride, H_2S, and its most stable allotrope, cyclo-S_8.

◼ Summary of Section 15.2

- Hydrocarbons contain only C and H atoms, so their physical properties depend on the strength of their dispersion forces.
- Names of organic compounds have a root for the longest chain, a prefix for any attached group, and a suffix for the type of compound.
- Alkanes (C_nH_{2n+2}) have only single bonds. Cycloalkanes (C_nH_{2n}) have ring structures that are typically nonplanar. Alkenes (C_nH_{2n}) have at least one C=C bond. Alkynes (C_nH_{2n-2}) have at least one C≡C bond. Aromatic hydrocarbons have at least one planar ring with delocalized π electrons.
- Isomers are compounds with the same molecular formula but different properties.
- Constitutional (structural) isomers have different atom arrangements.
- Stereoisomers (optical and geometric) have the same arrangement of atoms, but their atoms are oriented differently in space. Optical isomers cannot be superimposed on each other because they are asymmetric, with four different groups bonded to the C that is the chiral center. They have identical physical and chemical properties except in their rotation of plane-polarized light and their reaction with chiral reactants. Geometric (*cis-trans*) isomers have groups oriented differently around a C=C bond, which restricts rotation.
- Light converts a *cis* isomer of retinal to the all-*trans* form, which initiates the process of vision.
- ^{1}H-NMR spectroscopy indicates the relative numbers of H atoms in the various environments within an organic molecule.
- Boron, silicon, and sulfur also form catenated hydrides, but these are unstable.

15.3 • SOME IMPORTANT CLASSES OF ORGANIC REACTIONS

In Chapter 4, we classified chemical reactions based on the chemical process involved (precipitation, acid-base, or redox) and then briefly included a classification based on the number of reactants and products (combination, decomposition, or displacement). We take a similar approach here with organic reactions, but in reverse order.

From here on, we use an uppercase R with a single bond, R—, to signify a general organic group attached to one of the atoms shown; you can usually picture R— as an **alkyl group,** a saturated hydrocarbon group with one bond available to link to another atom. Thus, R—CH_2—Br has an alkyl group attached to a CH_2 group bonded to a Br atom; R—CH=CH_2 is an alkene with an alkyl group attached to one of the carbons in the double bond; and so forth. (Often, when more than one R group is present, we write R, R′, R″, and so forth, to indicate that these groups may be different.)

Types of Organic Reactions

Three important organic reaction types are *addition, elimination,* and *substitution* reactions, which can be identified by comparing the *number of bonds to C* in reactants and products.

Addition Reactions An **addition reaction** occurs when an unsaturated reactant becomes a saturated product:

$$R-CH=CH-R \; + \; X-Y \longrightarrow R-\overset{\overset{\displaystyle X}{|}}{C}H-\overset{\overset{\displaystyle Y}{|}}{C}H-R$$

Note the C atoms are bonded to *more* atoms in the product than in the reactant.

The C=C and C≡C bonds and the C=O bond commonly undergo addition reactions. In each case, the π bond breaks, leaving the σ bond intact. In the product, the two C atoms (or C and O) form two additional σ bonds. Let's examine the standard enthalpy of reaction (ΔH°_{rxn}) for a typical addition reaction to see why these reactions occur. Consider the reaction between ethene (common name, ethylene) and HCl:

$$CH_2=CH_2 \quad + \quad H-Cl \quad \longrightarrow \quad H-CH_2-CH_2-Cl$$

Reactants (bonds broken)	Product (bonds formed)
1 C=C = 614 kJ	1 C—C = −347 kJ
4 C—H = 1652 kJ	5 C—H = −2065 kJ
1 H—Cl = 427 kJ	1 C—Cl = −339 kJ
Total = 2693 kJ	Total = −2751 kJ

$$\Delta H^\circ_{rxn} = \Sigma \Delta H^\circ_{bonds\ broken} + \Sigma \Delta H^\circ_{bonds\ formed} = 2693\ kJ + (-2751\ kJ) = -58\ kJ$$

The reaction is exothermic. By looking at the *net* change in bonds, we see that the driving force for many additions is the formation of two σ bonds (in this case, C—H and C—Cl) from one σ bond (in this case, H—Cl) and one relatively weak π bond. An addition reaction is the basis of a color test for the presence of C=C bonds (Figure 15.14).

Elimination Reactions **Elimination reactions** are the opposite of addition reactions. They occur when a saturated reactant becomes an unsaturated product:

$$\underset{\underset{|}{\overset{Y\quad\ X}{R-CH-CH_2}}}{} \longrightarrow R-CH=CH_2 + X-Y$$

Note that the C atoms are bonded to *fewer* atoms in the product than in the reactant. A pair of halogen atoms, an H atom and a halogen atom, or an H atom and an —OH group are typically eliminated, but C atoms are not. Thus, the driving force for many elimination reactions is the formation of a small, stable molecule, such as HCl(g) or H$_2$O, which increases the entropy of the system (Section 13.3):

$$\underset{\underset{|\quad\ \ |}{\overset{OH\ \ H}{CH_3-CH-CH_2}}}{} \xrightarrow{H_2SO_4} CH_3-CH=CH_2 \quad + \quad H-OH$$

Substitution Reactions A **substitution reaction** occurs when an atom (or group) from an added reagent substitutes for one attached to a carbon in the organic reactant:

$$R-\overset{|}{\underset{|}{C}}-X + :Y \longrightarrow R-\overset{|}{\underset{|}{C}}-Y + :X$$

Note that the C atom is bonded to the *same number* of atoms in the product as in the reactant. The C atom may be saturated or unsaturated, and X and Y can be many different atoms, but generally *not* C. The main flavor ingredient in banana oil, for instance, forms through a substitution reaction; note that the O substitutes for the Cl:

$$\underset{\overset{\|}{CH_3-\overset{O}{C}-Cl}}{} + HO-CH_2-CH_2-\underset{\overset{|}{CH_3}}{\overset{}{CH}}-CH_3 \longrightarrow \underset{\overset{\|}{CH_3-\overset{O}{C}-O-CH_2-CH_2-\overset{|}{\underset{}{CH}}-CH_3}}{\overset{CH_3}{}} + H-Cl$$

Figure 15.14 A color test for C=C bonds. **A,** Br$_2$ (in pipet) reacts with a compound that has a C=C bond (in beaker), and its orange-brown color disappears:

$$\overset{}{\underset{}{C}}=\overset{}{\underset{}{C}} + Br_2 \longrightarrow -\overset{\overset{Br}{|}}{\underset{}{C}}-\overset{\overset{}{}}{\underset{\underset{Br}{|}}{C}}-$$

B, This compound has no C=C bond, so the Br$_2$ does not react.

Sample Problem 15.3 Recognizing the Type of Organic Reaction

Problem State whether each reaction is an addition, elimination, or substitution:

(a) $CH_3-CH_2-CH_2-Br \longrightarrow CH_3-CH=CH_2 + HBr$

(b) (pentagon) $+ H_2 \longrightarrow$ (pentagon)

(c) $CH_3\overset{\overset{\displaystyle O}{\|}}{C}-Br + CH_3CH_2OH \longrightarrow CH_3\overset{\overset{\displaystyle O}{\|}}{C}-OCH_2CH_3 + HBr$

Plan We determine the type of reaction by looking for any change in the number of atoms bonded to C:

• More atoms bonded to C is an *addition.*
• Fewer atoms bonded to C is an *elimination.*
• Same number of atoms bonded to C is a *substitution.*

Solution (a) Elimination: two bonds in the reactant, C—H and C—Br, are absent in the product, so fewer atoms are bonded to C.
(b) Addition: two more C—H bonds have formed in the product, so more atoms are bonded to C.
(c) Substitution: the reactant C—Br bond becomes a C—O bond in the product, so the same number of atoms are bonded to C.

Follow-Up Problem 15.3 Write a balanced equation for each of the following:
(a) An addition reaction between 2-butene and Cl_2
(b) A substitution reaction between $CH_3-CH_2-CH_2-Br$ and OH^-
(c) The elimination of H_2O from $(CH_3)_3C-OH$

The Redox Process in Organic Reactions

An important process in many organic reactions is *oxidation-reduction.* Even though a redox reaction always involves both an oxidation and a reduction, organic chemists typically *focus on the organic reactant only.* Instead of monitoring the change in oxidation numbers of the various C atoms in a redox reaction, chemists usually note the movement of electron density around a C atom by counting the number of bonds to more electronegative atoms (usually O) or to less electronegative atoms (usually H). A more electronegative atom takes some electron density from the C, whereas a less electronegative atom gives some electron density to the C. Therefore,

• When a C atom in the organic reactant forms more bonds to O or fewer bonds to H, thus losing some electron density, the reactant is oxidized, and the reaction is called an *oxidation.*
• When a C atom in the organic reactant forms fewer bonds to O or more bonds to H, thus gaining some electron density, the reactant is reduced, and the reaction is called a *reduction.*

The most dramatic redox reactions are combustion reactions. All organic compounds contain C and H atoms and burn in excess O_2 to form CO_2 and H_2O. For ethane, the reaction is

$$2CH_3-CH_3 + 7O_2 \longrightarrow 4CO_2 + 6H_2O$$

Obviously, when ethane is converted to CO_2 and H_2O, each of its C atoms has more bonds to O and fewer bonds to H. Thus, ethane is oxidized, and this reaction is referred to as an *oxidation,* even though O_2 is reduced as well.

Most oxidations do not involve a breakup of the entire molecule, however. When 2-propanol reacts with potassium dichromate in acidic solution (a common oxidizing agent in organic reactions), it forms 2-propanone (acetone):

$$CH_3-\underset{\underset{\displaystyle \text{OH}}{|}}{CH}-CH_3 \xrightarrow[\text{H}_2\text{SO}_4]{\text{K}_2\text{Cr}_2\text{O}_7} CH_3-\underset{\underset{\displaystyle O}{\|}}{C}-CH_3$$

2-propanol   2-propanone

Note that C-2 has one fewer bond to H and one more bond to O in 2-propanone than it does in 2-propanol. Thus, 2-propanol is oxidized, so this is an *oxidation*. Don't forget, however, that the dichromate ion is reduced at the same time:

$$Cr_2O_7^{2-} + 14H^+ + 6e^- \longrightarrow 2Cr^{3+} + 7H_2O$$

The addition reaction between H_2 and an alkene is also a *reduction:*

$$CH_2{=}CH_2 + H_2 \xrightarrow{\text{Pd}} CH_3{-}CH_3$$

Note that each C has more bonds to H in ethane than it has in ethene, so the ethene is reduced. The H_2 is oxidized in the process, and the palladium shown over the arrow acts as a catalyst to speed up the reaction (Section 16.7).

■ Summary of Section 15.3

- In an addition reaction, a π bond breaks, and the two C atoms (or one C and one O) are bonded to more atoms in the product.
- In an elimination reaction, a π bond forms, with the two C atoms bonded to fewer atoms in the product.
- In a substitution reaction, one atom bonded to C is replaced by another, but the total number of atoms bonded to the C does not change.
- In an organic redox reaction, the organic reactant is oxidized if at least one of its C atoms forms more bonds to O atoms (or fewer bonds to H atoms), and it is reduced if a C atom forms more bonds to H (or fewer bonds to O).

15.4 • PROPERTIES AND REACTIVITIES OF COMMON FUNCTIONAL GROUPS

The central organizing principle of organic chemistry is the *functional group. The distribution of electron density in a functional group is a major factor in the reactivity of the compound.* The electron density can be high, as in the C=C and C≡C bonds, or it can be low at one end of a bond and high at the other, as in the C—Cl and C—O bonds. Such electron-rich or polar bonds enhance the oppositely charged pole in the other reactant. As a result, the reactants attract each other and begin a sequence of bond-forming and bond-breaking steps that lead to a product. Thus, *the intermolecular forces that affect physical properties and solubility also affect reactivity.* Table 15.5 *(next page)* lists some of the important functional groups in organic compounds.

When we classify functional groups by bond order (single, double, and so forth), they tend to follow certain patterns of reactivity:

- Functional groups with only single bonds undergo elimination or substitution.
- Functional groups with double or triple bonds undergo addition.
- Functional groups with both single and double bonds undergo substitution.

We will learn how to name compounds that contain each functional group, examine some of their common properties, and summarize their common reactions.

Functional Groups with Only Single Bonds

The most common functional groups with only single bonds are alcohols, haloalkanes, and amines.

Alcohols The **alcohol** functional group consists of a carbon bonded to an —OH group, $-\overset{|}{\underset{|}{C}}-\overset{..}{\underset{..}{O}}-H$, and the general formula of an alcohol is R—OH. Alcohols are named by dropping the final -*e* from the parent hydrocarbon name and adding the suffix -*ol*. Thus, the two-carbon alcohol is ethanol (ethan- + -ol). The common name is the hydrocarbon *root*- + -*yl*, followed by "alcohol"; thus, the common name of ethanol is ethyl alcohol. (This substance, obtained from fermented grain, has been consumed by

Table 15.5 Important Functional Groups in Organic Compounds

Functional Group	Compound Type	Prefix or Suffix of Name	Example		
			Lewis Structure	Ball-and-Stick Model	Systematic Name (Common Name)
C=C	alkene	-ene	H, C=C, H (with H on each carbon)		ethene (ethylene)
—C≡C—	alkyne	-yne	H—C≡C—H		ethyne (acetylene)
—C—Ö—H	alcohol	-ol	H—C—Ö—H (with H above and below C)		methanol (methyl alcohol)
—C—Ẍ: (X = halogen)	haloalkane	halo-	H—C—C̈l: (with H above and below C)		chloromethane (methyl chloride)
—C—N̈—	amine	-amine	H—C—C—N̈—H (with H's)		ethanamine (ethylamine)
:O: ‖ —C—H	aldehyde	-al	H—C—C—H with :O: above second C		ethanal (acetaldehyde)
:O: ‖ —C—C—C—	ketone	-one	H—C—C—C—H with :O: above middle C		2-propanone (acetone)
:O: ‖ —C—Ö—H	carboxylic acid	-oic acid	H—C—C—Ö—H with :O: above second C		ethanoic acid (acetic acid)
:O: ‖ —C—Ö—C—	ester	-oate	H—C—C—Ö—C—H with :O: above second C		methyl ethanoate (methyl acetate)
:O: ‖ —C—N̈—	amide	-amide	H—C—C—N̈—H with :O: above second C		ethanamide (acetamide)
—C≡N:	nitrile	-nitrile	H—C—C≡N: (with H's)		ethanenitrile (acetonitrile, methyl cyanide)

people as an intoxicant in beverages since ancient times; today, it is recognized as the most abused drug in the world.) Alcohols are common organic reactants, and the functional group occurs in many biomolecules, including carbohydrates, sterols, and some amino acids. Figure 15.15 shows the names, structures, and uses of some important compounds that contain the alcohol group.

The physical properties of the smaller alcohols are similar to those of water. They have high melting and boiling points as a result of hydrogen bonding, and they dissolve polar molecules and some salts.

Alcohols undergo elimination and substitution reactions.

- The elimination of H and OH, called *dehydration*, requires acid and forms an alkene:

Methanol (methyl alcohol)
Byproduct in coal gasification; de-icing agent; gasoline substitute; precursor of organic compounds

1,2-Ethanediol (ethylene glycol)
Main component of auto antifreeze

$$\underset{\text{cyclohexanol}}{\text{[OH]}} \xrightarrow{\text{H}^+} \underset{\text{cyclohexene}}{\text{[ ]}} + \text{ H}_2\text{O}$$

The elimination of two H atoms is an *oxidation* and requires an inorganic oxidizing agent, such as potassium dichromate ($K_2Cr_2O_7$) in aqueous H_2SO_4. The product has a C=O group:

Serine
Amino acid found in most proteins

$$\underset{\text{2-butanol}}{\text{CH}_3\text{—CH}_2\text{—}\overset{\text{OH}}{\underset{|}{\text{CH}}}\text{—CH}_3} \xrightarrow[\text{H}_2\text{SO}_4]{\text{K}_2\text{Cr}_2\text{O}_7} \underset{\text{2-butanone}}{\text{CH}_3\text{—CH}_2\text{—}\overset{\text{O}}{\overset{||}{\text{C}}}\text{—CH}_3}$$

Alcohols with an OH group at the end of the chain (R—CH₂—OH) can be oxidized further to acids. (This is *not* an elimination.) Wine turns sour, for example, when the ethanol in contact with air is oxidized to acetic acid:

$$\underset{}{\text{CH}_3\text{—}\overset{\text{OH}}{\underset{|}{\text{CH}}_2}} \xrightarrow[-\text{H}_2\text{O}]{\frac{1}{2}\text{O}_2} \text{CH}_3\text{—}\overset{\text{O}}{\overset{||}{\text{CH}}} \xrightarrow{\frac{1}{2}\text{O}_2} \text{CH}_3\text{—}\overset{\text{O}}{\overset{||}{\text{C}}}\text{—OH}$$

- Substitution yields products with other single-bonded functional groups. Reactions of hydrohalic acids with many alcohols give haloalkanes:

$$\text{R}_2\text{CH—OH} + \text{HBr} \longrightarrow \text{R}_2\text{CH—Br} + \text{HOH}$$

As you'll see below, *the C atom undergoing the change in a substitution is bonded to a more electronegative element,* which makes it partially positive and, thus, a target for a negatively charged or electron-rich group of an incoming reactant.

Cholesterol
Major sterol in animals; essential for cell membranes; precursor of steroid hormones

Figure 15.15 Some molecules with the alcohol functional group.

Haloalkanes A *halogen* atom (X) bonded to a carbon gives the **haloalkane** functional group, $-\overset{|}{\underset{|}{\text{C}}}-\ddot{\text{X}}:$, and compounds with the general formula R—X. Haloalkanes (common name, **alkyl halides**) are named by identifying the halogen with a prefix on the hydrocarbon name and numbering the C atom to which the halogen is attached, as in bromomethane, 2-chloropropane, or 1,3-diiodohexane.

Like alcohols, haloalkanes undergo substitution and elimination reactions.

- Just as many alcohols undergo substitution to form alkyl halides when treated with halide ions in acid, many halides undergo substitution to form alcohols in base. For example, OH⁻ attacks the positive C end of the C—X bond and displaces X⁻:

$$\underset{\text{1-bromobutane}}{\text{CH}_3\text{—CH}_2\text{—CH}_2\text{—CH}_2\text{—Br}} + \text{OH}^- \longrightarrow \underset{\text{1-butanol}}{\text{CH}_3\text{—CH}_2\text{—CH}_2\text{—CH}_2\text{—OH}} + \text{Br}^-$$

Substitutions by groups such as —CN, —SH, —OR, and —NH₂ allow chemists to convert alkyl halides to a host of other families of compounds.

• Just as addition of HX *to* an alkene produces haloalkanes, elimination of HX *from* a haloalkane by reaction with a strong base, such as potassium ethoxide, produces an alkene:

2-chloro-2-methylpropane   potassium ethoxide   2-methylpropene

Haloalkanes have many important uses, but some, like the chlorofluorocarbons, cause serious environmental problems (Chemical Connections, pp. 664–665). Also, some halogenated aromatic hydrocarbons (*aryl* halides) are carcinogenic in mammals, have severe neurological effects in humans, and, to make matters worse, are very stable and accumulate in the environment. For example, the polychlorinated biphenyls (PCBs) (Figure 15.16), used as insulating fluids in electrical transformers, have accumulated for decades in rivers and lakes and have been incorporated into the food chain. PCBs in natural waters pose health risks and present an enormous cleanup problem.

Figure 15.16 A tetrachlorobiphenyl, one of 209 polychlorinated biphenyls (PCBs).

Amines The **amine** functional group is $-\overset{\displaystyle |}{\underset{\displaystyle |}{C}}-\overset{\displaystyle \cdot\cdot}{\underset{\displaystyle |}{N}}-$. Chemists classify amines as derivatives of ammonia, with R groups in place of one or more of the H atoms in NH_3. *Primary* (1°) amines are RNH_2, *secondary* (2°) amines are R_2NH, and *tertiary* (3°) amines are R_3N. Like ammonia, amines have trigonal pyramidal shapes and a lone pair of electrons on a partially negative N atom, which is the key to amine reactivity (Figure 15.17).

Figure 15.17 General structures of amines.

Primary, 1°   Secondary, 2°   Tertiary, 3°

Systematic names drop the final *-e* of the alkane and add the suffix *-amine,* as in ethanamine. However, there is still wide usage of common names, in which the suffix *-amine* follows the name of the alkyl group; thus, methylamine has one methyl group attached to N, diethylamine has two ethyl groups attached, and so forth. Figure 15.18 shows that the amine functional group occurs in many biomolecules.

Primary and secondary amines can form H bonds, so they have higher melting and boiling points than hydrocarbons and alkyl halides of similar molar mass. For example, dimethylamine ($\mathcal{M} = 45.09$ g/mol) boils 45°C higher than ethyl fluoride

Figure 15.18 Some biomolecules with the amine functional group.

Lysine (primary amine)
Amino acid found in most proteins

Adenine (primary amine)
Component of nucleic acids

Epinephrine (adrenaline; secondary amine)
Neurotransmitter in brain; hormone released during stress

Cocaine (tertiary amine)
Brain stimulant; widely abused drug

($\mathcal{M} = 48.06$ g/mol). Trimethylamine has a greater molar mass than dimethylamine, but it melts more than 20°C *lower* because trimethylamine molecules do not have an H atom attached to the N for H bonding.

Amines of low molar mass are fishy smelling, water soluble, and weakly basic because of the lone pair on N. The reaction with water proceeds only slightly to the right to reach equilibrium:

$$CH_3-\ddot{N}H_2 + H_2O \rightleftharpoons CH_3-\overset{+}{N}H_3 + OH^-$$

The lone pair is also the reason amines undergo substitution reactions: the lone pair attacks the partially positive C in alkyl halides to displace X^- and form a larger amine:

$$2\ CH_3-CH_2-\ddot{N}H_2\ +\ CH_3-CH_2-Cl\ \longrightarrow\ CH_3-CH_2-\ddot{N}H\ +\ CH_3-CH_2-\overset{+}{N}H_3Cl^-$$
$$\underset{\text{ethylamine}}{}\qquad\qquad \underset{\text{chloroethane}}{}\qquad\qquad \underset{\underset{\displaystyle CH_3-CH_2}{|}}{}\qquad\qquad \underset{\substack{\text{ethylammonium}\\\text{chloride}}}{}$$

diethylamine

(Two molecules of ethylamine are needed: one attacks the chloroethane, and the other binds the released H^+ to prevent it from remaining on the diethylamine product.)

Sample Problem 15.4   **Predicting the Reactions of Alcohols, Alkyl Halides, and Amines**

Problem Determine the reaction type and predict the product(s) for each reaction:

(a) $CH_3-CH_2-CH_2-I + NaOH \longrightarrow$

(b) $CH_3-CH_2-Br + 2\ CH_3-CH_2-CH_2-NH_2 \longrightarrow$

(c) $CH_3-\underset{\underset{\displaystyle OH}{|}}{CH}-CH_3 \xrightarrow[H_2SO_4]{Cr_2O_7^{2-}}$

Plan We first determine the functional group(s) of the reactant(s) and then examine any inorganic reagent(s) to decide on the reaction type, keeping in mind that, in general, these functional groups undergo substitution or elimination. In (a), the reactant is an alkyl halide, so the OH^- of the inorganic reagent substitutes for I^-. In (b), the reactants are an amine and an alkyl halide, so the N of the amine substitutes for the Br. In (c), the reactant is an alcohol, the inorganic reagents form a strong oxidizing agent, and the alcohol group undergoes elimination to form a $C=O$.

Solution (a) Substitution: The products are $CH_3-CH_2-CH_2-OH + NaI$

(b) Substitution: The products are $CH_3-CH_2-CH_2-\underset{\underset{\displaystyle CH_2-CH_3}{|}}{NH} + CH_3-CH_2-CH_2-\overset{+}{N}H_3Br^-$

(c) Elimination (oxidation): The product is $CH_3-\overset{\displaystyle \|}{\underset{\displaystyle O}{C}}-CH_3$

Check The only changes should be at the functional group.

Follow-Up Problem 15.4 Fill in the blank in each reaction. (*Hint:* Examine any inorganic compounds and the organic product to determine the organic reactant.)

(a) _____ + $CH_3-ONa \longrightarrow CH_3-CH=\overset{\overset{\displaystyle CH_3}{|}}{C}-CH_3 + NaCl + CH_3-OH$

(b) _____ $\xrightarrow[H_2SO_4]{Cr_2O_7^{2-}} CH_3-CH_2-\overset{\overset{\displaystyle O}{\|}}{C}-OH$

Variations on a Theme: Inorganic Compounds with Single Bonds to O, X, and N

The $-OH$ group occurs frequently in inorganic compounds. All oxoacids contain at least one $-OH$, usually bonded to a relatively electronegative nonmetal atom, which in most cases is bonded to other O atoms. Oxoacids are acidic in water because these additional O atoms pull electron density from the central nonmetal, which pulls electron density from the O—H bond, releasing an H^+ ion and stabilizing the oxoanion through resonance. Alcohols are *not* acidic in water because they lack the additional O atoms and the electronegative nonmetal.

Halides of nearly every nonmetal are known, and many undergo substitution reactions in base. As in the case of an alkyl halide, the process involves an attack on the partially positive central atom by OH⁻:

$$H-O^- \quad \text{C}-\text{Cl} \longrightarrow \quad \text{C}-OH + Cl^-$$

$$H-O^- \quad \text{B}-\text{Cl} \longrightarrow \quad \text{B}-OH + Cl^-$$

Thus, alkyl halides undergo the same general reaction as other nonmetal halides, such as BCl_3, SiF_4, and PCl_5.

The bonds between nitrogen and larger nonmetals, such as Si, P, and S, have significant double-bond character, which affects structure and reactivity. For example, $(SiH_3)_3N$, trisilylamine, the Si analog of trimethylamine, is trigonal planar, rather than trigonal pyramidal, because of the formation of a double bond between N and Si. Because the lone pair on N is delocalized in this π bond, trisilylamine is not basic.

Functional Groups with Double Bonds

The most important functional groups with double bonds are the C=C group of alkenes and the C=O group of aldehydes and ketones. Both appear in many organic and biological molecules. *Their most common reaction type is addition.*

Alkenes The C=C bond is the essential portion of the *alkene* functional group, $\text{C}=\text{C}$. Although they undergo elimination to alkynes, *alkenes typically undergo addition.* The electron-rich double bond is readily attracted to the partially positive H atoms of hydronium ions and hydrohalic acids, yielding alcohols and alkyl halides, respectively:

$$CH_3-\underset{\underset{\text{CH}_2}{|}}{\overset{\overset{CH_3}{|}}{C}}=CH_2 + H_3O^+ \longrightarrow CH_3-\underset{\underset{OH}{|}}{\overset{\overset{CH_3}{|}}{C}}-CH_3 + H^+$$

2-methylpropene

2-methyl-2-propanol

$$CH_3-CH=CH_2 + HCl \longrightarrow CH_3-\underset{\underset{Cl}{|}}{\overset{\overset{Cl}{|}}{CH}}-CH_3$$

propene

2-chloropropane

Figure 15.19 The stability of benzene.

Comparing the Reactivities of Alkenes and Aromatic Compounds

The *localized* unsaturation of alkenes is very different from the *delocalized* unsaturation of aromatic compounds. That is, despite the way we depict its resonance forms, benzene does *not* have double bonds. Thus, benzene does not decolorize Br_2.

In general, aromatic rings are much *less* reactive than alkenes because of their delocalized π electrons. For example, let's compare the enthalpies of reaction for the addition of H_2. Hydrogenation of cyclohexene, with one C=C bond, has a ΔH°_{rxn} of −120 kJ/mol. Then, for the imaginary molecule "cyclohexatriene," that is, the structure with three C=C bonds, the hypothetical ΔH°_{rxn} for hydrogenation would be three times as much, or −360 kJ/mol. Hydrogenation of benzene has a ΔH°_{rxn} of −208 kJ/mol. Thus, the ΔH°_{rxn} for hydrogenation of benzene is 152 kJ/mol *less* than that for "cyclohexatriene." This energy difference is attributed to the aromatic resonance stabilization of benzene (Figure 15.19).

This extra energy needed to break up the delocalized π system means *addition* reactions with benzene occur rarely. But, benzene does undergo many *substitution* reactions in which the delocalization is retained when an H atom attached to a ring C is replaced by another group:

benzene   bromobenzene

Aldehydes and Ketones The C=O bond, or **carbonyl group,** is one of the most chemically versatile.

- In the **aldehyde** functional group, the carbonyl C is bonded to H (and often to another C), so it occurs *at the end of a chain*, $R-\overset{\overset{\displaystyle H}{|}}{C}=\overset{..}{\overset{..}{O}}$. Aldehyde names drop the final *-e* from the alkane name and add *-al;* thus, the three-C aldehyde is propan*al*.

- In the **ketone** functional group, the carbonyl C is bonded to two other C atoms, $-\overset{|}{\underset{|}{C}}-\overset{\overset{\displaystyle :\!O:}{||}}{C}-\overset{|}{\underset{|}{C}}-$, so it occurs *within the chain*. Ketones, $R-\overset{\overset{\displaystyle O}{||}}{C}-R'$, are named by numbering the carbonyl C, dropping the final *-e* from the alkane name, and adding *-one*. For example, the unbranched, five-C ketone with the carbonyl C as C-2 in the chain is named 2-pentan*one*. Figure 15.20 shows some common carbonyl compounds.

Aldehydes and ketones are formed by the oxidation of alcohols:

$CH_3-CH_2-OH \xrightarrow{\text{oxidation}} CH_3-\overset{\overset{\displaystyle O}{||}}{C}-H$

ethanol

ethanal (common name, acetaldehyde)

3-pentanol

3-pentanone (common name, diethylketone)

Conversely, as a result of their unsaturation, carbonyl compounds can undergo *addition* and be reduced to alcohols:

 $\xrightarrow{\text{reduction}}$

cyclobutanone   cyclobutanol

Figure 15.20 Some common aldehydes and ketones.

Methanal (formaldehyde)
Used to make resins in plywood, dishware, countertops; biological preservative

Ethanal (acetaldehyde)
Narcotic product of ethanol metabolism; used to make perfumes, flavors, plastics, other chemicals

Benzaldehyde
Artificial almond flavoring

2-Propanone (acetone)
Solvent for fat, rubber, plastic, varnish, lacquer; chemical feedstock

2-Butanone (methyl ethyl ketone)
Important solvent

A Electron density model

$$R' \cdots C=\ddot{O} \longleftrightarrow R' \cdots C^+ - \ddot{O}:^-$$
$$R \qquad\qquad R$$

B Charged resonance form

Figure 15.21 The polar carbonyl group.

Like the C=C bond, the C=O bond is *electron rich;* unlike the C=C bond, it is *highly polar* ($\Delta EN = 1.0$). Figure 15.21 emphasizes this polarity with an orbital contour model (Figure 15.21A) and a charged resonance form (Figure 15.21B).

As a result of the bond polarity, addition often occurs with an electron-rich group bonding to the carbonyl C and an electron-poor group bonding to the carbonyl O. **Organometallic compounds,** which have a metal atom (usually Li or Mg) attached to an R group through a polar covalent bond, take part in this type of reaction. In a two-step sequence, they convert carbonyl compounds to alcohols with *different carbon skeletons:*

$$R\overset{\delta+}{-}\overset{\delta-}{CH}=O + \overset{\delta-}{R'}\overset{\delta+}{-}Li \xrightarrow{\ H_2O\ } R-\underset{\underset{\displaystyle OH}{|}}{CH}-R' + LiOH$$

In the following example, the electron-rich C bonded to Li in ethyllithium, CH_3CH_2—Li, attacks the electron-poor carbonyl C of 2-propanone, adding its ethyl group; at the same time, the Li adds to the carbonyl O. Treating the mixture with water forms the C—OH group in the product, 2-methyl-2-butanol:

$$CH_3-CH_2 + \underset{\underset{\displaystyle CH_3}{|}}{\overset{\displaystyle O}{\overset{\|}{C}}}-CH_3 \longrightarrow CH_3-CH_2-\underset{\underset{\displaystyle CH_3}{|}}{\overset{\overset{\displaystyle O^-Li^+}{|}}{C}}-CH_3 \xrightarrow{\ H_2O\ } CH_3-CH_2-\underset{\underset{\displaystyle CH_3}{|}}{\overset{\overset{\displaystyle OH}{|}}{C}}-CH_3 + LiOH$$

Note that the product skeleton combines the two reactant skeletons. The field of *organic synthesis* often employs organometallic compounds to create new compounds with different skeletons.

Sample Problem 15.5 **Predicting the Steps in a Reaction Sequence**

Problem Fill in the blanks in the following reaction sequence:

$$CH_3-CH_2-\underset{\underset{\displaystyle Br}{|}}{CH}-CH_3 \xrightarrow{\ OH^-\ } \underline{\hspace{1cm}} \xrightarrow[H_2SO_4]{Cr_2O_7{}^{2-}} \underline{\hspace{1cm}} \xrightarrow{\ CH_3-Li\ } \xrightarrow{\ H_2O\ } \underline{\hspace{1cm}}$$

Plan For each step, we examine the functional group of the reactant and the reagent above the yield arrow to decide on the most likely product.

Solution The sequence starts with an alkyl halide reacting with OH^-. Substitution gives an alcohol. Oxidation of this alcohol with acidic dichromate gives a ketone. Finally, a two-step reaction of a ketone with CH_3—Li and then water forms an alcohol with a carbon skeleton that has the CH_3— group attached to the carbonyl C:

$$CH_3-CH_2-\underset{\underset{\displaystyle Br}{|}}{CH}-CH_3 \xrightarrow{\ OH^-\ } CH_3-CH_2-\underset{\underset{\displaystyle OH}{|}}{CH}-CH_3 \xrightarrow[H_2SO_4]{Cr_2O_7{}^{2-}} CH_3-CH_2-\overset{\overset{\displaystyle O}{\|}}{C}-CH_3 \xrightarrow{\ CH_3-Li\ } \xrightarrow{\ H_2O\ } CH_3-CH_2-\underset{\underset{\displaystyle CH_3}{|}}{\overset{\overset{\displaystyle OH}{|}}{C}}-CH_3$$

$$\text{2-bromobutane} \qquad\qquad \text{2-butanol} \qquad\qquad \text{2-butanone} \qquad\qquad \text{2-methyl-2-butanol}$$

Check In this case, make sure that the first two reactions alter the functional group only and that the final steps change the C skeleton.

Follow-Up Problem 15.5 Choose reactants to obtain the following products:

(a) $\underline{\hspace{1cm}} \xrightarrow[H_2SO_4]{Cr_2O_7{}^{2-}}$ [structure: cyclohexanone with a CH_3 group]

(b) $\underline{\hspace{1cm}} \xrightarrow{\ CH_3-CH_2-Li\ } \xrightarrow{\ H_2O\ }$ [structure: cyclopentane ring attached to $CH-CH_2-CH_3$ with OH]

Variations on a Theme: Inorganic Compounds with Double Bonds Homonuclear (same kind of atom) double bonds are rare for atoms other than C. However, we've seen many double bonds between O and other nonmetals, for example, in the oxides of S, N, and the halogens. Like carbonyl compounds, these substances undergo addition reactions. For example, the partially negative O of water attacks the partially positive S of SO_3 to form sulfuric acid:

S bonded to 3 atoms   S bonded to 4 atoms

Functional Groups with Both Single and Double Bonds

A family of three functional groups contains C double bonded to O (a carbonyl group) *and* single bonded to O or N. The parent of the family is the **carboxylic acid** group, $-\overset{\overset{\displaystyle :O:}{\|}}{C}-\ddot{O}H$, also called the *carboxyl group* and written —COOH. *The most important reaction type of this family is substitution from one member to another.* Substitution for the —OH by the —OR of an alcohol gives the **ester** group, $-\overset{\overset{\displaystyle :O:}{\|}}{C}-\ddot{O}-R$; substitution by the $-\overset{\displaystyle ..}{N}-$ of an amine gives the **amide** group, $-\overset{\overset{\displaystyle :O:}{\|}}{C}-\overset{\displaystyle |}{\underset{\displaystyle ..}{N}}-$.

Carboxylic Acids Carboxylic acids, $R-\overset{\overset{\displaystyle O}{\|}}{C}-OH$, are named by dropping the *-e* from the alkane name and adding *-oic acid;* however, many common names are used. For example, the four-C acid is butanoic acid (the carboxyl C is counted when choosing the root); its common name is butyric acid. Figure 15.22 shows some important carboxylic acids. The carboxyl C already has three bonds, so it forms only one other. In formic acid (methanoic acid), the carboxyl C is bonded to an H, but in all other carboxylic acids it is bonded to a chain or ring.

Carboxylic acids are weak acids in water:

$$CH_3-\overset{\overset{\displaystyle O}{\|}}{C}-OH(l) + H_2O(l) \rightleftharpoons CH_3-\overset{\overset{\displaystyle O}{\|}}{C}-O^-(aq) + H_3O^+(aq)$$
ethanoic acid
(acetic acid)

At equilibrium in a solution of typical concentration, more than 99% of the acid molecules are undissociated at any given moment. In strong base, however, a carboxylic acid reacts completely to form a salt and water:

$$CH_3-\overset{\overset{\displaystyle O}{\|}}{C}-OH(l) + NaOH(aq) \longrightarrow CH_3-\overset{\overset{\displaystyle O}{\|}}{C}-O^-(aq) + Na^+(aq) + H_2O(l)$$

The anion of the salt is the *carboxylate ion,* named by dropping *-oic acid* and adding *-oate;* the sodium salt of butanoic acid, for instance, is sodium butanoate.

Carboxylic acids with long hydrocarbon chains are **fatty acids,** an essential group of compounds found in all cells. Animal fatty acids have saturated chains, whereas many fatty acids from plants are unsaturated, usually with the C=C bonds in the *cis* configuration. The double bonds make them much easier to metabolize. Nearly all fatty acid skeletons have an even number of C atoms—16 and 18 carbons are very common—because cells use two-carbon units in synthesizing them. Fatty acid salts, usually with a cation from Group 1A(1) or 2A(2), are soaps (Section 13.2).

Methanoic acid (formic acid)
An irritating component
of ant and bee stings

Butanoic acid (butyric acid)
Odor of rancid butter;
suspected component of
monkey sex attractant

Benzoic acid
Calorimetric standard;
used in preserving food,
dyeing fabric, curing tobacco

Octadecanoic acid (stearic acid)
Found in animal fats; used in
making candles and soaps

Figure 15.22 Some molecules with the carboxylic acid functional group.

Substitution of carboxylic acids and other members of this family occurs through a two-step sequence: *addition plus elimination equals substitution.* Addition to the trigonal planar C atom gives an unstable tetrahedral intermediate, which immediately undergoes elimination to revert to a trigonal planar product (in this case, X is OH):

$$
\underset{R}{\overset{O}{\underset{\|}{C}}}{}_X + Z-Y \xrightleftharpoons[]{\text{addition}} \left[\underset{R}{\overset{O-Z}{\underset{\underset{Y}{\|}}{C}}}{}_X \right] \xrightleftharpoons[]{\text{elimination}} \underset{R}{\overset{O}{\underset{\|}{C}}}{}_Y + Z-X
$$

Strong heating of a carboxylic acid forms an **acid anhydride** through a type of substitution called a *dehydration-condensation reaction* (Section 14.7), in which two molecules condense into one with loss of water:

$$
\underset{R}{\overset{O}{\underset{\|}{C}}}\boxed{-OH + H}O-\underset{\underset{\|}{O}}{C}-R \xrightarrow{\Delta} R-\overset{O}{\underset{\|}{C}}-O-\underset{\underset{\|}{O}}{C}-R + HOH
$$

Esters The ester group, $-\overset{O}{\underset{\|}{C}}-O-R$, is formed from an alcohol and a carboxylic acid. The first part of an ester name designates the alcohol portion and the second the acid portion (named in the same way as the carboxylate ion). For example, the ester formed between ethanol and ethanoic acid is ethyl ethanoate (common name, ethyl acetate), a solvent for nail polish and model glue.

The ester group occurs commonly in **lipids,** a large group of fatty biological substances. Most dietary fats are *triglycerides,* esters that are composed of three fatty acids linked to the alcohol 1,2,3-trihydroxypropane (common name, glycerol) and that function as energy stores. Some important lipids are shown in Figure 15.23; lecithin is one of several phospholipids that make up the lipid bilayer in all cell membranes (Section 13.2).

Esters, like acid anhydrides, form through a dehydration-condensation reaction; in this case, it is called an *esterification:*

$$
\underset{R}{\overset{O}{\underset{\|}{C}}}\boxed{-OH + H}-O-R' \xrightleftharpoons{H^+} R-\overset{O}{\underset{\|}{C}}-O-R' + HOH
$$

Note that the esterification reaction is reversible. The opposite of dehydration-condensation is **hydrolysis,** in which the O atom of water is attracted to the partially positive C atom of the ester, cleaving (lysing) the ester molecule into two parts. One part bonds to water's —OH, and the other part to water's other H. In the process of soap manufacture, or *saponification* (Latin *sapon,* "soap"), begun in ancient times, the ester bonds in animal or vegetable fats are hydrolyzed with a strong base:

$$
\begin{array}{c}
R-\overset{O}{\underset{\|}{C}}-O-CH_2 \\
R'-\overset{O}{\underset{\|}{C}}-O-CH \\
R''-\overset{O}{\underset{\|}{C}}-O-CH_2
\end{array}
\;+\; 3NaOH \xrightarrow{\Delta}
\begin{array}{c}
R-\overset{O}{\underset{\|}{C}}-O^-Na^+ \\
R'-\overset{O}{\underset{\|}{C}}-O^-Na^+ \\
R''-\overset{O}{\underset{\|}{C}}-O^-Na^+
\end{array}
\;+\;
\begin{array}{c}
HO-CH_2 \\
HO-CH \\
HO-CH_2
\end{array}
$$

a triglyceride   3 soaps   glycerol

Carboxylic acids and esters have some familiar and distinctive odors.

While carboxylic acids have pungent, vinegary, and cheesy odors, esters have pleasant odors. For example, ethyl butanoate has the scent of pineapple, and pentyl-pentanoate has the aroma of apples (*see photo*). Naturally occurring and synthetic esters are used to add fruity, floral, and herbal odors to foods, cosmetics, household deodorizers, and medicines.

Cetyl palmitate The most common lipid in whale blubber

Lecithin Phospholipid found in all cell membranes

Tristearin Typical dietary fat used as an energy store in animals

Figure 15.23 Some lipid molecules with the ester functional group.

Amides The product of a substitution between an amine (or NH_3) and an ester

is an amide with the functional group $-\overset{\overset{\displaystyle O}{\|}}{C}-\overset{\displaystyle |}{N}-$. The partially negative N of the amine is attracted to the partially positive C of the ester, an alcohol (ROH) is lost, and an amide forms:

$$CH_3-\overset{\overset{\displaystyle O}{\|}}{C}-O-CH_3 + H\overset{\displaystyle \cdot \cdot}{N}-CH_2-CH_3 \longrightarrow CH_3-\overset{\overset{\displaystyle O}{\|}}{C}-\overset{\overset{\displaystyle H}{|}}{N}-CH_2-CH_3 + CH_3-OH$$

methyl ethanoate (methyl acetate)　　ethanamine (ethylamine)　　N-ethylethanamide (N-ethylacetamide)　　methanol

Amides are named by denoting the amine portion with *N-* and replacing *-oic acid* from the parent carboxylic acid with *-amide*. In the amide produced in the preceding reaction, the ethyl group comes from the amine, and the acid portion comes from ethanoic acid (acetic acid). Some amides are shown in Figure 15.24. The most important example of the amide group is the *peptide bond* (discussed in Sections 13.2 and 15.6), which links amino acids in a protein.

An amide is hydrolyzed in hot water (or base) to a carboxylic acid and an amine. Thus, even though amides are not normally formed in the following way, they can be viewed as the result of a reversible dehydration-condensation:

$$R-\overset{\overset{\displaystyle O}{\|}}{C}\boxed{-OH + H}-\overset{\displaystyle |}{N}-R' \rightleftharpoons R-\overset{\overset{\displaystyle O}{\|}}{C}-\overset{\overset{\displaystyle H}{|}}{N}-R' + HOH$$

Compounds in the carboxylic acid family also undergo reduction to form other functional groups. For example, certain inorganic *reducing agents* convert acids or esters to alcohols and convert amides to amines:

$$R-\overset{\overset{\displaystyle O}{\|}}{C}-OH \text{ (or } R-\overset{\overset{\displaystyle O}{\|}}{C}-O-R') \xrightarrow{\text{reduction}} R-CH_2-OH + HOH \text{ (or } R'-OH)$$

$$R-\overset{\overset{\displaystyle O}{\|}}{C}-NH-R' \xrightarrow{\text{reduction}} R-CH_2-NH-R' + H_2O$$

Figure 15.24 Some molecules with the amide functional group.

Acetaminophen
Active ingredient in nonaspirin pain relievers; used to make dyes and photographic chemicals

N,N-Dimethylmethanamide (dimethylformamide)
Major organic solvent; used in production of synthetic fibers

Lysergic acid diethylamide (LSD-25) A potent hallucinogen

Sample Problem 15.6 Predicting Reactions of the Carboxylic Acid Family

Problem Predict the product(s) of the following reactions:

$$\text{(a)} \quad CH_3-CH_2-CH_2-\overset{\displaystyle O}{\overset{\displaystyle \|}{C}}-OH \; + \; CH_3-\overset{\displaystyle OH}{\overset{\displaystyle |}{CH}}-CH_3 \; \rightleftharpoons^{H^+}$$

$$\text{(b)} \quad CH_3-\overset{\displaystyle CH_3}{\overset{\displaystyle |}{CH}}-CH_2-CH_2-\overset{\displaystyle O}{\overset{\displaystyle \|}{C}}-NH-CH_2-CH_3 \; \xrightarrow[H_2O]{NaOH}$$

Plan We discussed substitution reactions (including addition-elimination and dehydration-condensation) and hydrolysis. **(a)** A carboxylic acid and an alcohol react, so the reaction must be a substitution to form an ester and water. **(b)** An amide reacts with OH⁻, so it is hydrolyzed to an amine and a sodium carboxylate.

Solution (a) Formation of an ester:

$$CH_3-CH_2-CH_2-\overset{\displaystyle O}{\overset{\displaystyle \|}{C}}-O-\overset{\displaystyle CH_3}{\overset{\displaystyle |}{CH}}-CH_3 \; + \; H_2O$$

(b) Basic hydrolysis of an amide:

$$CH_3-\overset{\displaystyle CH_3}{\overset{\displaystyle |}{CH}}-CH_2-CH_2-\overset{\displaystyle O}{\overset{\displaystyle \|}{C}}-O^- \; + \; Na^+ \; + \; H_2N-CH_2-CH_3$$

Check Note that in part (b), the carboxylate ion forms, rather than the acid, because the aqueous NaOH that is present reacts with the carboxylic acid.

Follow-Up Problem 15.6 Fill in the blanks in the following reactions:

$$\text{(a)} \quad \_\_\_\_ \; + \; CH_3-OH \; \rightleftharpoons^{H^+} \; \langle\bigcirc\rangle-CH_2-\overset{\displaystyle O}{\overset{\displaystyle \|}{C}}-O-CH_3 \; + \; H_2O$$

$$\text{(b)} \quad \_\_\_\_ \; + \; \_\_\_\_ \; \longrightarrow \; CH_3-CH_2-CH_2-\overset{\displaystyle O}{\overset{\displaystyle \|}{C}}-NH-CH_2-CH_3 \; + \; CH_3-OH$$

Acid	Anhydride
$2 \, R-\overset{:O:}{\overset{\|}{C}}-\ddot{O}H \xrightarrow{-H_2O}$	$R-\overset{:O:}{\overset{\|}{C}}-\ddot{O}-\overset{:O:}{\overset{\|}{C}}-R$
$2 \, H\ddot{O}-\overset{:O:}{\overset{\|}{\underset{:\ddot{O}H}{P}}}-\ddot{O}H \xrightarrow{-H_2O}$	$H\ddot{O}-\overset{:O:}{\overset{\|}{\underset{:\ddot{O}H}{P}}}-\ddot{O}-\overset{:O:}{\overset{\|}{\underset{:\ddot{O}H}{P}}}-\ddot{O}H$
$2 \, H\ddot{O}-\overset{:O:}{\underset{:O:}{\overset{\|}{\underset{\|}{S}}}}-\ddot{O}H \xrightarrow{-H_2O}$	$H\ddot{O}-\overset{:O:}{\underset{:O:}{\overset{\|}{\underset{\|}{S}}}}-\ddot{O}-\overset{:O:}{\underset{:O:}{\overset{\|}{\underset{\|}{S}}}}-\ddot{O}H$

Figure 15.25 The formation of carboxylic, phosphoric, and sulfuric acid anhydrides.

Variations on a Theme: Oxoacids, Esters, and Amides of Other Nonmetals

A nonmetal that has both double and single bonds to oxygens occurs in most inorganic oxoacids, such as phosphoric, sulfuric, and chlorous acids. Those with additional O atoms are stronger acids than carboxylic acids.

Diphosphoric and disulfuric acids are acid anhydrides formed by dehydration-condensation reactions, like the one that yields a carboxylic acid anhydride (Figure 15.25). Inorganic oxoacids form esters and amides that are part of many biological molecules. We already saw that certain lipids are phosphate esters (see Figure 15.23). The first compound formed when glucose is digested is a phosphate ester (Figure 15.26A); a similar phosphate ester is a major structural feature of nucleic acids, as we'll see shortly. Amides of organic sulfur-containing oxoacids, called *sulfonamides*,

A Glucose-6-phosphate

B Sulfanilamide

Figure 15.26 A phosphate ester and a sulfonamide.

are potent antibiotics; the simplest of these is depicted in Figure 15.26B. More than 10,000 different sulfonamides have been synthesized.

Functional Groups with Triple Bonds

Alkynes and nitriles are the only two important functional groups with triple bonds.

Alkynes Alkynes, with an electron-rich —C≡C— group, undergo addition (by H_2O, H_2, HX, X_2, and so forth) to form double-bonded or saturated compounds:

$$CH_3-C{\equiv}CH \xrightarrow{H_2} CH_3-CH{=}CH_2 \xrightarrow{H_2} CH_3-CH_2-CH_3$$

propyne   propene   propane

Nitriles Nitriles (R—C≡N) contain the **nitrile** group (—C≡N:) and are made by substituting a CN^- (cyanide) ion for X^- in a reaction with an alkyl halide:

$$CH_3-CH_2-Cl + NaCN \longrightarrow CH_3-CH_2-C{\equiv}N + NaCl$$

This reaction is useful because it *increases the chain by one C atom.* Nitriles are versatile because once they are formed, they can be reduced to amines or hydrolyzed to carboxylic acids:

$$CH_3-CH_2-CH_2-NH_2 \xleftarrow{\text{reduction}} CH_3-CH_2-C{\equiv}N \xrightarrow[\text{hydrolysis}]{H_3O^+, H_2O} CH_3-CH_2-\overset{\displaystyle O}{\overset{\|}{C}}-OH + NH_4^+$$

Variations on a Theme: Inorganic Compounds with Triple Bonds Triple bonds are as scarce in the inorganic world as in the organic world. Carbon monoxide (:C≡O:), elemental nitrogen (:N≡N:), and the cyanide ion ([:C≡N:]⁻) are the only common examples.

You've seen quite a few functional groups by this time, and it is especially important that you can recognize them in a complex organic molecule. Sample Problem 15.7 provides some practice.

Sample Problem 15.7   **Recognizing Functional Groups**

Problem Circle and name the functional groups in the following molecules:

(a)
(b)
(c)

Plan We use Table 15.5 (p. 592) to identify the various functional groups.

Solution

(a)   carboxylic acid   (b)   alcohol   (c)   ketone

       ester   2° amine   haloalkane
                                                 alkene

Follow-Up Problem 15.7   Circle and name the functional groups:

(a)

(b)

(Peroxide initiator)

Y–O–O–Y

Step 1
Formation of
free radical

2Y–O•

$H_2C{=}CH_2$

Step 2
Addition of
monomer

$Y–O–CH_2–CH_2{}^\bullet$

(n+1)

(n+1) $H_2C{=}CH_2$

Step 3
Addition of
more monomer

$Y–O–CH_2–CH_2{\Big[}CH_2–CH_2{\Big]}_n CH_2–CH_2{}^\bullet$

${}^\bullet CH_2–CH_2{\Big[}CH_2–CH_2{\Big]}_m O–Y$

Step 4
Chain termination by
joining of two free radicals

$Y–O–CH_2–CH_2{\Big[}CH_2–CH_2{\Big]}_{n+1}{\Big[}CH_2–CH_2{\Big]}_{m+1}O–Y$

Figure 15.27 Steps in the free-radical
polymerization of ethylene.

▇ Summary of Section 15.4

- Organic reactions are initiated when regions of high and low electron density in reactant molecules attract each other.
- Functional groups containing only single bonds—alcohols, amines, and alkyl halides—take part in substitution and elimination reactions.
- Functional groups with double or triple bonds—alkenes, aldehydes, ketones, alkynes, and nitriles—generally take part in addition reactions.
- Aromatic compounds typically undergo substitution, rather than addition, because delocalization of the π electrons stabilizes the ring.
- Functional groups with both double and single bonds—carboxylic acids, esters, and amides—generally take part in substitution reactions.
- Many reactions change one functional group to another, but some, including reactions with organometallic compounds and with the cyanide ion, change the carbon skeleton.

15.5 • THE MONOMER-POLYMER THEME I: SYNTHETIC MACROMOLECULES

In Chapter 12, you saw that polymers are extremely large molecules that consist of many monomeric repeat units. In that chapter, we focused on the mass, shape, and physical properties of polymers. Now we'll see how polymers are named and discuss the two types of organic reactions that link monomers covalently into a chain. To name a polymer, just add the prefix *poly-* to the monomer name, as in *polyethylene* or *polystyrene*. When the monomer has a two-word name, parentheses are used, as in *poly(vinyl chloride)*.

The two major types of reaction processes that form synthetic polymers lend their names to the resulting classes of polymer—addition and condensation.

Addition Polymers

Addition polymers form when monomers undergo an addition reaction with one another. These substances are also called *chain-reaction* (or *chain-growth*) *polymers* because as each monomer adds to the chain, it forms a new reactive site to continue the process. The monomers of most addition polymers have the $\diagup C{=}C\diagdown$ grouping. As you can see from Table 15.6, the essential chemical differences between an acrylic sweater, a plastic grocery bag, and a bowling ball are due to the different groups that are attached to the double-bonded C atoms of the monomer.

The *free-radical polymerization* of ethene (ethylene, $CH_2{=}CH_2$) to polyethylene is a simple example of the addition process (Figure 15.27). The monomer reacts to form a *free radical*, a species with an unpaired electron, that seeks an electron from another monomer to form a covalent bond:

Step 1. The process begins when an *initiator*, usually a peroxide, generates a free radical.

Step 2. The free radical attacks the π bond of an ethylene molecule, forming a σ bond with one of the *p* electrons and leaving the other unpaired, the new free radical.

Step 3. This new free radical then attacks the π bond of another ethylene molecule, joining it to the chain end, and the backbone of the polymer grows. As each ethylene adds, it leaves an unpaired electron on the growing end to find an electron "mate" and make the chain one repeat unit longer.

Step 4. This process stops when two free radicals form a covalent bond or when a very stable free radical is formed by addition of an *inhibitor* molecule.

Recent progress in controlling the high reactivity of free-radical species promises an even wider range of polymers. In one method, polymerization is initiated by the formation of a cation (or anion) instead of a free radical. The cationic (or anionic)

Table **15.6** Some Major Addition Polymers

Monomer		Polymer	Applications
ethylene (H₂C=CH₂)		polyethylene	Plastic bags; bottles; toys
tetrafluoroethylene (F₂C=CF₂)		polytetrafluoroethylene	Cooking utensils (e.g., Teflon)
propylene (H₂C=CHCH₃)		polypropylene	Carpeting (indoor-outdoor); bottles
vinyl chloride (H₂C=CHCl)		poly(vinyl chloride)	Plastic wrap; garden hose; indoor plumbing
styrene (H₂C=CH-phenyl)		polystyrene	Insulation; furniture; packing materials
acrylonitrile (H₂C=CHCN)		polyacrylonitrile	Yarns (e.g., Orlon, Acrilan), fabrics, and wigs
vinyl acetate (H₂C=CH-O-C(=O)-CH₃)		poly(vinyl acetate)	Adhesives; paints; textile coatings; computer disks
vinylidene chloride (H₂C=CCl₂)		poly(vinylidene chloride)	Food wrap (e.g., Saran)
methyl methacrylate (H₂C=C(CH₃)-C(=O)-O-CH₃)		poly(methyl methacrylate)	Glass substitute (e.g., Lucite, Plexiglas); bowling balls; paint

reactive end of the chain attacks the π bond of another monomer to form a new cationic (or anionic) end, and the process continues.

The most important polymerization reactions take place under relatively mild conditions through the use of catalysts that incorporate transition metals. In 1963, Karl Ziegler and Giulio Natta received the Nobel Prize in chemistry for developing *Ziegler-Natta catalysts,* which employ an organoaluminum compound, such as $Al(C_2H_5)_3$, and the tetrachloride of titanium or vanadium. Today, chemists use organometallic catalysts that are *stereoselective* to create polymers whose repeat units have groups spatially oriented in particular ways. Through the use of these catalysts, polyethylene chains with molar masses of 10^4 to 10^5 g/mol are made by varying conditions and reagents.

Similar methods are used to make polypropylenes, $-CH_2-CH-\}_n$, that have

$$CH_3$$

all the CH_3 groups of the repeat units oriented either on one side of the chain or on alternating sides. The different orientations lead to different packing efficiencies of the chains and, thus, different degrees of crystallinity, which lead to differences in such physical properties as density, rigidity, and elasticity (Section 12.7).

Condensation Polymers

The monomers of **condensation polymers** must have *two functional groups;* we can designate such a monomer as A—**R**—B (where A and B may or may not be the same, and **R** is the rest of the molecule). Most commonly, the monomers link when an A group on one undergoes a *dehydration-condensation reaction* with a B group on another:

$$\tfrac{1}{2}n\text{H}\text{—A—R—B—OH} + \tfrac{1}{2}n\text{H}\text{—A—R—B—OH} \xrightarrow{-(n-1)\text{HOH}} \text{H} \!\!\left[\text{A—R—B}\right]_{n}\!\!\text{OH}$$

Many condensation polymers are *copolymers,* those consisting of two or more different repeat units (Section 12.7). Two major types are polyamides and polyesters.

1. *Polyamides.* Condensation of carboxylic acid and amine monomers forms *polyamides (nylons).* One of the most common is *nylon-66,* manufactured by mixing equimolar amounts of a six-C diamine (1,6-diaminohexane) and a six-C diacid (1,6-hexanedioic acid). The basic amine reacts with the acid to form a "nylon salt." Heating drives off water and forms the amide bonds:

$$n\text{HO}\overset{\text{O}}{\overset{\|}{\text{—C—}}}(\text{CH}_2)_4\overset{\text{O}}{\overset{\|}{\text{—C—}}}\text{OH} + n\text{H}_2\text{N—}(\text{CH}_2)_6\text{—NH}_2 \xrightarrow[-(2n-1)\text{H}_2\text{O}]{\Delta} \text{HO}\!\!\left[\overset{\text{O}}{\overset{\|}{\text{C—}}}(\text{CH}_2)_4\overset{\text{O}}{\overset{\|}{\text{—C—}}}\text{NH—}(\text{CH}_2)_6\text{—NH}\right]_{n}\!\!\text{H}$$

In the laboratory, this nylon is made without heating by using a more reactive acid component (Figure 15.28). Covalent bonds within the chains give nylons great strength, and H bonds between chains give them great flexibility (see Table 2.8, p. 69). About half of all nylons are made to reinforce automobile tires; the others are used for rugs, clothing, fishing line, and so forth.

2. *Polyesters.* Condensation of carboxylic acid and alcohol monomers form *polyesters.* Dacron, a popular polyester fiber, is woven from polymer strands formed when equimolar amounts of 1,4-benzenedicarboxylic acid and 1,2-ethanediol react. Blending these polyester fibers with various amounts of cotton gives fabrics that are durable, easily dyed, and crease resistant. Extremely thin Mylar films, used for recording tape and food packaging, are also made from this polymer.

Variations on a Theme: Inorganic Polymers You already know that some synthetic polymers have inorganic backbones. In Chapter 14, we discussed the silicones, polymers with the repeat unit —(R_2)Si—O—. Depending on the chain crosslinks and the R groups, silicones range from oily liquids to elastic sheets to rigid solids and have applications that include artificial limbs and spacesuits. Polyphosphazenes exist as flexible chains even at low temperatures and have the repeat unit —(R_2)P=N—.

Figure 15.28 The formation of nylon-66. In the laboratory, the six-C diacid chloride, which is more reactive than the diacid, is used as one monomer; the polyamide forms between the two liquid phases.

■ Summary of Section 15.5

- Polymers are extremely large molecules that are made of repeat units called monomers.
- Addition polymers are formed from unsaturated monomers that commonly link through free-radical reactions.
- Most condensation polymers are formed by linking monomers that each have two functional groups through a dehydration-condensation reaction.
- Reaction conditions, catalysts, and monomers can be varied to produce polymers with different properties.

15.6 • THE MONOMER-POLYMER THEME II: BIOLOGICAL MACROMOLECULES

The monomer-polymer theme was being played out in nature eons before humans employed it to such great advantage. Biological macromolecules are condensation polymers created by nature's reaction chemistry and improved through evolution.

These remarkable molecules are the best demonstration of the versatility of carbon and its handful of atomic partners.

Natural polymers, such as polysaccharides, proteins, and nucleic acids, are the "stuff of life." Some have structures that make wood strong, hair curly, fingernails hard, and wool flexible. Others speed up the myriad reactions that occur in every cell or defend the body against infection. Still others possess the genetic information organisms need to forge other biomolecules. Remarkable as these giant molecules are, the functional groups of their monomers and the reactions that link them are identical to those of other, smaller organic molecules. Moreover, as you saw in Section 13.2, the same intermolecular forces that dissolve smaller molecules stabilize these giant molecules in the aqueous medium of the cell.

Sugars and Polysaccharides

In essence, the same chemical change occurs when you burn a piece of wood or eat a piece of bread. Wood and bread are mixtures of *carbohydrates,* substances that provide energy through oxidation.

Monomer Structure and Linkage Glucose and other simple sugars, from the three-C *trioses* to the seven-C *heptoses,* are called **monosaccharides** and consist of carbon chains with attached hydroxyl and carbonyl groups. In addition to their roles as individual molecules engaged in energy metabolism, they serve as the monomer units of **polysaccharides.** Most natural polysaccharides are formed from five- and six-C units. In aqueous solution, *an alcohol group and the aldehyde (or ketone) group of the same monosaccharide react with each other to form a cyclic molecule with either a five- or six-membered ring.* For example, a molecule of glucose undergoes an internal addition reaction between the aldehyde group of C-1 and the alcohol group of C-5 (Figure 15.29A).

When two monosaccharides undergo a dehydration-condensation reaction, a **disaccharide** forms. For example, sucrose (table sugar) is a disaccharide of glucose (linked at C-1) and fructose (linked at C-2) (Figure 15.29B); lactose (milk sugar) is a disaccharide of glucose (C-1) and galactose (C-4); and maltose, used in brewing and as a sweetener, is a disaccharide of two glucose units (C-1 to C-4).

Figure 15.29 The structure of glucose in aqueous solution **(A)** and the formation of a disaccharide **(B)**.

Lobster shells contain a polysaccharide called *chitin*.

Types of Polysaccharides A polysaccharide consists of *many* monosaccharide units linked together. The three major natural polysaccharides—cellulose, starch, and glycogen—consist entirely of glucose units, but they differ in the ring positions of the links, in the orientation of certain bonds, and in the extent of crosslinking. Some other polysaccharides contain nitrogen in their attached groups. One of these nitrogen-containing polysaccharides is chitin (pronounced "KY-tin"), the main component of the tough, brittle, external skeletons of insects and crustaceans (*see photo*).

1. *Cellulose* is the most abundant organic chemical on Earth. More than 50% of the carbon in plants occurs in the cellulose of stems and leaves; wood is largely cellulose, and cotton is more than 90% cellulose. Cellulose consists of long chains of glucose. The great strength of wood is due largely to the countless H bonds between cellulose chains. The monomers are linked in a particular way from C-1 in one unit to C-4 in the next. Humans lack the enzymes to break this link, so we cannot digest cellulose (unfortunately!); however, microorganisms in the digestive tracts of some animals, such as cows, sheep, and termites, can.

2. *Starch* is a mixture of polysaccharides of glucose and serves as an *energy store* in plants. When a plant needs energy, some starch is broken down by hydrolysis of the bonds between units, and the released glucose is oxidized through a multistep metabolic pathway. Starch occurs in plant cells as insoluble granules of amylose, a helical molecule of several thousand glucose units, and amylopectin, a highly branched, bush-like molecule of up to a million glucose units. Most of the glucose units are linked by C-1 to C-4 bonds, as in cellulose, but a different orientation around the chiral C-1 allows our digestive enzymes to break starch down into monomers. A C-6 to C-1 crosslink joins chains every 24 to 30 units.

3. *Glycogen* functions as the energy storage molecule in animals. It occurs in liver and muscle cells as large, insoluble granules consisting of glycogen molecules made from 1000 to more than 500,000 glucose units. In glycogen, these units are linked by C-1 to C-4 bonds, as in starch, but the molecule is more highly crosslinked than starch, with C-6 to C-1 crosslinks every 8 to 12 units.

Amino Acids and Proteins

As you saw in Section 15.5, synthetic polyamides (such as nylon-66) are formed from two monomers, one with a carboxyl group at each end and the other with an amine group at each end. **Proteins,** the polyamides of nature, are unbranched polymers formed from monomers called **amino acids.** As noted in Section 13.2, *each amino acid molecule has both a carboxyl group and an amine group.*

Monomer Structure and Linkage An amino acid has both its carboxyl group and its amine group attached to the α-*carbon,* the second C atom in the chain. Proteins are made up of about 20 different types of amino acids, each with its own particular R group, ranging from an H atom to a polycyclic N-containing aromatic structure (Figure 15.30). The R groups play a major role in the shape and function of the protein.

In the aqueous cell fluid, the NH_2 and COOH groups of amino acids are charged because the carboxyl groups each transfer an H^+ ion to H_2O to form H_3O^+. These H_3O^+ ions transfer the H^+ to the amine groups. The overall process can be viewed as an intramolecular acid-base reaction:

An H atom is the third group bonded to the α-carbon, and the fourth is the R group (also called the *side chain*).

Figure 15.30 The common amino acids. The R groups are screened gray, and the α-carbons (*boldface*), with carboxyl and amino groups, are screened yellow. Here the amino acids are shown with the charges they have under physiological conditions.

Each amino acid is linked to the next through a *peptide (amide) bond* formed by a dehydration-condensation reaction in which the carboxyl group of one monomer reacts with the amine group of the next.

$$H-\overset{\overset{\displaystyle H}{|}}{\underset{\underset{\displaystyle H}{|}}{N^+}}-\overset{\overset{\displaystyle H}{|}}{\underset{\underset{\displaystyle R_1}{|}}{C}}-\overset{\overset{\displaystyle O}{\|}}{C}-O^- \ + \ H-\overset{\overset{\displaystyle H}{|}}{\underset{\underset{\displaystyle H}{|}}{N^+}}-\overset{\overset{\displaystyle H}{|}}{\underset{\underset{\displaystyle R_2}{|}}{C}}-\overset{\overset{\displaystyle O}{\|}}{C}-O^- \ \longrightarrow \ H-\overset{\overset{\displaystyle H}{|}}{\underset{\underset{\displaystyle H}{|}}{N^+}}-\overset{\overset{\displaystyle H}{|}}{\underset{\underset{\displaystyle R_1}{|}}{C}}-\overset{\overset{\displaystyle O}{\|}}{C}-\overset{\overset{\displaystyle H}{|}}{\underset{\underset{\displaystyle H}{|}}{N}}-\overset{\overset{\displaystyle H}{|}}{\underset{\underset{\displaystyle R_2}{|}}{C}}-\overset{\overset{\displaystyle O}{\|}}{C}-O^- \ + \ H_2O$$

peptide bond

Therefore, as noted in Section 13.2, the polypeptide chain—the backbone of the protein—has a repeating structure that consists of an *α-carbon bonded to an amide group bonded to the next α-carbon bonded to the next amide group,* and so forth (see Figure 13.6, p. 483). The various R groups dangle from the α-carbons on alternate sides of the chain.

The Hierarchy of Protein Structure *Each type of protein has its own amino acid composition,* specific numbers and proportions of the various amino acids. However, it is not the composition that defines the protein's role in the cell; rather, *the sequence of*

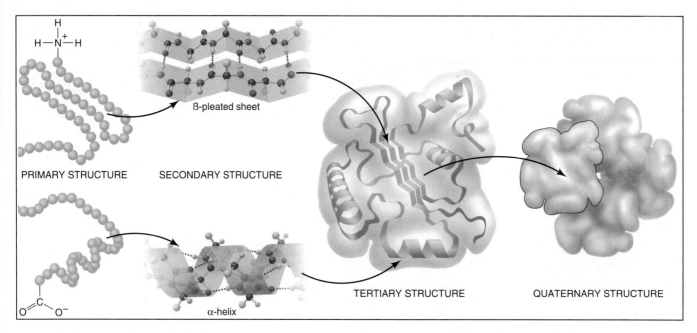

Figure 15.31 The structural hierarchy of proteins.

amino acids determines the protein's shape and function. Proteins range from about 50 to several thousand amino acids, yet from a purely mathematical point of view, even a small protein of 100 amino acids has a virtually limitless number of possible sequences of the 20 types of amino acids ($20^{100} \approx 10^{130}$). In fact, though, only a tiny fraction of these possibilities occur in actual proteins. For example, even in an organism as complex as a human being, there are only about 10^5 different types of protein.

A protein folds into its native shape as it is being synthesized in the cell. Some shapes are simple—long helical tubes or undulating sheets. Others are far more complex—baskets, Y shapes, spheroid blobs, and countless other globular forms. Biochemists define a hierarchy for the overall structure of a protein (Figure 15.31):

1. *Primary (1°) structure,* the most basic level, refers to the sequence of covalently bonded amino acids in the polypeptide chain.
2. *Secondary (2°) structure* refers to sections of the chain that, as a result of H bonding between nearby peptide groupings, adopt shapes called α-helices and β-pleated sheets.
3. *Tertiary (3°) structure* refers to the three-dimensional folding of the whole polypeptide chain. Research shows that in many proteins, certain folding patterns form characteristic regions that play a role in the protein's function—binding a hormone, attaching to a membrane, forming a membrane channel, and so forth.
4. *Quaternary (4°) structure,* the most complex level, occurs in proteins made up of several polypeptide chains (subunits) and refers to the way the chains assemble into the overall multi-subunit protein. Hemoglobin, for example, consists of four subunits arranged as in Figure 15.31.

Note that *only the 1° structure involves covalent bonds; the 2°, 3°, and 4° structures rely primarily on intermolecular forces,* as discussed in Section 13.2.

The Relation Between Structure and Function Two broad classes of proteins differ in the complexity of their amino acid compositions and sequences and, therefore, in their structure and function:

1. *Fibrous proteins* have relatively simple amino acid compositions and correspondingly simple structures. They are key components of hair, wool, skin, and connective tissue—materials that require strength and flexibility. Like synthetic polymers, these proteins have a small number of different amino acids in a repeating sequence.

- *Collagen,* the most common animal protein, makes up as much as 40% of human body weight. More than 30% of its amino acids are glycine (G) and another 20% are proline (P). It is formed of three chains, each an extended helix, that wind tightly around each other. The peptide C=O groups in one chain form H bonds to the peptide N—H groups in another. The result is a long, triple-helical cable with the sequence —G—X—P—G—X—P— and so on (where X is another amino acid), as shown in Figure 15.32A. As the main protein component of tendons, skin, and blood-vessel walls, collagen has a high tensile strength; in fact, a 1-mm thick strand can support a 10-kg weight!

- In *silk fibroin,* secreted by the silk moth caterpillar, more than 85% of the amino acids are glycine, alanine, and serine (Figure 15.32B). Fibroin chain segments bend back and forth, running alongside each other, and form interchain H bonds to create a *pleated sheet.* Stacks of sheets interact through dispersion forces, which make fibroin strong and flexible but not very extendable—perfect for a silkworm's cocoon.

● Glycine
● X
■ Proline

A Collagen

2. *Globular proteins* have much more complex compositions, often containing all 20 amino acids in varying proportions. As the name implies, globular proteins are typically more rounded and compact, with a wide variety of shapes and a correspondingly wide range of functions: defenders against bacterial invasion, messengers that trigger cell actions, catalysts of chemical change, membrane gatekeepers that maintain cellular concentrations, and many others.

The locations of particular amino-acid R groups are crucial to the protein's function. For example, in catalytic proteins, a few R groups form a crevice that closely matches the shape of reactant molecules. These groups typically hold the reactants through intermolecular forces and speed their reaction to products by bringing them together and twisting and stretching their bonds (Section 16.7). Experiment has established that a slight change in one of these critical R groups decreases the catalytic function dramatically. This fact supports the essential idea that *the protein's amino acid sequence determines its structure, which in turn determines its function:*

SEQUENCE ⟹ STRUCTURE ⟹ FUNCTION

Next, we'll see how the amino acid sequence of every protein in every organism is prescribed by the genetic information that is held within the organism's nucleic acids.

Glycine

B Silk fibroin Alanine (or serine)

Figure 15.32 The shapes of fibrous proteins.

Nucleotides and Nucleic Acids

An organism's nucleic acids construct its proteins. And, given that the proteins determine how the organism looks and behaves, no job could be more essential.

Monomer Structure and Linkage Nucleic acids are unbranched polymers that consist of linked monomer units called **mononucleotides,** which consist of an N-containing base, a sugar, and a phosphate group. The two types of nucleic acid, *ribonucleic acid* (RNA) and *deoxyribonucleic acid* (DNA), differ most obviously in the sugar portions of their mononucleotides. RNA contains *ribose,* a five-C sugar, and DNA contains *deoxyribose,* in which —H substitutes for —OH on the 2′ position of ribose. (Carbon atoms in the sugar portion are given numbers with a prime to distinguish them from carbon atoms in the base.)

Ribose in RNA   Deoxyribose in RNA

Attached to the sugar molecule at the 1′ carbon is one of four N-containing bases, either a pyrimidine (six-membered ring) or a purine (six- and five-membered rings sharing a side). The pyrimidines are cytosine (C), thymine (T), and uracil (U);

Figure 15.33 Nucleic acid precursors and their linkage.

Nucleoside triphosphate of ribonucleic acid (RNA)

Triphosphate group

Nucleoside triphosphate of deoxyribonucleic acid (DNA)

Triphosphate group

A

Portion of DNA polynucleotide chain

Phosphodiester bonds

B

thymine occurs only in DNA and uracil occurs only in RNA. The purines are guanine (G) and adenine (A).

Cytosine (C)
DNA, RNA

Thymine (T)
DNA

Uracil (U)
RNA

Guanine (G)
DNA, RNA

Adenine (A)
DNA, RNA

A phosphate group is attached to the 5′ carbon of the sugar. The cellular precursors that form a nucleic acid are *nucleoside triphosphates* (Figure 15.33A). Dehydration-condensation reactions between them release inorganic diphosphate ($H_2P_2O_7^{2-}$) and create a phosphodiester bond between the phosphate group on the 5′ carbon of one sugar and the —OH group on the 3′ carbon of a second sugar to form a polynucleotide chain. Therefore, *the repeating pattern of the nucleic acid backbone is sugar-phosphate-sugar-phosphate,* and so on (Figure 15.33B), with the bases dangling off the chain, much as R groups dangle off the polypeptide chain of a protein.

The Central Importance of Base Pairing In the nucleus of the cell, DNA exists as two chains wrapped around each other in a **double helix** (Figure 15.34). The polar sugar-phosphate backbone of each DNA chain faces the watery outside and the *nonpolar bases on each chain form H bonds to each other* in the DNA core, which holds

Figure 15.34 The double helix of DNA and a section showing base pairs.

the two chains together. A double helical DNA molecule may contain many millions of H-bonded bases in specified pairs. Two features of these **base pairs** are crucial to the structure and function of DNA:

- A pyrimidine and a purine are always paired, which gives the double helix a constant diameter.
- Each base is always paired with the same partner: A with T and G with C. Thus, *the base sequence on one chain is the complement of the sequence on the other.* For example, the sequence A—C—T on one chain is *always* paired with T—G—A on the other: A with T, C with G, and T with A.

Each DNA molecule is folded into a tangled mass that forms one of the cell's *chromosomes.* The DNA molecule is amazingly long and thin: if the largest human chromosome were stretched out, it would be 4 cm (more than 1.5 in) long; in the cell nucleus, however, it is wound into a structure only 5 nm in diameter—8 million times shorter! Segments of the DNA chains are the *genes* that contain the chemical information for synthesizing the organism's proteins.

Protein Synthesis *The information content of a gene resides in its base sequence.* In the **genetic code,** each base acts as a "letter," each three-base sequence as a "word," and *each word codes for a specific amino acid.* For example, the sequence C—A—C codes for the amino acid histidine, A—A—G codes for lysine, and so on. Through a complex series of interactions, greatly simplified in the overview in Figure 15.35 *(next page),* one amino acid at a time is positioned and linked to the next to gradually synthesize a protein. To fully appreciate this aspect of the chemical basis of biology, keep in mind that *this amazingly complex process occurs largely through H bonding between base pairs.*

There are two main steps in protein synthesis, transcription and translation. DNA occurs in the cell nucleus, but the genetic message is decoded outside the nucleus in

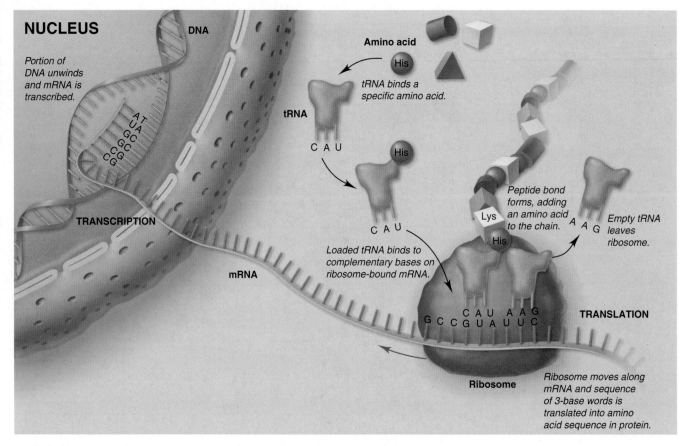

NUCLEUS

Portion of DNA unwinds and mRNA is transcribed.

DNA

Amino acid

His

tRNA binds a specific amino acid.

tRNA

C A U

His

TRANSCRIPTION

C A U

Loaded tRNA binds to complementary bases on ribosome-bound mRNA.

mRNA

Peptide bond forms, adding an amino acid to the chain.

Lys

His

A A G

Empty tRNA leaves ribosome.

C A U   A A G
G C C G U A U U C

TRANSLATION

Ribosome

Ribosome moves along mRNA and sequence of 3-base words is translated into amino acid sequence in protein.

Figure 15.35 Key stages in protein synthesis.

the cytoplasm of the cell. Therefore, the information must be sent from the DNA to the synthesis site. RNA serves this messenger role.

Transcription is the process of producing a *messenger RNA* (mRNA) copy of the DNA information:

1. A portion of the DNA is temporarily unwound, and one chain segment acts as a template for the formation of a complementary chain of mRNA made by linking individual mononucleoside triphosphates.
2. The DNA code words are transcribed into RNA code words through base pairing. Cytosine (C) and guanine (G) are complementary bases. Adenine (A) is the complementary base for thymine (T) in DNA, and for uracil (U) in RNA.
3. The DNA rewinds, and mRNA moves out of the nucleus through pores in its membrane.

Translation is the process that uses the mRNA produced through transcription to synthesize the protein:

1. The mRNA binds, again through base pairing, to an RNA-rich particle in the cell called a *ribosome*, which moves along the mRNA strand.
2. *Transfer RNA* (tRNA) is used to bring amino acid molecules to the mRNA bound to the ribosome. The tRNA molecule has two key portions on opposite ends. On one end is a three-base sequence that is *the complement of a word on the mRNA*. On the opposite end is a *covalent binding site for the amino acid* that is coded by that word. So tRNA is used to "shuttle" the correct amino acid to the correct position on the mRNA.
3. The ribosome moves along the bound mRNA, one three-letter word at a time, while the tRNA molecules H-bond to the mRNA to position their amino acids near one another.
4. When a tRNA molecule attaches to the mRNA at the ribosome, it releases its amino acid, and an enzyme (not shown) catalyzes formation of a peptide bond to the growing chain of amino acids in the protein. Once empty of its amino acid, the tRNA molecule leaves the site.

In essence, then, protein synthesis involves *transcribing* the DNA three-base words into an RNA message of three-base words, and then *translating* the word, via three-base RNA carriers, into the sequence of linked amino acids that make up a protein:

DNA BASE SEQUENCE ⇒ RNA BASE SEQUENCE ⇒ PROTEIN AMINO ACID SEQUENCE

DNA Replication Another complex series of interactions leads to *DNA replication,* the process in which DNA copies itself. When a cell divides, its chromosomes are replicated, or reproduced, ensuring that the new cells have the same number and types of genes. In this process (Figure 15.36):

- A small portion of the double helix is "unzipped," so each DNA chain can act as a template for a new chain.
- The bases in each DNA chain are H-bonded with the complementary bases of free mononucleoside triphosphate units.
- The new units are linked through phosphodiester bonds into a new chain in a process catalyzed by an enzyme called *DNA polymerase.*
- Gradually, each of the unzipped chains forms the complementary half of a double helix, which results in *two* double helices.

Because each base always pairs with its complement, the original double helix is copied and the genetic makeup of the cell preserved. (Base pairing is central to methods for learning the sequence of nucleotides in genes, and for analyzing evidence in criminal investigations, as the upcoming Chemical Connections essay shows.)

Figure 15.36 Key stages in DNA replication.

■ Summary of Section 15.6

- The three types of natural polymers—polysaccharides, proteins, and nucleic acids—are formed by dehydration-condensation reactions.
- Polysaccharides are formed from cyclic monosaccharides, such as glucose. Cellulose, starch, and glycogen have structural or energy-storage roles.
- Proteins are polyamides formed from as many as 20 different types of amino acids. Fibrous proteins have extended shapes and play structural roles. Globular proteins have compact shapes and play metabolic, immunologic, and hormonal roles. The amino acid sequence of a protein determines its shape and function.
- Nucleic acids (DNA and RNA) are polynucleotides consisting of four different mononucleotides. The base sequence of the DNA chain determines the sequence of amino acids in an organism's proteins. Hydrogen bonding between specific base pairs is the key to protein synthesis and DNA replication.
- DNA sequencing is used to determine the identity and order of nucleotides in a fragment of a DNA chain; DNA fingerprinting is used to identify a person from the unique pattern of repeating base sequences in his or her DNA.

Thanks to *DNA sequencing,* the process of determining the identity and order of DNA bases, we now know the sequence of the 3 billion nucleotide base pairs in the DNA of the entire human genome! Sequencing has become indispensable to molecular biology and biochemical genetics.

Just as indispensable to forensic science is *DNA fingerprinting* (or *DNA profiling*), a different process that employs similar methods. Since the discovery that portions of an individual's DNA are as unique as fingerprints, this technique has been applied in countless situations, such as identifying the remains of victims of the September 11, 2001 terrorist attacks.

DNA Sequencing

A given chromosome in the nucleus may have 100 million nucleotide bases, but the sequencing process can only deal with DNA fragments about 2000 bases long. Therefore, the chromosome is first broken into pieces by enzymes that cleave at specific sites. Then, to obtain enough sample for analysis, the DNA is replicated through a variety of "amplification" methods, which make many copies of the individual DNA "target" fragments.

The most popular sequencing method is the *Sanger chain-termination method,* which uses chemically altered bases to stop the growth of a complementary DNA chain at specific locations. As you've learned, the chain consists of linked 2′-deoxyribonucleoside monophosphate units (dNMP, where N represents A, T, G, or C). The link is a phosphodiester bond from the 3′-OH of one unit to the 5′-OH of the next. The free monomers used to construct the chain are 2′-deoxyribonucleoside triphosphates (dNTP) (Figure B15.5A). The Sanger method uses a modified monomer, called a *di*deoxyribonucleoside triphosphate (ddNTP), in which the 3′-OH group is also missing from the ribose unit (Figure B15.5B). As soon as the ddNTP is incorporated into the growing chain, polymerization stops because there is no —OH group on the 3′ position to form a phosphodiester bond to the next dNTP unit.

The procedure is shown in Figure B15.6. After several preparation steps, the sample to be sequenced consists of single-stranded

A

B

C

D

Figure B15.6 Steps in the Sanger method of DNA sequencing.

Figure B15.5 (left diagram)

N = A, G, C, or T

A Deoxynucleoside triphosphate (dNTP)

no 2′-OH

B Dideoxynucleoside triphosphate (ddNTP)

no 2′ and 3′-OH

Figure B15.5 Nucleoside triphosphate monomers.

DNA target fragments, each of which is attached to one strand of a double-stranded segment of DNA (Figure B15.6A). This sample is divided into four tubes, and to each tube is added a mixture of DNA polymerase, large amounts of all four dNTP's, and a small amount of one of the four ddNTP's. Thus, tube 1 contains polymerase, dATP, dGTP, dCTP, and dTTP, and, say, ddATP; tube 2 contains the same mixture, except ddGTP instead of ddATP; and so forth. After the polymerization reaction is complete, each tube contains the original target fragments paired to complementary chains of varying length (Figure B15.6B). The chain lengths vary because in tube 1, each complementary chain ends in ddA (designated A in the figure); in tube 2, each ends in ddG (G); in tube 3, each ends in ddC (C); and in tube 4, each ends in ddT (T).

Each double-stranded product is divided into single strands, and then the complementary chains are separated by means of *high-resolution polyacrylamide-gel electrophoresis*. This technique applies an electric field to separate charged species through differences in their rate of migration through pores in a gel: the smaller the species, the faster it moves. Polynucleotide fragments are commonly separated by electrophoresis because they have charged phosphate groups. High-resolution gels have pores that vary so slightly in size that they can separate fragments differing by only a single nucleotide.

In this step, each sample is applied to its own "lane" on a gel. After electrophoresis, the gel is scanned to locate the chains, which appear in bands. Because all four ddNTP's were used, all possible chain fragments are formed, so the sequence of the original DNA fragment can be determined (Figure B15.6C).

An automated approach begins with each ddNTP tagged with a different fluorescent dye that emits light of a distinct color. The entire mixture of complementary chains is introduced onto the gel and separated. The gel is scanned by a laser, which activates the dyes. The fluorescent intensity versus distance along the chain is detected and plotted by a computer (Figure B15.6D).

DNA Fingerprinting

Modern techniques of DNA fingerprinting require less than 1 ng of DNA. Thus, in addition to blood and semen, licked stamps and envelopes, chewed gum, and clothing containing dead skin cells can also be sources of DNA.

Currently, the most successful and widely used DNA profiling procedure is called *short tandem repeat (STR) analysis*. STRs are specific areas on a chromosome that contain short (3–7 bases) sequences that repeat themselves within the DNA molecule. There are hundreds of different types of STRs, but each person has a unique number and assortment of types. Therefore, the more STRs that are characterized, the more discriminating the analysis.

Once the STRs have been amplified, they are separated by electrophoresis, and an analyst determines the number of base repeats within each STR. In Figure B15.7, stained gels containing the STRs of DNA in blood samples from several suspects are compared with those from the blood found at a crime scene. Suspect 3 has a pattern of STRs identical to that in the crime scene sample.

Figure B15.7 STR analysis of DNA in the blood of seven suspects and that in blood found at a crime scene.

Problems

B15.4 If you were analyzing a DNA fragment with the base sequence TACAGGTTCAGT, how many complementary chain pieces would you obtain in the tube containing ddATP? In the tube containing ddCTP?

B15.5 A DNA fragment is sequenced and the following complementary chain pieces are obtained from the four tubes:

1. The ddATP tube contains ATG and ATATG.
2. The ddTTP tube contains TG and TATG.
3. The ddCTP tube contains CATATG.
4. The ddGPT tube contains G.

What is the sequence of bases in the DNA fragment? Draw a sketch of the electrophoresis gel for this fragment similar to the one shown in Figure B15.6C.

CHAPTER REVIEW GUIDE

Learning Objectives   Relevant section (§) and/or sample problem (SP) numbers appear in parentheses.

Understand These Concepts

1. How carbon's atomic properties give rise to its ability to form four strong covalent bonds, multiple bonds, and chains, which results in the great structural diversity of organic compounds (§15.1)
2. How carbon's atomic properties give rise to its ability to bond to various heteroatoms, which creates regions of charge imbalance that result in functional groups (§15.1)
3. Structures and names of alkanes, alkenes, and alkynes (§15.2)
4. The distinctions among constitutional, optical, and geometric isomers (§15.2)
5. The importance of optical isomerism in organisms (§15.2)
6. The effect of restricted rotation around a π bond on the structures and properties of alkenes (§15.2)
7. The nature of organic addition, elimination, and substitution reactions (§15.3)
8. The properties and reaction types of the various functional groups (§15.4):
   • Substitution and elimination for alcohols, alkyl halides, and amines
   • Addition for alkenes, alkynes, and aldehydes and ketones
   • Substitution for the carboxylic acid family (acids, esters, and amides)
9. Why delocalization of electrons causes aromatic rings to have lower reactivity than alkenes (§15.4)
10. The polarity of the carbonyl bond and the importance of organometallic compounds in addition reactions of carbonyl compounds (§15.4)
11. How addition plus elimination lead to substitution in the reactions of the carboxylic acid family (§15.4)
12. How addition and condensation polymers form (§15.5)
13. The three types of biopolymers and their monomers (§15.6)

14. How amino acid sequence determines protein shape, which determines function (§15.6)
15. How complementary base pairing controls the processes of protein synthesis and DNA replication (§15.6)
16. How DNA base sequence determines RNA base sequence, which determines amino acid sequence (§15.6)

Master These Skills

1. Drawing hydrocarbon structures given the number(s) of C atoms, multiple bonds, and rings (SP 15.1)
2. Naming hydrocarbons and drawing expanded, condensed, and carbon skeleton formulas (§15.2 and SP 15.2)
3. Drawing geometric isomers and identifying chiral centers of molecules (SP 15.2)
4. Recognizing the type of organic reaction from the structures of reactants and products (SP 15.3)
5. Recognizing an organic reaction as an oxidation or reduction from the structures of reactants and products (§15.3)
6. Determining reactants and products in reactions of alcohols, alkyl halides, and amines (SP 15.4 and Follow-Up)
7. Determining the products in a stepwise reaction sequence (SP 15.5)
8. Determining the reactants in reactions involving aldehydes and ketones (Follow-Up Problem 15.5)
9. Determining reactants and products in reactions of the carboxylic acid family (SP 15.6 and Follow-Up)
10. Recognizing and naming the functional groups in organic molecules (SP 15.7)
11. Drawing an abbreviated synthetic polymer structure based on monomer structures (§15.5)
12. Drawing small peptides from amino acid structures (§15.6)
13. Using the base-paired sequence of one DNA strand to predict the sequence of the other (§15.6)

Key Terms   Page numbers appear in parentheses.

Introduction
organic compounds (571)

Section 15.1
catenation (572)
heteroatom (573)
functional group (573)

Section 15.2
hydrocarbon (574)
alkane (C_nH_{2n+2}) (576)
homologous series (576)
saturated hydrocarbon (576)
cyclic hydrocarbon (578)
isomers (579)
constitutional (structural) isomers (579)
stereoisomers (580)
optical isomers (580)

chiral molecule (580)
polarimeter (581)
optically active (581)
alkene (C_nH_{2n}) (582)
unsaturated hydrocarbon (582)
geometric (*cis-trans*) isomers (582)
alkyne (C_nH_{2n-2}) (583)
aromatic hydrocarbon (584)
nuclear magnetic resonance (NMR) spectroscopy (586)

Section 15.3
alkyl group (588)
addition reaction (588)
elimination reaction (589)
substitution reaction (589)

Section 15.4
alcohol (591)
haloalkane (alkyl halide) (593)
amine (594)
carbonyl group (597)
aldehyde (597)
ketone (597)
organometallic compound (598)
carboxylic acid (599)
ester (599)
amide (599)
fatty acid (599)
acid anhydride (600)
lipid (600)
hydrolysis (600)
nitrile (603)

Section 15.5
addition polymer (604)
condensation polymer (606)

Section 15.6
monosaccharide (607)
polysaccharide (607)
disaccharide (607)
protein (608)
amino acid (608)
nucleic acid (611)
mononucleotide (611)
double helix (612)
base pair (613)
genetic code (613)
transcription (614)
translation (614)

Brief Solutions to Follow-Up Problems

15.1 (a)

[structural formulas of isomers of heptane / methylhexanes / dimethylpentanes, drawn as expanded Lewis structures]

(b)

$$H-\overset{H}{\underset{H}{C}}-\overset{H}{\underset{H}{C}}-\overset{H}{\underset{H}{C}}-C\equiv C-H \qquad H-\overset{H}{\underset{H}{C}}-\overset{H}{\underset{H}{C}}-C\equiv C-\overset{H}{\underset{H}{C}}-H \qquad H-\overset{H}{\underset{H}{C}}-\overset{H}{\underset{H}{\underset{\underset{C}{|}}{C}}}-C\equiv C-H$$

15.2 (a) $CH_3-CH_2-CH_2-CH_2-CH_2-\underset{\underset{CH_3}{|}}{\overset{\overset{CH_2-CH_3}{|}}{C}}-CH_2-CH_3$

(b)

[cyclohexane ring with $CH_2-CH_2-CH_3$ and CH_2-CH_3 substituents]   and   [cyclohexane ring with propyl and ethyl substituents]

(c) $HC\equiv C-\underset{\underset{CH_2-CH_3}{|}}{\overset{\overset{CH_2-CH_3}{|}}{C}}-CH_2-CH_2-CH_3$

(d) $\underset{CH_3}{\overset{CH_3-CH_2}{>}}C=C\underset{CH_2-CH_2-CH_3}{\overset{H}{<}}$

15.3 (a) $CH_3-CH=CH-CH_3 + Cl_2 \longrightarrow$

$CH_3-\underset{\underset{Cl}{|}}{\overset{\overset{Cl}{|}}{CH}}-CH-CH_3$

(b) $CH_3-CH_2-CH_2-Br + OH^- \longrightarrow$

$CH_3-CH_2-CH_2-OH + Br^-$

(c) $CH_3-\underset{\underset{OH}{|}}{\overset{\overset{CH_3}{|}}{C}}-CH_3 \xrightarrow{-H_2O} CH_3-\overset{\overset{CH_3}{|}}{C}=CH_2$

15.4 (a) $CH_3-\underset{\underset{Cl}{|}}{CH}-\overset{\overset{CH_3}{|}}{CH}-CH_3$ or $CH_3-CH_2-\underset{\underset{Cl}{|}}{\overset{\overset{CH_3}{|}}{C}}-CH_3$

(b) $CH_3-CH_2-CH_2-OH$

15.5 (a) [cyclohexane ring with OH and CH_3 on adjacent carbons]   (b) [cyclopentane ring with $-\overset{\overset{O}{||}}{C}-H$ group]

15.6 (a) [benzene ring]$-CH_2-\overset{\overset{O}{||}}{C}-OH$

(b) $CH_3-CH_2-CH_2-\overset{\overset{O}{||}}{C}-O-CH_3 + CH_3-CH_2-NH_2$

15.7 (a) [benzene ring]$-CH=CH-\overset{\overset{O}{||}}{C}-H$ alkene   aldehyde

(b) $H_2N-\overset{\overset{O}{||}}{C}-CH_2-\underset{\underset{Br}{|}}{CH}-CH_3$ amide   haloalkane

PROBLEMS

Problems with **colored** numbers are answered in Appendix E and worked in detail in the Student Solutions Manual. Problem sections match those in the text and provide the numbers of relevant sample problems. Most offer Concept Review Questions, Skill-Building Exercises (grouped in pairs covering the same concept), and Problems in Context. The Comprehensive Problems are based on material from any section or previous chapter.

The Special Nature of Carbon and the Characteristics of Organic Molecules

Concept Review Questions

15.1 Give the names and formulas of two carbon compounds that are organic and two that are inorganic.

15.2 Explain each statement in terms of atomic properties:
(a) Carbon engages in covalent rather than ionic bonding.
(b) Carbon has four bonds in all its organic compounds.
(c) Carbon forms neither stable cations, like many metals, nor stable anions, like many nonmetals.
(d) Carbon bonds to itself more extensively than does any other element.
(e) Carbon forms stable multiple bonds.

15.3 Carbon bonds to many elements other than itself.
(a) Name six elements that commonly bond to carbon in organic compounds.
(b) Which of these elements are heteroatoms?
(c) Which of these elements are more electronegative than carbon? Less electronegative?
(d) How does bonding of carbon to heteroatoms increase the number of organic compounds?

15.4 Silicon lies just below carbon in Group 4A(14) and also forms four covalent bonds. Why aren't there as many silicon compounds as carbon compounds?

15.5 What is the range of oxidation states for carbon? Name a compound in which carbon has its highest oxidation state and one in which it has its lowest.

15.6 Which of these bonds to carbon would you expect to be relatively reactive: C—H, C—C, C—I, C=O, C—Li? Explain.

The Structures and Classes of Hydrocarbons
(Sample Problems 15.1 and 15.2)

Concept Review Questions

15.7 (a) What structural feature is associated with each type of hydrocarbon: alkane, cycloalkane, alkene, and alkyne?
(b) Give the general formula for each type.
(c) Which hydrocarbons are considered saturated?

15.8 Define each type of isomer: (a) constitutional; (b) geometric; (c) optical. Which types of isomers are stereoisomers?

15.9 Among alkenes, alkynes, and aromatic hydrocarbons, only alkenes exhibit *cis-trans* isomerism. Why don't the others?

15.10 Which objects are asymmetric (have no plane of symmetry): (a) a circular clock face; (b) a football; (c) a dime; (d) a brick; (e) a hammer; (f) a spring?

15.11 Explain how a polarimeter works and what it measures.

15.12 How does an aromatic hydrocarbon differ from a cyclo-alkane in terms of its bonding? How does this difference affect structure?

Skill-Building Exercises (grouped in similar pairs)

15.13 Draw all possible skeletons for a 7-C compound with
(a) A 6-C chain and 1 double bond
(b) A 5-C chain and 1 double bond
(c) A 5-C ring and no double bonds

15.14 Draw all possible skeletons for a 6-C compound with
(a) A 5-C chain and 2 double bonds
(b) A 5-C chain and 1 triple bond
(c) A 4-C ring and no double bonds

15.15 Add the correct number of hydrogens to each of the skeletons in Problem 15.13.

15.16 Add the correct number of hydrogens to each of the skeletons in Problem 15.14.

15.17 Draw correct structures, by making a single change, for any that are incorrect:

(a) $CH_3-\overset{\overset{\displaystyle CH_3}{|}}{CH}-CH_2-CH_3$ (b) $CH_3=CH-CH_2-CH_3$

(c) $CH\equiv C-\underset{\underset{\displaystyle CH_3}{|}}{\overset{\overset{\displaystyle }{|}}{\underset{}{CH_2}}}-CH_2-CH_3$ (d) $CH_3-\langle\bigcirc\rangle-CH_3$

15.18 Draw correct structures, by making a single change, for any that are incorrect:

(a) $CH_3-CH=CH-CH_2-CH_3$ (b)

(c) $CH_3-C\equiv CH-CH_2-CH_3$ (d) $CH_3-CH_2-\overset{\overset{\displaystyle CH_3}{|}}{\underset{}{C}}-CH_2-CH_2-CH_3$

15.19 Draw the structure or give the name of each compound:
(a) 2,3-dimethyloctane   (b) 1-ethyl-3-methylcyclohexane

(c) $CH_3-CH_2-\underset{\underset{\displaystyle CH_3}{|}}{CH}-\overset{\overset{\displaystyle CH_3}{|}}{CH}-\underset{\underset{\displaystyle CH_2-CH_3}{|}}{CH_2}$ (d)

15.20 Draw the structure or give the name of each compound:

(a)   (b)

(c) 1,2-diethylcyclopentane (d) 2,4,5-trimethylnonane

15.21 Each of the following names is wrong. Draw structures based on them, and correct the names:
(a) 4-methylhexane   (b) 2-ethylpentane
(c) 2-methylcyclohexane   (d) 3,3-methyl-4-ethyloctane

15.22 Each of the following names is wrong. Draw structures based on them, and correct the names:

(a) 3,3-dimethylbutane   (b) 1,1,1-trimethylheptane
(c) 1,4-diethylcyclopentane   (d) 1-propylcyclohexane

15.23 Each of the following compounds can exhibit optical activity. Circle the chiral center(s) in each:
(a)   (b)

15.24 Each of the following compounds can exhibit optical activity. Circle the chiral center(s) in each:
(a)   (b)

15.25 Draw structures from the following names, and determine which compounds are optically active:
(a) 3-bromohexane   (b) 3-chloro-3-methylpentane
(c) 1,2-dibromo-2-methylbutane

15.26 Draw structures from the following names, and determine which compounds are optically active:
(a) 1,3-dichloropentane   (b) 3-chloro-2,2,5-trimethylhexane
(c) 1-bromo-1-chlorobutane

15.27 Which of the following structures exhibit geometric isomerism? Draw and name the two isomers in each case:
(a) $CH_3-CH_2-CH=CH-CH_3$ (b)

(c) $CH_3-\overset{\underset{\displaystyle |}{CH_3}}{C}=CH-\overset{\underset{\displaystyle |}{CH_3}}{CH}-CH_2-CH_3$

15.28 Which of the following structures exhibit geometric isomerism? Draw and name the two isomers in each case:
(a) $CH_3-\overset{\overset{\displaystyle CH_3}{|}}{\underset{\underset{\displaystyle CH_3}{|}}{C}}-CH=CH-CH_3$ (b)

(c) $Cl-CH_2-CH=\overset{\overset{\displaystyle CH_3}{|}}{C}-CH_2-CH_2-CH_2-CH_3$

15.29 Which compounds exhibit geometric isomerism? Draw and name the two isomers in each case:
(a) propene   (b) 3-hexene
(c) 1,1-dichloroethene   (d) 1,2-dichloroethene

15.30 Which compounds exhibit geometric isomerism? Draw and name the two isomers in each case:
(a) 1-pentene   (b) 2-pentene
(c) 1-chloropropene   (d) 2-chloropropene

15.31 Draw and name all the constitutional isomers of dichlorobenzene.

15.32 Draw and name all the constitutional isomers of trimethylbenzene.

Problems in Context

15.33 Butylated hydroxytoluene (BHT) is a common preservative added to cereals and other dry foods. Its systematic name is 1-hydroxy-2,6-di-*tert*-butyl-4-methylbenzene (where "*tert*-butyl" is 1,1-dimethylethyl). Draw the structure of BHT.

15.34 There are two compounds with the name 2-methyl-3-hexene, but only one with the name 2-methyl-2-hexene. Explain with structures.

15.35 Any tetrahedral atom with four different groups attached can be a chiral center. Which of these species is optically active?
(a) CHClBrF   (b) $NBrCl_2H^+$
(c) $PFClBrI^+$ (d) SeFClBrH

15.36 Breaking the C=C π bond in the molecule retinal in the eye requires approximately 250 kJ/mol of energy. Find the longest wavelength (in nm) of visible light that has the energy to break the π bond.

Some Important Classes of Organic Reactions
(Sample Problem 15.3)

Concept Review Questions

15.37 In terms of numbers of reactant and product substances, which organic reaction type corresponds to (a) a combination reaction, (b) a decomposition reaction, (c) a displacement reaction?

15.38 The same type of bond is broken in an addition reaction and formed in an elimination reaction. Name the type.

15.39 Can a redox reaction also be an addition, elimination, or substitution reaction? Explain with examples.

Skill-Building Exercises (grouped in similar pairs)

15.40 Determine the type of each of the following reactions:

(a) $CH_3-CH_2-\overset{\overset{\displaystyle Br}{|}}{CH}-CH_3 \xrightarrow[\Delta]{NaOH}$
$CH_3-CH=CH-CH_3 + NaBr + H_2O$

(b) $CH_3-CH=CH-CH_2-CH_3 + H_2 \xrightarrow{Pt}$
$CH_3-CH_2-CH_2-CH_2-CH_3$

15.41 Determine the type of each of the following reactions:

(a) $CH_3-\overset{\overset{\displaystyle O}{\|}}{CH} + HCN \longrightarrow CH_3-\overset{\overset{\displaystyle OH}{|}}{CH}-CN$

(b) $CH_3-\overset{\overset{\displaystyle O}{\|}}{C}-O-CH_3 + CH_3-NH_2 \xrightarrow{H^+}$
$CH_3-\overset{\overset{\displaystyle O}{\|}}{C}-NH-CH_3 + CH_3-OH$

15.42 Write equations for the following: (a) an addition reaction between H_2O and 3-hexene (H^+ is a catalyst); (b) an elimination reaction between 2-bromopropane and hot potassium ethoxide, CH_3-CH_2-OK (KBr and ethanol are also products); (c) a light-induced substitution reaction between Cl_2 and ethane to form 1,1-dichloroethane.

15.43 Write equations for the following: (a) a substitution reaction between 2-bromopropane and KI; (b) an addition reaction between cyclohexene and Cl_2; (c) an addition reaction between 2-propanone and H_2 (Ni metal is a catalyst).

15.44 Based on the number of bonds and the nature of the bonded atoms, state whether each of the following changes is an oxidation or a reduction:

(a) $=CH_2$ becomes $-CH_2-OH$

(b) $=CH-$ becomes $-CH_2-$

(c) $\equiv C-$ becomes $-CH_2-$

15.45 Based on the number of bonds and the nature of the bonded atoms, state whether each of the following changes is an oxidation or a reduction:

(a) $-\overset{|}{\underset{|}{C}}-OH$ becomes $-C=O$

(b) $-CH_2-OH$ becomes $=CH_2$

(c) $-\overset{O}{\overset{\|}{C}}-\overset{|}{\underset{|}{C}}-$ becomes $-\overset{O}{\overset{\|}{C}}-O-$

15.46 Is the organic reactant oxidized, reduced, or neither in each of the following reactions?

(a) 2-hexene $\xrightarrow[\text{cold OH}]{\text{KMnO}_4}$ 2,3-dihydroxyhexane

(b) cyclohexane $\xrightarrow[\text{catalyst}]{\Delta}$ benzene + $3H_2$

15.47 Is the organic reactant oxidized, reduced, or neither in each of the following reactions?

(a) 1-butyne + H_2 $\xrightarrow{\text{Pt}}$ 1-butene

(b) toluene $\xrightarrow[\text{H}_3\text{O}^+, \Delta]{\text{KMnO}_4}$ benzoic acid

Problems in Context

15.48 Phenylethylamine is a natural substance that is structurally similar to amphetamine. It is found in sources as diverse as almond oil and human urine, where it occurs at elevated concentrations as a result of stress and certain forms of schizophrenia. One method of synthesizing the compound for pharmacological and psychiatric studies involves two steps:

phenylethylamine

Classify each step as an addition, elimination, or substitution.

Properties and Reactivities of Common Functional Groups

(Sample Problems 15.4 to 15.7)

Concept Review Questions

15.49 Compounds with nearly identical molar masses often have very different physical properties. Choose the compound with the higher value for each of the following properties, and explain your choice.
(a) Solubility in water: chloroethane or methylethylamine
(b) Melting point: diethyl ether or 1-butanol
(c) Boiling point: trimethylamine or propylamine

15.50 Fill in each blank with a general formula for the type of compound formed:

15.51 Of the three major types of organic reactions, which do *not* occur readily with benzene? Why?

15.52 Why does the C=O group react differently from the C=C group? Show an example of the difference.

15.53 Many substitution reactions are initiated by electrostatic attraction between reactants. Show where this attraction arises in the formation of an amide from an amine and an ester.

15.54 Although both carboxylic acids and alcohols contain an —OH group, one is acidic in water and the other is not. Explain.

15.55 What reaction type is common to the formation of esters and acid anhydrides? What is the other product?

15.56 Both alcohols and carboxylic acids undergo substitution, but the processes are very different. Explain.

Skill-Building Exercises (grouped in similar pairs)

15.57 Name the type of organic compound from each description of the functional group: (a) polar group that has only single bonds and does not include O or N; (b) group that is polar and has a triple bond; (c) group that has single and double bonds and is acidic in water; (d) group that has a double bond and must be at the end of a C chain.

15.58 Name the type of organic compound from each description of the functional group: (a) N-containing group with single and double bonds; (b) group that is not polar and has a double bond; (c) polar group that has a double bond and cannot be at the end of a C chain; (d) group that has only single bonds and is basic in water.

15.59 Circle and name the functional group(s) in each compound:

(a) $CH_3-CH=CH-CH_2-OH$ (b)

(c)   (d) $N\equiv C-CH_2-\overset{O}{\overset{\|}{C}}-CH_3$

(e)

15.60 Circle and name the functional group(s) in each compound:

(a)   (b) $I-CH_2-CH_2-C\equiv CH$

(c) $CH_2=CH-CH_2-\overset{O}{\overset{\|}{C}}-O-CH_3$ (d) $CH_3-NH-\overset{O}{\overset{\|}{C}}-\overset{O}{\overset{\|}{C}}-O-CH_3$

(e) $CH_3-\overset{Br}{\overset{|}{C}}H-CH=CH-CH_2-NH-CH_3$

15.61 Draw all alcohols with the formula $C_5H_{12}O$.

15.62 Draw all aldehydes and ketones with the formula $C_5H_{10}O$.

15.63 Draw all amines with the formula $C_4H_{11}N$.

15.64 Draw all carboxylic acids with the formula $C_5H_{10}O_2$.

15.65 Draw the product resulting from mild oxidation of (a) 2-butanol; (b) 2-methylpropanal; (c) cyclopentanol.

15.66 Draw the alcohol you'd oxidize to produce (a) 2-methylpropanal; (b) 2-pentanone; (c) 3-methylbutanoic acid.

15.67 Draw the organic product formed when the following compounds undergo a substitution reaction: (a) acetic acid and methylamine; (b) butanoic acid and 2-propanol; (c) formic acid and 2-methyl-1-propanol.

15.68 Draw the organic product formed when the following compounds undergo a substitution reaction: (a) acetic acid and 1-hexanol; (b) propanoic acid and dimethylamine; (c) ethanoic acid and diethylamine.

15.69 Draw condensed formulas for the carboxylic acid and alcohol that form the following esters:

(a)

(b)

(c) $CH_3-CH_2-O-\overset{O}{\underset{\|}{C}}-CH_2-CH_2-$

15.70 Draw condensed formulas for the carboxylic acid and amine that form the following amides:

(a) $H_3C-$$-CH_2-\overset{O}{\underset{\|}{C}}-NH_2$

(b)

(c) $H\overset{O}{\underset{\|}{C}}-NH-$

15.71 Fill in the expected organic substances:

(a) $CH_3-CH_2-Br \xrightarrow{OH^-} \underline{\quad} \xrightarrow[H^+]{CH_3-CH_2-\overset{O}{\underset{\|}{C}}-OH} \underline{\quad}$

(b) $CH_3-CH_2-\overset{Br}{\underset{|}{CH}}-CH_3 \xrightarrow{CN^-} \underline{\quad} \xrightarrow{H_3O^+, H_2O} \underline{\quad}$

15.72 Fill in the expected organic substances:

(a) $CH_3-CH_2-CH=CH_2 \xrightarrow{H^+, H_2O} \underline{\quad} \xrightarrow{Cr_2O_7^{2-}, H^+} \underline{\quad}$

(b) $CH_3-CH_2-\overset{O}{\underset{\|}{C}}-CH_3 \xrightarrow{CH_3-CH_2-Li} \xrightarrow{H_2O} \underline{\quad}$

15.73 Supply the missing organic and/or inorganic substances:

(a) $CH_3-CH_2-OH + \underline{\quad} \xrightarrow{H_3O^+, H_2O}$
$CH_3-CH_2-O-\overset{O}{\underset{\|}{C}}-CH_2-CH_3$

(b) $CH_3-\overset{O}{\underset{\|}{C}}-O-CH_3 \xrightarrow{\ ?\ } CH_3-CH_2-NH-\overset{O}{\underset{\|}{C}}-CH_3$

15.74 Supply the missing organic and/or inorganic substances:

(a) $CH_3-\overset{Cl}{\underset{|}{CH}}-CH_3 \xrightarrow{\ ?\ } CH_3-CH=CH_2 \xrightarrow{\ ?\ } CH_3-\overset{Br}{\underset{|}{CH}}-\overset{Br}{\underset{|}{CH_2}}$

(b) $CH_3-CH_2-CH_2-OH \xrightarrow{\ ?\ } CH_3-CH_2-\overset{O}{\underset{\|}{C}}-OH + \underline{\quad} \xrightarrow{\ ?\ } \underline{\quad}$
$CH_3-CH_2-\overset{O}{\underset{\|}{C}}-O-CH_2-$

Problems in Context

15.75 (a) Draw the four isomers of $C_5H_{12}O$ that can be oxidized to an aldehyde. (b) Draw the three isomers of $C_5H_{12}O$ that can be oxidized to a ketone. (c) Draw the isomers of $C_5H_{12}O$ that cannot be easily oxidized to an aldehyde or ketone. (d) Name any isomer that is an alcohol.

15.76 Ethyl formate ($H\overset{O}{\underset{\|}{C}}-O-CH_2-CH_3$) is added to foods to give them the flavor of rum. How would you synthesize ethyl formate from ethanol, methanol, and any inorganic reagents?

The Monomer-Polymer Theme I: Synthetic Macromolecules

Concept Review Questions

15.77 Name the reaction processes that lead to the two types of synthetic polymers.

15.78 Which functional group occurs in the monomers of addition polymers? How are these polymers different from one another?

15.79 What is a free radical? How is it involved in polymer formation?

15.80 Which intermolecular force is primarily responsible for the different types of polyethylene? Explain.

15.81 Which of the two types of synthetic polymer is more similar chemically to biopolymers? Explain.

15.82 Which functional groups react to form nylons? Polyesters?

Skill-Building Exercises (grouped in similar pairs)

15.83 Draw an abbreviated structure for the following polymers, with brackets around the repeat unit:

(a) Poly(vinyl chloride) (PVC) from

(b) Polypropylene from

15.84 Draw an abbreviated structure for the following polymers, with brackets around the repeat unit:
(a) Teflon from   (b) Polystyrene from

Problems in Context

15.85 Polyethylene terephthalate (PET) is used to make synthetic fibers, such as Dacron, thin films, such as Mylar, and bottles for carbonated beverages.

PET

PET is produced from ethylene glycol and either of two monomers, depending on whether the reaction proceeds by dehydration-condensation or by displacement. Write equations for the two syntheses. (*Hint:* The displacement is reversed by adding methanol to PET at high *T* and *P*.)

15.86 Write a balanced equation for the reaction of dihydroxydimethylsilane (*right*) to form the condensation polymer known as Silly Putty.

$$HO-\underset{\underset{CH_3}{|}}{\overset{\overset{CH_3}{|}}{Si}}-OH$$

The Monomer-Polymer Theme II: Biological Macromolecules

Concept Review Questions

15.87 Which type of polymer is formed from each of the following monomers: (a) amino acids; (b) alkenes; (c) simple sugars; (d) mononucleotides?

15.88 What is the key structural difference between fibrous and globular proteins? How is it related, in general, to the proteins' amino acid composition?

15.89 Protein shape, function, and amino acid sequence are interrelated. Which determines which?

15.90 What linkage joins the monomers in each strand of DNA?

15.91 What is base pairing? How does it pertain to DNA structure?

15.92 RNA base sequence, protein amino acid sequence, and DNA base sequence are interrelated. Which determines which in the process of protein synthesis?

Skill-Building Exercises (grouped in similar pairs)

15.93 Draw the R group of (a) alanine; (b) histidine; (c) methionine.

15.94 Draw the R group of (a) glycine; (b) isoleucine; (c) tyrosine.

15.95 Draw the structure of each of the following tripeptides:
(a) Aspartic acid-histidine-tryptophan
(b) Glycine-cysteine-tyrosine with the charges that exist in cell fluid

15.96 Draw the structure of each of the following tripeptides:
(a) Lysine-phenylalanine-threonine
(b) Alanine-leucine-valine with the charges that exist in cell fluid

15.97 Write the sequence of the complementary DNA strand that pairs with each of the following DNA base sequences:
(a) TTAGCC   (b) AGACAT

15.98 Write the sequence of the complementary DNA strand that pairs with each of the following DNA base sequences:
(a) GGTTAC   (b) CCCGAA

15.99 Write the base sequence of the DNA template from which this RNA sequence was derived: UGUUACGGA. How many amino acids are coded for in this sequence?

15.100 Write the base sequence of the DNA template from which this RNA sequence was derived: GUAUCAAUGAACUUG. How many amino acids are coded for in this sequence?

Problems in Context

15.101 Protein shapes are maintained by a variety of forces that arise from interactions between the amino-acid R groups. Name the amino acid that possesses each R group and the force that could arise in each of the following interactions:
(a) $-CH_2-SH$ with $HS-CH_2-$

(b) $-(CH_2)_4-NH_3^+$ with $\overset{\overset{O}{\|}}{^-O-C-CH_2-}$

(c) $-CH_2-\overset{\overset{O}{\|}}{C}-NH_2$ with $HO-CH_2-$

(d) $-\overset{\overset{CH_3}{|}}{CH}-CH_3$ with $-CH_2-$

15.102 Amino acids have an average molar mass of 100 g/mol. How many bases on a single strand of DNA are needed to code for a protein with a molar mass of 5×10^5 g/mol?

Comprehensive Problems

15.103 Ethers (general formula R—O—R′) have many important uses. Until recently, methyl *tert*-butyl ether (MTBE, *right*) was used as an octane booster and fuel additive for gasoline. It increases the oxygen content of the fuel, which reduces CO emissions. MTBE is synthesized by the catalyzed reaction of 2-methylpropene with methanol.
(a) Write a balanced equation for the synthesis of MTBE. (*Hint:* Alcohols add to alkenes similarly to the way water does.)
(b) If the government required that auto fuel mixtures contain 2.7% oxygen by mass to reduce CO emissions, how many grams of MTBE would have to be added to each 100. g of gasoline?
(c) How many liters of MTBE would be in each liter of fuel mixture? (The density of both gasoline and MTBE is 0.740 g/mL.)
(d) How many liters of air (21% O_2 by volume) are needed at 24°C and 1.00 atm to fully combust 1.00 L of MTBE?

15.104 An alcohol is oxidized to a carboxylic acid, and 0.2003 g of the acid is titrated with 45.25 mL of 0.03811 *M* NaOH. (a) What is the molar mass of the acid? (b) What are the molar mass and molecular formula of the alcohol?

15.105 Some of the most useful compounds for organic synthesis are Grignard reagents (general formula R—MgX, where X is a halogen), which are made by combining an alkyl halide, R—X, with Mg. They are used to change the carbon skeleton of a starting carbonyl compound in a reaction similar to that with R—Li:

$$R'-\overset{\overset{O}{\|}}{C}-R'' + R-MgBr \longrightarrow R'-\overset{\overset{OMgBr}{|}}{\underset{\underset{R}{|}}{C}}-R'' \xrightarrow{H_2O}$$

$$R'-\overset{\overset{OH}{|}}{\underset{\underset{R}{|}}{C}}-R'' + Mg(OH)Br$$

(a) What is the product, after a final step with water, of the reaction between ethanal and the Grignard reagent of bromobenzene? (b) What is the product, after a final step with water, of the reaction between 2-butanone and the Grignard reagent of 2-bromopropane? (c) There are often two (or more) combinations of Grignard reagent and carbonyl compound that will give the same product. Choose another pair of reactants to give the product in (a). (d) What carbonyl compound must react with a Grignard reagent to yield a product with the —OH group at the *end* of the carbon chain? (e) What Grignard reagent and carbonyl compound would you use to prepare 2-methyl-2-butanol?

15.106 Starting with the given organic reactant and any necessary inorganic reagents, explain how you would perform each of the following syntheses:

(a) From $CH_3-CH_2-CH_2-OH$, make $CH_3-\overset{\overset{Br}{|}}{CH}-CH_2-Br$

(b) From $CH_3-CH_2-CH_2-OH$, make $CH_3-\overset{\overset{\displaystyle O}{\|}}{C}-O-CH_2-CH_3$

15.107 Compound A, composed of C, H, and O, is heated in a 1.00-L flask to 160.°C until all of the A has vaporized and displaced the air. The flask is then cooled, and 2.48 g of A remains. When 0.500 g of A burns in O_2, 0.409 g of H_2O and 1.00 g of CO_2 are produced. Compound A is not acidic, but it can be oxidized to compound B, which is weakly acidic: 1.000 g of B is neutralized with 33.9 mL of 0.5 M sodium hydroxide. When B is heated to 260°C, it gives off water and forms C, whose solution in $CDCl_3$ (where D is deuterium, ^2H) has one peak in its ^1H-NMR spectrum. (a) What are the structures of A, B, and C? (b) Compound A is a controlled substance because it is metabolized to the weakly acidic "date rape" drug GHB, $C_4H_8O_3$. What are the structure and name of GHB?

15.108 Cadaverine (1,5-diaminopentane) and putrescine (1,4-diaminobutane) are two compounds that are formed by bacterial action and are responsible for the odor of rotting flesh. Draw their structures. Suggest a series of reactions to synthesize putrescine from 1,2-dibromoethane and any inorganic reagents.

15.109 Pyrethrins, such as jasmolin II (*below*), are a group of natural compounds synthesized by flowers of the genus *Chrysanthemum* (known as pyrethrum flowers) to act as insecticides.
(a) Circle and name the functional groups in jasmolin II.
(b) What is the hybridization of the numbered carbons?
(c) Which, if any, of the numbered carbons are chiral centers?

15.110 Compound A is branched and optically active and contains C, H, and O. (a) A 0.500-g sample burns in excess O_2 to yield 1.25 g of CO_2 and 0.613 g of H_2O. Determine the empirical formula. (b) When 0.225 g of compound A vaporizes at 755 torr and 97°C, the vapor occupies 78.0 mL. Determine the molecular formula. (c) Careful oxidation of the compound yields a ketone. Name and draw compound A, and circle the chiral center.

15.111 Ibuprofen is one of the most common anti-inflammatory drugs. (a) Identify the functional group(s) and chiral center(s) in ibuprofen. (b) Write a four-step synthesis of a racemic mixture of ibuprofen from 4-isobutylbenzaldehyde, using inorganic reactants and one organometallic reactant (see Problem 15.105).

ibuprofen

4-isobutylbenzaldehyde

15.112 Which features of retinal make it so useful as a photon absorber in the visual systems of organisms?

15.113 The polypeptide chain in proteins does not exhibit free rotation because of the partial double-bond character of the peptide bond. Explain this fact with resonance structures.

15.114 Other nonmetals form compounds that are structurally analogous to those of carbon, but these inorganic compounds are usually more reactive. Predict any missing products and write balanced equations for each reaction: (a) the decomposition and chlorination of diborane to boron trichloride; (b) the combustion of pentaborane (B_5H_9) in O_2; (c) the hydrolysis of trisilane (Si_3H_8) to silica (SiO_2) and H_2; (d) the complete halogenation of disilane with Cl_2; (e) the thermal decomposition of H_2S_5 to hydrogen sulfide and sulfur molecules; (f) the hydrolysis of PCl_5.

15.115 In addition to their use in water treatment, ion-exchange resins are used to extract Au, Ag, and Pt ions from solution. One of the most common resins consists of a polymer with a benzene-containing backbone to which sulfonic acid groups ($-SO_3H$) are added. (a) What monomer can be used to prepare the polymer backbone? (b) This polymer typically contains 4–16% crosslinking. Draw the structure of the benzene-containing monomer used to crosslink the polymer.

15.116 Complete hydrolysis of a 100.00-g sample of a peptide gave the following amounts of individual amino acids (molar masses, in g/mol, appear in parentheses):

3.00 g of glycine (75.07)   0.90 g of alanine (89.10)
3.70 g of valine (117.15)   6.90 g of proline (115.13)
7.30 g of serine (105.10)   86.00 g of arginine (174.21)

(a) Why does the total mass of amino acids exceed the mass of peptide? (b) What are the relative numbers of amino acids in the peptide? (c) What is the minimum molar mass of the peptide?

15.117 2-Butanone is reduced by hydride ion donors, such as sodium borohydride ($NaBH_4$), to the alcohol 2-butanol. Even though the alcohol has a chiral center, the product isolated from the redox reaction is not optically active. Explain.

15.118 Wastewater from a cheese factory has the following composition: 8.0 g/L protein ($C_{16}H_{24}O_5N_4$); 12 g/L carbohydrate (CH_2O); and 2.0 g/L fat ($C_8H_{16}O$). What is the total organic carbon (TOC) of the wastewater in g of C/L?

15.119 Structures A, B, and C show the three common forms of vitamin A. (a) Match each structure with the correct vitamin A compound: retinal (an aldehyde), retinol (an alcohol), and retinoic acid (a carboxylic acid). (b) Retinal, the molecule responsible for the chemistry of vision, can be converted to retinol or to retinoic acid. Identify each of these reactions as a reduction or an oxidation. (c) Structure D is that of beta-carotene, found in carrots. Suggest a reason for the importance of beta-carotene in the vision process.

Nuclear Reactions and Their Applications

Concepts and skills to review before you study this chapter

- discovery of the atomic nucleus (Section 2.4)
- protons, neutrons, mass number, and the $^A_Z X$ notation (Section 2.5)
- half-life and first-order reaction rate (Section 16.4)

You might find it hard to believe that uranium within the fuel pellets used in nuclear power reactors has any measureable behavior in common with ordinary bananas, but both exhibit **radioactivity,** the spontaneous disintegration of an unstable nucleus by emission of radiation. A very small percentage of unstable potassium atoms in a banana are the source of its tiny amount of radioactivity. In fact, as we'll discuss, many everyday materials exhibit radioactivity. For example, the trees that produce Brazil nuts have such deep root systems that the nuts have 1000 times more radium than the next most radioactive food. (Despite these facts, the levels of radioactivity in bananas and Brazil nuts are miniscule and present no health risk.)

Up to this point, we have focused on the atom's electrons, treating the nucleus as their electrostatic anchor and examining the effect of its positive charge on atomic properties and, ultimately, chemical behavior. In this chapter, we *will* focus on the atom's tiny, dense core, which is held together by the strongest force in the universe. Scientists studying the structure and behavior of the nucleus see enormous potential as well as great mystery and wonder.

But society is ambivalent about some applications of nuclear research. The promise of abundant energy and treatments for disease is offset by the threat of nuclear waste contamination, reactor accidents, and unimaginable destruction from nuclear war or terrorism. Can the power of the nucleus be harnessed for our benefit, or are the risks too great? By studying this chapter, you'll learn the principles that can help you consider this vital question knowledgably.

The changes that occur in atomic nuclei differ strikingly from chemical changes. In chemical reactions, electrons are shared or transferred to form *compounds,* while nuclei remain unchanged. In nuclear reactions, the roles are reversed: electrons take part much less often, while nuclei undergo changes that, in nearly every case, form different *elements.* Nuclear reactions are often accompanied by energy changes a million times greater than those for chemical reactions, energy changes so large that changes in mass *are* detectable. Moreover, nuclear reaction yields and rates are *not* subject to the effects of pressure, temperature, and catalysis that chemical reactions are. Table 24.1 summarizes these general differences.

Table 24.1 Comparison of Chemical and Nuclear Reactions

Chemical Reactions	Nuclear Reactions
1. One substance is converted into another, but atoms never change identity.	1. Atoms of one element typically are converted into atoms of another element.
2. Electrons in orbitals are involved as bonds break and form; nuclear particles do not take part.	2. Protons, neutrons, and other nuclear particles are involved; electrons in orbitals take part much less often.
3. Reactions are accompanied by relatively small changes in energy and no measurable changes in mass.	3. Reactions are accompanied by relatively large changes in energy and measurable changes in mass.
4. Reaction rates are influenced by temperature, concentration, catalysts, and the compound in which an element occurs.	4. Reaction rates depend on number of nuclei, but are not affected by temperature, catalysts, or, except on rare occasions, the compound in which an element occurs.

IN THIS CHAPTER ... We survey the field of nuclear chemistry, examining radioactive nuclei and their decay processes, especially the effects and applications of radioactivity and the interconversion of matter and energy.

• We investigate nuclear stability to determine why some nuclei are stable and others are not and undergo radioactive decay.
• We learn how radioactivity is detected and how the kinetics of decay is applied.
• We see how nuclei synthesized in particle accelerators have extended the periodic table.
• We consider the effects of radioactive emissions on matter, especially living tissue, and focus on some major uses of radioisotopes in science, technology, and medicine.
• We discuss the mass difference that arises when a nucleus forms from its subatomic particles and the energy that is equivalent to this difference.
• We explore current and future attempts to harness the energy released when heavy nuclei split and lighter ones fuse.
• Finally, we look at the nuclear processes in stars that continue to create chemical elements.

24.1 • RADIOACTIVE DECAY AND NUCLEAR STABILITY

A stable nucleus remains intact indefinitely, but *the great majority of nuclei are unstable.* An unstable nucleus exhibits radioactivity, spontaneously decaying by emitting radiation. In Section 24.2, you'll see that each type of unstable nucleus has its own characteristic *rate* of radioactive decay. In this section, we cover important terms and notation for nuclei, discuss some key events in the discovery of radioactivity, define the types of emission, and describe various modes of radioactive decay and how to predict which occurs for a given nucleus.

The Components of the Nucleus: Terms and Notation

Recall from Chapter 2 that the nucleus contains essentially all the atom's mass but is only about 10^{-5} times its radius (or 10^{-15} times its volume), making the nucleus incredibly dense: about 10^{14} g/mL. ● *Protons* and *neutrons,* the elementary particles that make up the nucleus, are called **nucleons.** A **nuclide** is a nucleus with a particular composition, that is, with specific numbers of the two types of nucleons. Most elements occur in nature as a mixture of **isotopes,** atoms with the characteristic number of protons of the element but different numbers of neutrons. Each isotope of an element thus has a different nuclide. For example, oxygen has three naturally occurring isotopes—the most abundant contains eight protons and eight neutrons, whereas the least abundant contains eight protons and nine neutrons.

The relative mass and charge of a particle—nucleon, elementary particle, or nuclide—is described by the notation $^{A}_{Z}X$, where X is the *symbol* for the particle, A is the *mass number,* or the total number of nucleons, and Z is the *charge* of the particle; for nuclei, A is the *sum of protons and neutrons* and Z is the *number of protons* (atomic number). In this notation, the three subatomic elementary particles are

$$_{-1}^{0}e \text{ (electron)}, \quad _{1}^{1}p \text{ (proton)}, \quad \text{and} \quad _{0}^{1}n \text{ (neutron)}$$

(A proton is also sometimes represented as $_{1}^{1}H^{+}$.) The number of neutrons (*N*) in a nucleus is the mass number (*A*) minus the atomic number (*Z*): $N = A - Z$. The two naturally occurring stable isotopes of chlorine, for example, have 17 protons (*Z* = 17), but one has 18 neutrons ($_{17}^{35}Cl$, also written ^{35}Cl) and the other has 20 ($_{17}^{37}Cl$, or ^{37}Cl). Nuclides can also be designated with the element name followed by the mass number, for example, chlorine-35 and chlorine-37. In naturally occurring samples of an element or its compounds, *the isotopes of the element are present in specific proportions* that vary only very slightly. Thus, in a sample of sodium chloride (or any Cl-containing substance), 75.77% of the Cl atoms are chlorine-35 and the remaining 24.23% are chlorine-37.

● **Big Atom, Massive Core** If you could strip the electrons from the atoms in an object and compress the nuclei together, the object would lose only a fraction of a percent of its mass, but it would shrink to 0.0000000000001% (10^{-13}%) of its volume!

To understand this chapter, it's very important that you are comfortable with nuclear notations, so please take a moment to review Sample Problem 2.4 (pp. 49–50) and Problems 2.39 to 2.46 (p. 76).

The Discovery of Radioactivity and the Types of Emissions

In 1896, the French physicist Antoine-Henri Becquerel accidentally discovered that uranium minerals, even when wrapped in paper and stored in the dark, emit a penetrating radiation that can expose a photographic plate. Becquerel also found that the radiation creates an electric discharge in air, thus providing a means for measuring its intensity.

Two years later, a young doctoral student named Marie Sklodowska Curie began a search for other minerals that behaved in this way. She found that thorium minerals also emit radiation and, most importantly, that *the intensity of the radiation is directly proportional to the concentration of the element in the mineral, not to the formula of the mineral or compound.* Curie named the emissions *radioactivity* and showed that they are *unaffected by temperature, pressure, or other physical and chemical conditions.*

After months of painstaking chemical work, Curie and her husband, physicist Pierre Curie, isolated two new elements from pitchblende, the principal ore of uranium: polonium (Po; Z = 84), the most metallic member of Group 6A(16), and radium (Ra; Z = 88), the heaviest alkaline earth metal.

Then, starting with several tons of pitchblende residues from which the uranium had been extracted and working arduously for four years, Curie isolated 0.1 g of radium chloride, which she melted and electrolyzed to obtain pure metallic radium. Curie is the only person to have received two Nobel Prizes in science, one in physics for her research into radioactivity, and the other in chemistry for her discoveries of polonium and radium.

During the next few years, Henri Becquerel, the Curies, and P. Villard in France and Ernest Rutherford and his coworkers in England studied the nature of radioactive emissions. A key finding was the observation of Rutherford and his colleague Frederick Soddy that elements other than radium were formed when radium decayed. In 1902, they proposed that radioactive emission results in the change of one element into another. This explanation seemed like a return to alchemy and was met with disbelief and ridicule. We now know it to be true: *when a nuclide of one element decays, it emits radiation and usually changes into a nuclide of a different element.*

There are three natural types of radioactive emission:

- **Alpha particles** (symbolized α, $^4_2\alpha$, or $^4_2\text{He}^{2+}$) are identical to helium-4 nuclei.
- **Beta particles** (symbolized β, β^-, or sometimes $^0_{-1}\beta$) are high-speed electrons. (The emission of electrons from the nucleus may seem strange, but as you'll see shortly, they result from a nuclear reaction.)
- **Gamma rays** (symbolized γ, or sometimes $^0_0\gamma$) are very high-energy photons.

Figure 24.1 illustrates the behavior of these emissions in an electric field: the positively charged α particles curve to a small extent toward the negative plate, the negatively charged β particles curve to a greater extent toward the positive plate (because they have lower mass), and the uncharged γ rays are not affected by the electric field.

Figure 24.1 How the three types of radioactive emissions behave in an electric field.

Modes of Radioactive Decay; Balancing Nuclear Equations

When a nuclide decays, it forms a nuclide of lower energy, and the excess energy is carried off by the emitted radiation and the recoiling nucleus. The decaying, or reactant, nuclide is called the *parent;* the product nuclide is called the *daughter.* Nuclides can decay in several ways. As each of the major modes of decay is introduced (summarized in Table 24.2 on the next page), we'll show examples of that mode and apply the key principle used to balance nuclear reactions: *the total Z (charge, number of protons) and the total A (sum of protons and neutrons) of the reactants equal those of the products:*

$$\text{Total } ^A_Z \text{ Reactants} = \text{Total } ^A_Z \text{ Products} \qquad (24.1)$$

Table 24.2 Modes of Radioactive Decay*

Mode	Emission	Decay Process	Change in A	Z	N
α Decay	$\alpha(^4_2\text{He}^{2+})$	α expelled	−4	−2	−2
β^- Decay[†]	$\beta^-(^{\ 0}_{-1}\beta)$	nucleus with xp^+ and yn^0 → nucleus with $(x+1)p^+$ and $(y-1)n^0$ + $^{\ 0}_{-1}\beta$ β^- expelled	0	+1	−1
	Net:	^1_0n in nucleus → ^1_1p in nucleus + $^{\ 0}_{-1}\beta$ β^- expelled			
Positron (β^+) emission[†]	$\beta^+(^0_1\beta)$	nucleus with xp^+ and yn^0 → nucleus with $(x-1)p^+$ and $(y+1)n^0$ + $^0_1\beta$ β^+ expelled	0	−1	+1
	Net:	^1_1p in nucleus → ^1_0n in nucleus + $^0_1\beta$ β^+ expelled			
Electron (e^-) capture (EC)[†]	x-ray	low-energy orbital, nucleus with xp^+ and yn^0 → nucleus with $(x-1)p^+$ and $(y+1)n^0$	0	−1	+1
	Net:	$^{\ 0}_{-1}\text{e}$ absorbed from low-energy orbital + ^1_1p in nucleus → ^1_0n in nucleus			
Gamma (γ) emission	γ	excited nucleus → stable nucleus + γ γ photon radiated	0	0	0

*Nuclear chemists consider β^- decay, positron emission, and electron capture to be three decay modes of the more general process known as beta decay (see text).

[†]Neutrinos (ν) or antineutrinos ($\bar{\nu}$) are also formed during the three modes of beta decay. Although we will not include them in other equations in the chapter, keep in mind that antineutrinos are always expelled during β^- decay, and neutrinos are expelled during β^+ emission and e^- capture.

1. **Alpha (α) decay** involves the loss of an α particle from a nucleus. For each α particle emitted by the parent, *A decreases by 4 and Z decreases by 2* in the daughter. Every element beyond bismuth (Bi; $Z = 83$) is radioactive and exhibits α decay, which is *the most common means for a heavy, unstable nucleus to become more stable.* For example, radium undergoes α decay to yield radon (Rn; $Z = 86$):

$$^{226}_{88}\text{Ra} \longrightarrow \ ^{222}_{86}\text{Rn} + \ ^{4}_{2}\alpha$$

Note that the A value for Ra equals the sum of the A values for Rn and α ($226 = 222 + 4$), and that the Z value for Ra equals the sum of the Z values for Rn and α ($88 = 86 + 2$).

2. **Beta (β) decay** is a more general class of radioactive decay that includes three modes: β^- decay, β^+ emission, and electron capture.

- **β^- decay** (or *negatron emission*) occurs through the ejection of a β^- particle from the nucleus. This change does not involve expulsion of a β^- particle that was in the nucleus; rather, *a neutron is converted into a proton, which remains in the nucleus, and a β^- particle, which is expelled immediately:*

$$^{1}_{0}\text{n} \longrightarrow \ ^{1}_{1}\text{p} + \ ^{0}_{-1}\beta$$

As always, the totals of the A and the Z values for reactant and products are equal. Radioactive nickel-63 becomes stable copper-63 through β^- decay:

$$^{63}_{28}\text{Ni} \longrightarrow \ ^{63}_{29}\text{Cu} + \ ^{0}_{-1}\beta$$

Another example is the β^- decay of carbon-14, used in radiocarbon dating:

$$^{14}_{6}\text{C} \longrightarrow \ ^{14}_{7}\text{N} + \ ^{0}_{-1}\beta$$

Note that *β^- decay results in a product nuclide with the same A but with Z one higher (one more proton)* than in the reactant nuclide. In other words, an atom of the element with the next *higher* atomic number is formed. Although equations in this chapter do not include it, a neutral particle called an antineutrino ($\overline{\nu}$) is also emitted during β^- decay. The mass of the antineutrino is thought to be much less than 10^{-4} times that of an electron.

- **Positron (β^+) emission** is the emission of a β^+ particle from the nucleus. A key idea of modern physics is that most fundamental particles have corresponding *antiparticles* with the same mass but opposite charge. The **positron** is the antiparticle of the electron. Positron emission occurs through a process in which *a proton in the nucleus is converted into a neutron, and a positron is expelled:*

$$^{1}_{1}\text{p} \longrightarrow \ ^{1}_{0}\text{n} + \ ^{0}_{1}\beta$$

Also emitted during this process is a *neutrino* (ν), the antiparticle of the antineutrino. In terms of the effect on A and Z, *positron emission has the opposite effect of β^- decay: the daughter has the same A but Z is one lower (one fewer proton) than the parent.* Thus, an atom of the element with the next *lower* atomic number forms. Carbon-11, a synthetic radioisotope, decays to a stable boron isotope through β^+ emission:

$$^{11}_{6}\text{C} \longrightarrow \ ^{11}_{5}\text{B} + \ ^{0}_{1}\beta$$

- **Electron (e⁻) capture (EC)** occurs when the nucleus interacts with an electron in a low atomic energy level. The net effect is that *a proton is transformed into a neutron:*

$$^{1}_{1}\text{p} + \ ^{0}_{-1}\text{e} \longrightarrow \ ^{1}_{0}\text{n}$$

(We use the symbol "e" to distinguish an orbital electron from a beta particle, β.) The orbital vacancy is quickly filled by an electron that moves down from a higher energy level, and that process continues through still higher energy levels, with x-ray photons and neutrinos carrying off the energy difference in each step. Radioactive iron forms stable manganese through electron capture:

$$^{55}_{26}\text{Fe} + \ ^{0}_{-1}\text{e} \longrightarrow \ ^{55}_{25}\text{Mn} + h\nu \text{ (x-rays and neutrinos)}$$

Even though the processes are different, *electron capture has the same net effect as positron emission: Z lower by 1, A unchanged.*

3. **Gamma (γ) emission** involves the radiation of high-energy γ photons (also called γ rays) from an excited nucleus. Just as an atom in an excited *electronic*

state reduces its energy by emitting photons, usually in the UV and visible ranges (see Section 7.2), a nucleus in an excited state lowers its energy by emitting γ photons, which are of much higher energy (much shorter wavelength) than UV photons. Many nuclear processes leave the nucleus in an excited state, so γ *emission accompanies many other (mostly β) types of decay.* Several γ photons of different energies can be emitted from an excited nucleus as it returns to the ground state. Some of Marie Curie's experiments involved the release of γ rays, such as

$$^{215}_{84}\text{Po} \longrightarrow {}^{211}_{82}\text{Pb} + {}^{4}_{2}\alpha \text{ (several } \gamma \text{ emitted)}$$

Gamma emission often accompanies β^- decay:

$$^{99}_{43}\text{Tc} \longrightarrow {}^{99}_{44}\text{Ru} + {}^{0}_{-1}\beta \text{ (several } \gamma \text{ emitted)}$$

Because γ rays have no mass or charge, γ *emission does not change A or Z.* Two gamma rays are emitted when a particle and an antiparticle annihilate each other. In the medical technique known as *positron-emission tomography* (which we discuss in Section 24.5), a positron and an electron annihilate each other (with all A and Z values shown):

$$^{0}_{1}\beta + {}^{0}_{-1}e \longrightarrow 2{}^{0}_{0}\gamma$$

Sample Problem 24.1 Writing Equations for Nuclear Reactions

Problem Write balanced equations for the following nuclear reactions:
(a) Naturally occurring thorium-232 undergoes α decay.
(b) Zirconium-86 undergoes electron capture.

Plan We first write a skeleton equation that includes the mass numbers, atomic numbers, and symbols of all the particles on the correct sides of the equation, showing the unknown product particle as ${}^{A}_{Z}\text{X}$. Then, because the total of mass numbers and the total of charges on the left side and the right side must be equal, we solve for A and Z, and use Z to determine X from the periodic table.

Solution **(a)** Writing the skeleton equation, with the α particle as a product:

$$^{232}_{90}\text{Th} \longrightarrow {}^{A}_{Z}\text{X} + {}^{4}_{2}\alpha$$

Solving for A and Z and balancing the equation: For A, $232 = A + 4$, so $A = 228$. For Z, $90 = Z + 2$, so $Z = 88$. From the periodic table, we see that the element with $Z = 88$ is radium (Ra). Thus, the balanced equation is

$$^{232}_{90}\text{Th} \longrightarrow {}^{228}_{88}\text{Ra} + {}^{4}_{2}\alpha$$

(b) Writing the skeleton equation, with the captured electron as a reactant:

$$^{86}_{40}\text{Zr} + {}^{0}_{-1}e \longrightarrow {}^{A}_{Z}\text{X}$$

Solving for A and Z and balancing the equation: For A, $86 + 0 = A$, so $A = 86$. For Z, $40 + (-1) = Z$, so $Z = 39$. The element with $Z = 39$ is yttrium (Y), so we have

$$^{86}_{40}\text{Zr} + {}^{0}_{-1}e \longrightarrow {}^{86}_{39}\text{Y}$$

Check Always read across superscripts and then across subscripts, with the yield arrow as an equal sign, to check your arithmetic. In part (a), for example, $232 = 228 + 4$, and $90 = 88 + 2$.

Follow-Up Problem 24.1 Write a balanced equation for the reaction in which a nuclide undergoes β^- decay and changes to cesium-133.

Nuclear Stability and the Mode of Decay

Can we predict how, and whether, an unstable nuclide will decay? Our knowledge of the nucleus is much less complete than that of the whole atom, but some patterns emerge by observing naturally occurring nuclides.

The Band of Stability Two key factors determine the stability of a nuclide:

1. The number of neutrons (N), the number of protons (Z), and their ratio (N/Z), which we calculate from $(A - Z)/Z$. This factor relates primarily to nuclides that undergo one of the three modes of β decay.

2. The total mass of the nuclide, which mostly relates to nuclides that undergo α decay.

Figure 24.2A is a plot of number of neutrons vs. number of protons for all stable nuclides. Note the following:

- The points form a narrow **band of stability** that gradually curves above the line for $N = Z$ ($N/Z = 1$).
- The only stable nuclides with $N/Z < 1$ are $_1^1$H and $_2^3$He.
- Many lighter nuclides with $N = Z$ are stable, such as $_2^4$He, $_6^{12}$C, $_8^{16}$O, and $_{10}^{20}$Ne; the heaviest of these is $_{20}^{40}$Ca. Thus, for lighter nuclides, one neutron for each proton ($N = Z$) is enough to provide stability.
- The N/Z ratio of stable nuclides gradually increases as Z increases. For example, for $_{26}^{56}$Fe, $N/Z = 1.15$; for $_{47}^{107}$Ag, $N/Z = 1.28$; for $_{74}^{184}$W, $N/Z = 1.49$, and, finally, for $_{83}^{209}$Bi, $N/Z = 1.52$. Thus, for heavier stable nuclides, $N > Z$ ($N/Z > 1$), and N increases faster than Z. As we discuss below, and show in Figure 24.2B, if N/Z of a nuclide is either too high (above the band) or not high enough (below the band), the nuclide is unstable and undergoes one of the three modes of beta decay.
- All nuclides with $Z > 83$ are unstable.* This means that all nuclides with a higher Z—the largest members of main groups 1A(1) through 8A(18), actinium and the actinides ($Z = 89-103$), and the other elements of the fourth ($6d$) transition series ($Z = 104-112$)—are radioactive, and, as we point out below, undergo α decay.

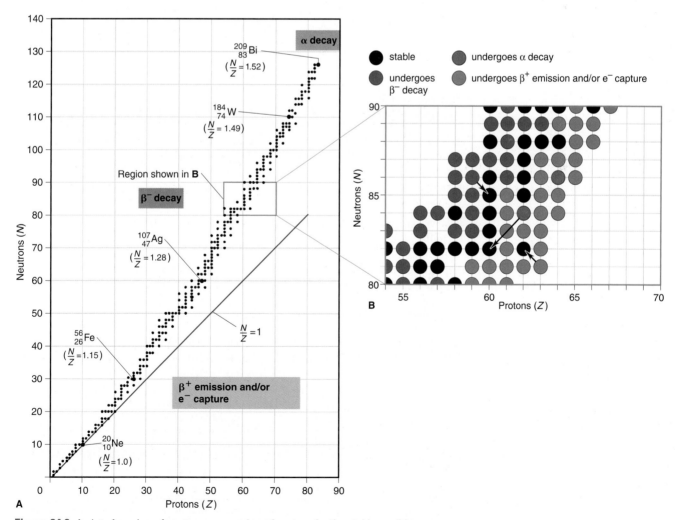

Figure 24.2 A plot of number of neutrons vs. number of protons for the stable nuclides.

Table 24.3 Number of Stable Nuclides for Elements 48 to 54*

Element	Atomic No. (Z)	No. of Nuclides
Cd	**48**	8
In	49	2
Sn	**50**	10
Sb	51	2
Te	**52**	8
I	53	1
Xe	**54**	9

*Even Z shown in boldface.

Table 24.4 An Even-Odd Breakdown of the Stable Nuclides

Z	N	No. of Nuclides
Even	Even	157
Even	Odd	53
Odd	Even	50
Odd	Odd	4
	TOTAL	264

Stability and Nuclear Structure Given that protons are positively charged and neutrons are uncharged, the first question to ask is what holds the nucleus together? Nuclear scientists answer this question and explain the importance of N and Z values in terms of two opposing forces: Electrostatic repulsive forces between protons would break the nucleus apart if not for an attractive force called the **strong force,** which exists between all nucleons (protons and neutrons). This force is 137 times stronger than the repulsive force but *operates only over the short distances within the nucleus.* Thus, the *attractive* strong force overwhelms the much weaker *repulsive* electrostatic force and keeps the nucleus together.

The oddness or evenness of N and Z values is related to some important patterns of nuclear stability. Two interesting points become apparent when we classify the known stable nuclides:

1. Elements with an even Z (number of protons) usually have a larger number of stable nuclides than elements with an odd Z. Table 24.3 demonstrates this point for cadmium ($Z = 48$) through xenon ($Z = 54$).
2. Well over half the stable nuclides have *both* even N and even Z (Table 24.4). Only four nuclides with odd N and odd Z are stable: ^2_1H, ^6_3Li, $^{10}_5B$, and $^{14}_7N$.

One model of nuclear structure that attempts to explain the stability of even values of N and Z postulates that protons and neutrons lie in *nucleon energy levels,* and that greater stability results from the *pairing of spins* of like nucleons. (Note the analogy to electron energy levels and the stability from pairing of electron spins.)

Just as noble gases—with 2, 10, 18, 36, 54, and 86 electrons—are exceptionally stable because they have filled *electron* levels, nuclides with N or Z values of 2, 8, 20, 28, 50, 82 (and $N = 126$) are exceptionally stable. These so-called *magic numbers* are thought to correspond to the numbers of protons or neutrons in filled *nucleon* levels. A few examples are $^{50}_{22}Ti$ ($N = 28$), $^{88}_{38}Sr$ ($N = 50$), and the ten stable nuclides of tin ($Z = 50$). Some extremely stable nuclides have two magic numbers: ^4_2He, $^{16}_8O$, $^{40}_{20}Ca$, and $^{208}_{82}Pb$ ($N = 126$).

Sample Problem 24.2 | **Predicting Nuclear Stability**

Problem Which of the following nuclides would you predict to be stable and which radioactive: (a) $^{18}_{10}Ne$; (b) $^{32}_{16}S$; (c) $^{236}_{90}Th$; (d) $^{123}_{56}Ba$? Explain.

Plan In order to evaluate the stability of each nuclide, we determine the N and Z values, the N/Z ratio from $(A - Z)/Z$, the value of Z, stable N/Z ratios (from Figure 24.2A), and whether Z and N are even or odd.

Solution (a) Radioactive. This nuclide has $N = 8$ ($18 - 10$) and $Z = 10$, so $N/Z = \dfrac{18 - 10}{10} = 0.8$. Except for hydrogen-1 and helium-3, no nuclides with $N < Z$ are stable; despite its even N and Z, this nuclide has too few neutrons to be stable.

(b) Stable. This nuclide has $N = Z = 16$, so $N/Z = 1.0$. With $Z < 20$ and even N and Z, this nuclide is most likely stable.

(c) Radioactive. This nuclide has $Z = 90$, and every nuclide with $Z > 83$ is radioactive.

(d) Radioactive. This nuclide has $N = 67$ and $Z = 56$, so $N/Z = 1.20$. For Z values of 55 to 60, Figure 24.2A shows $N/Z \geq 1.3$, so this nuclide has too few neutrons to be stable.

Check By consulting a table of isotopes, such as the one in the *CRC Handbook of Chemistry and Physics,* we find that our predictions are correct.

Follow-Up Problem 24.2 Why is $^{31}_{15}P$ stable but $^{30}_{15}P$ unstable?

---

*In 2003, French nuclear physicists discovered that $^{209}_{83}Bi$ actually undergoes α decay, but the half-life is 1.9×10^{19} yr, about a billion times longer than the estimated age of the universe. Bismuth ($Z = 83$) can thus be considered stable.

Predicting the Mode of Decay An unstable nuclide generally decays in a mode that shifts its N/Z ratio toward the band of stability. This fact is illustrated in Figure 24.2B, which expands the small region of $Z = 54$ to 70 in Figure 24.2A to show the stable *and* many of the unstable nuclides in that region, as well as their modes of decay. Note the following points:

1. *Neutron-rich nuclides.* Nuclides with too many neutrons for stability (a high N/Z) lie above the band of stability. They undergo β^- *decay,* which converts a neutron into a proton, thus reducing the value of N/Z.

2. *Proton-rich nuclides.* Nuclides with too many protons for stability (a low N/Z) lie below the band. They undergo β^+ *emission* and/or e^- *capture,* both of which convert a proton into a neutron, thus increasing the value of N/Z. (The rate of e^- capture increases with Z, so β^+ emission is more common among lighter elements and e^- capture more common among heavier elements.)

3. *Heavy nuclides.* Nuclides with $Z > 83$ (shown in Figure 24.2A) are too heavy to be stable and undergo α *decay,* which reduces their Z and N values by two units per emission.

With the information in Figure 24.2, predicting the mode of decay of an unstable nuclide means just comparing its N/Z ratio with those in the nearby region of the band of stability. But, even without Figure 24.2, we can often make an educated guess about mode of decay. The atomic mass of an element is the weighted average of its naturally occurring isotopes. Therefore,

- The mass number A of a *stable* nuclide will be relatively close to the atomic mass.
- If an *unstable* nuclide of an element (given Z) has an A value much higher than the atomic mass, it is neutron rich and will probably decay by β^- emission.
- If, on the other hand, the unstable nuclide has an A value much lower than the atomic mass, it is proton rich and will probably decay by β^+ emission and/or e^- capture.

In the next sample problem, we predict the mode of decay of some unstable nuclides.

Sample Problem 24.3 | Predicting the Mode of Nuclear Decay

Problem Use the atomic mass of the element to predict the mode(s) of decay of the following radioactive nuclides: **(a)** $^{12}_{5}B$; **(b)** $^{234}_{92}U$; **(c)** $^{81}_{33}As$; **(d)** $^{127}_{57}La$.

Plan If the nuclide is too heavy to be stable ($Z > 83$), it undergoes α decay. For other cases, we use the Z value to obtain its atomic mass from the periodic table. If the mass number of the nuclide is higher than the atomic mass, the nuclide has too many neutrons: N too high $\Rightarrow \beta^-$ decay. If the mass number is lower than the atomic mass, the nuclide has too many protons: Z too high $\Rightarrow \beta^+$ emission and/or e^- capture.

Solution **(a)** This nuclide has $Z = 5$, which is boron (B), and the atomic mass is 10.81. The nuclide's A value of 12 is significantly higher than its atomic mass, so this nuclide is neutron rich. It will probably undergo β^- decay.
(b) This nuclide has $Z = 92$, so it will undergo α decay and decrease its total mass.
(c) This nuclide has $Z = 33$, which is arsenic (As), and the atomic mass is 74.92. The A value of 81 is much higher, so this nuclide is neutron rich and will probably undergo β^- decay.
(d) This nuclide has $Z = 57$, which is lanthanum (La), and the atomic mass is 138.9. The A value of 127 is much lower, so this nuclide is proton rich and will probably undergo β^+ emission and/or e^- capture.

Check To confirm our predictions in (a), (c), and (d), let's compare each nuclide's N/Z ratio to those in the band of stability. **(a)** This nuclide has $N = 7$ and $Z = 5$, so $N/Z = 1.40$, which is too high for this region of the band, so it will undergo β^- decay. **(c)** This nuclide has $N = 48$ and $Z = 33$, so $N/Z = 1.45$, which is too high for this region of the band, so it undergoes β^- decay. **(d)** This nuclide has $N = 70$ and $Z = 57$, so $N/Z = 1.23$, which is too low for this region of the band, so it undergoes β^+ emission and/or e^- capture. Our predictions based on N/Z values were the same as those based on atomic mass.

Comment Both possible modes of decay are observed for the nuclide in part (d).

Follow-Up Problem 24.3 Use the A value for the nuclide and the atomic mass in the periodic table to predict the mode of decay of **(a)** $^{61}_{26}\text{Fe}$; **(b)** $^{241}_{95}\text{Am}$.

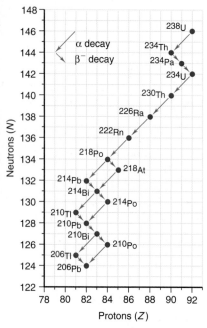

Figure 24.3 The ^{238}U decay series.

Decay Series A parent nuclide may undergo a series of decay steps before a stable daughter nuclide forms. The succession of steps is called a **decay series**, or **disintegration series**, and is typically depicted on a gridlike display. Figure 24.3 shows the decay series from uranium-238 to lead-206. Numbers of neutrons (N) are plotted against numbers of protons (Z) to form the grid, which displays a series of α and β$^-$ decays. The typical zigzag pattern arises because $N > Z$, which means that α decay, which reduces both N and Z by two units, decreases Z slightly more than it does N. Therefore, α decays result in neutron-rich daughters, which undergo β$^-$ decay to gain more stability. Note that a given nuclide can undergo both modes of decay. (Gamma emission accompanies many of these steps but does not affect the type of nuclide.)

The series in Figure 24.3 is one of three that occur in nature. All end with isotopes of lead whose nuclides all have one ($Z = 82$) or two ($N = 126$, $Z = 82$) magic numbers. A second series begins with uranium-235 and ends with lead-207, and a third begins with thorium-232 and ends with lead-208. (Neptunium-237 began a fourth series, but its half-life is so much less than the age of Earth that only traces of it remain today.)

◼ Summary of Section 24.1

- To become more stable, a radioactive nuclide may emit α particles ($^4_2\text{He}^{2+}$; helium-4 nuclei), β particles (β$^-$ or $_{-1}^0\beta$; high-speed electrons), positrons (β$^+$ or $_1^0\beta$), or γ rays (high-energy photons) or may capture an orbital electron ($_{-1}^0\text{e}$).
- A narrow band of neutron-to-proton ratios (N/Z) includes those of all the stable nuclides.
- Even values of N and Z are associated with stable nuclides, as are certain "magic numbers" of neutrons and protons.
- By comparing a nuclide's mass number with the atomic mass and its N/Z ratio with those in the band of stability, we can predict that, in general, neutron-rich nuclides undergo β$^-$ decay and proton-rich nuclides undergo β$^+$ emission and/or e$^-$ capture. Heavy nuclides ($Z > 83$) undergo α decay.
- Three naturally occurring decay series all end in isotopes of lead.

24.2 • THE KINETICS OF RADIOACTIVE DECAY

Both chemical and nuclear systems tend toward maximum stability. Just as the concentrations in a chemical system change in a predictable direction to give a stable equilibrium ratio, the type and number of nucleons in an unstable nucleus change in a predictable direction to give a stable N/Z ratio. As you know, however, the tendency of a chemical system to become more stable tells nothing about how long that process will take, and the same holds true for nuclear systems. In this section, we first see how radioactivity is detected and measured and then examine the kinetics of nuclear change; later, we'll examine the energetics of nuclear change.

Detection and Measurement of Radioactivity

Radioactive emissions interact with surrounding atoms. To determine the rate of nuclear decay, we measure radioactivity by observing the effects of these interactions over time. Because these effects can be electrically amplified billions of times, it is

Figure 24.4 Detection of radioactivity by an ionization counter.

possible to detect the decay of a single nucleus. Ionization counters and scintillation counters are two devices used to measure radioactive emissions.

Ionization Counters An *ionization counter* detects radioactive emissions as they ionize a gas. Ionization produces free electrons and gaseous cations, which are attracted to electrodes that conduct a current to a recording device. The most common type of ionization counter is a **Geiger-Müller counter** (Figure 24.4). It consists of a tube filled with an argon-methane mixture; the tube housing acts as the cathode, and a thin wire in the center of the tube acts as the anode. Emissions from the sample enter the tube through a thin window and strike argon atoms, producing Ar^+ ions that migrate toward the cathode and free electrons that are accelerated toward the anode. These electrons collide with other argon atoms and free more electrons in an *avalanche effect*. The current created is amplified and appears as a meter reading and/or an audible click. An initial release of 1 electron can release 10^{10} electrons in a microsecond, giving the Geiger-Müller counter great sensitivity.

Scintillation Counters In a **scintillation counter,** radioactive emissions are detected by their ability to excite atoms and cause them to emit light. The light-emitting substance in the counter, called a *phosphor,* is coated onto part of a *photomultiplier tube,* a device that increases the original electrical signal. Incoming radioactive particles strike the phosphor, which emits photons. Each photon, in turn, strikes a cathode, releasing an electron through the photoelectric effect (Section 7.1). This electron hits other portions of the tube that release increasing numbers of electrons, and the resulting current is recorded. Liquid scintillation counters employ an organic mixture that contains a phosphor and a solvent (Figure 24.5). This "cocktail" dissolves the radioactive sample *and* emits pulses of light when excited by the emission. The number of pulses is proportional to the concentration of the radioactive substance. These counters are often used to measure β^- emissions from dissolved biological samples, particularly those containing compounds of ^3H and ^{14}C.

Figure 24.5 A scintillation "cocktail" in tubes to be placed in the counter.

The Rate of Radioactive Decay

Radioactive nuclei decay at a characteristic rate, regardless of the chemical substance in which they occur. The *decay rate,* or **activity ($\mathscr{A}$),** of a radioactive sample is the change in number of nuclei ($\mathscr{N}$) divided by the change in time (t). As with chemical reaction rates (Section 16.2), because the number of nuclei is *decreasing,* a minus sign precedes the expression to obtain a positive decay rate:

$$\text{Decay rate } (\mathscr{A}) = -\frac{\Delta \mathscr{N}}{\Delta t}$$

The SI unit of radioactivity is the **becquerel (Bq),** defined as one disintegration per second (d/s): 1 Bq = 1 d/s. A much larger and more common unit of radioactivity is the **curie (Ci),** which was originally defined as the number of disintegrations per second in 1 g of radium-226, but is now a fixed quantity:

$$1 \text{ Ci} = 3.70 \times 10^{10} \text{ d/s} \qquad \text{(24.2)}$$

Because the curie is so large, the millicurie (mCi) and microcurie (μCi) are commonly seen. The radioactivity of a sample is often given as a *specific activity,* the decay rate per gram.

An activity is meaningful only when we consider the large number of nuclei in a macroscopic sample. Suppose there are 1×10^{15} radioactive nuclei of a particular type in a sample and they decay at a rate of 10% per hour. Although any particular nucleus in the sample might decay in a microsecond or in a million hours, the *average* of all decays results in 10% of the entire collection of nuclei disintegrating each hour. During the first hour, 10% of the *original* number, or 1×10^{14} nuclei, will decay. During the next hour, 10% of the remaining 9×10^{14} nuclei, or 9×10^{13} nuclei, will decay. During the next hour, 10% of those remaining will decay, and so forth. Thus, for a large collection of radioactive nuclei, *the number decaying per unit time is proportional to the number present:*

$$\text{Decay rate } (\mathscr{A}) \propto \mathscr{N} \qquad \text{or} \qquad \mathscr{A} = k\mathscr{N}$$

where k is called the **decay constant** and is characteristic of each type of nuclide. The larger the value of k, the higher is the decay rate: larger $k \Rightarrow$ higher $\mathscr{A}$.

Combining the two rate expressions just given, we obtain

$$\mathscr{A} = -\frac{\Delta \mathscr{N}}{\Delta t} = k\mathscr{N} \qquad \text{(24.3)}$$

Note that the activity depends only on $\mathscr{N}$ raised to the first power (and on the constant value of k). Therefore, *radioactive decay is a first-order process* (Section 16.4), but with respect to the *number* of nuclei rather than their concentration.

Half-Life of Radioactive Decay Decay rates are also commonly expressed in terms of the fraction of nuclei that decay over a given time interval. The **half-life ($t_{1/2}$)** of a nuclide has the same meaning as for a chemical change (Section 16.4) and can be expressed in terms of number of nuclei, mass of radioactive substance, and activity:

- *Number of nuclei.* Half-life is the time it takes for half the nuclei in a sample to decay—*the number of nuclei remaining is halved after each half-life.* Figure 24.6 shows the decay of carbon-14, which has a half-life of 5730 years, in terms of number of ^{14}C nuclei remaining:

$$^{14}_{6}\text{C} \longrightarrow ^{14}_{7}\text{N} + ^{0}_{-1}\beta$$

- *Mass.* As ^{14}C decays, the mass of ^{14}C decreases while the mass of ^{14}N increases. If we start with 1.0 g of ^{14}C, half that mass of ^{14}C (0.50 g) will be left after 5730 years, half of that mass (0.25 g) after another 5730 years, and so on.

- *Activity.* The activity depends on the number of nuclei, so the activity is halved after each succeeding half-life.

We determine the half-life of a nuclear reaction from its rate constant. Rearranging Equation 24.3 and integrating over time gives an expression for finding the number of nuclei remaining, $\mathscr{N}_t$, after a given time t:

$$\ln \frac{\mathscr{N}_t}{\mathscr{N}_0} = -kt \qquad \text{or} \qquad \mathscr{N}_t = \mathscr{N}_0 e^{-kt} \qquad \text{and} \qquad \ln \frac{\mathscr{N}_0}{\mathscr{N}_t} = kt \qquad \text{(24.4)}$$

Figure 24.6 Decrease in number of ^{14}C nuclei over time.

where $\mathcal{N}_0$ is the number of nuclei at $t = 0$. (Note the similarity to Equation 16.4, p. 642.) To calculate the half-life ($t_{1/2}$), we set $\mathcal{N}_t$ equal to $\frac{1}{2}\mathcal{N}_0$ and solve for $t_{1/2}$:

$$\ln \frac{\mathcal{N}_0}{\frac{1}{2}\mathcal{N}_0} = kt_{1/2} \quad \text{so} \quad t_{1/2} = \frac{\ln 2}{k} \qquad \text{(24.5)}$$

Exactly analogous to the half-life of a first-order chemical change, *this half-life is **not** dependent on the number of nuclei and is inversely related to the decay constant:*

large $k \Rightarrow$ short $t_{1/2}$ and small $k \Rightarrow$ long $t_{1/2}$

The decay constants and half-lives of radioactive nuclides vary over a very wide range, even for the nuclides of a given element (Table 24.5).

Table 24.5 Decay Constants (k) and Half-Lives ($t_{1/2}$) of Beryllium Isotopes

Nuclide	k	$t_{1/2}$
$^{7}_{4}Be$	1.30×10^{-2}/day	53.3 days
$^{8}_{4}Be$	1.0×10^{16}/s	6.7×10^{-17} s
$^{9}_{4}Be$	Stable	
$^{10}_{4}Be$	4.3×10^{-7}/yr	1.6×10^{6} yr
$^{11}_{4}Be$	5.02×10^{-2}/s	13.8 s

Sample Problem 24.4 Finding the Number of Radioactive Nuclei

Problem Strontium-90 is a radioactive byproduct of nuclear reactors that behaves biologically like calcium, the element above it in Group 2A(2). When ^{90}Sr is ingested by mammals, it is found in their milk and eventually in the bones of those drinking the milk. If a sample of ^{90}Sr has an activity of 1.2×10^{12} d/s, what are the activity and the fraction of nuclei that have decayed after 59 yr ($t_{1/2}$ of $^{90}Sr = 29$ yr)?

Plan The fraction of nuclei that have decayed is the change in number of nuclei, expressed as a fraction of the starting number. The activity of the sample ($\mathcal{A}$) is proportional to the number of nuclei ($\mathcal{N}$), so we know that

$$\text{Fraction decayed} = \frac{\mathcal{N}_0 - \mathcal{N}_t}{\mathcal{N}_0} = \frac{\mathcal{A}_0 - \mathcal{A}_t}{\mathcal{A}_0}$$

We are given $\mathcal{A}_0$ (1.2×10^{12} d/s), so we find $\mathcal{A}_t$ from the integrated form of the first-order rate equation (Equation 24.4), in which t is 59 yr. To solve that equation, we first need k, which we can calculate from the given $t_{1/2}$ (29 yr).

Solution Calculating the decay constant k:

$$t_{1/2} = \frac{\ln 2}{k} \quad \text{so} \quad k = \frac{\ln 2}{t_{1/2}} = \frac{0.693}{29 \text{ yr}} = 0.024 \text{ yr}^{-1}$$

Applying Equation 24.4 to calculate $\mathcal{A}_t$, the activity remaining at time t:

$$\ln \frac{\mathcal{N}_0}{\mathcal{N}_t} = \ln \frac{\mathcal{A}_0}{\mathcal{A}_t} = kt \quad \text{or} \quad \ln \mathcal{A}_0 - \ln \mathcal{A}_t = kt$$

So, $\quad \ln \mathcal{A}_t = -kt + \ln \mathcal{A}_0 = -(0.024 \text{ yr}^{-1} \times 59 \text{ yr}) + \ln (1.2 \times 10^{12} \text{ d/s})$
$\ln \mathcal{A}_t = -1.4 + 27.81 = 26.4$

$$\mathcal{A}_t = 2.9 \times 10^{11} \text{ d/s}$$

(All the data contain two significant figures, so we retained two in the answer.)
Calculating the fraction decayed:

$$\text{Fraction decayed} = \frac{\mathcal{A}_0 - \mathcal{A}_t}{\mathcal{A}_0} = \frac{1.2 \times 10^{12} \text{ d/s} - 2.9 \times 10^{11} \text{ d/s}}{1.2 \times 10^{12} \text{ d/s}} = \boxed{0.76}$$

Check The answer is reasonable: t is about 2 half-lives, so $\mathcal{A}_t$ should be about $\frac{1}{4}\mathcal{A}_0$, or about 0.3×10^{12}; therefore, the activity should have decreased by about $\frac{3}{4}$.

Comment 1. A useful substitution of Equation 24.4 for finding $\mathcal{A}_t$, the activity at time t, is $\mathcal{A}_t = \mathcal{A}_0 e^{-kt}$.

2. Another way to find the fraction of activity (or nuclei) remaining incorporates the number of half-lives ($t/t_{1/2}$). By combining Equations 24.4 and 24.5 and substituting $(\ln 2)/t_{1/2}$ for k, we obtain

$$\ln \frac{\mathcal{N}_0}{\mathcal{N}_t} = \left(\frac{\ln 2}{t_{1/2}}\right)t = \frac{t}{t_{1/2}}\ln 2 = \ln 2^{t/t_{1/2}}$$

Inverting the ratio gives

$$\ln \frac{\mathcal{N}_t}{\mathcal{N}_0} = \ln \left(\frac{1}{2}\right)^{t/t_{1/2}}$$

Taking the antilog gives

$$\text{Fraction remaining} = \frac{\mathcal{N}_t}{\mathcal{N}_0} = \left(\frac{1}{2}\right)^{t/t_{1/2}} = \left(\frac{1}{2}\right)^{59/29} = 0.24$$

So,

$$\text{Fraction decayed} = 1.00 - 0.24 = 0.76$$

Follow-Up Problem 24.4 Sodium-24 ($t_{1/2} = 15$ h) is used to study blood circulation. If a patient is injected with an aqueous solution of $^{24}\text{NaCl}$ whose activity is 2.5×10^9 d/s, how much of the activity is present in the patient's body and excreted fluids after 4.0 days?

Radioisotopic Dating

The historical record fades rapidly with time and virtually disappears for events of more than a few thousand years ago. Much knowledge of prehistory comes from **radioisotopic dating,** which uses **radioisotopes** to determine the ages of objects. This technique supplies data in fields such as art history, archeology, geology, and paleontology.

The technique of *radiocarbon dating,* for which the American chemist Willard F. Libby won the Nobel Prize in chemistry in 1960, is based on measuring the amounts of ^{14}C and ^{12}C in materials of biological origin. The accuracy of the method falls off after about six half-lives of ^{14}C ($t_{1/2} = 5730$ yr), so it is used to date objects up to about 36,000 years old.

Here is how radiocarbon dating works:

1. High-energy cosmic rays, consisting mainly of protons, enter the atmosphere from outer space and initiate a cascade of nuclear reactions, some of which produce neutrons that bombard ordinary ^{14}N atoms to form ^{14}C:

$$^{14}_{7}\text{N} + ^{1}_{0}\text{n} \longrightarrow ^{14}_{6}\text{C} + ^{1}_{1}\text{p}$$

Through the competing processes of formation and radioactive decay, the amount of ^{14}C in the atmosphere has remained nearly constant.*

2. The ^{14}C atoms combine with O_2, diffuse throughout the lower atmosphere, and enter the total carbon pool as gaseous $^{14}\text{CO}_2$ and aqueous $\text{H}^{14}\text{CO}_3^-$. They mix with ordinary $^{12}\text{CO}_2$ and $\text{H}^{12}\text{CO}_3^-$, reaching a constant $^{12}\text{C}/^{14}\text{C}$ ratio of about $10^{12}/1$.

3. The CO_2 is taken up by plants during photosynthesis, and then taken up and excreted by animals that eat the plants. Thus, the $^{12}\text{C}/^{14}\text{C}$ ratio of a living organism is the same as the ratio in the environment.

4. When an organism dies, it no longer absorbs or releases CO_2, so the $^{12}\text{C}/^{14}\text{C}$ ratio steadily increases because *the amount of ^{14}C decreases as it decays:*

$$^{14}_{6}\text{C} \longrightarrow ^{14}_{7}\text{N} + ^{0}_{-1}\beta$$

The difference between the $^{12}\text{C}/^{14}\text{C}$ ratio in a dead organism and the ratio in living organisms reflects the time elapsed since the organism died.

---

*Cosmic ray intensity does vary slightly with time, which affects the amount of atmospheric ^{14}C. From ^{14}C activity in ancient trees, we know the amount fell slightly about 3000 years ago to current levels. Recently, nuclear testing and fossil fuel combustion have also altered the fraction of ^{14}C slightly. Taking these factors into account improves the accuracy of the dating method.

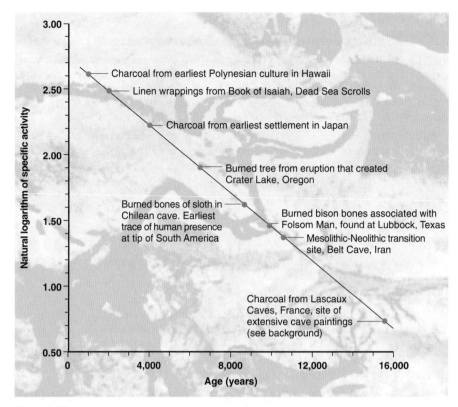

Figure 24.7 Ages of several objects determined by radiocarbon dating.

As you saw in Sample Problem 24.4, the first-order rate equation can be expressed in terms of a ratio of activities:

$$\ln \frac{\mathcal{N}_0}{\mathcal{N}_t} = \ln \frac{\mathcal{A}_0}{\mathcal{A}_t} = kt$$

We use this expression in radiocarbon dating, where $\mathcal{A}_0$ is the activity in a living organism and $\mathcal{A}_t$ is the activity in the object whose age is unknown. Solving for t gives the age of the object:

$$t = \frac{1}{k} \ln \frac{\mathcal{A}_0}{\mathcal{A}_t} \qquad (24.6)$$

A useful graphical method in radioisotopic dating shows a plot of the natural logarithm of the specific activity vs. time, which gives a straight line with a slope of $-k$, the negative of the decay constant. Using such a plot and measuring the ^{14}C specific activity of an object, we can determine its age; several examples appear in Figure 24.7.

One well-known example of the use of radiocarbon dating was in the determination of the age of the Shroud of Turin (*see photo*). One of the holiest Christian relics, the shroud is a piece of linen that bears a faint image of a man's body and was thought to be the burial cloth used to wrap the body of Jesus Christ. However, three labs in Europe and the United States independently measured the $^{12}C/^{14}C$ ratio of a 50-mg piece of the linen and determined that the flax from which the cloth was made was grown between 1260 A.D. and 1390 A.D.

To determine the ages of more ancient objects or of objects that do not contain carbon, different radioisotopes are measured. For example, comparing the ratio of ^{238}U ($t_{1/2} = 4.5\times10^9$ yr) to its final decay product, ^{206}Pb, in meteorites gives 4.7 billion years for the age of the Solar System, and therefore Earth. From this and other isotope ratios, such as $^{40}K/^{40}Ar$ ($t_{1/2}$ of $^{40}K = 1.3\times10^9$ yr) and $^{87}Rb/^{87}Sr$ ($t_{1/2}$ of $^{87}Rb = 4.9\times10^{10}$ yr), Moon rocks collected by Apollo astronauts have been dated at 4.2 billion years old.

The Shroud of Turin.

Sample Problem 24.5 Applying Radiocarbon Dating

Problem The charred bones of a sloth in a cave in Chile represent the earliest evidence of human presence at the southern tip of South America. A sample of the bone has a specific activity of 5.22 disintegrations per minute per gram of carbon (d/min·g). If the $^{12}C/^{14}C$ ratio for living organisms results in a specific activity of 15.3 d/min·g, how old are the bones ($t_{1/2}$ of ^{14}C = 5730 yr)?

Plan We calculate k from the given $t_{1/2}$ (5730 yr). Then we apply Equation 24.6 to find the age (t) of the bones, using the given activities of the bones ($\mathscr{A}_t$ = 5.22 d/min·g) and of a living organism ($\mathscr{A}_0$ = 15.3 d/min·g).

Solution Calculating k for ^{14}C decay:

$$k = \frac{\ln 2}{t_{1/2}} = \frac{0.693}{5730 \text{ yr}} = 1.21\times10^{-4} \text{ yr}^{-1}$$

Calculating the age (t) of the bones:

$$t = \frac{1}{k} \ln \frac{\mathscr{A}_0}{\mathscr{A}_t} = \frac{1}{1.21\times10^{-4} \text{ yr}^{-1}} \ln \left(\frac{15.3 \text{ d/min·g}}{5.22 \text{ d/min·g}} \right) = 8.89\times10^3 \text{ yr}$$

The bones are about 8900 years old.

Check The activity of the bones is between $\frac{1}{2}$ and $\frac{1}{4}$ the activity of a living organism, so the age should be between one and two half-lives (5730 to 11,460 yr).

Follow-Up Problem 24.5 A sample of wood from an Egyptian mummy case has a specific activity of 9.41 d/min·g. How old is the case?

Summary of Section 24.2

- Ionization and scintillation counters measure the number of emissions from a radioactive sample.
- The decay rate (activity) of a sample is proportional to the number of radioactive nuclei. Nuclear decay is a first-order process, so half-life is constant.
- Radioisotopic methods, such as ^{14}C dating, determine the age of an object by measuring the ratio of specific isotopes in it.

24.3 • NUCLEAR TRANSMUTATION: INDUCED CHANGES IN NUCLEI

The alchemists' dream of changing base metals into gold was never realized, but in the early 20th century, nuclear physicists *did* change one element into another. Research into **nuclear transmutation,** the *induced* conversion of the nucleus of one element into the nucleus of another, was closely linked to research into atomic structure and led to the discovery of the neutron and the production of artificial radioisotopes. Later, high-energy bombardment of nuclei in particle accelerators began the ongoing effort to create new nuclides and new elements, and, most recently, to understand fundamental questions of matter and energy.

Early Transmutation Experiments; Nuclear Shorthand Notation

The first recognized transmutation occurred in 1919, when Ernest Rutherford showed that α particles emitted from radium bombarded atmospheric nitrogen to form a proton and oxygen-17:

$$^{14}_{7}N + ^{4}_{2}\alpha \longrightarrow ^{1}_{1}p + ^{17}_{8}O$$

By 1926, experimenters had found that α bombardment transmuted most elements with low atomic numbers to the next higher element, with ejection of a proton.

A shorthand notation used specifically for nuclear transmutation reactions shows the reactant (target) nucleus to the left and the product nucleus to the right of a set of parentheses, within which a comma separates the projectile particle from the ejected particle(s):

> reactant nucleus (particle in, particle(s) out) product nucleus **(24.7)**

Using this notation, we write the previous reaction as $^{14}N\ (\alpha,p)\ ^{17}O$.

An unexpected finding in a transmutation experiment led to *the discovery of the neutron*. When lithium, beryllium, and boron were bombarded with α particles, they emitted highly penetrating radiation that could not be deflected by a magnetic or electric field. Unlike γ radiation, these emissions were massive enough to eject protons from the substances they penetrated. In 1932, James Chadwick, a student of Rutherford, proposed that the emissions consisted of neutral particles with a mass similar to that of a proton, which he named *neutrons*. He received the Nobel Prize in physics in 1935 for his discovery.

In 1933, Irene and Frederic Joliot-Curie (*see photo*), daughter and son-in-law of Marie and Pierre Curie, created the first artificial radioisotope, phosphorus-30. When they bombarded aluminum foil with α particles, phosphorus-30 and neutrons were formed:

$$^{27}_{13}Al + ^{4}_{2}\alpha \longrightarrow ^{1}_{0}n + ^{37}_{15}P \quad \text{or} \quad ^{27}Al(\alpha,n)\ ^{30}P$$

The Joliot-Curies in their laboratory.

Since then, other techniques for producing artificial radioisotopes have been developed. In fact, the majority of the nearly 1000 known radionuclides have been produced artificially.

Particle Accelerators and the Transuranium Elements

During the 1930s and 1940s, researchers probing the nucleus bombarded elements with neutrons, α particles, protons, and **deuterons** (nuclei of the stable hydrogen isotope deuterium, ^{2}H). Neutrons are especially useful as projectiles because they have no charge and thus are not repelled as they approach a target nucleus. The other particles are all positive, so early researchers found it difficult to give them enough energy to overcome their repulsion by the target nuclei. Beginning in the 1930s, however, **particle accelerators** were invented to impart high kinetic energies to particles by placing them in an electric field, usually in combination with a magnetic field. In the simplest and earliest design, protons are introduced at one end of a tube and attracted to the other end by a potential difference.

Linear Accelerator A major advance was the *linear accelerator*, a series of separated tubes of increasing length that, through a source of alternating voltage, change their charge from positive to negative in synchrony with the movement of the particle through them (Figure 24.8).

A proton, for example, exits the first tube just when that tube becomes positive and the next tube negative. Repelled by the first tube and attracted by the second, the proton accelerates across the gap between them. The process is performed in stages to achieve high particle energies without having to apply a single high voltage. A 40-ft linear accelerator with 46 tubes, built in California after World War II, accelerated protons to speeds several million times faster than earlier accelerators.

Figure 24.8 Schematic diagram of a linear accelerator.

Figure 24.9 Schematic diagram of a cyclotron.

A small section of the Large Hadron Collider.

Other Early Particle Accelerators The *cyclotron* (Figure 24.9), invented by E. O. Lawrence in 1930, applies the principle of the linear accelerator but uses electromagnets to give the particle a spiral path to save space. The magnets lie within an evacuated chamber above and below two "dees," open, D-shaped electrodes that act like the tubes in the linear design. The particle is accelerated as it passes from one dee, which is momentarily positive, to the other, which is momentarily negative. Its speed and path radius increase until it is deflected toward the target nucleus.

The *synchrotron* uses a synchronously increasing magnetic field to make the particle's path circular rather than spiral.

Powerful Modern Accelerators Some very powerful accelerators used to study the physics of high-energy particle collisions include both a linear section and a synchrotron section. The *tevatron* at the Fermi Lab near Chicago has a circumference of 3.9 miles and can accelerate particles to an energy slightly less than 1×10^{12} electron volts (1 TeV) before colliding them together.

The world's most powerful accelerator is the Large Hadron Collider (LHC) near Geneva, Switzerland (*photo*). The first successful collision of protons in the LHC was achieved in early 2010. When operating at peak capacity, the LHC will accelerate protons to an energy of 7 TeV as they travel around the main ring at a speed of 11,000 revolutions per second, attaining a final speed about 99.99% of the speed of light before colliding with other protons. Physicists are eager to study the results of these high-energy subatomic collisions for information on the nature of matter and the early universe.

Synthesis of Transuranium Elements Scientists use accelerators for many applications, from producing radioisotopes used in medical applications to studying the fundamental nature of matter. Perhaps the most specific application for chemists is the synthesis of **transuranium elements,** those with atomic numbers higher than uranium, the heaviest naturally occurring element. Some reactions that were used to form several of these elements appear in Table 24.6. The transuranium elements include the remaining actinides ($Z = 93$ to 103), in which the $5f$ sublevel is filled, and the elements in the fourth transition series ($Z = 104$ to 112), in which the $6d$ sublevel is filled, and the remaining elements in the $7p$ sublevel ($Z = 113$ to 118).

Conflicting claims of discovery by scientists in the United States and the former Soviet Union led to controversies about names for some of the more recently synthesized elements. To provide interim names until the disputes could be settled, the International Union of Pure and Applied Chemistry (IUPAC) adopted a system that

Table 24.6 Formation of Some Transuranium Nuclides*

Reaction					Half-life of Product
$^{239}_{94}\text{Pu}$	$+\ 2^1_0\text{n}$	$\longrightarrow$	$^{241}_{95}\text{Am}$	$+\ ^{\ 0}_{-1}\beta$	432 yr
$^{239}_{94}\text{Pu}$	$+\ ^4_2\alpha$	$\longrightarrow$	$^{242}_{96}\text{Cm}$	$+\ ^1_0\text{n}$	163 days
$^{241}_{95}\text{Am}$	$+\ ^4_2\alpha$	$\longrightarrow$	$^{243}_{97}\text{Bk}$	$+\ 2^1_0\text{n}$	4.5 h
$^{242}_{96}\text{Cm}$	$+\ ^4_2\alpha$	$\longrightarrow$	$^{245}_{98}\text{Cf}$	$+\ ^1_0\text{n}$	45 min
$^{253}_{99}\text{Es}$	$+\ ^4_2\alpha$	$\longrightarrow$	$^{256}_{101}\text{Md}$	$+\ ^1_0\text{n}$	76 min
$^{243}_{95}\text{Am}$	$+\ ^{18}_{8}\text{O}$	$\longrightarrow$	$^{256}_{103}\text{Lr}$	$+\ 5^1_0\text{n}$	28 s

*Like chemical reactions, nuclear reactions may occur in several steps. For example, the first reaction here is actually an overall process that occurs in three steps:
(1) $^{239}_{94}\text{Pu} + ^1_0\text{n} \longrightarrow ^{240}_{94}\text{Pu}$ (2) $^{240}_{94}\text{Pu} + ^1_0\text{n} \longrightarrow ^{241}_{94}\text{Pu}$ (3) $^{241}_{94}\text{Pu} \longrightarrow ^{241}_{95}\text{Am} + ^{\ 0}_{-1}\beta$

uses the atomic number as the basis for a Latin name. Thus, for example, element 104 was named unnilquadium (un = 1, nil = 0, quad = 4, ium = metal suffix), with the symbol Unq. After much compromise, IUPAC has finalized these names: 104, rutherfordium (Rf); 105, dubnium (Db); 106, seaborgium (Sg); 107, bohrium (Bh); 108, hassium (Hs); 109, meitnerium (Mt); 110, darmstadtium (Ds); 111, roentgenium (Rg); and 112, copernicium (Cn). Elements with atomic numbers 113 and higher have not yet been named.

■ Summary of Section 24.3

- One nucleus can be transmuted to another through bombardment with high-energy particles.
- Accelerators increase the kinetic energy of particles in nuclear bombardment experiments and are used to produce transuranium elements and radioisotopes for medical use.

24.4 • EFFECTS OF NUCLEAR RADIATION ON MATTER

In 1986, an accident at the Chernobyl nuclear facility in the former Soviet Union released radioactivity that, according to the World Health Organization, will cause thousands of cancer deaths. In the same year, isotopes used in medical treatment emitted radioactivity that prevented thousands of cancer deaths. In this section and Section 24.5, we examine radioactivity's harmful and beneficial effects.

The key to both of these effects is that *nuclear changes cause chemical changes in surrounding matter.* In other words, even though the nucleus of an atom may undergo a reaction with little or no involvement of the atom's electrons, the emissions from that reaction *do* affect the electrons of nearby atoms.

Virtually all radioactivity causes **ionization** in surrounding matter, as the emissions collide with atoms and dislodge electrons:

$$\text{Atom} \xrightarrow{\text{ionizing radiation}} \text{ion}^+ + \text{e}^-$$

From each ionization event, a cation and a free electron result, and the number of such *cation-electron pairs* produced is directly related to the energy of the incoming **ionizing radiation.**

Many applications of ionizing radiation depend not only on the ionizing event itself, but also on secondary processes. For example, in a Geiger-Müller counter, the free electron of the cation-electron pair often collides with another atom, which ejects a second electron, and in a scintillation counter, the initial ionization eventually results in the emission of light. In nuclear power plants (Section 24.7), the initial process as well as several secondary processes cause the release of heat that makes steam to create electricity.

Effects of Ionizing Radiation on Living Tissue

Ionizing radiation has a destructive effect on living tissue, and if the ionized atom is part of a key biological macromolecule or cell membrane, the results can be devastating to the cell and perhaps the organism.

The danger from a radionuclide depends on three factors: the type of radiation, its half-life, and, most importantly, its biological behavior. For example, both ^{235}U and ^{239}Pu emit α particles and have long half-lives, but uranium is rapidly excreted by the body, whereas plutonium behaves like calcium and, thus, is incorporated into bones and teeth. One of the most dangerous radionuclides is ^{90}Sr^{2+} (formed during a nuclear explosion) because it behaves very similarly to Ca^{2+} and is absorbed rapidly by bones. Let's first see how to measure radiation dose and then look in more detail at the damaging power of ionizing radiation.

Units of Radiation Dose and Its Effects To measure the effects of ionizing radiation, we need a unit for radiation dose. Units of radioactive decay, such as the becquerel and curie, measure the number of decay events in a given time but not their energy or absorption by matter. However, the number of cation-electron pairs produced in a given amount of living tissue *is* a measure of the energy absorbed by the tissue. The SI unit for such energy absorption is the **gray (Gy)**; it is equal to 1 joule of energy absorbed per kilogram of body tissue: 1 Gy = 1 J/kg. A more widely used unit is the **rad (radiation-absorbed dose),** which is one-hundredth as much:

$$1 \text{ rad} = 0.01 \text{ J/kg} = 0.01 \text{ Gy}$$

To measure actual tissue damage, we must account for differences in the strength of the radiation, the exposure time, and the type of tissue. To do this, we multiply the number of rads by a *relative biological effectiveness* (RBE) factor, which depends on the effect a given type of radiation has on a given tissue or body part. The product is the **rem (roentgen equivalent for man),** the unit of radiation dosage equivalent to a given amount of tissue damage in a human:

$$\text{no. of rems} = \text{no. of rads} \times \text{RBE}$$

Doses are often expressed in millirems (10^{-3} rem). The SI unit for dosage equivalent is the **sievert (Sv).** It is defined in the same way as the rem but with absorbed dose in grays; thus, 1 rem = 0.01 Sv.

Penetrating Power of Emissions The effect on living tissue of a radiation dose depends on the penetrating power *and* ionizing ability of the radiation. Since water is the main component of living tissue, penetrating power is often measured in terms of the depth of water that stops 50% of incoming radiation. In Figure 24.10, the average values of the penetrating distances are shown in actual size for the three common types of emissions. Note, in general, that *penetrating power is inversely related to the mass, charge, and energy of the emission.* In other words, if a particle interacts strongly with matter, it penetrates only slightly, and vice versa:

1. *Alpha particles.* Alpha particles are massive and highly charged, which means that they interact with matter most strongly of the three common emissions. As a result, they penetrate so little that a piece of paper, light clothing, or the outer layer of skin can stop α radiation from an external source. However, if ingested, an α emitter can cause grave localized internal damage through extensive ionization. For example, in the early 20th century, wristwatch and clock dials were painted by hand with paint containing radium so they would glow in the dark. To write numbers clearly, the women who applied the paint "tipped" fine brushes repeatedly between their lips. Small amounts of ingested $^{226}\text{Ra}^{2+}$ were incorporated into their bones along with normal Ca^{2+}, which led to numerous cases of bone fracture and jaw cancer.

2. *Beta particles and positrons.* Beta particles (β⁻) and positrons (β⁺) have less charge and much less mass than α particles, so they interact less strongly with matter. Even though a given particle has less chance of causing ionization, a β⁻ (or β⁺) emitter is a more destructive external source because the particles penetrate deeper. Specialized heavy clothing or a thick (0.5 cm) piece of metal is required to stop these particles. The relative danger from α and β⁻ emissions is shown by the poisoning of two former Russian intelligence agents. In 1957, an agent was poisoned by thallium-204, a β⁻ emitter, but he survived because β⁻ particles do relatively little radiation damage. In contrast, in 2006, another agent was poisoned with polonium-210, an α emitter, and died in three weeks because of the much greater radiation damage.

3. *Gamma rays.* Neutral, massless γ rays interact least with matter and, thus, penetrate most. A block of lead several inches thick is needed to stop them. Therefore, an external γ ray source is the most dangerous because the energy can ionize many layers of living tissue.

The extent of interaction with matter is variable for emitted *neutrons,* which are neutral and massive. Outside a nucleus, neutrons decay with a half-life of 10.6 min into a proton and an electron (and an antineutrino). With energies ranging from very low to very high, they may be scattered or captured by interaction with nuclei.

α (~0.03 mm)

β (~2 mm)

γ (~10 cm)

Figure 24.10 Penetrating power of radioactive emissions.

Molecular Interactions How does the damage take place on the molecular level? When ionizing radiation interacts with molecules, it causes the *loss of an electron from a bond or a lone pair.* The resulting charged species go on to form **free radicals,** molecular or atomic species with one or more unpaired electrons, which, as you know, are very reactive (Section 10.1, p. 370). They form electron pairs by attacking bonds in other molecules, often forming more free radicals.

When γ radiation strikes living tissue, for instance, the most likely molecule to absorb it is water, yielding an electron and a water ion-radical:

$$H_2O + \gamma \longrightarrow H_2O\bullet^+ + e^-$$

The products collide with other water molecules to form more free radicals:

$$H_2O\bullet^+ + H_2O \longrightarrow H_3O^+ + \bullet OH \quad \text{and} \quad e^- + H_2O \longrightarrow H\bullet + OH^-$$

These free radicals attack more H_2O and surrounding biomolecules, whose bonding and structure are intimately connected with their function (Section 15.6).

The double bonds in membrane lipids are highly susceptible to free-radical attack:

$$H\bullet + RCH{=}CHR' \longrightarrow RCH_2{-}\overset{\bullet}{C}HR'$$

In this reaction, one electron of the π bond forms a C—H bond between one of the double-bonded carbons and the H•, and the other electron resides on the other carbon to form a free radical. Changes to lipid structure cause damage that results in leakage through cell membranes and destruction of the protective fatty tissue around organs. Changes to critical bonds in enzymes lead to their malfunction as catalysts of metabolic reactions. Changes in the nucleic acids and proteins that govern the rate of cell division can cause cancer. Genetic damage and mutations may occur when bonds in the DNA of sperm and egg cells are altered by free radicals.

Sources of Ionizing Radiation

We are continuously exposed to ionizing radiation from natural and artificial sources (Table 24.7, *next page*). Indeed, life evolved in the presence of natural ionizing radiation, called **background radiation.** The same radiation that alters bonds in DNA and causes harmful mutations also causes beneficial ones that allow species to evolve.

Background radiation has several natural sources:

- *Cosmic radiation* increases with altitude because of decreased absorption by the atmosphere. Thus, people in Denver absorb twice as much cosmic radiation as people in Los Angeles; even a jet flight involves measurable absorption.
- Thorium and uranium minerals are present in rocks and soil. Radon, the heaviest noble gas [Group 8A(18)], is a radioactive product of uranium and thorium decay. Its concentration in the air we breathe is related to the presence of trace minerals in building materials and to the uranium content of local soil and rocks (Figure 24.11). Once it enters the body, radon poses a serious potential hazard as it decays to radioactive nuclides of Po, Pb, and Bi, through α, β^-, and γ emissions. The emissions damage lung tissue, and the heavy-metal atoms formed aggravate the problem. Recent EPA estimates indicate that radon contributes to 15% of annual lung cancer deaths.
- About 150 g of K^+ ions is dissolved in the water in the tissues of an average adult, and 0.0118% of these ions are radioactive ^{40}K. The presence of these substances and of atmospheric $^{14}CO_2$ makes *all* food (including bananas and Brazil nuts; see beginning of chapter), water, clothing, and building materials slightly radioactive.

The largest artificial source of radiation, and the one that is easiest to control, is from medical diagnostic techniques, especially x-rays. The radiation dosage from nuclear testing and radioactive waste disposal is miniscule for most people, but exposures for those living near test sites or disposal areas may be much higher.

Assessing the Risk from Ionizing Radiation

How much radiation is too much? To answer this question, we must ask several others: How strong is the exposure? How long is the exposure? Which tissue is exposed? Are children affected? One reason we lack clear data to answer

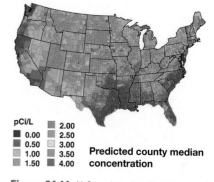

pCi/L
- 0.00
- 0.50
- 1.00
- 1.50
- 2.00
- 2.50
- 3.00
- 3.50
- 4.00

Predicted county median concentration

Figure 24.11 U.S. radon distribution.

Table 24.7 Typical Radiation Doses from Natural and Artificial Sources

Source of Radiation	Average Adult Exposure
Natural	
Cosmic radiation	30–50 mrem/yr
Radiation from the ground	
From clay soil and rocks	~25–170 mrem/yr
In wooden houses	10–20 mrem/yr
In brick houses	60–70 mrem/yr
In concrete (cinder block) houses	60–160 mrem/yr
Radiation from the air (mainly radon)	
Outdoors, average value	20 mrem/yr
In wooden houses	70 mrem/yr
In brick houses	130 mrem/yr
In concrete (cinder block) houses	260 mrem/yr
Internal radiation from minerals in tap water and daily intake of food (^{40}K, ^{14}C, Ra)	~40 mrem/yr
Artificial	
Diagnostic x-ray methods	0.04–0.2 rad/film
Lung (local)	1.5–3 rad/film
Kidney (local)	≤1 rad/film
Dental (dose to the skin)	Locally ≤ 10,000 rad
Therapeutic radiation treatment	
Other sources	
Jet flight (4 h)	~1 mrem
Nuclear testing	<4 mrem/yr
Nuclear power industry	<1 mrem/yr
Total average value	100–200 mrem/yr

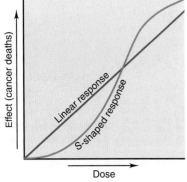

Figure 24.12 Two models of radiation risk.

these questions is that scientific ethical standards forbid the intentional exposure of humans in an experimental setting. However, accidentally exposed radiation workers and Japanese atomic bomb survivors have been studied extensively. Table 24.8 summarizes the immediate effects on humans of an acute single dose of ionizing radiation to the whole body. The severity of the effects increases with dose; a dose of 500 rem will kill about 50% of the exposed population within a month.

Most data come from laboratory animals, whose biological systems may differ greatly from ours. Nevertheless, studies with mice and dogs show that lesions and cancers appear after massive whole-body exposure, with rapidly dividing cells affected first. In an adult animal, these are cells of the bone marrow, organ linings, and reproductive organs, but many other tissues are affected in an immature animal or fetus. Studies in both animals and humans show an increase in the incidence of cancer from either a high, single exposure or a low, chronic exposure.

Two current models of radiation risk are shown in Figure 24.12:

- The *linear response model* proposes that radiation effects, such as cancer risks, accumulate over time regardless of dose and that populations should not be exposed to any radiation above background levels.
- The *S-shaped response model* implies there is a threshhold above which the effects are more significant: very low risk at low dose and high risk at high dose.

Reliable data on genetic effects of radiation are few. Studies on fruit flies show a linear increase in genetic defects with both dose and exposure time. However, in the mouse, whose genetic system is obviously much more similar to ours than is the fruit fly's, a total dose given over a long period created one-third as many genetic defects as the same dose given over a short period. Therefore, rate of exposure is a

Table 24.8 Acute Effects of a Single Dose of Whole-Body Irradiation			
Dose (rem)	Effect	Lethal Dose	
		Population (%)	No. of Days
5–20	Possible late effect; possible chromosomal aberrations	—	—
20–100	Temporary reduction in white blood cells	—	—
50+	Temporary sterility in men (100+ rem = 1-yr duration)	—	—
100–200	"Mild radiation sickness": vomiting, diarrhea, tiredness in a few hours Reduction in infection resistance Possible bone growth retardation in children	—	—
300+	Permanent sterility in women	—	—
500	"Serious radiation sickness": marrow/intestine destruction	50–70	30
400–1000	Acute illness, early deaths	60–95	30
3000+	Acute illness, death in hours to days	100	2

key factor. The children of atomic bomb survivors show higher-than-normal childhood cancer rates, implying that their parents' reproductive systems were affected.

Summary of Section 24.4

- All radioactive emissions cause ionization.
- The effect of ionizing radiation on living matter depends on the quantity of energy absorbed and the extent of ionization in a given type of tissue. Radiation dose for the human body is measured in rem.
- Ionization forms free radicals, some of which proliferate and destroy biomolecular function.
- All organisms are exposed to varying quantities of natural ionizing radiation.
- Studies show that either a large acute dose or a chronic small dose is harmful.

24.5 • APPLICATIONS OF RADIOISOTOPES

Radioisotopes are powerful tools for studying processes in biochemistry, medicine, materials science, environmental studies, and many other scientific and industrial fields. Such uses depend on the fact that *isotopes of an element exhibit **very similar chemical and physical behavior.** In other words, except for having a less stable nucleus, a radioisotope has nearly the same properties as a nonradioactive isotope of that element.* For example, the fact that $^{14}CO_2$ is utilized by a plant in the same way as $^{12}CO_2$ forms the basis of radiocarbon dating.

Radioactive Tracers

Just think how useful it could be to follow a substance through a complex process or from one region of a system to another. A tiny amount of a radioisotope mixed with

---

*Although this statement is generally correct, differences in isotopic mass *can* influence bond strengths and therefore reaction rates. Such behavior is called a *kinetic isotope effect* and is particularly important for isotopes of hydrogen—^1H, ^2H, and ^3H—because their masses differ by such large proportions. Section 22.4 discussed how the kinetic isotope effect is employed in the industrial production of heavy water, D_2O.

a large amount of the stable isotope can act as a **tracer,** a chemical "beacon" emitting radiation that signals the presence of the substance.

Reaction Pathways Tracers are used to identify simple and complex reaction pathways.

1. *Inorganic systems*: *the periodate-iodide reaction.* One well-studied example is the reaction between periodate and iodide ions:

$$IO_4^-(aq) + 2I^-(aq) + H_2O(l) \longrightarrow I_2(s) + IO_3^-(aq) + 2OH^-(aq)$$

Is IO_3^- the result of IO_4^- reduction or I^- oxidation? When we add "cold" (nonradioactive) IO_4^- to a solution of I^- that contains some "hot" (radioactive, indicated in red) $^{131}I^-$, we find that the I_2 is radioactive, not the IO_3^-:

$$IO_4^-(aq) + 2\,{}^{131}I^-(aq) + H_2O(l) \longrightarrow {}^{131}I_2(s) + IO_3^-(aq) + 2OH^-(aq)$$

These results show that IO_3^- forms through the reduction of IO_4^-, and that I_2 forms through the oxidation of I^-. To confirm this pathway, we add IO_4^- containing some $^{131}IO_4^-$ to a solution of I^-. As we expected, the IO_3^- is radioactive, not the I_2:

$$^{131}IO_4^-(aq) + 2I^-(aq) + H_2O(l) \longrightarrow I_2(s) + {}^{131}IO_3^-(aq) + 2OH^-(aq)$$

Thus, tracers act like "handles" we can "hold" to follow the changing reactants.

2. *Biochemical pathways: photosynthesis.* Far more complex pathways can be followed with tracers as well. The photosynthetic pathway, the most essential and widespread metabolic process on Earth, in which energy from sunlight is used to form the chemical bonds of glucose, has an overall reaction that looks quite simple:

$$6CO_2(g) + 6H_2O(l) \xrightarrow[\text{chlorophyll}]{\text{light}} C_6H_{12}O_6(s) + 6O_2(g)$$

However, the actual process is extremely complex: 13 enzyme-catalyzed steps are required to incorporate each C atom from CO_2, so the six CO_2 molecules incorporated to form a molecule of $C_6H_{12}O_6$ require six repetitions of the pathway. Melvin Calvin and his coworkers took seven years to determine the pathway, using ^{14}C in CO_2 as the tracer and chromatography as the means of separating the products formed after different times of light exposure. Calvin won the Nobel Prize in chemistry in 1961 for this remarkable achievement.

Physiological Studies Tracers are used in many studies of physiological function. Some recent studies examine challenges of living in outer space. In an animal study of red blood cell loss during extended space flight, blood plasma volume was measured with ^{125}I-labeled albumin (a blood protein), and red blood cells labeled with ^{51}Cr as a trace substitute for Fe were used to assess survival of blood cells. In another study, blood flow in skin under long periods of microgravity was monitored using injected ^{133}Xe.

Material Flow Tracers are used in studies of solid surfaces and the flow of materials. Metal atoms hundreds of layers deep within a solid have been shown to exchange with metal ions from the surrounding solution within a matter of minutes. Chemists and engineers use tracers to study material movement in semiconductor chips, paint, and metal plating, in detergent action, and in the process of corrosion, to mention just a few of many applications.

Hydrologic engineers use tracers to study the volume and flow of large bodies of water. By following radionuclides that formed during atmospheric nuclear bomb tests (^3H in H_2O, $^{90}Sr^{2+}$, and $^{137}Cs^+$), scientists have mapped the flow of water from land to lakes and streams to oceans. They also use tracers to study the surface and deep ocean currents that circulate around the globe, the mechanisms of hurricane formation, and the mixing of the troposphere and stratosphere. Industries employ tracers to study material flow during manufacturing processes, such as the flow of ore pellets in smelting kilns, the paths of wood chips and bleach in paper mills, the diffusion of fungicide into lumber, and in a particularly important application, the porosity and leakage of oil and gas wells in geological formations.

Activation Analysis Another use of tracers is in *neutron activation analysis* (NAA). In this method, neutrons bombard a nonradioactive sample, converting a small fraction of its atoms to radioisotopes, which exhibit characteristic decay patterns, such as γ-ray spectra, that reveal the elements present. Unlike chemical analysis, NAA leaves the sample virtually intact, so the method can be used to determine the composition of a valuable object or a very small sample. For example, a painting thought to be a 16th-century Dutch masterpiece was shown through NAA to be a 20th-century forgery, because a microgram-sized sample of its pigment contained much less silver and antimony than the pigments used by the Dutch masters. Forensic chemists use NAA to detect traces of ammunition on a suspect's hand or traces of arsenic in the hair of a victim of poisoning.

Automotive engineers employ NAA and γ-ray detectors to measure friction and wear of moving parts without having to take the engine apart. For example, when a steel surface that has been neutron-activated to form some radioactive ^{59}Fe moves against a second steel surface, the amount of radioactivity on the second surface indicates the amount of material rubbing off. The radioactivity appearing in a lubricant placed between the surfaces can demonstrate the lubricant's ability to reduce wear.

Medical Diagnosis The largest use of radioisotopes is in medical science. In fact, over 25% of U.S. hospital admissions are for diagnoses based on data from radioisotopes. Tracers with half-lives of a few minutes to a few days are employed to observe specific organs and body parts. For example, a healthy thyroid gland incorporates dietary I^- into iodine-containing hormones at a known rate. To assess thyroid function, the patient drinks a solution containing a trace amount of $Na^{131}I$; the thyroid gland absorbs $^{131}I^-$ ions, which undergo β^- decay, and the emissions produce an image of the gland (Figure 24.13A). Technetium-99 ($Z = 43$) is also used for imaging the thyroid (Figure 24.13B), as well as the heart, lungs, and liver. Technetium does not occur naturally, so the radioisotope (actually a metastable form, ^{99m}Tc) is prepared from radioactive molybdenum just before use:

$$^{99}_{42}\text{Mo} \longrightarrow ^{99m}_{43}\text{Tc} + ^{0}_{-1}\beta$$

Tracers are also used to measure physiological processes, such as blood flow. The rate at which the heart pumps blood, for example, can be observed by injecting ^{59}Fe, which becomes incorporated into the hemoglobin of blood cells. Several radioisotopes used in medical diagnosis are listed in Table 24.9.

Positron-emission tomography (PET) is a powerful imaging method for observing brain structure and function. A biological substance is synthesized with one of its atoms replaced by an isotope that emits positrons. The substance is injected into a patient's bloodstream, from which it is taken up into the brain. The isotope emits positrons, each of which annihilates a nearby electron. In this process, two γ photons are emitted simultaneously 180° from each other:

$$^{0}_{1}\beta + ^{0}_{-1}e \longrightarrow 2^{0}_{0}\gamma$$

Table **24.9** Some Radioisotopes Used as Medical Tracers	
Isotope	**Body Part or Process**
^{11}C, ^{18}F, ^{13}N, ^{15}O	PET studies of brain, heart
^{60}Co, ^{192}Ir	Cancer therapy
^{64}Cu	Metabolism of copper
^{59}Fe	Blood flow, spleen
^{67}Ga	Tumor imaging
^{123}I, ^{131}I	Thyroid
^{111}In	Brain, colon
^{42}K	Blood flow
^{81m}Kr	Lung
^{99m}Tc	Heart, thyroid, liver, lung, bone
^{201}Tl	Heart muscle
^{90}Y	Cancer, arthritis

A   **B**

Figure 24.13 The use of radioisotopes to image the thyroid gland. **A,** This ^{131}I scan shows an asymmetric image that is indicative of disease. **B,** A ^{99}Tc scan of a healthy thyroid.

Figure 24.14 PET and brain activity.
These PET scans show brain activity in a normal person (*left*) and in a patient with Alzheimer's disease (*right*). Red and yellow indicate relatively high activity within a region.

An array of detectors around the patient's head pinpoints the sites of γ emission, and the image is analyzed by computer. Two of the isotopes used are ^{15}O, injected as $H_2^{15}O$ to measure blood flow, and ^{18}F bonded to a glucose analog to measure glucose uptake, which is an indicator of energy metabolism. Among many fascinating PET findings are those that show how changes in blood flow and glucose uptake accompany normal or abnormal brain activity (Figure 24.14). Also, substances incorporating ^{11}C and ^{15}O are being investigated using PET to learn how molecules interact with and move along the surface of a catalyst.

Additional Applications of Ionizing Radiation

Many other uses of radioisotopes involve higher-energy ionizing radiation.

- *Radiation therapy.* Cancer cells divide more rapidly than normal cells, so radioisotopes that interfere with cell division kill more cancer cells than normal ones. Implants of ^{198}Au or of ^{90}Sr, which decays to the γ-emitting ^{90}Y, have been used to destroy pituitary and breast tumor cells, and γ rays from ^{60}Co have been used to destroy tumors of the brain and other body parts.

- *Destruction of microbes.* Irradiation of food increases shelf life by killing microorganisms that cause rotting or spoilage (Figure 24.15), but the practice is controversial. Advocates point to the benefits of preserving fresh foods, grains, and seeds for long periods, whereas opponents suggest that irradiation might lower the food's nutritional content or produce harmful byproducts. Irradiation also provides a way to destroy newer, more resistant bacterial strains that survive the increasing use of the more common antibiotics in animal feed. The United Nations has approved irradiation for potatoes, wheat, chicken, and strawberries, and, in 2003, the U.S. Food and Drug Administration approved it as well.

Nonirradiated   Irradiated

Figure 24.15 The increased shelf life of irradiated food.

- *Insect control.* Ionizing radiation has been used to control harmful insects. Captured males are sterilized by radiation and released to mate, thereby reducing the number of offspring. This method has been used to control the Mediterranean fruit fly in California and disease-causing insects, such as the tsetse fly and malarial mosquito, in other parts of the world.

- *Power for spacecraft instruments.* A nonharmful use of ionizing radiation relies on its secondary processes. Most spacecraft use solar energy to provide power for instruments. In deep-space missions, when solar energy is too weak, however, a radioisotope heater unit (RHU) has been used. It consists of a $^{238}PuO_2$ fuel pellet the size of a pencil eraser that is clad within a multilayered graphite and metal shell a little smaller than a flashlight battery. The whole RHU weighs only 40 g.

▌ Summary of Section 24.5

- Radioisotopic tracers have been used to study reaction mechanisms, material flow, elemental composition, and medical conditions.
- Ionizing radiation has been used in devices that destroy cancer tissue, kill organisms that spoil food, control insect populations, and power spacecraft instruments.

24.6 • THE INTERCONVERSION OF MASS AND ENERGY

Most of the nuclear processes we've considered so far have involved radioactive decay, in which a nucleus emits one or a few small particles or photons to become a more stable, slightly lighter nucleus. Two other nuclear processes cause much greater mass changes. In nuclear **fission,** a heavy nucleus splits into two much lighter nuclei, emitting several small particles at the same time. In nuclear **fusion,** the opposite process occurs: two lighter nuclei combine to form a heavier one. Both fission and fusion release enormous quantities of energy. Let's take a look at the origins of this energy by first examining the change in mass that accompanies the breakup of a nucleus into its nucleons and then considering the energy that is equivalent to this mass change.

The Mass Difference Between a Nucleus and Its Nucleons

For most of the 20th century, we have known that mass and energy are interconvertible. The separate mass and energy conservation laws are combined to state that *the total quantity of mass-energy in the universe is constant.* Therefore, when *any* reacting system releases or absorbs energy, it also loses or gains mass.

Mass Difference and Chemical Reactions The interconversion of mass and energy is not important for chemical reactions because the energy changes involved in breaking or forming chemical bonds are so small that the mass changes are negligible. For example, when 1 mol of water breaks up into its atoms, heat is absorbed and we have:

$$H_2O(g) \longrightarrow 2H(g) + O(g) \qquad \Delta H^{\circ}_{rxn} = 2 \times \text{BE of O—H} = 934 \text{ kJ}$$

We find the mass that is equivalent to this energy from *Einstein's equation:*

$$E = mc^2 \quad \text{or} \quad \Delta E = \Delta mc^2 \quad \text{so} \quad \Delta m = \frac{\Delta E}{c^2} \qquad (24.8)$$

where Δm is the mass difference between reactants and products:

$$\Delta m = m_{products} - m_{reactants}$$

Substituting the enthalpy of reaction (in J/mol) for ΔE and the numerical value for c (2.9979$\times$10^8 m/s), we obtain

$$\Delta m = \frac{9.34 \times 10^5 \text{ J/mol}}{(2.9979 \times 10^8 \text{ m/s})^2} = 1.04 \times 10^{-11} \text{ kg/mol} = 1.04 \times 10^{-8} \text{ g/mol}$$

(Units of kg/mol are obtained because the joule includes the kilogram: 1 J = 1 kg·m^2/s^2.) The mass of 1 mol of H$_2$O molecules (reactant) is about 10 ng *less* than the combined masses of 2 mol of H atoms and 1 mol of O atoms (products), a change difficult to measure with even the most sophisticated balance. Such minute mass changes when bonds break or form allow us to assume that, for all practical purposes, mass is conserved in *chemical* reactions.

Mass Difference and Nuclear Reactions The much larger mass change that accompanies a *nuclear* process is related to the enormous energy required to bind the nucleus together from its parts. In an analogy with the calculation above involving the water molecule, consider the change in mass that occurs when one ^{12}C nucleus breaks apart into its nucleons—six protons and six neutrons:

$$^{12}\text{C} \longrightarrow 6^1_1\text{p} + 6^1_0\text{n}$$

We calculate this mass difference in a special way. By combining the mass of six H *atoms* and six neutrons and then subtracting the mass of one ^{12}C *atom,* the masses of the electrons cancel: six e$^-$ (in six ^{1}H atoms) cancel six e$^-$ (in one ^{12}C atom). The mass of one ^{1}H atom is 1.007825 amu, and the mass of one neutron is 1.008665 amu, so

$$\text{Mass of six } ^1\text{H atoms} = 6 \times 1.007825 \text{ amu} = 6.046950 \text{ amu}$$
$$\underline{\text{Mass of six neutrons} = 6 \times 1.008665 \text{ amu} = 6.051990 \text{ amu}}$$
$$\text{Total mass} = 12.098940 \text{ amu}$$

The mass of the reactant, one ^{12}C atom, is 12 amu (exactly). The mass difference (Δm) we obtain is the total mass of the nucleons minus the mass of the nucleus:

$$\Delta m = 12.098940 \text{ amu} - 12.000000 \text{ amu}$$
$$= 0.098940 \text{ amu}/^{12}\text{C} = 0.098940 \text{ g/mol} \; ^{12}\text{C}$$

Two key points emerge from these calculations:

- *The mass of the nucleus is **less** than the combined masses of its nucleons:* there is *always* a mass decrease when nucleons form a nucleus.
- The mass change of this nuclear process (9.89×10^{-2} g/mol) is nearly 10 million times that of the chemical process (10.4×10^{-9} g/mol) we saw earlier and *can* be observed on any laboratory balance.

Nuclear Binding Energy and the Binding Energy per Nucleon

Einstein's equation for the relation between mass and energy allows us to find the energy equivalent of any mass change. For 1 mol of ^{12}C, after converting grams to kilograms, we have

$$\Delta E = \Delta mc^2 = (9.8940 \times 10^{-5} \text{ kg/mol})(2.9979 \times 10^8 \text{ m/s})^2$$
$$= 8.8921 \times 10^{12} \text{ J/mol} = 8.8921 \times 10^9 \text{ kJ/mol}$$

This quantity of energy is called the **nuclear binding energy** for carbon-12, and the positive value means *energy is absorbed.* This is the energy required to break 1 mol of ^{12}C atoms into neutrons and hydrogen atoms. Thus, the *nuclear binding energy* is the energy to *break 1 mol of nuclei into individual nucleons:*

$$\text{Nucleus} + \text{nuclear binding energy} \longrightarrow \text{nucleons}$$

Thus, the nuclear binding energy is qualitatively analogous to the sum of bond energies of a covalent compound or the lattice energy of an ionic compound. But, quantitatively, nuclear binding energies are typically several million times greater.

The Electron Volt as the Unit of Binding Energy We use joules to express the binding energy per mole of nuclei, but the joule is much too large a unit to express the binding energy of a single nucleus. Instead, nuclear scientists use the **electron volt (eV)**, the energy an electron acquires when it moves through a potential difference of 1 volt:

$$1 \text{ eV} = 1.602 \times 10^{-19} \text{ J}$$

Binding energies are commonly expressed in millions of electron volts, that is, in *mega–electron volts* (MeV):

$$1 \text{ MeV} = 10^6 \text{ eV} = 1.602 \times 10^{-13} \text{ J}$$

A particularly useful factor converts the atomic mass unit to its energy equivalent in electron volts:

$$1 \text{ amu} = 931.5 \times 10^6 \text{ eV} = 931.5 \text{ MeV} \qquad \text{(24.9)}$$

Earlier we found the mass change when ^{12}C breaks apart into its nucleons to be 0.098940 amu. The binding energy per ^{12}C nucleus, expressed in MeV, is

$$\frac{\text{Binding energy}}{^{12}\text{C nucleus}} = 0.098940 \text{ amu} \times \frac{931.5 \text{ MeV}}{1 \text{ amu}} = 92.16 \text{ MeV}$$

We can compare the stability of nuclides of different elements by determining the *binding energy per nucleon.* For ^{12}C, we have

$$\text{Binding energy per nucleon} = \frac{\text{binding energy}}{\text{no. of nucleons}} = \frac{92.16 \text{ MeV}}{12 \text{ nucleons}} = 7.680 \text{ MeV/nucleon}$$

Sample Problem 24.6 | Calculating the Binding Energy per Nucleon

Problem Iron-56 is an extremely stable nuclide. Compute the binding energy per nucleon for ^{56}Fe and compare it with that for ^{12}C (mass of ^{56}Fe atom = 55.934939 amu; mass of ^{1}H atom = 1.007825 amu; mass of neutron = 1.008665 amu).

Plan Iron-56 has 26 protons and 30 neutrons. We calculate the mass difference, Δm, when the nucleus forms by subtracting the given mass of one ^{56}Fe atom from the sum of the masses of 26 ^{1}H atoms and 30 neutrons. To find the binding energy per nucleon, we multiply Δm by the equivalent in MeV (931.5 MeV/amu) and divide by the number of nucleons (56).

Solution Calculating the mass difference, Δm:

$$\text{Mass difference} = \big[(26 \times \text{mass }^1\text{H atom}) + (30 \times \text{mass neutron})\big] - \text{mass }^{56}\text{Fe atom}$$

$$= \big[(26)(1.007825 \text{ amu}) + (30)(1.008665 \text{ amu})\big] - 55.934939 \text{ amu}$$

$$= 0.52846 \text{ amu}$$

Calculating the binding energy per nucleon:

$$\text{Binding energy per nucleon} = \frac{0.52846 \text{ amu} \times 931.5 \text{ MeV/amu}}{56 \text{ nucleons}} = \boxed{8.790 \text{ MeV/nucleon}}$$

An ^{56}Fe nucleus would require more energy per nucleon to break up into its nucleons than would ^{12}C (7.680 MeV/nucleon), so ^{56}Fe is more stable than ^{12}C.

Check The answer is consistent with the great stability of ^{56}Fe. Given the number of decimal places in the values, rounding to check the math is useful only to find a *major* error. The number of nucleons (56) is an exact number, so we retain four significant figures.

Follow-Up Problem 24.6 Uranium-235 is an essential component of the fuel in nuclear power plants. Calculate the binding energy per nucleon for ^{235}U. Is this nuclide more or less stable than ^{12}C (mass of ^{235}U atom = 235.043924 amu)?

Fission or Fusion: Means of Increasing the Binding Energy per Nucleon

Calculations similar to those in Sample Problem 24.6 for other nuclides show that the binding energy per nucleon varies considerably. The essential point is that *the greater the binding energy per nucleon, the more stable the nuclide is.*

Figure 24.16 shows a plot of the binding energy per nucleon vs. mass number. It provides information about nuclide stability and the two possible processes nuclides can undergo to form more stable nuclides. Most nuclides with fewer than 10 nucleons have a relatively small binding energy per nucleon. The ^{4}He nucleus is an exception—it is stable enough to be emitted intact as an α particle. Above $A = 12$, the binding energy per nucleon varies from about 7.6 to 8.8 MeV.

The most important observation is that *the binding energy per nucleon peaks at elements with $A \approx 60$.* In other words, nuclides become more stable with increasing mass number up to around 60 nucleons and then become less stable with higher numbers of nucleons. The existence of a peak of stability suggests that there are two ways nuclides can increase their binding energy per nucleon:

Figure 24.16 The variation in binding energy per nucleon.

- *Fission.* A heavier nucleus can *split into lighter ones (closer to A ≈ 60)* by undergoing fission. The product nuclei have greater binding energy per nucleon (are more stable) than the reactant nucleus, and the difference in *energy is released.* Nuclear power plants generate energy through fission, as do atomic bombs (Section 24.7).
- *Fusion.* Lighter nuclei, on the other hand, can *combine to form a heavier one (closer to A ≈ 60)* by undergoing fusion. Once again, the product is more stable than the reactants, and *energy is released.* The Sun and other stars generate energy through fusion, as do thermonuclear (hydrogen) bombs. In these examples and in all current research efforts for developing fusion as a useful energy source, hydrogen nuclei fuse to form the very stable helium-4 nucleus.

In Section 24.7, we examine fission and fusion and their applications.

▌ Summary of Section 24.6

- The mass of a nucleus is less than the sum of the masses of its nucleons. The energy equivalent to this mass difference is the nuclear binding energy, often expressed in units of MeV.
- The binding energy per nucleon is a measure of nuclide stability and varies with the number of nucleons. Nuclides with $A ≈ 60$ are most stable.
- Lighter nuclides join (fusion) or heavier nuclides split (fission) to create more stable products.

24.7 • APPLICATIONS OF FISSION AND FUSION

Of the many beneficial applications of nuclear reactions, the greatest is the potential for abundant quantities of energy, which is based on the multimillion-fold increase in energy yield of nuclear reactions over chemical reactions. Our experience with nuclear energy from power plants in the late 20th century, however, has shown that we must improve ways to tap this energy source safely and economically and deal with the waste generated. In this section, we discuss how fission and fusion occur and how we are applying them.

The Process of Nuclear Fission

During the mid-1930s, Enrico Fermi and coworkers bombarded uranium ($Z = 92$) with neutrons in an attempt to synthesize transuranium elements. Many of the unstable nuclides produced were tentatively identified as having $Z > 92$, but other scientists were skeptical. Four years later, the German chemist Otto Hahn and his associate F. Strassmann showed that one of these unstable nuclides was an isotope of barium ($Z = 56$). The Austrian physicist Lise Meitner, a coworker of Hahn, and her nephew Otto Frisch proposed that barium resulted from the *splitting* of the uranium nucleus into *smaller* nuclei, a process that they called *fission* as an analogy to cell division in biology. Element 109 was named *meitnerium* in honor of this extraordinary physicist who proposed the correct explanation of nuclear fission and discovered the element protactinium (Pa; $Z = 91$) as well as numerous radioisotopes.

   The ^{235}U nucleus can split in many different ways, giving rise to various daughter nuclei, but all routes have the same general features. Figure 24.17 depicts one of these fission patterns. Neutron bombardment results in a highly excited ^{236}U nucleus, which splits apart in 10^{-14} s. The products are two nuclei of unequal mass, two to four neutrons (average of 2.4), and a large quantity of energy. A single ^{235}U nucleus releases 3.5×10^{-11} J when it splits; 1 mol of ^{235}U (about $\frac{1}{2}$ lb) releases 2.1×10^{13} J— a billion times as much energy as burning $\frac{1}{2}$ lb of coal (about 2×10^4 J)!

Chain Reaction and Critical Mass We harness the energy of nuclear fission, much of which eventually appears as heat, by means of a **chain reaction** (Figure 24.18): the few neutrons that are released by the fission of one nucleus collide with other fissionable nuclei and cause them to split, releasing more neutrons, and so on,

Figure 24.17 Fission of ^{235}U caused by neutron bombardment.

in a self-sustaining process (with each step shown as a vertical dashed line). In this manner, the energy released increases rapidly because each fission event in a chain reaction releases about two-and-a-half times as much energy as the preceding one.

Whether a chain reaction occurs depends on the mass (and thus the volume) of the fissionable sample. If the piece of uranium is large enough, the product neutrons strike another fissionable nucleus *before* flying out of the sample, and a chain reaction takes place. The mass required to achieve a chain reaction is called the **critical mass.** If the sample has less than the critical mass (a *subcritical mass*), too many product neutrons leave the sample before they collide with and cause the fission of another ^{235}U nucleus, and thus a chain reaction does not occur.

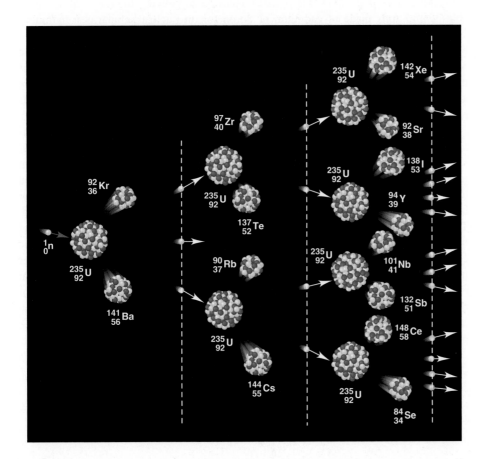

Figure 24.18 A chain reaction involving fission of ^{235}U.

Figure 24.19 An atomic bomb based on ^{235}U.

Uncontrolled Fission: The Atomic Bomb An uncontrolled chain reaction can be adapted to make an extremely powerful explosive, as several of the world's leading atomic physicists hypothesized just prior to World War II. In August 1939, Albert Einstein wrote the president of the United States, Franklin Delano Roosevelt, to this effect, warning of the danger of allowing the Nazi government to develop this power first. It was this concern that led to the Manhattan Project, an enormous scientific effort to develop a bomb based on nuclear fission, which was initiated in 1941.* In August 1945, the United States detonated two atomic bombs over Japan, and the horrible destructive power of these bombs was a major factor in the surrender of the Japanese a few days later.

In an atomic bomb, small explosions of trinitrotoluene (TNT) bring subcritical masses of fissionable material together to exceed the critical mass, and the ensuing chain reaction brings about the explosion (Figure 24.19). The proliferation of nuclear power plants, which use fissionable materials to generate energy for electricity, has increased concern that more countries (and unscrupulous individuals) may have access to such material for making bombs. Since the devastating terrorist attacks of September 11, 2001 in the United States, this concern has been heightened.

Controlled Fission: Nuclear Energy Reactors Like a coal-fired power plant, *a nuclear power plant generates heat to produce steam, which turns a turbine attached to an electric generator.* But a nuclear plant has the potential to produce electric power much more cleanly than by the combustion of coal.

1. *Operation of a nuclear power plant.* Heat generation takes place in the **reactor core** of a nuclear plant (Figure 24.20). The core contains the *fuel rods,* which consist of fuel enclosed in tubes of a corrosion-resistant zirconium alloy. The fuel is uranium(IV) oxide (UO_2) that has been *enriched* from 0.7% ^{235}U, the natural abundance of this fissionable isotope, to the 3% to 4% ^{235}U required to sustain a chain reaction in a practical volume. (Enrichment of nuclear fuel is the most important application of Graham's law, see p. 210.) Sandwiched between the fuel rods are movable *control rods* made of cadmium or boron (or, in nuclear submarines, hafnium), substances that absorb neutrons very efficiently. When the control rods are lowered between the fuel rods, the chain reaction slows because fewer neutrons are available to bombard uranium atoms; when they are raised, the chain reaction speeds up. Neutrons that leave the fuel-rod assembly collide with a *reflector,* usually made of a beryllium alloy, which absorbs very few neutrons. Reflecting the neutrons back to the fuel rods speeds the chain reaction.

Flowing around the fuel and control rods in the reactor core is the *moderator,* a substance that slows the neutrons, making them much better at causing fission than the fast ones emerging directly from the fission event. In most modern reactors, the moderator also acts as the *coolant,* the fluid that transfers the released heat to the steam-producing region. *Light-water reactors* use H_2O as the moderator because ^{1}H absorbs neutrons to some extent; in heavy-water reactors, D_2O is used. The advantage of D_2O is that it absorbs very few neutrons, leaving more available for fission, so heavy-water reactors can use uranium that has been *less enriched.* As the coolant flows around the encased fuel, pumps circulate it through coils that transfer its heat to the water reservoir. Steam formed in the reservoir turns the turbine that runs the generator. The steam then enters a condenser, where water from a lake or river is used to cool it back to liquid that is returned to the water reservoir. Often (although not shown here), large cooling towers aid in this step (see Figure 13.20, p. 493).

---

*For an excellent scientific and historical account of the development of the atomic bomb, see R. Rhodes, *The Making of the Atomic Bomb,* New York, Simon and Schuster, 1986.

Figure 24.20 A light-water nuclear reactor.

2. *Breeder reactors.* Because ^{235}U is not an abundant isotope, the *breeder reactor* was designed to consume one type of nuclear fuel as it produces another. Outside the moderator, fuel rods are surrounded by natural U_3O_8, which contains 99.3% *nonfissionable* ^{238}U atoms. As neutrons formed during ^{235}U fission escape the fuel rod, they collide with ^{238}U, transmuting it into ^{239}Pu, another fissionable nucleus:

$$^{238}_{92}U + ^{1}_{0}n \longrightarrow ^{239}_{92}U \qquad (t_{1/2} \text{ of } ^{239}_{92}U = 23.5 \text{ min})$$

$$^{239}_{92}U \longrightarrow ^{239}_{93}Np + ^{0}_{-1}\beta \qquad (t_{1/2} \text{ of } ^{239}_{93}Np = 2.35 \text{ days})$$

$$^{239}_{93}Np \longrightarrow ^{239}_{94}Pu + ^{0}_{-1}\beta \qquad (t_{1/2} \text{ of } ^{239}_{94}Pu = 2.4 \times 10^4 \text{ yr})$$

Although breeder reactors can make fuel as they operate, they are difficult and expensive to build, and ^{239}Pu is extremely toxic and long lived. Breeder reactors are not used in the United States, although several are operating in Europe and Japan.

3. *Power plant accidents and other concerns.* Some major accidents at nuclear plants have caused decidedly negative public reactions. In 1979, malfunctions of coolant pumps and valves at the Three-Mile Island facility in Pennsylvania led to melting of some of the fuel and damage to the reactor core, but the release of only a very small amount (about 1 Ci) of radioactive gases into the atmosphere. In 1986, a million times as much radioactivity (1 MCi) was released when a cooling system failure at the Chernobyl plant in Ukraine caused a much greater melting of fuel and an uncontrolled reaction. High-pressure steam and ignited graphite moderator rods caused the reactor building to explode and expel radioactive debris. Carried by prevailing winds, the radioactive particles contaminated vegetables and milk in much of Europe. And, as we said earlier, health officials have evidence that thousands of people living near the accident have already developed or may eventually develop cancer from radiation exposure. The design of the Chernobyl plant was particularly unsafe because, unlike reactors in the United States and western Europe, the reactor was not contained in a massive, concrete building.*

4. *Current use of nuclear power.* Despite potential safety problems, nuclear power remains an important source of electricity. In the late 1990s, nearly every European country employed nuclear power, and it is the major power source in some countries—Sweden creates 50% of its electricity this way and France almost 80%. Currently, the United States obtains about 20% of its electricity from nuclear power, and Canada slightly less. As our need for energy grows and climate change from fossil-fuel consumption worsens, safer reactors are being designed and are likely to be built.

5. *Thermal pollution and waste disposal.* However, even a smoothly operating plant has certain inherent problems. The problem of *thermal pollution* is common to all power plants. Water used to condense the steam is several degrees warmer when returned to its source, which can harm aquatic organisms (Section 13.4). A more serious problem is *nuclear waste disposal.* Many of the fission products formed in nuclear reactors have long half-lives, and no satisfactory plan for their permanent disposal has yet been devised. Proposals to place the waste in containers and bury them in deep bedrock cannot possibly be field-tested for the thousands of years the material will remain harmful. Leakage of radioactive material into groundwater is a danger, and earthquakes can occur even in geologically stable regions. It remains to be seen whether we can operate fission reactors *and* dispose of the waste safely and economically.

The Promise of Nuclear Fusion

Nuclear fusion in the Sun is the ultimate source of nearly all the energy—and chemical elements—on Earth. In fact, *all the elements heavier than hydrogen were formed in fusion and decay processes within stars,* as the next Chemical Connections essay describes.

Much research is being devoted to making nuclear fusion a practical, direct source of energy on Earth. To understand the advantages of fusion, let's consider one of the most discussed fusion reactions, in which deuterium and tritium react:

$$\,^2_1H + \,^3_1H \longrightarrow \,^4_2He + \,^1_0n$$

This reaction produces 1.7×10^9 kJ/mol, an enormous quantity of energy with no radioactive byproducts. Moreover, the reactant nuclei are relatively easy to come by.

---

*An even greater release of radioactivity (1.1 MCi), involving several radionuclides including the extremely dangerous ^{90}Sr, occurred in 1957 in Kyshtym, a town in the South Ural Mountains of Russia. As a result, radioactivity spread globally, but the accident was kept secret by the former Soviet government until 1980.

Vacuum container
for plasma   Plasma   Magnets

Figure 24.21 The tokamak design for magnetic containment of a fusion plasma.

We obtain deuterium from the electrolysis of water (Section 22.4). In nature, tritium forms through the cosmic (neutron) irradiation of ^{14}N:

$$^{14}_{7}N + ^{1}_{0}n \longrightarrow ^{3}_{1}H + ^{12}_{6}C$$

However, this process results in a natural abundance of only $10^{-7}\%$ ^{3}H. More practically, tritium is produced in nuclear accelerators by bombarding lithium-6 or by surrounding the fusion reactor itself with material containing lithium-6:

$$^{6}_{3}Li + ^{1}_{0}n \longrightarrow ^{3}_{1}H + ^{4}_{2}He$$

Thus, in principle, fusion *seems* promising and may represent an ideal source of power. However, some extremely difficult technical problems remain. Fusion requires enormous energy in the form of heat to give the positively charged nuclei enough kinetic energy to force themselves together. The fusion of deuterium and tritium, for example, occurs at practical rates at about 10^{8} K, a temperature hotter than the Sun's core! How can such conditions be achieved? Two current research approaches have promise. In one, atoms are stripped of their electrons at high temperatures, which results in a gaseous *plasma,* a neutral mixture of positive nuclei and electrons. Because of the extreme temperatures needed for fusion, no *material* can contain the plasma. The most successful approach to date has been to enclose the plasma within a magnetic field. The *tokamak* design has a donut-shaped container in which a helical magnetic field confines the plasma and prevents it from contacting the walls (Figure 24.21). Scientists at the Princeton University Plasma Physics facility have achieved some success in generating energy from fusion this way. In another approach, the high temperature is reached by using many focused lasers to compress and heat the fusion reactants. In any event, one or more major breakthroughs are needed before fusion will be a practical, everyday source of energy.

▌ Summary of Section 24.7

- In nuclear fission, neutron bombardment causes a nucleus to split into two smaller nuclei and release neutrons that split other nuclei, giving rise to a chain reaction.
- A nuclear power plant controls the rate of the chain reaction to produce heat that creates steam, which is used to generate electricity.
- Potential hazards, such as radiation leaks, thermal pollution, and disposal of nuclear waste, remain current concerns.
- Nuclear fusion holds great promise as a source of clean abundant energy, but it requires extremely high temperatures and is not yet practical.
- The elements were formed through a complex series of nuclear reactions in evolving stars.

How did the universe begin? Where did matter come from? How were the elements formed? The most accepted model proposes that a sphere of unimaginable properties—diameter of 10^{-28} cm, density of 10^{96} g/mL (density of a nucleus ≈ 10^{14} g/mL), and temperature of 10^{32} K—exploded in a "Big Bang," for reasons not yet known, and distributed its contents through the void of space. Cosmologists consider this moment the beginning of time.

One second later, the universe was an expanding mixture of neutrons, protons, and electrons, denser than rock and hotter than an exploding hydrogen bomb (about 10^{10} K). In the next few minutes, it became a gigantic fusion reactor creating the first atomic nuclei other than ^1H: ^2H, ^3He, and ^4He. After 10 min, more than 25% of the mass of the universe existed as ^4He, and only about 0.025% as ^2H. About 100 million years later, or about 15 billion years ago, gravitational forces pulled this cosmic mixture into primitive, contracting stars.

This account of the origin of the universe is based on the observation of spectra from the Sun, other stars, nearby galaxies, and cosmic (interstellar) dust. Spectral analysis of planets and chemical analysis of Earth and Moon rocks, meteorites, and cosmic-ray particles furnish data about isotope abundance. From these, a model has been developed for **stellar nucleosynthesis**, the creation of the elements in stars. The overall process occurs in several stages during a star's evolution, and the entire sequence of steps occurs only in very massive stars, having 10

to 100 times the mass of the Sun. Each step involves a contraction of the volume of the star that results in higher temperature and yields heavier nuclei. Such events are forming elements in stars today. The key stages in the process are shown in Figure B24.1 and described below:

1. *Hydrogen burning produces He.* The initial contraction of a star heats its core to about 10^7 K, at which point a fusion process called *hydrogen burning* begins. Through three possible reactions (one is shown below), helium nuclei are produced from the abundant protons:

$$4{}^1_1H \longrightarrow {}^4_2He + 2{}^0_1\beta + 2\nu + energy$$

2. *Helium burning produces C, O, Ne, and Mg.* After several billion years of hydrogen burning, about 10% of the ^1H is consumed, and the star contracts further. The ^4He forms a dense core, hot enough (2×10^8 K) to fuse ^4He nuclei. The energy released during *helium burning* expands the remaining ^1H into a vast envelope: the star becomes a *red giant,* more than 100 times its original diameter. Within its core, pairs of ^4He nuclei (α particles) fuse into unstable ^8Be nuclei ($t_{1/2} = 7\times10^{-17}$ s), which play the role of an activated complex in chemical reactions. A ^8Be nucleus collides with another ^4He to form ^{12}C. Then, further fusion with ^4He creates nuclei up to ^{24}Mg:

$$^{12}C \xrightarrow{\alpha} {}^{16}O \xrightarrow{\alpha} {}^{20}Ne \xrightarrow{\alpha} {}^{24}Mg$$

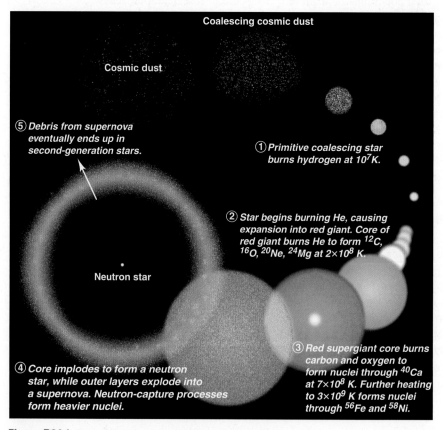

Figure B24.1 Element synthesis in the life cycle of a star.

3. *Elements through Fe and Ni form.* For another 10 million years, ^{4}He is consumed, and the heavier nuclei created form a core. This core contracts and heats, expanding the star into a *supergiant.* Within the hot core (7×10^8 K), *carbon and oxygen burning* occur:

$$^{12}C + {}^{12}C \longrightarrow {}^{23}Na + {}^{1}H$$
$$^{12}C + {}^{16}O \longrightarrow {}^{28}Si + \gamma$$

Absorption of α particles forms nuclei up to ^{40}Ca:

$$^{12}C \xrightarrow{\alpha} {}^{16}O \xrightarrow{\alpha} {}^{20}Ne \xrightarrow{\alpha} {}^{24}Mg \xrightarrow{\alpha}$$
$$^{28}Si \xrightarrow{\alpha} {}^{32}S \xrightarrow{\alpha} {}^{36}Ar \xrightarrow{\alpha} {}^{40}Ca$$

Further contraction and heating to a temperature of 3×10^9 K allow reactions in which nuclei release neutrons, protons, and α particles and then recapture them. As a result, nuclei with lower binding energies supply nucleons to create those with higher binding energies. In stars of moderate mass, less than 10 times the mass of the Sun, this process stops at iron-56 and nickel-58, the nuclei with the highest binding energies.

4. *Heavier elements form.* In very massive stars, the next stage is the most spectacular. With all the fuel consumed, the core collapses within a second. Many Fe and Ni nuclei break down into neutrons and protons. Protons capture electrons to form neutrons, and the entire core forms an incredibly dense *neutron star.* (An Earth-sized star that became a neutron star would fit in the Houston Astrodome!) As the core implodes, the outer layers explode in a *supernova,* which expels material throughout space. A supernova occurs an average of every few hundred years in each galaxy or once every second somewhere in the universe. The heavier elements are formed during supernova events and are found in

second-generation stars, those that coalesce from interstellar ^{1}H and ^{4}He and the debris of exploded first-generation stars.

Heavier elements form through *neutron-capture* processes. In the *s-process* (*slow* neutron-capture process), a nucleus captures a neutron, sometime over a period of 10 to 1000 years. If the resulting nucleus is unstable, it undergoes β^- decay to form the next element, as in this conversion of ^{68}Zn to ^{70}Ge:

$$^{68}Zn \xrightarrow{n} {}^{69}Zn \xrightarrow{\beta^-} {}^{69}Ga \xrightarrow{n} {}^{70}Ga \xrightarrow{\beta^-} {}^{70}Ge$$

The stable isotopes of most heavy elements up to ^{209}Bi form by the s-process.

Less stable isotopes and those with A greater than 230 cannot form by the s-process because their half-lives are too short. These form by the *r-process* (*rapid* neutron-capture process) during the fury of the supernova. Many neutron captures, followed by many β^- decays, occur in a second, as when ^{56}Fe is converted to ^{79}Br:

$$^{56}_{26}Fe + 23{}^{1}_{0}n \longrightarrow {}^{79}_{26}Fe \longrightarrow {}^{79}_{35}Br + 9{}^{0}_{-1}\beta$$

We know from the heavy elements present in the Sun that it is at least a second-generation star presently undergoing hydrogen burning. Together with its planets, it was formed from the dust of exploded stars about 4.6×10^9 years ago. This means that many of the atoms on Earth, including some within you, came from exploded stars and are older than the Solar System itself!

Any theory of element formation must be consistent with the element abundances we observe (Section 22.1). Although local compositions, such as those of Earth and the Sun, differ, and mineral grains in meteorites may have abnormal isotopic compositions, large regions of the universe have, on average, similar compositions. Scientists believe element forming reaches a dynamic equilibrium, resulting in *relatively constant amounts of the isotopes.*

Problems

B24.1 Compare the *s*- and *r*-processes in stellar nucleosynthesis in terms of rate, number of neutrons absorbed, and types of isotopes formed.

B24.2 The overall reaction taking place during hydrogen burning in a young star is

$$4{}^{1}_{1}H \longrightarrow {}^{4}_{2}He + 2{}^{0}_{1}\beta + 2\nu + energy$$

How much energy (in MeV) is released per He nucleus formed? Per mole of He formed? (Masses of atoms: $^{1}_{1}H$ atom = 1.007825 amu; $^{4}_{2}$He atom = 4.00260 amu; mass of positron = 5.48580×10^{-4} amu.)

B24.3 Cosmologists modeling the origin of the elements postulate nuclides with very short half-lives. One of these short-lived nuclides, ^{8}Be ($t_{1/2} = 7 \times 10^{-17}$ s), is thought to

play a key role in stellar nucleosynthesis by fusing with ^{4}He to form ^{12}C. Another model proposes the simultaneous fusion of three ^{4}He nuclei to form ^{12}C. Comment on the validity of this alternative mechanism.

B24.4 The *s*-process produces isotopes of elements up to ^{209}Bi. This process is terminated when ^{209}Bi captures a neutron to produce ^{210}Bi, which subsequently undergoes β^- decay to produce nuclide A, which then decays by emitting an α particle to form nuclide B. This nuclide captures three neutrons to produce nuclide C, which undergoes β^- decay to produce nuclide D, starting the cycle again. Write balanced nuclear equations for the formation of nuclides A through D.

CHAPTER REVIEW GUIDE

Learning Objectives   Relevant section (§) and/or sample problem (SP) numbers appear in parentheses.

Understand These Concepts

1. How nuclear changes differ, in general, from chemical changes (Introduction)
2. The meanings of *radioactivity, nucleon, nuclide,* and *isotope* (§24.1)
3. Characteristics of three types of radioactive emissions: α, β, and γ (§24.1)
4. The various modes of radioactive decay and how each changes the values of A and Z (§24.1)
5. How the N/Z ratio, the even-odd nature of N and Z, and magic numbers correlate with nuclear stability (§24.1)
6. How an unstable nuclide's mass number or N/Z ratio correlates with its mode of decay (§24.1)
7. How a decay series combines numerous decay steps and ends with a stable nuclide (§24.1)
8. How ionization and scintillation counters detect and measure radioactivity (§24.2)
9. Why radioactive decay is a first-order process; the meanings of *decay rate* and *specific activity* (§24.2)
10. The meaning of *half-life* in the context of radioactive decay (§24.2)
11. How the specific activity of an isotope in an object is used to determine the object's age (§24.2)
12. How particle accelerators and reactors are used to synthesize new nuclides (§24.3)
13. The units of radiation dose; the effects on living tissue of various dosage levels; the inverse relationship between the mass and charge of an emission and its penetrating power (§24.4)
14. How ionizing radiation creates free radicals that damage tissue; sources and risks of ionizing radiation (§24.4)
15. How radioisotopes are used in research, analysis, and medical diagnosis (§24.5)

16. Why the mass of a nucleus is less than the total mass of its nucleons and how this mass difference is related to the nuclear binding energy (§24.6)
17. How nuclear stability is related to binding energy per nucleon (§24.6)
18. How heavy nuclides undergo fission and lighter ones undergo fusion to increase the binding energy per nucleon (§24.6)
19. The current application of fission and potential application of fusion to produce energy (§24.7)

Master These Skills

1. Expressing the mass and charge of a particle with the $_{Z}^{A}X$ notation (§24.1; see also §2.5)
2. Using changes in the values of A and Z to write and balance nuclear equations (SP 24.1)
3. Using the N/Z ratio, the even-odd nature of N and Z, and the presence of magic numbers to predict nuclear stability (SP 24.2)
4. Using the atomic mass of the element or the N/Z ratio to predict the mode of decay of an unstable nuclide (SP 24.3)
5. Converting units of radioactivity (§24.2)
6. Calculating specific activity, decay constant, half-life, and number of nuclei (§24.2 and SP 24.4)
7. Estimating the age of an object from the specific activity and half-life of carbon-14 (SP 24.5)
8. Writing notations and balancing equations for nuclear transmutation (§24.3)
9. Calculating radiation dose and converting units (§24.4)
10. Calculating the mass difference between a nucleus and its nucleons and the energy equivalent (§24.6)
11. Calculating the binding energy per nucleon and using it to compare stabilities of nuclides (SP 24.6)

Key Terms   Page numbers appear in parentheses.

radioactivity (977)

Section 24.1
nucleon (978)
nuclide (978)
isotope (978)
alpha (α) particle (979)
beta (β) particle (979)
gamma (γ) ray (979)
alpha (α) decay (981)
beta (β) decay (981)
β⁻ decay (981)
positron (β⁺) emission (981)
positron (981)
electron (e⁻) capture (EC) (981)
gamma (γ) emission (982)

band of stability (983)
strong force (984)
decay (disintegration) series (986)

Section 24.2
Geiger-Müller counter (987)
scintillation counter (987)
activity ($\mathscr{A}$) (988)
becquerel (Bq) (988)
curie (Ci) (988)
decay constant (988)
half-life ($t_{1/2}$) (988)
radioisotopic dating (990)
radioisotope (990)

Section 24.3
nuclear transmutation (992)

deuteron (993)
particle accelerator (993)
transuranium element (994)

Section 24.4
ionization (995)
ionizing radiation (995)
gray (Gy) (996)
rad (*radiation-absorbed dose*) (996)
rem (*roentgen equivalent for man*) (996)
sievert (Sv) (996)
free radical (997)
background radiation (997)

Section 24.5
tracer (1000)

Section 24.6
fission (1003)
fusion (1003)
nuclear binding energy (1004)
electron volt (eV) (1004)

Section 24.7
chain reaction (1006)
critical mass (1007)
reactor core (1008)
stellar nucleosynthesis (1012)

Key Equations and Relationships   Page numbers appear in parentheses.

24.1 Balancing a nuclear equation (979):

$$\text{Total } _{\text{Total } Z}^{A}\text{Reactants} = \text{Total } _{\text{Total } Z}^{A}\text{Products}$$

24.2 Defining the unit of radioactivity (curie, Ci) (988):

$$1 \text{ Ci} = 3.70 \times 10^{10} \text{ disintegrations per second (d/s)}$$

24.3 Expressing the decay rate (activity) for radioactive nuclei (988):

$$\text{Decay rate } (\mathcal{A}) = -\frac{\Delta \mathcal{N}}{\Delta t} = k\mathcal{N}$$

24.4 Finding the number of nuclei remaining after a given time, $\mathcal{N}_t$ (988):

$$\ln \frac{\mathcal{N}_t}{\mathcal{N}_0} = -kt \quad \text{or} \quad \mathcal{N}_t = \mathcal{N}_0 e^{-kt}$$

24.5 Finding the half-life of a radioactive nuclide (989):

$$t_{1/2} = \frac{\ln 2}{k}$$

24.6 Calculating the time to reach a given specific activity (age of an object in radioisotopic dating) (991):

$$t = \frac{1}{k} \ln \frac{\mathcal{A}_0}{\mathcal{A}_t}$$

24.7 Writing a transmutation in shorthand notation (993):

reactant nucleus (particle in, particle(s) out) product nucleus

24.8 Adapting Einstein's equation to calculate mass difference and/or nuclear binding energy (1003):

$$\Delta m = \frac{\Delta E}{c^2} \quad \text{or} \quad \Delta E = \Delta mc^2$$

24.9 Relating the atomic mass unit to its energy equivalent in MeV (1004):

$$1 \text{ amu} = 931.5 \times 10^6 \text{ eV} = 931.5 \text{ MeV}$$

Brief Solutions to Follow-Up Problems

24.1 $^{133}_{54}\text{Xe} \longrightarrow ^{133}_{55}\text{Cs} + _{-1}^{0}\beta$

24.2 ^{31}P has an even N (16), but ^{30}P has both N and Z odd. ^{31}P also has a slightly higher N/Z ratio that is closer to the band of stability.

24.3 (a) $Z = 26$ is iron (Fe), and the atomic mass is 55.85. The A value of 61 is higher: β^- decay; (b) $Z > 83$, which is too high for stability: α decay

24.4 $\ln \mathcal{A}_t = -kt + \ln \mathcal{A}_0$

$$= -\left(\frac{\ln 2}{15 \text{ h}} \times 4.0 \text{ days} \times \frac{24 \text{ h}}{1 \text{ day}}\right) + \ln (2.5 \times 10^9)$$

$$= 17.20$$

$$\mathcal{A} = 3.0 \times 10^7 \text{ d/s}$$

24.5 $t = \frac{1}{k} \ln \frac{\mathcal{A}_0}{\mathcal{A}_t} = \frac{5730 \text{ yr}}{\ln 2} \ln \left(\frac{15.3 \text{ d/min·g}}{9.41 \text{ d/min·g}}\right)$

$$= 4.02 \times 10^3 \text{ yr}$$

The mummy case is about 4000 years old.

24.6 ^{235}U has 92 $_{1}^{1}\text{p}$ and 143 $_{0}^{1}\text{n}$.

$\Delta m = [(92 \times 1.007825 \text{ amu}) + (143 \times 1.008665 \text{ amu})]$

$$- 235.043924 \text{ amu}$$

$$= 1.9151 \text{ amu}$$

$$\frac{\text{Binding energy}}{\text{nucleon}} = \frac{1.9151 \text{ amu} \times \dfrac{931.5 \text{ MeV}}{1 \text{ amu}}}{235 \text{ nucleons}}$$

$$= 7.591 \text{ MeV/nucleon}$$

Therefore, ^{235}U is less stable than ^{12}C.

PROBLEMS

Problems with **colored** numbers are answered in Appendix E and worked in detail in the Student Solutions Manual. Problem sections match those in the text and provide the numbers of relevant sample problems. Most offer Concept Review Questions, Skill-Building Exercises (grouped in pairs covering the same concept), and Problems in Context. The Comprehensive Problems are based on material from any section or previous chapter.

Radioactive Decay and Nuclear Stability
(Sample Problems 24.1 to 24.3)

Concept Review Questions

24.1 How do chemical and nuclear reactions differ in
(a) Magnitude of the energy change?
(b) Effect on rate of increasing temperature?

(c) Effect on rate of higher reactant concentration?
(d) Effect on yield of higher reactant concentration?

24.2 Sulfur has four naturally occurring stable isotopes. The one with the lowest mass number is sulfur-32, which is also the most abundant (95.02%).
(a) What percentage of the S atoms in a matchhead are ^{32}S?
(b) The isotopic mass of ^{32}S is 31.972070 amu. Is the atomic mass of S larger, smaller, or equal to this mass? Explain.

24.3 What led Marie Curie to draw the following conclusions?
(a) Radioactivity is a property of the element and not the compound in which it is found. (b) A highly radioactive element, aside from uranium, occurs in pitchblende.

24.4 Which of the following produce an atom of a *different* element: (a) α decay; (b) β^- decay; (c) γ emission; (d) β^+ emission;

(e) e^- capture? Show how Z and N change, if at all, with each process.

24.5 Why is $^3_2$He stable, but $^2_2$He has never been detected?

24.6 How do the modes of decay differ for a neutron-rich nuclide and a proton-rich nuclide?

24.7 Why might it be difficult to use only a nuclide's N/Z ratio to predict whether it will decay by β^+ emission or by e^- capture? What other factor is important?

Skill-Building Exercises (grouped in similar pairs)

24.8 Write balanced nuclear equations for the following:
(a) Alpha decay of $^{234}_{92}$U
(b) Electron capture by neptunium-232
(c) Positron emission by $^{12}_{7}$N

24.9 Write balanced nuclear equations for the following:
(a) β^- decay of sodium-26
(b) β^- decay of francium-223
(c) Alpha decay of $^{212}_{83}$Bi

24.10 Write balanced nuclear equations for the following:
(a) β^- emission by magnesium-27
(b) β^+ emission by $^{23}_{12}$Mg
(c) Electron capture by $^{103}_{46}$Pd

24.11 Write balanced nuclear equations for the following:
(a) β^- decay of silicon-32
(b) Alpha decay of polonium-218
(c) Electron capture by $^{110}_{49}$In

24.12 Write balanced nuclear equations for the following:
(a) Formation of $^{48}_{22}$Ti through positron emission
(b) Formation of silver-107 through electron capture
(c) Formation of polonium-206 through α decay

24.13 Write balanced nuclear equations for the following:
(a) Formation of $^{241}_{95}$Am through β^- decay
(b) Formation of $^{228}_{89}$Ac through β^- decay
(c) Formation of $^{203}_{83}$Bi through α decay

24.14 Write balanced nuclear equations for the following:
(a) Formation of ^{186}Ir through electron capture
(b) Formation of francium-221 through α decay
(c) Formation of iodine-129 through β^- decay

24.15 Write balanced nuclear equations for the following:
(a) Formation of ^{52}Mn through positron emission
(b) Formation of polonium-215 through α decay
(c) Formation of ^{81}Kr through electron capture

24.16 Which nuclide(s) would you predict to be stable? Why?
(a) $^{20}_{8}$O   (b) $^{59}_{27}$Co   (c) $^{9}_{3}$Li

24.17 Which nuclide(s) would you predict to be stable? Why?
(a) $^{146}_{60}$Nd   (b) $^{114}_{48}$Cd   (c) $^{88}_{42}$Mo

24.18 Which nuclide(s) would you predict to be stable? Why?
(a) ^{127}I   (b) tin-106   (c) ^{68}As

24.19 Which nuclide(s) would you predict to be stable? Why?
(a) ^{48}K   (b) ^{79}Br   (c) argon-32

24.20 What is the most likely mode of decay for each?
(a) $^{238}_{92}$U   (b) $^{48}_{24}$Cr   (c) $^{50}_{25}$Mn

24.21 What is the most likely mode of decay for each?
(a) $^{111}_{47}$Ag   (b) $^{41}_{17}$Cl   (c) $^{110}_{44}$Ru

24.22 What is the most likely mode of decay for each?
(a) ^{15}C   (b) ^{120}Xe   (c) ^{224}Th

24.23 What is the most likely mode of decay for each?
(a) ^{106}In   (b) ^{141}Eu   (c) ^{241}Am

24.24 Why is $^{52}_{24}$Cr the most stable isotope of chromium?

24.25 Why is $^{40}_{20}$Ca the most stable isotope of calcium?

Problems in Context

24.26 ^{237}Np is the parent nuclide of a decay series that starts with α emission, followed by β^- emission, and then two more α emissions. Write a balanced nuclear equation for each step.

24.27 Why is helium found in deposits of uranium and thorium ores? What kind of radioactive emission produces it?

24.28 In a natural decay series, how many α and β^- emissions per atom of uranium-235 result in an atom of lead-207?

The Kinetics of Radioactive Decay
(Sample Problems 24.4 and 24.5)

Concept Review Questions

24.29 What electronic process is the basis for detecting radioactivity in (a) a scintillation counter; (b) a Geiger-Müller counter?

24.30 What is the reaction order of radioactive decay? Explain.

24.31 After 1 minute, three radioactive nuclei remain from an original sample of six. Is it valid to conclude that $t_{1/2}$ equals 1 minute? Is this conclusion valid if the original sample contained 6×10^{12} nuclei and 3×10^{12} remain after 1 minute? Explain.

24.32 Radioisotopic dating depends on the constant rate of decay and formation of various nuclides in a sample. How is the proportion of ^{14}C kept relatively constant in living organisms?

Skill-Building Exercises (grouped in similar pairs)

24.33 What is the specific activity (in Ci/g) if 1.65 mg of an isotope emits 1.56×10^6 α particles per second?

24.34 What is the specific activity (in Ci/g) if 2.6 g of an isotope emits 4.13×10^8 β^- particles per hour?

24.35 What is the specific activity (in Bq/g) if 8.58 μg of an isotope emits 7.4×10^4 α particles per minute?

24.36 What is the specific activity (in Bq/g) if 1.07 kg of an isotope emits 3.77×10^7 β^- particles per minute?

24.37 If one-trillionth of the atoms of a radioactive isotope disintegrate each day, what is the decay constant of the process?

24.38 If $2.8 \times 10^{-10}\%$ of the atoms of a radioactive isotope disintegrate in 1.0 yr, what is the decay constant of the process?

24.39 If 1.00×10^{-12} mol of ^{135}Cs emits 1.39×10^5 β^- particles in 1.00 yr, what is the decay constant?

24.40 If 6.40×10^{-9} mol of ^{176}W emits 1.07×10^{15} β^+ particles in 1.00 h, what is the decay constant?

24.41 The isotope $^{212}_{83}$Bi has a half-life of 1.01 yr. What mass (in mg) of a 2.00-mg sample will remain after 3.75×10^3 h?

24.42 The half-life of radium-226 is 1.60×10^3 yr. How many hours will it take for a 2.50-g sample to decay to the point where 0.185 g of the isotope remains?

24.43 A rock contains 270 μmol of ^{238}U ($t_{1/2} = 4.5\times10^9$ yr) and 110 μmol of ^{206}Pb. Assuming that all the ^{206}Pb comes from decay of the ^{238}U, estimate the rock's age.

24.44 A fabric remnant from a burial site has a $^{14}C/^{12}C$ ratio of 0.735 of the original value. How old is the fabric?

Problems in Context

24.45 Due to decay of ^{40}K, cow's milk has a specific activity of about 6×10^{-11} mCi per milliliter. How many disintegrations of ^{40}K nuclei are there per minute in an 8.0-oz glass of milk?

24.46 Plutonium-239 ($t_{1/2} = 2.41\times10^4$ yr) represents a serious nuclear waste hazard. If seven half-lives are required to reach a tolerable level of radioactivity, how long must ^{239}Pu be stored?

24.47 A rock that contains 3.1×10^{-15} mol of ^{232}Th ($t_{1/2} = 1.4\times10^{10}$ yr) has 9.5×10^4 fission tracks, each track representing the fission of one atom of ^{232}Th. How old is the rock?

24.48 A volcanic eruption melts a large chunk of rock, and all gases are expelled. After cooling, $^{40}_{18}Ar$ accumulates from the ongoing decay of $^{40}_{19}K$ in the rock ($t_{1/2} = 1.25\times10^9$ yr). When a piece of rock is analyzed, it is found to contain 1.38 mmol of ^{40}K and 1.14 mmol of ^{40}Ar. How long ago did the rock cool?

Nuclear Transmutation: Induced Changes in Nuclei

Concept Review Questions

24.49 Irene and Frederic Joliot-Curie converted $^{27}_{13}Al$ to $^{30}_{15}P$ in 1933. Why was this transmutation significant?

24.50 Early workers mistakenly thought neutron beams were γ radiation. Why? What evidence led to the correct conclusion?

24.51 Why must the electrical polarity of the tubes in a linear accelerator be reversed at very short time intervals?

24.52 Why does bombardment with protons usually require higher energies than bombardment with neutrons?

Skill-Building Exercises (grouped in similar pairs)

24.53 Determine the missing species in these transmutations, and write a full nuclear equation from the shorthand notation:
(a) ^{10}B (α,n) __
(b) ^{28}Si (d,__) ^{29}P (where d is a deuteron, ^2H)
(c) __ (α,2n) ^{244}Cf

24.54 Name the unidentified species, and write each transmutation process in shorthand notation: (a) gamma irradiation of a nuclide yields a proton, a neutron, and ^{29}Si; (b) bombardment of ^{252}Cf with ^{10}B yields five neutrons and a nuclide; (c) bombardment of ^{238}U with a particle yields three neutrons and ^{239}Pu.

Problems in Context

24.55 Elements 104, 105, and 106 have been named rutherfordium (Rf), dubnium (Db), and seaborgium (Sg), respectively. These elements are synthesized from californium-249 by bombarding with carbon-12, nitrogen-15, and oxygen-18 nuclei, respectively. Four neutrons are formed in each reaction as well. (a) Write balanced nuclear equations for the formation of these elements. (b) Write the equations in shorthand notation.

Effects of Nuclear Radiation on Matter

Concept Review Questions

24.56 The effects on matter of γ rays and α particles differ. Explain.

24.57 What is a cation-electron pair, and how does it form?

24.58 Why is ionizing radiation more harmful to children than adults?

24.59 Why is ·OH more dangerous than OH⁻ in an organism?

Skill-Building Exercises (grouped in similar pairs)

24.60 A 135-lb person absorbs 3.3×10^{-7} J of energy from radioactive emissions. (a) How many rads does she receive? (b) How many grays (Gy) does she receive?

24.61 A 3.6-kg laboratory animal receives a single dose of 8.92×10^{-4} Gy. (a) How many rads did the animal receive? (b) How many joules did the animal absorb?

24.62 A 70.-kg person exposed to ^{90}Sr absorbs 6.0×10^5 β⁻ particles, each with an energy of 8.74×10^{-14} J. (a) How many grays does the person receive? (b) If the RBE is 1.0, how many millirems is this? (c) What is the equivalent dose in sieverts (Sv)?

24.63 A laboratory rat weighs 265 g and absorbs 1.77×10^{10} β⁻ particles, each with an energy of 2.20×10^{-13} J. (a) How many rads does the animal receive? (b) What is this dose in Gy? (c) If the RBE is 0.75, what is the equivalent dose in Sv?

Problems in Context

24.64 If 2.50 pCi [1 pCi (picocurie) $= 1\times10^{-12}$ Ci] of radioactivity from ^{239}Pu is emitted in a 95-kg human for 65 h, and each disintegration has an energy of 8.25×10^{-13} J, how many grays does the person receive?

24.65 A small region of a cancer patient's brain is exposed for 24.0 min to 475 Bq of radioactivity from ^{60}Co for treatment of a tumor. If the brain mass exposed is 1.858 g and each β⁻ particle emitted has an energy of 5.05×10^{-14} J, what is the dose in rads?

Applications of Radioisotopes

Concept Review Questions

24.66 What two ways are radioactive tracers used in organisms?

24.67 Why is neutron activation analysis (NAA) useful to art historians and criminologists?

24.68 Positrons cannot penetrate matter more than a few atomic diameters, but positron emission of radiotracers can be monitored in medical diagnosis. Explain.

24.69 A steel part is treated to form some iron-59. Oil used to lubricate the part emits 298 β⁻ particles (with the energy characteristic of ^{59}Fe) per minute per milliliter of oil. What other information would you need to calculate the rate of removal of the steel from the part during use?

Problems in Context

24.70 The oxidation of methanol to formaldehyde can be accomplished by reaction with chromic acid:

$$6H^+(aq) + 3CH_3OH(aq) + 2H_2CrO_4(aq) \longrightarrow$$
$$3CH_2O(aq) + 2Cr^{3+}(aq) + 8H_2O(l)$$

The reaction can be studied with the stable isotope tracer ^{18}O and mass spectrometry. When a small amount of $CH_3^{18}OH$ is present in the alcohol reactant, $CH_2^{18}O$ forms. When a small amount of $H_2Cr^{18}O_4$ is present, $H_2^{18}O$ forms. Does chromic acid or methanol supply the O atom to the aldehyde? Explain.

The Interconversion of Mass and Energy
(Sample Problem 24.6)

Note: Data for problems in this section: mass of ^1H atom = 1.007825 amu; mass of neutron = 1.008665 amu.

Concept Review Questions

24.71 Many scientists at first reacted skeptically to Einstein's equation, $E = mc^2$. Why?

24.72 How does a change in mass arise when a nuclide forms from nucleons?

24.73 When a nucleus forms from nucleons, is energy absorbed or released? Why?

24.74 What is the binding energy per nucleon? Why is the binding energy per nucleon, rather than per nuclide, used to compare nuclide stability?

Skill-Building Exercises (grouped in similar pairs)

24.75 A ^{3}H nucleus decays with an energy of 0.01861 MeV. Convert this energy into (a) electron volts; (b) joules.

24.76 Arsenic-84 decays with an energy of 1.57×10^{-15} kJ per nucleus. Convert this energy into (a) eV; (b) MeV.

24.77 How many joules are released when 1.5 mol of ^{239}Pu decays, if each nucleus releases 5.243 MeV?

24.78 How many MeV are released per nucleus when 3.2×10^{-3} mol of chromium-49 releases 8.11×10^5 kJ?

24.79 Oxygen-16 is one of the most stable nuclides. The mass of a ^{16}O atom is 15.994915 amu. Calculate the binding energy (a) per nucleon in MeV; (b) per atom in MeV; (c) per mole in kJ.

24.80 Lead-206 is the end product of ^{238}U decay. One ^{206}Pb atom has a mass of 205.974440 amu. Calculate the binding energy (a) per nucleon in MeV; (b) per atom in MeV; (c) per mole in kJ.

24.81 Cobalt-59 is the only stable isotope of this transition metal. One ^{59}Co atom has a mass of 58.933198 amu. Calculate the binding energy (a) per nucleon in MeV; (b) per atom in MeV; (c) per mole in kJ.

24.82 Iodine-131 is one of the most important isotopes used in the diagnosis of thyroid cancer. One atom has a mass of 130.906114 amu. Calculate the binding energy (a) per nucleon in MeV; (b) per atom in MeV; (c) per mole in kJ.

Problems in Context

24.83 The ^{80}Br nuclide decays either by β^- decay or by electron capture. (a) What is the product of each process? (b) Which process releases more energy? (Masses of atoms: ^{80}Br = 79.918528 amu; ^{80}Kr = 79.916380 amu; ^{80}Se = 79.916520 amu; neglect the mass of electrons involved because these are atomic, not nuclear, masses.)

Applications of Fission and Fusion

Concept Review Questions

24.84 What is the minimum number of neutrons from each fission event that must be absorbed by other nuclei for a chain reaction to be sustained?

24.85 In what main way is fission different from radioactive decay? Are all fission events in a chain reaction identical? Explain.

24.86 What is the purpose of enrichment in the preparation of fuel rods? How is it accomplished?

24.87 Describe the nature and purpose of these components of a nuclear reactor: (a) control rods; (b) moderator; (c) reflector.

24.88 State an advantage and a disadvantage of heavy-water reactors compared to light-water reactors.

24.89 What are the expected advantages of fusion reactors over fission reactors?

24.90 Why is iron the most abundant element in Earth's core?

Problems in Context

24.91 The reaction that will probably power the first commercial fusion reactor is

$$^3_1H + ^2_1H \longrightarrow ^4_2He + ^1_0n$$

How much energy would be produced per mole of reaction? (Masses of atoms: ^3_1H = 3.01605 amu; ^2_1H = 2.0140 amu; ^4_2He = 4.00260 amu; mass of ^1_0n = 1.008665 amu.)

Comprehensive Problems

24.92 Some $^{243}_{95}$Am was present when Earth formed, but it all decayed in the next billion years. The first three steps in this decay series are emissions of an α particle, a β^- particle, and another α particle. What other isotopes were present on the young Earth in a rock that contained some $^{243}_{95}$Am?

24.93 Curium-243 undergoes α decay to plutonium-239:

$$^{243}Cm \longrightarrow ^{239}Pu + \alpha$$

(a) Find the change in mass, Δm (in kg). (Masses: ^{243}Cm = 243.0614 amu; ^{239}Pu = 239.0522 amu; ^4He = 4.0026 amu; 1 amu = 1.661×10^{-24} g.)
(b) Find the energy released in joules.
(c) Find the energy released in kJ/mol of reaction, and comment on the difference between this value and a typical heat of reaction for a chemical change, which is a few hundred kJ/mol.

24.94 Plutonium "triggers" for nuclear weapons were manufactured at the Rocky Flats plant in Colorado. An 85-kg worker inhaled a dust particle containing 1.00 μg of $^{239}_{94}$Pu, which resided in his body for 16 h ($t_{1/2}$ of ^{239}Pu = 2.41×10^4 yr; each disintegration released 5.15 MeV). (a) How many rads did he receive? (b) How many grays?

24.95 Archeologists removed some charcoal from a Native American campfire, burned it in O_2, and bubbled the CO_2 formed into $Ca(OH)_2$ solution (limewater). The $CaCO_3$ that precipitated was filtered and dried. If 4.58 g of the $CaCO_3$ had a radioactivity of 3.2 d/min, how long ago was the campfire?

24.96 A 5.4-μg sample of ^{226}RaCl$_2$ has a radioactivity of 1.5×10^5 Bq. Calculate $t_{1/2}$ of ^{226}Ra.

24.97 How many rads does a 65-kg human receive each year from the approximately 10^{-8} g of $^{14}_6$C naturally present in her body ($t_{1/2}$ = 5730 yr; each disintegration releases 0.156 MeV)?

24.98 A sample of AgCl emits 175 nCi/g. A saturated solution prepared from the solid emits 1.25×10^{-2} Bq/mL due to radioactive Ag^+ ions. What is the molar solubility of AgCl?

24.99 The scene below depicts a neutron bombarding ^{235}U:

$$^1_0 + ^{235}_{92} \longrightarrow ^{144}_{55} + ? + 2^1_0$$

(a) Is this an example of fission or of fusion? (b) Identify the other nuclide formed. (c) What is the most likely mode of decay of the nuclide with Z = 55?

24.100 What fraction of the ^{235}U ($t_{1/2} = 7.0 \times 10^8$ yr) created when Earth was formed would remain after 2.8×10^9 yr?

24.101 ^{238}U ($t_{1/2} = 4.5 \times 10^9$ yr) begins a decay series that ultimately forms ^{206}Pb. The scene below depicts the relative number of ^{238}U atoms (red) and ^{206}Pb atoms (green) in a mineral. If all the Pb comes from ^{238}U, calculate the age of the sample.

24.102 Technetium-99m is a metastable nuclide used in numerous cancer diagnostic and treatment programs. It is prepared just before use because it decays rapidly through γ emission:

$$^{99m}\text{Tc} \longrightarrow {}^{99}\text{Tc} + \gamma$$

Use the data below to determine (a) the half-life of ^{99m}Tc; (b) the percentage of the isotope that is lost if it takes 2.0 h to prepare and administer the dose.

Time (h)	γ Emission (photons/s)
0	5000.
4	3150.
8	2000.
12	1250.
16	788
20	495

24.103 How many curies are produced by 1.0 mol of ^{40}K ($t_{1/2} = 1.25 \times 10^9$ yr)? How many becquerels?

24.104 The fraction of a radioactive isotope remaining at time t is $(\frac{1}{2})^{t/t_{1/2}}$, where $t_{1/2}$ is the half-life. If the half-life of carbon-14 is 5730 yr, what fraction of carbon-14 in a piece of charcoal remains after (a) 10.0 yr; (b) 10.0×10^3 yr; (c) 10.0×10^4 yr? (d) Why is radiocarbon dating more reliable for the fraction remaining in part (b) than that in part (a) or in part (c)?

24.105 The isotopic mass of $^{210}_{86}$Rn is 209.989669 amu. When this nuclide decays by electron capture, it emits 2.368 MeV. What is the isotopic mass of the resulting nuclide?

24.106 Exactly 0.1 of the radioactive nuclei in a sample decay per hour. Thus, after n hours, the fraction of nuclei remaining is $(0.900)^n$. Find the value of n equal to one half-life.

24.107 In neutron activation analysis (NAA), stable isotopes are bombarded with neutrons. Depending on the isotope and the energy of the neutron, various emissions are observed. What are the products when the following neutron-activated species decay? Write an overall equation in shorthand notation for the reaction starting with the stable isotope before neutron activation.
(a) $^{52}_{23}$V* $\longrightarrow$ [β^- emission]   (b) $^{64}_{29}$Cu* $\longrightarrow$ [β^+ emission]
(c) $^{28}_{13}$Al* $\longrightarrow$ [β^- emission]

24.108 In the 1950s, radioactive material was spread over the land from aboveground nuclear tests. A woman drinks some contaminated milk and ingests 0.0500 g of ^{90}Sr, which is taken up by bones and teeth and not eliminated. (a) How much ^{90}Sr ($t_{1/2} = 29$ yr) is present in her body after 10 yr? (b) How long will it take for 99.9% of the ^{90}Sr to decay?

24.109 The scene below represents a reaction (with neutrons gray and protons purple) that occurs during the lifetime of a star. (a) Write a balanced nuclear equation for the reaction. (b) If the mass difference is 7.7×10^{-2} amu, find the energy (kJ) released.

24.110 What volume of radon will be produced per hour at STP from 1.000 g of ^{226}Ra ($t_{1/2} = 1599$ yr; 1 yr = 8766 h; mass of one ^{226}Ra atom = 226.025402 amu)?

24.111 ^{90}Kr ($t_{1/2} = 32$ s) is used to study respiration. How soon after being made must a sample be administered to the patient if the activity must be at least 90% of the original activity?

24.112 Which isotope in each pair is more stable? Why?
(a) $^{140}_{55}$Cs or $^{133}_{55}$Cs   (b) $^{79}_{35}$Br or $^{78}_{35}$Br
(c) $^{28}_{12}$Mg or $^{24}_{12}$Mg   (d) $^{14}_{7}$N or $^{18}_{7}$N

24.113 A bone sample containing strontium-90 ($t_{1/2} = 29$ yr) emits 7.0×10^4 β^- particles per month. How long will it take for the emission to decrease to 1.0×10^4 particles per month?

24.114 The 23rd-century starship *Enterprise* uses a substance called "dilithium crystals" as its fuel.
(a) Assuming this material is the result of fusion, what is the product of the fusion of two ^{6}Li nuclei?
(b) How much energy is released per kilogram of dilithium formed? (Mass of one ^{6}Li atom is 6.015121 amu.)
(c) When four ^{1}H atoms fuse to form ^{4}He, how many positrons are released?
(d) To determine the energy potential of the fusion processes in parts (b) and (c), compare the changes in mass per kilogram of dilithium and of ^{4}He.
(e) Compare the change in mass per kilogram in part (b) to that for the formation of ^{4}He by the method used in current fusion reactors (see p. 1010). (For masses, see Problem 24.91.)
(f) Using early 21st-century fusion technology, how much tritium can be produced per kilogram of ^{6}Li in the following reaction: $^6_3$Li + $^1_0$n $\longrightarrow$ $^4_2$He + $^3_1$H? When this amount of tritium is fused with deuterium, what is the change in mass? How does this quantity compare with the use of dilithium in part (b)?

24.115 Uranium and radium are found in many rocky soils throughout the world. Both undergo radioactive decay, and one of the products is radon-222, the heaviest noble gas ($t_{1/2} = 3.82$ days). Inhalation of this gas contributes to many lung cancers. According to Environmental Protection Agency recommendations, the level of radioactivity from radon in homes should not exceed 4.0 pCi/L of air.
(a) What is the safe level of radon in Bq/L of air?
(b) A home has a radon measurement of 41.5 pCi/L. The owner vents the basement in such a way that no more radon enters the living area. What is the activity of the radon remaining in the room air (in Bq/L) after 9.5 days?
(c) How many more days does it take to reach the EPA recommended level?

24.116 Nuclear disarmament could be accomplished if weapons were not "replenished." The tritium in warheads decays to helium with a half-life of 12.26 yr and must be replaced or the weapon is useless. What fraction of the tritium is lost in 5.50 yr?

24.117 A decay series starts with the synthetic isotope $^{239}_{92}U$. The first four steps are emissions of a β^- particle, another β^-, an α particle, and another α. Write a balanced nuclear equation for each step. Which natural series could start by this sequence?

24.118 How long can a 54-lb child be exposed to 1.0 mCi of radiation from ^{222}Rn before accumulating 1.0 mrad if the energy of each disintegration is 5.59 MeV?

24.119 An earthquake in the area of present-day San Francisco is to be dated by measuring the ^{14}C activity ($t_{1/2}$ = 5730 yr) of parts of a tree uprooted during the event. The tree parts have an activity of 12.9 d/min·g C, and a living tree has an activity of 15.3 d/min·g C. How long ago did the earthquake occur?

24.120 Were organisms a billion years ago exposed to more or less ionizing radiation than similar organisms today? Explain.

24.121 Tritium (^3H; $t_{1/2}$ = 12.26 yr) is continually formed in the upper troposphere by interaction of solar particles with nitrogen. As a result, natural waters contain a small amount of tritium. Two samples of wine are analyzed, one known to be made in 1941 and another made earlier. The water in the 1941 wine has 2.23 times as much tritium as the water in the other. When was the other wine produced?

24.122 Even though plutonium-239 ($t_{1/2}$ = 2.41×10⁴ yr) is one of the main fission fuels, it is still a radiation hazard present in spent uranium fuel from nuclear power plants. How many years does it take for 99% of the plutonium-239 in spent fuel to decay?

24.123 Carbon from the remains of an extinct Australian marsupial, called *Diprotodon*, has a specific activity of 0.61 pCi/g. Modern carbon has a specific activity of 6.89 pCi/g. How long ago did the *Diprotodon* apparently become extinct?

24.124 The reaction that allows for radiocarbon dating is the continual formation of carbon-14 in the upper atmosphere:

$$^{14}_{7}N + ^{1}_{0}n \longrightarrow ^{14}_{6}C + ^{1}_{1}H$$

What is the energy change associated with this process in eV/reaction and in kJ/mol reaction? (Masses of atoms: $^{14}_{7}N$ = 14.003074 amu; $^{14}_{6}C$ = 14.003241 amu; $^{1}_{1}H$ = 1.007825 amu; mass of $^{1}_{0}n$ = 1.008665 amu.)

24.125 What is the nuclear binding energy of a lithium-7 nucleus in units of kJ/mol and eV/nucleus? (Mass of a lithium-7 atom = 7.016003 amu.)

24.126 Gadolinium-146 undergoes electron capture. Identify the product, and use Figure 24.2 to find the modes of decay and the other two nuclides in the series below:

24.127 Using 21st-century technology, hydrogen fusion requires temperatures around 10⁸ K. But, lower initial temperatures are used if the hydrogen is compressed. In the late 24th century, the starship *Leinad* uses such methods to fuse hydrogen at 10⁶ K.
(a) What is the kinetic energy of an H atom at 1.00×10⁶ K?
(b) How many H atoms are heated to 1.00×10⁶ K from the energy of one H and one anti-H atom annihilating each other?
(c) If these H atoms fuse into ^4He atoms (with the loss of two positrons per ^4He formed), how much energy (in J) is generated?
(d) How much more energy is generated by the fusion in (c) than by the hydrogen-antihydrogen collision in (b)?
(e) Should the captain of the *Leinad* change the technology and produce ^3He (mass = 3.01603 amu) instead of ^4He?

24.128 A metastable (excited) form of ^{50}Sc changes to its stable form by emitting γ radiation with a wavelength of 8.73 pm. What is the change in mass of 1 mol of the isotope when it undergoes this change?

24.129 A sample of cobalt-60 ($t_{1/2}$ = 5.27 yr), a powerful γ emitter used to treat cancer, was purchased by a hospital on March 1, 2007. The sample must be replaced when its activity reaches 70.% of the original value. On what date must it be replaced?

24.130 Uranium-233 decays to thorium-229 by α decay, but the emissions have different energies and products: 83% emit an α particle with energy of 4.816 MeV and give ^{229}Th in its ground state; 15% emit an α particle of 4.773 MeV and give ^{229}Th in excited state I; and 2% emit a lower energy α particle and give ^{229}Th in the higher excited state II. Excited state II emits a γ ray of 0.060 MeV to reach excited state I. (a) Find the γ-ray energy and wavelength that would convert excited state I to the ground state. (b) Find the energy of the α particle that would convert ^{233}U to excited state II.

24.131 Uranium-238 undergoes a slow decay step ($t_{1/2}$ = 4.5×10⁹ yr) followed by a series of fast steps to form the stable isotope ^{206}Pb. Thus, on a time scale of billions of years, ^{238}U effectively decays "directly" to ^{206}Pb, and the relative amounts of these isotopes are used to find the age of some rocks. Two students derive equations relating number of half-lives (n) since the rock formed to the amounts of the isotopes:

Student 1: $$\left(\tfrac{1}{2}\right)^n = \frac{^{238}_{92}U}{^{206}_{82}Pb}$$

Student 2: $$\left(\tfrac{1}{2}\right)^n = \frac{^{238}_{92}U}{^{238}_{92}U + ^{206}_{82}Pb}$$

(a) Which equation is correct, and why?
(b) If a rock contains exactly twice as much ^{238}U as ^{206}Pb, what is its age in years?

24.132 In the naturally occurring thorium-232 decay series, the steps emit this sequence of particles: α, β^-, β^-, α, α, α, α, β^-, β^-, and α. Write a balanced equation for each step.

24.133 At death, a nobleman in ancient Egypt was mummified and his body contained 1.4×10⁻³ g of ^{40}K ($t_{1/2}$ = 1.25×10⁹ yr), 1.2×10⁻⁸ g of ^{14}C ($t_{1/2}$ = 5730 yr), and 4.8×10⁻¹⁴ g of ^3H ($t_{1/2}$ = 12.26 yr). Which nuclide would give the most accurate estimate of the mummy's age? Explain.

24.134 Assuming that many radioactive nuclides can be considered safe after 20 half-lives, how long will it take for each of the following nuclides to be safe: (a) ^{242}Cm ($t_{1/2}$ = 163 days); (b) ^{214}Po ($t_{1/2}$ = 1.6×10⁻⁴ s); (c) ^{232}Th ($t_{1/2}$ = 1.39×10¹⁰ yr)?

24.135 An ancient sword has a blade from the early Roman Empire, around 100 AD, but the wooden handle, inlaid wooden decorations, leather ribbon, and leather sheath have different styles. Given the following activities, estimate the age of each part. Which part was made near the time of the blade ($t_{1/2}$ of ^{14}C = 5730 yr; $\mathscr{A}_0$ = 15.3 d/min·g)?

Part	$\mathscr{A}_t$ (d/min·g)
Handle	10.1
Inlaid wood	13.8
Ribbon	12.1
Sheath	15.0

24.136 The starship *Voyager*, like many other vessels of the newly designed 24th-century fleet, uses antimatter as fuel.

(a) How much energy is released when 1.00 kg each of antimatter and matter annihilate each other?

(b) When the antimatter is atomic antihydrogen, a small amount of it is mixed with excess atomic hydrogen (gathered from interstellar space during flight). The annihilation releases so much heat that the remaining hydrogen nuclei fuse to form ^{4}He. If each hydrogen-antihydrogen collision releases enough heat to fuse 1.00×10^5 hydrogen atoms, how much energy (in kJ) is released per kilogram of antihydrogen?

(c) Which produces more energy per kilogram of antihydrogen, the procedure in part (a) or that in part (b)?

24.137 Use Einstein's equation, the mass in grams of 1 amu, and the relation between electron volts and joules to find the energy equivalent (in MeV) of a mass difference of 1 amu.

24.138 Determine the age of a rock containing 0.065 g of uranium-238 ($t_{1/2} = 4.5 \times 10^9$ yr) and 0.023 g of lead-206. (Assume all the lead-206 came from ^{238}U decay.)

24.139 Plutonium-242 decays to uranium-238 by emission of an α particle with an energy of 4.853 MeV. The ^{238}U that forms is unstable and emits a γ ray ($\lambda = 0.02757$ nm). (a) Write balanced equations for these reactions. (b) What would be the energy of the α particle if ^{242}Pu decayed directly to the more stable ^{238}U?

24.140 Seaborgium-263 (Sg), the first isotope of element 106 synthesized, was made, together with four neutrons, by bombarding californium-249 with oxygen-18. It then underwent a series of decays starting with three α emissions. Write balanced equations for the synthesis and the three α emissions of ^{263}Sg.

24.141 Some nuclear power plants use plutonium-239, which is produced in breeder reactors. The rate-determining step is the second β$^-$ emission. How long does it take to make 1.00 kg of ^{239}Pu if the reaction is complete when the product is 90.% ^{239}Pu?

24.142 A random-number generator can be used to simulate the probability of a given atom decaying over a given time. For example, the formula "=RAND()" in the Excel spreadsheet returns a random number between 0 and 1; thus, for one radioactive atom and a time of one half-life, a number less than 0.5 means the atom decays and a number greater than 0.5 means it doesn't.

(a) Place the "=RAND()" formula in cells A1 to A10 of an Excel spreadsheet. In cell B1, place "=IF(A1<0.5, 0, 1)." This formula returns 0 if A1 is <0.5 (the atom decays) and 1 if A1 is >0.5 (the atom does not decay). Place analogous formulas in cells B2 to B10 (using the "Fill Down" procedure in Excel). To determine the number of atoms remaining after one half-life, sum cells B1 to B10 by placing "=SUM(B1:B10)" in cell B12. To create a new set of random numbers, click on an empty cell (e.g., B13) and hit "Delete." Perform 10 simulations, each time recording the total number of atoms remaining. Do half of the atoms remain after each half-life? If not, why not?

(b) Increase the number of atoms to 100 by placing suitable formulas in cells A1 to A100, B1 to B100, and B102. Perform 10 simulations, and record the number of atoms remaining each time. Are these results more realistic for radioactive decay? Explain.

24.143 In the following Excel-based simulation, the fate of 256 atoms is followed over five half-lives. Set up formulas in columns A and B, as in Problem 24.142, and simulate the fate of the sample of 256 atoms over one half-life. Cells B1 to B256 should contain 1 or 0. In cell C1, enter "=IF(B1=0, 0, RAND())." This returns 0 if the original atom decayed in the previous half-life or a random number between 0 and 1 if it did not. Fill the formula in C1 down to cell C256. Column D should have formulas similar to those in B, but with modified references, as should columns F, H, and J. Columns E, G, and I should have formulas similar to those in C, but with modified references. In cell B258, enter "=SUM(B1:B256)." This records the number of atoms remaining after the first half-life. Put formulas in cells D258, F258, H258, and J258 to record atoms remaining after subsequent half-lives.

(a) Ideally, how many atoms should remain after each half-life?

(b) Make a table of the atoms remaining after each half-life in four separate simulations. Compare these outcomes to the ideal outcome. How would you make the results more realistic?

24.144 Representations of three nuclei (with neutrons gray and protons purple) are shown below. Nucleus 1 is stable, but 2 and 3 are not. (a) Write the symbol for each isotope. (b) What is (are) the most likely mode(s) of decay for 2 and 3?

1   2   3

Common Mathematical Operations in Chemistry

In addition to basic arithmetic and algebra, four mathematical operations are used frequently in general chemistry: manipulating logarithms, using exponential notation, solving quadratic equations, and graphing data. Each is discussed briefly below.

MANIPULATING LOGARITHMS

Meaning and Properties of Logarithms

A *logarithm* is an exponent. Specifically, if $x^n = A$, we can say that the logarithm to the base x of the number A is n, and we can denote it as

$$\log_x A = n$$

Because logarithms are exponents, they have the following properties:

$$\log_x 1 = 0$$
$$\log_x (A \times B) = \log_x A + \log_x B$$
$$\log_x \frac{A}{B} = \log_x A - \log_x B$$
$$\log_x A^y = y \log_x A$$

Types of Logarithms

Common and natural logarithms are used in chemistry and the other sciences.

1. For *common* logarithms, the base (x in the examples above) is 10, but they are written without specifying the base; that is, $\log_{10} A$ is written more simply as $\log A$; thus, the notation *log* means base 10. The common logarithm of 1000 is 3; in other words, you must raise 10 to the 3rd power to obtain 1000:

$$\log 1000 = 3 \qquad \text{or} \qquad 10^3 = 1000$$

Similarly, we have

$$\log 10 = 1 \qquad \text{or} \qquad 10^1 = 10$$
$$\log 1{,}000{,}000 = 6 \qquad \text{or} \qquad 10^6 = 1{,}000{,}000$$
$$\log 0.001 = -3 \qquad \text{or} \qquad 10^{-3} = 0.001$$
$$\log 853 = 2.931 \qquad \text{or} \qquad 10^{2.931} = 853$$

The last example illustrates an important point about significant figures with all logarithms: *the number of significant figures in the number equals the number of digits to the right of the decimal point in the logarithm.* That is, the number 853 has three significant figures, and the logarithm 2.931 has three digits to the right of the decimal point.

To find a common logarithm with an electronic calculator, enter the number and press the LOG button.

2. For *natural* logarithms, the base is the number e, which is 2.71828 . . . , and $\log_e A$ is written ln A; thus, the notation *ln* means base e. The relationship between the common and natural logarithms is easily obtained:

$$\log 10 = 1 \qquad \text{and} \qquad \ln 10 = 2.303$$

Therefore, we have

$$\ln A = 2.303 \log A$$

To find a natural logarithm with an electronic calculator, enter the number and press the LN button. If your calculator does not have an LN button, enter the number, press the LOG button, and multiply by 2.303.

Antilogarithms

The *antilogarithm* is the base raised to the logarithm:

$$\text{antilogarithm (antilog) of } n \text{ is } 10^n$$

Using two of the earlier examples, the antilog of 3 is 1000, and the antilog of 2.931 is 853. To obtain the antilog with a calculator, enter the number and press the 10^x button. Similarly, to obtain the natural antilogarithm, enter the number and press the e^x button. [On some calculators, enter the number and first press INV and then the LOG (or LN) button.]

USING EXPONENTIAL (SCIENTIFIC) NOTATION

Many quantities in chemistry are very large or very small. For example, in the conventional way of writing numbers, the number of gold atoms in 1 gram of gold is

59,060,000,000,000,000,000,000 atoms (to four significant figures)

As another example, the mass in grams of one gold atom is

0.000000000000000000003272 g (to four significant figures)

Exponential (scientific) notation provides a much more practical way of writing such numbers. In exponential notation, we express numbers in the form

$$A \times 10^n$$

where A (the coefficient) is greater than or equal to 1 and less than 10 (that is, $1 \leq A < 10$), and n (the exponent) is an integer.

If the number we want to express in exponential notation is larger than 1, the exponent is positive ($n > 0$); if the number is smaller than 1, the exponent is negative ($n < 0$). The size of n tells the number of places the decimal point (in conventional notation) must be moved to obtain a coefficient A greater than or equal to 1 and less than 10 (in exponential notation). In exponential notation, 1 gram of gold contains 5.906×10^{22} atoms, and each gold atom has a mass of 3.272×10^{-22} g.

Changing Between Conventional and Exponential Notation

In order to use exponential notation, you must be able to convert to it from conventional notation, and vice versa.

1. To change a number from conventional to exponential notation, move the decimal point to the left for numbers equal to or greater than 10 and to the right for numbers between 0 and 1:

    75,000,000 changes to 7.5×10^7 (decimal point 7 places to the left)
    0.006042 changes to 6.042×10^{-3} (decimal point 3 places to the right)

2. To change a number from exponential to conventional notation, move the decimal point the number of places indicated by the exponent to the right for numbers with positive exponents and to the left for numbers with negative exponents:

    1.38×10^5 changes to 138,000 (decimal point 5 places to the right)
    8.41×10^{-6} changes to 0.00000841 (decimal point 6 places to the left)

3. An exponential number with a coefficient greater than 10 or less than 1 can be changed to the standard exponential form by converting the coefficient to the standard form and adding the exponents:

$$582.3 \times 10^6 \text{ changes to } 5.823 \times 10^2 \times 10^6 = 5.823 \times 10^{(2+6)} = 5.823 \times 10^8$$
$$0.0043 \times 10^{-4} \text{ changes to } 4.3 \times 10^{-3} \times 10^{-4} = 4.3 \times 10^{[(-3)+(-4)]} = 4.3 \times 10^{-7}$$

Using Exponential Notation in Calculations

In calculations, you can treat the coefficient and exponents separately and apply the properties of exponents (see earlier section on logarithms).

1. To multiply exponential numbers, multiply the coefficients, add the exponents, and reconstruct the number in standard exponential notation:

$$(5.5 \times 10^3)(3.1 \times 10^5) = (5.5 \times 3.1) \times 10^{(3+5)} = 17 \times 10^8 = 1.7 \times 10^9$$
$$(9.7 \times 10^{14})(4.3 \times 10^{-20}) = (9.7 \times 4.3) \times 10^{[14+(-20)]} = 42 \times 10^{-6} = 4.2 \times 10^{-5}$$

2. To divide exponential numbers, divide the coefficients, subtract the exponents, and reconstruct the number in standard exponential notation:

$$\frac{2.6 \times 10^6}{5.8 \times 10^2} = \frac{2.6}{5.8} \times 10^{(6-2)} = 0.45 \times 10^4 = 4.5 \times 10^3$$

$$\frac{1.7 \times 10^{-5}}{8.2 \times 10^{-8}} = \frac{1.7}{8.2} \times 10^{[(-5)-(-8)]} = 0.21 \times 10^3 = 2.1 \times 10^2$$

3. To add or subtract exponential numbers, change all numbers so that they have the same exponent, then add or subtract the coefficients:

$$(1.45 \times 10^4) + (3.2 \times 10^3) = (1.45 \times 10^4) + (0.32 \times 10^4) = 1.77 \times 10^4$$
$$(3.22 \times 10^5) - (9.02 \times 10^4) = (3.22 \times 10^5) - (0.902 \times 10^5) = 2.32 \times 10^5$$

SOLVING QUADRATIC EQUATIONS

A *quadratic equation* is one in which the highest power of x is 2. The general form of a quadratic equation is

$$ax^2 + bx + c = 0$$

where a, b, and c are numbers. For given values of a, b, and c, the values of x that satisfy the equation are called *solutions* of the equation. We calculate x with the quadratic formula:

$$x = \frac{-b \pm \sqrt{b^2 - 4ac}}{2a}$$

We commonly require the quadratic formula when solving for some concentration in an equilibrium problem. For example, we might have an expression that is rearranged into the quadratic equation

$$\underset{a}{4.3x^2} + \underset{b}{0.65x} - \underset{c}{8.7} = 0$$

Applying the quadratic formula, with $a = 4.3$, $b = 0.65$, and $c = -8.7$, gives

$$x = \frac{-0.65 \pm \sqrt{(0.65)^2 - 4(4.3)(-8.7)}}{2(4.3)}$$

The "plus or minus" sign ($\pm$) indicates that there are always two possible values for x. In this case, they are

$$x = 1.3 \quad \text{and} \quad x = -1.5$$

In any real physical system, however, only one of the values will have any meaning. For example, if x were $[H_3O^+]$, the negative value would give a negative concentration, which has no physical meaning.

GRAPHING DATA IN THE FORM OF A STRAIGHT LINE

Visualizing changes in variables by means of a graph is used throughout science. In many cases, it is most useful if the data can be graphed in the form of a straight line. Any equation will appear as a straight line if it has, or can be rearranged to have, the following general form:

$$y = mx + b$$

where y is the dependent variable (typically plotted along the vertical axis), x is the independent variable (typically plotted along the horizontal axis), m is the slope of the line, and b is the intercept of the line on the y axis. The intercept is the value of y when $x = 0$:

$$y = m(0) + b = b$$

The slope of the line is the change in y for a given change in x:

$$\text{Slope } (m) = \frac{y_2 - y_1}{x_2 - x_1} = \frac{\Delta y}{\Delta x}$$

The *sign* of the slope tells the *direction* of the line. If y increases as x increases, m is positive, and the line slopes upward with higher values of x; if y decreases as x increases, m is negative, and the line slopes downward with higher values of x. The *magnitude* of the slope indicates the *steepness* of the line. A line with $m = 3$ is three times as steep (y changes three times as much for a given change in x) as a line with $m = 1$.

Consider the linear equation $y = 2x + 1$. A graph of this equation is shown in Figure A.1. In practice, you can find the slope by drawing a right triangle to the line, using the line as the hypotenuse. Then, one leg gives Δy, and the other gives Δx. In the figure, $\Delta y = 8$ and $\Delta x = 4$.

At several places in the text, an equation is rearranged into the form of a straight line in order to determine information from the slope and/or the intercept. For example, in Chapter 16, we obtained the following expression:

$$\ln \frac{[A]_0}{[A]_t} = kt$$

Based on the properties of logarithms, we have

$$\ln [A]_0 - \ln [A]_t = kt$$

Rearranging into the form of an equation for a straight line gives

$$\ln [A]_t = -kt + \ln [A]_0$$
$$y \quad\;\; = mx + \quad b$$

Thus, a plot of $\ln [A]_t$ vs. t is a straight line, from which you can see that the slope is $-k$ (the negative of the rate constant) and the intercept is $\ln [A]_0$ (the natural logarithm of the initial concentration of A).

At many other places in the text, linear relationships occur that were not shown in graphical terms. For example, the conversion of temperature scales in Chapter 1 can also be expressed in the form of a straight line:

$$°F = \tfrac{9}{5}°C + 32$$
$$y = mx \quad + b$$

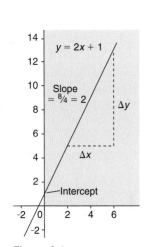

Figure A.1

Standard Thermodynamic Values for Selected Substances*

Substance or Ion	ΔH°_f (kJ/mol)	ΔG°_f (kJ/mol)	S° (J/mol·K)	Substance or Ion	ΔH°_f (kJ/mol)	ΔG°_f (kJ/mol)	S° (J/mol·K)
$e^-(g)$	0	0	20.87	$CaCO_3(s)$	−1206.9	−1128.8	92.9
Aluminum				$CaO(s)$	−635.1	−603.5	38.2
$Al(s)$	0	0	28.3	$Ca(OH)_2(s)$	−986.09	−898.56	83.39
$Al^{3+}(aq)$	−524.7	−481.2	−313	$Ca_3(PO_4)_2(s)$	−4138	−3899	263
$AlCl_3(s)$	−704.2	−628.9	110.7	$CaSO_4(s)$	−1432.7	−1320.3	107
$Al_2O_3(s)$	−1676	−1582	50.94	Carbon			
Barium				$C(graphite)$	0	0	5.686
$Ba(s)$	0	0	62.5	$C(diamond)$	1.896	2.866	2.439
$Ba(g)$	175.6	144.8	170.28	$C(g)$	715.0	669.6	158.0
$Ba^{2+}(g)$	1649.9	—	—	$CO(g)$	−110.5	−137.2	197.5
$Ba^{2+}(aq)$	−538.36	−560.7	13	$CO_2(g)$	−393.5	−394.4	213.7
$BaCl_2(s)$	−806.06	−810.9	126	$CO_2(aq)$	−412.9	−386.2	121
$BaCO_3(s)$	−1219	−1139	112	$CO_3^{2-}(aq)$	−676.26	−528.10	−53.1
$BaO(s)$	−548.1	−520.4	72.07	$HCO_3^-(aq)$	−691.11	587.06	95.0
$BaSO_4(s)$	−1465	−1353	132	$H_2CO_3(aq)$	−698.7	−623.42	191
Boron				$CH_4(g)$	−74.87	−50.81	186.1
$B(\beta\text{-rhombo-hedral})$	0	0	5.87	$C_2H_2(g)$	227	209	200.85
				$C_2H_4(g)$	52.47	68.36	219.22
$BF_3(g)$	−1137.0	−1120.3	254.0	$C_2H_6(g)$	−84.667	−32.89	229.5
$BCl_3(g)$	−403.8	−388.7	290.0	$C_3H_8(g)$	−105	−24.5	269.9
$B_2H_6(g)$	35	86.6	232.0	$C_4H_{10}(g)$	−126	−16.7	310
$B_2O_3(s)$	−1272	−1193	53.8	$C_6H_6(l)$	49.0	124.5	172.8
$H_3BO_3(s)$	−1094.3	−969.01	88.83	$CH_3OH(g)$	−201.2	−161.9	238
Bromine				$CH_3OH(l)$	−238.6	−166.2	127
$Br_2(l)$	0	0	152.23	$HCHO(g)$	−116	−110	219
$Br_2(g)$	30.91	3.13	245.38	$HCOO^-(aq)$	−410	−335	91.6
$Br(g)$	111.9	82.40	174.90	$HCOOH(l)$	−409	−346	129.0
$Br^-(g)$	−218.9	—	—	$HCOOH(aq)$	−410	−356	164
$Br^-(aq)$	−120.9	−102.82	80.71	$C_2H_5OH(g)$	−235.1	−168.6	282.6
$HBr(g)$	−36.3	−53.5	198.59	$C_2H_5OH(l)$	−277.63	−174.8	161
Cadmium				$CH_3CHO(g)$	−166	−133.7	266
$Cd(s)$	0	0	51.5	$CH_3COOH(l)$	−487.0	−392	160
$Cd(g)$	112.8	78.20	167.64	$C_6H_{12}O_6(s)$	−1273.3	−910.56	212.1
$Cd^{2+}(aq)$	−72.38	−77.74	−61.1	$C_{12}H_{22}O_{11}(s)$	−2221.7	−1544.3	360.24
$CdS(s)$	−144	−141	71	$CN^-(aq)$	151	166	118
Calcium				$HCN(g)$	135	125	201.7
$Ca(s)$	0	0	41.6	$HCN(l)$	105	121	112.8
$Ca(g)$	192.6	158.9	154.78	$HCN(aq)$	105	112	129
$Ca^{2+}(g)$	1934.1	—	—	$CS_2(g)$	117	66.9	237.79
$Ca^{2+}(aq)$	−542.96	−553.04	−55.2	$CS_2(l)$	87.9	63.6	151.0
$CaF_2(s)$	−1215	−1162	68.87	$CH_3Cl(g)$	−83.7	−60.2	234
$CaCl_2(s)$	−795.0	−750.2	114	$CH_2Cl_2(l)$	−117	−63.2	179

*All values at 298 K.

(*continued*)

Substance or Ion	ΔH_f° (kJ/mol)	ΔG_f° (kJ/mol)	S° (J/mol·K)	Substance or Ion	ΔH_f° (kJ/mol)	ΔG_f° (kJ/mol)	S° (J/mol·K)
$CHCl_3(l)$	−132	−71.5	203	$Fe^{2+}(aq)$	−87.9	−84.94	113
$CCl_4(g)$	−96.0	−53.7	309.7	$FeCl_2(s)$	−341.8	−302.3	117.9
$CCl_4(l)$	−139	−68.6	214.4	$FeCl_3(s)$	−399.5	−334.1	142
$COCl_2(g)$	−220	−206	283.74	$FeO(s)$	−272.0	−251.4	60.75
Cesium				$Fe_2O_3(s)$	−825.5	−743.6	87.400
$Cs(s)$	0	0	85.15	$Fe_3O_4(s)$	−1121	−1018	145.3
$Cs(g)$	76.7	49.7	175.5	Lead			
$Cs^+(g)$	458.5	427.1	169.72	$Pb(s)$	0	0	64.785
$Cs^+(aq)$	−248	−282.0	133	$Pb^{2+}(aq)$	1.6	−24.3	21
$CsF(s)$	−554.7	−525.4	88	$PbCl_2(s)$	−359	−314	136
$CsCl(s)$	−442.8	−414	101.18	$PbO(s)$	−218	−198	68.70
$CsBr(s)$	−395	−383	121	$PbO_2(s)$	−276.6	−219.0	76.6
$CsI(s)$	−337	−333	130	$PbS(s)$	−98.3	−96.7	91.3
Chlorine				$PbSO_4(s)$	−918.39	−811.24	147
$Cl_2(g)$	0	0	223.0	Lithium			
$Cl(g)$	121.0	105.0	165.1	$Li(s)$	0	0	29.10
$Cl^-(g)$	−234	−240	153.25	$Li(g)$	161	128	138.67
$Cl^-(aq)$	−167.46	−131.17	55.10	$Li^+(g)$	687.163	649.989	132.91
$HCl(g)$	−92.31	−95.30	186.79	$Li^+(aq)$	−278.46	−293.8	14
$HCl(aq)$	−167.46	−131.17	55.06	$LiF(s)$	−616.9	−588.7	35.66
$ClO_2(g)$	102	120	256.7	$LiCl(s)$	−408	−384	59.30
$Cl_2O(g)$	80.3	97.9	266.1	$LiBr(s)$	−351	−342	74.1
Chromium				$LiI(s)$	−270	−270	85.8
$Cr(s)$	0	0	23.8	Magnesium			
$Cr^{3+}(aq)$	−1971	—	—	$Mg(s)$	0	0	32.69
$CrO_4^{2-}(aq)$	−863.2	−706.3	38	$Mg(g)$	150	115	148.55
$Cr_2O_7^{2-}(aq)$	−1461	−1257	214	$Mg^{2+}(g)$	2351	—	—
Copper				$Mg^{2+}(aq)$	−461.96	−456.01	118
$Cu(s)$	0	0	33.1	$MgCl_2(s)$	−641.6	−592.1	89.630
$Cu(g)$	341.1	301.4	166.29	$MgCO_3(s)$	−1112	−1028	65.86
$Cu^+(aq)$	51.9	50.2	−26	$MgO(s)$	−601.2	−569.0	26.9
$Cu^{2+}(aq)$	64.39	64.98	−98.7	$Mg_3N_2(s)$	−461	−401	88
$Cu_2O(s)$	−168.6	−146.0	93.1	Manganese			
$CuO(s)$	−157.3	−130	42.63	$Mn(s, \alpha)$	0	0	31.8
$Cu_2S(s)$	−79.5	−86.2	120.9	$Mn^{2+}(aq)$	−219	−223	−84
$CuS(s)$	−53.1	−53.6	66.5	$MnO_2(s)$	−520.9	−466.1	53.1
Fluorine				$MnO_4^-(aq)$	−518.4	−425.1	190
$F_2(g)$	0	0	202.7	Mercury			
$F(g)$	78.9	61.8	158.64	$Hg(l)$	0	0	76.027
$F^-(g)$	−255.6	−262.5	145.47	$Hg(g)$	61.30	31.8	174.87
$F^-(aq)$	−329.1	−276.5	−9.6	$Hg^{2+}(aq)$	171	164.4	−32
$HF(g)$	−273	−275	173.67	$Hg_2^{2+}(aq)$	172	153.6	84.5
Hydrogen				$HgCl_2(s)$	−230	−184	144
$H_2(g)$	0	0	130.6	$Hg_2Cl_2(s)$	−264.9	−210.66	196
$H(g)$	218.0	203.30	114.60	$HgO(s)$	−90.79	−58.50	70.27
$H^+(aq)$	0	0	0	Nitrogen			
$H^+(g)$	1536.3	1517.1	108.83	$N_2(g)$	0	0	191.5
Iodine				$N(g)$	473	456	153.2
$I_2(s)$	0	0	116.14	$N_2O(g)$	82.05	104.2	219.7
$I_2(g)$	62.442	19.38	260.58	$NO(g)$	90.29	86.60	210.65
$I(g)$	106.8	70.21	180.67	$NO_2(g)$	33.2	51	239.9
$I^-(g)$	−194.7	—	—	$N_2O_4(g)$	9.16	97.7	304.3
$I^-(aq)$	−55.94	−51.67	109.4	$N_2O_5(g)$	11	118	346
$HI(g)$	25.9	1.3	206.33	$N_2O_5(s)$	−43.1	114	178
Iron				$NH_3(g)$	−45.9	−16	193
$Fe(s)$	0	0	27.3	$NH_3(aq)$	−80.83	26.7	110
$Fe^{3+}(aq)$	−47.7	−10.5	−293	$N_2H_4(l)$	50.63	149.2	121.2

(continued)

Substance or Ion	ΔH_f° (kJ/mol)	ΔG_f° (kJ/mol)	S° (J/mol·K)	Substance or Ion	ΔH_f° (kJ/mol)	ΔG_f° (kJ/mol)	S° (J/mol·K)
$NO_3^-(aq)$	−206.57	−110.5	146	$AgF(s)$	−203	−185	84
$HNO_3(l)$	−173.23	−79.914	155.6	$AgCl(s)$	−127.03	−109.72	96.11
$HNO_3(aq)$	−206.57	−110.5	146	$AgBr(s)$	−99.51	−95.939	107.1
$NF_3(g)$	−125	−83.3	260.6	$AgI(s)$	−62.38	−66.32	114
$NOCl(g)$	51.71	66.07	261.6	$AgNO_3(s)$	−45.06	19.1	128.2
$NH_4Cl(s)$	−314.4	−203.0	94.6	$Ag_2S(s)$	−31.8	−40.3	146
Oxygen				**Sodium**			
$O_2(g)$	0	0	205.0	$Na(s)$	0	0	51.446
$O(g)$	249.2	231.7	160.95	$Na(g)$	107.76	77.299	153.61
$O_3(g)$	143	163	238.82	$Na^+(g)$	609.839	574.877	147.85
$OH^-(aq)$	−229.94	−157.30	−10.54	$Na^+(aq)$	−239.66	−261.87	60.2
$H_2O(g)$	−241.826	−228.60	188.72	$NaF(s)$	−575.4	−545.1	51.21
$H_2O(l)$	−285.840	−237.192	69.940	$NaCl(s)$	−411.1	−384.0	72.12
$H_2O_2(l)$	−187.8	−120.4	110	$NaBr(s)$	−361	−349	86.82
$H_2O_2(aq)$	−191.2	−134.1	144	$NaOH(s)$	−425.609	−379.53	64.454
Phosphorus				$Na_2CO_3(s)$	−1130.8	−1048.1	139
$P_4(s, white)$	0	0	41.1	$NaHCO_3(s)$	−947.7	−851.9	102
$P(g)$	314.6	278.3	163.1	$NaI(s)$	−288	−285	98.5
$P(s, red)$	−17.6	−12.1	22.8	**Strontium**			
$P_2(g)$	144	104	218	$Sr(s)$	0	0	54.4
$P_4(g)$	58.9	24.5	280	$Sr(g)$	164	110	164.54
$PCl_3(g)$	−287	−268	312	$Sr^{2+}(g)$	1784	—	
$PCl_3(l)$	−320	−272	217	$Sr^{2+}(aq)$	−545.51	−557.3	−39
$PCl_5(g)$	−402	−323	353	$SrCl_2(s)$	−828.4	−781.2	117
$PCl_5(s)$	−443.5	—	—	$SrCO_3(s)$	−1218	−1138	97.1
$P_4O_{10}(s)$	−2984	−2698	229	$SrO(s)$	−592.0	−562.4	55.5
$PO_4^{3-}(aq)$	−1266	−1013	−218	$SrSO_4(s)$	−1445	−1334	122
$HPO_4^{2-}(aq)$	−1281	−1082	−36	**Sulfur**			
$H_2PO_4^-(aq)$	−1285	−1135	89.1	$S(rhombic)$	0	0	31.9
$H_3PO_4(aq)$	−1277	−1019	228	$S(monoclinic)$	0.3	0.096	32.6
Potassium				$S(g)$	279	239	168
$K(s)$	0	0	64.672	$S_2(g)$	129	80.1	228.1
$K(g)$	89.2	60.7	160.23	$S_8(g)$	101	49.1	430.211
$K^+(g)$	514.197	481.202	154.47	$S^{2-}(aq)$	41.8	83.7	22
$K^+(aq)$	−251.2	−282.28	103	$HS^-(aq)$	−17.7	12.6	61.1
$KF(s)$	−568.6	−538.9	66.55	$H_2S(g)$	−20.2	−33	205.6
$KCl(s)$	−436.7	−409.2	82.59	$H_2S(aq)$	−39	−27.4	122
$KBr(s)$	−394	−380	95.94	$SO_2(g)$	−296.8	−300.2	248.1
$KI(s)$	−328	−323	106.39	$SO_3(g)$	−396	−371	256.66
$KOH(s)$	−424.8	−379.1	78.87	$SO_4^{2-}(aq)$	−907.51	−741.99	17
$KClO_3(s)$	−397.7	−296.3	143.1	$HSO_4^-(aq)$	−885.75	−752.87	126.9
$KClO_4(s)$	−432.75	−303.2	151.0	$H_2SO_4(l)$	−813.989	−690.059	156.90
Rubidium				$H_2SO_4(aq)$	−907.51	−741.99	17
$Rb(s)$	0	0	69.5	**Tin**			
$Rb(g)$	85.81	55.86	169.99	$Sn(white)$	0	0	51.5
$Rb^+(g)$	495.04	—	—	$Sn(gray)$	3	4.6	44.8
$Rb^+(aq)$	−246	−282.2	124	$SnCl_4(l)$	−545.2	−474.0	259
$RbF(s)$	−549.28	—	—	$SnO_2(s)$	−580.7	−519.7	52.3
$RbCl(s)$	−435.35	−407.8	95.90	**Titanium**			
$RbBr(s)$	−389.2	−378.1	108.3	$Ti(s)$	0	0	30.7
$RbI(s)$	−328	−326	118.0	$TiCl_4(l)$	−804.2	−737.2	252.3
Silicon				$TiO_2(s)$	−944.0	−888.8	50.6
$Si(s)$	0	0	18.0	**Zinc**			
$SiF_4(g)$	−1614.9	−1572.7	282.4	$Zn(s)$	0	0	41.6
$SiO_2(s)$	−910.9	−856.5	41.5	$Zn(g)$	130.5	94.93	160.9
Silver				$Zn^{2+}(aq)$	−152.4	−147.21	−106.5
$Ag(s)$	0	0	42.702	$ZnO(s)$	−348.0	−318.2	43.9
$Ag(g)$	289.2	250.4	172.892	$ZnS(s, zinc$ $blende)$	−203	−198	57.7
$Ag^+(aq)$	105.9	77.111	73.93				

Equilibrium Constants for Selected Substances*

Dissociation (Ionization) Constants (K_a) of Selected Acids

Name and Formula	Lewis Structure[†]	K_{a1}	K_{a2}	K_{a3}
Acetic acid CH_3COOH		1.8×10^{-5}		
Acetylsalicylic acid $CH_3COOC_6H_4COOH$		3.6×10^{-4}		
Adipic acid $HOOC(CH_2)_4COOH$		3.8×10^{-5}	3.8×10^{-6}	
Arsenic acid H_3AsO_4		6×10^{-3}	1.1×10^{-7}	3×10^{-12}
Ascorbic acid $H_2C_6H_6O_6$		1.0×10^{-5}	5×10^{-12}	
Benzoic acid C_6H_5COOH		6.3×10^{-5}		
Carbonic acid H_2CO_3		4.5×10^{-7}	4.7×10^{-11}	
Chloroacetic acid $ClCH_2COOH$		1.4×10^{-3}		
Chlorous acid $HClO_2$		1.1×10^{-2}		

*All values at 298 K, except for acetylsalicylic acid, which is at 37°C (310 K) in 0.15 M NaCl.

[†]Acidic (ionizable) proton(s) shown in red. Structures have lowest formal charges. Benzene rings show one resonance form.

(continued)

Dissociation (Ionization) Constants (K_a) of Selected Acids

Name and Formula	Lewis Structure[†]	K_{a1}	K_{a2}	K_{a3}
Citric acid HOOCCH$_2$C(OH)(COOH)CH$_2$COOH		7.4×10^{-4}	1.7×10^{-5}	4.0×10^{-7}
Formic acid HCOOH		1.8×10^{-4}		
Glyceric acid HOCH$_2$CH(OH)COOH		2.9×10^{-4}		
Glycolic acid HOCH$_2$COOH		1.5×10^{-4}		
Glyoxylic acid HC(O)COOH		3.5×10^{-4}		
Hydrocyanic acid HCN		6.2×10^{-10}		
Hydrofluoric acid HF		6.8×10^{-4}		
Hydrosulfuric acid H$_2$S		9×10^{-8}	1×10^{-17}	
Hypobromous acid HBrO		2.3×10^{-9}		
Hypochlorous acid HClO		2.9×10^{-8}		
Hypoiodous acid HIO		2.3×10^{-11}		
Iodic acid HIO$_3$		1.6×10^{-1}		
Lactic acid CH$_3$CH(OH)COOH		1.4×10^{-4}		
Maleic acid HOOCCH=CHCOOH		1.2×10^{-2}	4.7×10^{-7}	

(continued)

Dissociation (Ionization) Constants (K_a) of Selected Acids (*continued*)

Name and Formula	Lewis Structure[†]	K_{a1}	K_{a2}	K_{a3}
Malonic acid $HOOCCH_2COOH$		1.4×10^{-3}	2.0×10^{-6}	
Nitrous acid HNO_2		7.1×10^{-4}		
Oxalic acid $HOOCCOOH$		5.6×10^{-2}	5.4×10^{-5}	
Phenol C_6H_5OH		1.0×10^{-10}		
Phenylacetic acid $C_6H_5CH_2COOH$		4.9×10^{-5}		
Phosphoric acid H_3PO_4		7.2×10^{-3}	6.3×10^{-8}	4.2×10^{-13}
Phosphorous acid $HPO(OH)_2$		3×10^{-2}	1.7×10^{-7}	
Propanoic acid CH_3CH_2COOH		1.3×10^{-5}		
Pyruvic acid $CH_3C(O)COOH$		2.8×10^{-3}		
Succinic acid $HOOCCH_2CH_2COOH$		6.2×10^{-5}	2.3×10^{-6}	
Sulfuric acid H_2SO_4		Very large	1.0×10^{-2}	
Sulfurous acid H_2SO_3		1.4×10^{-2}	6.5×10^{-8}	

(*continued*)

Dissociation (Ionization) Constants (K_b) of Selected Amine Bases

Name and Formula	Lewis Structure[†]	K_{b1}	K_{b2}
Ammonia NH_3		1.76×10^{-5}	
Aniline $C_6H_5NH_2$		4.0×10^{-10}	
Diethylamine $(CH_3CH_2)_2NH$		8.6×10^{-4}	
Dimethylamine $(CH_3)_2NH$		5.9×10^{-4}	
Ethanolamine $HOCH_2CH_2NH_2$		3.2×10^{-5}	
Ethylamine $CH_3CH_2NH_2$		4.3×10^{-4}	
Ethylenediamine $H_2NCH_2CH_2NH_2$		8.5×10^{-5}	7.1×10^{-8}
Methylamine CH_3NH_2		4.4×10^{-4}	
tert-Butylamine $(CH_3)_3CNH_2$		4.8×10^{-4}	
Piperidine $C_5H_{10}NH$		1.3×10^{-3}	
n-Propylamine $CH_3CH_2CH_2NH_2$		3.5×10^{-4}	

[†]Blue type indicates the basic nitrogen and its lone pair.   (*continued*)

Dissociation (Ionization) Constants (K_b) of Selected Amine Bases (*continued*)

Name and Formula	Lewis Structure[†]	K_{b1}	K_{b2}
Isopropylamine $(CH_3)_2CHNH_2$		4.7×10^{-4}	
1,3-Propylenediamine $H_2NCH_2CH_2CH_2NH_2$		3.1×10^{-4}	3.0×10^{-6}
Pyridine C_5H_5N		1.7×10^{-9}	
Triethylamine $(CH_3CH_2)_3N$		5.2×10^{-4}	
Trimethylamine $(CH_3)_3N$		6.3×10^{-5}	

Dissociation (Ionization) Constants (K_a) of Some Hydrated Metal Ions

Free Ion	Hydrated Ion	K_a
Fe^{3+}	$Fe(H_2O)_6^{3+}(aq)$	6×10^{-3}
Sn^{2+}	$Sn(H_2O)_6^{2+}(aq)$	4×10^{-4}
Cr^{3+}	$Cr(H_2O)_6^{3+}(aq)$	1×10^{-4}
Al^{3+}	$Al(H_2O)_6^{3+}(aq)$	1×10^{-5}
Cu^{2+}	$Cu(H_2O)_6^{2+}(aq)$	3×10^{-8}
Pb^{2+}	$Pb(H_2O)_6^{2+}(aq)$	3×10^{-8}
Zn^{2+}	$Zn(H_2O)_6^{2+}(aq)$	1×10^{-9}
Co^{2+}	$Co(H_2O)_6^{2+}(aq)$	2×10^{-10}
Ni^{2+}	$Ni(H_2O)_6^{2+}(aq)$	1×10^{-10}

Formation Constants (K_f) of Some Complex Ions

Complex Ion	K_f
$Ag(CN)_2^-$	3.0×10^{20}
$Ag(NH_3)_2^+$	1.7×10^{7}
$Ag(S_2O_3)_2^{3-}$	4.7×10^{13}
AlF_6^{3-}	4×10^{19}
$Al(OH)_4^-$	3×10^{33}
$Be(OH)_4^{2-}$	4×10^{18}
CdI_4^{2-}	1×10^{6}
$Co(OH)_4^{2-}$	5×10^{9}
$Cr(OH)_4^-$	8.0×10^{29}
$Cu(NH_3)_4^{2+}$	5.6×10^{11}
$Fe(CN)_6^{4-}$	3×10^{35}
$Fe(CN)_6^{3-}$	4.0×10^{43}
$Hg(CN)_4^{2-}$	9.3×10^{38}
$Ni(NH_3)_6^{2+}$	2.0×10^{8}
$Pb(OH)_3^-$	8×10^{13}
$Sn(OH)_3^-$	3×10^{25}
$Zn(CN)_4^{2-}$	4.2×10^{19}
$Zn(NH_3)_4^{2+}$	7.8×10^{8}
$Zn(OH)_4^{2-}$	3×10^{15}

Solubility-Product Constants (K_{sp}) of Slightly Soluble Ionic Compounds

Name, Formula	K_{sp}	Name, Formula	K_{sp}
Carbonates		Cobalt(II) hydroxide, $Co(OH)_2$	1.3×10^{-15}
Barium carbonate, $BaCO_3$	2.0×10^{-9}	Copper(II) hydroxide, $Cu(OH)_2$	2.2×10^{-20}
Cadmium carbonate, $CdCO_3$	1.8×10^{-14}	Iron(II) hydroxide, $Fe(OH)_2$	4.1×10^{-15}
Calcium carbonate, $CaCO_3$	3.3×10^{-9}	Iron(III) hydroxide, $Fe(OH)_3$	1.6×10^{-39}
Cobalt(II) carbonate, $CoCO_3$	1.0×10^{-10}	Magnesium hydroxide, $Mg(OH)_2$	6.3×10^{-10}
Copper(II) carbonate, $CuCO_3$	3×10^{-12}	Manganese(II) hydroxide, $Mn(OH)_2$	1.6×10^{-13}
Lead(II) carbonate, $PbCO_3$	7.4×10^{-14}	Nickel(II) hydroxide, $Ni(OH)_2$	6×10^{-16}
Magnesium carbonate, $MgCO_3$	3.5×10^{-8}	Zinc hydroxide, $Zn(OH)_2$	3×10^{-16}
Mercury(I) carbonate, Hg_2CO_3	8.9×10^{-17}	**Iodates**	
Nickel(II) carbonate, $NiCO_3$	1.3×10^{-7}	Barium iodate, $Ba(IO_3)_2$	1.5×10^{-9}
Strontium carbonate, $SrCO_3$	5.4×10^{-10}	Calcium iodate, $Ca(IO_3)_2$	7.1×10^{-7}
Zinc carbonate, $ZnCO_3$	1.0×10^{-10}	Lead(II) iodate, $Pb(IO_3)_2$	2.5×10^{-13}
Chromates		Silver iodate, $AgIO_3$	3.1×10^{-8}
Barium chromate, $BaCrO_4$	2.1×10^{-10}	Strontium iodate, $Sr(IO_3)_2$	3.3×10^{-7}
Calcium chromate, $CaCrO_4$	1×10^{-8}	Zinc iodate, $Zn(IO_3)_2$	3.9×10^{-6}
Lead(II) chromate, $PbCrO_4$	2.3×10^{-13}	**Oxalates**	
Silver chromate, Ag_2CrO_4	2.6×10^{-12}	Barium oxalate dihydrate, $BaC_2O_4 \cdot 2H_2O$	1.1×10^{-7}
Cyanides		Calcium oxalate monohydrate, $CaC_2O_4 \cdot H_2O$	2.3×10^{-9}
Mercury(I) cyanide, $Hg_2(CN)_2$	5×10^{-40}	Strontium oxalate monohydrate,	
Silver cyanide, $AgCN$	2.2×10^{-16}	$SrC_2O_4 \cdot H_2O$	5.6×10^{-8}
Halides		**Phosphates**	
Fluorides		Calcium phosphate, $Ca_3(PO_4)_2$	1.2×10^{-29}
Barium fluoride, BaF_2	1.5×10^{-6}	Magnesium phosphate, $Mg_3(PO_4)_2$	5.2×10^{-24}
Calcium fluoride, CaF_2	3.2×10^{-11}	Silver phosphate, Ag_3PO_4	2.6×10^{-18}
Lead(II) fluoride, PbF_2	3.6×10^{-8}	**Sulfates**	
Magnesium fluoride, MgF_2	7.4×10^{-9}	Barium sulfate, $BaSO_4$	1.1×10^{-10}
Strontium fluoride, SrF_2	2.6×10^{-9}	Calcium sulfate, $CaSO_4$	2.4×10^{-5}
Chlorides		Lead(II) sulfate, $PbSO_4$	1.6×10^{-8}
Copper(I) chloride, $CuCl$	1.9×10^{-7}	Radium sulfate, $RaSO_4$	2×10^{-11}
Lead(II) chloride, $PbCl_2$	1.7×10^{-5}	Silver sulfate, Ag_2SO_4	1.5×10^{-5}
Silver chloride, $AgCl$	1.8×10^{-10}	Strontium sulfate, $SrSO_4$	3.2×10^{-7}
Bromides		**Sulfides**	
Copper(I) bromide, $CuBr$	5×10^{-9}	Cadmium sulfide, CdS	1.0×10^{-24}
Silver bromide, $AgBr$	5.0×10^{-13}	Copper(II) sulfide, CuS	8×10^{-34}
Iodides		Iron(II) sulfide, FeS	8×10^{-16}
Copper(I) iodide, CuI	1×10^{-12}	Lead(II) sulfide, PbS	3×10^{-25}
Lead(II) iodide, PbI_2	7.9×10^{-9}	Manganese(II) sulfide, MnS	3×10^{-11}
Mercury(I) iodide, Hg_2I_2	4.7×10^{-29}	Mercury(II) sulfide, HgS	2×10^{-50}
Silver iodide, AgI	8.3×10^{-17}	Nickel(II) sulfide, NiS	3×10^{-16}
Hydroxides		Silver sulfide, Ag_2S	8×10^{-48}
Aluminum hydroxide, $Al(OH)_3$	3×10^{-34}	Tin(II) sulfide, SnS	1.3×10^{-23}
Cadmium hydroxide, $Cd(OH)_2$	7.2×10^{-15}	Zinc sulfide, ZnS	2.0×10^{-22}
Calcium hydroxide, $Ca(OH)_2$	6.5×10^{-6}		

Appendix D

Standard Electrode (Half-Cell) Potentials*

Half-Reaction	$E°$ (V)
$F_2(g) + 2e^- \rightleftharpoons 2F^-(aq)$	+2.87
$O_3(g) + 2H^+(aq) + 2e^- \rightleftharpoons O_2(g) + H_2O(l)$	+2.07
$Co^{3+}(aq) + e^- \rightleftharpoons Co^{2+}(aq)$	+1.82
$H_2O_2(aq) + 2H^+(aq) + 2e^- \rightleftharpoons 2H_2O(l)$	+1.77
$PbO_2(s) + 3H^+(aq) + HSO_4^-(aq) + 2e^- \rightleftharpoons PbSO_4(s) + 2H_2O(l)$	+1.70
$Ce^{4+}(aq) + e^- \rightleftharpoons Ce^{3+}(aq)$	+1.61
$MnO_4^-(aq) + 8H^+(aq) + 5e^- \rightleftharpoons Mn^{2+}(aq) + 4H_2O(l)$	+1.51
$Au^{3+}(aq) + 3e^- \rightleftharpoons Au(s)$	+1.50
$Cl_2(g) + 2e^- \rightleftharpoons 2Cl^-(aq)$	+1.36
$Cr_2O_7^{2-}(aq) + 14H^+(aq) + 6e^- \rightleftharpoons 2Cr^{3+}(aq) + 7H_2O(l)$	+1.33
$MnO_2(s) + 4H^+(aq) + 2e^- \rightleftharpoons Mn^{2+}(aq) + 2H_2O(l)$	+1.23
$O_2(g) + 4H^+(aq) + 4e^- \rightleftharpoons 2H_2O(l)$	+1.23
$Br_2(l) + 2e^- \rightleftharpoons 2Br^-(aq)$	+1.07
$NO_3^-(aq) + 4H^+(aq) + 3e^- \rightleftharpoons NO(g) + 2H_2O(l)$	+0.96
$2Hg^{2+}(aq) + 2e^- \rightleftharpoons Hg_2^{2+}(aq)$	+0.92
$Hg_2^{2+}(aq) + 2e^- \rightleftharpoons 2Hg(l)$	+0.85
$Ag^+(aq) + e^- \rightleftharpoons Ag(s)$	+0.80
$Fe^{3+}(aq) + e^- \rightleftharpoons Fe^{2+}(aq)$	+0.77
$O_2(g) + 2H^+(aq) + 2e^- \rightleftharpoons H_2O_2(aq)$	+0.68
$MnO_4^-(aq) + 2H_2O(l) + 3e^- \rightleftharpoons MnO_2(s) + 4OH^-(aq)$	+0.59
$I_2(s) + 2e^- \rightleftharpoons 2I^-(aq)$	+0.53
$O_2(g) + 2H_2O(l) + 4e^- \rightleftharpoons 4OH^-(aq)$	+0.40
$Cu^{2+}(aq) + 2e^- \rightleftharpoons Cu(s)$	+0.34
$AgCl(s) + e^- \rightleftharpoons Ag(s) + Cl^-(aq)$	+0.22
$SO_4^{2-}(aq) + 4H^+(aq) + 2e^- \rightleftharpoons SO_2(g) + 2H_2O(l)$	+0.20
$Cu^{2+}(aq) + e^- \rightleftharpoons Cu^+(aq)$	+0.15
$Sn^{4+}(aq) + 2e^- \rightleftharpoons Sn^{2+}(aq)$	+0.13
$2H^+(aq) + 2e^- \rightleftharpoons H_2(g)$	0.00
$Pb^{2+}(aq) + 2e^- \rightleftharpoons Pb(s)$	−0.13
$Sn^{2+}(aq) + 2e^- \rightleftharpoons Sn(s)$	−0.14
$N_2(g) + 5H^+(aq) + 4e^- \rightleftharpoons N_2H_5^+(aq)$	−0.23
$Ni^{2+}(aq) + 2e^- \rightleftharpoons Ni(s)$	−0.25
$Co^{2+}(aq) + 2e^- \rightleftharpoons Co(s)$	−0.28
$PbSO_4(s) + H^+(aq) + 2e^- \rightleftharpoons Pb(s) + HSO_4^-(aq)$	−0.31
$Cd^{2+}(aq) + 2e^- \rightleftharpoons Cd(s)$	−0.40
$Fe^{2+}(aq) + 2e^- \rightleftharpoons Fe(s)$	−0.44
$Cr^{3+}(aq) + 3e^- \rightleftharpoons Cr(s)$	−0.74
$Zn^{2+}(aq) + 2e^- \rightleftharpoons Zn(s)$	−0.76
$2H_2O(l) + 2e^- \rightleftharpoons H_2(g) + 2OH^-(aq)$	−0.83
$Mn^{2+}(aq) + 2e^- \rightleftharpoons Mn(s)$	−1.18
$Al^{3+}(aq) + 3e^- \rightleftharpoons Al(s)$	−1.66
$Mg^{2+}(aq) + 2e^- \rightleftharpoons Mg(s)$	−2.37
$Na^+(aq) + e^- \rightleftharpoons Na(s)$	−2.71
$Ca^{2+}(aq) + 2e^- \rightleftharpoons Ca(s)$	−2.87
$Sr^{2+}(aq) + 2e^- \rightleftharpoons Sr(s)$	−2.89
$Ba^{2+}(aq) + 2e^- \rightleftharpoons Ba(s)$	−2.90
$K^+(aq) + e^- \rightleftharpoons K(s)$	−2.93
$Li^+(aq) + e^- \rightleftharpoons Li(s)$	−3.05

*All values at 298 K. Written as reductions; $E°$ value refers to all components in their standard states: 1 M for dissolved species; 1 atm pressure for the gas behaving ideally; the pure substance for solids and liquids.

Answers to Selected Problems

Chapter 1

1.2 Gas molecules fill the entire container; the volume of a gas is the volume of the container. Solids and liquids have a definite volume. The volume of the container does not affect the volume of a solid or liquid. (a) gas (b) liquid (c) liquid **1.4** Physical property: a characteristic shown by a substance itself, without any interaction with or change into other substances. Chemical property: a characteristic of a substance that appears as it interacts with, or transforms into, other substances. (a) Color (yellow-green and silvery to white) and physical state (gas and metal to crystals) are physical properties. The interaction between chlorine gas and sodium metal is a chemical property. (b) Color and magnetism are physical properties. No chemical changes. **1.6**(a) Physical change; there is only a temperature change. (b) Chemical change; the change in appearance indicates an irreversible chemical change. (c) Physical change; there is only a change in size, not composition. (d) Chemical change; the wood (and air) become different substances with different compositions. **1.8**(a) fuel (b) wood **1.13** Lavoisier measured the total mass of the reactants and products, not just the mass of the solids. The total mass of the reactants and products remained constant. His measurements showed that a gas was involved in the reaction. He called this gas *oxygen* (one of his key discoveries). **1.16** A well-designed experiment must have the following essential features: (1) There must be at least two variables that are expected to be related; (2) there must be a way to control all the variables, so that only one at a time may be changed; (3) the results must be reproducible. **1.19**(a) $(2.54 \text{ cm})^2/(1 \text{ in})^2$ and $(1 \text{ m})^2/(100 \text{ cm})^2$ (b) $(1000 \text{ m})^2/(1 \text{ km})^2$ and $(100 \text{ cm})^2/(1 \text{ m})^2$ (c) $(1.609 \times 10^3 \text{ m/mi})$ and $(1 \text{ h}/3600 \text{ s})$ (d) $(1000 \text{ g}/2.205 \text{ lb})$ and $(3.531 \times 10^{-5} \text{ ft}^3/\text{cm}^3)$ **1.21** An extensive property depends on the amount of material present. An intensive property is the same regardless of how much material is present. (a) extensive property (b) intensive property (c) extensive property (d) intensive property **1.23**(a) increases (b) remains the same (c) decreases (d) increases (e) remains the same **1.26** 1.43 nm **1.28** 3.94×10^3 in **1.30**(a) 2.07×10^{-9} km^2 (b) \$10.43 **1.32** Answers will vary, depending on the person's mass. **1.34**(a) 5.52×10^3 kg/m^3 (b) 345 lb/ft^3 **1.36**(a) 2.56×10^{-9} mm^3 (b) 10^{-10} L **1.38** 9.626 cm^3 (b) 64.92 g **1.40** 2.70 g/cm^3 **1.42**(a) 20.°C; 293 K (b) 109 K; $-263°$F (c) $-273°$C; $-460.°$F **1.45**(a) 2.47×10^{-7} m (b) 67.6 Å **1.52**(a) none (b) none (c) 0.04$\underline{1}$0 (d) 4.$\underline{0}$1$\underline{00}$×10^4 **1.54**(a) 0.00036 (b) 35.83 (c) 22.5 **1.56** 6×10^2 **1.58**(a) 1.34 m (b) 21,621 mm^3 (c) 443 cm **1.60**(a) 1.310000×10^5 (b) 4.7×10^{-4} (c) 2.10006×10^5 (d) 2.1605×10^3 **1.62**(a) 5550 (b) 10,070. (c) 0.000000885 (d) 0.003004 **1.64**(a) 8.025×10^4 (b) 1.0098×10^{-3} (c) 7.7×10^{-11}

1.66(a) 4.06×10^{-19} J (b) 1.61×10^{24} molecules (c) 1.82×10^5 J/mol **1.68**(a) Height measured, not exact. (b) Planets counted, exact. (c) Number of grams in a pound is not a unit definition, not exact. (d) Definition of "millimeter," exact. **1.70** 7.50 ± 0.05 cm **1.72**(a) $I_{avg} = 8.72$ g; $II_{avg} = 8.72$ g; $III_{avg} = 8.50$ g; $IV_{avg} = 8.56$ g; sets I and II are most accurate. (b) Set III is the most precise, but is the least accurate. (c) Set I has the best combination of high accuracy and high precision. (d) Set IV has both low accuracy and low precision. **1.74**(a)

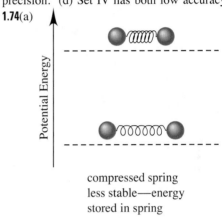

compressed spring
less stable—energy
stored in spring

(b)

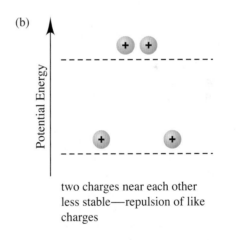

two charges near each other
less stable—repulsion of like
charges

1.76 7.7/1 **1.78**(a) density $= 0.21$ g/L, will float (b) CO_2 is denser than air, will sink (c) density $= 0.30$ g/L, will float (d) O_2 is denser than air, will sink (e) density $= 1.38$ g/L, will sink (f) 0.55 g for empty ball; 0.50 g for ball filled with hydrogen **1.80**(a) 8.0×10^{12} g (b) 4.1×10^5 m^3 (c) 9.5×10^{13} dollars **1.82**(a) $-195.79°$C (b) $-320.42°$F (c) 5.05 L **1.83**(a) 2.6 m/s (b) 16 km (c) 12:45 pm **1.85** freezing point $= -3.7°$X; boiling point $= 63.3°$X **1.86** 2.3×10^{25} g oxygen; 1.4×10^{25} g silicon; 5×10^{15} g ruthenium and rhodium

Chapter 2

Answers to Boxed Reading Problems: B2.1 (a) 5 peaks (b) m/e ratio of heaviest particle = 74; m/e ratio of lightest particle = 35 **B2.3** (a) Since salt dissolves in water and pepper does not, add water to mixture and filter to remove solid pepper. Evaporate water to recover solid salt. (d) Heat the mixture; the ethanol will boil off (distill), while the sugar will remain behind.

• **2.1** Compounds contain different types of atoms; there is only one type of atom in an element. **2.4**(a) The presence of more than one element makes pure calcium chloride a compound. (b) There is only one kind of atom, so sulfur is an element. (c) The presence of more than one compound makes baking powder a mixture. (d) The presence of more than one type of atom means cytosine cannot be an element. The specific, not variable, arrangement means it is a compound. **2.12**(a) elements, compounds, and mixtures (b) compounds (c) compounds **2.14**(a) Law of definite composition: the composition is the same regardless of its source. (b) Law of mass conservation: the total quantity of matter does not change. (c) Law of multiple proportions: two elements can combine to form two different compounds that have different proportions of those elements. **2.16**(a) No, the percent by mass of each element in a compound is fixed. (b) Yes, the *mass* of each element in a compound depends on the amount of compound. **2.18** The two experiments demonstrate the law of definite composition. The unknown compound decomposes the same way both times. The experiments also demonstrate the law of conservation of mass since the total mass before reaction equals the total mass after reaction. **2.20**(a) 1.34 g F (b) 0.514 Ca; 0.486 F (c) 51.4 mass % Ca; 48.6 mass % F **2.22**(a) 0.603 (b) 322 g Mg **2.24** 3.498×10^6 g Cu; 1.766×10^6 g S **2.26** compound 1: 0.905 S/Cl; compound 2: 0.451 S/Cl; ratio: 2.00/1.00 **2.29** Coal A **2.31** Dalton postulated that atoms of an element are identical and that compounds result from the chemical combination of specific ratios of different elements. **2.32** If you know the ratio of any two quantities and the value of one of them, the other can always be calculated; in this case, the charge and the mass/charge ratio were known. **2.36** The atomic number is the number of protons in an atom's nucleus. When the atomic number changes, the identity of the element changes. The mass number is the total number of protons and neutrons in the nucleus. The identity of an element is based on the number of protons, not the number of neutrons. The mass number can vary (by a change in number of neutrons) without changing the identity of the element. **2.39** All three isotopes have 18 protons and 18 electrons. Their respective mass numbers are 36, 38, and 40, with the respective numbers of neutrons being 18, 20, and 22. **2.41**(a) These have the same number of protons and electrons, but different numbers of neutrons; same Z. (b) These have the same number of neutrons, but different numbers of protons and electrons; same N. (c) These have different numbers of protons, neutrons, and electrons; same A.

2.43(a) $^{38}_{18}$Ar (b) $^{55}_{25}$Mn (c) $^{109}_{47}$Ag
2.45(a) $^{48}_{22}$Ti   (b) $^{79}_{34}$Se   (c) $^{11}_{5}$B

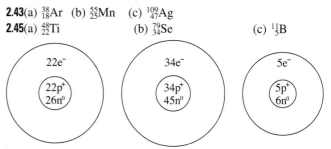

2.47 69.72 amu **2.49** ^{35}Cl = 75.774%, ^{37}Cl = 24.226% **2.52**(a) In the modern periodic table, the elements are arranged in order of increasing atomic number. (b) Elements in a group (or family) have similar chemical properties. (c) Elements can be classified as metals, metalloids, or nonmetals. **2.55** The alkali metals [Group 1A(1)] are metals and readily lose one electron to form cations; the halogens [Group 7A(17)] are nonmetals and readily gain one electron to form anions. **2.56**(a) germanium; Ge; 4A(14); metalloid (b) phosphorus; P; 5A(15); nonmetal (c) helium; He; 8A(18); nonmetal (d) lithium; Li; 1A(1); metal (e) molybdenum; Mo; 6B(6); metal **2.58**(a) Ra; 88 (b) Si; 14 (c) Cu; 63.55 amu (d) Br; 79.90 amu **2.60** Atoms of these two kinds of substances will form ionic bonds, in which one or more electrons are transferred from the metal atom to the nonmetal atom to form a cation and an anion, respectively. **2.63** Coulomb's law states the energy of attraction in an ionic bond is directly proportional to the product of charges and inversely proportional to the distance between charges. The product of charges in MgO [(2+) (2−)] is greater than that in LiF [(1+) (1−)]. Thus, MgO has stronger ionic bonding. **2.66** The Group 1A(1) elements form cations, and the Group 7A(17) elements form anions. **2.68** Each potassium atom loses one electron to form an ion with a 1+ charge. Each sulfur atom gains two electrons to form an ion with a 2− charge. Two potassiums, losing one electron each, are required for each sulfur, which gains two electrons. The oppositely charged ions attract each other to form an ionic solid, K_2S. **2.70** K^+; I^- **2.72**(a) oxygen; 17; 6A(16); 2 (b) fluorine; 19; 7A(17); 2 (c) calcium; 40; 2A(2); 4 **2.74** Lithium forms the Li^+ ion; oxygen forms the O^{2-} ion. Number of O^{2-} ions = 4.2×10^{21} O^{2-} ions. **2.76** NaCl **2.78** The subscripts in a formula give the numbers of ions in a formula unit of the compound. The subscripts indicate that there are two F^- ions for each Mg^{2+} ion. Using this information and the mass of each element, we can calculate percent mass of each element in the compound. **2.80** The two samples are similar in that both contain 20 billion oxygen atoms and 20 billion hydrogen atoms. They differ in that they contain different types of molecules: H_2O_2 molecules in the hydrogen peroxide sample, and H_2 and O_2 molecules in the mixture. In addition, the mixture contains 20 billion molecules (10 billion H_2 and 10 billion O_2), while the hydrogen peroxide sample contains 10 billion molecules. **2.84**(a) Na_3N, sodium nitride (b) SrO, strontium oxide (c) $AlCl_3$, aluminum chloride **2.86**(a) MgF_2, magnesium fluoride (b) ZnS, zinc sulfide (c) $SrCl_2$, strontium chloride **2.88**(a) $SnCl_4$ (b) iron(III) bromide

(c) CuBr (d) manganese(III) oxide   **2.90**(a) cobalt(II) oxide
(b) Hg_2Cl_2 (c) lead(II) acetate trihydrate (d) Cr_2O_3
2.92(a) BaO (b) $Fe(NO_3)_2$ (c) MgS   **2.94**(a) H_2SO_4; sulfuric
acid (b) HIO_3; iodic acid (c) HCN; hydrocyanic acid
(d) H_2S; hydrosulfuric acid   **2.96**(a) ammonium ion, NH_4^+;
ammonia, NH_3 (b) magnesium sulfide, MgS; magnesium
sulfite, $MgSO_3$; magnesium sulfate, $MgSO_4$ (c) hydrochloric
acid, HCl; chloric acid, $HClO_3$; chlorous acid, $HClO_2$
(d) cuprous bromide, CuBr; cupric bromide, $CuBr_2$ **2.98** Disulfur tetrafluoride, S_2F_4 **2.100**(a) calcium chloride (b) copper(I)
oxide (c) stannic fluoride (d) hydrochloric acid   **2.102**(a) 12
oxygen atoms; 342.2 amu (b) 9 hydrogen atoms; 132.06 amu
(c) 8 oxygen atoms; 344.6 amu   **2.104**(a) $(NH_4)_2SO_4$; 132.15 amu
(b) NaH_2PO_4; 119.98 amu (c) $KHCO_3$; 100.12 amu
2.106(a) 108.02 amu (b) 331.2 amu (c) 72.08 amu
2.108(a) SO_3; sulfur trioxide; 80.07 amu (b) C_3H_8; propane;
44.09 amu   **2.112** Separating the components of a mixture
requires physical methods only; that is, no chemical changes
(no changes in composition) take place, and the components
maintain their chemical identities and properties throughout.
Separating the components of a compound requires a chemical
change (change in composition).   **2.115**(a) compound (b) homogeneous mixture (c) heterogeneous mixture (d) homogeneous
mixture (e) homogeneous mixture   **2.117**(a) filtration
(b) chromatography   **2.119**(a) fraction of volume = 5.2×10^{-13}
(b) mass of nucleus = 6.64466×10^{-24} g; fraction of mass =
0.999726   **2.120** strongest ionic bonding: MgO; weakest ionic
bonding: RbI   **2.124**(a) I = NO; II = N_2O_3; III = N_2O_5 (b) I has
1.14 g O per 1.00 g N; II, 1.71 g O; III, 2.86 g O   **2.128**(a) Cl^-,
1.898 mass %; Na^+, 1.056 mass %; SO_4^{2-}, 0.265 mass %;
Mg^{2+}, 0.127 mass %; Ca^{2+}, 0.04 mass %; K^+, 0.038 mass %;
HCO_3^-, 0.014 mass % (b) 30.72% (c) Alkaline earth metal
ions, total mass % = 0.17%; alkali metal ions, total mass % =
1.094% (d) Anions (2.177 mass %) make up a larger mass
fraction than cations (1.26 mass %).   **2.131** Molecular formula,
$C_4H_6O_4$; molecular mass, 118.09 amu; 40.68% by mass C;
5.122% by mass H; 54.20% by mass O   **2.134**(a) Formulas and
masses in amu: $^{15}N_2^{18}O$, 48; $^{15}N_2^{16}O$, 46; $^{14}N_2^{18}O$, 46; $^{14}N_2^{16}O$,
44; $^{15}N^{14}N^{18}O$, 47; $^{15}N^{14}N^{16}O$, 45 (b) $^{15}N_2^{18}O$, least common;
$^{14}N_2^{16}O$, most common   **2.136** 58.091 amu   **2.138** nitroglycerin,
39.64 mass % NO; isoamyl nitrate, 22.54 mass % NO
2.139 0.370 lb C; 0.0222 lb H; 0.423 lb O; 0.185 lb N
2.144(1) chemical change (2) physical change (3) chemical
change (4) chemical change (5) physical change

Chapter 3

3.2(a) 12 mol C atoms (b) 1.445×10^{25} C atoms   **3.7**(a) left
(b) left (c) left (d) neither   **3.8**(a) 121.64 g/mol
(b) 76.02 g/mol (c) 106.44 g/mol (d) 152.00 g/mol
3.10(a) 134.7 g/mol (b) 175.3 g/mol (c) 342.17 g/mol
(d) 125.84 g/mol   **3.12**(a) 1.1×10^2 g $KMnO_4$ (b) 0.188 mol O
atoms (c) 1.5×10^{20} O atoms   **3.14**(a) 9.73 g $MnSO_4$ (b) 44.6 mol
$Fe(ClO_4)_3$ (c) 1.74×10^{21} N atoms   **3.16**(a) 1.56×10^3 g
Cu_2CO_3 (b) 0.0725 g N_2O_5 (c) 0.644 mol $NaClO_4$; 3.88×10^{23}
formula units $NaClO_4$ (d) 3.88×10^{23} Na^+ ions; 3.88×10^{23}

ClO_4^- ions; 3.88×10^{23} Cl atoms; 1.55×10^{24} O atoms
3.18(a) 6.375 mass % H (b) 71.52 mass % O   **3.20**(a) 0.1252
mass fraction C (b) 0.3428 mass fraction O   **3.23**(a) 0.9507 mol
cisplatin (b) 3.5×10^{24} H atoms   **3.25**(a) 195 mol rust
(b) 195 mol Fe_2O_3 (c) 2.18×10^4 g Fe   **3.27** $CO(NH_2)_2 >$
$NH_4NO_3 > (NH_4)_2SO_4 > KNO_3$ **3.28**(a) 883 mol PbS
(b) 1.88×10^{25} Pb atoms   **3.32**(b) From the mass percent, determine the empirical formula. Add up the total number of atoms
in the empirical formula, and divide that number into the total
number of atoms in the molecule. The result is the multiplier
that converts the empirical formula into the molecular formula.

Road Map

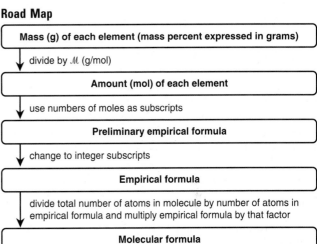

(c) Find the empirical formula from the mass percents. Compare the number of atoms given for the one element to the
number in the empirical formula. Multiply the empirical formula by the factor that is needed to obtain the given number
of atoms for that element.

Road Map

First three steps are the same as in road map for part (b).

Empirical formula
divide the number of atoms given for the one element by the number of atoms of that element in the empirical formula and multiply the empirical formula by that factor
Molecular formula

(e) Count the numbers of the various types of atoms in the
structural formula and put these into a molecular formula.

Road Map

Structural formula
use the numbers of atoms of the elements as subscripts
Molecular formula

3.34(a) CH_2; 14.03 g/mol (b) CH_3O; 31.03 g/mol (c) N_2O_5;
108.02 g/mol (d) $Ba_3(PO_4)_2$; 601.8 g/mol (e) TeI_4; 635.2 g/mol
3.36 Disulfur dichloride; SCl; 135.04 g/mol   **3.38**(a) C_3H_6
(b) N_2H_4 (c) N_2O_4 (d) $C_5H_5N_5$ **3.40**(a) Cl_2O_7 (b) $SiCl_4$
(c) CO_2 **3.42**(a) NO_2 (b) N_2O_4 **3.44**(a) 1.20 mol F (b) 24.0 g M

(c) calcium **3.47** $C_{21}H_{30}O_5$ **3.49** $C_{10}H_{20}O$ **3.50** A balanced equation provides information on the identities of reactants and products, the physical states of reactants and products, and the molar ratios by which reactants form products. **3.53** b

3.54(a) $16Cu(s) + S_8(s) \longrightarrow 8Cu_2S(s)$

(b) $P_4O_{10}(s) + 6H_2O(l) \longrightarrow 4H_3PO_4(l)$

(c) $B_2O_3(s) + 6NaOH(aq) \longrightarrow 2Na_3BO_3(aq) + 3H_2O(l)$

(d) $4CH_3NH_2(g) + 9O_2(g) \longrightarrow$
$$4CO_2(g) + 10H_2O(g) + 2N_2(g)$$

3.56(a) $2SO_2(g) + O_2(g) \longrightarrow 2SO_3(g)$

(b) $Sc_2O_3(s) + 3H_2O(l) \longrightarrow 2Sc(OH)_3(s)$

(c) $H_3PO_4(aq) + 2NaOH(aq) \longrightarrow Na_2HPO_4(aq) + 2H_2O(l)$

(d) $C_6H_{10}O_5(s) + 6O_2(g) \longrightarrow 6CO_2(g) + 5H_2O(g)$

3.58(a) $4Ga(s) + 3O_2(g) \longrightarrow 2Ga_2O_3(s)$

(b) $2C_6H_{14}(l) + 19O_2(g) \longrightarrow 12CO_2(g) + 14H_2O(g)$

(c) $3CaCl_2(aq) + 2Na_3PO_4(aq) \longrightarrow$
$$Ca_3(PO_4)_2(s) + 6NaCl(aq)$$

3.64 Balance the equation for the reaction: $aA + bB \longrightarrow cC$. Since A is the limiting reactant, A is used to determine the amount of C. Divide the mass of A by its molar mass to obtain the number of moles of A. Use the molar ratio from the balanced equation to find the number of moles of C. Multiply the number of moles of C by its molar mass to obtain the mass of C.

Road Map

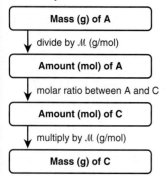

3.66(a) 0.455 mol Cl_2 (b) 32.3 g Cl_2 **3.68**(a) 1.42×10^3 mol KNO_3 (b) 1.43×10^5 g KNO_3 **3.70** 195.8 g H_3BO_3; 19.16 g H_2 **3.72** 2.60×10^3 g Cl_2

3.74(a) $I_2(s) + Cl_2(g) \longrightarrow 2ICl(s)$
$ICl(s) + Cl_2(g) \longrightarrow ICl_3(s)$

(b) $I_2(s) + 3Cl_2(g) \longrightarrow 2ICl_3(s)$

(c) 1.33×10^3 g I_2

3.76(a) 0.105 mol CaO (b) 0.175 mol CaO (c) calcium (d) 5.88 g CaO **3.78** 1.36 mol HIO_3, 239 g HIO_3; 44.9 g H_2O in excess **3.80** 4.40 g CO_2; 4.80 g O_2 in excess **3.82** 12.2 g $Al(NO_2)_3$, no NH_4Cl, 48.7 g $AlCl_3$, 30.7 g N_2, 39.5 g H_2O **3.84** 50.% **3.86** 90.5% **3.88** 24.0 g CH_3Cl **3.90**(a) 39.7 g CF_4 **3.91** A **3.95**(a) C (b) B (c) C (d) B **3.98** No, instructions should read: "Take 100.0 mL of the 10.0 M solution and, with stirring, add water until the total volume is 1000. mL." **3.99**(a) 7.85 g $Ca(C_2H_3O_2)_2$ (b) 0.254 M KI (c) 124 mol NaCN **3.101**(a) 4.65 g K_2SO_4 (b) 0.0653 M $CaCl_2$ (c) 1.11×10^{20} Mg^{2+} ions **3.103**(a) 0.0617 M KCl (b) 0.00363 M $(NH_4)_2SO_4$ (c) 0.138 M Na^+ **3.105**(a) 987 g HNO_3/L (b) 15.7 M HNO_3 **3.107** 845 mL **3.109** 0.88 g $BaSO_4$ **3.112**(a) Instructions: Be

sure to wear goggles to protect your eyes! Pour approximately 2.0 gal of water into the container. Add to the water, slowly and with mixing, 0.90 gal of concentrated HCl. Dilute to 3.0 gal with more water.

(b) 22.6 mL **3.117** $x = 3$ **3.118** ethane > propane > cetyl palmitate > ethanol > benzene **3.123**(a) $Fe_2O_3(s) + 3CO(g) \longrightarrow 2Fe(s) + 3CO_2(g)$ (b) 3.39×10^7 g CO **3.125** 89.8% **3.127**(a) $2AB_2 + B_2 \longrightarrow 2AB_3$ (b) AB_2 (c) 5.0 mol AB_3 (d) 0.5 mol B_2 **3.129** B, C, and D have the same empirical formula, C_2H_4O; 44.05 g/mol **3.130** 44.3% **3.133**(a) C (b) B (c) D **3.140**(a) 586 g CO_2 (b) 10.5% CH_4 by mass **3.142** 10/0.66/1.0 **3.147**(a) 192.12 g/mol; $C_6H_8O_7$ (b) 0.549 mol

3.148(a) $N_2(g) + O_2(g) \longrightarrow 2NO(g)$
$2NO(g) + O_2(g) \longrightarrow 2NO_2(g)$
$3NO_2(g) + H_2O(g) \longrightarrow 2HNO_3(aq) + NO(g)$

(b) $2N_2(g) + 5O_2(g) + 2H_2O(g) \longrightarrow 4HNO_3(aq)$

(c) 6.07×10^3 t HNO_3

3.149 A **3.151**(a) 0.039 g heme (b) 6.3×10^{-5} mol heme (c) 3.5×10^{-3} g Fe (d) 4.1×10^{-2} g hemin **3.153**(a) 46.65 mass % N in urea; 31.98 mass % N in arginine; 21.04 mass % N in ornithine (b) 28.45 g N **3.155** 29.54% **3.157**(a) 89.3% (b) 1.47 g ethylene **3.159**(a) 125 g salt (b) 65.6 L H_2O

Chapter 4

4.2 Ionic or polar covalent compounds **4.3** Ions must be present, and they come from ionic compounds or from electrolytes such as acids and bases. **4.6** B **4.10**(a) Benzene is likely to be insoluble in water because it is nonpolar and water is polar. (b) Sodium hydroxide, an ionic compound, is likely to be very soluble in water. (c) Ethanol (CH_3CH_2OH) is likely to be soluble in water because the alcohol group (—OH) is very polar, like the water molecule. (d) Potassium acetate, an ionic compound, is likely to be very soluble in water.

4.12(a) Yes, CsBr is a soluble salt. (b) Yes, HI is a strong acid. **4.14**(a) 0.64 mol (b) 0.242 mol (c) 1.18×10^{-4} mol **4.16**(a) 3.0 mol (b) 7.57×10^{-5} mol (c) 0.148 mol **4.18**(a) 0.058 mol Al^{3+}; 3.5×10^{22} Al^{3+} ions; 0.18 mol Cl^-; 1.1×10^{23} Cl^- ions (b) 4.62×10^{-4} mol Li^+; 2.78×10^{20} Li^+ ions; 2.31×10^{-4} mol SO_4^{2-}; 1.39×10^{20} SO_4^{2-} ions (c) 1.50×10^{-2} mol K^+; 9.02×10^{21} K^+ ions; 1.50×10^{-2} mol Br^-; 9.02×10^{21} Br^- ions **4.20**(a) 0.35 mol H^+ (b) 6.3×10^{-3} mol H^+ (c) 0.22 mol H^+ **4.24** Spectator ions do not appear in a net ionic equation because they are not involved in the reaction and serve only to balance charges. **4.28** Assuming that the left beaker contains $AgNO_3$ (because it has gray Ag^+ ions), the right must contain NaCl. Then, NO_3^- is blue, Na^+ is brown, and Cl^- is green.

Molecular equation: $AgNO_3(aq) + NaCl(aq) \longrightarrow$
$$AgCl(s) + NaNO_3(aq)$$

Total ionic equation: $Ag^+(aq) + NO_3^-(aq) + Na^+(aq) +$
$$Cl^-(aq) \longrightarrow AgCl(s) + Na^+(aq) + NO_3^-(aq)$$

Net ionic equation: $Ag^+(aq) + Cl^-(aq) \longrightarrow AgCl(s)$

4.29(a) Molecular: $Hg_2(NO_3)_2(aq) + 2KI(aq) \longrightarrow$
$$Hg_2I_2(s) + 2KNO_3(aq)$$

Total ionic: $Hg_2^{2+}(aq) + 2NO_3^-(aq) + 2K^+(aq) +$
  $2I^-(aq) \longrightarrow Hg_2I_2(s) + 2K^+(aq) + 2NO_3^-(aq)$
Net ionic: $Hg_2^{2+}(aq) + 2I^-(aq) \longrightarrow Hg_2I_2(s)$
Spectator ions are K^+ and NO_3^-.
(b) Molecular: $FeSO_4(aq) + Sr(OH)_2(aq) \longrightarrow$
  $Fe(OH)_2(s) + SrSO_4(s)$
Total ionic: $Fe^{2+}(aq) + SO_4^{2-}(aq) + Sr^{2+}(aq) +$
  $2OH^-(aq) \longrightarrow Fe(OH)_2(s) + SrSO_4(s)$
Net ionic: This is the same as the total ionic equation, because there are no spectator ions.
4.31(a) No precipitate will form. (b) A precipitate will form because silver ions, Ag^+, and bromide ions, Br^-, will combine to form a solid salt, silver bromide, AgBr. The ammonium and nitrate ions do not form a precipitate.
Molecular: $NH_4Br(aq) + AgNO_3(aq) \longrightarrow$
  $AgBr(s) + NH_4NO_3(aq)$
Total ionic: $NH_4^+(aq) + Br^-(aq) + Ag^+(aq) + NO_3^-(aq) \longrightarrow$
  $AgBr(s) + NH_4^+(aq) + NO_3^-(aq)$
Net ionic: $Ag^+(aq) + Br^-(aq) \longrightarrow AgBr(s)$
4.33(a) No precipitate will form.
  (b) $BaSO_4$ will precipitate.
Molecular: $(NH_4)_2SO_4(aq) + BaCl_2(aq) \longrightarrow$
  $BaSO_4(s) + 2NH_4Cl(aq)$
Total ionic: $2NH_4^+(aq) + SO_4^{2-}(aq) + Ba^{2+}(aq)$
  $+ 2Cl^-(aq) \longrightarrow BaSO_4(s) + 2NH_4^+(aq) + 2Cl^-(aq)$
Net ionic: $SO_4^{2-}(aq) + Ba^{2+}(aq) \longrightarrow BaSO_4(s)$
4.35 0.0354 M Pb^{2+} **4.37**(a) $PbSO_4$ (b) $Pb^{2+}(aq) +$
$SO_4^{2-}(aq) \longrightarrow PbSO_4(s)$ (c) 1.5 g $PbSO_4$ **4.39** Potassium carbonate, K_2CO_3 **4.41** 2.206 mass % Cl^- **4.47**(a) Formation of a gas, $SO_2(g)$, and of a nonelectrolyte (water) will cause the reaction to go to completion. (b) Formation of a precipitate $Ba_3(PO_4)_2(s)$, and of a nonelectrolyte (water) will cause the reaction to go to completion.
4.49(a) Molecular equation: $KOH(aq) + HBr(aq) \longrightarrow$
  $KBr(aq) + H_2O(l)$
Total ionic equation: $K^+(aq) + OH^-(aq) + H^+(aq)$
  $+ Br^-(aq) \longrightarrow K^+(aq) + Br^-(aq) + H_2O(l)$
Net ionic equation: $OH^-(aq) + H^+(aq) \longrightarrow H_2O(l)$
The spectator ions are $K^+(aq)$ and $Br^-(aq)$.
(b) Molecular equation: $NH_3(aq) + HCl(aq) \longrightarrow$
  $NH_4Cl(aq)$
Total ionic equation: $NH_3(aq) + H^+(aq) + Cl^-(aq) \longrightarrow$
  $NH_4^+(aq) + Cl^-(aq)$
NH_3, a weak base, is written in the molecular (undissociated) form. HCl, a strong acid, is written as dissociated ions. NH_4Cl is a soluble compound because all ammonium compounds are soluble.
Net ionic equation: $NH_3(aq) + H^+(aq) \longrightarrow NH_4^+(aq)$
Cl^- is the only spectator ion.
4.51 Total ionic equation: $CaCO_3(s) + 2H^+(aq) + 2Cl^-(aq) \longrightarrow$
  $Ca^{2+}(aq) + 2Cl^-(aq) + H_2O(l) + CO_2(g)$
Net ionic equation: $CaCO_3(s) + 2H^+(aq) \longrightarrow$
  $Ca^{2+}(aq) + H_2O(l) + CO_2(g)$
4.53 0.05839 M CH_3COOH **4.64**(a) S has O.N. = $+6$ in SO_4^{2-} (i.e., H_2SO_4) and O.N. = $+4$ in SO_2, so S has been

reduced (and I^- oxidized); H_2SO_4 acts as an oxidizing agent. (b) The oxidation numbers remain constant throughout; H_2SO_4 transfers an H^+ to F^- to produce HF, so it acts as an acid. **4.66**(a) $+4$ (b) $+3$ (c) $+4$ (d) -3 **4.68**(a) -1
(b) $+2$ (c) -3 (d) $+3$ **4.70**(a) -3 (b) $+5$ (c) $+3$
4.72(a) $+6$ (b) $+3$ (c) $+7$ **4.74**(a) MnO_4^- is the oxidizing agent; $H_2C_2O_4$ is the reducing agent. (b) Cu is the reducing agent; NO_3^- is the oxidizing agent. **4.76**(a) Oxidizing agent is NO_3^-; reducing agent is Sn. (b) Oxidizing agent is MnO_4^-; reducing agent is Cl^-.
4.78(a) $8HNO_3(aq) + K_2CrO_4(aq) + 3Fe(NO_3)_2(aq) \longrightarrow$
  $2KNO_3(aq) + 3Fe(NO_3)_3(aq) + Cr(NO_3)_3(aq) + 4H_2O(l)$
  Oxidizing agent is K_2CrO_4; reducing agent is $Fe(NO_3)_2$.
(b) $8HNO_3(aq) + 3C_2H_6O(l) + K_2Cr_2O_7(aq) \longrightarrow$
  $2KNO_3(aq) + 3C_2H_4O(l) + 7H_2O(l) + 2Cr(NO_3)_3(aq)$
  Oxidizing agent is $K_2Cr_2O_7$; reducing agent is C_2H_6O.
(c) $6HCl(aq) + 2NH_4Cl(aq) + K_2Cr_2O_7(aq) \longrightarrow$
  $2KCl(aq) + 2CrCl_3(aq) + N_2(g) + 7H_2O(l)$
  Oxidizing agent is $K_2Cr_2O_7$; reducing agent is NH_4Cl.
(d) $KClO_3(aq) + 6HBr(aq) \longrightarrow$
  $3Br_2(l) + 3H_2O(l) + KCl(aq)$
  Oxidizing agent is $KClO_3$; reducing agent is HBr.
4.80(a) 4.54×10^{-3} mol MnO_4^- (b) 0.0113 mol H_2O_2
(c) 0.386 g H_2O_2 (d) 2.61 mass % H_2O_2 (e) H_2O_2
4.86 A combination reaction that is also a redox reaction is $2Mg(s) + O_2(g) \longrightarrow 2MgO(s)$. A combination reaction that is not a redox reaction is $CaO(s) + H_2O(l) \longrightarrow Ca(OH)_2(aq)$.
4.87(a) $Ca(s) + 2H_2O(l) \longrightarrow$
  $Ca(OH)_2(aq) + H_2(g)$; displacement
(b) $2NaNO_3(s) \longrightarrow 2NaNO_2(s) + O_2(g)$; decomposition
(c) $C_2H_2(g) + 2H_2(g) \longrightarrow C_2H_6(g)$; combination
4.89(a) $2Sb(s) + 3Cl_2(g) \longrightarrow 2SbCl_3(s)$; combination
(b) $2AsH_3(g) \longrightarrow 2As(s) + 3H_2(g)$; decomposition
(c) $Zn(s) + Fe(NO_3)_2(aq) \longrightarrow$
  $Zn(NO_3)_2(aq) + Fe(s)$; displacement
4.91(a) $Sr(s) + Br_2(l) \longrightarrow SrBr_2(s)$
(b) $2Ag_2O(s) \xrightarrow{\Delta} 4Ag(s) + O_2(g)$
(c) $Mn(s) + Cu(NO_3)_2(aq) \longrightarrow Mn(NO_3)_2(aq) + Cu(s)$
4.93(a) $N_2(g) + 3H_2(g) \longrightarrow 2NH_3(g)$
(b) $2NaClO_3(s) \xrightarrow{\Delta} 2NaCl(s) + 3O_2(g)$
(c) $Ba(s) + 2H_2O(l) \longrightarrow Ba(OH)_2(aq) + H_2(g)$
4.95(a) $2Cs(s) + I_2(s) \longrightarrow 2CsI(s)$
(b) $2Al(s) + 3MnSO_4(aq) \longrightarrow Al_2(SO_4)_3(aq) + 3Mn(s)$
(c) $2SO_2(g) + O_2(g) \longrightarrow 2SO_3(g)$
(d) $2C_4H_{10}(g) + 13O_2(g) \longrightarrow 8CO_2(g) + 10H_2O(g)$
(e) $2Al(s) + 3Mn^{2+}(aq) \longrightarrow 2Al^{3+}(aq) + 3Mn(s)$
4.97 315 g O_2; 3.95 kg Hg **4.99**(a) O_2 is in excess.
(b) 0.117 mol Li_2O (c) 0 g Li, 3.49 g Li_2O, and 4.63 g O_2
4.101 67.2 mass % $KClO_3$ **4.103** 2.79 kg Fe **4.104** 99.9 g compound B, which is $FeCl_2$ **4.108** The reaction is $2NO + Br_2 \rightleftharpoons 2NOBr$, which can proceed in either direction. If NO and Br_2 are placed in a container, they will react to form NOBr, and NOBr will decompose to form NO and Br_2. Eventually, the concentrations of NO, Br_2, and NOBr

adjust so that the rates of the forward and reverse reactions become equal, and equilibrium is reached.
4.110(a) $Fe(s) + 2H^+(aq) \longrightarrow Fe^{2+}(aq) + H_2(g)$
O.N.:   0   +1   +2   0
(b) 3.1×10^{21} Fe^{2+} ions
4.112 5.11 g C_2H_5OH; 24.9 L CO_2
4.114(a) $Ca^{2+}(aq) + C_2O_4^{2-}(aq) \longrightarrow CaC_2O_4(s)$
(b) $5H_2C_2O_4(aq) + 2MnO_4^-(aq) + 6H^+(aq) \longrightarrow$
          $10CO_2(g) + 2Mn^{2+}(aq) + 8H_2O(l)$
(c) $KMnO_4$ (d) $H_2C_2O_4$ (e) 55.06 mass % $CaCl_2$
4.117 2.809 mass % $CaMg(CO_3)_2$ **4.119**(a) Step 1: oxidizing agent is O_2; reducing agent is NH_3. Step 2: oxidizing agent is O_2; reducing agent is NO. Step 3: oxidizing agent is NO_2; reducing agent is NO_2. (b) 1.2×10^4 kg NH_3 **4.123** 627 L air
4.125 0.75 kg SiO_2; 0.26 kg Na_2CO_3; 0.18 kg $CaCO_3$
4.128(a) 4 mol IO_3^- (b) 12 mol I_2; IO_3^- is oxidizing agent and I^- is reducing agent. (c) 12.87 mass % thyroxine
4.131 3.0×10^{-3} mol CO_2 (b) 0.11 L CO_2 **4.133**(a) $C_7H_5O_4Bi$
(b) $C_{21}H_{15}O_{12}Bi_3$ (c) $Bi(OH)_3(s) + 3HC_7H_5O_3(aq) \longrightarrow$
$Bi(C_7H_5O_3)_3(s) + 3H_2O(l)$ (d) 0.490 mg $Bi(OH)_3$
4.135(a) Ethanol: $C_2H_5OH(l) + 3O_2(g) \longrightarrow 2CO_2(g) + 3H_2O(l)$
Gasoline: $2C_8H_{18}(l) + 25O_2(g) \longrightarrow 16CO_2(g) + 18H_2O(g)$
(b) 2.50×10^3 g O_2 (c) 1.75×10^3 L O_2 (d) 8.38×10^3 L air
4.137 yes

Chapter 5

Answers to Boxed Reading Problems: B5.1 The density of the atmosphere decreases with increasing altitude. High density causes more drag on the aircraft. At high altitudes, low density means that there are relatively few gas particles present to collide with the aircraft. **B5.3** 0.934 %, 7.10 torr

• **5.1**(a) The volume of the liquid remains constant, but the volume of the gas increases to the volume of the larger container. (b) The volume of the container holding the gas sample increases when heated, but the volume of the container holding the liquid sample remains essentially constant when heated. (c) The volume of the liquid remains essentially constant, but the volume of the gas is reduced. **5.6** 990 cmH_2O **5.8**(a) 566 mmHg (b) 1.32 bar (c) 3.60 atm (d) 107 kPa **5.10** 0.9408 atm **5.12** 0.966 atm **5.18** At constant temperature and volume, the pressure of a gas is directly proportional to number of moles of the gas. **5.20**(a) Volume decreases to one-third of the original volume. (b) Volume increases by a factor of 3.0. (c) Volume increases by a factor of 4. **5.22**(a) Volume decreases by a factor of 2. (b) Volume increases by a factor of 1.48. (c) Volume decreases by a factor of 3. **5.24** $-144°C$ **5.26** 35.3 L **5.28** 0.085 mol Cl_2 **5.30** 1.16 g ClF_3 **5.33** yes **5.35** Beaker is inverted for H_2 and upright for CO_2. The molar mass of CO_2 is greater than the molar mass of air, which, in turn, has a greater molar mass than H_2. **5.39** 5.86 g/L **5.41** 1.78×10^{-3} mol AsH_3; 3.48 g/L **5.43** 51.1 g/mol **5.45** 1.33 atm **5.47** 39.2 g P_4 **5.49** 41.2 g PH_3 **5.51** 0.0249 g Al **5.55** C_5H_{12} **5.57**(a) 0.90 mol (b) 6.76 torr **5.58** 286 mL SO_2 **5.60** 0.0997 atm SiF_4 **5.65** At STP, the volume occupied by a mole of any gas is the same.

At the same temperature, all gases have the same average kinetic energy, resulting in the same pressure. **5.68**(a) $P_A > P_B > P_C$ (b) $E_A = E_B = E_C$ (c) $rate_A > rate_B > rate_C$ (d) total $E_A >$ total $E_B >$ total E_C (e) $d_A = d_B = d_C$ (f) collision frequency in A > collision frequency in B > collision frequency in C **5.69** 13.21 **5.71**(a) curve 1 (b) curve 1 (c) curve 1; fluorine and argon have about the same molar mass **5.73** 14.9 min **5.75** 4 atoms per molecule **5.78** negative deviations; $N_2 < Kr < CO_2$ **5.80** At 1 atm; at lower pressures, the gas molecules are farther apart and intermolecular forces are less important. **5.83** 6.81×10^4 g/mol **5.86**(a) 22.1 atm (b) 20.9 atm **5.90**(a) 597 torr N_2; 159 torr O_2; 0.3 torr CO_2; 3.5 torr H_2O (b) 74.9 mol % N_2; 13.7 mol % O_2; 5.3 mol % CO_2; 6.2 mol % H_2O (c) 1.6×10^{21} molecules O_2 **5.92**(a) 4×10^2 mL (b) 0.013 mol N_2 **5.93** 35.7 L NO_2 **5.98** Al_2Cl_6 **5.100** 1.52×10^{-2} mol SO_3 **5.104**(a) 1.95×10^3 g Ni (b) 3.5×10^4 g Ni (c) 63 m^3 CO **5.106**(a) 9 volumes of $O_2(g)$ (b) CH_5N **5.109** The lungs would expand by a factor of 4.86; the diver can safely ascend 52.5 ft to a depth of 73 ft. **5.111** 6.07 g H_2O_2 **5.116** 6.53×10^{-3} g N_2 **5.120**(a) xenon (b) water vapor (c) mercury vapor (d) water vapor **5.124** 17.2 g CO_2; 17.8 g Kr **5.130** Ne, 676 m/s; Ar, 481 m/s; He, 1.52×10^3 m/s **5.132**(a) 0.052 g (b) 1.1 mL **5.139**(a) 16.5 L CO_2 (b) $P_{H_2O} = 48.8$ torr; $P_{O_2} = P_{CO_2} = 3.7\times10^2$ torr **5.144** 332 steps **5.146** 1.4 **5.150** $P_{total} = 245$ torr; $P_{I_2} = 25.2$ torr

Chapter 6

Answers to Boxed Reading Problem: B6.2 (a) $2C(coal) + 2H_2O(g) \longrightarrow CH_4(g) + CO_2(g)$ (b) 12 kJ (c) -3.30×10^4 kJ

• **6.4** Increase: eating food, lying in the sun, taking a hot bath. Decrease: exercising, taking a cold bath, going outside on a cold day. **6.6** The amount of the change in internal energy is the same for heater and air conditioner. Since both devices consume the same amount of electrical energy, the change in energy of the heater equals that of the air conditioner. **6.8** 0 J **6.10** 1.54×10^3 J **6.12**(a) 6.6×10^7 kJ (b) 1.6×10^7 kcal (c) 6.3×10^7 Btu **6.15** 8.8 h **6.17** Measuring the heat transfer at constant pressure is more convenient than measuring at constant volume. **6.19**(a) exothermic (b) endothermic (c) exothermic (d) exothermic (e) endothermic (f) endothermic (g) exothermic

6.22

6.24(a) Combustion of ethane: $2C_2H_6(g) + 7O_2(g) \longrightarrow 4CO_2(g) + 6H_2O(g) +$ heat

(b) Freezing of water: $H_2O(l) \longrightarrow H_2O(s)$ + heat

$$H \begin{array}{l} \uparrow H_2O(l) \\ \overline{} \text{(initial)} \\ \\ \qquad \Delta H = (-), \text{(exothermic)} \\ \\ \downarrow H_2O(s) \\ \overline{} \text{(final)} \end{array}$$

6.26(a) $2CH_3OH(l) + 3O_2(g) \longrightarrow 2CO_2(g) + 4H_2O(g)$ + heat

$$H \begin{array}{l} \uparrow 2CH_3OH + 3O_2 \\ \overline{} \text{(initial)} \\ \downarrow \\ \qquad \Delta H = (-), \text{(exothermic)} \\ 2CO_2 + 4H_2O \\ \overline{} \text{(final)} \end{array}$$

(b) $\frac{1}{2}N_2(g) + O_2(g)$ + heat $\longrightarrow NO_2(g)$

$$H \begin{array}{l} \uparrow NO_2 \\ \overline{} \text{(final)} \\ \qquad \uparrow \\ \qquad \Delta H = (+), \text{(endothermic)} \\ \frac{1}{2}N_2 + O_2 \\ \overline{} \text{(initial)} \end{array}$$

6.28(a) This is a phase change from the solid phase to the gas phase. Heat is absorbed by the system so q_{sys} is positive (+). (b) The volume of the system is expanding as more moles of gas are present after the phase change than were present before the phase change. So the system has done work of expansion, and w is negative. Since $\Delta E_{sys} = q + w$, q is positive, and w is negative, the sign of ΔE_{sys} cannot be predicted. It will be positive if $q > w$ and negative if $q < w$. (c) $\Delta E_{univ} = 0$. If the system loses energy, the surroundings gain an equal amount of energy. The sum of the energy of the system and the energy of the surroundings remains constant. **6.31** To determine the specific heat capacity of a substance, you need its mass, the heat added (or lost), and the change in temperature. **6.33** Heat capacity is the quantity of heat required to raise the temperature of an object 1 K. Specific heat capacity is the quantity of heat required to raise 1 g of a material by 1 K. Molar heat capacity is the quantity of heat required to raise the temperature of 1 mol of a substance by 1 K. **6.35** 6.9×10^3 J **6.37** 295°C **6.39** 77.5°C **6.41** 45°C **6.43** 36.6°C **6.50** The reaction has a positive ΔH, because it requires the input of energy to break the oxygen-oxygen bond. **6.51** ΔH is negative; it is opposite in sign and half of the value for the vaporization of 2 mol of H_2O. **6.52**(a) exothermic (b) 20.2 kJ (c) -4.2×10^2 kJ (d) -15.7 kJ

6.54(a) $\frac{1}{2}N_2(g) + \frac{1}{2}O_2(g) \longrightarrow NO(g)$; $\Delta H = 90.29$ kJ
(b) -10.5 kJ
6.56 -1.88×10^6 kJ
6.60(a) $C_2H_4(g) + 3O_2(g) \longrightarrow 2CO_2(g) + 2H_2O(g)$;
$\Delta H_{rxn} = -1411$ kJ
(b) 1.39 g C_2H_4
6.64 -110.5 kJ **6.65** -813.4 kJ **6.67** $N_2(g) + 2O_2(g) \longrightarrow$ $2NO_2(g)$; $\Delta H_{overall} = 66.4$ kJ; equation 1 is A, equation 2 is B, and equation 3 is C. **6.69** 44.0 kJ **6.72** The standard enthalpy of reaction, ΔH_{rxn}°, is the enthalpy change for a reaction where all substances are in their standard states. The standard

enthalpy of formation, ΔH_f°, is the enthalpy change that accompanies the formation of one mole of a compound in its standard state from elements in their standard states.
6.74(a) $\frac{1}{2}Cl_2(g) + Na(s) \longrightarrow NaCl(s)$
(b) $H_2(g) + \frac{1}{2}O_2(g) \longrightarrow H_2O(g)$
(c) no changes
6.75(a) $Ca(s) + Cl_2(g) \longrightarrow CaCl_2(s)$
(b) $Na(s) + \frac{1}{2}H_2(g) + C(\text{graphite}) + \frac{3}{2}O_2(g) \longrightarrow$
$$NaHCO_3(s)$$
(c) $C(\text{graphite}) + 2Cl_2(g) \longrightarrow CCl_4(l)$
(d) $\frac{1}{2}H_2(g) + \frac{1}{2}N_2(g) + \frac{3}{2}O_2(g) \longrightarrow HNO_3(l)$
6.77(a) -1036.9 kJ (b) -433 kJ **6.79** -157.3 kJ/mol
6.81(a) 503.9 kJ (b) $-\Delta H_1 + 2\Delta H_2 = 504$ kJ
6.82(a) $C_{18}H_{36}O_2(s) + 26O_2(g) \longrightarrow 18CO_2(g) + 18H_2O(g)$
(b) $-10,488$ kJ (c) -36.9 kJ; -8.81 kcal (d) 8.81 kcal/g
$\times$ 11.0 g = 96.9 kcal **6.84**(a) initial = 23.6 L/mol; final = 24.9 L/mol (b) 187 J (c) -1.2×10^2 J (d) 3.1×10^2 J
(e) 310 J (f) $\Delta H = \Delta E + P\Delta V = \Delta E - w = (q + w) - w = q_P$ **6.93**(a) 1.1×10^3 J (b) 1.1×10^8 J (c) 1.3×10^2 mol CH_4 (d) \$0.0050/mol (e) \$0.85 **6.98**(a) $\Delta H_{rxn1}^{\circ} = -657.0$ kJ; $\Delta H_{rxn2}^{\circ} = 32.9$ kJ (b) -106.6 kJ **6.99**(a) -6.81×10^3 J
(b) $+243$°C **6.100** -22.2 kJ **6.101**(a) 34 kJ/mol
(b) -757 kJ **6.103**(a) -1.25×10^3 kJ (b) 2.24×10^{3}°C

Chapter 7

Answers to Boxed Reading Problem: B7.1 (a) slope = $1.3 \times 10^4/M$; y-intercept = 0.00

(b) diluted solution = 1.8×10^{-5} M; original solution = 1.4×10^{-4} M

• 7.2(a) x-ray < ultraviolet < visible < infrared < microwave < radio waves (b) radio < microwave < infrared < visible < ultraviolet < x-ray
(c) radio < microwave < infrared < visible < ultraviolet < x-ray **7.7** 316 m; 3.16×10^{11} nm; 3.16×10^{12} Å **7.9** 2.5×10^{-23} J
7.11 red < yellow < blue **7.13** 1.3483×10^7 nm; 1.3483×10^8 Å
7.16(a) 1.24×10^{15} s^{-1}; 8.21×10^{-19} J (b) 1.4×10^{15} s^{-1};
9.0×10^{-19} J **7.18** Bohr's key assumption was that the electron in an atom does not radiate energy while in a stationary state, and it can move to a different orbit only by absorbing or emitting a photon whose energy is equal to the difference in energy between two states. These differences in energy correspond to the wavelengths in the known line spectra for the hydrogen atom. A solar system model does not allow for the movement of electrons between levels. **7.20**(a) absorption (b) emission (c) emission (d) absorption **7.22** Yes, the predicted line spectra are accurate. The energies could be predicted from

$$E_n = \frac{-(Z^2)(2.18 \times 10^{-18} \text{ J})}{n^2}, \text{ where } Z \text{ is the atomic number for}$$

the atom or ion. The energy levels for Be^{3+} will be greater by a factor of 16 ($Z = 4$) than those for the hydrogen atom. This means that the pattern of lines will be similar, but the lines will be at different wavelengths. **7.23** 434.17 nm **7.25** 1875.6 nm **7.27** -2.76×10^5 J/mol **7.29** d < a < c < b **7.31** $n = 4$ **7.37** Macroscopic objects do exhibit a wavelike motion, but the wavelength is too small for humans to perceive. **7.39**(a) 7.10×10^{-37} m (b) 1×10^{-35} m **7.41** 2.2×10^{-26} m/s **7.43** 3.75×10^{-36} kg **7.47** The total probability of finding the $1s$ electron in any distance r from the H nucleus is greatest when the value of r is 0.529 Å. The probability is greater for the $1s$ orbital. **7.48**(a) principal determinant of the electron's energy or distance from the nucleus (b) determines the shape of the orbital (c) determines the orientation of the orbital in three-dimensional space **7.49**(a) one (b) five (c) three (d) nine **7.51**(a) m_l: $-2, -1, 0, +1, +2$ (b) m_l: 0 (if $n = 1$, then $l = 0$) (c) m_l: $-3, -2, -1, 0, +1, +2, +3$

7.53(a)

(b)

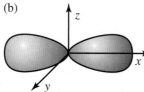

7.55

Sublevel	Allowable m_l values	No. of orbitals
(a) d ($l = 2$)	$-2, -1, 0, +1, +2$	5
(b) p ($l = 1$)	$-1, 0, +1$	3
(c) f ($l = 3$)	$-3, -2, -1, 0, +1, +2, +3$	7

7.57(a) $n = 5$ and $l = 0$; one orbital (b) $n = 3$ and $l = 1$; three orbitals (c) $n = 4$ and $l = 3$; seven orbitals **7.59**(a) no; $n = 2, l = 1, m_l = -1; n = 2, l = 0, m_l = 0$ (b) allowed (c) allowed (d) no; $n = 5, l = 3, m_l = +3; n = 5, l = 2, m_l = 0$ **7.62**(a) $E = -(2.180 \times 10^{-18}$ J$)(1/n^2)$. This is identical to the expression from Bohr's theory. (b) 3.028×10^{-19} J (c) 656.1 nm **7.63**(a) The attraction of the nucleus for the electrons must be overcome. (b) The electrons in silver are more tightly held by the nucleus. (c) silver (d) Once the electron is freed from the atom, its energy increases in proportion to the frequency of the light. **7.66** Li^{2+} **7.68**(a) $2 \longrightarrow 1$ (b) $5 \longrightarrow 2$ (c) $4 \longrightarrow 2$ (d) $3 \longrightarrow 2$ (e) $6 \longrightarrow 3$ **7.72**(a) $l = 1$ or 2 (b) $l = 1$ or 2 (c) $l = 3, 4, 5$, or 6 (d) $l = 2$ or 3 **7.74**(a) $\Delta E =$

$$(-2.18 \times 10^{-18} \text{ J})\left(\frac{1}{\infty^2} - \frac{1}{n_{initial}^2}\right)Z^2\left(\frac{6.022 \times 10^{23}}{1 \text{ mol}}\right)$$

(b) 3.28×10^7 J/mol (c) 205 nm (d) 22.8 nm **7.76**(a) 5.293×10^{-11} m (b) 5.293×10^{-9} m **7.78** 6.4×10^{27} photons **7.80**(a) no overlap (b) overlap (c) two (d) At longer wavelengths, the hydrogen spectrum begins to become a continuous band. **7.82**(a) 7.56×10^{-18} J; 2.63×10^{-8} m (b) 5.122×10^{-17} J; 3.881×10^{-9} m (c) 1.2×10^{-18} J; 1.66×10^{-7} m **7.84**(a) 1.87×10^{-19} J (b) 3.58×10^{-19} J **7.86**(a) red; green (b) 5.89 kJ (Sr); 5.83 kJ (Ba) **7.88**(a) This is

the wavelength of maximum absorbance, so it gives the highest sensitivity. (b) ultraviolet region (c) 1.93×10^{-2} g vitamin A/g oil **7.92** 1.0×10^{18} photons/s **7.95** $3s \longrightarrow 2p$; $3d \longrightarrow 2p$; $4s \longrightarrow 2p$; $3p \longrightarrow 2s$

Chapter 8

8.1 Elements are listed in the periodic table in an ordered, systematic way that correlates with a periodicity of their chemical and physical properties. The theoretical basis for the table in terms of atomic number and electron configuration does not allow for a "new element" between Sn and Sb. **8.3**(a) predicted atomic mass = 54.23 amu (b) predicted melting point = 6.3°C **8.6** The quantum number m_s relates to just the electron; all the others describe the orbital. **8.9** Shielding occurs when electrons protect, or shield, other electrons from the full nuclear attraction. The effective nuclear charge is the nuclear charge an electron actually experiences. As the number of electrons, especially inner electrons, increases, the effective nuclear charge decreases. **8.11**(a) 6 (b) 10 (c) 2 **8.13**(a) 6 (b) 2 (c) 14 **8.16** Hund's rule states that electrons will occupy empty orbitals in a given sublevel (with parallel spins) before filling half-filled orbitals. The lowest energy arrangement has the maximum number of unpaired electrons with parallel spins.

N: $1s^2 2s^2 2p^3$

$1s$ $2s$ $2p$

8.18 Main-group elements from the same group have similar outer electron configurations, and the (old) group number equals the number of outer electrons. Outer electron configurations vary in a periodic manner within a period, with each succeeding element having an additional electron. **8.20** The maximum number of electrons in any energy level n is $2n^2$, so the $n = 4$ energy level holds a maximum of $2(4^2) = 32$ electrons. **8.21**(a) $n = 5, l = 0, m_l = 0$, and $m_s = +\frac{1}{2}$ (b) $n = 3, l = 1, m_l = +1$, and $m_s = -\frac{1}{2}$ (c) $n = 5, l = 0, m_l = 0$, and $m_s = +\frac{1}{2}$ (d) $n = 2, l = 1, m_l = +1$, and $m_s = -\frac{1}{2}$ **8.23**(a) Rb: $1s^2 2s^2 2p^6 3s^2 3p^6 4s^2 3d^{10} 4p^6 5s^1$ (b) Ge: $1s^2 2s^2 2p^6 3s^2 3p^6 4s^2 3d^{10} 4p^2$ (c) Ar: $1s^2 2s^2 2p^6 3s^2 3p^6$ **8.25**(a) Cl: $1s^2 2s^2 2p^6 3s^2 3p^5$ (b) Si: $1s^2 2s^2 2p^6 3s^2 3p^2$ (c) Sr: $1s^2 2s^2 2p^6 3s^2 3p^6 4s^2 3d^{10} 4p^6 5s^2$ **8.27**(a) Ti: [Ar] $4s^2 3d^2$

↑↓	↑	↑						

$4s$ $3d$ $4p$

(b) Cl: [Ne] $3s^2 3p^5$

↑↓	↑↓	↑↓	↑

$3s$ $3p$

(c) V: [Ar] $4s^2 3d^3$

↑↓	↑	↑	↑					

$4s$ $3d$ $4p$

8.29(a) Mn: [Ar] $4s^2 3d^5$

(b) P: [Ne] $3s^2 3p^3$

↑↓		↑	↑	↑	
$3s$			$3p$		

(c) Fe: [Ar] $4s^2 3d^6$

↑↓		↑↓	↑	↑	↑	↑				
$4s$				$3d$					$4p$	

8.31(a) O; Group 6A(16); Period 2

↑↓		↑↓	↑	↑
$2s$			$2p$	

(b) P; Group 5A(15); Period 3

↑↓		↑	↑	↑
$3s$			$3p$	

8.33(a) Cl; Group 7A(17); Period 3

↑↓		↑↓	↑↓	↑
$3s$			$3p$	

(b) As; Group 5A(15); Period 4

↑↓		↑	↑	↑
$4s$			$4p$	

8.35(a) [Ar] $4s^2 3d^{10} 4p^1$; Group 3A(13) (b) [He] $2s^2 2p^6$; Group 8A(18)

8.37

	Inner Electrons	Outer Electrons	Valence Electrons
(a) O	2	6	6
(b) Sn	46	4	4
(c) Ca	18	2	2
(d) Fe	18	2	8
(e) Se	28	6	6

8.39(a) B; Al, Ga, In, and Tl (b) S; O, Se, Te, and Po (c) La; Sc, Y, and Ac **8.41**(a) C; Si, Ge, Sn, and Pb (b) V; Nb, Ta, and Db (c) P; N, As, Sb, and Bi

8.43 Na (first excited state): $1s^2 2s^2 2p^6 3p^1$

↑↓		↑↓		↑↓	↑↓	↑↓					↑	
$1s$		$2s$			$2p$			$3s$			$3p$	

8.50 A high IE_1 and a very negative EA_1 suggest that the elements are halogens, in Group 7A(17), which form $1-$ ions. **8.53**(a) K < Rb < Cs (b) O < C < Be (c) Cl < S < K (d) Mg < Ca < K **8.55**(a) Ba < Sr < Ca (b) B < N < Ne (c) Rb < Se < Br (d) Sn < Sb < As **8.57** $1s^2 2s^2 2p^1$ (boron, B) **8.59**(a) Na (b) Na (c) Be **8.61**(1) Metals conduct electricity; nonmetals do not. (2) Metal ions have a positive charge; nonmetal ions have a negative charge. (3) Metal oxides are mostly ionic and act as bases; nonmetal oxides are mostly covalent and act as acids. **8.62** Metallic character increases down a group and decreases to the right across a period. These trends are the same as those for atomic size and opposite those for ionization energy. **8.65** Possible ions are $2+$ and $4+$. The $2+$ ions form by loss of the outermost two p electrons; the $4+$ ions form by loss of these and the outermost two s electrons. **8.69**(a) Rb (b) Ra (c) I **8.71**(a) As (b) P (c) Be **8.73** acidic solution; $SO_2(g) + H_2O(l) \longrightarrow H_2SO_3(aq)$

8.75(a) Cl^-: $1s^2 2s^2 2p^6 3s^2 3p^6$ (b) Na^+: $1s^2 2s^2 2p^6$ (c) Ca^{2+}: $1s^2 2s^2 2p^6 3s^2 3p^6$ **8.77**(a) Al^{3+}: $1s^2 2s^2 2p^6$ (b) S^{2-}: $1s^2 2s^2 2p^6 3s^2 3p^6$ (c) Sr^{2+}: $1s^2 2s^2 2p^6 3s^2 3p^6 4s^2\ 3d^{10} 4p^6$ **8.79**(a) 0 (b) 3 (c) 0 (d) 1 **8.81** a, b, and d **8.83**(a) V^{3+}: [Ar] $3d^2$, paramagnetic (b) Cd^{2+}: [Kr] $4d^{10}$, diamagnetic (c) Co^{3+}: [Ar] $3d^6$, paramagnetic (d) Ag^+: [Kr] $4d^{10}$, diamagnetic **8.85** For palladium to be diamagnetic, all of its electrons must be paired. (a) You might first write the condensed electron configuration for Pd as [Kr] $5s^2 4d^8$. However, the partial orbital diagram is not consistent with diamagnetism.

↑↓		↑↓	↑↓	↑↓	↑	↑				
$5s$				$4d$					$5p$	

(b) This is the only configuration that supports diamagnetism, [Kr] $4d^{10}$.

		↑↓	↑↓	↑↓	↑↓	↑↓				
$5s$				$4d$					$5p$	

(c) Promoting an s electron into the d sublevel still leaves two electrons unpaired.

↑		↑↓	↑↓	↑↓	↑↓	↑				
$5s$				$4d$					$5p$	

8.87(a) $Li^+ < Na^+ < K^+$ (b) $Rb^+ < Br^- < Se^{2-}$ (c) $F^- < O^{2-} < N^{3-}$ **8.90** Ce: [Xe] $6s^2 4f^1 5d^1$; Ce^{4+}: [Xe]; Eu: [Xe] $6s^2 4f^7$; Eu^{2+}: [Xe] $4f^7$. Ce^{4+} has a noble-gas configuration; Eu^{2+} has a half-filled f subshell. **8.91**(a) Cl_2O, dichlorine monoxide (b) Cl_2O_3, dichlorine trioxide (c) Cl_2O_5, dichlorine pentaoxide (d) Cl_2O_7, dichlorine heptaoxide (e) SO_3, sulfur trioxide (f) SO_2, sulfur dioxide (g) N_2O_5, dinitrogen pentaoxide (h) N_2O_3, dinitrogen trioxide (i) CO_2, carbon dioxide (j) P_4O_{10}, tetraphosphorus decaoxide **8.94**(a) $SrBr_2$, strontium bromide (b) CaS, calcium sulfide (c) ZnF_2, zinc fluoride (d) LiF, lithium fluoride **8.95**(a) 2009 kJ/mol (b) -549 kJ/mol **8.97** All ions except Fe^{8+} and Fe^{14+} are paramagnetic; Fe^+ and Fe^{3+} would be most attracted.

Chapter 9

Answers to Boxed Reading Problems: B9.1 The C=C bond shows absorption of IR at shorter wavelength (higher energy) because it is a stronger bond than C—C. The C≡C bond would show absorption at a shorter wavelength (higher energy) than the C=C bond since the triple bond has a larger bond energy than the double bond. **B9.2** (a) 7460 nm (symmetric stretch), 1.50×10^4 nm (bending), 4260 nm (asymmetrical stretch) (b) 2.66×10^{-20} J (symmetric stretch), 1.33×10^{-20} J (bending), 4.67×10^{-20} J (asymmetrical stretch); bending requires the least amount of energy.

• **9.1**(a) Greater ionization energy decreases metallic character. (b) Larger atomic radius increases metallic character. (c) Higher number of outer electrons decreases metallic character. (d) Larger effective nuclear charge decreases metallic character. **9.4**(a) Cs (b) Rb (c) As **9.6**(a) ionic (b) covalent (c) metallic **9.8**(a) covalent (b) ionic (c) covalent **9.10**(a) Rb· (b) ·Ṡi· (c) :Ï: **9.12**(a) ·Sr· (b) :Ṗ· (c) :S̈· **9.14**(a) 6A(16); [noble gas] $ns^2 np^4$ (b) 3(A)13; [noble gas] $ns^2 np^1$ **9.20**(a) Ba^{2+}, [Xe]; Cl^-, [Ne] $3s^2 3p^6$, :C̈l:⁻ ; $BaCl_2$

(b) Sr^{2+}, [Kr]; O^{2-}, [He] $2s^22p^6$, $:\!\ddot{O}\!:^{2-}$; SrO (c) Al^{3+}, [Ne]; F^-, [He] $2s^22p^6$, $:\!\ddot{F}\!:^-$; AlF_3 (d) Rb^+, [Kr]; O^{2-}, [He] $2s^22p^6$, $:\!\ddot{O}\!:^{2-}$; Rb_2O. **9.22**(a) 2A(2) (b) 6A(16) (c) 1A(1) **9.24**(a) 3A(13) (b) 2A(2) (c) 6A(16) **9.26**(a) BaS; the charge on each ion is twice the charge on the ions in CsCl. (b) LiCl; Li^+ is smaller than Cs^+. **9.28**(a) BaS; Ba^{2+} is larger than Ca^{2+}. (b) NaF; the charge on each ion is less than the charge on Mg and O. **9.30** 788 kJ; the lattice energy for NaCl is less than that for LiF, because the Na^+ and Cl^- ions are larger than Li^+ and F^- ions. **9.33** -336 kJ **9.34** When two chlorine atoms are far apart, there is no interaction between them. As the atoms move closer together, the nucleus of each atom attracts the electrons of the other atom. The closer the atoms, the greater this attraction; however, the repulsions of the two nuclei and the electrons also increase at the same time. The final internuclear distance is the distance at which maximum attraction is achieved in spite of the repulsion. **9.35** The bond energy is the energy required to break the bond between H atoms and Cl atoms in one mole of HCl molecules in the gaseous state. Energy is needed to break bonds, so bond breaking is always endothermic and $\Delta H^\circ_{\text{bond breaking}}$ is positive. The quantity of energy needed to break the bond is released upon its formation, so $\Delta H^\circ_{\text{bond forming}}$ has the same magnitude as $\Delta H^\circ_{\text{bond breaking}}$ but is opposite in sign (always exothermic and negative). **9.39**(a) I—I < Br—Br < Cl—Cl (b) S—Br < S—Cl < S—H (c) C—N < C=N < C≡N **9.41**(a) C—O < C=O; the C=O bond (bond order = 2) is stronger than the C—O bond (bond order = 1). (b) C—H < O—H; O is smaller than C so the O—H bond is shorter and stronger than the C—H bond. **9.43** Less energy is required to break weak bonds. **9.45** Both are one-carbon molecules. Since methane contains fewer carbon-oxygen bonds, it will have the greater heat of reaction per mole for combustion. **9.47** -168 kJ **9.49** -22 kJ **9.50** -59 kJ **9.51** Electronegativity increases from left to right and increases from bottom to top within a group. Fluorine and oxygen are the two most electronegative elements. Cesium and francium are the two least electronegative elements. **9.53** The H—O bond in water is polar covalent. A nonpolar covalent bond occurs between two atoms with identical electronegativities. A polar covalent bond occurs when the atoms have differing electronegativities. Ionic bonds result from electron transfer between atoms.
9.56(a) Si < S < O (b) Mg < As < P
9.58(a) N > P > Si (b) As > Ga > Ca
9.60(a) $\overset{\longleftrightarrow}{N-B}$ (b) $\overset{\longrightarrow}{N-O}$ (c) $\overset{\text{none}}{C-S}$

(d) $\overset{\longrightarrow}{S-O}$ (e) $\overset{\longrightarrow}{N-H}$ (f) $\overset{\longrightarrow}{Cl-O}$

9.62 a, d, and e **9.64**(a) nonpolar covalent (b) ionic (c) polar covalent (d) polar covalent (e) nonpolar covalent (f) polar covalent; $SCl_2 < SF_2 < PF_3$

9.66(a) $\overset{\longrightarrow}{H-I}$ < $\overset{\longrightarrow}{H-Br}$ < $\overset{\longrightarrow}{H-Cl}$

(b) $\overset{\longrightarrow}{H-C}$ < $\overset{\longrightarrow}{H-O}$ < $\overset{\longrightarrow}{H-F}$

(c) $\overset{\longrightarrow}{S-Cl}$ < $\overset{\longrightarrow}{P-Cl}$ < $\overset{\longrightarrow}{Si-Cl}$

9.69(a) Shiny, conducts heat, conducts electricity, and is malleable. (b) Metals lose electrons to form positive ions, and metals form basic oxides. **9.73**(a) 800. kJ/mol, which is lower than the value in Table 9.2 (b) -2.417×10^4 kJ (c) 1690. g CO_2 (d) 65.2 L O_2 **9.75**(a) -125 kJ (b) yes, since ΔH°_f is negative (c) -392 kJ (d) No, ΔH°_f for $MgCl_2$ is much more negative than that for MgCl. **9.77**(a) 406 nm (b) 2.93×10^{-19} J (c) 1.87×10^4 m/s **9.80** C—Cl: 3.53×10^{-7} m; bond in O_2: 2.40×10^{-7} m **9.81** XeF_2: 132 kJ/mol; XeF_4: 150. kJ/mol; XeF_6: 146 kJ/mol **9.83**(a) The presence of the very electronegative fluorine atoms bonded to one of the carbons makes the C—C bond polar. This polar bond will tend to undergo heterolytic rather than homolytic cleavage. More energy is required to achieve heterolytic cleavage. (b) 1420 kJ **9.86** 13,286 kJ **9.88** 8.70×10^{14} s^{-1}; 3.45×10^{-7} m; the ultraviolet region of the electromagnetic spectrum **9.90**(a) $CH_3OCH_3(g)$: -326 kJ; $CH_3CH_2OH(g)$: -369 kJ (b) The formation of gaseous ethanol is more exothermic. (c) 43 kJ

Chapter 10

Answers to Boxed Reading Problem: B10.1 resonance form on the left: trigonal planar around C, trigonal pyramidal around N; resonance form on the right: trigonal planar around both C and N.

• **10.1** He cannot serve as a central atom because it does not bond. H cannot because it forms only one bond. Fluorine cannot because it needs only one electron to complete its valence level, and it does not have d orbitals available to expand its valence level. Thus, it can bond to only one other atom. **10.3** All the structures obey the octet rule except c and g. **10.5**(a) (b) (c)

10.7(a) (b) (c) $:\!\ddot{S}\!=\!C\!=\!\ddot{S}\!:$

10.9(a) $\left[\ddot{O}\!=\!N\!=\!\ddot{O}\right]^+$
(b)

10.11(a) $[:\!\ddot{N}\!=\!N\!=\!\ddot{N}\!:]^- \longleftrightarrow [:\!\ddot{N}\!-\!N\!\equiv\!N:]^- \longleftrightarrow [:N\!\equiv\!N\!-\!\ddot{N}\!:]^-$
(b) $[:\!\ddot{O}\!=\!N\!-\!\ddot{O}\!:]^- \longleftrightarrow [:\!\ddot{O}\!-\!N\!=\!\ddot{O}\!:]^-$

10.13(a)   formal charges: I = 0, F = 0

(b)   formal charges: H = 0, Al = -1

10.15(a) $[:\!C\!\equiv\!N\!:]^-$ formal charges: C = -1, N = 0

(b) $[:\!\ddot{C}l\!-\!\ddot{O}\!:]^-$ formal charges: Cl = 0, O = -1

10.17(a) $\left[\ddot{O}=\overset{..}{Br}=\ddot{O}\right]^{-}$ with :O: below

formal charges: Br = 0, doubly bonded O = 0, singly bonded O = −1 O.N.: Br = +5; O = −2

(b) $\left[:\ddot{O}-\overset{..}{S}-\ddot{O}:\right]^{2-}$ with :O: below

formal charges: S = 0, singly bonded O = −1, doubly bonded O = 0 O.N.: S = +4; O = −2

10.19(a) B has 6 valence electrons in BH₃, so the molecule is electron deficient. (b) As has an expanded valence level with 10 electrons. (c) Se has an expanded valence level with 10 electrons.

(a) BH₃ structure (b) [AsF₄]⁻ structure (c) SeCl₂ structure

(a)   (b)   (c)

10.21(a) Br expands its valence level to 10 electrons. (b) I has an expanded valence level of 10 electrons. (c) Be has only 4 valence electrons in BeF₂, so the molecule is electron deficient.

(a) $:\ddot{F}-\overset{..}{Br}-\ddot{F}:$ with :F: below (b) $[:\ddot{Cl}-\ddot{I}-\ddot{Cl}:]^{-}$ (c) $:\ddot{F}-Be-\ddot{F}:$

10.23

$:\ddot{Cl}-Be-\ddot{Cl}:$ + $\begin{bmatrix}[:\ddot{Cl}:]^{-}\\ [:\ddot{Cl}:]^{-}\end{bmatrix}$ ⟶ $\left[:\ddot{Cl}-Be-\ddot{Cl}:\right]^{2-}$ with :Cl: above and :Cl: below

10.26 structure A   **10.28** The molecular shape and the electron-group arrangement are the same when no lone pairs are present on the central atom.   **10.30** tetrahedral, AX₄; trigonal pyramidal, AX₃E; bent or V shaped, AX₂E₂

10.32(a) A with X, X bent (b) X–A–X with X below (trigonal planar) (c) X–A with X, X, X (d) X–A–X with X below (e) A with X's (f) A with X's

10.34(a) trigonal planar, bent, 120° (b) tetrahedral, trigonal pyramidal, 109.5° (c) tetrahedral, trigonal pyramidal, 109.5°
10.36(a) trigonal planar, trigonal planar, 120° (b) trigonal planar, bent, 120° (c) tetrahedral, tetrahedral, 109.5°
10.38(a) trigonal planar, AX₃, 120° (b) trigonal pyramidal, AX₃E, 109.5° (c) trigonal bipyramidal, AX₅, 90° and 120°   **10.40**(a) bent, 109.5°, less than 109.5° (b) trigonal bipyramidal, 90° and 120°, angles are ideal (c) seesaw, 90° and 120°, less than ideal (d) linear, 180°, angle is ideal
10.42(a) C: tetrahedral, 109.5°; O: bent, < 109.5° (b) N: trigonal planar, 120°   **10.44**(a) C in CH₃: tetrahedral, 109.5°; C with C=O: trigonal planar, 120°; O with H: bent, < 109.5°
(b) O: bent, < 109.5°   **10.46** OF₂ < NF₃ < CF₄ < BF₃ < BeF₂
10.48(a) The C and N each have three groups, so the ideal angles are 120°; the O has four groups, so the ideal angle is

109.5°. The N and O have lone pairs, so the angles are less than ideal. (b) All central atoms have four pairs, so the ideal angles are 109.5°. The lone pairs on the O reduce this value. (c) The B has three groups and an ideal bond angle of 120°. All the O's have four groups (ideal bond angles of 109.5°), two of which are lone pairs that reduce the angle.

10.51 PCl₅ structures (three Lewis structures)

In the gas phase, PCl₅ is AX₅, so the shape is trigonal bipyramidal, and the bond angles are 120° and 90°. The PCl₄⁺ ion is AX₄, so the shape is tetrahedral, and the bond angles are 109.5°. The PCl₆⁻ ion is AX₆, so the shape is octahedral, and the bond angles are 90°.   **10.52** Molecules are polar if they have polar bonds that are not arranged to cancel each other. A polar bond is present any time there is a bond between elements with differing electronegativities.   **10.55**(a) CF₄ (b) BrCl and SCl₂   **10.57**(a) SO₂, because it is polar and SO₃ is not.
(b) IF has a greater electronegativity difference between its atoms. (c) SF₄, because it is polar and SiF₄ is not. (d) H₂O has a greater electronegativity difference between its atoms.

10.59 Three C=C structures labeled X, Y, Z

Yes, compound Y has a dipole moment.

10.61(a) H–N̈–N̈–H with H, H (Hydrazine)   H–N̈=N̈–H (Diazene)   :N≡N: (Nitrogen)

The single N—N bond (bond order = 1) is weaker and longer than the others. The triple bond (bond order = 3) is stronger and shorter than the others. The double bond (bond order = 2) has an intermediate strength and length.
(b) ΔH°_{rxn} = −367 kJ

H–N̈–N̈=N̈–N̈–H ⟶ H–N̈–N̈–H + :N≡N:

10.65(a) formal charges: Al = −1, end Cl = 0, bridging Cl = +1; I = −1, end Cl = 0, bridging Cl = +1 (b) The iodine atoms are each AX₄E₂, and the shape around each is square planar. These square planar portions are adjacent, giving a planar molecule.

10.70

$\overset{H_3C}{\underset{H}{}}C=CH_2$ + H₂O₂ ⟶ $H_3C-\overset{O}{\underset{}{C}}-CH_2$ + H₂O

(a) In propylene oxide, the shape around each C is tetrahedral, with ideal angles of 109.5°. (b) The C that is not part of the three-membered ring should have close to the ideal angle. The atoms in the ring form an equilateral triangle, so the angles around the two C's in the ring are reduced from the ideal 109.5° to 60°.   **10.75**(a) −1267 kJ/mol (b) −1226 kJ/mol (c) −1234.8 kJ/mol. The two answers differ by less than 10 kJ/mol. This is very good agreement since average bond energies were used to calculate answers a and b. (d) −37 kJ

10.77 H—Ö—C—C—Ö—H
         ‖ ‖
        :O: :O:

10.80 CH_4: -409 kJ/mol O_2; H_2S: -398 kJ/mol O_2

10.82(a) The O in the OH species has only 7 valence electrons, which is less than an octet, and 1 electron is unpaired. (b) 426 kJ (c) 508 kJ **10.84**(a) The F atoms will substitute at the axial positions first. (b) PF_5 and PCl_3F_2

10.86 $H_2C_2O_4$:

H—Ö: :Ö—H
    \   /
     C—C
    /   \
  :O: :O:

$HC_2O_4^-$:

$\begin{bmatrix} :Ö: & :Ö—H \\ & C—C \\ :O: & :O: \end{bmatrix}^- \longleftrightarrow \begin{bmatrix} :O: & :Ö—H \\ & C—C \\ :O: & :Ö: \end{bmatrix}^-$

$C_2O_4^{2-}$:

$\begin{bmatrix} :Ö: & :Ö: \\ & C—C \\ :O: & :O: \end{bmatrix}^{2-} \longleftrightarrow \begin{bmatrix} :O: & :Ö: \\ & C—C \\ :O: & :O: \end{bmatrix}^{2-}$

$\longleftrightarrow \begin{bmatrix} :O: & :Ö: \\ & C—C \\ :O: & :O: \end{bmatrix}^{2-} \longleftrightarrow \begin{bmatrix} :Ö: & :Ö: \\ & C—C \\ :O: & :O: \end{bmatrix}^{2-}$

In $H_2C_2O_4$, there are two shorter and stronger C=O bonds and two longer and weaker C—O bonds. In $HC_2O_4^-$, the carbon-oxygen bonds on the side retaining the H remain as one long, weak C—O and one short, strong C=O. The carbon-oxygen bonds on the other side of the molecule have resonance forms with a bond order of 1.5, so they are intermediate in length and strength. In $C_2O_4^{2-}$, all the carbon-oxygen bonds have a bond order of 1.5. **10.90** 22 kJ **10.91** Trigonal planar molecules are nonpolar, so AY_3 cannot be that shape. Trigonal pyramidal molecules and T-shaped molecules are polar, so AY_3 could have either of these shapes. **10.95**(a) 339 pm (b) 316 pm and 223 pm (c) 270 pm

Chapter 11

11.1(a) sp^2 (b) sp^3d^2 (c) sp (d) sp^3 (e) sp^3d **11.3** C has only $2s$ and $2p$ atomic orbitals, allowing for a maximum of four hybrid orbitals. Si has $3s$, $3p$, and $3d$ atomic orbitals, allowing it to form more than four hybrid orbitals. **11.5**(a) six, sp^3d^2 (b) four, sp^3 **11.7**(a) sp^2 (b) sp^2 (c) sp^2 **11.9**(a) sp^3 (b) sp^3 (c) sp^3 **11.11**(a) Si: one s and three p atomic orbitals form four sp^3 hybrid orbitals. (b) C: one s and one p atomic orbital forms two sp hybrid orbitals. (c) S: one s, three p, and one d atomic orbital mix to form five sp^3d hybrid orbitals. (d) N: one s and three p atomic orbitals mix to form four sp^3 hybrid orbitals. **11.13**(a) B ($sp^3 \longrightarrow sp^3$) (b) A ($sp^2 \longrightarrow sp^3$)

11.15

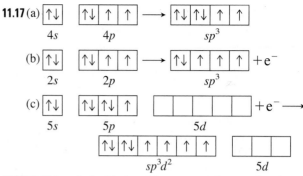

11.20(a) False. A double bond is one σ and one π bond. (b) False. A triple bond consists of one σ and two π bonds. (c) True (d) True (e) False. A π bond consists of a second pair of electrons after a σ bond has been previously formed. (f) False. End-to-end overlap results in a bond with electron density along the bond axis. **11.21**(a) Nitrogen uses sp^2 to form three σ bonds and one π bond. (b) Carbon uses sp to form two σ bonds and two π bonds. (c) Carbon uses sp^2 to form three σ bonds and one π bond.

11.23(a) N: sp^2, forming 2 σ bonds and 1 π bond

:F̈—N̈=Ö:

(b) C: sp^2, forming 3 σ bonds and 1 π bond

:F̈   F̈:
  \   /
   C=C
  /   \
:F̈   F̈:

(c) C: sp, forming 2 σ bonds and 2 π bonds

:N≡C—C≡N:

11.25

H   H   CH₃   H
 \   /   \   /
  C=C   C=C
 /   \   /   \
CH₃   CH₃   H   CH₃

   cis   *trans*

The single bonds are all σ bonds. The double bond is one σ bond and one π bond. **11.26** Four MOs form from the four p atomic orbitals. The total number of MOs must equal the number of atomic orbitals. **11.28**(a) Bonding MOs have lower energy than antibonding MOs. Lower energy means more stable. (b) Bonding MOs do not have a nodal plane perpendicular to the bond. (c) Bonding MOs have higher electron density between nuclei than antibonding MOs. **11.30**(a) two (b) two (c) four **11.32**(a) A is π^*_{2p}, B is σ_{2p}, C is π_{2p}, and D is σ^*_{2p}. (b) π^*_{2p} (A), σ_{2p} (B), and π_{2p} (C) have at least one electron. (c) π^*_{2p} (A) has only one electron. **11.34**(a) stable (b) paramagnetic (c) $(\sigma_{2s})^2(\sigma^*_{2s})^1$ **11.36**(a) $C_2^+ < C_2 < C_2^-$ (b) $C_2^- < C_2 < C_2^+$ **11.40**(a) C (ring): sp^2; C (all others): sp^3; O (all): sp^3; N: sp^3 (b) 26 (c) 6 **11.42**(a) 17 (b) All carbons are sp^2; the ring N is sp^2, the other N's are sp^3. **11.44**(a) B changes from sp^2 to sp^3. (b) P changes from sp^3 to sp^3d. (c) C changes from sp to sp^2. Two electron groups surround C in C_2H_2, and three electron groups surround C in C_2H_4. (d) Si changes from sp^3 to sp^3d^2. (e) no change for S **11.46** P: tetrahedral, sp^3; N: trigonal pyramid, sp^3; C_1 and C_2: tetrahedral, sp^3; C_3: trigonal planar, sp^2 **11.51**(a) B and D are present. (b) Yes, sp hybrid orbitals. (c) Two sets of sp orbitals,

four sets of sp^2 orbitals, and three sets of sp^3 orbitals.
11.52 Through resonance, the C—N bond gains some double-bond character, which hinders rotation about that bond.

11.55(a) C in —CH$_3$: sp^3; all other C atoms: sp^2; O in two C—O bonds: sp^3; O in two C=O bonds: sp^2 (b) two (c) eight; one **11.56**(a) four (b) eight

Chapter 12

Answer to Boxed Reading Problem: B12.1 1.76×10^{-10} m

• **12.1** In a solid, the energy of attraction of the particles is greater than their energy of motion; in a gas, it is less. Gases have high compressibility and the ability to flow, while solids have neither. **12.4**(a) Because the intermolecular forces are only partially overcome when fusion occurs but need to be totally overcome in vaporization. (b) Because solids have greater intermolecular forces than liquids do. (c) $\Delta H_{vap} = -\Delta H_{cond}$ **12.5**(a) intermolecular (b) intermolecular (c) intramolecular (d) intramolecular **12.7**(a) condensation (b) fusion (c) vaporization **12.9** The gas molecules slow down as the gas is compressed. Therefore, much of the kinetic energy lost by the propane molecules is released to the surroundings. **12.13** At first, the vaporization of liquid molecules from the surface predominates, which increases the number of gas molecules and hence the vapor pressure. As more molecules enter the gas phase, more gas molecules hit the surface of the liquid and "stick" more frequently, so the condensation rate increases. When the vaporization and condensation rates become equal, the vapor pressure becomes constant. **12.14** As intermolecular forces increase, (a) critical temperature increases, (b) boiling point increases, (c) vapor pressure decreases, and (d) heat of vaporization increases. **12.18** because the condensation of the vapor supplies an additional 40.7 kJ/mol **12.19** 7.67×10^3 J **12.21** 0.777 atm **12.23** 2×10^4 J/mol
12.25

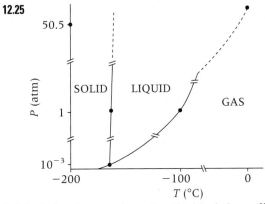

Solid ethylene is more dense than liquid ethylene. **12.28** 32 atm
12.32 O is smaller and more electronegative than Se; so the electron density on O is greater, which attracts H more strongly. **12.34** All particles (atoms and molecules) exhibit dispersion forces, but the total force is weak for small molecules.

Dipole-dipole forces between small polar molecules dominate the dispersion forces. **12.37**(a) hydrogen bonding (b) dispersion forces (c) dispersion forces **12.39**(a) dipole-dipole forces (b) dispersion forces (c) hydrogen bonding
12.41(a)

$$CH_3-CH-\overset{..}{O}:\cdots H-\overset{..}{O}-CH-CH_3$$

with CH_3 above the right O, CH_3 and H below.

(b)

12.43(a) dispersion forces (b) hydrogen bonding (c) dispersion forces **12.45**(a) I$^-$ (b) CH$_2$=CH$_2$ (c) H$_2$Se. In (a) and (c) the larger particle has the higher polarizability. In (b), the less tightly held π electron clouds are more easily distorted. **12.47**(a) C$_2$H$_6$; it is a smaller molecule exhibiting weaker dispersion forces than C$_4$H$_{10}$. (b) CH$_3$CH$_2$F; it has no H—F bonds, so it exhibits only dipole-dipole forces, which are weaker than the hydrogen bonds of CH$_3$CH$_2$OH. (c) PH$_3$; it has weaker intermolecular forces (dipole-dipole) than NH$_3$ (hydrogen bonding). **12.49**(a) HCl; it has dipole-dipole forces, and there are stronger ionic bonds in LiCl. (b) PH$_3$; it has dipole-dipole forces, and there is stronger hydrogen bonding in NH$_3$. (c) Xe; it exhibits weaker dispersion forces since its smaller size results in lower polarizability than the larger I$_2$ molecules. **12.51**(a) C$_4$H$_8$ (cyclobutane), because it is more compact than C$_4$H$_{10}$. (b) PBr$_3$; the dipole-dipole forces in PBr$_3$ are weaker than the ionic bonds in NaBr. (c) HBr; the dipole-dipole forces in HBr are weaker than the hydrogen bonds in water. **12.53** As atomic size decreases and electronegativity increases, the electron density of an atom increases. Thus, the attraction to an H atom on another molecule increases while its bonded H atom becomes more positive. Fluorine is the smallest of the three and the most electronegative, so the H bonds in hydrogen fluoride are the strongest. Oxygen is smaller and more electronegative than nitrogen, so H bonds in water are stronger than H bonds in ammonia. **12.57** The cohesive forces in water and mercury are stronger than the adhesive forces to the nonpolar wax on the floor. Weak adhesive forces result in spherical drops. The adhesive forces overcome the even weaker cohesive forces in the oil, and so the oil drop spreads out. **12.59** Surface tension is defined as the energy needed to increase the surface area by a given amount, so units of energy per area are appropriate. **12.61** CH$_3$CH$_2$CH$_2$OH < HOCH$_2$CH$_2$OH < HOCH$_2$CH(OH)CH$_2$OH.
More hydrogen bonding means more attraction between molecules, so more energy is needed to increase surface area. **12.63** HOCH$_2$CH(OH)CH$_2$OH > HOCH$_2$CH$_2$OH > CH$_3$CH$_2$CH$_2$OH. More hydrogen bonding means more attraction between molecules, so they flow less easily. **12.68** Water is a good solvent for polar and ionic substances and a poor solvent for nonpolar substances. Water is a polar molecule and dissolves polar substances because their intermolecular forces are of similar strength. **12.69** A single water molecule can form four H bonds. The two hydrogen atoms each form one H bond to oxygen atoms on neighboring water molecules. The two

lone pairs on the oxygen atom form H bonds with hydrogen atoms on two neighboring molecules. **12.72** Water exhibits strong capillary action, which allows it to be easily absorbed by the plant's roots and transported upward to the leaves. **12.78** simple cubic **12.81** The energy gap is the energy difference between the highest filled energy level (valence band) and the lowest unfilled energy level (conduction band). In conductors and superconductors, the energy gap is zero because the valence band overlaps the conduction band. In semiconductors, the energy gap is small. In insulators, the gap is large. **12.83** atomic mass and atomic radius **12.84**(a) face-centered cubic (b) body-centered cubic (c) face-centered cubic **12.86**(a) The change in unit cell is from a sodium chloride structure in CdO to a zinc blende structure in CdSe. (b) Yes, the coordination number of Cd changes from 6 in CdO to 4 in CdSe. **12.88**(a) Nickel forms a metallic solid since it is a metal whose atoms are held together by metallic bonds. (b) Fluorine forms a molecular solid since the F_2 molecules are held together by dispersion forces. (c) Methanol forms a molecular solid since the CH_3OH molecules are held together by hydrogen bonds. (d) Tin forms a metallic solid since it is a metal whose atoms are held together by metallic bonds. (e) Silicon is in the same group as carbon, so it exhibits similar bonding properties. Since diamond and graphite are both network covalent solids, it makes sense that Si forms a network covalent solid as well. (f) Xe is an atomic solid since its individual atoms are held together by dispersion forces. **12.90** four **12.92**(a) four Se^{2-} ions, four Zn^{2+} ions (b) 577.48 amu (c) 1.77×10^{-22} cm^3 (d) 5.61×10^{-8} cm **12.94**(a) insulator (b) conductor (c) semiconductor **12.96**(a) Conductivity increases. (b) Conductivity increases. (c) Conductivity decreases. **12.98** 1.68×10^{-8} cm **12.105** A substance whose properties are the same in all directions is isotropic; otherwise, the substance is anisotropic. Liquid crystals have a degree of order only in certain directions, so they are anisotropic. **12.111**(a) n-type semiconductor (b) p-type semiconductor **12.113** $n = 3.4 \times 10^3$ **12.115** 8.4 pm **12.118**(a) 19.8 torr (b) 0.0485 g **12.124** 259 K **12.126**(a) 2.23×10^{-2} atm (b) 6.23 L **12.129**(a) furfuryl alcohol

2-furoic acid

(b) furfuryl alcohol   2-furoic acid

12.130(a) 49.3 metric tons H_2O (b) -1.11×10^8 kJ **12.131** 2.9 g/m^3 **12.136**(a) 1.1 min (b) 10. min (c)

12.137 2.98×10^5 g BN **12.140** 45.98 amu

Chapter 13

Answers to Boxed Reading Problem: B13.1 (a) The colloidal particles in water generally have negatively charged surfaces and so repel each other, slowing the settling process. Cake alum, $Al_2(SO_4)_3$, is added to coagulate the colloids. The Al^{3+} ions neutralize the negative surface charges and allow the particles to aggregate and settle. (b) Water that contains large amounts of divalent cations (such as Ca^{2+}, and Mg^{2+}) is called hard water. During cleaning, these ions combine with the fatty-acid anions in soaps to produce insoluble deposits. (c) In reverse osmosis, a pressure greater than the osmotic pressure is applied to the solution, forcing the water back through the membrane, leaving the ions behind. (d) Chlorine may give the water an unpleasant odor, and can form carcinogenic chlorinated compounds. (e) The high concentration of NaCl displaces the divalent and polyvalent ions from the ion-exchange resin.

• **13.2** When a salt such as NaCl dissolves, ion-dipole forces cause the ions to separate, and many water molecules cluster around each ion in hydration shells. Ion-dipole forces bind the first shell to an ion. The water molecules in that shell form H bonds to others to create the next shell, and so on. **13.4** Sodium stearate is a more effective soap because the hydrocarbon chain in the stearate ion is longer than that in the acetate ion. The longer chain allows for more dispersion forces with grease molecules. **13.7** KNO_3 is an ionic compound and is therefore more soluble in water. **13.9**(a) ion-dipole forces (b) hydrogen bonding (c) dipole–induced dipole forces **13.11**(a) hydrogen bonding (b) dipole–induced dipole forces (c) dispersion forces **13.13**(a) HCl(g), because the molecular interactions (dipole-dipole forces) in ether are like those in HCl but not like the ionic bonding in NaCl. (b) $CH_3CHO(l)$, because the molecular interactions with ether (dipole-dipole) can replace those between CH_3CHO, but not the H bonds in water. (c) $CH_3CH_2MgBr(s)$, because the molecular interactions (dipole-dipole and dispersion forces) are greater than between ether and the ions in $MgBr_2$. **13.16** Gluconic acid is soluble in water due to extensive hydrogen bonding by the —OH groups attached to five of its carbons. The dispersion forces in the nonpolar tail of caproic acid are more similar to the dispersion forces in hexane; thus, caproic acid is soluble in hexane.   **13.18** The nitrogen-containing bases form H bonds to their complementary bases. The flat, N-containing bases stack above each other, which allows extensive dispersion forces. The exterior negatively charged sugar-phosphate chains form ion-dipole and H bonds with water molecules in the aqueous surroundings, which also stabilizes the structure.   **13.21** Dispersion forces are present between the nonpolar tails of the lipid molecules within the bilayer. The polar heads interact with the aqueous surroundings through H bonds and ion-dipole forces.   **13.25** The enthalpy changes needed to separate the solvent ($\Delta H_{solvent}$) and to mix the solvent and solute (ΔH_{mix}) combine to give $\Delta H_{solvation}$.   **13.29** very soluble, because a decrease in enthalpy and an increase in entropy both favor the formation of a solution

13.30

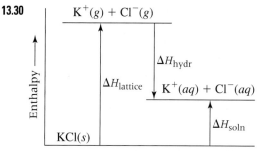

13.32(a) The volume of Na^+ is smaller. (b) Sr^{2+} has a larger ionic charge and a smaller volume. (c) Na^+ is smaller than Cl^-. (d) O^{2-} has a larger ionic charge with a similar ion volume. (e) OH^- has a smaller volume than SH^-. (f) Mg^{2+} has a smaller volume. (g) Mg^{2+} has both a smaller volume and a larger ionic charge. (h) CO_3^{2-} has both a smaller volume and a larger ionic charge. **13.34**(a) Na^+ (b) Sr^{2+} (c) Na^+ (d) O^{2-} (e) OH^- (f) Mg^{2+} (g) Mg^{2+} (h) CO_3^{2-} **13.36**(a) -704 kJ/mol (b) The K^+ ion contributes more because it is smaller and, therefore, has a greater charge density. **13.38**(a) increases (b) decreases (c) increases **13.41** Add a pinch of X to each solution. Addition of a "seed" crystal of solute to a supersaturated solution causes the excess solute to crystallize immediately, leaving behind a saturated solution. The solution in which the added X dissolves is the unsaturated solution. The solution in which the added X remains undissolved is the saturated solution. **13.44**(a) increase (b) decrease **13.46**(a) 0.102 g O_2 (b) 0.0214 g O_2 **13.49** 0.20 mol/L **13.52**(a) molarity and % w/v or % v/v (b) parts-by-mass (% w/w) (c) molality **13.54** With just this information, you can convert between molality and molarity, but you need to know the molar mass of the solvent to convert to mole fraction. **13.56**(a) 0.944 M $C_{12}H_{22}O_{11}$ (b) 0.167 M $LiNO_3$ **13.58**(a) 0.0749 M NaOH (b) 0.36 M HNO_3 **13.60**(a) Add 4.25 g KH_2PO_4 to enough water to make 365 mL of aqueous solution. (b) Add 125 mL of 1.25 M NaOH to enough water to make 465 mL of solution. **13.62**(a) Weigh out 48.0 g KBr, dissolve it in about 1 L distilled water, and then dilute to 1.40 L with distilled water. (b) Measure 82.7 mL of the 0.264 M $LiNO_3$ solution and add distilled water to make a total of 255 mL. **13.64**(a) 0.896 m glycine (b) 1.21 m glycerol **13.66** 4.48 m C_6H_6 **13.68**(a) Add 2.39 g $C_2H_6O_2$ to

308 g H_2O. (b) Add 0.0508 kg of 52.0% HNO_3 by mass to 1.15 kg H_2O to make 1.20 kg of 2.20% HNO_3 by mass. **13.70**(a) 0.29 (b) 58 mass % (c) 23 m C_3H_7OH **13.72** 42.6 g CsBr; mole fraction = 7.16×10^{-3}; 7.84% by mass **13.74** 5.11 m NH_3; 4.53 M NH_3; mole fraction = 0.0843 **13.76** 2.5 ppm Ca^{2+}; 0.56 ppm Mg^{2+} **13.80** It conducts a "strong" current. A strong electrolyte dissociates completely into ions in solution. **13.82** The boiling point is higher and the freezing point is lower for the solution than for the solvent. **13.85** A dilute solution of an electrolyte behaves more ideally than a concentrated one. With increasing concentration, the effective concentration deviates from the molar concentration because of ionic attractions. Thus, 0.050 m NaF has a boiling point closer to its predicted value. **13.88**(a) strong electrolyte (b) strong electrolyte (c) nonelectrolyte (d) weak electrolyte **13.90**(a) 0.6 mol of solute particles (b) 0.13 mol (c) 2×10^{-4} mol (d) 0.06 mol **13.92**(a) CH_3OH in H_2O (b) H_2O in CH_3OH solution **13.94**(a) $\Pi_{II} < \Pi_I < \Pi_{III}$ (b) $bp_{II} < bp_I < bp_{III}$ (c) $fp_{III} < fp_I < fp_{II}$ (d) $vp_{III} < vp_I < vp_{II}$ **13.96** 23.4 torr **13.98** $-0.467°C$ **13.100** 79.5°C **13.102** 1.18×10^4 g $C_2H_6O_2$ **13.104**(a) NaCl: 0.173 m and $i = 1.84$ (b) CH_3COOH: 0.0837 m and $i = 1.02$ **13.107** 209 torr for CH_2Cl_2; 48.1 torr for CCl_4 **13.108** The fluid inside a bacterial cell is both a solution and a colloid. It is a solution of ions and small molecules and a colloid of large molecules (proteins and nucleic acids). **13.112** Soap micelles have nonpolar tails pointed inward and anionic heads pointed outward. The like charges on the heads of one micelle repel those on the heads of a neighboring micelle. This repulsion between micelles keeps them from coagulating. Soap is more effective in freshwater than in seawater because the divalent cations in seawater combine with the anionic heads to form a precipitate. **13.116** 3.4×10^9 L **13.120** 0.0°C: 4.53×10^{-4} M O_2; 20.0°C: 2.83×10^{-4} M O_2; 40.0°C: 2.00×10^{-4} M O_2 **13.122**(a) 89.9 g/mol (b) C_2H_5O; $C_4H_{10}O_2$ (c) Forms H bonds:

$$HO-\overset{\overset{\displaystyle H}{|}}{C}-\overset{\overset{\displaystyle H}{|}}{C}-\overset{\overset{\displaystyle H}{|}}{C}-\overset{\overset{\displaystyle H}{|}}{C}-OH$$
$$\underset{\underset{\displaystyle H}{|}}{}\underset{\underset{\displaystyle H}{|}}{}\underset{\underset{\displaystyle H}{|}}{}\underset{\underset{\displaystyle H}{|}}{}$$

Does not form H bonds:

$$H-\overset{\overset{\displaystyle H}{|}}{C}-O-\overset{\overset{\displaystyle H}{|}}{C}-O-\overset{\overset{\displaystyle H}{|}}{C}-\overset{\overset{\displaystyle H}{|}}{C}-H$$

13.126(a) 9.45 g NaF (b) 0.0017 g F^- **13.129**(a) 68 g/mol (b) 2.1×10^2 g/mol (c) The molar mass of CaN_2O_6 is 164.10 g/mol. This value is less than the 2.1×10^2 g/mol calculated when the compound is assumed to be a strong electrolyte and is greater than the 68 g/mol calculated when the compound is assumed to be a nonelectrolyte. Thus, the compound forms a nonideal solution because the ions interact but do not dissociate completely in solution. (d) $i = 2.4$ **13.133**(a) 1.82×10^4 g/mol (b) $3.41 \times 10^{-5}°C$ **13.134** 8.2×10^5 ng/L **13.138**(a) 0.02 (b) 5×10^{-3} atm·L/mol (c) yes **13.140** Weigh 3.11 g of $NaHCO_3$ and dissolve in 247 g of water. **3.144** $M = m$

(kg solvent/L solution) $= m \times d_{solution}$. Thus, for very dilute solutions, molality $\times$ density $=$ molarity. For an aqueous solution, the number of liters of solution is approximately the same as the kg of solvent because the density of water is close to 1 kg/L, so $m = M$. **13.146**(a) 2.5×10^{-3} M SO_2 (b) The base reacts with the sulfur dioxide to produce calcium sulfite. The reaction of sulfur dioxide makes "room" for more sulfur dioxide to dissolve. **13.151**(a) 7.83×10^{-3} mol L·atm (b) 4×10^{-5} M (c) 3×10^{-6} (d) 1 ppm **13.155**(a) 0.0212 mol/L·atm (b) 8.86 ppm (c) k_H: $C_6F_{14} > C_6H_{14} >$ ethanol $>$ water. To dissolve oxygen in a solvent, the solvent molecules must be moved apart to make room for the gas. The stronger the intermolecular forces in the solvent, the more difficult it is to separate solvent particles and the lower the solubility of the gas. In both C_6F_{14} and C_6H_{14} have weak dispersion forces, with C_6F_{14} having the weaker forces due to the electronegative fluorine atoms repelling each other. In both ethanol and water, the molecules are held together by strong hydrogen bonds with those bonds being stronger in water, as the boiling point indicates. **13.157**(a) Yes, the phases of water can still coexist at some temperature and can therefore establish equilibrium. (b) The triple point would occur at a lower pressure and lower temperature because the dissolved air would lower the vapor pressure of the solvent. (c) Yes, this is possible because the gas-solid phase boundary exists below the new triple point. (d) No; at both temperatures, the presence of the solute lowers the vapor pressure of the liquid. **13.159**(a) 2.8×10^{-4} g/mL (b) 81 mL

Chapter 14

14.1 The outermost electron is attracted by a smaller effective nuclear charge in Li because of shielding by the inner electrons, and it is farther from the nucleus in Li. Both of these factors lead to a lower ionization energy for Li.
14.3(a) NH_3 will hydrogen bond.

:F̈—N̈—F̈:   H—N̈—H
    | |
   :F̈:   H

(b) CH_3CH_2OH will hydrogen bond.

H   H   H H
| | | |
H—C—Ö—C—H   H—C—C—Ö—H
| | | |
H   H   H H

14.5(a) $2Al(s) + 6HCl(aq) \longrightarrow 2AlCl_3(aq) + 3H_2(g)$
(b) $LiH(s) + H_2O(l) \longrightarrow LiOH(aq) + H_2(g)$
14.7(a) $NaBH_4$: +1 for Na, +3 for B, -1 for H
$Al(BH_4)_3$: +3 for Al, +3 for B, -1 for H
$LiAlH_4$: +1 for Li, +3 for Al, -1 for H
(b) tetrahedral

$$\left[\begin{array}{c} H \\ | \\ H—B—H \\ | \\ H \end{array}\right]^{-}$$

14.10 For Groups 1A(1) to 4A(14), the number of covalent bonds equals the (old) group number. For Groups 5A(15) to 7A(17), it equals 8 minus the (old) group number. There are

exceptions in Period 3 to Period 6 because it is possible for the 3A(13) to 7A(17) elements to use d orbitals and form more bonds. **14.13**(a) Group 3A(13) or 3B(3) (b) If E is in Group 3B(3), the oxide will be more basic and the fluoride will be more ionic; if E is in Group 3A(13), the oxide will be more acidic and the fluoride will be more covalent.
14.16(a) reducing agent (b) Alkali metals have relatively low ionization energies, which means they easily lose the outermost electron.
(c) $2Na(s) + 2H_2O(l) \longrightarrow 2Na^+(aq) + 2OH^-(aq) + H_2(g)$
$2Na(s) + Cl_2(g) \longrightarrow 2NaCl(s)$
14.18 Density and ionic size increase down a group; the other three properties decrease down a group.
14.20 $2Na(s) + O_2(g) \longrightarrow Na_2O_2(s)$
14.22 $K_2CO_3(s) + 2HI(aq) \longrightarrow 2KI(aq) + H_2O(l) + CO_2(g)$
14.26 Group 2A(2) metals have an additional valence electron to increase the strength of metallic bonding, which leads to higher melting points, higher boiling points, greater hardness, and greater density.
14.27(a) $CaO(s) + H_2O(l) \longrightarrow Ca(OH)_2(s)$
(b) $2Ca(s) + O_2(g) \longrightarrow 2CaO(s)$
14.30(a) $BeO(s) + H_2O(l) \longrightarrow$ no reaction
(b) $BeCl_2(l) + 2Cl^-(solvated) \longrightarrow BeCl_4^{2-}(solvated)$
Be behaves like other Group 2A(2) elements in reaction (b).
14.33 The electron removed from Group 2A(2) atoms occupies the outer s orbital, whereas in Group 3A(13) atoms, the electron occupies the outer p orbital. For example, the electron configuration for Be is $1s^22s^2$ and for B it is $1s^22s^22p^1$. It is easier to remove the p electron of B than an s electron of Be, because the energy of a p orbital is higher than that of the s orbital of the same level. Even though atomic size decreases because of increasing Z_{eff}, IE decreases from 2A(2) to 3A(13).
14.34(a) Most atoms form stable compounds when they complete their outer shell (octet). Some compounds of Group 3A(13) elements, like boron, have only six electrons around the central atom. Having fewer than eight electrons is called *electron deficiency*.
(b) $BF_3(g) + NH_3(g) \longrightarrow F_3B—NH_3(g)$
$B(OH)_3(aq) + OH^-(aq) \longrightarrow B(OH)_4^-(aq)$
14.36 $In_2O_3 < Ga_2O_3 < Al_2O_3$ **14.38** Apparent O.N., +3; actual O.N., +1. $\left[:\ddot{I}—\ddot{I}—\ddot{I}:\right]^{-}$ The anion I_3^- has the general formula AX_2E_3 and bond angles of 180°. $(Tl^{3+})(I^-)_3$ does not exist because of the low strength of the Tl—I bond.
14.43(a) $B_2O_3(s) + 2NH_3(g) \longrightarrow 2BN(s) + 3H_2O(g)$
(b) 1.30×10^2 kJ (c) 5.3 kg borax **14.44** Basicity in water is greater for the oxide of a metal. Tin(IV) oxide is more basic in water than carbon dioxide because tin has more metallic character than carbon. **14.46**(a) Ionization energy generally decreases down a group. (b) The deviations (increases) from the expected trend are due to the presence of the first transition series between Si and Ge and of the lanthanides between Sn and Pb. (c) Group 3A(13) **14.49** Atomic size increases down a group. As atomic size increases, ionization energy decreases and so it is easier to form a positive ion. An atom that is easier to ionize exhibits greater metallic character.

14.51(a)

(b)

14.54(a) diamond, C (b) calcium carbonate, $CaCO_3$ (c) carbon dioxide, CO_2 (d) carbon monoxide, CO (e) silicon, Si
14.58(a) -3 to $+5$ (b) For a group of nonmetals, the oxidation states range from the lowest, group number $- 8$, or $5 - 8 = -3$ for Group 5A, to the highest, equal to the group number, or $+5$ for Group 5A. **14.61** $H_3AsO_4 < H_3PO_4 < HNO_3$
14.63(a) $4As(s) + 5O_2(g) \longrightarrow 2As_2O_5(s)$
  (b) $2Bi(s) + 3F_2(g) \longrightarrow 2BiF_3(s)$
  (c) $Ca_3As_2(s) + 6H_2O(l) \longrightarrow 3Ca(OH)_2(s) + 2AsH_3(g)$
14.65(a) $N_2(g) + 2Al(s) \overset{\Delta}{\longrightarrow} 2AlN(s)$
  (b) $PF_5(g) + 4H_2O(l) \longrightarrow H_3PO_4(aq) + 5HF(g)$
14.67 trigonal bipyramidal, with axial F atoms and equatorial Cl atoms;

14.71(a)

(b)

(c)

(d)

14.73(a) $2KNO_3(s) \overset{\Delta}{\longrightarrow} 2KNO_2(s) + O_2(g)$ (b) $4KNO_3(s) \overset{\Delta}{\longrightarrow} 2K_2O(s) + 2N_2(g) + 5O_2(g)$ **14.75**(a) Boiling point and conductivity vary in similar ways down both groups. (b) Degree of metallic character and types of bonding vary in similar ways down both groups. (c) Both P and S have allotropes, and both bond covalently with almost every other nonmetal. (d) Both N and O are diatomic gases at normal temperatures and pressures. (e) O_2 is a reactive gas, whereas N_2 is not. Nitrogen can have any of six oxidation states, whereas oxygen has two. **14.77**(a) $NaHSO_4(aq) + NaOH(aq) \longrightarrow Na_2SO_4(aq) + H_2O(l)$
  (b) $S_8(s) + 24F_2(g) \longrightarrow 8SF_6(g)$
  (c) $FeS(s) + 2HCl(aq) \longrightarrow H_2S(g) + FeCl_2(aq)$
  (d) $Te(s) + 2I_2(s) \longrightarrow TeI_4(s)$
14.79(a) acidic (b) acidic (c) basic (d) amphoteric (e) basic
14.81 $H_2O < H_2S < H_2Te$ **14.84**(a) O_3, ozone (b) SO_3, sulfur trioxide (c) SO_2, sulfur dioxide (d) H_2SO_4, sulfuric acid (e) $Na_2S_2O_3 \cdot 5H_2O$, sodium thiosulfate pentahydrate
14.86 $S_2F_{10}(g) \longrightarrow SF_4(g) + SF_6(g)$; O.N. of S in S_2F_{10} is $+5$; O.N. of S in SF_4 is $+4$; O.N. of S in SF_6 is $+6$. **14.88**(a) -1, $+1$, $+3$, $+5$, $+7$ (b) The electron configuration for Cl is [Ne] $3s^23p^5$. By gaining one electron, Cl achieves an octet. By forming covalent bonds, Cl completes or expands its valence level by maintaining electron pairs in bonds or as lone pairs. (c) Fluorine has only the -1 oxidation state because its small size and absence of d orbitals prevent it from forming more than one covalent bond. **14.90**(a) Cl—Cl bond is stronger

than Br—Br bond. (b) Br—Br bond is stronger than I—I bond. (c) Cl—Cl bond is stronger than F—F bond. The fluorine atoms are so small that electron-electron repulsion of the lone pairs decreases the strength of the bond.
14.92(a) $3Br_2(l) + 6OH^-(aq) \longrightarrow$
$$5Br^-(aq) + BrO_3^-(aq) + 3H_2O(l)$$
  (b) $ClF_5(l) + 6OH^-(aq) \longrightarrow$
$$5F^-(aq) + ClO_3^-(aq) + 3H_2O(l)$$
14.93(a) $2Rb(s) + Br_2(l) \longrightarrow 2RbBr(s)$
  (b) $I_2(s) + H_2O(l) \longrightarrow HI(aq) + HIO(aq)$
  (c) $Br_2(l) + 2I^-(aq) \longrightarrow I_2(s) + 2Br^-(aq)$
  (d) $CaF_2(s) + H_2SO_4(l) \longrightarrow CaSO_4(s) + 2HF(g)$
14.95 $HIO < HBrO < HClO < HClO_2$ **14.99** $I_2 < Br_2 < Cl_2$, because Cl_2 is able to oxidize Re to the $+6$ oxidation state, Br_2 only to $+5$, and I_2 only to $+4$ **14.100** helium; argon
14.102 Only dispersion forces hold atoms of noble gases together. **14.106** $\Delta H_{soln} = -411$ kJ **14.110**(a) Second ionization energies for alkali metals are so high because the electron being removed is from the next lower energy level and these are very tightly held by the nucleus. Also, the alkali metal would lose its noble gas electron configuration.
  (b) $2CsF_2(s) \longrightarrow 2CsF(s) + F_2(g)$; -405 kJ/mol
14.112(a) hyponitrous acid, $H_2N_2O_2$; nitroxyl, HNO
  (b)

  (c) In both species the shape is bent about the N atoms.
  (d)

cis   *trans*

14.116 13 t **14.118** In a disproportionation reaction, a substance acts as both a reducing agent and an oxidizing agent because atoms of an element within the substance attain both higher and lower oxidation states in the products. The disproportionation reactions are b, c, d, e, and f. **14.120**(a) Group 5A(15) (b) Group 7A(17) (c) Group 6A(16) (d) Group 1A(1) (e) Group 3A(13) (f) Group 8A(18)
14.122 117.2 kJ
14.127

The nitronium ion (NO_2^+) has a linear shape because the central N atom has two surrounding electron groups, which achieve maximum repulsion at 180°. The nitrite ion (NO_2^-) bond angle is more compressed than the nitrogen dioxide (NO_2) bond angle because the lone pair of electrons takes up more space than the lone electron. **14.129** 2.29×10^4 g UF_6
14.133 O^+, O^-, and O^{2+} **14.134**(a) 39.96 mass % in $CuHAsO_3$; As, 62.42 mass % in $(CH_3)_3As$ (b) 0.35 g $CuHAsO_3$

Chapter 15

Answers to Boxed Reading Problems: B15.1 butane, 2 peaks; 2-methylpropane, 2 peaks; pentane, 3 peaks; 2-methylbutane, 4 peaks; 2,2-dimethylpropane, 1 peak **B15.2** 0.08 J/mol
B15.4 ddATP: four complementary chain pieces; ddCTP: three complementary chain pieces

• **15.2**(a) Carbon's electronegativity is midway between the most metallic and most nonmetallic elements of Period 2. To attain a filled outer shell, carbon forms covalent bonds to other atoms in molecules, network covalent solids, and polyatomic ions. (b) Since carbon has four valence shell electrons, it forms four covalent bonds to attain an octet. (c) To reach the He electron configuration, a carbon atom must lose four electrons, requiring too much energy to form the C^{4+} cation. To reach the Ne electron configuration, the carbon atom must gain four electrons, also requiring too much energy to form the C^{4-} anion. (d) Carbon is able to bond to itself extensively because its small size allows for close approach and great orbital overlap. The extensive orbital overlap results in a strong, stable bond. (e) The C—C σ bond is short enough to allow sideways overlap of unhybridized p orbitals of neighboring C atoms. The sideways overlap of p orbitals results in the π bonds that are part of double and triple bonds. **15.3**(a) H, O, N, P, S, and halogens (b) Heteroatoms are atoms of any element other than carbon and hydrogen. (c) More electronegative than C: N, O, F, Cl, and Br; less electronegative than C: H and P. Sulfur and iodine have the same electronegativity as carbon. (d) Since carbon can bond to a wide variety of heteroatoms and to carbon atoms, it can form many different compounds. **15.6** The C—H and C—C bonds are unreactive because electronegativities are close and the bonds are short. The C—I bond is somewhat reactive because it is long and weak. The C=O bond is reactive because oxygen is more electronegative than carbon and the electron-rich π bond makes it attract electron-poor atoms. The C—Li bond is also reactive because the bond polarity results in an electron-rich region around carbon and an electron-poor region around lithium. **15.7**(a) An alkane and a cycloalkane are organic compounds that consist of carbon and hydrogen and have only single bonds. A cycloalkane has a ring of carbon atoms. An alkene is a hydrocarbon with at least one double bond. An alkyne is a hydrocarbon with at least one triple bond. (b) alkane = C_nH_{2n+2}, cycloalkane = C_nH_{2n}, alkene = C_nH_{2n}, alkyne = C_nH_{2n-2} (c) Alkanes and cycloalkanes are saturated hydrocarbons. **15.10** a, c, and f

15.13(a)

(b)

(c)

15.15(a)

(b) CH₂=C—CH—CH₂—CH₃   CH₂=C—CH₂—CH—CH₃
       | | | |
       CH₃ CH₃   CH₃   CH₃

              CH₃
              |
CH₂=CH—C—CH₂—CH₃   CH₂=CH—CH—CH—CH₃
            | | |
              CH₃   CH₃ CH₃

              CH₃
              |
CH₂=CH—CH₂—C—CH₃   CH₂=CH—CH—CH₂—CH₃
                | |
              CH₃   CH₂—CH₃

CH₃—C=C—CH₂—CH₃   CH₃—C=CH—CH—CH₃
       | | | |
       CH₃ CH₃   CH₃   CH₃

                        CH₃
                        |
CH₃—CH=C—CH—CH₃   CH₃—CH=CH—C—CH₃
              | | |
              CH₃ CH₃   CH₃

CH₃—CH=C—CH₂—CH₃
              |
              CH₂—CH₃

(c)   CH₂   CH₂
      / \   / \
   CH₂ CH—CH₂—CH₃   CH₂ CH—CH₃
    | | | |
   H₂C—CH₂   H₂C—CH—CH₃

        CH₂   CH₂   CH₃
      / \   / \ /
  H₂C CH—CH₃   H₂C C
    | | | \
 H₃C—HC—CH₂   H₂C—CH₂ CH₃

15.17(a)   CH₃   (b) H₂C=CH—CH₂— CH₃
             |
     CH₃—C—CH₂—CH₃
            |
            CH₃

(c) HC≡C—CH—CH₃   (d) Structure is correct.
             |
             CH₂
             |
             CH₃

              CH₃
              |
15.19(a) CH₃—CH—CH—CH₂—CH₂—CH₂—CH₂—CH₃
                 |
               CH₃

(b)   CH₂—CH₃

    6   2
                 3
   5   CH₃
       4

(c) 3,4-dimethylheptane (d) 2,2-dimethylbutane

15.21(a)   CH₃
                     |
    CH₃—CH₂—CH₂—CH—CH₂—CH₃
    Correct name is 3-methylhexane.

(b)   CH₂—CH₃
                   |
    CH₃—CH₂—CH₂—CH—CH₃
    Correct name is 3-methylhexane.

(c)   CH₃

Correct name is methylcyclohexane.

(d)   CH₃
                    |
    CH₃—CH₂—C—CH—CH₂—CH₂—CH₂—CH₃
                | |
                CH₃ CH₂—CH₃

Correct name is 4-ethyl-3,3-dimethyloctane.

15.23(a)   H   H
            \ /
             C
     H—Ⓒ—Ⓒ—CH₃
         | |
         Cl H

(b)   H   CH₃
               | |
    CH₃—CH₂—Ⓒ—C—CH₃
               | |
             CH₃ H

15.25(a) 3-Bromohexane is optically active.
    CH₃—CH₂—ⒸH—CH₂—CH₂—CH₃
              |
              Br

(b) 3-Chloro-3-methylpentane is not optically active.
               CH₃
               |
    CH₃—CH₂—C—CH₂—CH₃
               |
              Cl

(c) 1,2-Dibromo-2-methylbutane is optically active.
               CH₃
               |
    CH₂—Ⓒ—CH₂—CH₃
     | |
    Br Br

15.27(a)   H   H   H   CH₃
          \   /   \   /
          C=C   C=C
         /   \   /   \
   CH₃CH₂   CH₃   CH₃CH₂   H
     cis-2-pentene   *trans*-2-pentene

(b)   H   H   H   CH₃
          \ /   \ /
          C=C   C=C
         /   \   /   \
              CH₃   H
  cis-1-cyclohexylpropene *trans*-1-cyclohexylpropene

(c) no geometric isomers

15.29(a) no geometric isomers

(b) CH₃—CH₂   CH₂—CH₃   CH₃—CH₂   H
         \   /   \   /
          C=C   C=C
         /   \   /   \
       H   H   H   CH₂—CH₃
      cis-3-hexene   *trans*-3-hexene

(c) no geometric isomers

(d)   Cl   Cl   Cl   H
      \   /   \   /
      C=C   C=C
     /   \   /   \
    H   H   H   Cl

  cis-1,2-dichloroethene   *trans*-1,2-dichloroethene

15.31

1,2-dichlorobenzene   1,3-dichlorobenzene   1,4-dichlorobenzene
(*o*-dichlorobenzene)   (*m*-dichlorobenzene)   (*p*-dichlorobenzene)

15.33

CH₃—C(CH₃)₂ ... OH ... C(CH₃)₂—CH₃ ... CH₃

15.34

cis-2-methyl-3-hexene   trans-2-methyl-3-hexene

The compound 2-methyl-2-hexene does not have *cis-trans* isomers. **15.38** π bond **15.40**(a) elimination (b) addition
15.42(a) $CH_3CH_2CH=CHCH_2CH_3 + H_2O \xrightarrow{H^+}$
$CH_3CH_2CH_2CH(OH)CH_2CH_3$
(b) $CH_3CHBrCH_3 + CH_3CH_2OK \longrightarrow$
$CH_3CH=CH_2 + CH_3CH_2OH + KBr$
(c) $CH_3CH_3 + 2Cl_2 \xrightarrow{h\nu} CHCl_2CH_3 + 2HCl$
15.44(a) oxidation (b) reduction (c) reduction **15.46**(a) oxidized (b) oxidized **15.49**(a) Methylethylamine is more soluble because it has the ability to form H bonds with water molecules. (b) 1-Butanol has a higher melting point because it can form intermolecular H bonds. (c) Propylamine has a higher boiling point because it contains N—H bonds that allow H bonding, and trimethylamine cannot form H bonds. **15.52** Both groups react by addition to the π bond. The very polar C=O bond attracts the electron-rich O of water to the partially positive C. There is no such polarity in the alkene, so either C atom can be attacked, and two products result.

$CH_3—CH_2—C(=O)—CH_2—CH_3 + H_2O \xrightarrow{H^+}$

$CH_3—CH_2—C(OH)_2—CH_2—CH_3$ (with OH above and OH below central C)

$CH_3—CH_2—CH=CH—CH_3 + H_2O \xrightarrow{H^+}$

$CH_3—CH_2—CH(OH)—CH_2—CH_3 + CH_3—CH_2—CH_2—CH(OH)—CH_3$

15.55 Esters and acid anhydrides form through dehydration-condensation reactions, and water is the other product.
15.57(a) alkyl halide (b) nitrile (c) carboxylic acid (d) aldehyde
15.59(a) CH₃—(CH=CH)—(CH₂—OH)
  alkene   alcohol
(b) (Cl—CH₂)—⬡—(C(=O)—OH)
  haloalkane   carboxylic acid

(c) alkene / amide: C(=O)—N(H)—CH₃

(d) (N≡C)—(CH₂—C(=O)—CH₃)
  nitrile   ketone

(e) ⬜—(C(=O)—O—CH₂—CH₃)
  ester

15.61 $H_3C—CH_2—CH_2—CH_2—CH_2—OH$
$H_3C—CH_2—CH_2—CH(OH)—CH_3$

$H_3C—CH(CH_3)—CH(OH)—CH_3$
$H_3C—CH_2—CH(OH)—CH_2—CH_3$
$H_3C—CH_2—CH(CH_3)—CH_2—OH$
$H_3C—C(OH)(CH_3)—CH_2—CH_3$
$H_3C—CH(CH_3)—CH_2—CH_2—OH$
$H_3C—C(CH_3)_2—CH_2—OH$

15.63 $H_3C—CH_2—CH_2—CH_2—NH_2$
$H_3C—CH_2—CH(NH_2)—CH_3$
$H_3C—CH(CH_3)—CH_2—NH_2$
$H_3C—C(CH_3)(NH_2)—CH_3$ [with CH₃ above]
$H_3C—CH_2—N(H)—CH_2—CH_3$
$H_3C—CH_2—CH_2—N(H)—CH_3$
$H_3C—CH_2—N(CH_3)—CH_3$
$H_3C—CH(CH_3)—N(H)—CH_3$

15.65(a) $CH_3—C(=O)—CH_2—CH_3$ (b) $CH_3—CH(CH_3)—C(=O)—OH$
(c) cyclopentanone (ring with =O)

15.67(a) $CH_3—C(=O)—N(H)—CH_3$
(b) $CH_3—CH_2—CH_2—C(=O)—O—CH(CH_3)—CH_3$
(c) $H—C(=O)—O—CH_2—CH(CH_3)—CH_3$

15.69(a) $CH_3—(CH_2)_4—C(=O)—OH$ and $HO—CH_2—CH_3$
(b) ⬡—C(=O)—OH and $HO—CH_2—CH_2—CH_3$
(c) $CH_3—CH_2—OH$ and $HO—C(=O)—CH_2—CH_2—$⬡

15.71(a) CH_3-CH_2-OH

(b)

$$CH_3-CH_2-\overset{\overset{\displaystyle O}{\|}}{C}-O-CH_2-CH_3$$

$$\underset{\underset{\displaystyle CH_3-CH_2-CH-CH_3}{|}}{C\equiv N}$$

$$\underset{\underset{\displaystyle CH_3-CH_2-CH-CH_3}{|}}{\overset{\overset{\displaystyle OH}{|}}{C=O}}$$

15.73(a) propanoic acid (b) ethylamine **15.77** addition reactions and condensation reactions **15.80** Dispersion forces strongly attract the long, unbranched chains of high-density polyethylene (HDPE). Low-density polyethylene (LDPE) has branching in the chains that prevents packing and weakens the attractions. **15.82** An amine and a carboxylic acid react to form nylon; a carboxylic acid and an alcohol form a polyester.

15.83(a)

$$\left[\begin{matrix} H & H \\ | & | \\ -C-C- \\ | & | \\ H & Cl \end{matrix}\right]_n$$

(b)

$$\left[\begin{matrix} H & H \\ | & | \\ -C-C- \\ | & | \\ H & CH_3 \end{matrix}\right]_n$$

15.87(a) condensation (b) addition (c) condensation (d) condensation **15.89** The amino acid sequence in a protein determines its shape and structure, which determine its function. **15.92** The DNA base sequence determines the RNA base sequence, which determines the protein amino acid sequence.

15.93(a)   (b)   (c)

15.95(a)

(b)

15.97(a) AATCGG (b) TCTGTA **15.99** ACAATGCCT; this sequence codes for three amino acids. **15.101**(a) Both R groups are from cysteine, which can form a disulfide bond (covalent bond). (b) Lysine and aspartic acid give a salt link. (c) Asparagine and serine will hydrogen bond. (d) Valine

and phenylalanine interact through dispersion forces.
15.106(a) Perform an acid-catalyzed dehydration of the alcohol followed by addition of Br_2. (b) Oxidize 1 mol of ethanol to acetic acid, then react 1 mol of acetic acid with 1 mol of ethanol to form the ester.

15.108

$$H_2N-CH_2-CH_2-CH_2-CH_2-CH_2-NH_2$$
cadaverine

$$H_2N-CH_2-CH_2-CH_2-CH_2-NH_2$$
putrescine

$$Br-CH_2CH_2-Br + 2CN^- \longrightarrow$$
$$N\equiv C-CH_2CH_2-C\equiv N + 2Br^-$$

$$N\equiv C-CH_2CH_2-C\equiv N \xrightarrow{reduction}$$
$$H_2N-CH_2CH_2CH_2CH_2-NH_2$$

15.109(a)

(b) Carbon 1 is sp^2 hybridized. Carbon 2 is sp^3 hybridized. Carbon 3 is sp^3 hybridized. Carbon 4 is sp^2 hybridized. Carbon 5 is sp^3 hybridized. Carbons 6 and 7 are sp^2 hybridized.
(c) Carbons 2, 3, and 5 are chiral centers, as they are each bonded to four different groups.
15.113 The resonance structures show that the bond between carbon and nitrogen will have some double bond character that restricts rotation around the bond.

15.116(a) Hydrolysis requires the addition of water to break the peptide bonds. (b) glycine, 4; alanine, 1; valine, 3; proline, 6; serine, 7; arginine, 49 (c) 10,700 g/mol **15.117** When 2-butanone is reduced, equal amounts of both isomers are produced because the reaction does not favor the production of one over the other. The mixture is not optically active since the rotation of light to the right by one isomer cancels the rotation of light to the left by the other isomer.

Chapter 16

Answers to Boxed Reading Problems:

B16.2 (a) Step 1 $\cancel{NO(g)} + O_3(g) \longrightarrow \cancel{NO_2(g)} + O_2(g)$
          Step 2 $\cancel{NO_2(g)} + O(g) \longrightarrow \cancel{NO(g)} + O_2(g)$
          Overall $O_3(g) + O(g) \longrightarrow 2O_2(g)$
(b) rate $= 3 \times 10^7$ molecule/s
B16.3 (a) Step 1 with Cl will have the higher value for the p factor. Since Cl is a single atom, no matter how it collides with the ozone molecule, the two particles should react, if the collision has enough energy. NO is a molecule. If the O_3 molecule collides with the N atom in the NO molecule, reaction can occur as a bond can form between N and O; if the O_3

molecule collides with the O atom in the NO molecule, reaction will not occur as the bond between N and O cannot form. The probability of a successful collision is smaller with NO.

(b) $:\ddot{\underset{..}{Cl}}\text{-----}\ddot{\underset{..}{O}}\text{------}\overset{\displaystyle\ddot{O}}{\text{ }}\text{=}\ddot{O}$

• **16.2** Reaction rate is proportional to concentration. An increase in pressure will increase the concentration, resulting in an increased rate.   **16.3** The addition of water will lower the concentrations of all dissolved solutes, and the rate will decrease.   **16.5** An increase in temperature increases the rate by increasing the number of collisions between particles, but more importantly, it increases the energy of collisions.   **16.8**(a) The instantaneous rate is the rate at one point in time during the reaction. The average rate is the average over a period of time. On a graph of reactant concentration vs. time, the instantaneous rate is the slope of the tangent to the curve at any point. The average rate is the slope of the line connecting two points on the curve. The closer together the two points (the shorter the time interval), the closer the average rate is to the instantaneous rate.   (b) The initial rate is the instantaneous rate at the point on the graph where $t = 0$, that is, when reactants are mixed.

16.10

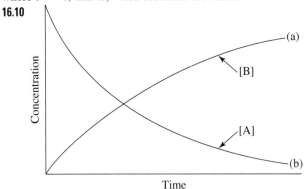

16.12(a) $\text{rate} = -\left(\dfrac{1}{2}\right)\dfrac{\Delta AX_2}{\Delta t}$

$= -\left(\dfrac{1}{2}\right)\dfrac{(0.0088\ M - 0.0500\ M)}{(20.0\ s - 0\ s)}$

$= 0.0010\ M/s$

(b)

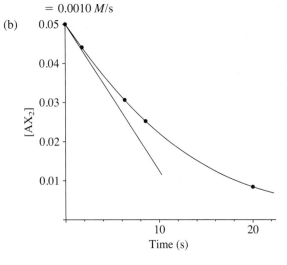

The initial rate is higher than the average rate because the rate decreases as reactant concentration decreases.

16.14 $\text{rate} = -\dfrac{1}{2}\dfrac{\Delta[A]}{\Delta t} = \dfrac{\Delta[B]}{\Delta t} = \dfrac{\Delta[C]}{\Delta t}$; 4 mol/L·s

16.16 $\text{rate} = -\dfrac{\Delta[A]}{\Delta t} = -\dfrac{1}{2}\dfrac{\Delta[B]}{\Delta t} = \dfrac{\Delta[C]}{\Delta t}$; 0.2 mol/L·s

16.18 $2N_2O_5(g) \longrightarrow 4NO_2(g) + O_2(g)$

16.21 $\text{rate} = -\dfrac{\Delta[N_2]}{\Delta t} = -\dfrac{1}{3}\dfrac{\Delta[H_2]}{\Delta t} = \dfrac{1}{2}\dfrac{\Delta[NH_3]}{\Delta t}$

16.22(a) $\text{rate} = -\dfrac{1}{3}\dfrac{\Delta[O_2]}{\Delta t} = \dfrac{1}{2}\dfrac{[\Delta O_3]}{\Delta t}$

(b) 1.45×10^{-5} mol/L·s

16.23(a) k is the rate constant, the proportionality constant in the rate law; it is reaction and temperature specific.   (b) m represents the order of the reaction with respect to [A], and n represents the order of the reaction with respect to [B]. The order of a reactant does not necessarily equal its stoichiometric coefficient in the balanced equation.   (c) $L^2/mol^2\cdot min$ **16.25**(a) Rate doubles.   (b) Rate decreases by a factor of 4.   (c) Rate increases by a factor of 9.   **16.26** first order in BrO_3^-; first order in Br^-; second order in H^+; fourth order overall   **16.28**(a) Rate doubles.   (b) Rate is halved.   (c) The rate increases by a factor of 16.   **16.30** second order in NO_2; first order in Cl; third order overall   **16.32**(a) Rate increases by a factor of 9.   (b) Rate increases by a factor of 8.   (c) Rate is halved.   **16.34**(a) second order in A; first order in B   (b) rate = $k[A]^2[B]$ (c) 5.00×10^3 $L^2/mol^2\cdot min$ **16.36**(a) $time^{-1}$ (b) L/mol·time   (c) $L^2/mol^2\cdot time$ (d) $L^{3/2}/mol^{3/2}\cdot time$ **16.39**(a) first order   (b) second order   (c) zero order   **16.41** 7 s   **16.43**(a) $k = 0.0660$ min^{-1} (b) 21.0 min

16.45(a)

x-axis (time, s)	[NH₃]	y-axis (ln [NH₃])
0	4.000 M	1.38629
1.000	3.986 M	1.38279
2.000	3.974 M	1.37977

$k = 3\times10^{-3}$ s^{-1}

(b) $t_{1/2} = 2\times10^2$ s

16.47 No, other factors that affect the rate are the energy and orientation of the collisions.   **16.50** Measure the rate constant at a series of temperatures and plot ln k versus $1/T$. The slope of the line equals $-E_a/R$.   **16.53** No, reaction is reversible and will eventually reach a state where the forward and reverse rates are equal. When this occurs, there are no concentrations equal to zero. Since some reactants are reformed from EF, the

amount of EF will be less than 4×10^{-5} mol. **16.54** At the same temperature, both reaction mixtures have the same average kinetic energy, but the reactant molecules do not have the same average velocity. The trimethylamine molecule has greater mass than the ammonia molecule, so trimethylamine molecules will collide less often with HCl. Moreover, the bulky groups bonded to nitrogen in trimethylamine mean that collisions with HCl having the correct orientation occur less frequently. Therefore, the rate of the reaction between NH_3 and HCl is higher. **16.55** 12 unique collisions **16.57** 2.96×10^{-18} **16.59** 0.033 s^{-1}
16.61(a)

(b) 2.70×10^2 kJ/mol

(c)

16.64(a) Because the enthalpy change is positive, the reaction is endothermic.

(b) 3 kJ (c) :Cl⋯⋯Cl⋯⋯N≋O:

16.65 The rate of an overall reaction depends on the rate of the slowest step. The rate of the overall reaction will be lower than the average of the individual rates because the average includes higher rates as well. **16.69** The probability of three particles colliding with one another with the proper energy and orientation is much less than the probability for two particles.
16.70 No, the overall rate law must contain only reactants (no intermediates), and the overall rate is determined by the slow step.
16.72(a) $A(g) + B(g) + C(g) \longrightarrow D(g)$

(b) X and Y are intermediates.

(c)

Step	Molecularity	Rate Law
$A(g) + B(g) \rightleftharpoons X(g)$	bimolecular	$rate_1 = k_1[A][B]$
$X(g) + C(g) \longrightarrow Y(g)$	bimolecular	$rate_2 = k_2[X][C]$
$Y(g) \longrightarrow D(g)$	unimolecular	$rate_3 = k_3[Y]$

(d) yes (e) yes **16.74** The proposed mechanism is valid because the individual steps are chemically reasonable, they add to give the overall equation, and the rate law for the mechanism matches the observed rate law. **16.77** No. A catalyst changes the mechanism of a reaction to one with lower activation energy. Lower activation energy means a faster reaction. An increase in temperature does not influence the activation energy, but increases the fraction of collisions with sufficient energy to equal or exceed the activation energy. **16.78**(a) No. The spark provides energy that is absorbed by the H_2 and O_2 molecules to achieve the activation energy. (b) Yes. The powdered metal acts as a heterogeneous catalyst, providing a surface on which the oxygen-hydrogen reaction can proceed with a lower activation energy.
16.83(a) Water does not appear as a reactant in the rate-determining step.

(b) Step 1: $rate_1 = k_1[(CH_3)_3CBr]$
Step 2: $rate_2 = k_2[(CH_3)_3C^+]$
Step 3: $rate_3 = k_3[(CH_3)_3COH_2^+]$

(c) $(CH_3)_3C^+$ and $(CH_3)_3COH_2^+$

(d) The rate-determining step is step 1. The rate law for this step agrees with the rate law observed with $k = k_1$.

16.85 4.61×10^4 J/mol **16.89**(a) Rate increases 2.5 times.
(b) Rate is halved. (c) Rate decreases by a factor of 0.01.
(d) Rate does not change. **16.90** second order **16.93** 57 yr
16.96(a) 0.21 h^{-1}; 3.3 h (b) 6.6 h (c) If the concentration of sucrose is relatively low, the concentration of water remains nearly constant even with small changes in the amount of water. This gives an apparent zero-order reaction with respect to water. Thus, the reaction is first order overall because the rate does not change with changes in the amount of water.
16.99(a) 0.68 M (b) 0.57 **16.102** 71 kPa **16.106** 7.3×10^3 J/mol
16.108(a) 2.4×10^{-15} M (b) 2.4×10^{-11} mol/L·s **16.111**(a) 2.8 days
(b) 7.4 days (c) 4.5 mol/m³ **6.114**(a) $rate_1 = 1.7\times10^{-5}$ M s^{-1}; $rate_2 = 3.4\times10^{-5}$ M s^{-1}; $rate_3 = 3.4\times10^{-5}$ M s^{-1} (b) zero order with respect to $S_2O_8^{2-}$; first order with respect to I^-
(c) 4.3×10^{-4} s^{-1} (d) rate $= (4.3\times10^{-4}$ $s^{-1})[KI]$
16.117(a) 7×10^4 cells/L (b) 2.0×10^1 min **16.120**(a) Use the Monod equation.

(b) 8.2×10^3 cells/m³ (c) 8.4×10^3 cells/m³
16.125(a) 8.0×10^1 s (b) 59 s (c) 2.6×10^2 s

Chapter 17

Answers to Boxed Reading Problem: B17.1 (a) Enzyme 3 (d) If F inhibited enzyme 6, then the second branch would not take place when enough F was made.

• **17.1** If the change is one of concentrations, it results temporarily in more products and less reactants. After equilibrium is re-established, K_c remains unchanged because the ratio of products and reactants remains the same. **17.7** The equilibrium constant expression is $K = [O_2]$. If the temperature remains constant, K remains constant. If the initial amount of Li_2O_2 present is sufficient to reach equilibrium, the amount of O_2 obtained will be constant.

17.8(a) $Q = \dfrac{[HI]^2}{[H_2][I_2]}$

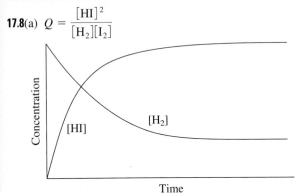

The value of Q increases as a function of time until it reaches the value of K. (b) no **17.11** Yes. If Q_1 is for the formation of 1 mol NH_3 from H_2 and N_2, and Q_2 is for the formation of NH_3 from H_2 and 1 mol of N_2, then $Q_2 = Q_1^2$.

17.12(a) $4NO(g) + O_2(g) \rightleftharpoons 2N_2O_3(g)$;

$$Q_c = \dfrac{[N_2O_3]^2}{[NO]^4[O_2]}$$

(b) $SF_6(g) + 2SO_3(g) \rightleftharpoons 3SO_2F_2(g)$;

$$Q_c = \dfrac{[SO_2F_2]^3}{[SF_6][SO_3]^2}$$

(c) $2SClF_5(g) + H_2(g) \rightleftharpoons S_2F_{10}(g) + 2HCl(g)$;

$$Q_c = \dfrac{[S_2F_{10}][HCl]^2}{[SClF_5]^2[H_2]}$$

17.14(a) $2NO_2Cl(g) \rightleftharpoons 2NO_2(g) + Cl_2(g)$;

$$Q_c = \dfrac{[NO_2]^2[Cl_2]}{[NO_2Cl]^2}$$

(b) $2POCl_3(g) \rightleftharpoons 2PCl_3(g) + O_2(g)$;

$$Q_c = \dfrac{[PCl_3]^2[O_2]}{[POCl_3]^2}$$

(c) $4NH_3(g) + 3O_2(g) \rightleftharpoons 2N_2(g) + 6H_2O(g)$;

$$Q_c = \dfrac{[N_2]^2[H_2O]^6}{[NH_3]^4[O_2]^3}$$

17.16(a) 7.9 (b) 3.2×10^{-5}

17.18(a) $2Na_2O_2(s) + 2CO_2(g) \rightleftharpoons 2Na_2CO_3(s) + O_2(g)$;

$$Q_c = \dfrac{[O_2]}{[CO_2]^2}$$

(b) $H_2O(l) \rightleftharpoons H_2O(g)$; $Q_c = [H_2O(g)]$

(c) $NH_4Cl(s) \rightleftharpoons NH_3(g) + HCl(g)$; $Q_c = [NH_3][HCl]$

17.20(a) $2NaHCO_3(s) \rightleftharpoons Na_2CO_3(s) + CO_2(g) + H_2O(g)$;

$Q_c = [CO_2][H_2O]$

(b) $SnO_2(s) + 2H_2(g) \rightleftharpoons Sn(s) + 2H_2O(g)$;

$$Q_c = \dfrac{[H_2O]^2}{[H_2]^2}$$

(c) $H_2SO_4(l) + SO_3(g) \rightleftharpoons H_2S_2O_7(l)$;

$$Q_c = \dfrac{1}{[SO_3]}$$

17.23(a) (1) $Cl_2(g) + F_2(g) \rightleftharpoons 2ClF(g)$

(2) $2ClF(g) + 2F_2(g) \rightleftharpoons 2ClF_3(g)$

overall: $Cl_2(g) + 3F_2(g) \rightleftharpoons 2ClF_3(g)$

(b) $Q_{overall} = Q_1 Q_2 = \dfrac{[\cancel{ClF}]^2}{[Cl_2][F_2]} \times \dfrac{[ClF_3]^2}{[\cancel{ClF}]^2[F_2]^2}$

$$= \dfrac{[ClF_3]^2}{[Cl_2][F_2]^3}$$

17.25 K_c and K_p are equal when $\Delta n_{gas} = 0$. **17.26**(a) smaller (b) Assuming that $RT > 1$ ($T > 12.2$ K), $K_p > K_c$ if there are more moles of products than reactants at equilibrium, and $K_p < K_c$ if there are more moles of reactants than products. **17.27**(a) 3 (b) −1 (c) 3 **17.29**(a) 3.2 (b) 28.5 **17.31**(a) 0.15 (b) 3.6×10^{-7} **17.33** The reaction quotient (Q) and equilibrium constant (K) are determined by the ratio [products]/[reactants]. When $Q < K$, the reaction proceeds to the right to form more products. **17.35** no; to the left **17.38** At equilibrium, equal concentrations of $CFCl_3$ and HCl exist, regardless of starting reactant concentrations, because the product coefficients are equal. **17.40**(a) The approximation applies when the change in concentration from initial concentration to equilibrium concentration is so small that it is insignificant; this occurs when K is small and initial concentration is large. (b) This approximation should not be used when the change in concentration is greater than 5%. This can occur when $[reactant]_{initial}$ is very small or when change in [reactant] is relatively large due to a large K. **17.41** 50.8

17.43

Concentration (M)	$PCl_5(g)$	$\rightleftharpoons$	$PCl_3(g) +$	$Cl_2(g)$
Initial	0.075		0	0
Change	$-x$		$+x$	$+x$
Equilibrium	$0.075 - x$		x	x

17.45 28 atm **17.47** 0.33 atm **17.49** 3.5×10^{-3} M **17.51** [HI] = 0.0152 M; $[I_2]$ = 0.00328 M **17.53** $[I_2]_{eq} = [Cl_2]_{eq} = 0.0199$ M; $[ICl]_{eq} = 0.0601$ M **17.55** 6.01×10^{-6} **17.58** Equilibrium position refers to the specific concentrations or pressures of reactants and products that exist at equilibrium, whereas equilibrium constant is the overall ratio of equilibrium concentrations or pressures. Equilibrium position changes as a result of a change in reactant and product concentrations. **17.59**(a) B, because the amount of product increases with temperature (b) A, because the lowest temperature will give the least product **17.63**(a) shifts toward products (b) shifts toward products (c) does not shift (d) shifts toward reactants **17.65**(a) more F and less F_2 (b) more C_2H_2 and H_2 and less CH_4 **17.67**(a) no effect (b) less H_2 and O_2 and more H_2O **17.69**(a) no change (b) increase volume **17.71**(a) amount decreases (b) amounts increase (c) amounts increase (d) amount decreases **17.73** 2.0 **17.76**(a) lower temperature, higher pressure (b) Q decreases; no change in K (c) Reaction rates are lower at lower temperatures, so a catalyst is used to speed up the reaction. **17.78**(a) $P_{N_2} = 31$ atm; $P_{H_2} = 93$ atm; $P_{total} = 174$ atm (b) $P_{N_2} = 18$ atm; $P_{H_2} = 111$ atm; $P_{total} = 179$ atm; not a valid argument **17.81** 0.204 atm **17.84**(a) 3×10^{-3} atm (b) high pressure; low temperature (c) 2×10^5 (d) No, because water condenses at a higher temperature. **17.87**(a) 0.016 atm (b) $K_c = 5.6 \times 10^2$; $P_{O_2} = 0.16$ atm **17.89** 12.5 g $CaCO_3$ **17.93** Both concentrations increased by a factor of 2.2. **17.95**(a) 3.0×10^{-14} atm (b) 0.013 pg CO/L **17.97**(a) 98.0% (b) 99.0% (c) 2.60×10^5 J/mol **17.99**(a) $2CH_4(g) + O_2(g) + 2H_2O(g) \rightleftharpoons 2CO_2(g) + 6H_2(g)$ (b) 1.76×10^{29} (c) 3.19×10^{23} (d) 48 atm **17.100**(a) 4.0×10^{-21} atm (b) 5.5×10^{-8} atm (c) 29 N atoms/L; 4.0×10^{14} H atoms/L (d) The more reasonable step is $N_2(g) + H(g) \longrightarrow NH(g) + N(g)$. With only 29 N atoms in 1.0 L, the first reaction would produce virtually no $NH(g)$ molecules. There are orders of magnitude more N_2 molecules than N atoms, so the second reaction is the more reasonable step. **17.103**(a) $P_{N_2} = 0.780$ atm; $P_{O_2} = 0.210$ atm; $P_{NO} = 2.67 \times 10^{-16}$ atm (b) 0.990 atm (c) $K_c = K_p = 4.35 \times 10^{-31}$ **17.105**(a) 1.26×10^{-3} (b) 794 (c) -51.8 kJ (d) 1.2×10^4 J/mol **17.109**(a) 1.52 (b) 0.9626 atm (c) 0.2000 mol CO (d) 0.01097 M

Chapter 18

18.2 All Arrhenius acids have H in their formula and produce hydronium ion (H_3O^+) in aqueous solution. All Arrhenius bases have OH in their formula and produce hydroxide ion (OH^-) in aqueous solution. Neutralization occurs when each H_3O^+ ion combines with an OH^- ion to form two molecules of H_2O. Chemists found the reaction of any strong base with any strong acid always had a ΔH of -56 kJ/mol H_2O produced.
18.4 Strong acids and bases dissociate completely into ions when dissolved in water. Weak acids and bases dissociate only partially. The characteristic property of all weak acids is that a great majority of the acid molecules are undissociated.
18.5 a, c, and d
18.7 b and d

18.9(a) $K_a = \dfrac{[CN^-][H_3O^+]}{[HCN]}$

(b) $K_a = \dfrac{[CO_3^{2-}][H_3O^+]}{[HCO_3^-]}$

(c) $K_a = \dfrac{[HCOO^-][H_3O^+]}{[HCOOH]}$

18.11(a) $K_a = \dfrac{[NO_2^-][H_3O^+]}{[HNO_2]}$

(b) $K_a = \dfrac{[CH_3COO^-][H_3O^+]}{[CH_3COOH]}$

(c) $K_a = \dfrac{[BrO_2^-][H_3O^+]}{[HBrO_2]}$

18.13 $CH_3COOH < HF < HIO_3 < HI$ **18.15**(a) weak acid (b) strong base (c) weak acid (d) strong acid **18.17**(a) strong base (b) strong acid (c) weak acid (d) weak acid
18.22(a) The acid with the smaller K_a (4×10^{-5}) has the higher pH, because less dissociation yields fewer hydronium ions. (b) The acid with the larger pK_a (3.5) has the higher pH, because it has a smaller K_a and, thus, lower $[H_3O^+]$. (c) Lower concentration (0.01 M) contains fewer hydronium ions. (d) A 0.1 M weak acid solution contains fewer hydronium ions. (e) The 0.01 M base solution contains more hydroxide ions, so fewer hydronium ions. (f) The solution that has pOH = 6.0 has the higher pH: pH = $14.0 - 6.0 = 8.0$.
18.23(a) 12.05; basic (b) 11.13; acidic **18.25**(a) 2.212; acidic (b) -0.708; basic
18.27(a) $[H_3O^+] = 1.4 \times 10^{-10}$ M, $[OH^-] = 7.1 \times 10^{-5}$ M, pOH = 4.15

(b) $[H_3O^+] = 2.7 \times 10^{-5}$ M, $[OH^-] = 3.7 \times 10^{-10}$ M, pH = 4.57

18.29(a) $[H_3O^+] = 1.7 \times 10^{-5}$ M, $[OH^-] = 5.9 \times 10^{-10}$ M, pOH = 9.23

(b) $[H_3O^+] = 4.5 \times 10^{-9}$ M, $[OH^-] = 2.2 \times 10^{-6}$ M, pH = 8.36

18.31 4.8×10^{-4} mol OH^-/L **18.33** 1.4×10^{-4} mol OH^-
18.36(a) Rising temperature increases the value of K_w. (b) $K_w = 2.5 \times 10^{-14}$; pOH = 6.80; $[OH^-] = 1.6 \times 10^{-7}$ M
18.37 The Brønsted-Lowry theory defines acids as proton donors and bases as proton acceptors, while the Arrhenius definition looks at acids as containing ionizable hydrogen atoms and at bases as containing hydroxide ions. In both definitions, an acid produces H_3O^+ ions and a base produces OH^- ions when added to water. Ammonia and carbonate ion are two Brønsted-Lowry bases that are not Arrhenius bases because they do not contain OH^- ions. Brønsted-Lowry acids must contain an ionizable hydrogen atom in order to be proton donors, so a Brønsted-Lowry acid is also an Arrhenius acid. **18.40** An amphiprotic species is one that can lose a proton to act as an acid or gain a proton to act as a base. The dihydrogen phosphate ion, $H_2PO_4^-$, is an example.

$H_2PO_4^-(aq) + OH^-(aq) \longrightarrow H_2O(l) + HPO_4^{2-}(aq)$
$H_2PO_4^-(aq) + HCl(aq) \longrightarrow H_3PO_4(aq) + Cl^-(aq)$

18.41(a) $H_3PO_4(aq) + H_2O(l) \rightleftharpoons H_2PO_4^-(aq) + H_3O^+(aq)$

$K_a = \dfrac{[H_3O^+][H_2PO_4^-]}{[H_3PO_4]}$

(b) $C_6H_5COOH(aq) + H_2O(l) \rightleftharpoons C_6H_5COO^-(aq) + H_3O^+(aq)$

$K_a = \dfrac{[H_3O^+][C_6H_5COO^-]}{[C_6H_5COOH]}$

(c) $HSO_4^-(aq) + H_2O(l) \rightleftharpoons SO_4^{2-}(aq) + H_3O^+(aq)$

$K_a = \dfrac{[H_3O^+][SO_4^{2-}]}{[HSO_4^-]}$

18.43(a) Cl^- (b) HCO_3^- (c) OH^- **18.45**(a) NH_4^+ (b) NH_3 (c) $C_{10}H_{14}N_2H^+$

18.47(a) $HCl + H_2O \rightleftharpoons Cl^- + H_3O^+$
　　acid　　base　　　base　　acid
Conjugate acid-base pairs: HCl/Cl^- and H_3O^+/H_2O
(b) $HClO_4 + H_2SO_4 \rightleftharpoons ClO_4^- + H_3SO_4^+$
　　acid　　　base　　　　base　　acid
Conjugate acid-base pairs: $HClO_4/ClO_4^-$ and $H_3SO_4^+/H_2SO_4$
(c) $HPO_4^{2-} + H_2SO_4 \rightleftharpoons H_2PO_4^- + HSO_4^-$
　　base　　　acid　　　　acid　　　base
Conjugate acid-base pairs: H_2SO_4/HSO_4^- and $H_2PO_4^-/HPO_4^{2-}$

18.49(a) $NH_3 + H_3PO_4 \rightleftharpoons NH_4^+ + H_2PO_4^-$
　　base　　acid　　　　acid　　　base
Conjugate acid-base pairs: $H_3PO_4/H_2PO_4^-$ and NH_4^+/NH_3
(b) $CH_3O^- + NH_3 \rightleftharpoons CH_3OH + NH_2^-$
　　base　　　acid　　　acid　　　base
Conjugate acid-base pairs: NH_3/NH_2^- and CH_3OH/CH_3O^-
(c) $HPO_4^{2-} + HSO_4^- \rightleftharpoons H_2PO_4^- + SO_4^{2-}$
　　base　　　acid　　　acid　　　base
Conjugate acid-base pairs: HSO_4^-/SO_4^{2-} and $H_2PO_4^-/HPO_4^{2-}$

18.51(a) $OH^-(aq) + H_2PO_4^-(aq) \rightleftharpoons H_2O(l) + HPO_4^{2-}(aq)$
Conjugate acid-base pairs: $H_2PO_4^-/HPO_4^{2-}$ and H_2O/OH^-
(b) $HSO_4^-(aq) + CO_3^{2-}(aq) \rightleftharpoons$
　　　　　　　　　　　$SO_4^{2-}(aq) + HCO_3^-(aq)$
Conjugate acid-base pairs: HSO_4^-/SO_4^{2-} and HCO_3^-/CO_3^{2-}

18.53 $K_c > 1$: $HS^- + HCl \rightleftharpoons H_2S + Cl^-$
$K_c < 1$: $H_2S + Cl^- \rightleftharpoons HS^- + HCl$
18.55 $K_c > 1$ for both a and b **18.57** $K_c < 1$ for both a and b
18.59(a) A strong acid is 100% dissociated, so the acid concentration will be very different after dissociation. (b) A weak acid dissociates to a very small extent, so the acid concentration before and after dissociation is nearly the same. (c) same as b, but with the extent of dissociation greater (d) same as a
18.60 No. HCl is a strong acid and dissociates to a greater extent than the weak acid CH_3COOH. The K_a of the acid, not the concentration of H_3O^+, determines the strength of the acid. **18.63** 1.5×10^{-5} **18.65** $[H_3O^+] = [NO_2^-] = 2.1 \times 10^{-2}$ M; $[OH^-] = 4.8 \times 10^{-13}$ M **18.67** $[H_3O^+] = [ClCH_2COO^-] = 0.041$ M; $[ClCH_2COOH] = 1.21$ M; pH = 1.39
18.69(a) $[H_3O^+] = 6.0 \times 10^{-3}$ M; pH = 2.22; $[OH^-] = 1.7 \times 10^{-12}$ M; pOH = 11.78 (b) 1.9×10^{-4} **18.71** 2.2×10^{-7}
18.73(a) 2.37 (b) 11.53 **18.75**(a) 2.290 (b) 12.699 **18.77** 1.1%
18.79 $[H_3O^+] = [HS^-] = 9 \times 10^{-5}$ M; pH = 4.0; $[OH^-] = 1 \times 10^{-10}$ M; pOH = 10.0; $[H_2S] = 0.10$ M; $[S^{2-}] = 1 \times 10^{-17}$ M **18.82** 1.5% **18.83** All Brønsted-Lowry bases contain at least one lone pair of electrons, which binds an H^+ and allows the base to act as a proton acceptor.
18.86(a) $C_5H_5N(aq) + H_2O(l) \rightleftharpoons OH^-(aq) + C_5H_5NH^+(aq)$

$$K_b = \frac{[C_5H_5NH^+][OH^-]}{[C_5H_5N]}$$

(b) $CO_3^{2-}(aq) + H_2O(l) \rightleftharpoons OH^-(aq) + HCO_3^-(aq)$

$$K_b = \frac{[HCO_3^-][OH^-]}{[CO_3^{2-}]}$$

18.88(a) $HONH_2(aq) + H_2O(l) \rightleftharpoons OH^-(aq) + HONH_3^+(aq)$

$$K_b = \frac{[HONH_3^+][OH^-]}{[HONH_2]}$$

(b) $HPO_4^{2-}(aq) + H_2O(l) \rightleftharpoons H_2PO_4^-(aq) + OH^-(aq)$

$$K_b = \frac{[H_2PO_4^-][OH^-]}{[HPO_4^{2-}]}$$

18.90 11.79 **18.92** 11.45 **18.94**(a) 5.6×10^{-10} (b) 2.5×10^{-5}
18.96(a) 12.04 (b) 10.77 **18.98**(a) 11.19 (b) 5.56
18.100(a) 8.78 (b) 4.66 **18.102** $[OH^-] = 5.5 \times 10^{-4}$ M; pH = 10.74 **18.104** As a nonmetal becomes more electronegative, the acidity of its binary hydride increases. The electronegative nonmetal attracts the electrons more strongly in the polar bond, shifting the electron density away from H, thus making H^+ more easily transferred to a water molecule to form H_3O^+.
18.107 Chlorine is more electronegative than iodine, and $HClO_4$ has more oxygen atoms than HIO. **18.108**(a) H_2SeO_4
(b) H_3PO_4 (c) H_2Te **18.110**(a) H_2Se (b) $B(OH)_3$ (c) $HBrO_2$
18.112(a) 0.5 M $AlBr_3$ (b) 0.3 M $SnCl_2$ **18.114**(a) 0.2 M $Ni(NO_3)_2$ (b) 0.35 M $Al(NO_3)_3$ **18.117** NaF contains the anion of the weak acid HF, so F^- acts as a base. NaCl contains the anion of the strong acid HCl.
18.119(a) $KBr(s) \xrightarrow{H_2O} K^+(aq) + Br^-(aq)$; neutral
(b) $NH_4I(s) \xrightarrow{H_2O} NH_4^+(aq) + I^-(aq)$
$NH_4^+(aq) + H_2O(l) \rightleftharpoons NH_3(aq) + H_3O^+(aq)$; acidic
(c) $KCN(s) \xrightarrow{H_2O} K^+(aq) + CN^-(aq)$
$CN^-(aq) + H_2O(l) \rightleftharpoons HCN(aq) + OH^-(aq)$; basic
18.121(a) $Na_2CO_3(s) \xrightarrow{H_2O} 2Na^+(aq) + CO_3^{2-}(aq)$
$CO_3^{2-}(aq) + H_2O(l) \rightleftharpoons$
　　　　　　　　　$HCO_3^-(aq) + OH^-(aq)$; basic
(b) $CaCl_2(s) \xrightarrow{H_2O} Ca^{2+}(aq) + 2Cl^-(aq)$; neutral
(c) $Cu(NO_3)_2(s) \xrightarrow{H_2O} Cu^{2+}(aq) + 2NO_3^-(aq)$
$Cu(H_2O)_6^{2+}(aq) + H_2O(l) \rightleftharpoons$
　　　　　　　　　$Cu(H_2O)_5OH^+(aq) + H_3O^+(aq)$; acidic
18.123(a) $SrBr_2(s) \xrightarrow{H_2O} Sr^{2+}(aq) + 2Br^-(aq)$; neutral
(b) $Ba(CH_3COO)_2(s) \xrightarrow{H_2O} Ba^{2+}(aq) + 2CH_3COO^-(aq)$
$CH_3COO^-(aq) + H_2O(l) \rightleftharpoons$
　　　　　　　　　$CH_3COOH(aq) + OH^-(aq)$; basic
(c) $(CH_3)_2NH_2Br(s) \xrightarrow{H_2O} (CH_3)_2NH_2^+(aq) + Br^-(aq)$
$(CH_3)_2NH_2^+(aq) + H_2O(l) \rightleftharpoons$
　　　　　　　　　$(CH_3)_2NH(aq) + H_3O^+(aq)$; acidic
18.125(a) $NH_4^+(aq) + H_2O(l) \rightleftharpoons NH_3(aq) + H_3O^+(aq)$
$PO_4^{3-}(aq) + H_2O(l) \rightleftharpoons HPO_4^{2-}(aq) + OH^-(aq)$;
$K_b > K_a$; basic
(b) $SO_4^{2-}(aq) + H_2O(l) \rightleftharpoons HSO_4^-(aq) + OH^-(aq)$;
Na^+ gives no reaction; basic
(c) $ClO^-(aq) + H_2O(l) \rightleftharpoons HClO(aq) + OH^-(aq)$;
Li^+ gives no reaction; basic

18.127(a) $Fe(NO_3)_2 < KNO_3 < K_2SO_3 < K_2S$

(b) $NaHSO_4 < NH_4NO_3 < NaHCO_3 < Na_2CO_3$

18.129 Since both bases produce OH^- ions in water, both bases appear equally strong. $CH_3O^-(aq) + H_2O(l) \longrightarrow OH^-(aq) + CH_3OH(aq)$ and $NH_2^-(aq) + H_2O(l) \longrightarrow OH^-(aq) + NH_3(aq)$. **18.131** Ammonia, NH_3, is a more basic solvent than H_2O. In a more basic solvent, weak acids such as HF act like strong acids and are 100% dissociated. **18.133** A Lewis acid is an electron-pair acceptor while a Brønsted-Lowry acid is a proton donor. The proton of a Brønsted-Lowry acid is a Lewis acid because it accepts an electron pair when it bonds with a base. All Lewis acids are not Brønsted-Lowry acids. A Lewis base is an electron-pair donor and a Brønsted-Lowry base is a proton acceptor. All Brønsted-Lowry bases are Lewis bases, and vice versa. **18.134**(a) No,

$Ni(H_2O)_6{}^{2+}(aq) + 6NH_3(aq) \rightleftharpoons Ni(NH_3)_6{}^{2+} + 6H_2O(l)$; NH_3 is a weak Brønsted-Lowry base, but a strong Lewis base. (b) cyanide ion and water (c) cyanide ion **18.137**(a) Lewis acid (b) Lewis base (c) Lewis acid (d) Lewis base **18.139**(a) Lewis acid (b) Lewis base (c) Lewis base (d) Lewis acid **18.141**(a) Lewis acid: Na^+; Lewis base: H_2O (b) Lewis acid: CO_2; Lewis base: H_2O (c) Lewis acid: BF_3; Lewis base: F^- **18.143**(a) Lewis (b) Brønsted-Lowry and Lewis (c) none (d) Lewis **18.146** 3.5×10^{-8} to 4.5×10^{-8} M H_3O^+; 5.2×10^{-7} to 6.6×10^{-7} M OH^- **18.147**(a) Acids vary in the extent of dissociation depending on the acid-base character of the solvent. (b) Methanol is a weaker base than water since phenol dissociates less in methanol than in water.

(c) $C_6H_5OH(solvated) + CH_3OH(l) \rightleftharpoons$
$\qquad CH_3OH_2{}^+(solvated) + C_6H_5O^-(solvated)$

(d) $CH_3OH(l) + CH_3OH(l) \rightleftharpoons CH_3O^-(solvated)$
$\qquad + CH_3OH_2{}^+(solvated)$; $K = [CH_3O^-][CH_3OH_2{}^+]$

18.150(a) $SnCl_4$ is the Lewis acid; $(CH_3)_3N$ is the Lewis base (b) $5d$ **18.151** pH = 5.00, 6.00, 6.79, 6.98, 7.00 **18.157** 3×10^{18} **18.160** 10.48 **18.162** 2.41 **18.164** amylase, 2×10^{-7} M; pepsin, 1×10^{-2} M; trypsin, 3×10^{-10} M **18.168** 1.47×10^{-3} **18.170**(a) Ca^{2+} does not react with water; $CH_3CH_2COO^-(aq) + H_2O(l) \rightleftharpoons CH_3CH_2COOH(aq) + OH^-(aq)$; basic (b) 9.08 **18.176** 4.5×10^{-5} **18.179**(a) The concentration of oxygen is higher in the lungs, so the equilibrium shifts to the right. (b) In an oxygen-deficient environment, the equilibrium shifts to the left to release oxygen. (c) A decrease in $[H_3O^+]$ shifts the equilibrium to the right. More oxygen is absorbed, but it will be more difficult to remove the O_2. (d) An increase in $[H_3O^+]$ shifts the equilibrium to the left. Less oxygen is bound to Hb, but it will be easier to remove it. **18.181**(a) 1.012 M (b) 0.004 M (c) 0.4% **18.182**(a) 10.0 (b) The pK_b for the 3° amine group is much smaller than that for the aromatic ring, thus the K_b is significantly larger (yielding a much greater amount of OH^-). (c) 4.7 (d) 5.1

Chapter 19

Answers to Boxed Reading Problem: B19.2 (a) 65 mol (b) 6.28 (c) 4.0×10^3 g HCO_3^-

• **19.2** The acid component neutralizes added base, and the base component neutralizes added acid, so the pH of the buffer solution remains relatively constant. The components of a buffer do not neutralize one another because they are a conjugate acid-base pair. **19.7** The buffer range, the pH over which the buffer acts effectively, is greatest when the buffer-component concentration ratio is 1; the range decreases as this ratio deviates from 1. **19.9**(a) Ratio and pH increase; added OH^- reacts with HA. (b) Ratio and pH decrease; added H^+ reacts with A^-. (c) Ratio and pH increase; added A^- increases $[A^-]$. (d) Ratio and pH decrease; added HA increases $[HA]$. **19.11** $[H_3O^+] = 5.6 \times 10^{-6}$ M; pH = 5.25 **19.13** $[H_3O^+] = 5.2 \times 10^{-4}$ M; pH = 3.28 **19.15** 3.89 **19.17** 10.03 **19.19** 9.47 **19.21**(a) K_{a2} (b) 10.55 **19.23** 3.6 **19.25** 0.20 **19.27** 3.37 **19.29** 8.82 **19.31**(a) 4.81 (b) 0.66 g KOH **19.33**(a) $HOOC(CH_2)_4COOH/HOOC(CH_2)_4COO^-$ or $C_6H_5NH_3{}^+/C_6H_5NH_2$ (b) $H_2PO_4^-/HPO_4{}^{2-}$ or $H_2AsO_4^-/HAsO_4{}^{2-}$ **19.35**(a) $HOCH_2CH(OH)COOH/HOCH_2CH(OH)COO^-$ or $CH_3COOC_6H_4COOH/CH_3COOC_6H_4COO^-$ (b) $C_5H_5NH^+/C_5H_5N$ **19.38** 1.6 **19.40** To see a distinct color in a mixture of two colors, you need one to have about 10 times the intensity of the other. For this to be the case, the concentration ratio $[HIn]/[In^-]$ has to be greater than $10/1$ or less than $1/10$. This occurs when pH = $pK_a - 1$ or pH = $pK_a + 1$, respectively, giving a pH range of about 2 units. **19.42** The equivalence point in a titration is the point at which the number of moles of base is stoichiometrically equivalent to the number of moles of acid. The endpoint is the point at which the added indicator changes color. If an appropriate indicator is selected, the endpoint is close to the equivalence point, but they are not usually the same. The pH at the endpoint, or color change, may precede or follow the pH at the equivalence point, depending on the indicator chosen. **19.44**(a) initial pH: *strong acid*–strong base < *weak acid*–strong base < *weak base*–strong acid (b) pH at equivalence point: *weak base*–strong acid < *strong acid*–strong base < *weak acid*–strong base **19.46** At the center of the buffer region, the concentrations of weak acid and conjugate base are equal, so the pH = pK_a of the acid. **19.48** pH range from 7.5 to 9.5 **19.50**(a) bromthymol blue (b) thymol blue or phenolphthalein **19.52**(a) methyl red (b) bromthymol blue **19.54**(a) 1.0000 (b) 1.6368 (c) 2.898 (d) 3.903 (e) 7.00 (f) 10.10 (g) 12.05 **19.56**(a) 2.91 (b) 4.81 (c) 5.29 (d) 6.09 (e) 7.41 (f) 8.76 (g) 10.10 (h) 12.05 **19.58**(a) 59.0 mL and 8.54 (b) 66.0 mL and 7.13, total 132.1 mL and 9.69 **19.60**(a) 123 mL and 5.17 (b) 194 mL and 5.80 **19.63** Fluoride ion is the conjugate base of a weak acid and reacts with H_2O: $F^-(aq) + H_2O(l) \rightleftharpoons HF(aq) + OH^-(aq)$. As the pH increases, the equilibrium shifts to the left and $[F^-]$ increases. As the pH decreases, the equilibrium shifts to the right and $[F^-]$ decreases. The changes in $[F^-]$ influence the solubility of BaF_2. Chloride ion is the conjugate base of a strong acid, so it does not react with water and its concentration is not influenced by pH. **19.65** The compound precipitates. **19.66**(a) $K_{sp} = [Ag^+]^2[CO_3{}^{2-}]$ (b) $K_{sp} = [Ba^{2+}][F^-]^2$ (c) $K_{sp} = [Cu^{2+}][HS^-][OH^-]$

19.68(a) $K_{sp} = [Ca^{2+}][CrO_4^{2-}]$ (b) $K_{sp} = [Ag^+][CN^-]$
(c) $K_{sp} = [Ni^{2+}][HS^-][OH^-]$ **19.70** 1.3×10^{-4} **19.72** 2.8×10^{-11}
19.74(a) 2.3×10^{-5} M (b) 4.2×10^{-9} M **19.76**(a) 1.7×10^{-3} M
(b) 2.0×10^{-4} M **19.78**(a) $Mg(OH)_2$ (b) PbS
(c) Ag_2SO_4 **19.80**(a) $CaSO_4$ (b) $Mg_3(PO_4)_2$ (c) $PbSO_4$
19.82(a) $AgCl(s) \rightleftharpoons Ag^+(aq) + Cl^-(aq)$. The chloride ion
is the anion of a strong acid, so it does not react with H_3O^+.
No change with pH.
(b) $SrCO_3(s) \rightleftharpoons Sr^{2+}(aq) + CO_3^{2-}(aq)$. The strontium ion is
the cation of a strong base, so pH will not affect its solubility.
The carbonate ion acts as a base:
$CO_3^{2-}(aq) + H_2O(l) \rightleftharpoons HCO_3^-(aq) + OH^-(aq)$; also
$CO_2(g)$ forms and escapes: $CO_3^{2-}(aq) + 2H_3O^+(aq) \longrightarrow$
$CO_2(g) + 3H_2O(l)$. Therefore, the solubility of $SrCO_3$
will increase with addition of H_3O^+ (decreasing pH).
19.84(a) $Fe(OH)_2(s) \rightleftharpoons Fe^{2+}(aq) + 2OH^-(aq)$. The OH^- ion
reacts with added H_3O^+: $OH^-(aq) + H_3O^+(aq) \longrightarrow 2H_2O(l)$.
The added H_3O^+ consumes the OH^-, driving the equilibrium
toward the right to dissolve more $Fe(OH)_2$. Solubility
increases with addition of H_3O^+ (decreasing pH).
(b) $CuS(s) + H_2O(l) \rightleftharpoons Cu^{2+}(aq) + HS^-(aq) + OH^-(aq)$.
Both HS^- and OH^- are anions of weak acids, so both ions
react with added H_3O^+. Solubility increases with addition of
H_3O^+ (decreasing pH).   **19.86** yes   **19.88** yes   **19.91**(a) $Fe(OH)_3$
(b) The two metal ions are separated by adding just enough
NaOH to precipitate iron(III) hydroxide.   (c) 2.0×10^{-7} M
19.94 No, because it indicates that a complex ion forms
between the lead ion and hydroxide ions:
$$Pb^{2+}(aq) + nOH^-(aq) \rightleftharpoons Pb(OH)_n^{2-n}(aq)$$
19.95 $Hg(H_2O)_4^{2+}(aq) + 4CN^-(aq) \rightleftharpoons$
$$Hg(CN)_4^{2-}(aq) + 4H_2O(l)$$
19.97 $Ag(H_2O)_2^+(aq) + 2S_2O_3^{2-}(aq) \rightleftharpoons$
$$Ag(S_2O_3)_2^{3-}(aq) + 2H_2O(l)$$
19.99 8.1×10^{-15} M **19.101** 0.05 M **19.103** 1.0×10^{-16} M Zn^{2+};
0.025 M $Zn(CN)_4^{2-}$; 0.049 M CN^- **19.105** 0.035 L of 2.00 M
NaOH and 0.465 L of 0.200 M HCOOH   **19.107**(a) 0.99
(b) assuming the volumes are additive: 0.468 L of 1.0 M
HCOOH and 0.232 L of 1.0 M NaOH   (c) 0.34 M
19.110 1.3×10^{-4} M **19.113**(a) 14   (b) 1 g from the second
beaker   **19.116**(a) 0.088 (b) 0.14 **19.117** 0.260 M TRIS; pH $=$
8.53 **19.119** Lower the pH below 6.6   **19.123** 8×10^{-5}
19.125(a)

V (mL)	pH	ΔpH/ΔV	V_avg (mL)
0.00	1.00		
10.00	1.22	0.022	5.00
20.00	1.48	0.026	15.00
30.00	1.85	0.037	25.00
35.00	2.18	0.066	32.50
39.00	2.89	0.18	37.00
39.50	3.20	0.62	39.25
39.75	3.50	1.2	39.63
39.90	3.90	2.7	39.83
39.95	4.20	6	39.93
39.99	4.90	18	39.97

V (mL)	pH	ΔpH/ΔV	V_avg (mL)
40.00	7.00	200	40.00
40.01	9.40	200	40.01
40.05	9.80	10	40.03
40.10	10.40	10	40.08
40.25	10.50	0.67	40.18
40.50	10.79	1.2	40.38
41.00	11.09	0.60	40.75
45.00	11.76	0.17	43.00
50.00	12.05	0.058	47.50
60.00	12.30	0.025	55.00
70.00	12.43	0.013	65.00
80.00	12.52	0.009	75.00

(b)

Maximum slope (equivalence point) is at $V_{avg} = 40.00$ mL.
19.127 4.05 **19.133** H_2CO_3/HCO_3^- and $H_2PO_4^-/HPO_4^{2-}$;
$[HPO_4^{2-}]/[H_2PO_4^-] = 5.8$ **19.134** 3.8 **19.136**(a) 58.2 mL
(b) 7.85 mL   (c) 6.30 **19.138** 170 mL   **19.142** 5.68
19.144 3.9×10^{-9} μg $Pb^{2+}/100$ mL blood   **19.146** No NaCl will
precipitate.   **19.147**(a) A and D   (b) $pH_A = 4.35$; $pH_B = 8.67$;
$pH_C = 2.67$; $pH_D = 4.57$ (c) C, A, D, B   (d) B

Chapter 20

Answer to Boxed Reading Problem: B20.2 -12.6 kJ/mol

• **20.2** A spontaneous process occurs by itself, whereas a nonspontaneous process requires a continuous input of energy to
make it happen. It is possible to cause a nonspontaneous process to occur, but the process stops once the energy source is
removed. A reaction that is nonspontaneous under one set of
conditions may be spontaneous under a different set of conditions.   **20.5** The transition from liquid to gas involves a greater
increase in dispersal of energy and freedom of motion than
does the transition from solid to liquid.   **20.6** In an exothermic
reaction, $\Delta S_{surr} > 0$. In an endothermic reaction, $\Delta S_{surr} < 0$. A
chemical cold pack for injuries is an example of an application
using a spontaneous endothermic process.   **20.8** a, b, and c
20.10 a and b   **20.12**(a) positive   (b) negative   (c) negative
20.14(a) positive   (b) positive   (c) positive   **20.16**(a) negative
(b) negative   (c) positive   **20.18**(a) positive   (b) negative
(c) positive   **20.20**(a) positive   (b) negative   (c) positive
20.22(a) Butane. The double bond in 2-butene restricts freedom
of rotation.   (b) $Xe(g)$. It has the greater molar mass.
(c) $CH_4(g)$. Gases have greater entropy than liquids.
20.24(a) $C_2H_5OH(l)$. It is a more complex molecule.

(b) $KClO_3(aq)$. Ions in solution have their energy more dispersed than those in a solid. (c) $K(s)$. It has a greater molar mass. **20.26**(a) Diamond < graphite < charcoal. Freedom of motion is least in the network solid; more freedom between graphite sheets; most freedom in amorphous solid. (b) Ice < liquid water < water vapor. Entropy increases as a substance changes from solid to liquid to gas. (c) O atoms < O_2 < O_3. Entropy increases with molecular complexity. **20.28**(a) $ClO_4^-(aq) > ClO_3^-(aq) > ClO_2^-(aq)$; decreasing molecular complexity (b) $NO_2(g) > NO(g) > N_2(g)$. N_2 has lower standard molar entropy because it consists of two of the same atoms; the other species have two different types of atoms. NO_2 is more complex than NO. (c) $Fe_3O_4(s) > Fe_2O_3(s) > Al_2O_3(s)$. Fe_3O_4 is more complex and more massive. Fe_2O_3 is more massive than Al_2O_3. **20.31** For a system at equilibrium, $\Delta S_{univ} = \Delta S_{sys} + \Delta S_{surr} = 0$. For a system moving to equilibrium, $\Delta S_{univ} > 0$. **20.32** $S^\circ_{Cl_2O(g)} = 2S^\circ_{HClO(g)} - S^\circ_{H_2O(g)} - \Delta S^\circ_{rxn}$ **20.33**(a) negative; $\Delta S^\circ = -172.4$ J/K (b) positive; $\Delta S^\circ = 141.6$ J/K (c) negative; $\Delta S^\circ = -837$ J/K **20.35** $\Delta S^\circ = 93.1$ J/K; yes, the positive sign of ΔS is expected because there is a net increase in the number of gas molecules. **20.37** $\Delta S^\circ = -311$ J/K; yes, the negative entropy change matches the decrease in moles of gas. **20.39** -75.6 J/K **20.41** -242 J/K **20.44** -97.2 J/K **20.46** A spontaneous process has $\Delta S_{univ} > 0$. Since the absolute temperature is always positive, ΔG_{sys} must be negative ($\Delta G_{sys} < 0$) for a spontaneous process. **20.48** ΔH° is positive and ΔS° is positive. Melting is an example. **20.49** The entropy changes little within a phase. As long as the substance does not change phase, the value of ΔS° is relatively unaffected by temperature. **20.50**(a) -1138.0 kJ (b) -1379.4 kJ (c) -224 kJ **20.52**(a) -1138 kJ (b) -1379 kJ (c) -226 kJ **20.54**(a) Entropy decreases (ΔS° is negative) because the number of moles of gas decreases. The combustion of CO releases energy (ΔH° is negative). (b) -257.2 kJ or -257.3 kJ, depending on the method **20.56**(a) -0.409 kJ/mol·K (b) -197 kJ/mol **20.58**(a) $\Delta H^\circ_{rxn} = 90.7$ kJ; $\Delta S^\circ_{rxn} = 221$ J/K (b) At 28°C, $\Delta G^\circ = 24.3$ kJ; at 128°C, $\Delta G^\circ = 2.2$ kJ; at 228°C, $\Delta G^\circ = -19.9$ kJ (c) For the substances in their standard states, the reaction is nonspontaneous at 28°C, near equilibrium at 128°C, and spontaneous at 228°C. **20.60** $\Delta H^\circ = 30910$ J, $\Delta S^\circ = 93.15$ J/K, $T = 331.8$ K **20.62**(a) $\Delta H^\circ_{rxn} = -241.826$ kJ, $\Delta S^\circ_{rxn} = -44.4$ J/K, $\Delta G^\circ_{rxn} = -228.60$ kJ (b) Yes. The reaction will become nonspontaneous at higher temperatures. (c) The reaction is spontaneous below 5.45×10^3 K. **20.64**(a) ΔG° is a relatively large positive value. (b) $K \gg 1$. Q depends on initial conditions, not equilibrium conditions. **20.67** The standard free energy change, ΔG°, applies when all components of the system are in their standard states; $\Delta G^\circ = \Delta G$ when all concentrations equal 1 M and all partial pressures equal 1 atm. **20.68**(a) 1.7×10^6 (b) 3.89×10^{-34} (c) 1.26×10^{48} **20.70**(a) 6.57×10^{173} (b) 4.46×10^{-15} (c) 3.46×10^4 **20.72** 4.89×10^{-51} **20.74** 3.36×10^5 **20.76** 2.7×10^4 J/mol; no **20.78**(a) 2.9×10^4 J/mol (b) The reverse direction, formation of reactants, is spontaneous, so the reaction proceeds to the left. (c) 7.0×10^3

J/mol; the reaction proceeds to the left to reach equilibrium. **20.80**(a) no T (b) 163 kJ (c) 1×10^2 kJ/mol **20.83**(a) spontaneous (b) + (c) + (d) − (e) −, not spontaneous (f) − **20.87**(a) 2.3×10^2 (b) The treatment is to administer oxygen-rich air; increasing the concentration of oxygen shifts the equilibrium to the left, in the direction of $Hb \cdot O_2$. **20.89** -370. kJ **20.91**(a) $2N_2O_5(g) + 6F_2(g) \longrightarrow 4NF_3(g) + 5O_2(g)$ (b) $\Delta G^\circ_{rxn} = -569$ kJ (c) $\Delta G_{rxn} = -5.60 \times 10^2$ kJ/mol **20.93** $\Delta H^\circ_{rxn} = -137.14$ kJ; $\Delta S^\circ_{rxn} = -120.3$ J/K; $\Delta G^\circ_{rxn} = -101.25$ kJ **20.101**(a) 1.67×10^3 J/mol (b) 7.37×10^3 J/mol (c) -4.04×10^3 J/mol (d) 0.19 **20.105**(a) 465 K (b) 6.59×10^{-4} (c) The reaction rate is higher at the higher temperature. The shorter time required (kinetics) overshadows the lower yield (thermodynamics).

Chapter 21

Answers to Boxed Reading Problem: B21.1 (a) reduction: $Fe^{3+} + e^- \longrightarrow Fe^{2+}$; oxidation: $Cu^+ \longrightarrow Cu^{2+} + e^-$ (b) Overall: $Fe^{3+} + Cu^+ \longrightarrow Fe^{2+} + Cu^{2+}$

• **21.1** Oxidation is the loss of electrons and results in a higher oxidation number; reduction is the gain of electrons and results in a lower oxidation number. **21.3** No, one half-reaction cannot take place independently because there is a transfer of electrons from one substance to another. If one substance loses electrons, another substance must gain them. **21.6** To remove H^+ ions from an equation, add an equal number of OH^- ions to both sides to neutralize the H^+ ions and produce water. **21.8** Spontaneous reactions, for which $\Delta G_{sys} < 0$, take place in voltaic cells (also called galvanic cells). Nonspontaneous reactions, for which $\Delta G_{sys} > 0$, take place in electrolytic cells. **21.10**(a) Cl^- (b) MnO_4^- (c) MnO_4^- (d) Cl^- (e) from Cl^- to MnO_4^- (f) $8H_2SO_4(aq) + 2KMnO_4(aq) + 10KCl(aq) \longrightarrow$ $2MnSO_4(aq) + 5Cl_2(g) + 8H_2O(l) + 6K_2SO_4(aq)$ **21.12**(a) $ClO_3^-(aq) + 6H^+(aq) + 6I^-(aq) \longrightarrow$ $Cl^-(aq) + 3H_2O(l) + 3I_2(s)$ Oxidizing agent is ClO_3^- and reducing agent is I^-. (b) $2MnO_4^-(aq) + H_2O(l) + 3SO_3^{2-}(aq) \longrightarrow$ $2MnO_2(s) + 3SO_4^{2-}(aq) + 2OH^-(aq)$ Oxidizing agent is MnO_4^- and reducing agent is SO_3^{2-}. (c) $2MnO_4^-(aq) + 6H^+(aq) + 5H_2O_2(aq) \longrightarrow$ $2Mn^{2+}(aq) + 8H_2O(l) + 5O_2(g)$ Oxidizing agent is MnO_4^- and reducing agent is H_2O_2. **21.14**(a) $Cr_2O_7^{2-}(aq) + 14H^+(aq) + 3Zn(s) \longrightarrow$ $2Cr^{3+}(aq) + 7H_2O(l) + 3Zn^{2+}(aq)$ Oxidizing agent is $Cr_2O_7^{2-}$ and reducing agent is Zn. (b) $MnO_4^-(aq) + 3Fe(OH)_2(s) + 2H_2O(l) \longrightarrow$ $MnO_2(s) + 3Fe(OH)_3(s) + OH^-(aq)$ Oxidizing agent is MnO_4^- and reducing agent is $Fe(OH)_2$. (c) $2NO_3^-(aq) + 12H^+(aq) + 5Zn(s) \longrightarrow$ $N_2(g) + 6H_2O(l) + 5Zn^{2+}(aq)$ Oxidizing agent is NO_3^- and reducing agent is Zn. **21.16**(a) $4NO_3^-(aq) + 4H^+(aq) + 4Sb(s) \longrightarrow$ $4NO(g) + 2H_2O(l) + Sb_4O_6(s)$ Oxidizing agent is NO_3^- and reducing agent is Sb.

(b) $5BiO_3^-(aq) + 14H^+(aq) + 2Mn^{2+}(aq) \longrightarrow$
$\qquad 5Bi^{3+}(aq) + 7H_2O(l) + 2MnO_4^-(aq)$
Oxidizing agent is BiO_3^- and reducing agent is Mn^{2+}.
(c) $Pb(OH)_3^-(aq) + 2Fe(OH)_2(s) \longrightarrow$
$\qquad Pb(s) + 2Fe(OH)_3(s) + OH^-(aq)$
Oxidizing agent is $Pb(OH)_3^-$ and reducing agent is $Fe(OH)_2$.
21.18(a) $5As_4O_6(s) + 8MnO_4^-(aq) + 18H_2O(l) \longrightarrow$
$\qquad 20AsO_4^{3-}(aq) + 8Mn^{2+}(aq) + 36H^+(aq)$
Oxidizing agent is MnO_4^- and reducing agent is As_4O_6.
(b) $P_4(s) + 6H_2O(l) \longrightarrow$
$\qquad 2HPO_3^{2-}(aq) + 2PH_3(g) + 4H^+(aq)$
P_4 is both the oxidizing agent and the reducing agent.
(c) $2MnO_4^-(aq) + 3CN^-(aq) + H_2O(l) \longrightarrow$
$\qquad 2MnO_2(s) + 3CNO^-(aq) + 2OH^-(aq)$
Oxidizing agent is MnO_4^- and reducing agent is CN^-.
21.21(a) $Au(s) + 3NO_3^-(aq) + 4Cl^-(aq) + 6H^+(aq) \longrightarrow$
$AuCl_4^-(aq) + 3NO_2(g) + 3H_2O(l)$ (b) Oxidizing agent is NO_3^- and reducing agent is Au. (c) HCl provides chloride ions that combine with the gold(III) ion to form the stable $AuCl_4^-$ ion. **21.22**(a) A (b) E (c) C (d) A (e) E (f) E
21.25 An active electrode is a reactant or product in the cell reaction. An inactive electrode does not take part in the reaction and is present only to conduct a current. Platinum and graphite are commonly used as inactive electrodes. **21.26**(a) A (b) B (c) A (d) Hydrogen bubbles will form when metal A is placed in acid. Metal A is a better reducing agent than metal B, so if metal B reduces H^+ in acid, then metal A will also.
21.27(a) Oxidation: $Zn(s) \longrightarrow Zn^{2+}(aq) + 2e^-$
$\qquad$ Reduction: $Sn^{2+}(aq) + 2e^- \longrightarrow Sn(s)$
$\qquad$ Overall: $Zn(s) + Sn^{2+}(aq) \longrightarrow Zn^{2+}(aq) + Sn(s)$
(b)

21.29(a) left to right (b) left (c) right (d) Ni (e) Fe (f) Fe (g) 1 M $NiSO_4$ (h) K^+ and NO_3^- (i) neither (j) from right to left
(k) Oxidation: $Fe(s) \longrightarrow Fe^{2+}(aq) + 2e^-$
$\qquad$ Reduction: $Ni^{2+}(aq) + 2e^- \longrightarrow Ni(s)$
$\qquad$ Overall: $Fe(s) + Ni^{2+}(aq) \longrightarrow Fe^{2+}(aq) + Ni(s)$
21.31(a) Reduction: $Fe^{2+}(aq) + 2e^- \longrightarrow Fe(s)$
$\qquad$ Oxidation: $Mn(s) \longrightarrow Mn^{2+}(aq) + 2e^-$
$\qquad$ Overall: $Fe^{2+}(aq) + Mn(s) \longrightarrow Fe(s) + Mn^{2+}(aq)$

(b)

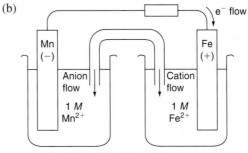

21.33(a) $Al(s) \mid Al^{3+}(aq) \parallel Cr^{3+}(aq) \mid Cr(s)$
(b) $Pt(s) \mid SO_2(g) \mid SO_4^{2-}(aq), H^+(aq) \parallel Cu^{2+}(aq) \mid Cu(s)$
21.36 A negative E_{cell}° indicates that the redox reaction is not spontaneous at the standard state, that is, $\Delta G^\circ > 0$. The reverse reaction is spontaneous with $E_{cell}^\circ > 0$. **21.37** Similar to other state functions, E° changes sign when a reaction is reversed. Unlike ΔG°, ΔH°, and S°, E° (the ratio of energy to charge) is an intensive property. When the coefficients in a reaction are multiplied by a factor, the values of ΔG°, ΔH°, and S° are multiplied by that factor. However, E° does not change because both the energy and charge are multiplied by the factor and thus their ratio remains unchanged.
21.38(a) Oxidation: $Se^{2-}(aq) \longrightarrow Se(s) + 2e^-$
$\qquad$ Reduction: $2SO_3^{2-}(aq) + 3H_2O(l) + 4e^- \longrightarrow$
$\qquad\qquad\qquad\qquad\qquad\qquad S_2O_3^{2-}(aq) + 6OH^-(aq)$
(b) $E_{anode}^\circ = E_{cathode}^\circ - E_{cell}^\circ = -0.57\ V - 0.35\ V$
$\qquad\qquad = -0.92\ V$
21.40(a) $Br_2 > Fe^{3+} > Cu^{2+}$ (b) $Ca^{2+} < Ag^+ < Cr_2O_7^{2-}$
21.42(a) $Co(s) + 2H^+(aq) \longrightarrow Co^{2+}(aq) + H_2(g)$
$\qquad E_{cell}^\circ = 0.28\ V$; spontaneous
(b) $2Mn^{2+}(aq) + 5Br_2(l) + 8H_2O(l) \longrightarrow$
$\qquad\qquad\qquad 2MnO_4^-(aq) + 10Br^-(aq) + 16H^+(aq)$
$\qquad E_{cell}^\circ = -0.44\ V$; not spontaneous
(c) $Hg_2^{2+}(aq) \longrightarrow Hg^{2+}(aq) + Hg(l)$
$\qquad E_{cell}^\circ = -0.07\ V$; not spontaneous
21.44(a) $2Ag(s) + Cu^{2+}(aq) \longrightarrow 2Ag^+(aq) + Cu(s)$
$\qquad E_{cell}^\circ = -0.46\ V$; not spontaneous
(b) $Cr_2O_7^{2-}(aq) + 3Cd(s) + 14H^+(aq) \longrightarrow$
$\qquad\qquad\qquad 2Cr^{3+}(aq) + 3Cd^{2+}(aq) + 7H_2O(l)$
$\qquad E_{cell}^\circ = 1.73\ V$; spontaneous
(c) $Pb(s) + Ni^{2+}(aq) \longrightarrow Pb^{2+}(aq) + Ni(s)$
$\qquad E_{cell}^\circ = -0.12\ V$; not spontaneous
21.46 $3N_2O_4(g) + 2Al(s) \longrightarrow 6NO_2^-(aq) + 2Al^{3+}(aq)$
$\qquad E_{cell}^\circ = 0.867\ V - (-1.66\ V) = 2.53\ V$
$\qquad 2Al(s) + 3SO_4^{2-}(aq) + 3H_2O(l) \longrightarrow$
$\qquad\qquad\qquad 2Al^{3+}(aq) + 3SO_3^{2-}(aq) + 6OH^-(aq)$
$\qquad E_{cell}^\circ = 2.59\ V$
$\qquad SO_4^{2-}(aq) + 2NO_2^-(aq) + H_2O(l) \longrightarrow$
$\qquad\qquad\qquad SO_3^{2-}(aq) + N_2O_4(g) + 2OH^-(aq)$
$\qquad E_{cell}^\circ = 0.06\ V$
$\qquad$ Oxidizing agents: $Al^{3+} < N_2O_4 < SO_4^{2-}$
$\qquad$ Reducing agents: $SO_3^{2-} < NO_2^- < Al$

21.48 $2HClO(aq) + Pt(s) + 2H^+(aq) \longrightarrow$
$$Cl_2(g) + Pt^{2+}(aq) + 2H_2O(l)$$
$E^{\circ}_{cell} = 0.43$ V
$2HClO(aq) + Pb(s) + SO_4^{2-}(aq) + 2H^+(aq) \longrightarrow$
$$Cl_2(g) + PbSO_4(s) + 2H_2O(l)$$
$E^{\circ}_{cell} = 1.94$ V
$Pt^{2+}(aq) + Pb(s) + SO_4^{2-}(aq) \longrightarrow Pt(s) + PbSO_4(s)$
$E^{\circ}_{cell} = 1.51$ V
Oxidizing agents: $PbSO_4 < Pt^{2+} < HClO$
Reducing agents: $Cl_2 < Pt < Pb$
21.50 yes; C > A > B **21.53** $A(s) + B^+(aq) \longrightarrow A^+(aq)$
$+ B(s)$ with $Q = [A^+]/[B^+]$. (a) $[A^+]$ increases and $[B^+]$
decreases. (b) E_{cell} decreases. (c) $E_{cell} = E^{\circ}_{cell} - (RT/nF)$
ln $([A^+]/[B^+])$; $E_{cell} = E^{\circ}_{cell}$ when (RT/nF) ln $([A^+]/[B^+]) =$
0. This occurs when ln $([A^+]/[B^+]) = 0$, that is, $[A^+]$ equals
$[B^+]$. (d) Yes, when $[A^+] > [B^+]$. **21.55** In a concentration
cell, the overall reaction decreases the concentration of the
more concentrated electrolyte because it is reduced in the
cathode compartment. **21.56**(a) 3×10^{35} (b) 4×10^{-31}
21.58(a) 1×10^{-67} (b) 6×10^{9} **21.60**(a) -2.03×10^5 J
(b) 1.74×10^5 J **21.62**(a) 3.82×10^5 J (b) -5.6×10^4 J
21.64 $E^{\circ} = 0.28$ V; $\Delta G^{\circ} = -2.7\times10^4$ J **21.66** $E^{\circ}_{cell} = 0.054$ V;
$\Delta G^{\circ} = -1.0\times10^4$ J **21.68** 8.8×10^{-5} M **21.70**(a) 0.05 V
(b) 0.50 M (c) $[Co^{2+}] = 0.91$ M; $[Ni^{2+}] = 0.09$ M **21.72** A;
0.083 V **21.74** Electrons flow from the anode, where oxidation
occurs, to the cathode, where reduction occurs. The electrons
always flow from the anode to the cathode no matter what
type of battery. **21.76** A D-sized alkaline battery is larger than
an AAA-sized one, so it contains greater amounts of the cell
components. The cell potential is an intensive property and
does not depend on the amounts of the cell components. The
total charge, however, does depend on the amount of cell components, so the D-sized battery produces more charge.
21.78 The Teflon spacers keep the two metals separated so that
the copper cannot conduct electrons that would promote the
corrosion (rusting) of the iron skeleton. **21.81** Sacrificial anodes
are made of metals with E° less than that of iron, -0.44 V, so
they are more easily oxidized than iron. Only b, f, and g will
work for iron: a will form an oxide coating that prevents further oxidation; c will react with groundwater quickly; d and e
are less easily oxidized than iron. **21.83** To reverse the reaction
requires 0.34 V with the cell in its standard state. A 1.5 V cell
supplies more than enough potential, so the Cd metal is oxidized to Cd^{2+} and Cr metal plates out. **21.85** The oxidation
number of N in NO_3^- is $+5$, the maximum O.N. for N. In the
nitrite ion, NO_2^-, the O.N. of N is $+3$, so nitrogen can be further oxidized. **21.87**(a) Br_2 (b) Na **21.89** I_2 gas forms at the
anode; magnesium (liquid) forms at the cathode. **21.91** Bromine gas forms at the anode; calcium metal forms at the cathode.
21.93 copper and bromine **21.95** iodine, zinc, and silver
21.97(a) Anode: $2H_2O(l) \longrightarrow O_2(g) + 4H^+(aq) + 4e^-$
    Cathode: $2H_2O(l) + 2e^- \longrightarrow H_2(g) + 2OH^-(aq)$
(b) Anode: $2H_2O(l) \longrightarrow O_2(g) + 4H^+(aq) + 4e^-$
    Cathode: $Sn^{2+}(aq) + 2e^- \longrightarrow Sn(s)$
21.99(a) Anode: $2H_2O(l) \longrightarrow O_2(g) + 4H^+(aq) + 4e^-$

Cathode: $NO_3^-(aq) + 4H^+(aq) + 3e^- \longrightarrow$
$$NO(g) + 2H_2O(l)$$
(b) Anode: $2Cl^-(aq) \longrightarrow Cl_2(g) + 2e^-$
    Cathode: $2H_2O(l) + 2e^- \longrightarrow H_2(g) + 2OH^-(aq)$
21.101(a) 3.75 mol e^- (b) 3.62×10^5 C (c) 28.7 A
21.103 0.275 g Ra **21.105** 9.20×10^3 s **21.107**(a) The sodium and
sulfate ions conduct a current, facilitating electrolysis. Pure
water, which contains very low (10^{-7} M) concentrations of H^+
and OH^-, conducts electricity very poorly. (b) The reduction
of H_2O has a more positive half-potential than does the reduction of Na^+; the oxidation of H_2O is the only reaction possible
because SO_4^{2-} cannot be oxidized. Thus, it is easier to reduce
H_2O than Na^+ and easier to oxidize H_2O than SO_4^{2-}.
21.109 62.6 g Zn **21.111**(a) 3.3×10^{11} C (b) 4.8×10^{11} J
(c) 1.2×10^4 kg **21.114** 64.3 mass % Cu **21.115**(a) 8 days
(b) 32 days (c) $940 **21.118** (a) 2.4×10^4 days (b) 2.1 g
(c) 6.1×10^{-5} dollars **21.121**(a) Pb/Pb^{2+}: $E^{\circ}_{cell} = 0.13$ V;
Cu/Cu^{2+}: $E^{\circ}_{cell} = 0.34$ V (b) The anode (negative electrode) is
Pb. The anode in the other cell is platinum in the standard
hydrogen electrode. (c) The precipitation of PbS decreases
$[Pb^{2+}]$, which increases the potential. (d) -0.13 V
21.124 The three steps equivalent to the overall reaction
$M^+(aq) + e^- \longrightarrow M(s)$ are
(1) $M^+(aq) \longrightarrow M^+(g)$ ΔH is $-\Delta H_{hydration}$
(2) $M^+(g) + e^- \longrightarrow M(g)$ ΔH is $-IE$
(3) $M(g) \longrightarrow M(s)$ ΔH is $-\Delta H_{atomization}$
The energy for step 3 is similar for all three elements, so the
difference in energy for the overall reaction depends on the
values for $\Delta H_{hydration}$ and IE. The Li^+ ion has a much greater
hydration energy than Na^+ and K^+ because it is smaller, with
a larger charge density that holds the water molecules more
tightly. The energy required to remove the waters surrounding
Li^+ offsets the lower ionization energy, making the overall
energy for the reduction of lithium larger than expected.
21.125 The very high and very low standard electrode potentials
involve extremely reactive substances, such as F_2 (a powerful
oxidizer) and Li (a powerful reducer). These substances react
directly with water because any aqueous cell with a voltage of
more than 1.23 V has the ability to electrolyze water into
hydrogen and oxygen.
21.127(a) 1.073×10^5 s (b) 1.5×10^4 kW·h (c) 0.92¢
21.129 If metal E and a salt of metal F are mixed, the salt is
reduced, producing metal F because E has the greatest reducing strength of the three metals; F < D < E.
21.131(a) Cell I: 4 mol electrons; $\Delta G = -4.75\times10^5$ J
        Cell II: 2 mol electrons; $\Delta G = -3.94\times10^5$ J
        Cell III: 2 mol electrons; $\Delta G = -4.53\times10^5$ J
    (b) Cell I: -13.2 kJ/g
        Cell II: -0.613 kJ/g
        Cell III: -2.63 kJ/g
        Cell I has the highest ratio (most energy released per
        gram) because the reactants have very low mass,
        while Cell II has the lowest ratio because the reactants
        have large masses.
21.135(a) 9.7 g Cu (b) 0.56 M Cu^{2+}

21.137 $Sn^{2+}(aq) + 2e^- \longrightarrow Sn(s)$
$Cr^{3+}(aq) + e^- \longrightarrow Cr^{2+}(aq)$
$Fe^{2+}(aq) + 2e^- \longrightarrow Fe(s)$
$U^{4+}(aq) + e^- \longrightarrow U^{3+}(aq)$
21.141(a) 3.6×10^{-9} M (b) 0.3 M
21.143(a) Nonstandard cell:

$$E_{waste} = E^{\circ}_{cell} - (0.0592\ V/1)\ \log\ [Ag^+]_{waste}$$

Standard cell:

$$E_{standard} = E^{\circ}_{cell} - (0.0592\ V/1)\ \log\ [Ag^+]_{standard}$$

(b) $[Ag^+]_{waste} = $ antilog $\left(\dfrac{E_{standard} - E_{waste}}{0.0592}\right)[Ag^+]_{standard}$

(c) $C_{Ag^+,\ waste} = $ antilog $\left(\dfrac{E_{standard} - E_{waste}}{0.0592}\right)C_{Ag^+,\ standard}$,

where C is concentration in ng/L
(d) 900 ng/L
(e) $[Ag^+]_{waste} =$

$$\text{antilog}\left[\frac{(E_{standard} - E_{waste})\dfrac{nF}{2.303R} + T_{standard}\ \log[Ag^+]_{standard}}{T_{waste}}\right]$$

21.145 (a) 1.08×10^3 C (b) 0.629 g Cd, 1.03 g NiO(OH), 0.202 g H_2O; total mass of reactants = 1.86 g (c) 10.1%
21.147 Li > Ba > Na > Al > Mn > Zn > Cr > Fe > Ni > Sn > Pb > Cu > Ag > Hg > Au. Metals with potentials lower than that of water (-0.83 V) can displace H_2 from water: Li, Ba, Na, Al, and Mn. Metals with potentials lower than that of hydrogen (0.00 V) can displace H_2 from acid: Li, Ba, Na, Al, Mn, Zn, Cr, Fe, Ni, Sn, and Pb. Metals with potentials greater than that of hydrogen (0.00 V) cannot displace H_2: Cu, Ag, Hg, and Au. **21.150**(a) 5.3×10^{-11}
(b) 0.20 V (c) 0.43 V (d) 8.2×10^{-4} M NaOH
21.153(a) -1.18×10^5 kJ (b) 1.20×10^4 L (c) 9.43×10^4 s
(d) 157 kW·h (e) 22.0¢ **21.154** 2.94

Chapter 22

22.2 Fe from Fe_2O_3; Ca from $CaCO_3$; Na from NaCl; Zn from ZnS **22.3**(a) Differentiation refers to the processes involved in the formation of Earth into regions (core, mantle, and crust) of differing composition. Substances separated according to their densities, with the more dense material in the core and the less dense in the crust. (b) O, Si, Al, and Fe (c) O **22.7** Plants produced O_2, slowly increasing the oxygen concentration in the atmosphere and creating an environment for oxidizing metals. The oxygen-free decay of plant and animal material created large fossil fuel deposits. **22.9** Fixation refers to the process of converting a substance in the atmosphere into a form more readily usable by organisms. Carbon and nitrogen; fixation of carbon dioxide gas by plants and fixation of nitrogen gas by nitrogen-fixing bacteria. **22.12** Atmospheric nitrogen is fixed by three pathways: atmospheric, industrial, and biological. Atmospheric fixation requires high-temperature reactions (e.g., initiated by lightning) to convert N_2 into NO and other oxidized species. Industrial fixation involves mainly the formation of ammonia, NH_3, from N_2 and H_2. Biological fixation occurs in nitrogen-fixing bacteria that live on the roots of legumes.

Human activity is an example of industrial fixation. It contributes about 17% of the fixed nitrogen. **22.14**(a) the atmosphere (b) Plants excrete acid from their roots to convert PO_4^{3-} ions into more soluble $H_2PO_4^-$ ions, which the plant can absorb. Through excretion and decay, organisms return soluble phosphate compounds to the cycle. **22.17**(a) 1.1×10^3 L
(b) 4.2×10^2 m^3 **22.18**(a) The iron(II) ions form an insoluble salt, $Fe_3(PO_4)_2$, that decreases the yield of phosphorus. (b) 8.8 t
22.20(a) Roasting consists of heating the mineral in air at high temperatures to convert the mineral to the oxide. (b) Smelting is the reduction of the metal oxide to the free metal using heat and a reducing agent such as coke. (c) Flotation is a separation process in which the ore is removed from the gangue by exploiting the difference in density in the presence of detergent. The gangue sinks to the bottom and the lighter ore-detergent mix is skimmed off the top. (d) Refining is the final step in the purification process to yield the pure metal.
22.25(a) Slag is a byproduct of steel-making and contains the impurity SiO_2. (b) Pig iron is the impure product of iron metallurgy (containing 3–4% C and other impurities). (c) Steel refers to iron alloyed with other elements to attain desirable properties. (d) The basic-oxygen process is used to purify pig iron and obtain carbon steel. **22.27** Iron and nickel are more easily oxidized and less easily reduced than copper. They are separated from copper in the roasting step and converted to slag. In the electrorefining process, all three metals are in solution, but only Cu^{2+} ions are reduced at the cathode to form Cu(s). **22.30** Le Châtelier's principle says that the system shifts toward formation of K as the gaseous metal leaves the cell.
22.31(a) $E^{\circ}_{half-cell} = -3.05$ V, -2.93 V, and -2.71 V for Li^+, K^+, and Na^+, respectively. In all of these cases, it is energetically more favorable to reduce H_2O to H_2 than to reduce M^+ to M. (b) $2RbX + Ca \longrightarrow CaX_2 + 2Rb$, where $\Delta H = IE_1(Ca) + IE_2(Ca) - 2IE_1(Rb) = 929$ kJ/mol. Based on the IEs and positive ΔH for the forward reaction, it seems more reasonable that Rb metal will reduce Ca^{2+} than the reverse. (c) If the reaction is carried out at a temperature greater than the boiling point of Rb, the product mixture will contain gaseous Rb, which can be removed from the reaction vessel; this would cause a shift in equilibrium to form more Rb as product. (d) $2CsX + Ca \longrightarrow CaX_2 + 2Cs$, where $\Delta H = IE_1(Ca) + IE_2(Ca) - 2IE_1(Cs) = 983$ kJ/mol. This reaction is more unfavorable than for Rb, but Cs has a lower boiling point. **22.32**(a) 4.5×10^4 L (b) 1.30×10^8 C
(c) 1.69×10^6 s **22.35**(a) Mg^{2+} is more difficult to reduce than H_2O, so $H_2(g)$ would be produced instead of Mg metal. $Cl_2(g)$ forms at the anode due to overvoltage. (b) The ΔH°_f of $MgCl_2(s)$ is -641.6 kJ/mol. High temperature favors the reverse (endothermic) reaction, the formation of magnesium metal and chlorine gas. **22.37**(a) Sulfur dioxide is the reducing agent and is oxidized to the +6 state (SO_4^{2-}). (b) $HSO_4^-(aq)$
(c) $H_2SeO_3(aq) + 2SO_2(g) + H_2O(l) \longrightarrow Se(s) + 2HSO_4^-(aq) + 2H^+(aq)$ **22.42**(a) O.N. for Cu: in Cu_2S, +1; in Cu_2O, +1; in Cu, 0 (b) Cu_2S is the reducing agent, and Cu_2O is the oxidizing agent. **22.44**(a) 1.3×10^6 C (b) 1.2×10^3 A

22.47 $2ZnS(s) + C(graphite) \longrightarrow 2Zn(s) + CS_2(g); \Delta G_{rxn}^\circ =$ 463 kJ. Since ΔG_{rxn}° is positive, this reaction is not spontaneous at standard-state conditions. $2ZnO(s) + C(s) \longrightarrow 2Zn(s) + CO_2(g); \Delta G_{rxn}^\circ = 242.0$ kJ. This reaction is also not spontaneous, but is less unfavorable. **22.48** The formation of sulfur trioxide is very slow at ordinary temperatures. Increasing the temperature can speed up the reaction, but because the reaction is exothermic, increasing the temperature decreases the yield. Adding a catalyst increases the rate of the reaction, allowing a lower temperature to be used to enhance the yield. **22.51**(a) Cl_2, H_2, and NaOH (b) The mercury-cell method yields higher purity NaOH, but releases some Hg, which is released into the environment. **22.52**(a) $\Delta G^\circ = -142$ kJ; yes (b) The rate of the reaction is very low at 25°C. (c) $\Delta G_{500}^\circ = -53$ kJ, so the reaction is spontaneous. (d) $K_{25} = 7.8 \times 10^{24} > K_{500} = 3.8 \times 10^3$ (e) 1.05×10^3 K **22.53** 7×10^2 lb Cl_2 **22.56**(a) $P_4O_{10}(s) + 6H_2O(l) \longrightarrow 4H_3PO_4(l)$ (b) 1.52 **22.58**(a) 9.006×10^9 g CO_2 (b) The 4.3×10^{10} g CO_2 produced by automobiles is much greater than that from the blast furnace. **22.60**(a) If $[OH^-] > 1.1 \times 10^{-4}$ M (i.e., if pH $>$ 10.04), $Mg(OH)_2$ will precipitate. (b) 1 (To the correct number of significant figures, all the magnesium precipitates.) **22.61**(a) K_{25}(step 1) $= 1 \times 10^{168}$; K_{25}(side rxn) $= 7 \times 10^{228}$ (b) K_{900}(step 1) $= 4.5 \times 10^{49}$; K_{900}(side rxn) $= 1.4 \times 10^{63}$ (c) 8.8×10^7 dollars (d) 6.4×10^7 dollars

22.64(1) $2H_2O(l) + 2FeS_2(s) + 7O_2(g) \longrightarrow$
$$2Fe^{2+}(aq) + 4SO_4{}^{2-}(aq) + 4H^+(aq)$$
increases acidity

(2) $4H^+(aq) + 4Fe^{2+}(aq) + O_2(g) \longrightarrow$
$$4Fe^{3+}(aq) + 2H_2O(l)$$

(3) $Fe^{3+}(aq) + 3H_2O(l) \longrightarrow Fe(OH)_3(s) + 3H^+(aq)$
increases acidity

(4) $8H_2O(l) + FeS_2(s) + 14Fe^{3+}(aq) \longrightarrow$
$$15Fe^{2+}(aq) + 2SO_4{}^{2-}(aq) + 16H^+(aq)$$
increases acidity

22.65 density of ferrite: 7.86 g/cm^3; density of austenite: 7.55 g/cm^3 **22.67**(a) Cathode: $Na^+(l) + e^- \longrightarrow Na(l)$
Anode: $4OH^-(l) \longrightarrow O_2(g) + 2H_2O(g) + 4e^-$
(b) 50% **22.70**(a) $nCO_2(g) + nH_2O(l) \longrightarrow (CH_2O)_n(s) + nO_2(g)$ (b) 27 L (c) 7.6×10^4 L **22.71** 73 mg/L **22.72** 891 kg Na_3AlF_6 **22.73**(a) 23.2 min (b) 14 effusion steps **22.75**(a) 1.890 t Al_2O_3 (b) 0.3339 t C (c) 100% (d) 74% (e) 2.813×10^3 m^3 **22.80** Acid rain increases the leaching of phosphate into the groundwater, due to the protonation of $PO_4{}^{3-}$ to form $HPO_4{}^{2-}$ and $H_2PO_4{}^-$. As shown in calculations for parts (a) and (b), solubility of $Ca_3(PO_4)_2$ increases from 6.4×10^{-7} M (in pure water) to 1.1×10^{-2} M (in acidic rainwater). (a) 6.4×10^{-7} M (b) 1.1×10^{-2} M **22.81**(a) 1.00 mol % (b) 238.9 g/mol **22.83** density of silver $= 10.51$ g/cm^3; density of sterling silver $= 10.2$ g/cm^3

Chapter 23

Answer to Boxed Reading Problem: B23.2 Zinc ions prefer a tetrahedral environment. The other ions listed prefer other environments (Ni^{2+} forms square planar complex ions while Fe^{2+} and Mn^{2+} form octahedral complex ions). If these ions are placed in a tetrahedral environment in place of the zinc, they cannot function as well as zinc since the enzyme catalyst would have a different shape.

• **23.2**(a) $1s^22s^22p^63s^23p^64s^23d^{10}4p^65s^24d^x$
(b) $1s^22s^22p^63s^23p^64s^23d^{10}4p^65s^24d^{10}5p^66s^24f^{14}5d^x$ **23.4** Five; examples are Mn, [Ar] $4s^23d^5$, and Fe^{3+}, [Ar] $3d^5$. **23.6**(a) The elements should increase in size as they increase in mass from Period 5 to Period 6. Because there are 14 inner transition elements in Period 6, the effective nuclear charge increases significantly; so the atomic size decreases, or "contracts." This effect is significant enough that Zr^{4+} and Hf^{4+} are almost the same size but differ greatly in atomic mass. (b) The atomic size increases from Period 4 to Period 5, but stays fairly constant from Period 5 to Period 6. (c) Atomic mass increases significantly from Period 5 to Period 6, but atomic radius (and thus volume) increases slightly, so Period 6 elements are very dense. **23.9**(a) A paramagnetic substance is attracted to a magnetic field, while a diamagnetic substance is slightly repelled by one. (b) Ions of transition elements often have half-filled d orbitals whose unpaired electrons make the ions paramagnetic. Ions of main-group elements usually have a noble-gas configuration with no partially filled levels. (c) Some d orbitals in the transition element ions are empty, which allows an electron from one d orbital to move to a slightly higher energy one. The energy required for this transition is small and falls in the visible wavelength range. All orbitals are filled in ions of main-group elements, so enough energy would have to be added to move an electron to the next principal energy level, not just another orbital within the same energy level. This amount of energy is very large and much greater than the visible range of wavelengths.

23.10(a) $1s^22s^22p^63s^23p^64s^23d^3$
(b) $1s^22s^22p^63s^23p^64s^23d^{10}4p^65s^24d^1$ (c) [Xe] $6s^24f^{14}5d^{10}$ **23.12**(a) [Xe] $6s^24f^{14}5d^6$ (b) [Ar] $4s^23d^7$ (c) [Kr] $5s^14d^{10}$ **23.14**(a) [Ar], no unpaired electrons (b) [Ar] $3d^9$, one unpaired electron (c) [Ar] $3d^5$, five unpaired electrons (d) [Kr] $4d^2$, two unpaired electrons **23.16**(a) $+5$ (b) $+4$ (c) $+7$ **23.18** Cr, Mo, and W **23.20** in CrF_2, because the chromium is in a lower oxidation state **23.22** Atomic size increases slightly down a group of transition elements, but nuclear charge increases much more, so the first ionization energy generally increases. The reduction potential for Mo is lower, so it is more difficult to oxidize Mo than Cr. In addition, the ionization energy of Mo is higher than that of Cr, so it is more difficult to remove electrons from Mo. **23.24** CrO_3, with Cr in a higher oxidation state, yields a more acidic aqueous solution. **23.28**(a) seven (b) This corresponds to a half-filled f subshell. **23.30**(a) [Xe] $6s^25d^1$ (b) [Xe] $4f^1$ (c) [Rn] $7s^25f^{11}$ (d) [Rn] $5f^2$ **23.32**(a) Eu^{2+}: [Xe] $4f^7$; Eu^{3+}: [Xe] $4f^6$; Eu^{4+}: [Xe] $4f^5$. The stability of the half-filled f subshell makes Eu^{2+} most stable. (b) Tb^{2+}: [Xe] $4f^9$; Tb^{3+}: [Xe] $4f^8$; Tb^{4+}: [Xe] $4f^7$. Tb should show a $+4$ oxidation state because that gives a half-filled subshell. **23.34** Gd has the electron configuration [Xe] $6s^24f^75d^1$ with eight unpaired electrons. Gd^{3+} has seven unpaired electrons: [Xe] $4f^7$. **23.37** The coordination number

indicates the number of ligand atoms bonded to the metal ion. The oxidation number represents the number of electrons lost to form the ion. The coordination number is unrelated to the oxidation number. **23.39** 2, linear; 4, tetrahedral or square planar; 6, octahedral **23.42** The complex ion has a negative charge. **23.45**(a) hexaaquanickel(II) chloride (b) tris(ethylenediamine)chromium(III) perchlorate (c) potassium hexacyanomanganate(II) **23.47**(a) 2+, 6 (b) 3+, 6 (c) 2+, 6 **23.49**(a) potassium dicyanoargentate(I) (b) sodium tetrachlorocadmate(II) (c) tetraammineaquabromocobalt(III) bromide **23.51**(a) 1+, 2 (b) 2+, 4 (c) 3+, 6 **23.53**(a) $[Zn(NH_3)_4]SO_4$ (b) $[Cr(NH_3)_5Cl]Cl_2$ (c) $Na_3[Ag(S_2O_3)_2]$ **23.55**(a) 4, two ions (b) 6, three ions (c) 2, four ions **23.57**(a) $[Cr(H_2O)_6]_2(SO_4)_3$ (b) $Ba[FeBr_4]_2$ (c) $[Pt(en)_2]CO_3$ **23.59**(a) 6, five ions (b) 4, three ions (c) 4, two ions **23.61**(a) The nitrite ion forms linkage isomers because it can bind to the metal ion through the lone pair on the N atom or any lone pair on either O atom.

$$[:\ddot{O}-\ddot{N}=\ddot{O}]^-$$

(b) Sulfur dioxide molecules form linkage isomers because the lone pair on the S atom or any lone pair on either O atom can bind the central metal ion.

$$\ddot{O}=\ddot{S}=\ddot{O}$$

(c) Nitrate ions have an N atom with no lone pair and three O atoms, all with lone pairs that can bind to the metal ion. But all of the O atoms are equivalent, so these ions do not form linkage isomers.

$$\left[:\ddot{O}-N=\ddot{O}\atop {\underset{:\ddot{O}:}{|}}\right]^-$$

23.63(a) geometric isomerism

Br   Br   Br   NH₂CH₃
  \ /   \ /
   Pt   and   Pt
  / \   / \
CH₃NH₂ NH₂CH₃   CH₃NH₂   Br
   cis   trans

(b) geometric isomerism

H₃N   NH₃   H₃N   F
  \ /   \ /
   Pt   and   Pt
  / \   / \
 Cl   F   Cl   NH₃
   cis   trans

(c) geometric isomerism

H₂O   NH₃   H₂O   NH₃   H₂O   F
  \ /   \ /   \ /
   Pt   and   Pt   and   Pt
  / \   / \   / \
 Cl   F   F   Cl   Cl   NH₃

23.65(a) geometric isomerism

$$\left[\begin{matrix}Cl & & Cl\\ & Pt & \\ Br & & Br\end{matrix}\right]^{2-} \text{ and } \left[\begin{matrix}Cl & & Br\\ & Pt & \\ Br & & Cl\end{matrix}\right]^{2-}$$
cis   trans

(b) linkage isomerism

$$\left[\begin{matrix} & NH_3 & \\ H_3N & & NH_3 \\ & Cr & \\ H_3N & & NO_2 \\ & NH_3 & \end{matrix}\right]^{2+} \text{ and } \left[\begin{matrix} & NH_3 & \\ H_3N & & NH_3 \\ & Cr & \\ H_3N & & ONO \\ & NH_3 & \end{matrix}\right]^{2+}$$

(c) geometric isomerism

$$\left[\begin{matrix} & NH_3 & \\ H_3N & & I \\ & Pt & \\ H_3N & & I \\ & NH_3 & \end{matrix}\right]^{2+} \text{ and } \left[\begin{matrix} & NH_3 & \\ H_3N & & I \\ & Pt & \\ I & & NH_3 \\ & NH_3 & \end{matrix}\right]^{2+}$$
cis   trans

23.67 The compound with the traditional formula is $CrCl_3 \cdot 4NH_3$; the actual formula is $[Cr(NH_3)_4Cl_2]Cl$. **23.69**(a) $K[Pd(NH_3)Cl_3]$ (b) $[PdCl_2(NH_3)_2]$ (c) $K_2[PdCl_6]$ (d) $[Pd(NH_3)_4Cl_2]Cl_2$ **23.71**(a) dsp^2 (b) sp^3 **23.74** absorption of orange or yellow light **23.75**(a) The crystal field splitting energy (Δ) is the energy difference between the two sets of d orbitals that result from electrostatic effects of ligands on a central transition metal atom. (b) In an octahedral field of ligands, the ligands approach along the x, y, and z axes. The $d_{x^2-y^2}$ and d_{z^2} orbitals are located *along* the x, y, and z axes, so ligand interaction is higher in energy. The other orbital-ligand interactions are lower in energy because the d_{xy}, d_{yz}, and d_{xz} orbitals are located *between* the x, y, and z axes. (c) In a tetrahedral field of ligands, the ligands do not approach along the x, y, and z axes. The ligand interaction is greater for the d_{xy}, d_{yz}, and d_{xz} orbitals and lesser for the $d_{x^2-y^2}$ and d_{z^2} orbitals. Therefore, the crystal field splitting is reversed, and the d_{xy}, d_{yz}, and d_{xz} orbitals are higher in energy than the $d_{x^2-y^2}$ and d_{z^2} orbitals. **23.78** If Δ is greater than $E_{pairing}$, electrons will pair their spins in the lower energy set of d orbitals before entering the higher energy set of d orbitals as unpaired electrons. If Δ is less than $E_{pairing}$, electrons will occupy the higher energy set of d orbitals as unpaired electrons before pairing in the lower energy set of d orbitals. **23.80**(a) no d electrons (b) eight d electrons (c) six d electrons **23.82**(a) five (b) ten (c) seven

23.84

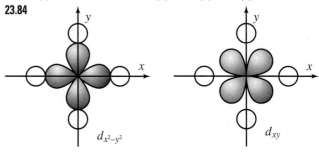

In an octahedral field of ligands, the ligands approach along the x, y, and z axes. The $d_{x^2-y^2}$ orbital is located along the x and y axes, so ligand interaction is greater. The d_{xy} orbital is offset from the x and y axes by 90°, so ligand interaction is less. The greater interaction of the $d_{x^2-y^2}$ orbital results in its higher energy.

23.86 a and d

23.88

23.90

(a) 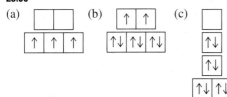 (b) (c)

23.92 $[Cr(H_2O)_6]^{3+} < [Cr(NH_3)_6]^{3+} < [Cr(NO_2)_6]^{3-}$
23.94 A violet complex absorbs yellow-green light. The light absorbed by a complex with a weaker field ligand would be at a lower energy and higher wavelength. Light of lower energy than yellow-green light is yellow, orange, or red. The color observed would be blue or green. **23.97** The H_2O ligand is weaker than the NH_3 ligand. The weaker field ligand results in a lower splitting energy and absorbs visible light of lower energy. The hexaaqua complex appears green because it absorbs red light. The hexaammine complex appears violet because it absorbs yellow light, which has higher energy (shorter λ) than red light. **23.101** Hg^+ is [Xe] $6s^1 4f^{14} 5d^{10}$ and Cu^+ is [Ar] $3d^{10}$. The mercury(I) ion has one electron in the $6s$ orbital that can form a covalent bond with the electron in the $6s$ orbital of another mercury(I) ion. In the copper(I) ion there are no electrons in the s orbital, so these ions cannot bond with one another. **23.102**(a) 6 (b) +3 (c) two (d) 1 mol
23.109 geometric (*cis-trans*) and linkage isomerism

$$\begin{bmatrix} NCS & NH_3 \\ & Pt & \\ NCS & NH_3 \end{bmatrix}$$
cis-diamminedithiocyanatoplatinum(II)

$$\begin{bmatrix} NCS & NH_3 \\ & Pt & \\ H_3N & SCN \end{bmatrix}$$
trans-diamminedithiocyanatoplatinum(II)

$$\begin{bmatrix} SCN & NH_3 \\ & Pt & \\ SCN & NH_3 \end{bmatrix}$$
cis-diamminediisothiocyanatoplatinum(II)

$$\begin{bmatrix} SCN & NH_3 \\ & Pt & \\ H_3N & NCS \end{bmatrix}$$
trans-diamminediisothiocyanatoplatinum(II)

$$\begin{bmatrix} SCN & NH_3 \\ & Pt & \\ NCS & NH_3 \end{bmatrix}$$
cis-diammineisothiocyanatothiocyanatoplatinum(II)

$$\begin{bmatrix} SCN & NH_3 \\ & Pt & \\ H_3N & SCN \end{bmatrix}$$
trans-diammineisothiocyanatothiocyanatoplatinum(II)

23.110 $[Co(NH_3)_4(H_2O)Cl]^{2+}$

tetraammineaquachlorocobalt(III) ion

2 geometric isomers

$$\begin{bmatrix} H_3N & NH_3 & Cl \\ & Co & \\ H_3N & NH_3 & OH_2 \end{bmatrix}^{2+} \quad \begin{bmatrix} H_3N & NH_3 & Cl \\ & Co & \\ H_2O & NH_3 & NH_3 \end{bmatrix}^{2+}$$
cis   *trans*

$[Cr(H_2O)_3Br_2Cl]$
triaquadibromochlorochromium(III)

3 geometric isomers

$$\begin{bmatrix} H_2O & H_2O & Br \\ & Cr & \\ Br & H_2O & Cl \end{bmatrix} \quad \begin{bmatrix} H_2O & H_2O & Br \\ & Cr & \\ Cl & H_2O & Br \end{bmatrix} \quad \begin{bmatrix} H_2O & Cl & Br \\ & Cr & \\ H_2O & H_2O & Br \end{bmatrix}$$
Br's are *trans*   Br's are *cis*   Br's and H₂O's are *cis*
H₂O's are *cis* and *trans*

$[Cr(NH_3)_2(H_2O)_2Br_2]^+$
diamminediaquadibromochromium(III) ion

6 isomers (5 geometric)

$$\begin{bmatrix} H_2O & NH_3 & Br \\ & Cr & \\ Br & NH_3 & OH_2 \end{bmatrix}^+ \quad \begin{bmatrix} H_2O & NH_3 & Br \\ & Cr & \\ H_2O & NH_3 & Br \end{bmatrix}^+ \quad \begin{bmatrix} H_2O & NH_3 & Br \\ & Cr & \\ Br & H_2O & NH_3 \end{bmatrix}^+$$
all ligands are *trans*   only NH₃ is *trans*   only Br is *trans*

$$\begin{bmatrix} H_2O & NH_3 & NH_3 \\ & Cr & \\ Br & Br & OH_2 \end{bmatrix}^+ \quad \begin{bmatrix} H_2O & NH_3 & NH_3 \\ & Cr & \\ H_2O & Br & Br \end{bmatrix}^+ \quad \begin{bmatrix} H_3N & NH_3 & OH_2 \\ & Cr & \\ Br & Br & OH_2 \end{bmatrix}^+$$
only H₂O is *trans*   optical isomers
all three ligands are *cis*

23.115(a) no optical isomers (b) no optical isomers (c) no optical isomers (d) no optical isomers (e) optical isomers
23.116 $Pt[P(C_2H_5)_3]_2Cl_2$

$$\begin{array}{ccc} Cl & & Cl \\ & Pt & \\ (C_2H_5)_3P & & P(C_2H_5)_3 \end{array}$$
cis-dichlorobis(triethylphosphine)platinum(II)

$$\begin{array}{ccc} Cl & & P(C_2H_5)_3 \\ & Pt & \\ (C_2H_5)_3P & & Cl \end{array}$$
trans-dichlorobis(triethylphosphine)platinum(II)

23.118(a) The first reaction shows no change in the number of particles. In the second reaction, the number of reactant particles is greater than the number of product particles. A decrease in the number of particles means a decrease in entropy. Based on entropy change only, the first reaction is favored. (b) The ethylenediamine complex will be more stable with respect to ligand exchange in water because the entropy change for that exchange is unfavorable (negative).

Chapter 24

Answers to Boxed Reading Problems: B24.1 In the *s*-process, a nucleus captures a neutron sometime over a long period of time. Then the nucleus emits a beta particle to form another element. The stable isotopes of most heavy elements up to ^{209}Bi form by the *s*-process. The *r*-process very quickly forms less stable isotopes and those with *A* greater than 230 by multiple neutron captures, followed by multiple beta decays. **B24.3** The simultaneous fusion of three nuclei is a termolecular process. Termolecular processes have a very low probability of occurring. The bimolecular fusion of ^{8}Be with ^{4}He is more likely. **B24.4** $^{210}_{83}\text{Bi} \longrightarrow {}^{0}_{-1}\beta + {}^{210}_{84}\text{Po}$ (nuclide A); $^{210}_{84}\text{Po} \longrightarrow {}^{4}_{2}\alpha + {}^{206}_{82}\text{Pb}$ (nuclide B); $^{206}_{82}\text{Pb} + 3^{1}_{0}\text{n} \longrightarrow {}^{209}_{82}\text{Pb}$ (nuclide C); $^{209}_{82}\text{Pb} \longrightarrow {}^{0}_{-1}\beta + {}^{210}_{83}\text{Bi}$ (nuclide D)

• **24.1**(a) Chemical reactions are accompanied by relatively small changes in energy; nuclear reactions are accompanied by relatively large changes in energy. (b) Increasing temperature increases the rate of a chemical reaction but has no effect on a nuclear reaction. (c) Both chemical and nuclear reaction rates increase with higher reactant concentrations. (d) If the reactant is limiting in a chemical reaction, then more reactant produces more product and the yield increases. The presence of more radioactive reactant results in more decay product, so a higher reactant concentration increases the yield. **24.2**(a) 95.02% (b) The atomic mass is larger than the isotopic mass of ^{32}S. Sulfur-32 is the lightest isotope. **24.4**(a) *Z* down by 2, *N* down by 2 (b) *Z* up by 1, *N* down by 1 (c) no change in *Z* or *N* (d) *Z* down by 1, *N* up by 1 (e) *Z* down by 1, *N* up by 1   A different element is produced in all cases except c. **24.6** A neutron-rich nuclide decays by beta (minus) decay. A neutron-poor nuclide undergoes positron decay or electron capture.
24.8(a) $^{234}_{92}\text{U} \longrightarrow {}^{4}_{2}\alpha + {}^{230}_{90}\text{Th}$ (b) $^{232}_{93}\text{Np} + {}^{0}_{-1}\text{e} \longrightarrow {}^{232}_{92}\text{U}$ (c) $^{12}_{7}\text{N} \longrightarrow {}^{0}_{1}\beta + {}^{12}_{6}\text{C}$ **24.10**(a) $^{27}_{12}\text{Mg} \longrightarrow {}^{0}_{-1}\beta + {}^{27}_{13}\text{Al}$ (b) $^{23}_{12}\text{Mg} \longrightarrow {}^{0}_{1}\beta + {}^{23}_{11}\text{Na}$ (c) $^{103}_{46}\text{Pd} + {}^{0}_{-1}\text{e} \longrightarrow {}^{103}_{45}\text{Rh}$ **24.12**(a) $^{48}_{23}\text{V} \longrightarrow {}^{48}_{22}\text{Ti} + {}^{0}_{1}\beta$ (b) $^{107}_{48}\text{Cd} + {}^{0}_{-1}\text{e} \longrightarrow {}^{107}_{47}\text{Ag}$ (c) $^{210}_{86}\text{Rn} \longrightarrow {}^{206}_{84}\text{Po} + {}^{4}_{2}\alpha$ **24.14**(a) $^{186}_{78}\text{Pt} + {}^{0}_{-1}\text{e} \longrightarrow {}^{186}_{77}\text{Ir}$ (b) $^{225}_{89}\text{Ac} \longrightarrow {}^{221}_{87}\text{Fr} + {}^{4}_{2}\alpha$ (c) $^{129}_{52}\text{Te} \longrightarrow {}^{129}_{53}\text{I} + {}^{0}_{-1}\beta$
24.16(a) Appears stable because its *N* and *Z* values are both magic numbers, but its *N/Z* ratio (1.50) is too high; it is unstable. (b) Appears unstable because its *Z* value is an odd number, but its *N/Z* ratio (1.19) is in the band of stability, so it is stable. (c) Unstable because its *N/Z* ratio is too high.
24.18(a) The *N/Z* ratio for ^{127}I is 1.4; it is stable. (b) The *N/Z* ratio for ^{106}Sn is 1.1; it is unstable because this ratio is too low. (c) The *N/Z* ratio is 1.1 for ^{68}As. The ratio is within the range of stability, but the nuclide is most likely unstable because there are odd numbers of both protons and neutrons. **24.20**(a) alpha decay (b) positron decay or electron capture (c) positron decay or electron capture **24.22**(a) beta (minus) decay (b) positron decay or electron capture (c) alpha decay **24.24** Stability results from a favorable *N/Z* ratio, even numbered *N* and/or *Z*, and the occurrence of magic numbers. The *N/Z* ratio of ^{52}Cr is 1.17, which is within the band of stability. The fact that *Z* is even does not account for the variation in stability because all isotopes of chromium have the same *Z*.

However, ^{52}Cr has 28 neutrons, so *N* is both an even number and a magic number for this isotope only. **24.28** seven α emissions and four β⁻ emissions **24.31** No, it is not valid to conclude that $t_{1/2}$ equals 1 min because the number of nuclei is so small. Decay rate is an average rate and is only meaningful when the sample is macroscopic and contains a large number of nuclei. For the sample containing 6×10^{12} nuclei, the conclusion is valid. **24.33** 2.56×10^{-2} Ci/g **24.35** 1.4×10^8 Bq/g **24.37** 1×10^{-12} day^{-1} **24.39** 2.31×10^{-7} yr^{-1} **24.41** 1.49 mg **24.43** 2.2×10^9 yr **24.45** 30 dpm **24.47** 1.0×10^6 yr **24.50** Neither γ radiation nor neutron beams have charge, so neither is deflected by a magnetic or electric field. Neutron beams differ from γ radiation in that a neutron has a mass approximately equal to that of a proton. It was observed that a neutron beam induces the emission of protons from a substance; γ radiation does not cause such emission. **24.52** Protons are repelled from the target nuclei due to interaction with like (positive) charges. Higher energy is required to overcome the repulsion.
24.53(a) $^{10}_{5}\text{B} + {}^{4}_{2}\alpha \longrightarrow {}^{1}_{0}\text{n} + {}^{13}_{7}\text{N}$ (b) $^{28}_{14}\text{Si} + {}^{2}_{1}\text{H} \longrightarrow {}^{1}_{0}\text{n}$ $+ {}^{29}_{15}\text{P}$ (c) $^{242}_{96}\text{Cm} + {}^{4}_{2}\alpha \longrightarrow 2^{1}_{0}\text{n} + {}^{244}_{98}\text{Cf}$ **24.58** Ionizing radiation is more dangerous to children because their rapidly dividing cells are more susceptible to radiation than adults' slowly dividing cells. **24.60**(a) 5.4×10^{-7} rad (b) 5.4×10^{-9} Gy **24.62**(a) 7.5×10^{-10} Gy (b) 7.5×10^{-5} mrem (c) 7.5×10^{-10} Sv **24.65** 1.86×10^{-3} rad **24.67** NAA does not destroy the sample, while chemical analyses do. Neutrons bombard a nonradioactive sample, inducing some atoms within the sample to be radioactive. The radioisotopes decay by emitting radiation characteristic of each isotope. **24.73** Energy is released when a nucleus forms from nucleons. The nuclear binding energy is the quantity of energy holding 1 mol of nuclei together. This energy must be absorbed to break up the nucleus into nucleons and is released when nucleons come together.
24.75(a) 1.861×10^4 eV (b) 2.981×10^{-15} J **24.77** 7.6×10^{11} J **24.79**(a) 7.976 MeV/nucleon (b) 127.6 MeV/atom (c) 1.231×10^{10} kJ/mol **24.81**(a) 8.768 MeV/nucleon (b) 517.3 MeV/atom (c) 4.99×10^{10} kJ/mol **24.85** Radioactive decay is a spontaneous process in which unstable nuclei emit radioactive particles and energy. Fission occurs as the result of high-energy bombardment of nuclei with small particles that cause the nuclei to break into smaller nuclides, radioactive particles, and energy. All fission events are not the same. The nuclei split in a number of ways to produce several different products. **24.88** The water serves to slow the neutrons so that they are better able to cause a fission reaction. Heavy water is a better moderator because it does not absorb neutrons as well as light water does; thus, more neutrons are available to initiate the fission process. However, D_2O does not occur naturally in great abundance, so its production adds to the cost of a heavy-water reactor. **24.93**(a) 1.1×10^{-29} kg (b) 9.9×10^{-13} J (c) 5.9×10^8 kJ/mol; this is approximately 1 million times larger than a typical enthalpy of reaction. **24.95** 8.0×10^3 yr **24.98** 1.35×10^{-5} *M* **24.100** 6.2×10^{-2} **24.102**(a) 5.99 h (b) 21% **24.104**(a) 0.999 (b) 0.298 (c) 5.58×10^{-6}

(d) Radiocarbon dating is more reliable for the fraction in part (b) because a significant amount of ^{14}C has decayed and a significant amount remains. Therefore, a change in the amount of ^{14}C will be noticeable. For the fraction in part (a), very little ^{14}C has decayed, and for (c) very little ^{14}C remains. In either case, it will be more difficult to measure the change, so the error will be relatively large. **24.106** 6.58 h **24.110** 4.904×10^{-9} L/h **24.113** 81 yr **24.115**(a) 0.15 Bq/L (b) 0.27 Bq/L (c) 3.3 d; a total of 12.8 d **24.118** 7.4 s **24.121** 1926

24.124 6.27×10^5 eV/reaction, 6.05×10^7 kJ/mol reaction **24.127**(a) 2.07×10^{-17} J (b) 1.45×10^7 H atoms (c) 1.4960×10^{-5} J (d) 1.4959×10^{-5} J (e) No, the captain should continue using the current technology. **24.130**(a) 0.043 MeV, 2.9×10^{-11} m (b) 4.713 MeV **24.134**(a) 3.26×10^3 d (b) 3.2×10^{-3} s (c) 2.78×10^{11} yr **24.136**(a) 1.80×10^{17} J (b) 6.15×10^{16} kJ (c) The procedure in part (b) produces more energy per kilogram of antihydrogen. **24.137** 9.316×10^2 MeV **24.141** 7.81 d

Numbers in parentheses refer to the page(s) on which a term is introduced and/or discussed.

A

absolute scale (also *Kelvin scale*) The preferred temperature scale in scientific work, which has absolute zero (0 K, or $-273.15°C$) as the lowest temperature. (23) [See also *kelvin (K)*.]

absorption spectrum The spectrum produced when atoms absorb specific wavelengths of incoming light and become excited from lower to higher energy levels. (273)

abundance The amount of an element in a particular region of the natural world. (905)

accuracy The closeness of a measurement to the actual value. (29)

acid In common laboratory terms, any species that produces H^+ ions when dissolved in water. (145) [See also *Arrhenius, Brønsted-Lowry,* and *Lewis acid-base definitions.*]

acid anhydride A compound, usually formed by a dehydration-condensation reaction of an oxoacid, that yields two molecules of the acid when it reacts with water. (600)

acid-base buffer (also *buffer*) A solution that resists changes in pH when a small amount of either strong acid or strong base is added. (765)

acid-base indicator An organic molecule whose color is different in acid and in base and is used to monitor the equivalence point of a titration or the pH of a solution. (728)

acid-base reaction Any reaction between an acid and a base. (145) (See also *neutralization reaction.*)

acid-base titration curve A plot of the pH of a solution of acid (or base) versus the volume of base (or acid) added to the solution. (774)

acid-dissociation (acid-ionization) constant (K_a) An equilibrium constant for the dissociation of an acid (HA) in H_2O to yield the conjugate base (A^-) and H_3O^+:

$$K_a = \frac{[H_3O^+][A^-]}{[HA]} \qquad (722)$$

actinides The Period 7 elements that constitute the second inner transition series (5*f* block), which includes thorium (Th; $Z = 90$) through lawrencium (Lr; $Z = 103$). (306, 952)

activated complex (See *transition state.*)

activation energy (E_a) The minimum energy with which molecules must collide to react. (649)

active site The region of an enzyme formed by specific amino acid side chains at which catalysis occurs. (662)

activity ($\mathscr{A}$) (also *decay rate*) The change in number of nuclei ($\mathscr{N}$) of a radioactive sample divided by the change in time (t). (988)

activity series of the metals A listing of metals arranged in order of decreasing strength of the metal as a reducing agent in aqueous reactions. (165)

actual yield The amount of product actually obtained in a chemical reaction. (112)

addition polymer (also *chain-reaction,* or *chain-growth, polymer*) A polymer formed when monomers (usually containing C=C) combine through an addition reaction. (604)

addition reaction A type of organic reaction in which atoms linked by a multiple bond become bonded to more atoms. (588)

adduct The product of a Lewis acid-base reaction characterized by the formation of a new covalent bond. (751)

adenosine triphosphate (ATP) A high-energy molecule that serves most commonly as a store and source of energy in organisms. (836)

alcohol An organic compound (ending, *-ol*) that contains a $-\overset{\displaystyle |}{\underset{\displaystyle |}{C}}-\overset{\displaystyle \cdot\cdot}{O}-H$ functional group. (591)

aldehyde An organic compound (ending, *-al*) that contains the carbonyl functional group ($C=\overset{\cdot\cdot}{O}$) in which the carbonyl C is also bonded to H. (597)

alkane A hydrocarbon that contains only single bonds and no rings (general formula, C_nH_{2n+2}). (576)

alkene A hydrocarbon that contains at least one C=C bond (general formula, C_nH_{2n}). (582)

alkyl group A saturated hydrocarbon chain with one bond available. (588)

alkyl halide (See *haloalkane.*)

alkyne A hydrocarbon that contains at least one C≡C bond (general formula, C_nH_{2n-2}). (583)

allotrope One of two or more crystalline or molecular forms of an element. In general, one allotrope is more stable than another at a particular pressure and temperature. (539)

alloy A mixture with metallic properties that consists of solid phases of two or more pure elements, a solid-solid solution, or distinct intermediate phases. (354, 482, 921)

alpha (α) decay A radioactive process in which an alpha particle is emitted from a nucleus. (981)

alpha particle (α or $^4_2He^{2+}$) A positively charged particle, identical to a helium-4 nucleus, that is one of the common types of radioactive emissions. (979)

amide An organic compound that contains the $-\overset{\displaystyle \overset{\displaystyle \parallel}{O}}{C}-\overset{\displaystyle |}{\underset{\displaystyle |}{N}}-$ functional group. (599)

amine An organic compound (general formula, $-\overset{\displaystyle |}{\underset{\displaystyle |}{C}}-\overset{\displaystyle |}{\underset{\displaystyle |}{N}}-$) derived structurally by replacing one or more H atoms of ammonia with organic groups; a weak organic base. (594, 754)

amino acid An organic compound [general formula, $H_2N-CH(R)-COOH$] with at least one carboxyl and one amine group on the same molecule; the monomer unit of a protein. (483, 608)

amorphous solid A solid that has a poorly defined shape because it lacks extensive molecular-level ordering of its particles. (441)

ampere (A) The SI unit of electric current; 1 ampere of current results when 1 coulomb flows through a conductor in 1 second. (890)

amphoteric Able to act as either an acid or a base. (316)

amplitude The height of the crest (or depth of the trough) of a wave; related to the intensity of the energy (brightness of the light). (262)

angular momentum quantum number (*l*) An integer from 0 to $n - 1$ that is related to the shape of an atomic orbital. (281)

anion   A negatively charged ion. (55)

anode   The electrode at which oxidation occurs in an electrochemical cell. Electrons are given up by the reducing agent and leave the cell at the anode. (856)

antibonding MO   A molecular orbital formed when wave functions are subtracted from each other, which decreases electron density between the nuclei and leaves a node. Electrons occupying such an orbital destabilize the molecule. (406)

apatite   A compound of general formula $Ca_5(PO_4)_3X$, where X is generally F, Cl, or OH; a source of phosphorus. (914)

aqueous solution   A solution in which water is the solvent. (70)

aromatic hydrocarbon   A compound of C and H with one or more rings of C atoms (often drawn with alternating $C—C$ and $C=C$ bonds), in which there is extensive delocalization of π electrons. (584)

Arrhenius acid-base definition   A model of acid-base behavior in which an acid is a substance that has H in its formula and dissociates in water to yield H_3O^+, and a base is a substance that has OH in its formula and produces OH^- in water. (720)

Arrhenius equation   An equation that expresses the exponential relationship between temperature and the rate constant: $k = Ae^{-E_a/RT}$. (649)

atmosphere   The mixture of gases that extends from a planet's surface and eventually merges with outer space; the gaseous portion of Earth's crust. (212, 908) (For the unit, see *standard atmosphere*.)

atom   The smallest particle of an element that retains the chemical nature of the element. A neutral, spherical entity composed of a positively charged central nucleus surrounded by one or more negatively charged electrons. (43)

atomic mass (also *atomic weight*)   The average of the masses of the naturally occurring isotopes of an element weighted according to their abundances. (50)

atomic mass unit (amu) (also *dalton, Da*)   A mass exactly equal to $\frac{1}{12}$ the mass of a carbon-12 atom. (50)

atomic number (Z)   The unique number of protons in the nucleus of each atom of an element (equal to the number of electrons in the neutral atom). An integer that expresses the positive charge of a nucleus or subatomic particle in multiples of the electronic charge. (48)

atomic orbital (also *wave function*)   A mathematical expression that describes the motion of the electron's matter-wave in terms of time and position in the region of the nucleus. The term is used qualitatively to mean the region of space in which there is a high probability of finding the electron. (279)

atomic solid   A solid consisting of individual atoms held together by dispersion forces; the frozen noble gases are the only examples. (449)

atomic symbol (also *element symbol*)   A one- or two-letter abbreviation for the English, Latin, or Greek name of an element. (49)

atomic weight   (See *atomic mass*.)

aufbau principle   The conceptual approach for building up atoms by adding one proton at a time to the nucleus and one electron around it to obtain the ground-state electron configurations of the elements. (299)

autoionization (also *self-ionization*)   A reaction in which two molecules of a substance react to give ions. The most important example is for water:

$$2H_2O(l) \rightleftharpoons H_3O^+(aq) + OH^-(aq) \qquad (724)$$

average rate   The change in concentration of reactants (or products) divided by a finite time period. (630)

Avogadro's law   The gas law stating that, at fixed temperature and pressure, equal volumes of any ideal gas contain equal numbers of particles, and, therefore, the volume of a gas is directly proportional to its amount (mol): $V \propto n$. (190)

Avogadro's number   A number (6.022×10^{23} to four significant figures) equal to the number of atoms in exactly 12 g of carbon-12; the number of atoms, molecules, or formula units in one mole of an element or compound. (83)

axial group   An atom (or group) that lies above or below the trigonal plane of a trigonal bipyramidal molecule, or a similar structural feature in a molecule. (377)

B

background radiation   Natural ionizing radiation, the most important form of which is cosmic radiation. (997)

balancing coefficient (also *stoichiometric coefficient*)   A numerical multiplier of all the atoms in the formula immediately following it in a balanced chemical equation. (99)

band of stability   The band of stable nuclides that appears on a plot of number of neutrons versus number of protons for all nuclides. (983)

band theory   An extension of molecular orbital (MO) theory that explains many properties of metals and other solids, in particular, the differences in electrical conductivity of conductors, semiconductors, and insulators. (452)

barometer   A device used to measure atmospheric pressure. Most commonly, a tube open at one end, which is filled with mercury and inverted into a dish of mercury. (183)

base   In common laboratory terms, any species that produces OH^- ions when dissolved in water. (146) [See also *Arrhenius, Brønsted-Lowry,* and *Lewis acid-base definitions.*]

base-dissociation (base-ionization) constant (K_b)   An equilibrium constant for the reaction of a base (B) with H_2O to yield the conjugate acid (BH^+) and OH^-:

$$K_b = \frac{[BH^+][OH^-]}{[B]} \qquad (740)$$

base pair   Two complementary mononucleotide bases that are H bonded to each other; guanine (G) always pairs with cytosine (C), and adenine (A) always pairs with thymine (T) (or uracil, U). (613)

base unit (also *fundamental unit*)   A unit that defines the standard for one of the seven physical quantities in the International System of Units (SI). (17)

basic-oxygen process   The method used to convert pig iron to steel, in which O_2 is blown over and through molten pig iron to oxidize impurities and decrease the content of carbon. (925)

battery   A group of voltaic cells arranged in series; primary and secondary types are self-contained, but flow batteries are not. (878)

becquerel (Bq)   The SI unit of radioactivity; 1 Bq = 1 d/s (disintegration per second). (988)

bent shape (also *V shape*)   A molecular shape that arises when a central atom is bonded to two other atoms and has one or two lone pairs; occurs as the AX_2E shape class (bond angle < 120°) in the trigonal planar arrangement and as the AX_2E_2 shape class (bond angle < 109.5°) in the tetrahedral arrangement. (375)

beta (β) decay   A radioactive change that encompasses any of three specific processes— $β^-$ decay, $β^+$ emission, and e^- capture. (981)

beta (β⁻) decay A radioactive process in which a beta particle is emitted from a nucleus. (981)

beta particle (β, β⁻, or ₋₁⁰β) A negatively charged particle, identified as a high-speed electron, that is one of the common types of radioactive emissions. (979)

bimolecular reaction An elementary reaction involving the collision of two reactant species. (655)

binary covalent compound A compound that consists of atoms of two elements in which bonding occurs primarily through electron sharing. (65)

binary ionic compound A compound that consists of the oppositely charged ions of two elements. (55)

biomass conversion The process of applying chemical and biological methods to convert plant or animal matter into fuels. (249)

biosphere The living systems that inhabit Earth. (908)

blast furnace A tower-shaped furnace made of brick material in which intense heat and blasts of air are used to convert iron ore and coke to iron metal and carbon dioxide. (924)

body-centered cubic unit cell A unit cell in which a particle lies at each corner and in the center of a cube. (442)

boiling point (bp or T_b) The temperature at which the vapor pressure of a gas equals the external (atmospheric) pressure. (428)

boiling point elevation (ΔT_b) The increase in the boiling point of a solvent caused by the presence of dissolved solute. (501)

bond angle The angle formed by the nuclei of two surrounding atoms with the nucleus of the central atom at the vertex. (374)

bond energy (BE) (also *bond enthalpy* or *bond strength*) The enthalpy change (always >0) accompanying the breakage of a given bond in 1 mol of gaseous molecules. (339)

bond length The distance between the nuclei of two bonded atoms. (340)

bond order The number of electron pairs shared by two bonded atoms. (339)

bonding MO A molecular orbital formed when wave functions are added to each other, which increases electron density between the nuclei. Electrons occupying such an orbital stabilize the molecule. (406)

bonding pair (also *shared pair*) An electron pair shared by two nuclei; the mutual attraction between the nuclei and the electron pair forms a covalent bond. (339)

Born-Haber cycle A series of hypothetical steps and their enthalpy changes that convert elements to an ionic compound; it is used to calculate the lattice energy. (333)

Boyle's law The gas law stating that, at constant temperature and amount of gas, the volume occupied by a gas is inversely proportional to the applied (external) pressure: $V \propto 1/P$. (187)

branch A side chain appended to a polymer backbone or longest sequence of atoms in an organic compound. (465)

bridge bond (also *three-center, two-electron bond*) A covalent bond in which three atoms are held together by two electrons. (536)

Brønsted-Lowry acid-base definition A model of acid-base behavior based on proton transfer, in which an acid and a base are defined, respectively, as species that donate and accept a proton. (729)

buffer (See *acid-base buffer.*)

buffer capacity A measure of the ability of a buffer to resist a change in pH; related to the total concentrations and relative proportions of buffer components. (770)

buffer range The pH range over which a buffer acts effectively. (771)

C

calibration The process of correcting for systematic error of a measuring device by comparing it to a known standard. (29)

calorie (cal) A unit of energy defined as exactly 4.184 joules; originally defined as the heat needed to raise the temperature of 1 g of water 1°C (from 14.5°C to 15.5°C). (233)

calorimeter A device used to measure the heat released or absorbed by a physical or chemical process taking place within it. (239)

capillarity (or *capillary action*) A property that results in a liquid rising through a narrow space against the pull of gravity. (438)

carbon steel The steel that is produced by the basic-oxygen process, contains about 1% to 1.5% C and other impurities, and is alloyed with metals that prevent corrosion and increase strength. (925)

carbonyl group The $C=O$ grouping of atoms. (597)

carboxylic acid An organic compound (ending, *-oic acid*) that contains the $-\overset{\overset{\displaystyle :O:}{\|}}{C}-\overset{..}{O}H$ group. (599)

catalyst A substance or mixture that increases the rate of a reaction without being used up in the process. (660)

catenation The process by which atoms of an element bond to each other in chains; most common with carbon in organic compounds but also occurs with boron, silicon, sulfur, and several other elements. (572)

cathode The electrode at which reduction occurs in an electrochemical cell. Electrons enter the cell and are acquired by the oxidizing agent at the cathode. (856)

cathode ray The ray of light emitted by the cathode (negative electrode) in a gas discharge tube; travels in straight lines, unless deflected by magnetic or electric fields. (45)

cation A positively charged ion. (55)

cell potential (E_{cell}) (also *electromotive force, or emf; cell voltage*) The potential difference between the electrodes of an electrochemical cell when no current flows. (861)

Celsius scale (formerly *centigrade scale*) A temperature scale in which the freezing and boiling points of water are defined as 0°C and 100°C, respectively. (23)

ceramic A nonmetallic, nonpolymeric solid that is hardened by heating it to high temperatures and, in most cases, consists of silicate microcrystals suspended in a glassy cementing medium. (459)

chain reaction In nuclear fission, a self-sustaining process in which neutrons released by splitting of one nucleus cause other nuclei to split, which releases more neutrons, and so on. (1006)

change in enthalpy (ΔH) The change in internal energy plus the product of the constant pressure and the change in volume: $\Delta H = \Delta E + P\Delta V$; the heat lost or gained at constant pressure: $\Delta H = q_P$. (235)

charge density The ratio of the charge of an ion to its volume. (489)

Charles's law The gas law stating that at constant pressure, the volume occupied by a fixed amount of gas is directly proportional to its absolute temperature: $V \propto T$. (188)

chelate A complex ion in which the metal ion is bonded to a bidentate or polydentate ligand. (955)

chemical bond The force that holds two atoms together in a molecule (or formula unit). (55)

chemical change (also *chemical reaction*) A change in which one or more substances are converted into one or more substances with different composition and properties. (4)

chemical equation A statement that uses chemical formulas to express the identities and quantities of the substances involved in a chemical or physical change. (98)

chemical formula A notation of atomic symbols and numerical subscripts that shows the type and number of each atom in a molecule or formula unit of a substance. (59)

chemical kinetics The study of the rates and mechanisms of reactions. (627)

chemical property A characteristic of a substance that appears as it interacts with, or transforms into, other substances. (4)

chemical reaction (See *chemical change.*)

chemistry The scientific study of matter and its properties, the changes it undergoes, and the energy associated with those changes. (4)

chiral molecule One that is not superimposable on its mirror image; an optically active molecule. In organic compounds, a chiral molecule typically contains a C atom bonded to four different groups (asymmetric C). (580)

chlor-alkali process An industrial method that electrolyzes concentrated aqueous NaCl and produces Cl_2, H_2, and NaOH. (936)

chromatography A separation technique in which a mixture is dissolved in a fluid (gas or liquid), and the components are separated through differences in adsorption to (or solubility in) a solid surface (or viscous liquid). (72)

***cis-trans* isomers** (See *geometric isomers.*)

Clausius-Clapeyron equation An equation that expresses the linear relationship between vapor pressure P of a liquid and temperature T; in two-point form, it is

$$\ln \frac{P_2}{P_1} = \frac{-\Delta H_{vap}}{R}\left(\frac{1}{T_2} - \frac{1}{T_1}\right) \qquad (427)$$

coal gasification An industrial process for altering the large molecules in coal to sulfur-free gaseous fuels. (249)

colligative property A property of a solution that depends on the number, not the identity, of solute particles. (499) (See also *boiling point elevation, freezing point depression, osmotic pressure,* and *vapor pressure lowering.*)

collision frequency The average number of collisions per second that a particle undergoes. (211)

collision theory A model that explains reaction rate as based on the number, energy, and orientation of colliding particles. (648)

colloid A heterogeneous mixture in which a solute-like phase is dispersed throughout a solvent-like phase. (508)

combustion The process of burning in air, often with release of heat and light. (10)

combustion analysis A method for determining the formula of a compound from the amounts of its combustion products; used commonly for organic compounds. (95)

common-ion effect The shift in the position of an ionic equilibrium away from an ion involved in the process that is caused by the addition or presence of that ion. (766)

complex (See *coordination compound.*)

complex ion An ion consisting of a central metal ion bonded covalently to molecules and/or anions called ligands (792, 953)

composition The types and amounts of simpler substances that make up a sample of matter. (4)

compound A substance composed of two or more elements that are chemically combined in fixed proportions. (38)

concentration A measure of the quantity of solute dissolved in a given quantity of solution (or solvent). (114)

concentration cell A voltaic cell in which both compartments contain the same components but at different concentrations. (874)

condensation The process of a gas changing into a liquid. (420)

condensation polymer A polymer formed by monomers with two functional groups that are linked together in a dehydration-condensation reaction. (606)

conduction band In band theory, the empty, higher energy portion of the band of molecular orbitals into which electrons move when conducting heat and electricity. (453)

conductor A substance (usually a metal) that conducts an electric current well. (453)

conjugate acid-base pair Two species related to each other through the gain or loss of a proton; the acid has one more proton than its conjugate base. (729)

constitutional isomers (also *structural isomers*) Compounds with the same molecular formula but different arrangements of atoms. (579, 957)

contact process An industrial process for the manufacture of sulfuric acid based on the catalyzed oxidation of SO_2. (934)

controlled experiment An experiment that measures the effect of one variable at a time by keeping other variables constant. (12)

conversion factor A ratio of equivalent quantities that is equal to 1 and used to convert the units of a quantity. (13)

coordinate covalent bond A covalent bond formed when one atom donates both electrons to provide the shared pair and, once formed, is identical to any covalent single bond. (961)

coordination compound (also *complex*) A substance containing at least one complex ion and counter ion(s). (953)

coordination isomers Two or more coordination compounds with the same composition in which the complex ions have different ligand arrangements. (957)

coordination number In a crystal, the number of nearest neighbors surrounding a particle. (442) In a complex, the number of ligand atoms bonded to the central metal ion. (953)

copolymer A polymer that consists of two or more types of monomer. (465)

core The dense, innermost region of Earth. (906)

core electrons (See *inner electrons.*)

corrosion The natural redox process that results in unwanted oxidation of a metal. (882)

coulomb (C) The SI unit of electric charge. One coulomb is the charge of 6.242×10^{18} electrons; one electron possesses a charge of 1.602×10^{-19} C. (862)

Coulomb's law A law stating that the electrostatic energy between particles A and B is directly proportional to the product of their charges and inversely proportional to the distance between them:

$$\text{electrostatic energy} \propto \frac{\text{charge A} \times \text{charge B}}{\text{distance}} \qquad (335)$$

counter ion A simple ion associated with a complex ion in a coordination compound. (953)

coupling of reactions   The pairing of reactions of which one releases enough free energy for the other to occur. (834)

covalent bond   A type of bond in which atoms are bonded through the sharing of electrons; the mutual attraction of the nuclei and an electron pair that holds atoms together in a molecule. (58, 338)

covalent bonding   The idealized bonding type that is based on localized electron-pair sharing between two atoms with little difference in their tendencies to lose or gain electrons (most commonly nonmetals). (330)

covalent compound   A compound that consists of atoms bonded together by shared electron pairs. (55)

covalent radius   One-half the shortest distance between nuclei of identical covalently bonded atoms. (308)

critical mass   The minimum mass needed to achieve a chain reaction. (1007)

critical point   The point on a phase diagram above which the vapor cannot be condensed to a liquid; the end of the liquid-gas curve. (429)

crosslink   A branch that covalently joins one polymer chain to another. (465)

crust   The thin, light, heterogeneous outer layer of Earth, which consists of gasous, liquid, and solid regions. (906)

crystal defect   Any of a variety of disruptions in the regularity of a crystal structure. (455)

crystal field splitting energy (Δ)   The difference in energy between two sets of metal-ion d orbitals that results from electrostatic interactions with the surrounding ligands. (964)

crystal field theory   A model that explains the color and magnetism of coordination compounds based on the effects of ligands on metal-ion d-orbital energies. (962)

crystalline solid   Solid with a well-defined shape because of the orderly arrangement of the atoms, molecules, or ions. (441)

crystallization   A technique used to separate and purify the components of a mixture through differences in solubility in which a component comes out of solution as crystals. (72)

cubic closest packing   A crystal structure based on the face-centered cubic unit cell in which the layers have an *abcabc . . .* pattern. (444)

cubic meter (m^3)   The SI-derived unit of volume. (18)

curie (Ci)   The most common unit of radioactivity, defined as the number of nuclei disintegrating each second in 1 g of radium-226; $1 \text{ Ci} = 3.70 \times 10^{10}$ d/s (disintegrations per second). (988)

cyclic hydrocarbon   A hydrocarbon with one or more rings in its structure. (578)

D

d orbital   An atomic orbital with $l = 2$. (286)

dalton (Da)   A unit of mass identical to *atomic mass unit.* (50)

Dalton's law of partial pressures   A gas law stating that, in a mixture of unreacting gases, the total pressure is the sum of the partial pressures of the individual gases: $P_{total} = P_1 + P_2 + \cdots$. (199)

data   Pieces of quantitative information obtained by observation. (12)

de Broglie wavelength   The wavelength of a moving particle obtained from the de Broglie equation: $\lambda = h/mu$. (276)

decay constant   The rate constant k for radioactive decay. (988)

decay series (also *disintegration series*)   The succession of steps a parent nucleus undergoes as it decays into a stable daughter nucleus. (986)

degree of polymerization (n)   The number of monomer repeat units in a polymer chain. (461)

dehydration-condensation reaction   A reaction in which an H_2O molecule is lost for every pair of OH groups that join. (550)

delocalization   (See *electron-pair delocalization.*)

density (d)   An intensive physical property of a substance at a given temperature and pressure, defined as the ratio of the mass to the volume: $d = m/V$. (22)

deposition   The process of changing directly from gas to solid. (421)

derived unit   Any of various combinations of the seven SI base units. (17)

desalination   A process used to remove large amounts of ions from seawater, usually by reverse osmosis. (511)

deuterons   Nuclei of the stable hydrogen isotope deuterium, ^2H. (993)

diagonal relationship   Physical and chemical similarities between a Period 2 element and one located diagonally down and to the right in Period 3. (533)

diamagnetism   The tendency of a species not to be attracted (or to be slightly repelled) by a magnetic field as a result of its electrons being paired. (319)

diastereomers   (See *geometric isomers.*)

differentiation   The geochemical process of forming regions in Earth based on differences in composition and density. (906)

diffraction   The phenomenon in which a wave striking the edge of an object bends around it. A wave passing through a slit as wide as its wavelength forms a circular wave. (264)

diffusion   The movement of one fluid through another. (210)

dimensional analysis (also *factor-label method*)   A calculation method in which arithmetic steps are accompanied by canceling units that represent physical dimensions. (15)

dipole-dipole force   The intermolecular attraction between oppositely charged poles of nearby polar molecules. (432)

dipole–induced dipole force   The intermolecular attraction between a polar molecule and the oppositely charged pole it induces in a nearby molecule. (478)

dipole moment (μ)   A measure of molecular polarity; the magnitude of the partial charges on the ends of a molecule (in coulombs) times the distance between them (in meters). (383)

disaccharide   An organic compound formed by a dehydration-condensation reaction between two simple sugars (monosaccharides). (607)

disintegration series   (See *decay series.*)

dispersion force (also *London force*)   The intermolecular attraction between all particles as a result of instantaneous polarizations of their electron clouds; the intermolecular force primarily responsible for the condensed states of nonpolar substances. (435)

disproportionation   A reaction in which a given substance is both oxidized and reduced. (547)

distillation   A separation technique in which a more volatile component of a mixture vaporizes and condenses separately from the less volatile components. (72)

donor atom   An atom that donates a lone pair of electrons to form a covalent bond, usually from ligand to metal ion in a complex. (954)

doping   Adding small amounts of other elements into the crystal structure of a semiconductor to enhance a specific property, usually conductivity. (455)

double bond   A covalent bond that consists of two bonding pairs; two atoms sharing four electrons in the form of one σ and one π bond. (339)

double helix   The two intertwined polynucleotide strands held together by H bonds that form the structure of DNA (deoxyribonucleic acid). (487, 612)

Downs cell   An industrial apparatus that electrolyzes molten NaCl to produce sodium and chlorine. (923)

dynamic equilibrium   The condition at which the forward and reverse reactions are taking place at the same rate, so there is no net change in the amounts of reactants or products. (167)

E

e_g orbitals   The set of orbitals (composed of $d_{x^2-y^2}$ and d_{z^2}) that results when the energies of the metal-ion d orbitals are split by a ligand field. This set is higher in energy than the other (t_{2g}) set in an octahedral field of ligands and lower in energy in a tetrahedral field. (964)

effective collision   A collision in which the particles meet with sufficient energy and an orientation that allows them to react. (651)

effective nuclear charge (Z_{eff})   The nuclear charge an electron actually experiences as a result of shielding effects due to the presence of other electrons. (297)

effusion   The process by which a gas escapes from its container through a tiny hole into an evacuated space. (209)

elastomer   A polymeric material that can be stretched and springs back to its original shape when released. (465)

electrochemical cell   A system that incorporates a redox reaction to produce or use electrical energy. (851)

electrochemistry   The study of the relationship between chemical change and electrical work. (851)

electrode   The part of an electrochemical cell that conducts the electricity between the cell and the surroundings. (855)

electrolysis   The nonspontaneous lysing (splitting) of a substance, often to its component elements, by supplying electrical energy. (886)

electrolyte   A substance that conducts a current when it dissolves in water. (137, 499) A mixture of ions, in which the electrodes of an electrochemical cell are immersed, that conducts a current. (855)

electrolytic cell   An electrochemical system that uses electrical energy to drive a nonspontaneous chemical reaction ($\Delta G > 0$). (855)

electromagnetic radiation (also *electromagnetic energy* or *radiant energy*)   Oscillating, perpendicular electric and magnetic fields moving simultaneously through space as waves and manifested as visible light, x-rays, microwaves, radio waves, and so on. (261)

electromagnetic spectrum   The continuum of wavelengths of radiant energy. (262)

electromotive force (emf)   (See *cell potential*.)

electron (e^-)   A subatomic particle that possesses a unit negative charge (-1.60218×10^{-19} C) and occupies the space around the atomic nucleus. (48)

electron affinity (EA)   The energy change (in kJ) accompanying the addition of one mole of electrons to one mole of gaseous atoms or ions. (314)

electron capture (EC)   A type of radioactive decay in which a nucleus draws in an orbital electron, usually one from the lowest energy level, and releases energy. (981)

electron cloud depiction   An imaginary representation of an electron's rapidly changing position around the nucleus over time. (280)

electron configuration   The distribution of electrons within the orbitals of the atoms of an element; also the notation for such a distribution. (295)

electron deficient   Referring to a bonded atom, such as Be or B, that has fewer than eight valence electrons. (369)

electron density diagram (also *electron probability density diagram*)   The pictorial representation for a given energy sublevel of the quantity ψ^2 (the probability density of the electron lying within a particular tiny volume) as a function of r (distance from the nucleus). (280)

electron-pair delocalization (also *delocalization*)   The process by which electron density is spread over several atoms rather than remaining between two. (367)

electron-sea model   A qualitative description of metallic bonding proposing that metal atoms pool their valence electrons into a delocalized "sea" of electrons in which the metal cores (metal ions) are submerged in an orderly array. (354)

electron volt (eV)   The energy (in joules, J) that an electron acquires when it moves through a potential difference of 1 volt; $1 \text{ eV} = 1.602 \times 10^{-19}$ J. (1004)

electronegativity (EN)   The relative ability of a bonded atom to attract shared electrons. (349)

electronegativity difference (ΔEN)   The difference in electronegativities between the atoms in a bond. (351)

electrorefining   An industrial, electrolytic purification process in which a sample of impure metal acts as the anode and a sample of the pure metal acts as the cathode. (921)

element   The simplest type of substance with unique physical and chemical properties. An element consists of only one kind of atom, so it cannot be broken down into simpler substances. (38)

element symbol   (See *atomic symbol*.)

elementary reaction (also *elementary step*)   A simple reaction that describes a single molecular event in a proposed reaction mechanism. (655)

elimination reaction   A type of organic reaction in which C atoms are bonded to fewer atoms in the product than in the reactant, which leads to multiple bonding. (589)

emission spectrum   The line spectrum produced when excited atoms return to lower energy levels and emit photons characteristic of the element. (273)

empirical formula   A chemical formula that shows the lowest relative number of atoms of each element in a compound. (92)

enantiomers   (See *optical isomers*.)

end point   The point in a titration at which the indicator changes color. (152, 776)

endothermic process   A process that occurs with an absorption of heat from the surroundings and therefore an increase in the enthalpy of the system ($\Delta H > 0$). (237)

energy   The capacity to do work, that is, to move matter. (8) [See also *kinetic energy* (E_k) and *potential energy* (E_p).]

enthalpy (H)   A thermodynamic quantity that is the sum of the internal energy plus the product of the pressure and volume. (235)

enthalpy diagram   A graphic depiction of the enthalpy change of a system. (237)

enthalpy of formation (ΔH_f) (also *heat of formation*)   The enthalpy change occurring when 1 mol of a compound forms from its elements. When all components are in their standard states, this is called the *standard enthalpy of formation* (ΔH_f°). (246)

enthalpy of fusion   (See *heat of fusion.*)

enthalpy of hydration   (See *heat of hydration.*)

enthalpy of reaction (ΔH_{rxn}) (also *heat of reaction*)   The enthalpy change that occurs during a reaction. When all components are in their standard states, this is called the *standard enthalpy of reaction* (ΔH_{rxn}°). (246)

enthalpy of solution   (See *heat of solution.*)

enthalpy of sublimation   (See *heat of sublimation.*)

enthalpy of vaporization   (See *heat of vaporization.*)

entropy (S)   A thermodynamic quantity related to the number of ways the energy of a system can be dispersed through the motions of its particles. (490, 814)

environmental cycle   The physical, chemical, and biological paths through which the atoms of an element move within Earth's crust. (911)

enzyme   A biological macromolecule (usually a protein) that acts as a catalyst. (662)

enzyme-substrate complex (ES)   The intermediate in an enzyme-catalyzed reaction, which consists of enzyme and substrate(s) and whose concentration determines the rate of product formation. (663)

equatorial group   An atom (or group) that lies in the trigonal plane of a trigonal bipyramidal molecule, or a similar structural feature in a molecule. (377)

equilibrium constant (K)   The value obtained when equilibrium concentrations are substituted into the reaction quotient. (679)

equilibrium vapor pressure   (See *vapor pressure.*)

equivalence point   The point in a titration when the number of moles of the added species is stoichiometrically equivalent to the original number of moles of the other species. (152, 775)

ester   An organic compound that contains the $-\overset{\displaystyle :O:}{\overset{\displaystyle \|}{C}}-\overset{..}{\underset{..}{O}}-\overset{|}{\underset{|}{C}}-$ group. (599)

exact number   A quantity, usually obtained by counting or based on a unit definition, that has no uncertainty associated with it and, therefore, contains as many significant figures as a calculation requires. (28)

exchange reaction   (See *metathesis reaction.*)

excited state   Any electron configuration of an atom or molecule other than the lowest energy (ground) state. (269)

exclusion principle   A principle developed by Wolfgang Pauli stating that no two electrons in an atom can have the same set of four quantum numbers. The principle arises from the fact that an orbital has a maximum occupancy of two electrons and their spins are paired. (297)

exothermic process   A process that occurs with a release of heat to the surroundings and therefore a decrease in the enthalpy of the system ($\Delta H < 0$). (236)

expanded valence shell   A valence level that can accommodate more than eight electrons by using available d orbitals; occurs only with central nonmetal atoms from Period 3 or higher. (370)

experiment   A set of procedural steps that tests a hypothesis. (12)

extensive property   A property, such as mass, that depends on the quantity of substance present. (25)

F

face-centered cubic unit cell   A unit cell in which a particle occurs at each corner and in the center of each face of a cube. (442)

Faraday constant (F)   The physical constant representing the charge of 1 mol of electrons: $F = 96{,}485$ C/mol e$^-$. (870)

fatty acid   A carboxylic acid that has a long hydrocarbon chain and is derived from a natural source. (599)

filtration   A method of separating the components of a mixture on the basis of differences in particle size. (72)

first law of thermodynamics   (See *law of conservation of energy.*)

fission   The process by which a heavier nucleus splits into lighter nuclei with the release of energy. (1003)

fixation   A chemical/biochemical process that converts a gaseous substance in the environment into a condensed form that can be used by organisms. (911)

flame test   A procedure for identifying the presence of metal ions in which a granule of a compound or a drop of its solution is placed in a flame to observe a characteristic color. (273)

flotation   A metallurgical process in which oil and detergent are mixed with pulverized ore in water to create a slurry that separates the mineral from the gangue. (917)

formal charge   The hypothetical charge on an atom in a molecule or ion, equal to the number of valence electrons minus the sum of all the unshared and half the shared valence electrons. (368)

formation constant (K_f)   An equilibrium constant for the formation of a complex ion from the hydrated metal ion and ligands. (794)

formation equation   An equation in which 1 mole of a compound forms from its elements. (246)

formula mass   The sum (in amu) of the atomic masses of a formula unit of a (usually ionic) compound. (66)

formula unit   The chemical unit of a compound that contains the relative numbers of the types of atoms or ions expressed in the chemical formula. (60)

fossil fuel   Any fuel, including coal, petroleum, and natural gas, derived from the products of the decay of dead organisms. (249)

fraction by mass (also *mass fraction*)   The portion of a compound's mass contributed by an element; the mass of an element in a compound divided by the mass of the compound. (41)

fractional distillation   A physical process involving numerous vaporization-condensation steps used to separate two or more volatile components. (505)

free energy (G)   A thermodynamic quantity that is the difference between the enthalpy and the product of the absolute temperature and the entropy: $G = H - TS$. (827)

free energy change (ΔG)   The change in free energy that occurs during a reaction. (827)

free radical   A molecular or atomic species with one or more unpaired electrons, which typically make it very reactive. (370, 996)

freezing   The process of cooling a liquid until it solidifies. (420)

freezing point depression (ΔT_f)   The lowering of the freezing point of a solvent caused by the presence of dissolved solute particles. (502)

frequency (ν)   The number of cycles a wave undergoes per second, expressed in units of 1/second, or s^{-1} [also called *hertz* (Hz)]; related inversely to wavelength. (261)

frequency factor (A)   The product of the collision frequency Z and an orientation probability factor p that is specific for a reaction. (651)

fuel cell (also *flow battery*)   A battery that is not self-contained and in which electricity is generated by the controlled oxidation of a fuel. (881)

functional group   A specific combination of atoms, typically containing a carbon-carbon multiple bond and/or carbon-heteroatom bond, that reacts in a characteristic way no matter what molecule it occurs in. (573)

fundamental unit   (See *base unit*.)

fusion   (See *melting*.)

fusion (nuclear)   The process by which light nuclei combine to form a heavier nucleus with the release of energy. (1003)

G

galvanic cell   (See *voltaic cell*.)

gamma emission   The type of radioactive decay in which gamma rays are emitted from an excited nucleus. (981)

gamma (γ) ray   A very high-energy photon. (979)

gangue   In an ore, the debris, such as sand, rock, and clay, attached to the mineral. (917)

gas   One of the three states of matter. A gas fills its container regardless of the shape because its particles are far apart. (6)

Geiger-Müller counter   An ionization counter that detects radioactive emissions through their ionization of gas atoms within the instrument. (987)

genetic code   The set of three-base sequences that is translated into specific amino acids during the process of protein synthesis. (613)

geometric isomers (also *cis-trans isomers* or *diastereomers*)   Stereoisomers in which the molecules have the same connections between atoms but differ in the spatial arrangements of the atoms. The *cis* isomer has similar groups on the same side of a double bond; the *trans* isomer has them on opposite sides. (582, 958)

Graham's law of effusion   A gas law stating that the rate of effusion of a gas is inversely proportional to the square root of its density (or molar mass):

$$\text{rate} \propto \frac{1}{\sqrt{\mathcal{M}}} \qquad (209)$$

gray (Gy)   The SI unit of absorbed radiation dose; 1 Gy = 1 J/kg tissue. (996)

green chemistry   Field that is focused on developing methods to synthesize compounds efficiently and reduce or prevent the release of harmful products into the environment. (113)

ground state   The electron configuration of an atom or ion that is lowest in energy. (269)

group   A vertical column in the periodic table; elements in a group usually have the same outer electron configuration and, thus, similar chemical behavior. (53)

H

H bond   (See *hydrogen bond*.)

Haber process   An industrial process used to form ammonia from its elements. (706)

half-cell   A portion of an electrochemical cell in which a half-reaction takes place. (857)

half-life ($t_{1/2}$)   In chemical processes, the time required for half the initial reactant concentration to be consumed. (644) In nuclear processes, the time required for half the initial number of nuclei in a sample to decay. (988)

half-reaction method   A method of balancing redox reactions by treating the oxidation and reduction half-reactions separately. (852)

haloalkane (also *alkyl halide*)   A hydrocarbon with one or more halogen atoms (X) in place of H; contains a $-\overset{|}{\underset{|}{C}}-\ddot{\underset{\cdot\cdot}{X}}$: group. (593)

hard water   Water that contains large amounts of divalent cations, especially Ca^{2+} and Mg^{2+}. (510)

heat (q) (also *thermal energy*)   The energy transferred between objects because of a difference in their temperatures only. (23, 230)

heat capacity   The quantity of heat required to change the temperature of an object by 1 K. (238)

heat of formation   (See *enthalpy of formation*.)

heat of fusion (ΔH_{fus}) (also *enthalpy of fusion*)   The enthalpy change occurring when 1 mol of a solid substance melts; designated ΔH°_{fus} at the standard state. (421)

heat of hydration (ΔH_{hydr}) (also *enthalpy of hydration*)   The enthalpy change occurring when 1 mol of a gaseous species (often an ion) is hydrated. The sum of the enthalpies from separating water molecules and mixing the gaseous species with them; designated ΔH°_{hydr} at the standard state. (489)

heat of reaction (ΔH_{rxn}) (See *enthalpy of reaction*.)

heat of solution (ΔH_{soln}) (also *enthalpy of solution*)   The enthalpy change occurring when a solution forms from solute and solvent. The sum of the enthalpies from separating solute and solvent substances and mixing them; designated ΔH°_{soln} at the standard state. (488)

heat of sublimation (ΔH_{subl}) (also *enthalpy of sublimation*)   The enthalpy change occurring when 1 mol of a solid substance changes directly to a gas. The sum of the heats of fusion and vaporization; designated ΔH°_{subl} at the standard state. (421)

heat of vaporization (ΔH_{vap}) (also *enthalpy of vaporization*)   The enthalpy change occurring when 1 mol of a liquid substance vaporizes; designated ΔH°_{vap} at the standard state. (421)

heating-cooling curve   A plot of temperature vs. time for a substance when heat is absorbed or released by the system at a constant rate. (422)

Henderson-Hasselbalch equation   An equation for calculating the pH of a buffer system:

$$pH = pK_a + \log\left(\frac{[\text{base}]}{[\text{acid}]}\right) \qquad (770)$$

Henry's law   A law stating that the solubility of a gas in a liquid is directly proportional to the partial pressure of the gas above the liquid: $S_{gas} = k_H \times P_{gas}$. (494)

Hess's law   A law stating that the enthalpy change of an overall process is the sum of the enthalpy changes of the individual steps. (244)

heteroatom   Any atom in an organic compound other than C or H. (573)

heterogeneous catalyst   A catalyst that occurs in a different phase from the reactants, usually a solid interacting with gaseous or liquid reactants. (661)

heterogeneous mixture   A mixture that has one or more visible boundaries among its components. (70)

hexagonal closest packing   A crystal structure based on the hexagonal unit cell in which the layers have an *abab . . .* pattern. (444)

high-spin complex   Complex ion that has the same number of unpaired electrons as in the isolated metal ion; contains weak-field ligands. (966)

homogeneous catalyst   A catalyst (gas, liquid, or soluble solid) that exists in the same phase as the reactants. (660)

homogeneous mixture (also *solution*)   A mixture that has no visible boundaries among its components. (70)

homologous series   A series of organic compounds in which each member differs from the next by a —CH$_2$— (methylene) group. (576)

homonuclear diatomic molecule   A molecule composed of two identical atoms. (408)

Hund's rule   A principle stating that when orbitals of equal energy are available, the electron configuration of lowest energy has the maximum number of unpaired electrons with parallel spins. (300)

hybrid orbital   An atomic orbital postulated to form during bonding by the mathematical mixing of specific combinations of nonequivalent orbitals in a given atom. (396)

hybridization   A postulated process of orbital mixing to form hybrid orbitals. (396)

hydrate   A compound in which a specific number of water molecules are associated with each formula unit. (63)

hydration   Solvation in water. (489)

hydration shell   The oriented cluster of water molecules that surrounds an ion in aqueous solution. (478)

hydrocarbon   An organic compound that contains only H and C atoms. (574)

hydrogen bond (H bond)   A type of dipole-dipole force that arises between molecules that have an H atom bonded to a small, highly electronegative atom with lone pairs, usually N, O, or F. (432)

hydrogenation   The addition of hydrogen to a carbon-carbon multiple bond to form a carbon-carbon single bond. (662)

hydrolysis   Cleaving a molecule by reaction with water, in which one part of the molecule bonds to the water —OH and the other to the water H. (600)

hydronium ion (H$_3$O$^+$)   A proton covalently bonded to a water molecule. (720)

hydrosphere   The liquid portion of Earth's crust. (908)

hypothesis   A testable proposal made to explain an observation. If inconsistent with experimental results, a hypothesis is revised or discarded. (12)

ideal gas   A hypothetical gas that exhibits linear relationships among volume, pressure, temperature, and amount (mol) at all conditions; approximated by simple gases at ordinary conditions. (186)

ideal gas law (also *ideal gas equation*)   An equation that expresses the relationships among volume, pressure, temperature, and amount (mol) of an ideal gas: $PV = nRT$. (191)

ideal solution   A solution whose vapor pressure equals the mole fraction of the solvent times the vapor pressure of the pure solvent; approximated only by very dilute solutions. (500) (See also *Raoult's law*.)

indicator   (See *acid-base indicator*.)

induced-fit model   A model of enzyme action that pictures the binding of the substrate as inducing the active site to change its shape and become catalytically active. (663)

infrared (IR)   The region of the electromagnetic spectrum between the microwave and visible regions. (262)

infrared (IR) spectroscopy   An instrumental technique for determining the types of bonds in a covalent molecule by measuring the absorption of IR radiation. (343)

initial rate   The instantaneous rate occurring as soon as the reactants are mixed, that is, at $t = 0$. (631)

inner electrons (also *core electrons*)   Electrons that fill all the energy levels of an atom except the valence level; electrons also present in atoms of the previous noble gas and any completed transition series. (306)

inner transition elements   The elements of the periodic table in which f orbitals are being filled; the lanthanides and actinides. (306, 952)

instantaneous rate   The reaction rate at a particular time, given by the slope of a tangent to a plot of reactant concentration vs. time. (631)

insulator   A substance (usually a nonmetal) that does not conduct an electric current. (453)

integrated rate law   A mathematical expression for reactant concentration as a function of time. (642)

intensive property   A property, such as density, that does not depend on the quantity of substance present. (25)

interhalogen compound   A compound consisting entirely of halogens. (558)

intermolecular forces (also *interparticle forces*)   The attractive and repulsive forces among the particles—molecules, atoms, or ions—in a sample of matter. (419)

internal energy (E)   The sum of the kinetic and potential energies of all the particles in a system. (230)

ion   A charged particle that forms from an atom (or covalently bonded group of atoms) when it gains or loses one or more electrons. (55)

ion-dipole force   The intermolecular attractive force between an ion and a polar molecule (dipole). (432)

ion exchange   A process of softening water by exchanging one type of ion (usually Ca^{2+}) for another (usually Na^+) by binding the ions on a specially designed resin. (511)

ion–induced dipole force   The attractive force between an ion and the dipole it induces in the electron cloud of a nearby nonpolar molecule. (478)

ion pair   A pair of ions that form a gaseous ionic molecule; sometimes formed when a salt boils. (337)

ion-product constant for water (K_w)   The equilibrium constant for the autoionization of water; equal to 1.0×10^{-14} at 298 K.

$$K_w = [H_3O^+][OH^-] \qquad (724)$$

ionic atmosphere   A cluster of ions of net opposite charge surrounding a given ion in solution. (506)

ionic bonding   The idealized type of bonding based on the attraction of oppositely charged ions that arise through electron transfer between atoms with large differences in their tendencies to lose or gain electrons (typically metals and nonmetals). (330)

ionic compound   A compound that consists of oppositely charged ions. (55)

ionic radius   The size of an ion as measured by the distance between the nuclei of adjacent ions in a crystalline ionic compound. (320)

ionic solid   A solid whose unit cell contains cations and anions. (449)

ionization   In nuclear chemistry, the process by which a substance absorbs energy from high-energy radioactive particles and loses an electron to become ionized. (995)

ionization energy (IE)   The energy (in kJ) required to remove completely one mole of electrons from one mole of gaseous atoms or ions. (311)

ionizing radiation   The high-energy radiation from natural and artificial sources that forms ions in a substance by causing electron loss. (995)

isoelectronic   Having the same number and configuration of electrons as another species. (317)

isomer   One of two or more compounds with the same molecular formula but different properties, often as a result of different arrangements of atoms. (97, 579, 957)

isotopes   Atoms of a given atomic number (that is, of a specific element) that have different numbers of neutrons and therefore different mass numbers. (49, 978)

isotopic mass   The mass (in amu) of an isotope relative to the mass of carbon-12. (50)

J

joule (J)   The SI unit of energy; $1\ J = 1\ kg\cdot m^2/s^2$. (233)

K

kelvin (K)   The SI base unit of temperature. The kelvin is the same size as the Celsius degree. (23)

Kelvin scale   (See *absolute scale*.)

ketone   An organic compound (ending, *-one*) that contains a carbonyl group bonded to two other C atoms, $-\overset{\displaystyle |}{\underset{\displaystyle |}{C}}-\overset{\displaystyle \overset{:O:}{\|}}{C}-\overset{\displaystyle |}{\underset{\displaystyle |}{C}}-$. (597)

kilogram (kg)   The SI base unit of mass. (20)

kinetic energy (E_k)   The energy an object has because of its motion. (8)

kinetic-molecular theory   The model that explains gas behavior in terms of particles in random motion whose volumes and interactions are negligible. (204)

L

lanthanide contraction   The additional decrease in atomic and ionic size, beyond the expected trend, caused by the poor shielding of the increasing nuclear charge by f electrons in the elements following the lanthanides. (949)

lanthanides   (also *rare earths*)   The Period 6 ($4f$) series of inner transition elements, which includes cerium (Ce; $Z = 58$) through lutetium (Lu; $Z = 71$). (306, 952)

lattice   The three-dimensional arrangement of points created by choosing each point to be at the same location within each particle of a crystal; thus, the lattice consists of all points with identical surroundings. (442)

lattice energy ($\Delta H^\circ_{lattice}$)   The enthalpy change (always positive) that accompanies the separation of 1 mol of a solid ionic compound into gaseous ions. (333)

law   (See *natural law*.)

law of chemical equilibrium   (also *law of mass action*)   The law stating that when a system reaches equilibrium at a given temperature, the ratio of quantities that make up the reaction quotient has a constant numerical value. (680)

law of conservation of energy   (also *first law of thermodynamics*)   A basic observation that the total energy of the universe is constant; thus, $\Delta E_{universe} = \Delta E_{system} + \Delta E_{surroundings} = 0$. (233)

law of definite (or constant) composition   A mass law stating that, no matter what its source, a particular compound is composed of the same elements in the same parts (fractions) by mass. (41)

law of mass action   (See *law of chemical equilibrium*.)

law of mass conservation   A mass law stating that the total mass of substances does not change during a chemical reaction. (40)

law of multiple proportions   A mass law stating that if elements A and B react to form two or more compounds, the different masses of B that combine with a fixed mass of A can be expressed as a ratio of small whole numbers. (42)

Le Châtelier's principle   A principle stating that if a system in a state of equilibrium is disturbed, it will undergo a change that shifts its equilibrium position in a direction that reduces the effect of the disturbance. (698)

leaching   A hydrometallurgical process that extracts a metal selectively, usually through formation of a complex ion. (918)

level   (also *shell*)   A specific energy state of an atom given by the principal quantum number n. (282)

leveling effect   The inability of a solvent to distinguish the strength of an acid (or base) that is stronger than the conjugate acid (or conjugate base) of the solvent. (750)

Lewis acid-base definition   A model of acid-base behavior in which acids and bases are defined, respectively, as species that accept and donate an electron pair. (751)

Lewis electron-dot symbol   A notation in which the element symbol represents the nucleus and inner electrons, and surrounding dots represent the valence electrons. (331)

Lewis structure   (also *Lewis formula*)   A structural formula consisting of electron-dot symbols, with lines as bonding pairs and dots as lone pairs. (363)

ligand   A molecule or anion bonded to a central metal ion in a complex ion. (792, 953)

like-dissolves-like rule   An empirical observation stating that substances having similar kinds of intermolecular forces dissolve in each other. (478)

limiting reactant   (also *limiting reagent*)   The reactant that is consumed when a reaction occurs and, therefore, the one that determines the maximum amount of product that can form. (107)

line spectrum   A series of separated lines of different colors representing photons whose wavelengths are characteristic of an element. (267) (See also *emission spectrum*.)

linear arrangement   The geometric arrangement obtained when two electron groups maximize their separation around a central atom. (374)

linear shape   A molecular shape formed by three atoms lying in a straight line, with a bond angle of $180°$ (shape class AX_2 or AX_2E_3). (374)

linkage isomers   Coordination compounds with the same composition but with different ligand donor atoms linked to the central metal ion. (957)

lipid   Any of a class of biomolecules, including fats, that are soluble in nonpolar solvents and not soluble in water. (600)

lipid bilayer   An extended sheetlike double layer of phospholipid molecules that forms in water and has the charged heads of the molecules on the surfaces of the bilayer and the nonpolar tails within the interior. (485)

liquid One of the three states of matter. A liquid fills a container to the extent of its own volume and thus forms a surface. (5)

liquid crystal A substance that flows like a liquid but packs like a crystalline solid at the molecular level. (456)

liter (L) A non-SI unit of volume equivalent to 1 cubic decimeter (0.001 m^3). (18)

lithosphere The solid portion of Earth's crust. (908)

lock-and-key model A model of enzyme function that pictures the enzyme active site and the substrate as rigid shapes that fit together as a lock and key, respectively. (663)

London force (See *dispersion force.*)

lone pair (also *unshared pair*) An electron pair that is part of an atom's valence level but not involved in covalent bonding. (339)

low-spin complex Complex ion that has fewer unpaired electrons than in the free metal ion because of the presence of strong-field ligands. (966)

M

macromolecule (See *polymer.*)

magnetic quantum number (m_l) An integer from $-l$ through 0 to $+l$ that specifies the orientation of an atomic orbital in the three-dimensional space about the nucleus. (281)

manometer A device used to measure the pressure of a gas in a laboratory experiment. (184)

mantle A thick homogeneous layer of Earth's internal structure that lies between the core and the crust. (906)

mass The quantity of matter an object contains. Balances are designed to measure mass. (20)

mass-action expression (See *reaction quotient.*)

mass fraction (See *fraction by mass.*)

mass number (A) The total number of protons and neutrons in the nucleus of an atom. (49)

mass percent (also *mass %* or *percent by mass*) The fraction by mass expressed as a percentage. (41) A concentration term [% (w/w)] expressed as the mass of solute dissolved in 100. parts by mass of solution. (496)

mass spectrometry An instrumental method for measuring the relative masses of particles in a sample by creating charged particles and separating them according to their mass-charge ratio. (50)

matter Anything that possesses mass and occupies volume. (4)

mean free path The average distance a molecule travels between collisions at a given temperature and pressure. (211)

melting (also *fusion*) The change of a substance from a solid to a liquid. (420)

melting point (mp or T_f) The temperature at which the solid and liquid forms of a substance are at equilibrium. (429)

metabolic pathway A biochemical reaction sequence that flows in one direction and has each reaction enzyme catalyzed. (708)

metal A substance or mixture that is relatively shiny and malleable and is a good conductor of heat and electricity. In reactions, metals tend to transfer electrons to nonmetals and form ionic compounds. (54)

metallic bonding An idealized type of bonding based on the attraction between metal ions and their delocalized valence electrons. (331) (See also *electron-sea model.*)

metallic radius One-half the shortest distance between the nuclei of adjacent individual atoms in a crystal of an element. (308)

metallic solid A solid whose individual atoms are held together by metallic bonding. (451)

metalloid (also *semimetal*) An element with properties between those of metals and nonmetals. (54)

metallurgy The branch of materials science concerned with the extraction and utilization of metals. (917)

metathesis reaction (also *double-displacement reaction*) A reaction in which atoms or ions of two compounds exchange bonding partners. (143)

meter (m) The SI base unit of length. The distance light travels in a vacuum in 1/299,792,458 second. (18)

methanogenesis The process of producing methane by anaerobic biodegradation of plant and animal waste. (249)

milliliter (mL) A volume (0.001 L) equivalent to 1 cm^3. (18)

millimeter of mercury (mmHg) A unit of pressure based on the difference in the heights of mercury in a barometer or manometer. Renamed the *torr* in honor of Torricelli. (185)

mineral The portion of an ore that contains the element of interest, a mineral is a naturally occurring, homogeneous, crystalline inorganic solid, with a well-defined composition. (917)

miscible Soluble in any proportion. (478)

mixture A group of two or more elements and/or compounds that are physically intermingled. (39)

MO bond order One-half the difference between the number of electrons in bonding and antibonding MOs. (407)

model (also *theory*) A simplified conceptual picture based on experiment that explains how a natural phenomenon occurs. (12)

molality (m) A concentration term expressed as number of moles of solute dissolved in 1000 g (1 kg) of solvent. (495)

molar heat capacity (C) The quantity of heat required to change the temperature of 1 mol of a substance by 1 K. (238)

molar mass ($\mathcal{M}$) The mass of 1 mol of entities (atoms, molecules, or formula units) of a substance, in units of g/mol. (84)

molarity (M) A concentration term expressed as the moles of solute dissolved in 1 L of solution. (114)

mole (mol) The SI base unit for amount of a substance. The amount that contains a number of objects equal to the number of atoms in exactly 12 g of carbon-12 (which is 6.022×10^{23}). (83)

mole fraction (X) A concentration term expressed as the ratio of moles of one component of a mixture to the total moles present. (200, 496)

molecular equation A chemical equation showing a reaction in solution in which reactants and products appear as intact, undissociated compounds. (140)

molecular formula A formula that shows the actual number of atoms of each element in a molecule of a compound. (68, 92)

molecular mass (also *molecular weight*) The sum (in amu) of the atomic masses of the elements in a molecule (or formula unit) of a compound. (66)

molecular orbital (MO) An orbital of given energy and shape that extends over a molecule and can be occupied by no more than two paired electrons. (405)

molecular orbital (MO) diagram A depiction of the relative energy and number of electrons in each MO, as well as the atomic orbitals from which the MOs form. (406)

molecular orbital (MO) theory A model that describes a molecule as a collection of nuclei and electrons in which the electrons occupy orbitals that extend over the entire molecule. (405)

molecular polarity The overall distribution of electronic charge in a molecule, determined by its shape and bond polarities. (383)

molecular shape   The three-dimensional structure defined by the relative positions of the atomic nuclei in a molecule. (373)

molecular solid   A solid held together by intermolecular forces between individual molecules. (449)

molecular weight   (See *molecular mass*.)

molecularity   The number of reactant particles involved in an elementary step. (655)

molecule   A structure consisting of two or more atoms that are bound chemically and behave as an independent unit. (38)

monatomic ion   An ion derived from a single atom. (55)

monomer   A small molecule, linked covalently to others of the same or similar type to form a polymer; the repeat unit of the polymer. (461)

mononucleotide   A monomer unit of a nucleic acid, consisting of an N-containing base, a sugar, and a phosphate group. (487, 611)

monosaccharide   A simple sugar; a polyhydroxy ketone or aldehyde with three to nine C atoms. (607)

N

nanotechnology   The science and engineering of nanoscale (1–100 nm) systems. (466)

natural law (also *law*)   A summary, often in mathematical form, of a universal observation. (12)

Nernst equation   An equation stating that the voltage of an electrochemical cell under any conditions depends on the standard cell voltage and the concentrations of the cell components:

$$E_{cell} = E_{cell}^\circ = \frac{RT}{nF} \ln Q \qquad (872)$$

net ionic equation   A chemical equation of a reaction in solution in which spectator ions have been eliminated to show the actual chemical change. (141)

network covalent solid   A solid in which all the atoms are bonded covalently so that individual molecules are not present. (451)

neutralization   Process that occurs when an H^+ ion from an acid combines with an OH^- ion from a base to form H_2O. (720)

neutralization reaction   An acid-base reaction that yields water and a solution of a salt; when the H^+ ions of a strong acid react with an equivalent amount of the OH^- ions of a strong base, the solution is neutral. (145)

neutron (n^0)   An uncharged subatomic particle found in the nucleus, with a mass slightly greater than that of a proton. (48)

nitrile   An organic compound containing the $-C\equiv N$: group. (603)

node   A region of an orbital where the probability of finding the electron is zero. (285)

nonbonding MO   A molecular orbital that is not involved in bonding. (412)

nonelectrolyte   A substance whose aqueous solution does not conduct an electric current. (139, 499)

nonmetal   An element that lacks metallic properties. In reactions, nonmetals tend to share electrons with each other to form covalent compounds or accept electrons from metals to form ionic compounds. (54)

nonpolar covalent bond   A covalent bond between identical atoms such that the bonding pair is shared equally. (351)

nuclear binding energy   The energy required to break 1 mole of nuclei of an element into individual nucleons. (1004)

nuclear magnetic resonance (NMR) spectroscopy   An instrumental technique used to determine the molecular environment of a given type of nucleus, most often ^{1}H, from its absorption of radio waves in a magnetic field. (586)

nuclear transmutation   The induced conversion of one nucleus into another by bombardment with a particle. (992)

nucleic acid   An unbranched polymer consisting of mononucleotides that occurs as two types, DNA and RNA (deoxyribonucleic and ribonucleic acids), which differ chemically in the nature of the sugar portion of the mononucleotides. (487, 611)

nucleon   A subatomic particle found in the nucleus; a proton or neutron. (978)

nucleus   The tiny central region of the atom that contains all the positive charge and essentially all the mass. (47)

nuclide   A nuclear species with specified numbers of protons and neutrons. (978)

O

observation   A fact obtained with the senses, often with the aid of instruments. Quantitative observations provide data that can be compared. (12)

occurrence (also *source*)   The form(s) in which an element exists in nature. (909)

octahedral arrangement   The geometric arrangement obtained when six electron groups maximize their space around a central atom; when all six groups are bonding groups, the molecular shape is octahedral (AX_6; ideal bond angle = 90°). (378)

octet rule   The observation that when atoms bond, they often lose, gain, or share electrons to attain a filled outer level of eight electrons (or two for H and Li). (331)

optical isomers (also *enantiomers*)   A pair of stereoisomers consisting of a molecule and its mirror image that cannot be superimposed on each other. (580, 959)

optically active   Able to rotate the plane of polarized light. (581)

orbital diagram   A depiction of orbital occupancy in terms of electron number and spin shown by means of arrows in a series of small boxes, lines, or circles. (299)

ore   A naturally occurring compound or mixture of compounds from which an element can be profitably extracted. (909)

organic compound   A compound in which carbon is nearly always bonded to itself and to hydrogen, and often to other elements. (571)

organometallic compound   An organic compound in which carbon has a polar covalent bond to a metal atom. (598)

osmosis   The process by which solvent flows through a semipermeable membrane from a dilute to a concentrated solution. (503)

osmotic pressure (Π)   The pressure that results from the ability of solvent, but not solute, particles to cross a semipermeable membrane. The pressure required to prevent the net movement of solvent across the membrane. (503)

outer electrons   Electrons that occupy the highest energy level (highest n value) and are, on average, farthest from the nucleus. (306)

overall (net) equation   A chemical equation that is the sum of two or more balanced sequential equations in which a product of one becomes a reactant for the next. (106)

overvoltage   The additional voltage, usually associated with gaseous products forming at an electrode, that is required above the standard cell voltage to accomplish electrolysis. (888)

oxidation   The loss of electrons by a species, accompanied by an increase in oxidation number. (154)

oxidation number (O.N.) (also *oxidation state*)   A number equal to the magnitude of the charge an atom would have if its shared electrons were held completely by the atom that attracts them more strongly. (155)

oxidation number method   A method for balancing redox reactions in which the change in oxidation numbers is used to determine balancing coefficients. (158)

oxidation-reduction reaction (also *redox reaction*)   A process in which there is a net movement of electrons from one reactant (reducing agent) to another (oxidizing agent). (153)

oxidation state   (See *oxidation number.*)

oxidizing agent   The substance that accepts electrons in a reaction and undergoes a decrease in oxidation number. (154)

oxoanion   An anion in which an element is bonded to one or more oxygen atoms. (63)

P

***p* orbital**   An atomic orbital with $l = 1$. (285)

packing efficiency   The percentage of the available volume occupied by atoms, ions, or molecules in a unit cell. (444)

paramagnetism   The tendency of a species with unpaired electrons to be attracted by an external magnetic field. (319)

partial ionic character   An estimate of the actual charge separation in a bond (caused by the electronegativity difference of the bonded atoms) relative to complete separation. (351)

partial pressure   The portion of the total pressure contributed by a gas in a mixture of gases. (199)

particle accelerator   A device used to impart high kinetic energies to nuclear particles. (993)

pascal (Pa)   The SI unit of pressure; $1 \text{ Pa} = 1 \text{ N/m}^2$. (185)

penetration   The process by which an outer electron moves through the region occupied by the core electrons to spend part of its time closer to the nucleus; penetration increases the average effective nuclear charge for that electron. (298)

percent by mass (mass %)   (See *mass percent.*)

percent yield (% yield)   The actual yield of a reaction expressed as a percentage of the theoretical yield. (112)

period   A horizontal row of the periodic table. (53)

periodic law   A law stating that when the elements are arranged by atomic number, they exhibit a periodic recurrence of properties. (295)

periodic table of the elements   A table in which the elements are arranged by atomic number into columns (groups) and rows (periods). (53)

pH   The negative common logarithm of $[H_3O^+]$. (726)

phase   A physically distinct and homogeneous part of a system. (419)

phase change   A physical change from one phase to another, usually referring to a change in physical state. (420)

phase diagram   A diagram used to describe the stable phases and phase changes of a substance as a function of temperature and pressure. (429)

photoelectric effect   The observation that when monochromatic light of sufficient frequency shines on a metal, an electric current is produced. (266)

photon   A quantum of electromagnetic radiation. (266)

photovoltaic cell   A device capable of converting light directly into electricity. (251)

physical change   A change in which the physical form (or state) of a substance, but not its composition, is altered. (4)

physical property   A characteristic shown by a substance itself, without interacting with or changing into other substances. (4)

pi (π) bond   A covalent bond formed by sideways overlap of two atomic orbitals that has two regions of electron density, one above and one below the internuclear axis. (403)

pi (π) MO   A molecular orbital formed by combination of two atomic (usually *p*) orbitals whose orientations are perpendicular to the internuclear axis. (408)

Planck's constant (*h*)   A proportionality constant relating the energy and frequency of a photon, equal to 6.626×10^{-34} J·s. (266)

plastic   A material that, when deformed, retains its new shape. (465)

polar covalent bond   A covalent bond in which the electron pair is shared unequally, so the bond has partially negative and partially positive poles. (351)

polar molecule   A molecule with an unequal distribution of charge as a result of its polar bonds and shape. (136)

polarimeter   A device used to measure the rotation of plane-polarized light by an optically active compound. (581)

polarizability   The ease with which a particle's electron cloud can be distorted. (434)

polyatomic ion   An ion in which two or more atoms are bonded covalently. (59)

polymer (also *macromolecule*)   An extremely large molecule that results from the covalent linking of many simpler molecular units (monomers). (461)

polyprotic acid   An acid with more than one ionizable proton. (737)

polysaccharide   A macromolecule composed of many simple sugars linked covalently. (607)

positron (β⁺)   The antiparticle of an electron. (981)

positron emission   A type of radioactive decay in which a positron is emitted from a nucleus. (981)

potential energy (*E*ₚ)   The energy an object has as a result of its position relative to other objects or because of its composition. (8)

precipitate   The insoluble product of a precipitation reaction. (141)

precipitation reaction   A reaction in which two soluble ionic compounds form an insoluble product, a precipitate. (141)

precision (also *reproducibility*)   The closeness of a measurement to other measurements of the same phenomenon in a series of experiments. (28)

pressure (*P*)   The force exerted per unit of surface area. (183)

pressure-volume work (*PV* work)   A type of work in which a volume change occurs against an external pressure. (235)

principal quantum number (*n*)   A positive integer that specifies the energy and relative size of an atomic orbital; a number that specifies an energy level in an atom. (281)

probability contour   A shape that defines the volume around an atomic nucleus within which an electron spends a given percentage of its time. (281)

product   A substance formed in a chemical reaction. (99)

property   A characteristic that gives a substance its unique identity. (4)

protein   A natural, linear polymer composed of any of about 20 types of amino acid monomers linked together by peptide bonds. (483, 608)

proton (p$^+$) A subatomic particle found in the nucleus that has a unit positive charge (1.60218×10^{-19} C). (48)

proton acceptor A substance that accepts an H$^+$ ion; a Brønsted-Lowry base. (729)

proton donor A substance that donates an H$^+$ ion; a Brønsted-Lowry acid. (729)

pseudo–noble gas configuration The $(n-1)d^{10}$ configuration of a p-block metal ion that has an empty outer energy level. (317)

Q

quantum A packet of energy equal to $h\nu$. The smallest quantity of energy that can be emitted or absorbed. (266)

quantum mechanics The branch of physics that examines the wave motion of objects on the atomic scale. (279)

quantum number A number that specifies a property of an orbital or an electron. (266)

R

rad (radiation-absorbed dose) The quantity of radiation that results in 0.01 J of energy being absorbed per kilogram of tissue; 1 rad = 0.01 J/kg tissue = 10^{-2} Gy. (996)

radial probability distribution plot The graphic depiction of the total probability distribution (sum of ψ^2) of an electron in the region near the nucleus. (280)

radioactivity The emissions resulting from the spontaneous disintegration of an unstable nucleus. (977)

radioisotope An isotope with an unstable nucleus that decays through radioactive emissions. (990)

radioisotopic dating A method for determining the age of an object based on the rate of decay of a particular radioactive nuclide relative to a stable nuclide. (990)

radius of gyration (R_g) A measure of the size of a coiled polymer chain, expressed as the average distance from the center of mass of the chain to its outside edge. (463)

random coil The shape adopted by most polymer chains and caused by random rotation about the bonds joining the repeat units. (462)

random error Error that occurs in all measurements (with its size depending on the measurer's skill and the instrument's precision) and results in values *both* higher and lower than the actual value. (29)

Raoult's law A law stating that the vapor pressure of solvent above a solution equals the mole fraction of solvent times the vapor pressure of pure solvent: $P_{\text{solvent}} = X_{\text{solvent}} \times P^{\circ}_{\text{solvent}}$. (500)

rare earths (See *lanthanides.*)

rate constant (k) The proportionality constant that relates reaction rate to reactant (and product) concentrations. (634)

rate-determining step (also *rate-limiting step*) The slowest step in a reaction mechanism and therefore the step that limits the overall rate. (656)

rate law (also *rate equation*) An equation that expresses the rate of a reaction as a function of reactant (and product) concentrations. (634)

reactant A starting substance in a chemical reaction. (99)

reaction energy diagram A graph that shows the potential energy of a reacting system as it progresses from reactants to products. (652)

reaction intermediate A substance that is formed and used up during the overall reaction and therefore does not appear in the overall equation. (657)

reaction mechanism A series of elementary steps that sum to the overall reaction and is consistent with the rate law. (655)

reaction order The exponent of a reactant concentration in a rate law that shows how the rate is affected by changes in that concentration. (634)

reaction quotient (Q) (also *mass-action expression*) A ratio of terms for a given reaction consisting of product concentrations multiplied together and divided by reactant concentrations multiplied together, each raised to the power of their balancing coefficient. The value of Q changes until the system reaches equilibrium, at which point it equals K. (680)

reaction rate The change in the concentrations of reactants (or products) with time. (627)

reactor core The part of a nuclear reactor that contains the fuel rods and generates heat from fission. (1008)

redox reaction (See *oxidation-reduction reaction.*)

reducing agent The substance that donates electrons in a redox reaction and undergoes an increase in oxidation number. (154)

reduction The gain of electrons by a species, accompanied by a decrease in oxidation number. (154)

refraction A phenomenon in which a wave changes its speed and therefore its direction as it passes through a phase boundary into a different medium. (263)

rem (roentgen equivalent for man) The unit of radiation dosage for a human based on the product of the number of rads and a factor related to the biological tissue; 1 rem = 10^{-2} Sv. (996)

reproducibility (See *precision.*)

resonance hybrid The weighted average of the resonance structures of a molecule. (367)

resonance structure (also *resonance form*) One of two or more Lewis structures for a molecule that cannot be adequately depicted by a single structure. Resonance structures differ only in the position of bonding and lone electron pairs. (367)

reverse osmosis A process for preparing drinkable water that uses an applied pressure greater than the osmotic pressure to remove ions from an aqueous solution, typically seawater. (511)

rms (root-mean-square) speed (u_{rms}) The speed of a molecule having the average kinetic energy; very close to the most probable speed. (209)

roasting A pyrometallurgical process in which metal sulfides are converted to oxides. (918)

round off The process of removing digits based on a series of rules to obtain an answer with the proper number of significant figures (or decimal places). (27)

S

s orbital An atomic orbital with $l = 0$. (284)

salt An ionic compound that results from an Arrhenius acid-base reaction after solvent is removed. (148)

salt bridge An inverted U tube containing a solution of a nonreacting electrolyte that connects the compartments of a voltaic cell and maintains neutrality by allowing ions to flow between compartments. (859)

saturated hydrocarbon A hydrocarbon in which each C is bonded to four other atoms. (576)

saturated solution A solution that contains the maximum amount of dissolved solute at a given temperature (prepared with undissolved solute present). (492)

scanning tunneling microscopy   An instrumental technique that uses electrons moving across a minute gap to observe the topography of a surface on the atomic scale. (447)

Schrödinger equation   An equation that describes how the electron matter-wave changes in space around the nucleus. Solutions of the equation provide allowable energy levels of the atom. (279)

scientific method   A process of creative thinking and testing aimed at objective, verifiable discoveries of the causes of natural events. (12)

scintillation counter   A device used to measure radioactivity through its excitation of atoms and their subsequent emission of light. (987)

screening   (See *shielding.*)

second (s)   The SI base unit of time. (25)

second law of thermodynamics   A law stating that a process occurs spontaneously in the direction that increases the entropy of the universe. (817)

seesaw shape   A molecular shape caused by the presence of one equatorial lone pair in a trigonal bipyramidal arrangement (AX_4E). (377)

selective precipitation   The process of separating ions through differences in the solubility of their compounds with a given precipitating ion. (791)

self-ionization   (See *autoionization.*)

semiconductor   A substance whose electrical conductivity is poor at room temperature but increases significantly with rising temperature. (453)

semimetal   (See *metalloid.*)

semipermeable membrane   A membrane that allows solvent, but not solute, to pass through. (503)

shared pair   (See *bonding pair.*)

shell   (See *level.*)

shielding   (also *screening*)   The ability of other electrons, especially those occupying inner orbitals, to lessen the nuclear attraction for an outer electron. (297)

SI unit   A unit composed of one or more of the base units of the Système International d'Unités, a revised metric system. (17)

side reaction   An undesired chemical reaction that consumes some of the reactant and reduces the overall yield of the desired product. (112)

sievert (Sv)   The SI unit of human radiation dosage; 1 Sv = 100 rem. (996)

sigma (σ) bond   A type of covalent bond that arises through end-to-end orbital overlap and has most of its electron density along an imaginary line joining the nuclei. (403)

sigma (σ) MO   A molecular orbital that is cylindrically symmetrical about an imaginary line that runs through the nuclei of the component atoms. (406)

significant figures   The digits obtained in a measurement. The greater the number of significant figures, the greater the certainty of the measurement. (25)

silicate   A type of compound found throughout rocks and soil and consisting of repeating —Si—O groupings and, in most cases, metal cations. (542)

silicone   A type of synthetic polymer containing —Si—O repeat units, with organic groups and crosslinks. (542)

simple cubic unit cell   A unit cell in which a particle occupies each corner of a cube. (442)

single bond   A bond that consists of one electron pair. (339)

slag   A molten waste product formed in a blast furnace by the reaction of acidic silica with a basic metal oxide. (925)

smelting   Heating a mineral with a reducing agent, such as coke, to obtain a metal. (919)

soap   The salt formed in a reaction between a fatty acid and a strong base, usually a Group 1A(1) or 2A(2) hydroxide. (485)

solid   One of the three states of matter. A solid has a fixed shape that does not conform to the container shape. (5)

solubility (S)   The maximum amount of solute that dissolves in a fixed quantity of a particular solvent at a specified temperature. (478)

solubility-product constant (K_{sp})   An equilibrium constant for a slightly soluble ionic compound dissolving in water. (783)

solute   The substance that dissolves in the solvent. (114, 478)

solution   (See *homogeneous mixture.*)

solvated   Surrounded closely by solvent molecules. (136)

solvation   The process of surrounding a solute particle with solvent particles. (489)

solvent   The substance in which the solute(s) dissolve. (114, 478)

source   (See *occurrence.*)

sp hybrid orbital   An orbital formed by the mixing of one s and one p orbital of a central atom. (396)

sp^2 hybrid orbital   An orbital formed by the mixing of one s and two p orbitals of a central atom. (398)

sp^3 hybrid orbital   An orbital formed by the mixing of one s and three p orbitals of a central atom. (398)

sp^3d hybrid orbital   An orbital formed by the mixing of one s, three p, and one d orbital of a central atom. (399)

sp^3d^2 hybrid orbital   An orbital formed by the mixing of one s, three p, and two d orbitals of a central atom. (400)

specific heat capacity (c)   The quantity of heat required to change the temperature of 1 gram of a material by 1 K. (238)

spectator ion   An ion that is present as part of a reactant but is not involved in the chemical change. (141)

spectrochemical series   A ranking of ligands in terms of their ability to split d-orbital energies. (965)

spectrometry   Any instrumental technique that uses a portion of the electromagnetic spectrum to measure the atomic and molecular energy levels of a substance. (273)

speed of light (c)   A fundamental constant giving the speed at which electromagnetic radiation travels in a vacuum: $c = 2.99792458 \times 10^8$ m/s. (262)

spin quantum number (m_s)   A number, either $+\frac{1}{2}$ or $-\frac{1}{2}$, that indicates the direction of electron spin. (296)

spontaneous change   A change that occurs by itself, that is, without an ongoing input of external energy. (811)

square planar shape   A molecular shape (AX_4E_2) caused by the presence of two lone pairs at opposite vertices in an octahedral arrangement. (378)

square pyramidal shape   A molecular shape (AX_5E) caused by the presence of one lone pair in an octahedral arrangement. (378)

standard atmosphere (atm)   The average atmospheric pressure measured at sea level and 0°C, defined as 1.01325×10^5 Pa. (185)

standard cell potential (E°_{cell})   The potential of a cell measured with all components in their standard states and no current flowing. (862)

standard electrode potential ($E^\circ_{\text{half-cell}}$) (also *standard half-cell potential*)   The standard potential of a half-cell, with the half-reaction written as a reduction. (862)

standard enthalpy of formation (ΔH°_f) (also *standard heat of formation*)   The enthalpy change occurring when 1 mol of a compound forms from its elements with all components in their standard states. (246)

standard enthalpy of reaction ($\Delta H^\circ_{\text{rxn}}$) (also *standard heat of reaction*)   The enthalpy change that occurs during a reaction when all components are in their standard states. (246)

standard entropy of reaction ($\Delta S^\circ_{\text{rxn}}$)   The entropy change that occurs when all components are in their standard states. (822)

standard free energy change (ΔG°)   The free energy change that occurs when all components are in their standard states. (828)

standard free energy of formation (ΔG°_f)   The standard free energy change that occurs when 1 mol of a compound is made from its elements with all components in their standard states. (829)

standard half-cell potential   (See *standard electrode potential*.)

standard heat of formation   (See *standard enthalpy of formation*.)

standard heat of reaction   (See *standard enthalpy of reaction*.)

standard hydrogen electrode   (See *standard reference half-cell*.)

standard molar entropy (S°)   The entropy of 1 mol of a substance in its standard state. (817)

standard molar volume   The volume of 1 mol of an ideal gas at standard temperature and pressure: 22.4141 L. (190)

standard reference half-cell (also *standard hydrogen electrode*)   A specially prepared platinum electrode immersed in 1 M $H^+(aq)$ through which H_2 gas at 1 atm is bubbled. $E^\circ_{\text{half-cell}}$ is defined as 0 V. (863)

standard state   A set of specifications used to compare thermodynamic data: 1 atm for gases behaving ideally, 1 M for dissolved species, or the pure substance for liquids and solids. (246)

standard temperature and pressure (STP)   The reference conditions for a gas:

$$0°C \; (273.15 \text{ K}) \text{ and } 1 \text{ atm } (760 \text{ torr}) \qquad (190)$$

state function   A property of the system determined by its current state, regardless of how it arrived at that state. (234)

state of matter   One of the three physical forms of matter: solid, liquid, or gas. (5)

stationary state   In the Bohr model, one of the allowable energy levels of the atom in which it does not release or absorb energy. (269)

steel   An alloy of iron with small amounts of carbon and usually other metals. (924)

stellar nucleosynthesis   The process by which elements are formed in the stars through nuclear fusion. (1012)

stereoisomers   Molecules with the same connections of atoms but different orientations of groups in space. (580, 958) (See also *geometric isomers* and *optical isomers*.)

stoichiometric coefficient   (See *balancing coefficient*.)

stoichiometry   The study of the mass-mole-number relationships of chemical formulas and reactions. (83)

strong-field ligand   A ligand that causes larger crystal field splitting energy and therefore is part of a low-spin complex. (964)

strong force   An attractive force that exists between all nucleons and is many times stronger than the electrostatic repulsive force. (984)

structural formula   A formula that shows the actual number of atoms, their relative placement, and the bonds between them. (68, 92)

structural isomers   (See *constitutional isomers*.)

sublevel (also *subshell*)   An energy substate of an atom within a level. Given by the n and l values, the sublevel designates the size and shape of the atomic orbitals. (282)

sublimation   The process by which a solid changes directly into a gas. (421)

substance   A type of matter, either an element or a compound, that has a fixed composition. (38)

substitution reaction   An organic reaction that occurs when an atom (or group) from one reactant substitutes for one in another reactant. (589)

substrate   A reactant that binds to the active site in an enzyme-catalyzed reaction. (662)

superconductivity   The ability to conduct a current with no loss of energy to resistive heating. (454)

supersaturated solution   An unstable solution in which more solute is dissolved than in a saturated solution. (492)

surface tension   The energy required to increase the surface area of a liquid by a given amount. (437)

surroundings   All parts of the universe other than the system being considered. (230)

suspension   A heterogeneous mixture containing particles that are distinct from the surrounding medium. (508)

synthetic natural gas (SNG)   A gaseous fuel mixture, mostly methane, formed from coal. (249)

system   The defined part of the universe under study. (230)

systematic error   A type of error producing values that are all either higher or lower than the actual value, often caused by faulty equipment or a consistent flaw in technique. (29)

T

t_{2g} orbitals   The set of orbitals (composed of d_{xy}, d_{yz}, and d_{xz}) that results when the energies of the metal-ion d orbitals are split by a ligand field. This set is lower in energy than the other (e_g) set in an octahedral field and higher in energy in a tetrahedral field. (964)

T shape   A molecular shape caused by the presence of two equatorial lone pairs in a trigonal bipyramidal arrangement (AX_3E_2). (377)

temperature (T)   A measure of how hot or cold a substance is relative to another substance. (23) A measure of the average kinetic energy of the particles in a sample. (208)

tetrahedral arrangement   The geometric arrangement formed when four electron groups maximize their separation around a central atom; when all four groups are bonding groups, the molecular shape is tetrahedral (AX_4; ideal bond angle 109.5°). (375)

theoretical yield   The amount of product predicted by the stoichiometrically equivalent molar ratio in the balanced equation. (112)

theory   (See *model*.)

thermochemical equation   A chemical equation that shows the heat involved for the amounts of substances specified. (242)

thermochemistry   The branch of thermodynamics that focuses on the heat involved in chemical and physical change. (229)

thermodynamics   The study of heat (thermal energy) and its interconversions. (229)

thermometer   A device for measuring temperature that contains a fluid that expands or contracts within a graduated tube. (23)

third law of thermodynamics   A law stating that the entropy of a perfect crystal is zero at 0 K. (817)

titration   A method of determining the concentration of a solution by monitoring relative amounts during its reaction with a solution of known concentration. (152)

torr   A unit of pressure identical to 1 mmHg. (185)

total ionic equation   An equation for an aqueous reaction that shows all the soluble ionic substances dissociated into ions. (141)

tracer   A radioisotope that signals the presence of the species of interest by radioactive emissions. (1000)

transcription   The process of producing messenger RNA from DNA. (614)

transition element   An element that occupies the *d* block of the periodic table; one whose *d* orbitals are being filled. (303, 945)

transition state (also *activated complex*)   An unstable species formed in an effective collision of reactants that exists momentarily when the system is highest in energy and that can either form products or re-form reactants. (652)

transition state theory   A model that explains how the energy of reactant collisions is used to form a high-energy transitional species that can change to reactant or product. (652)

translation   The process by which messenger RNA specifies the sequence of amino acids and synthesizes proteins. (614)

transuranium element   An element with atomic number higher than that of uranium ($Z = 92$). (994)

trigonal bipyramidal arrangement   The geometric arrangement formed when five electron groups maximize their separation around a central atom. When all five groups are bonding groups, the molecular shape is trigonal bipyramidal (AX_5; ideal bond angles, axial-center-equatorial 90° and equatorial-center-equatorial 120°). (376)

trigonal planar arrangement   The geometric arrangement formed when three electron groups maximize their separation around a central atom. When all three groups are bonding groups, the molecular shape is trigonal planar (AX_3; ideal bond angle 120°). (374)

trigonal pyramidal shape   A molecular shape (AX_3E) caused by the presence of one lone pair in a tetrahedral arrangement. (376)

triple bond   A covalent bond that consists of three bonding pairs, two atoms sharing six electrons; one σ and two π bonds. (339)

triple point   The pressure and temperature at which three phases of a substance are in equilibrium. In a phase diagram, the point at which three phase-transition curves meet. (429)

Tyndall effect   The scattering of light by a colloid. (509)

U

ultraviolet (UV)   Radiation in the region of the electromagnetic spectrum between the visible and the x-ray regions. (262)

uncertainty   A characteristic of every measurement that results from the inexactness of the measuring device and the need to estimate when taking a reading. (25)

uncertainty principle   The principle stated by Werner Heisenberg that it is impossible to know simultaneously the exact position and velocity of a particle; the principle becomes important only for particles of very small mass. (278)

unimolecular reaction   An elementary reaction that involves the decomposition or rearrangement of a single particle. (655)

unit cell   The smallest portion of a crystal that, if repeated in all three directions, gives the crystal. (442)

universal gas constant (R)   A proportionality constant that relates the energy, amount of substance, and temperature of a system; $R = 0.0820578$ atm·L/mol·K = 8.31447 J/mol·K. (191)

unsaturated hydrocarbon   A hydrocarbon with at least one carbon-carbon multiple bond; one in which at least two C atoms are bonded to fewer than four atoms. (582)

unsaturated solution   A solution in which more solute can be dissolved at a given temperature. (492)

unshared pair   (See *lone pair.*)

V

V shape   (See *bent shape.*)

valence band   In band theory, the lower energy portion of the band of molecular orbitals, which is filled with valence electrons. (453)

valence bond (VB) theory   A model that attempts to reconcile the shapes of molecules with those of atomic orbitals through the concepts of orbital overlap and hybridization. (395)

valence electrons   The electrons involved in compound formation; in main-group elements, the electrons in the valence (outer) level. (306)

valence-shell electron-pair repulsion (VSEPR) theory   A model explaining that the shapes of molecules and ions result from minimizing electron-pair repulsions around a central atom. (373)

van der Waals constants   Experimentally determined positive numbers used in the van der Waals equation to account for the intermolecular attractions and molecular volume of real gases. (216)

van der Waals equation   An equation that accounts for the behavior of real gases. (216)

van der Waals radius   One-half of the shortest distance between the nuclei of identical nonbonded atoms. (431)

vapor pressure (also *equilibrium vapor pressure*)   The pressure exerted by a vapor at equilibrium with its liquid in a closed system. (426)

vapor pressure lowering (ΔP)   The lowering of the vapor pressure of a solvent caused by the presence of dissolved solute particles. (499)

vaporization   The process of changing from a liquid to a gas. (420)

variable   A quantity that can have more than a single value. (12) (See also *controlled experiment.*)

viscosity   A measure of the resistance of a liquid to flow. (439)

volatility   The tendency of a substance to become a gas. (72)

volt (V)   The SI unit of electric potential: 1 V = 1 J/C. (862)

voltage   (See *cell potential.*)

voltaic cell (also *galvanic cell*)   An electrochemical cell that uses a spontaneous redox reaction to generate electric energy. (855)

volume (V)   The space occupied by a sample of matter. (18)

volume percent [% (v/v)]   A concentration term defined as the volume of solute in 100. volumes of solution. (496)

W

wastewater   Used water, usually containing industrial and/or residential waste, that is treated before being returned to the environment. (511)

water softening   The process of replacing the hard-water ions Ca^{2+} and Mg^{2+} with Na^+ ions. (510)

wave function   (See *atomic orbital*.)

wave-particle duality   The principle stating that both matter and energy have wavelike and particle-like properties. (277)

wavelength (λ)   The distance between any point on a wave and the corresponding point on the next wave, that is, the distance a wave travels during one cycle. (262)

weak-field ligand   A ligand that causes smaller crystal field splitting energy and therefore is part of a high-spin complex. (964)

weight   The force exerted by a gravitational field on an object that is directly proportional to its mass. (20)

work (w)   The energy transferred when an object is moved by a force. (231)

X

x-ray diffraction analysis   An instrumental technique used to determine dimensions of a crystal structure by measuring the diffraction patterns caused by x-rays impinging on the crystal. (447)

Z

zone refining   A process used to purify metals and metalloids in which impurities are removed from a bar of the element by concentrating them in a thin molten zone. (921)

Chapter 1

Opener: © The McGraw-Hill Companies, Inc./John Thoeming Photographer; 1.1A: © Paul Morrell/Stone/Getty Images; 1.1B: © The McGraw-Hill Companies, Inc./Stephen Frisch Photographer; Table 1.1A: © The McGraw-Hill Companies, Inc./Stephen Frisch Photographer; Table 1.1B: © Ruth Melnick; Table 1.1C-E: © The McGraw-Hill Companies, Inc./Stephen Frisch Photographer; p. 7: Gallileo Project, SSI, University of Arizona; 1.4: © SSPL/The Image Works; 1.5A: © George Haling/Photo Researchers, Inc.; 1.5B: © Javier Soriano/AFP/Getty Images; 1.5C: © Kiselev Andrey Velerevich/Shutterstock.com; 1.5D: © ayazad/Shutterstock.com; 1.8A: © The McGraw-Hill Companies, Inc./Stephen Frisch Photographer; 1.8B: © BrandTech Scientific, Inc.; 1.13A-B: © The McGraw-Hill Companies, Inc./Stephen Frisch Photographer.

Chapter 2

Opener: © Mark Schneider/Visuals Unlimited; Table 2.1(all), 2.2A-B: © The McGraw-Hill Companies, Inc./Stephen Frisch Photographer; 2.3(top): © Punchstock RF; 2.3(bottom): © Alexander Cherednichenko/Shutterstock.com; p. 45: © Roman Crochuk/Shutterstock.com; 2.10(all), 2.11A(both), 2.11E: © The McGraw-Hill Companies, Inc./Stephen Frisch Photographer; 2.16: © Mark Schneider/Visuals Unlimited; 2.19A-B: © The McGraw-Hill Companies, Inc./Stephen Frisch Photographer.

Chapter 3

Opener: © Stepan Jezek/Shutterstock.com; 3.1, 3.7(all): © The McGraw-Hill Companies, Inc./Charles Winters Photographer; p. 104: © The McGraw-Hill Companies, Inc./Stephen Frisch Photographer; p. 105: © Richard Megna/Fundamental Photographs, NYC; 3.14A-D, 3.15(both): © The McGraw-Hill Companies, Inc./Stephen Frisch Photographer.

Chapter 4

Opener: © Paul Avis/Stone Getty Images; 4.3A-C, 4.4(both): © The McGraw-Hill Companies, Inc./Stephen Frisch Photographer; 4.5: © The McGraw-Hill Companies, Inc./Richard Megna, Photographer; 4.6, 4.8A-B: © The McGraw-Hill Companies, Inc./Stephen Frisch Photographer; 4.10: © The McGraw-Hill Companies, Inc./Charles Winters Photographer; 4.11A-C, p. 158, 4.14(both), 4.15(all), 4.16(all), 4.17(all), 4.18, 4.19(both): © The McGraw-Hill Companies, Inc./Stephen Frisch Photographer.

Chapter 5

Opener: © The McGraw-Hill Companies, Inc./John Thoeming Photographer; 5.1A-C, 5.2A-B: © The McGraw-Hill Companies, Inc./Stephen Frisch Photographer; 5.10: © The McGraw-Hill Companies, Inc./Charles Winters Photographer; p. 198: © Charles F. McCarthy/Shutterstock.com; p. 203: © The McGraw-Hill Companies, Inc./Stephen Frisch Photographer.

Chapter 6

Opener: © The McGraw-Hill Companies, Inc./Charles Winters Photographer; 6.1: © The McGraw-Hill Companies, Inc./Stephen Frisch Photographer.

Chapter 7

Opener: © Orla/Shutterstock.com; p. 264: © Anthony McAulay/Shutterstock.com; 7.5A: © Richard Megna/Fundamental Photographs, NYC; 7.6A: © Ravi/Shutterstock.com; 7.6B: © The McGraw-Hill Companies, Inc./Charles Winters Photographer; 7.6C: © Feng Yu/Shutterstock.com; B7.1A(both): © The McGraw-Hill Companies, Inc./Stephen Frisch Photographer; B7.1B: Washington DC Convention & Visitors Association; 7.13A-B: PSSC Physics © 1965, Education Development Center, Inc.; D.C. Heath & Company/Education Development Center, Inc.; 7.14: © Dennis Kunkel/Phototake.com.

Chapter 8

CO8: © bbostjan/Shutterstock.com; 8.9A-B, 8.21(all), 8.23: © The McGraw-Hill Companies, Inc./Stephen Frisch Photographer.

Chapter 9

Opener(crystal): © E. R. Degginger/Photo Researchers, Inc.; Opener(candle): © Dolgisch/Shutterstock.com; Opener(copper): © The McGraw-Hill Companies, Inc./Stephen Frisch Photographer; 9.6A-B, 9.9A, 9.10(all), 9.15, 9.26, 9.29: © The McGraw-Hill Companies, Inc./Stephen Frisch Photographer; p. 355: © Diane Hirsch/Fundamental Photographs, NYC.

Chapter 10

Opener: © Jill Braaten; 10.2A(all), 10.6(both): © The McGraw-Hill Companies, Inc./Stephen Frisch Photographer.

Chapter 11

11.23: © The McGraw-Hill Companies, Inc./Charles Winters Photographer.

Chapter 12

Opener: © Cathleen Howland/Shutterstock.com; p. 420: © Christopher Meder Photography/Shutterstock.com; 12.1A: © dinadesign/Shutterstock.com; 12.1B: © Jill Birschbach Photo Services; 12.9: © The McGraw-Hill Companies, Inc./Richard Megna Photographer; p. 438(strider): © Nuridsany & Perennou /Photo Researchers, Inc.; p. 438(dew): © Rod Planck/Photo Researchers, Inc.; 12.21A-B: © The McGraw-Hill Companies, Inc./Stephen Frisch Photographer; 12.23B: © Scott Camazine/Photo Researchers, Inc.; 12.25A: © Jeffrey A. Scovil Photography (Wayne Thompson Minerals); 12.25B: © Mark Schneider/Visuals Unlimited; 12.25C: © Jeffrey A. Scovil Photography; 12.25D: © Jeffrey A. Scovil Photography (Francis Benjamin Collection); Page 444: © Bryan Busovicki/Shutterstock.com; B12.3: Courtesy National Institute of Standards and Technology; 12.43A: © J. R. Factor/Photo Researchers, Inc.; 12.43B: © James Dennis/Phototake.com; p. 465: © Ingram Publishing/Alamy; 12.49: Courtesy of Benoit Dubertret; 12.50: © & by permission from Ferrotec (USA) Corporation. May not be reproduced without written permission; 12.51: T. Sasaki/Rice University (Image courtesy of Rice University Office of Media Relations and Information).

Chapter 13

Opener: © CNRI/Photo Researchers, Inc.; 13.4A: © Ruth Melnick; 13.4B: © Ingram Publishing/AGE Fotostock RF; 13.18A-C: © The McGraw-Hill Companies, Inc./Stephen Frisch Photographer; 13.20: © Photodisc/Getty RF; p. 494: © Peter Scoones/Photo Researchers, Inc.; 13.22A-C: © The McGraw-Hill Companies, Inc./Stephen Frisch Photographer; 13.29A-C: © David M. Phillips/Photo Researchers, Inc.; 13.30A: © Ed Degginger/Color-Pic; 13.30B: © Corbis RF; 13.31: © Earth Satellite Corporation/SPL/Photo Researchers, Inc.; B13.3A: © Robert Essel/Corbis.

Chapter 14

Opener(left): © Joseph T. & Suzanne L. Collins/Photo Researchers, Inc.; Opener(right): © Joel Sartore/National Geographic Stock; Table 14.1, p. 529,

Page numbers followed by *f* indicate figures; *mn*, marginal notes; *n*, footnotes; and *t*, tables. Page numbers preceded by "A-" indicate pages in the *Appendix*. Page numbers preceded by "G-" indicate pages in the *Glossary*.